Chemistry

FOR THE IB DIPLOMA

SECOND EDITION

**Christopher Talbot,
Richard Harwood and
Christopher Coates**

HODDER
EDUCATION
AN HACHETTE UK COMPANY

This work has been developed independently from and is not endorsed by the International Baccalaureate (IB).

All proprietary drug names and brand names in Chapters 22–25 are protected by their respective registered trademarks.

Although every effort has been made to ensure that website addresses are correct at time of going to press, Hodder Education cannot be held responsible for the content of any website mentioned in this book. It is sometimes possible to find a relocated web page by typing in the address of the home page for a website in the URL window of your browser.

Hachette UK's policy is to use papers that are natural, renewable and recyclable products and made from wood grown in well-managed forests and other controlled sources. The logging and manufacturing processes are expected to conform to the environmental regulations of the country of origin.

Orders: please contact Hachette UK Distribution, Hely Hutchinson Centre, Milton Road, Didcot, Oxfordshire, OX11 7HH. Telephone: +44 (0)1235 827827. Email education@hachette.co.uk Lines are open from 9 a.m. to 5 p.m., Monday to Friday. You can also order through our website: www.hoddereducation.com

© Christopher Talbot, Richard Harwood and Christopher Coates 2015

First edition published in 2010

This second edition published 2015

by Hodder Education

An Hachette UK Company

Carmelite House, 50 Victoria Embankment, London EC4Y 0DZ

Impression number   5 4

Year   2025 2024 2023 2022 2021

Cover photo © ESA/Herschel/PACS/MESS Key Programme Supernova Remnant Team; NASA, ESA and Allison Loll/ Jeff Hester (Arizona State University)

Illustrations by Ken Vail Graphic Design and Aptara Inc.

Typeset in Goudy Oldstyle 10/12 pt by Aptara inc.

Printed and bound by CPI Group (UK) Ltd, Croydon, CR0 4YY

A catalogue record for this title is available from the British Library

ISBN: 978 1471 829055

Contents

Options

Available on the website accompanying this book: www.hoddereducation.com/IBextras

Answers and glossary

Answers and glossary appear on the website accompanying this book:

www.hoddereducation.com/IBextras

Introduction

Welcome to the second edition of *Chemistry for the IB Diploma*. The content and structure of this second edition has been completely revised to meet the demands of the 2014 *IB Diploma Programme Chemistry Guide*.

Within the IB Diploma Programme, the chemistry content is organized into compulsory core topics plus a number of options, from which all students select one. The organization of this resource exactly follows the *IB Chemistry Guide* sequence:

- **Core:** Chapters 1–11 cover the common core topics for Standard *and* Higher Level students.
- **Additional Higher Level (AHL):** Chapters 12–21 cover the additional topics for Higher Level students.
- **Options:** Chapters 22–25 cover Options A, B, C and D respectively. Each of these is available to both Standard and Higher Level students. (Higher Level students study more topics within the same option.) These are available on the Hodder website.

The syllabus is presented as topics, each of which (for the core and AHL topics) is the subject of a corresponding single chapter in the *Chemistry for the IB Diploma* printed book.

The Options (Chapters 22–25) are available on the website accompanying this book, as are a comprehensive Glossary and the answers to the end-of-chapter exam and exam-style questions: www.hoddereducation.com/IBextras.

Special features of the chapters of *Chemistry for the IB Diploma* are:

- Each chapter begins with **Essential Ideas** that summarize the concepts on which it is based.
- The text is written in **straightforward language**, without phrases or idioms that might confuse students for whom English is a second language. The text is also suitable for students of all abilities.
- The **depth of treatment** of topics has been carefully planned to accurately reflect the objectives of the IB syllabus and the requirements of the examinations.
- Photographs and full-colour illustrations support the relevant text, with annotations which elaborate on the context, function, language, history or applications of chemistry.
- The **Nature of Science** is an important new aspect of the IB Chemistry course, which aims to broaden students' interests and knowledge beyond the confines of its specific chemistry content. Throughout this book we hope that students will develop an appreciation of the processes and applications of chemistry and technology. Some aspects of the *Nature of Science* may be examined in IB Chemistry examinations and important discussion points are highlighted in the margins.

- The **Utilizations** and **Additional Perspectives** sections also reflect the Nature of Science, but they are designed to take students beyond the limits of the IB syllabus in a variety of ways. They may, for example, provide a historical context, extend theory or offer an interesting application. They are sometimes accompanied by more challenging, or research style, questions. They do not contain any knowledge which is essential for the IB examinations.

- Science and technology have developed over the centuries with contributions from scientists from all around the world. In the modern world science knows few boundaries and the flow of information is usually quick and easy. Some international applications of science have been indicated with the **International Mindedness** icon.

- **Worked examples** are provided in each chapter whenever new equations are introduced. A large number of **self-assessment questions** and some research questions are also placed throughout the chapters close to the relevant theory. They are phrased in order to assist comprehension and recall, and to help familiarize students with the assessment implications of the command terms.

- It is not an aim of this book to provide detailed information about experimental work or the use of computers. However, our **Applications and Skills** icon has been placed in the margin to indicate wherever such work may usefully aid understanding.

- A selection of **IB examination-style questions** are provided at the end of each chapter, as well as some past IB Chemistry examination questions. **Answers** to these are provided on the website accompanying this book.

- Extensive links to the interdisciplinary **Theory of Knowledge (ToK)** element of the IB Diploma course, including ethics, are made in all chapters.
- Comprehensive **glossaries** of words and terms, including IB command terms, for Core and AHL topics are included in the website which accompanies this book.

- This icon denotes links to material available on the website that accompanies this book: www.hoddereducation.com/IBextras.

Using this book

The sequence of chapters in *Chemistry for the IB Diploma* deliberately follows the sequence of the syllabus content. However, the *IB Diploma Chemistry Guide* is not designed as a teaching syllabus, so the order in which the syllabus content is presented is not necessarily the order in which it will be taught. Different schools and colleges should design course delivery based on their individual circumstances.

In addition to the study of the chemistry principles contained in this book, IB science students carry out experiments and investigations, as well as collaborating in a Group 4 Project. These are assessed within the school (Internal Assessment) based on well-established criteria.

Author profiles

Christopher Talbot

Chris teaches IB Chemistry and ToK at a leading IB World School in Singapore. He has also taught IB Biology, MYP Science and a variety of IGCSE Science courses. He has moderated IB Chemistry coursework and prepared students for the Singapore Chemistry Olympiad.

Richard Harwood

Richard was a Biochemistry researcher at Manchester Medical School and University College, Cardiff, before returning to teaching science in England and Switzerland. Most recently he has been involved in projects with various Ministries of Education evaluating science courses and providing teacher training nationally, and in individual schools, in Mongolia, Kazakhstan, Zimbabwe, India and Ghana.

Christopher Coates

Chris has previously taught in Suffolk, Yorkshire and Hong Kong at King George V School, and is currently Head of Science in the Senior School at the Tanglin Trust School, Singapore. He has taught A-level and IB Chemistry as well as ToK and MYP Science.

Authors' acknowledgements

We are indebted to the following lecturers who reviewed early drafts of the chapters for the second edition: Dr David L. Cooper, University of Liverpool (Chapters 2 and 14), Professor Mike Williamson, University of Sheffield (Chapters 21 and 23), Professor James Hanson, University of Sussex (Chapter 20), Professor Laurence Harwood, University of Reading (Chapter 20), Professor Robin Walsh, University of Reading (Chapters 6 and 16), Professor Howard Maskill, University of Newcastle (Chapter 20), Dr Norman Billingham, University of Sussex (Chapter 22), Dr Jon Nield, Queen Mary College, (Chapter 23), Professor Jon Cooper, University College London (Chapter 23), Dr Duncan Bruce, University of York (Chapter 22), Professor David Mankoff, University of Pennsylvania (Chapter 25), Dr Philip Walker, University of Surrey and Dr Eli Zysman-Colman (University of St Andrews (Chapter 22), and Dr Graham Patrick (Chapter 25), University of the West of Scotland.

I also acknowledge the contributions of Dr David Fairley (Overseas Family School, Singapore) who gave me invaluable advice and guidance on the many chemical issues I encountered when writing the book.

A special word of thanks must go to Mr Nick Lee, experienced chemistry and TOK teacher, workshop leader and IB examiner, for his most helpful comments on the final drafts.

Finally, we are indebted to the Hodder Education team that produced this book, led by Eleanor Miles and So-Shan Au at Hodder Education.

Chris Talbot
Singapore, June 2015

Acknowledgements

The Publishers would like to thank the following for permission to reproduce copyright material:

■ Photo credits

All photos by kind permission of Cesar Reyes except:

p.1 *t* Chris Talbot; **p.6** Science photo library/Michael W Davidson; **p.7** *t* Chris Talbot, *b* NASA/Johnson Space Center; **p.10** *t, b* Andrew Lambert Photography/Science Photo Library; **p.22** Chris Talbot; **p.26** Reproduced with permission of the BIPM, which retains full internationally protected copyright (photograph courtesy of the BIPM); **p.56** IBM Research; **p.63** Tim Beddow/Science Photo Library; **p.67** *l* Andrew Lambert Photography/Science Photo Library, *c* David Talbot, *r* Robert Balcer; **p.68** Carlos Santa Maria – Fotolia; **p.73** CERN; **p.87** *tl* Andrew Lambert Photography/Science Photo Library; **p.103** Prof. Mark J Winter/http://www.webelments.com; **p.108** *tr* Andrew Lambert Photography/Science Photo Library; **p.111** *b* JoLin/istockphoto.com; **p.122** Robert Balcer; **p.124** Se7enimage – Fotolia; **p.129** Chris Talbot; **p.141** *t* Chris Talbot; **p.143** Harry Kroto and used with the permission of The Sussex Fullerene Research Centre and photographer Nicholas Sinclair; **p.144** Public Domain/Http://Commons.Wikimedia.Org/Wiki/File:Graphene-3D-Balls.Png; **p.162** Dirk Wiersma/Science Photo Library; **p.167** *t, b* David Talbot; **p.192** NASA/Goddard Space Flight Center; **p.199** *l* Roger Harris/Science Photo Library, *r* Noaa/Science Photo Library; **p.204** J C Revy /Science Photo Library; **p.205** *t* Dr Colin Baker; **p.223** *t* Anh Ngo – Fotolia, *b* Gigi200043 – Fotolia; **p.224** *t, b* Richard Harwood; **p.226** Richard Harwood; **p.233** Richard Harwood; **p.235** Science Photo Library; **p.237** Richard Harwood; **p.239** *t, b* Richard Harwood; **p.245** Bettmann/CORBIS; **p.255** Juan Gartner/Science Photo Library; **p.259** *l, r* Richard Harwood; **p.274** Leungchopan – Fotolia; **p.283** *b* David Talbot; **p.285** Phil Degginger/Alamy; **p.295** *b* sequence Chris Talbot; **p.304** *t, b* Chris Talbot; **p.305** *t* Chris Talbot; **p.306** Dr Colin Baker; **p.307** Andrew Lambert Photography/Science Photo Library; **p.309** Martyn F. Chillmaid/Science Photo Library; **p.317** Frank Scullion/http://www.franklychemistry.co.uk/electrolysis_lead_bromide_video.html; **p.322** Klaus Boller/Science Photo Library; **p.323** *t, b* Chris Talbot; **p.324** Richard Harwood; **p.328** *t* Mandritoiu – Fotolia, *b* David Talbot; **p.331** Richard Harwood; **p.332** Richard Harwood; **p.336** Rasmol Library/Richard Harwood; **p.339** Richard Harwood; **p.342** Chris Talbot; **p.346** *t* Geraint Lewis/Rex, *b* Richard Harwood; **p.348** *t* Richard Harwood, *b* IBM Research; **p.351** *t* Chris Talbot, *c* Full Image – Fotolia, *bl* Science Photo LibraryDavid Taylor/Cordelia Molly, *br* David Taylor/Science Photo Library; **p.352** *t* Science Photo Library/Paul Rapson, *b* CSIRO/Science Photo Library; **p.353** *l* Eye Ubiquitous/Alamy, *r* Robert Brook/Science Photo Library; **p.354** Paul Rapson/Science Photo Library; **p.355** Chris Talbot; **p.356** David Talbot; **p.358** Chris Talbot; **p.359** Chris Talbot; **p.360** Andrew Lambert/Science Photo Library; **p.361** David Talbot; **p.365** *l* Roger Job/Science Photo Library, *r* Vanessa Vick/Science Photo Library; **p.366** Andrew Lambert/Science Photo Library; **p.368** *t* Chris Talbot, *b* Andrew Lambert/Science Photo Library; **p.370** Chris Talbot; **p.375** Ted Kinsman/Science Photo Library; **p.381** SciLabware; **p.395** JPL/NASA; **p.405** Chris Talbot; **p.408** Chris Talbot; **p.410** Dr Jon Hare; **p.423** Dr Jon Hare; **p.427** Mikhail Basov – Fotolia; **p.430** James Steidl/Fotolia.Com; **p.431** *t* Zephyr/Science Photo Library, *b* Dr Jon Hare; **p.441** CNRI/Science Photo Library; **p.458** Roger-Viollet/Topfoto; **p.460** Mark A. Wilson (Department Of Geology, The College Of Wooster)/Public Domain (http://Commons.Wikimedia.Org/Wiki/File:Qtubironpillar.JPG); **p.469** Chris Talbot; **p.474** Chris Talbot; **p.480** *t* Bruce Balick (University of Washington), Vincent Icke (Leiden University, The Netherlands), Garrelt Mellema (Stockholm University), and NASA/ESA, *c* Jose Ignacio Soto – Fotolia; **p.481** Andrew Lambert Photography/Science Photo Library; **p.516** Charles D. Winters/Science Photo Library; **p.526** Richard Harwood; **p.537** *t* David Talbot; **p.549** Public Domain/Http://Schneider.Ncifcrf.Gov/Images/Boltzmann/Boltzmann-Tomb-3.Html; **p.585** *t* TUDGAY, Frederick, 1841–1921, The "Dunedin" off the English Coast, 1875, oil on canvas: 487 x 790 mm, accession: 02/01, Hocken Collections, Uare Taoka o Hākena, University of Otago, *b* Everett Collection/Rex; **p.586** Chris Talbot; **p.587** Treetstreet – Fotolia; **p.597** Claude Nuridsany and Marie Perennou/Science Photo Library; **p.603** Sovereign, ISM/Science Photo Library; **p.628** Richard Harwood;

p.632 Chris Talbot; **p.652** CNRI/Science Photo Library; **p.659** Chris Talbot; **p.661** David Talbot; **p.667** David Talbot; **p.668** David Talbot; **p.671** Chris Talbot; **p.678** Andrew Lambert Photography/Science Photo Library; **p.684** Richard Harwood; **p.685** Andrew Lambert Photography/Science Photo Library; **p.688** Richard Harwood; **p.701** Richard Harwood; **p.706** David Talbot; **p.707** *t* Chris Talbot, *b* David Talbot; **p.708** David Talbot; **p.715** Richard Harwood; **p.727** Sovereign, ISM/Science Photo Library; **p.730** Chris Talbot; **p.733** Science Source/Science Photo Library; **p.735** Chris Talbot.

Artwork credits

p.25 Fig. 1.37 Jon Harwood; **p.37** Fig. 1.48 Kim Gyeoul; **p.54** Fig. 2.3 Kirstie Gannaway; **p.56** Fig. 2.10, **p.91** Fig. 3.16 Jon Harwood; **p.245** Fig. 7.26 Jon Harwood; **p.252** Fig. 8.1 Kim Gyeoul; **p.253** Fig. 8.2, **p.322** Fig. 10.2, **p.494** Fig. 14.17, **p.495** Fig. 14.20, **p.575** Fig. 16.21 Jon Harwood.

Examination questions credits

Examination questions have been reproduced with kind permission from the International Baccalaureate Organization.

Every effort has been made to trace all copyright holders, but if any have been inadvertently overlooked the Publishers will be pleased to make the necessary arrangements at the first opportunity.

1 Stoichiometric relationships

- Physical and chemical properties depend on the ways in which different atoms combine.
- The mole makes it possible to correlate the number of particles with the mass that can be measured.
- Mole ratios in chemical equations can be used to calculate reacting ratios by mass and gas volume.

1.1 Introduction to the particulate nature of matter and chemical change – *physical and chemical properties depend on the ways in which different atoms combine*

Chemistry is the study of chemical substances. The collective name for chemical substances is matter. Matter may be in the form of a solid, a liquid, or a gas. These are called the three states of matter and are convertible.

Matter may contain one chemical substance or a mixture of different chemical substances. Part of a chemist's work is to separate one substance from another and to identify single or pure substances.

■ **Figure 1.1** Hawaii National Park with volcano emitting steam (temperature above 100 °C), above which are clouds of water vapour (air temperature)

States of matter

There are three phases or states of matter: solids, liquids and gases. Any substance can exist in each of these three states depending on temperature and pressure.

A solid, at a given temperature, has a definite volume and shape, which may be affected by changes in temperature. Solids usually increase slightly in size (in all directions) when heated (thermal expansion) and usually decrease in size if cooled (thermal contraction).

A liquid, at a given temperature, has a fixed volume and will take up the shape of the bottom of any container it is poured into. Like a solid, a liquid's volume is slightly affected by changes in temperature.

A gas (Figure 1.1), at a given temperature, has neither a definite shape nor a definite volume. It will take up the shape of any container and will spread out evenly within it, by a process known as diffusion. The volumes of gases are greatly affected by changes in temperature.

Liquids and gases, unlike solids, are relatively compressible. This means that their volumes are decreased by applying pressure. Gases are much more compressible than liquids.

■ **Figure 1.2**
A sample of the element phosphorus (red allotropic form)

Elements

The chemical elements (Figure 1.2) are the simplest substances and are each composed of a single type of atom (see Chapter 2). (Many elements exist as a mixture of atoms of differing masses, known as isotopes – see Chapter 2). Elements cannot be split up or decomposed into simpler substances by a chemical reaction.

The elements can be classified into three groups based upon the state of matter they exist in at 25 °C. Most of the elements are solids, for example iron, but bromine and mercury are liquids at room temperature and the remainder of the elements are gases, for example oxygen and neon.

O=O
oxygen molecule O_2

N≡N
nitrogen molecule N_2

H—H
hydrogen molecule H_2

Cl—Cl
chlorine molecule Cl_2

sulfur molecule S_8

■ **Figure 1.3**
Diagram of oxygen, nitrogen, hydrogen, chlorine and sulfur molecules

The elements can also be classified into two groups: metals and non-metals (see Chapter 4), based on their chemical and physical properties. For example, aluminium is a metal and chlorine is a non-metal.

Many elements exist as atoms, for example metals and the noble gases. However, many non-metals exist as atoms bonded together into molecules (Figure 1.3). Examples of non-metal molecules include oxygen, O_2, chlorine, Cl_2, nitrogen, N_2, phosphorus, P_4, and sulfur, S_8. Oxygen, nitrogen and chlorine exist as diatomic molecules.

Allotropy is the existence of two or more crystalline forms of an element. These different forms are called allotropes. Allotropes exist where there is more than one possible arrangement of bonded atoms. For example, solid carbon can exist in three allotropes: diamond, carbon-60 (C_{60}) or buckminsterfullerene, graphite (and graphene which is a single layer of graphite) (see Chapter 4); oxygen can exist in two allotropes: dioxygen (O_2) and trioxygen (ozone, O_3).

ToK Link
Priestley and Lavoisier's discovery of oxygen

Oxygen was first prepared in a reasonably pure state in the 18th century, and its preparation was followed by a theory of burning (combustion) which is still accepted. It completely replaced a theory called the phlogiston theory in a paradigm shift. This occurs when a scientific model or way of thinking is quickly and completely replaced by a very different scientific model or way of thinking.

Priestley strongly heated a red powder (mercury oxide) which he called calx of mercury. This substance decomposed into two substances: mercury and a gas (now known to be oxygen). He also discovered that flammable substances burned much more strongly in this gas (100% oxygen) than in normal air (20% oxygen). Priestley informed Lavoisier of his discovery, and Lavoisier carried out an experiment (Figure 1.4) in which he demonstrated that the gas which Priestley had made was identical to that 20% of the air which supports combustion (burning).

He kept the mercury in the retort, at a temperature just lower than its boiling point, for several days. He observed that the volume of gas had been reduced by 20%, this being shown by a rise in the level of the mercury in the bell jar. He also observed that a red powder (mercury oxide) had been formed on the surface of the hot mercury in the retort. The gas (now known to be nitrogen and noble gases) remaining in his apparatus would not support combustion.

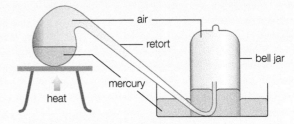

■ **Figure 1.4** Lavoisier's preparation of oxygen

On the basis of his and Priestley's observations, Lavoisier proposed the following explanation of combustion and the composition of air: 20% of air consists of oxygen; when substances burn they chemically combine with oxygen, forming oxides. When a substance burns completely, the mass of the oxide formed equals the combined mass of the original substance and the mass of the oxygen with which it has chemically combined.

■ Compounds

Many mixtures of elements undergo a chemical reaction when they are mixed together and heated. The formation of a compound (Figure 1.5) from its elements is termed synthesis. Heat energy is usually released during this reaction (see Chapter 5).

■ **Figure 1.5**
A model showing the structure of the compound calcium carbonate, $CaCO_3$ (black spheres represent carbon, red oxygen and clear calcium)

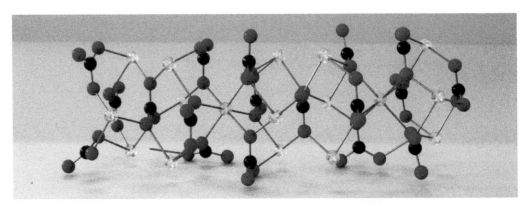

When a mixture of iron and sulfur is heated, large amounts of heat energy are released as the compound iron(II) sulfide, FeS, is formed (Figure 1.6). (Synthesis reactions like this are examples of redox reactions – see Chapter 9). Figure 1.6 describes this reaction in terms of atoms in iron and sulfur (Figure 1.7) reacting to form iron(II) sulfide.

■ **Figure 1.6**
A description of the formation of iron(II) sulfide in terms of atoms

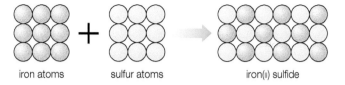

iron atoms   sulfur atoms   iron(II) sulfide

The word equation for this reaction is:

iron + sulfur → iron(II) sulfide

Mixtures of elements are easily separated by a physical method, since the atoms of the different elements are not bonded together. For example, iron can be separated from sulfur by the use of a magnet.

However, when a compound is formed the atoms it contains are chemically bonded together, so the compound will have different physical and chemical properties from the constituent elements (Table 1.1). For example, iron is magnetic, but the compound iron(II) sulfide is non-magnetic (Figure 1.8). A compound will contain either molecules or ions (Chapter 4).

■ **Table 1.1**
A summary of the different properties of iron, sulfur, an iron/sulfur mixture and iron(II) sulfide

Substance	Appearance	Effect of a magnet	Effect of dilute hydrochloric acid
Iron	Dark grey powder	Attracted to it	Very little reaction when cold. When warm, an odourless gas (hydrogen) is produced
Sulfur	Yellow powder	No effect	No reaction when hot or cold
Iron–sulfur mixture	Dirty yellow powder	Iron powder particles attracted to it	Iron powder reacts as described above
Iron(II) sulfide	Dark grey solid	No effect	A foul smelling gas (hydrogen sulfide) is produced

The splitting of a chemical compound into its constituent elements is termed decomposition. This process requires an input of energy, either heat (thermal decomposition) or electricity (electrolysis) (Chapter 9).

■ **Figure 1.7** The elements iron and sulfur

■ **Figure 1.8** A sample of iron(II) sulfide and a mixture of iron and sulfur

---

1   A mixture of magnesium and iodine was heated. A red glow spread through the mixture during the reaction. At the end of the experiment a white solid had been formed.
 a State one observation which shows that a chemical reaction has occurred.
 b Write a word equation to describe the reaction.
 c State two differences between compounds and elements.

■ Molecular kinetic theory

The simple diagram in Figure 1.9 shows the relationship between the states of matter and the arrangement (idealized, simplified and in two dimensions only) of their particles (ions, atoms or molecules). The arrows represent physical changes termed changes of state. In a physical change no new chemical substance is formed.

In a crystalline solid the particles (atoms, ions or molecules) are close together and packed in a regular pattern (known as a lattice). Studies using X-ray crystallography have confirmed how particles are arranged in crystal structures (see Chapter 22 on the accompanying website.)

■ **Figure 1.9**
The three states of matter and their interconversion

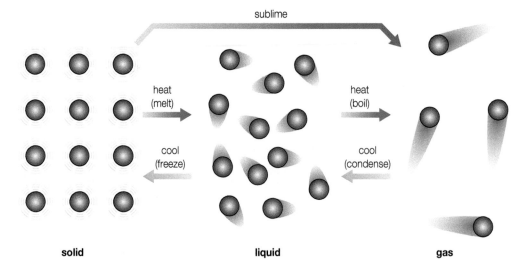

The particles vibrate around fixed positions and these vibrations become stronger as the temperature increases. The particles in a solid are strongly attracted to each other. In a liquid the particles are close together, but are free to move within the liquid. They are attracted to the other particles in the liquid. The particles move faster as the temperature increases. In a gas the particles are far apart and are free to move. The particles move so fast that there is little attraction between gas particles. The particles travel faster as the temperature increases.

This model about the way in which particles behave in the three states of matter is known as kinetic molecular theory. It describes all substances as being made up of particles in motion. It is a scientific model that explains how the arrangement of particles relates to the physical properties of the three states of matter.

■ Changes of state

The kinetic molecular model can be used to explain how a pure substance changes from one state of matter to another. If a crystalline solid is heated, the particles (atoms, ions or molecules) vibrate faster and with greater amplitude as they gain kinetic energy. This makes them 'push' their neighbouring particles further away from themselves. This causes an increase in the volume of the solid, which expands.

Eventually with a further increase in temperature the heat energy causes the forces of attraction between particles to weaken. The regular pattern of the particles in the lattice breaks down and the particles can now move around each other. The solid has melted and the temperature at which this occurs is the melting point. The temperature of a pure solid will remain constant until it has all melted. When the substance is a liquid there are still strong attractive forces operating between the particles.

There are energy changes which occur during changes of state. During melting and boiling heat is absorbed (from the surroundings). During condensing and freezing heat is released (to the surroundings). The heat supplied during melting and boiling is used to overcome or 'break' the attractive forces between particles by increasing their kinetic energy. The heat released during condensing and freezing is derived from the reduction in the average kinetic energy of the particles.

Certain solids, for example frozen carbon dioxide (dry ice), can change directly to a gas without passing through the liquid state. This is known as sublimation and the substance is said to sublime. This means molecules leave the solid with enough kinetic energy to exist as gas particles. If the temperature is lowered the gas particles slow down and re-form the solid without passing through the liquid state. This is known as vapour deposition or simply deposition.

Solids that have high melting points have stronger attractive forces (bonds or intermolecular forces) acting between their particles than those with low melting points. Table 1.2 shows a list of some substances (elements and compounds) with their corresponding melting and boiling points.

■ **Table 1.2** Selected melting and boiling points

Substance and formula	Melting point/°C	Boiling point/°C
Aluminium, Al	661	2467
Ethanol, C_2H_5OH	−117	79
Mercury, Hg	−30	357
Oxygen, O_2	−218	−183
Sodium chloride, NaCl	801	1413
Water, H_2O	0	100

If the liquid is heated, the particles (usually molecules) will move around even faster as their average kinetic energy increases. Their kinetic energy constantly changes due to collisions. Some particles at the surface of the liquid have enough kinetic energy to overcome the forces of attraction between themselves and the other particles in the liquid and they escape from the surface to form a gas. This process is known as evaporation and takes place at all temperatures below the boiling point. If the temperature is lowered the reverse process, known as condensation, occurs. The gas particles move more slowly and enter the surface of the liquid.

Eventually, a temperature is reached (the boiling point) at which the particles are trying to escape from the liquid so quickly that bubbles of gas form inside the bulk of the liquid. This is known as boiling. At the boiling point the pressure of the gas created above the liquid equals that in the air (atmospheric pressure) (Chapter 7).

Liquids with high boiling points have stronger forces (bonds or intermolecular forces) operating between their particles than liquids with low boiling points. Chemical bonding and intermolecular forces are discussed in Chapter 4.

When a gas is cooled, the average kinetic energy (speed) of the particles decreases and the particles (usually molecules) move closer and their average separation decreases. The forces of attraction become significant, and if the temperature is lowered to the condensation point the gas will condense to form a liquid. When a liquid is cooled to its freezing point (equal in value to the melting point) it freezes to a solid. During condensing and freezing heat energy is released.

The changes of state are physical changes: no new chemical substances are formed. Ice, water and steam all contain molecules with the formula H_2O. Whenever a change in state occurs the temperature remains constant during the change.

2 Identify the change of state which describes the following processes:
   a Solid ethanol changing to liquid ethanol
   b Molten metal solidifying in a mould
   c Water changing to steam at 100°C
   d Bubbles of ethanol gas forming in liquid ethanol
   e Ice forming from water vapour on the freezer compartment of a fridge
   f Solid aluminium chloride forming a gas on gentle heating

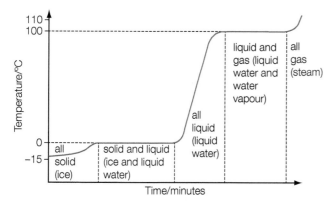

■ **Figure 1.10** Graph of temperature against time for the change from ice at −15°C to water to steam at 120°C

Heating and cooling curves

The graph shown in Figure 1.10 was constructed from data-logger measurements by plotting the temperature of water as it was heated steadily from −15°C to 120°C (at 1 atmosphere pressure). The heating curve shows that two changes of state have taken place. When the temperature was first measured only ice was present. After a short period of time the curve flattens, showing that even through heat energy is being absorbed, the temperature remains constant. This indicates that a change in state is occurring.

In ice the molecules of water are close together and are attracted to one another by intermolecular forces.

For ice to melt, the molecules must obtain sufficient kinetic energy to overcome the forces of attraction between the water particles to allow relative movement to take place. This is what the heat energy is doing. The temperature will begin to rise again only after all the ice has

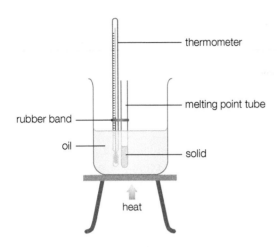

■ **Figure 1.11** Simple apparatus to find the melting point of a solid (in the melting point tube)

melted. Generally, the heating curve for a pure solid always stops rising at its melting point and gives rise to a sharp melting point. The addition or presence of impurities lowers the melting point. Figure 1.11 shows a simple apparatus used to find the melting point of a solid. Commercial melting point apparatus uses a heating block to melt the sample.

The purity of substances is very important. Consumers must be certain that foods and medicines do not contain harmful substances. Very small amounts of some chemicals can cause death. The food and drug industries must check constantly to ensure that the substances they use are pure.

To boil a liquid such as water, it has be to given some extra heat energy. This can be seen on the graph (Figure 1.10) where the curve levels out at 100 °C, which is the boiling point of water (at 1 atmosphere pressure). The reverse processes of condensing and freezing occur on cooling. This time, however, heat energy is given out when the gas condenses to the liquid and the liquid freezes to give the solid. Both changes of state occur at constant temperature.

3   A solid molecular compound X was heated at constant power for 20 minutes. Its temperature varied as shown in the graph below.

a Deduce the melting and boiling points of substance X.
b State the physical state of X at 25, 50 and 100 °C.
c Explain what is happening during the melting and boiling of X.

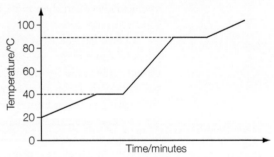

Utilization: Unusual states of matter

Liquid crystals

Liquid crystals (Figure 1.12) are a state of matter that look and flow like liquids (see Chapter 22 on the accompanying website). However, they have some order in the arrangement of their particles (molecules), and so in some ways behave like crystals. Liquid crystals are widely used in displays for digital watches, calculators, lap-top computer displays and in portable televisions. They are also useful in thermometers because certain liquid crystals change colour with temperature changes.

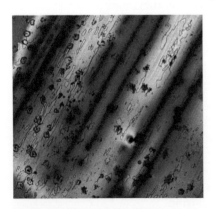

■ **Figure 1.12** A polarized light micrograph of liquid crystals

Plasma

A plasma is the superheated gaseous state consisting of a mixture of electrons and highly charged positive ions. It is found at extremely high temperatures in the interiors of stars or in intense electrical fields, such as low pressure discharge tubes (see Chapter 2). Astronomical studies have revealed that 99% of the matter in the Universe is present in the plasma state. Inductively coupled plasma spectroscopy is an important technique for detecting and quantifying small amounts of metals (see Chapter 22 on the accompanying website).

the coolant uses heat energy
from the air in the cabinet
to vaporize in the coils
around the ice box

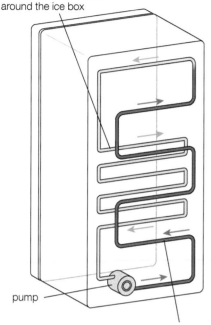

pump

the coolant condenses in these pipes, giving
out thermal energy which heats the air

■ **Figure 1.13** The coolant system of a refrigerator

■ **Figure 1.14** A domestic air conditioner

■ **Figure 1.15** An astronaut eating a freeze-dried
meal on board Space Shuttle Discovery

Utilization of heat changes during changes of state: Refrigeration

It is difficult to over-estimate the importance of the invention of the modern refrigerator in the context of food transportation and storage. The invention of refrigerated transport for food led to a revolution in the globalization of markets and the availability of important commodities across, and between, continents.

A refrigerator takes advantage of the heat energy transfers when a volatile (low boiling point) liquid evaporates and condenses. The key stage of the system depends on the fact that evaporation absorbs heat from the surroundings. Within the body of the refrigerator (Figure 1.13) a pump circulates a low boiling point liquid around a circuit of pipes. This volatile liquid vaporizes in the pipes inside the refrigerator, taking in heat energy from the air inside the refrigerator and keeping the food and drinks inside cold.

Continuing around the circuit, the vapour (gas) is compressed by the pump as it flows out at the bottom of the refrigerator. The compressed vapour is hot. As it flows through the pipes at the back of the refrigerator the vapour cools and condenses back to a liquid, releasing heat energy and heating up the air around the back of the cabinet. Overall, heat energy is transferred from inside the refrigerator to the air in the room.

The use of the reversible evaporation–condensation cycle of volatile liquids in refrigeration and air conditioning (Figure 1.14) is one of the features of modern living. In the past, many air conditioners commonly used CFCs (chlorofluorocarbons) as their volatile liquid. However, in most countries the manufacture and use of CFCs is either banned or restricted. This is because when CFC molecules reach the upper atmosphere ultraviolet radiation from the Sun breaks the carbon–chlorine bond, yielding a chlorine atom. These chlorine atoms catalyse the breakdown of ozone (trioxygen) into dioxygen, depleting the ozone layer that protects the Earth's surface from strong ultraviolet radiation.

Utilization of removal of water at low pressure: Freeze-drying

The basic idea of freeze-drying is to completely remove water from food while leaving the basic structure and composition unchanged. Removing water keeps food from spoiling for a long period of time. Food spoils when bacteria digest the food and decompose it. Bacteria may release toxins that cause disease, or they may just release chemicals that make food taste bad. Additionally, naturally occurring enzymes in food can react with oxygen to cause spoiling and ripening. Bacteria need water to survive, so if water is removed from food it will not spoil. Enzymes also need to be hydrated to react with food, so dehydrating food will also stop spoiling.

Freeze-drying also significantly reduces the total mass of the food. Most food is largely made up of water and removing this water makes the food a lot lighter, which means it is easier to transport. The military and camping supply companies freeze-dry foods to make them easier for one person to carry. NASA has also freeze-dried foods for the cramped quarters on board spacecraft and the International Space Station (Figure 1.15).

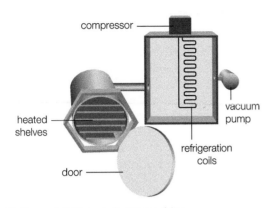

■ **Figure 1.16** Freeze-drying machine

Freeze-drying is not normally carried out by simple evaporation. It is difficult to remove water completely using evaporation because most of the water is not directly exposed to air. Unless all the water is removed then there will be some bacterial and enzyme activity. In addition, the heat involved in the evaporation process changes the shape, texture and composition of the food.

The fundamental principle in freeze-drying is sublimation, the phase change from a solid directly into a gas (at constant temperature). A lowering of the pressure (below 0.6 atmospheres) and an increase in temperature results in water being converted to a gas, rather than liquid water.

A typical freeze-drying machine (Figure 1.16) consists of a freeze-drying chamber with several shelves attached to heating units, a freezing coil connected to a refrigerator compressor, and a vacuum pump.

The machine runs the compressors to lower the temperature in the chamber. The food is frozen solid, which separates the water from everything around it, on a molecular level, even though the water is still present.

The heating units supply a small amount of heat to the shelves, causing the ice to change phase. Since the pressure is so low, the ice turns directly into water vapour. The water vapour flows out of the freeze-drying chamber, past the freezing coil. The water vapour condenses onto the freezing coil in solid ice form, in the same way as water condenses as frost on a cold day.

Utilization: Atom economy in chemical reactions

The atom economy examines the theoretical potential of a reaction, by considering the quantity of starting atoms in all the reactants that end up in the desired product.

$$\% \text{ atom economy} = \frac{\text{atomic mass of all utilized atoms}}{\text{atomic mass of all reactants}}$$

Taking the laboratory preparation of copper(II) sulfate from copper(II) oxide and sulfuric acid as an example, this is an acid–base reaction. This calculation is explained later in the chapter and involves calculating the mass of one mole of each substance from the formula and the relative atomic masses of the elements.

$$CuO(s) + H_2SO_4(aq) \rightarrow CuSO_4(aq) + H_2O(l)$$

Mass of starting atoms is
$CuO = 63.5 + 16 = 79.5\,g$
$H_2SO_4 = 2 + 32 + 64 = 98\,g$
Total = 177.5 g

Mass of desired product is
$CuSO_4 = 63.5 + 32 + 64 = 159.5\,g$

$$\% \text{ atom economy} = \frac{159.5}{177.5} \times 100 = 89.9\%$$

The atom economy for the production of ethanol from ethene and steam is shown below. This is known as an addition or hydration reaction.

$$C_2H_4(g) + H_2O(g) \rightarrow C_2H_5OH(l)$$

$$\% \text{ atom economy} = \frac{46}{46} \times 100 = 100\% \text{ (there are no unwanted products)}$$

4   Calculate the atom economy for the reaction between carbon and steam to form carbon dioxide and hydrogen.

A higher atom economy means that there is a higher utilization of the atoms of reactants into the final useful products. That is, there is a better use of materials and also less waste formation.

Green chemistry

Green chemistry consists of chemicals and chemical processes designed to reduce or eliminate impacts on the environment. The use and production of these chemicals may involve reduced waste products, non-toxic chemicals, and improved efficiency. Industrial chemists evaluate chemical pathways and their economic and environmental costs by calculating the relative efficiency of the chemical reactions involved. Percentage yield provides a means of comparison of the theoretical and actual quantity of product, and used to be the main way of evaluating reaction efficiency. However, calculation of 'atom economy' has become a more important means of comparing the efficiency of chemical reactions. Atom economy is a measure of the proportion of reactant atoms that is incorporated into the desired product of a chemical reaction. Calculation of atom economy therefore also gives an indication of the proportion of reactant atoms forming waste products.

Mixtures

In a mixture of two elements there are two types of atoms present, but they are not chemically bonded to each other. Figure 1.17 shows a mixture of elements existing as atoms and a mixture of two elements existing as diatomic molecules.

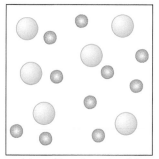 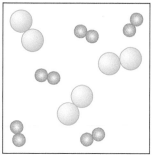

a mixture of two elements existing as atoms

b mixture of two elements existing as molecules

■ **Figure 1.17** Particle representations of a mixture of atoms and a mixture of molecules

A compound always contains the same proportion (by mass) of each element. For example, iron(II) sulfide has iron and sulfur in the ratio of 55.85 to 32.06, i.e. 1.742 to 1.000. However, a mixture can have any proportion of each element. For example, the percentage (by mass) of sulfur in an iron–sulfur mixture can range from close to 0% to almost 100%.

Alloys are mixtures of metals and other elements (often carbon) that have been melted together and then allowed to solidify. Common alloys include brass (a mixture of copper and zinc) and bronze (copper and tin).

The major differences between mixtures of elements and compounds are summarized below in Table 1.3.

■ **Table 1.3**
The major differences between mixtures of elements and compounds

Mixture	Compound
It contains two or more substances (elements or compounds)	It is a single pure substance
The composition is variable	The composition (by mass) is fixed
No chemical reaction takes place when a mixture is formed	A chemical reaction occurs when a compound is formed
The properties are those of the individual elements or compounds	The properties are very different to those of the component elements

5   State whether each of the boxes below contains an element, a compound or a mixture.

a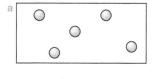

b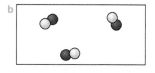

c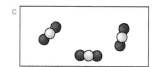

d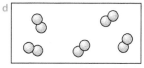

e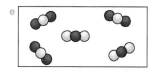

f

Types of mixtures

There are many different types of mixtures. One classification of mixtures is to classify them as homogeneous or heterogeneous. For example, if gaseous bromine is introduced into a gas jar filled with air (mainly nitrogen) it will diffuse and spread evenly through both gas jars (Figure 1.18). The concentrations of bromine and nitrogen will be the same throughout both gas jars. Mixtures of gases are described as being homogeneous since they have a uniform or constant composition. Figure 1.19 shows how kinetic molecular theory can be used to explain diffusion in gases. Gases diffuse quickly because the particles are moving rapidly and there are large spaces between the molecules.

■ **Figure 1.18** After 24 hours the orange bromine fumes have diffused throughout both gas jars

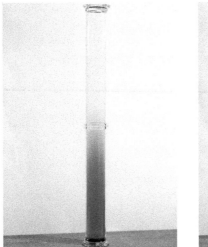
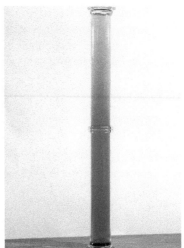

■ **Figure 1.19** A particle description of diffusion in gases

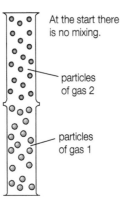
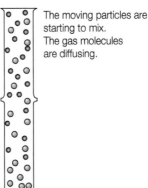
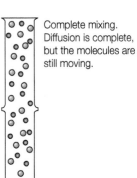

Diffusion also takes place in liquids (Figure 1.20) but it is a much slower process than with gases. This is because the particles in a liquid move much more slowly because they have less kinetic energy. The resulting solution is homogenous and the concentration of nickel(II) sulfate will be the same at any point within the solution.

■ **Figure 1.20** Diffusion within nickel(II) sulfate solution can take days to reach the stage shown on the right

The process of the dissolving of the nickel(II) sulfate can be readily explained using the kinetic molecular theory. Particles of water (the solvent) collide with the particles of the substance being dissolved (the solute). When they collide, they attract each other. Water molecules pull off and interact with the solute particles (nickel and sulfate ions) from the solid solute (nickel(II) sulfate). The water molecules surround the solute particles. As the water molecules move, the solute particles spread through the solution. Figure 1.21 shows solvent particles dissolving a single type of solute particle. This process is known as hydration.

■ **Figure 1.21**
A simplified particle
description of
dissolving

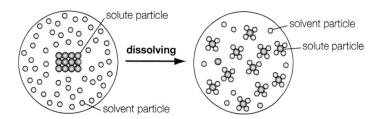

In a heterogeneous mixture the composition is not uniform (the same) throughout the mixture and sometimes the different components can be observed. For example, if water is mixed with oil, two separate layers are seen. The two liquids do not mix and are said to be immiscible. In contrast, if water is mixed with ethanol a uniform layer is observed. The two liquids are said to be miscible and a homogeneous mixture is formed.

At the macroscopic or bulk level, matter can be classified into mixtures or pure substances. These can be further sub-divided as shown in Figure 1.22.

6   Classify each of the following mixtures as homogenous or heterogeneous. vinegar (ethanoic acid in water), cooking oil and water, mixture of helium and hydrogen gases, iron and sulfur, sea water, blood, air, solder (a low melting point mixture of metals).

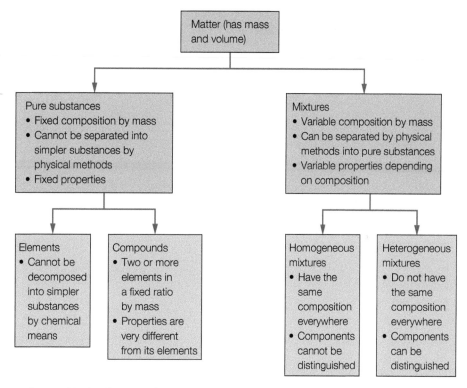

■ **Figure 1.22 Classification of matter**

Chemists usually want pure substances because if a substance is pure it always has the same physical and chemical properties. The properties of an impure substance will vary. Nearly all pure substances have been through two stages: they have been separated from a mixture and been tested to determine their purity.

 Elements and compounds can be detected by a variety of instrumental methods (see Chapter 21, and Chapter 22 on the accompanying website), for example mass spectrometry (MS), nuclear magnetic resonance (NMR), various forms of chromatography, inductive coupled plasma spectroscopy (ICP) and infrared spectroscopy (IR). These instruments allow chemists to probe and discover which elements are present in the substance, their quantities and, in some cases, give information about the structure of the substance. Forensic scientists also make use of these techniques because they are very accurate and sensitive: they only require tiny amounts of sample.

Separating mixtures

If the substances in a mixture are to be separated then the chemist needs to find some physical difference between them. Table 1.4 summarizes some common separation techniques.

■ **Table 1.4** Common separation techniques

Type of mixture	Name of separation technique	Physical difference	Examples of mixtures separated
Insoluble solid and liquid	Filtration	Solubility	Sand and water; calcium carbonate (chalk) and water
Two miscible liquids	Distillation (simple and fractional)	Boiling point	Ethanol (alcohol) and water
Soluble solid and liquid	Crystallization or evaporation	Volatility	Sodium chloride (salt) and water
Soluble solids	Paper chromatography	Solubility	Food colourings; plant pigments
Two immiscible liquids	Separating funnel	Insolubility	Water and petrol; water and oil

■ Chemical symbols

Each chemical element is represented by a chemical symbol (Table 1.5). The symbol consists of either one or two letters. The first letter is always a capital or upper case letter and the second letter is always small or lower case. These chemical symbols are international (Figure 1.23).

Name of chemical element	Chemical symbol	Comment
Hydrogen	H	The first letter of the name
Calcium	Ca	The first two letters of the name
Chlorine	Cl	The first letter and one other letter in the name
Sodium	Na	Two letters derived from a non-English name: *natrium* (Latin)

■ **Table 1.5** Selected chemical elements and symbols

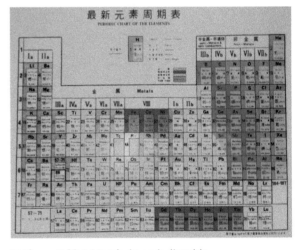

■ **Figure 1.23** A Mandarin periodic table

A number of chemical elements are named after people, mythical characters or places (Table 1.6).

■ **Table 1.6** Selected chemical elements and the origins of their names

Name and symbol of element	Origin of the name	Additional note
Gallium (Ga)	Named after France (*Gallia*), Latin for France	The discoverer of the metal, Lecoq de Boisbaudran, subtly attached an association with his name: Lecoq (rooster) in Latin is *gallus*
Niobium (Nb)	Niobe, a mortal woman in Greek mythology	Niobe is a character in the film *Matrix Reloaded* (unrelated to the naming of the element)
Vanadium (V)	Scandinavian goddess *Vanadis* (*Freyja*)	
Helium (He)	*Helios* is the Greek name for the Sun	Helium was discovered in the Sun before being discovered on Earth
Mendelevium (Md)	Named after Dmitri Mendeleev who formulated the first periodic table in 1869	The element was synthesized in 1955 by a team including Glenn Seaborg

International chemical symbols and equations

The current system of chemical notation was invented by the Swedish chemist Berzelius (1779–1848). In this typographical system chemical symbols are not abbreviations – though each consists of letters of the Latin alphabet – they are symbols intended to be used by people of all languages and alphabets. The chemical elements were assigned unique chemical symbols, based on the name of the element, but not necessarily in English. For example, tungsten has the chemical symbol 'W' after the German *Wolfram*. Chemical symbols are understood internationally when element names might need to be translated. There are sometimes differences; for example, the Germans have used 'J' instead of 'I' for iodine, so the character would not be confused with a Roman numeral.

The 'language' of chemistry frequently transcends cultural, linguistic and national boundaries. Although the symbols for the chemical elements are international, the names of the elements are sometimes language dependent, often with the end of the name characterizing the specific language. For example, magnesium changes to *magnésium* in French, *magnesio* in Spanish, *magnesion* in Greek and *magnij* in Russian. In Japanese, *katakama* reproduces the sound of the English 'magnesium'.

■ **Figure 1.24**
The Japanese *kanji* (pictogram) for sulfur (translated as 'yellow substance')

Chemical formulas

Each chemical compound is represented by a unique chemical formula. The formula of any compound can be determined by performing a suitable experiment. The formulas of many compounds can be deduced using the list of ions shown in Table 1.7. A polyatomic or compound ion is an ion that contains more than two covalently bound atoms with an associated charge; a simple ion is formed by a single element.

■ **Table 1.7** List of common ions

Positive ions			Negative ions		
Simple ions		**Formula**	**Simple ions**		**Formula**
Sodium		Na^+	Chloride		Cl^-
Potassium		K^+	Bromide		Br^-
Hydrogen		H^+	Iodide		I^-
			Oxide		O^{2-}
Copper(II)		Cu^{2+}	Sulfide		S^{2-}
Iron(II)		Fe^{2+}			
Magnesium		Mg^{2+}	**Compound or polyatomic ions**		
Calcium		Ca^{2+}	Nitrate		NO_3^-
			Nitrite		NO_2^-
Iron(III)		Fe^{3+}	Sulfate		SO_4^{2-}
Aluminium		Al^{3+}	Sulfite		SO_3^{2-}
			Carbonate		CO_3^{2-}
Compound or polyatomic ions			Phosphate(v)		PO_4^{3-}
Ammonium		NH_4^+	Hydroxide		OH^-

■ **Figure 1.25**
A sample of the compound copper(II) carbonate, $CuCO_3$ [Cu^{2+} CO_3^{2-}]

7 Deduce the formulas of iron(II) phosphate, ammonium iodide, aluminium nitrate, calcium bromide and iron(III) oxide.

In forming compounds (Figure 1.25) the number of ions used is such that the number of positive charges is equal to the number of negative charges. Ionic compounds are electrically neutral.

Examples of using the charges on ions to deduce the formula of a compound are given below:

■ Sodium sulfate is composed of sodium ions, Na^+, and sulfate ions, SO_4^{2-}. Twice as many sodium ions as sulfate ions are necessary in order to have electrical neutrality. Hence, the formula of sodium sulfate is Na_2SO_4 [$2Na^+$ SO_4^{2-}].

■ Magnesium hydroxide is composed of magnesium ions, Mg^{2+}, and hydroxide ions, OH^-. Twice as many hydroxide ions as magnesium ions are necessary in order to have electrical neutrality. Hence, the formula of magnesium hydroxide is $Mg(OH)_2$ [Mg^{2+} $2OH^-$].

The subscript number after a bracket (as in $(OH)_2$ in the formula for magnesium hydroxide) multiplies all the compound or polyatomic ions inside the bracket.

Chemical equations

Chemical reactions are at the centre of chemistry and it is important that the transition from reactants to products is represented with as much precision as possible. Each reaction has an equation. The reaction of iron with chlorine is used as an example to show how to write a correct chemical equation.

■ Write down the equation as a word equation, for example:

iron + chlorine → iron(III) chloride

The addition sign means 'reacts together' and the arrow means 'yields' and shows the direction of the reaction. (Note that some reactions are reversible, indicated by a double headed arrow ($\rightleftharpoons$), and that both forward and backward reactions will be occurring at the same time (Chapter 7).

■ Insert the correct chemical formulas for the reactant and products.

$$Fe + Cl_2 \rightarrow FeCl_3$$

This equation is unbalanced: the reactants contain (in total) one iron atom and two chlorine atoms, but the products (in total) contain one iron atom and three chlorine atoms.

■ Balance the equation by ensuring that the total numbers of atoms of elements on the two sides of the equation are equal. This is achieved by inserting integer numbers termed coefficients which multiply all the following formulas. The chemical formulas should *not* be altered.

The selection of coefficients is done on a 'trial and error' or inspection basis, although one common approach is to start with any odd numbers in formulas and double them to convert them to even numbers. Elements represented by molecules should be left until last since their coefficients will not unbalance any other molecules. Applying this approach to the example equation gives:

$$Fe + Cl_2 \rightarrow 2FeCl_3$$

followed by:

$$2Fe + Cl_2 \rightarrow 2FeCl_3$$

and finally:

$$2Fe + 3Cl_2 \rightarrow 2FeCl_3$$

This equation is now balanced: the total numbers of atoms of each element on both sides of the equation are equal, namely two iron atoms and six chlorine atoms.

The balancing of an equation is a consequence of the law of conservation of mass, which states that during a chemical reaction atoms cannot be created or destroyed. The coefficients in a balanced symbol equation indicate the reacting proportions in moles for stoichiometric amounts of the reactants. For example, the equation above indicates that two moles of iron atoms react with three moles of chlorine molecules to produce two moles of iron(III) chloride (formula units).

■ Finally, the physical states of reactants and products should be included in brackets after the chemical formulas:

$$2Fe(s) + 3Cl_2(g) \rightarrow 2FeCl_3(s)$$

Here the state symbol (s) represents a solid, (l) represents a pure liquid, (g) represents a pure gas and (aq) represents an aqueous solution.

■ If an element occurs in more than one substance on one side of the equation then leave it to last to balance. Also keep polyatomic ions, for example NO_3^- and SO_4^{2-}, as a unit during balancing.

Equations may also have additional information that indicates the size of the heat change during the reaction. This will depend on the physical states of the reactants and products, which shows the importance of including state symbols in symbol equations. For example:

$$2Fe(s) + 3Cl_2(g) \rightarrow 2FeCl_3(s) \quad \Delta H^\ominus = -1500 \, kJ \, mol^{-1}$$

indicates that when two moles of iron(III) chloride are formed by direct synthesis under standard conditions (25°C and 1 atmosphere pressure), 1500 kilojoules of heat energy are released. This is known as a thermochemical equation (Chapter 5).

An equation can be interpreted at both the atomic and the macroscopic or visible levels. The addition of state symbols or an enthalpy change makes the equation macroscopic.

It is good practice to include state symbols in chemical equations and their absence can cause errors. In the absence of state symbols, the reactants and products are assumed to be in their usual physical states at room temperature and pressure.

$$HCl + NaOH \rightarrow NaCl + H_2O$$

The precise interpretation of the equation above is 'one mole of gaseous hydrogen chloride and one mole of solid sodium hydroxide react to give one mole of solid sodium chloride and one mole of liquid water', but, under anhydrous conditions (in the absence of water), such a chemical reaction would be unlikely to occur because the HCl needs to dissolve in water to react. Presumably, the equation was meant to summarize the neutralization reaction between aqueous solutions of hydrochloric acid and sodium hydroxide:

$$HCl(aq) + NaOH(aq) \rightarrow NaCl(aq) + H_2O(l)$$

State symbols are vital if thermochemical equations (see Chapter 5) are written summarising a chemical equation and its associated energy change. State symbols must be included when writing an equation summarizing a phase change (see Chapter 7), for example, the sublimation of iodine:

$$I_2(s) \rightarrow I_2(g)$$

If the focus is purely stoichiometric, that is, on reacting amounts, then state symbols may be redundant, for example:

$$C_6H_5CH_3 + Cl_2 \rightarrow C_6H_5CH_2Cl + HCl$$

one mole of methylbenzene will react with one mole of chlorine to form one mole of chloromethylbenzene and one mole of hydrogen chloride. This reaction will occur regardless of what physical states the reactants are in. Of course, the reaction will be very slow if one or both reactants are solids (see Chapter 6) maintained at low temperatures.

It should also be noted that some reactions do not occur, even though balanced equations can be written, for example

$$Cu(s) + 2HCl(aq) \rightarrow CuCl_2(aq) + H_2(g)$$

Hence, the reactivity or electrochemical series (Chapter 9) should be consulted before equations for replacement reactions are written.

Additional points about chemical equations

When constructing a balanced equation, ensure that your final set of coefficients are all whole numbers with no common factors other than 1. For example, this equation is balanced:

$$4H_2(g) + 2O_2(g) \rightarrow 4H_2O(l)$$

However, all the coefficients have the common factor of 2. Divide through by 2 to eliminate common factors:

$$2H_2(g) + O_2(g) \rightarrow 2H_2O(l)$$

It is allowable, and sometimes necessary, to use fractional coefficients in the balancing process, for example:

$$C_2H_6(g) + \tfrac{7}{2}O_2(g) \rightarrow 2CO_2(g) + 3H_2O(l)$$

Generally, the fractional coefficient is not retained in the final answer. Multiplying the coefficients through by 2 removes the fraction:

$$2C_2H_6(g) + 7O_2(g) \rightarrow 4CO_2(g) + 6H_2O(l)$$

However, if an equation represents the standard molar enthalpy of combustion, then fractional coefficients may have to be used. The standard molar enthalpy of combustion represents the energy change when one mole of a compound undergoes complete combustion in the presence of excess oxygen (Chapter 5).

Hence the equation:

$$C_2H_6(g) + \frac{7}{2}O_2(g) \rightarrow 2CO_2(g) + 3H_2O(l)$$

correctly represents the standard molar enthalpy of combustion of ethane.

It should also be noted that some reactions do *not* occur, even though balanced equations can be written. Examples include:

$$Cu(s) + H_2SO_4(aq) \rightarrow CuSO_4(aq) + H_2(g)$$

and

$$Ag(s) + NaCl(aq) \rightarrow AgCl(aq) + Na(aq)$$

Information conveyed by a chemical reaction

Qualitatively, a chemical equation gives the names (via naming rules) of the various reactants and products, and directly gives their physical states. Quantitatively, it expresses the following information:

- the relative numbers of chemical entities of the reactants and products involved in the chemical reaction
- the relative amounts (in moles) of the reactant and products
- the relative reacting masses of reactants and products
- the relative volumes of gaseous reactants and products.

Consider the following equation:

$$H_2(g) + Cl_2(g) \rightarrow 2HCl(g)$$

Qualitatively, it indicates that hydrogen reacts with chlorine to form hydrogen chloride. The hydrogen, chlorine and hydrogen chloride are all in the gaseous form.

Quantitatively, it conveys the following information:

- one mole of hydrogen molecules reacts with one mole of chlorine molecules to form two moles of hydrogen chloride molecules
- 2 grams of hydrogen react with 71 grams of chlorine to form 73 grams of hydrogen chloride
- one volume of hydrogen reacts with one volume of chlorine to form two volumes of hydrogen chloride (see Avogadro's law).

An introduction to the different types of chemical reactions that will be encountered during the IB Chemistry programme may be found on the accompanying website.

Deducing chemical equations when reactants and products are specified

Magnesium burns in oxygen to form magnesium oxide. Write a balanced equation for this reaction.

Replace the names with their formulas:

$$Mg + O_2 \rightarrow MgO$$

This equation is unbalanced. There are two oxygen atoms on the left-hand side and one on the right-hand side. This is impossible as atoms cannot be created or destroyed in a chemical reaction.

The equation needs to be balanced. The correct equation is

$$2Mg + O_2 \rightarrow 2MgO$$

A balanced equation must contain the same number of atoms of each element on both sides of the arrow. Equations are balanced by placing coefficients in front of the formulas.

---

8   Write balanced equations showing the reaction between silicon tetrachloride and water to form silicic acid ($Si(OH)_4$) and hydrochloric acid and the decomposition of potassium chlorate(v), $KClO_3$, to form potassium chloride and oxygen.

Equations should have state symbols inserted to indicate the physical states of the substances, for example

$$2Mg(s) + O_2(g) \rightarrow 2MgO(s)$$

The condition of the reaction must be taken into account when writing state symbols. For example, copper(II) hydroxide reacts with hydrogen according to the following equation:

$$CuO + H_2 \rightarrow Cu + H_2O$$

This reaction only occurs on heating, so the water will be steam and not a liquid. Hence the equation is written:

$$CuO(s) + H_2(g) \rightarrow Cu(s) + H_2O(g)$$

ToK Link

Chemical equations are the 'language' of chemistry. How does the use of universal languages help and hinder the pursuit of knowledge?

Chemical equations (provided the existence of atoms and electrons is accepted) are unarguably universal, but only one of a number of items that make up the 'language' of chemistry. They are a representation of knowledge bridging the gap between sub-microscopic and macroscopic phenomena. In addition there is a vast nomenclature (naming rules for compounds), a wide range of chemical terms and mathematical relationships that help to make up the 'language'.

The chemical symbols introduced by Berzelius provided the tools necessary for modern chemistry to develop from alchemy. Having standardized names for compounds and elements (IUPAC nomenclature) was one of the main keys to further progress. So it could be argued that the benefits outweigh the drawbacks or hindrances. However, the development of specialized terms or jargon can make each field of chemistry increasingly opaque (unclear) to 'outsiders', so cross-transfer of developments in one field may be long delayed in being acquired by other scientific fields where the same principles could apply.

ToK Link

Lavoisier's discovery of oxygen, which overturned the phlogiston theory of combustion, is an example of a paradigm shift. How does scientific knowledge progress?

Phlogiston theory was proposed by Johann Becher (1635–1682) and Georg Stahl (1660–1734). It was a theory of combustion (burning) and rusting that had considerable influence upon the progress of chemistry. Their main hypothesis was that all materials that could be burnt contained a substance resembling fire known as phlogiston (Greek, fire-stuff).

According to the theory, burning and rusting both represent the escape of phlogiston, and air is necessary for both processes because phlogiston is absorbed into it. When the air becomes saturated with phlogiston, the phlogiston has no place to go and the flame goes out or the rusting stops.

Although the theory made qualitative sense and helped explain burning and rusting, it suffered from a quantitative defect: it could not adequately account for the observed changes in mass that accompany burning and rusting. It was known as early as 1630 that when a piece of iron rusts, the rust formed weighs more than the original iron. A few phlogistonists tried to explain this by asserting that phlogiston had negative mass. However, when a lump of charcoal (carbon) burns, again presumably with the loss of phlogiston, its mass decreases. The theory was later falsified (disproved) by the work of the French chemist Lavoisier and the English chemist Priestley.

■ Ionic equations

When a soluble ionic substance is dissolved in water, the ions separate and behave independently. For example, if barium chloride is dissolved in water, hydrated barium and chloride ions are formed:

$$BaCl_2(s) + (aq) \rightarrow BaCl_2(aq) \rightarrow Ba^{2+}(aq) + 2Cl^-(aq)$$

■ **Figure 1.26**
Precipitate of barium sulfate

The barium and chloride ions undergo their characteristic reactions regardless of which other ions may be present in the solution. For example, barium ions in solution react with sulfate ions in solution to form a white precipitate of barium sulfate (Figure 1.26).

If a solution of barium chloride, $BaCl_2$, and a solution of sodium sulfate, Na_2SO_4, are mixed, a white precipitate of barium sulfate, $BaSO_4$, is rapidly produced. The following equations describe the precipitate formation:

$$BaCl_2(aq) + Na_2SO_4(aq) \rightarrow BaSO_4(s) + 2NaCl(aq)$$

or

$$Ba^{2+}(aq) + 2Cl^-(aq) + 2Na^+(aq) + SO_4^{2-}(aq) \rightarrow BaSO_4(s) + 2Na^+(aq) + 2Cl^-(aq)$$

The second equation shows that the sodium and chloride ions have *not* undergone any change: they existed as independent ions both before and after the reaction took place. They are termed spectator ions and can be removed from the equation to generate a net ionic equation:

$$Ba^{2+}(aq) + SO_4^{2-}(aq) \rightarrow BaSO_4(s)$$

This equation may be interpreted to mean that any soluble barium salt will react with any soluble sulfate to produce barium sulfate.

The solubility of common salts is summarized below:

- All sodium, potassium and ammonium salts are soluble.
- All nitrates are soluble.
- All chlorides are soluble *except* silver chloride and lead(II) chloride.
- All sulfates are soluble except calcium sulfate, barium sulfate and lead(II) sulfate.
- Sodium, potassium and ammonium carbonates are soluble *but* all other carbonates are insoluble.

Net ionic equations must always have the same net charge on both sides of the equation. In the net ionic equation above, the net charge on both sides of the equation is zero.

Net ionic equations may be written whenever reactions occur in aqueous solution in which some of the ions originally present are removed from solution or when ions not originally present are formed. Ions are removed from solution by the following processes:

- formation of an insoluble precipitate
- formation of molecules containing only covalent bonds
- formation of a new ionic chemical species
- formation of a gas.

---

9 Write balanced 'molecular' and ionic equations showing the following reactions: silver nitrate and sodium chloride solutions to form silver chloride and sodium nitrate; hydrochloric acid and sodium hydroxide to form sodium chloride and water; zinc and copper(II) sulfate solution to form zinc sulfate and copper; sodium carbonate and hydrochloric acid to form sodium chloride, water and carbon dioxide.

■ IUPAC

The IUPAC is the International Union of Pure and Applied Chemistry. It is an international scientific organization, not associated with any government. The IUPAC sets global standards for names of inorganic and organic substances (nomenclature), chemical symbols and units. The IUPAC was formed in 1919 by chemists who recognized a need for standardization in chemistry. In addition to setting guidelines, the IUPAC sometimes helps to resolve disputes. An example is the decision to use the name 'sulfur' instead of 'sulphur'.

Nature of Science   **Making quantitative measurements with replicates to ensure reliability – the laws of chemical combination**

The laws of chemical combination listed below are all consequences of the atomic theory of matter. These are experimentally based laws derived from precise and repeated measurements of the masses of the reactants and products of chemical reactions. The law of definite proportions and the law of multiple proportions form the basis of stoichiometry.

Law of conservation of mass

There is no increase or decrease in mass during a chemical reaction (Figure 1.27). The atoms of a chemical substance cannot be created or destroyed during a chemical reaction. If the reacting substances are weighed before a chemical reaction and the products are accurately weighed after a chemical reaction, the mass is unchanged.

■ **Figure 1.27**
An illustration of the law of conservation mass

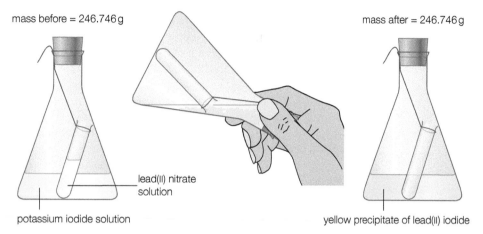

mass before = 246.746 g

lead(II) nitrate solution

potassium iodide solution

mass after = 246.746 g

yellow precipitate of lead(II) iodide

The law applies provided the product(s) do not escape and the mass of all the products is measured. However, if the reaction between calcium carbonate and dilute aqueous acid is performed in an open beaker, then there is a steady decrease in the total mass due to loss of the carbon dioxide, a gaseous product.

Law of constant composition

Some compounds can be prepared by a number of different methods. However, the chemical composition of the compound is identical regardless of the method used. For example, copper(II) oxide can be prepared by heating copper(II) carbonate or copper(II) nitrate.

$$CuCO_3(s) \rightarrow CuO(s) + CO_2(g)$$
$$2Cu(NO_3)_2(s) \rightarrow 2CuO(s) + 4NO_2(g) + O_2(g)$$

The copper(II) oxide produced by these and other reactions can be converted to copper by reaction with hydrogen.

$$CuO(s) + H_2(g) \rightarrow Cu(s) + H_2O(l)$$

Equal masses of copper(II) oxide, produced by different methods, form equal masses of copper when converted to the element.

Law of multiple proportions

The law of multiple proportions applies when two elements form more than one compound, for example, copper(II) oxide, CuO, and copper(I) oxide, Cu_2O. If two elements (A and B) combine together to form more than one compound, then the different masses of A that combine with a fixed mass of B are in a simple ratio. For example, if equal masses of two copper oxides are converted to copper by reaction with hydrogen, the masses of copper that combine with 1 gram of oxygen are in the ratio 2 : 1.

Law of definite proportions

The law of definite proportions states that a chemical compound always contains exactly the same proportion of elements by mass. An equivalent statement is the law of constant composition. For example, oxygen makes up about $\frac{8}{9}$ of the mass of any sample of water, while hydrogen makes up the remaining $\frac{1}{9}$ of the mass.

10 Lead forms two compounds with oxygen. The first lead oxide contains 2.980 g of lead and 0.461 g of oxygen. The second lead oxide contains 9.890 g of lead and 0.763 g of oxygen. For a given mass of oxygen, deduce the lowest integer mass ratio of lead in the two compounds.

Figure 1.28 The mole concept applied to two solid elements: magnesium and carbon (graphite)

1.2 The mole concept – *the mole makes it possible to correlate the number of particles with the mass that can be measured*

■ The mole concept and the Avogadro constant

Chemists are interested in the ratios in which chemical elements and compounds react together during chemical reactions. This is important when preparing a pure substance in the laboratory, and even more so in the chemical industry. Using excess reactant, unless necessary, will result in additional costs in order to remove it from the product.

Atoms are very small with very small masses, for example a hydrogen atom ($_1^1$H) weighs only 1.67355×10^{-27} kg. However, the masses of atoms of different elements are different, for example a carbon-12 atom is twelve times more massive than an atom of hydrogen-1.

For this reason, weighing out the same mass of different elements results in different numbers of atoms being present in the samples. It is very difficult for chemists to count large numbers of atoms directly so instead a chemist counts atoms *indirectly* by weighing samples of elements.

For example, 12 grams of carbon-12 atoms and 1 gram of hydrogen-1 atoms both contain the same number of atoms. These samples are described as having the same amount of atoms in moles. In this simple example the two samples of elements both contain one mole of atoms. The mole concept (Figure 1.28) allows chemists to weigh out samples of substances with equal numbers of particles (atoms, ions or molecules). For elements, one mole of atoms is present when the relative atomic mass of the element is weighed out in grams.

The amount of substance (symbol n) is a quantity that is directly proportional to the number of particles in a sample of substance. It is one of the seven base quantities of the SI unit system. The unit of amount is the mole (mol).

One mole of a substance contains 6.02×10^{23} particles of the substance. This is the same number of particles as there are atoms in exactly 12 grams of the isotope carbon-12 ($_6^{12}$C) (see Figure 1.29). The value 6.02×10^{23} mol^{-1} is called the Avogadro constant (symbol L or N_A).

Figure 1.29 An illustration of the Avogadro constant

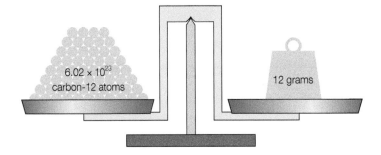

The particles may be atoms (e.g. Ar), molecules (e.g. Br$_2$), ions (e.g. Na$^+$), formula units (e.g. NaCl) or electrons (Figure 1.30), but should be specified, for example 1 mol of chlorine atoms or 2 mol of chlorine molecules. (Stoichiometric calculations involving electrons can be found in Chapter 19.)

Figure 1.30 A summary of the mole concept applied to different particles

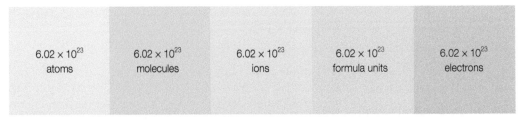

one mole of particles

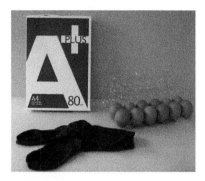

The mole is simply a convenient counting unit for chemists, large enough to be seen, handled and measured. It is no different from other counting units: a dozen eggs, a gross (144) of nails and a ream (500 sheets) of paper (Figure 1.31). Note that as the objects become *smaller*, the number in the unit amount becomes *larger*. The value of the Avogadro constant is given on page 2 of the IB *Chemistry data booklet*.

The equation below describes the relationship between the amount of a substance and the number of particles:

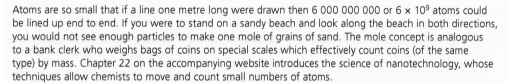

$$\text{amount of substance (mol)} = \frac{\text{number of particles}}{6.02 \times 10^{23} \text{ mol}^{-1}}$$

The formula may be rearranged to make the number of particles the subject.

■ **Figure 1.31** Counting units: from left to right, a pair of socks, a ream of paper and a dozen eggs

11 Calculate the number of molecules of water in 0.01 mol of water.

12 Calculate the amount of nitric(v) acid, HNO_3, that contains 9×10^{23} molecules.

13 Calculate the number of oxygen atoms present in 9×10^{23} molecules of nitric(v) acid, HNO_3.

ToK Link

The magnitude of the Avogadro constant is beyond the scale of our everyday experience. How does our everyday experience limit our intuition?

Atoms are so small that if a line one metre long were drawn then 6 000 000 000 or 6×10^9 atoms could be lined up end to end. If you were to stand on a sandy beach and look along the beach in both directions, you would not see enough particles to make one mole of grains of sand. The mole concept is analogous to a bank clerk who weighs bags of coins on special scales which effectively count coins (of the same type) by mass. Chapter 22 on the accompanying website introduces the science of nanotechnology, whose techniques allow chemists to move and count small numbers of atoms.

Our everyday experience is based on and is limited to large macroscopic objects, visible to the naked eye, and to low velocities. Our limited sense perception places limitations on our intuition, and to understand atoms we use mathematical theories supported by experimental data. Intuition as well as observation is valued in science. Great discoveries in science have often come from bold intuitive suggestions. Flashes of intuition and even dreams are allowed in science because they can be experimentally tested and then, if falsified, rejected.

Einstein recalled that at the age of 16 he imagined chasing after a beam of light, and he suggested that this may have played a role in his later development of the theory of special relativity. Einstein also used 'thought experiments' (*Gedanken* in German) when he developed his theory of mass–energy equivalence ($E = mc^2$) (Chapter 24 on the accompanying website). He imagined a stationary box floating deep in space containing a photon (light particle).

Unfortunately for humans, our powers of observation are limited by our five senses. We can only hear a limited range of sounds, and the visible spectrum is a relatively small proportion of the electromagnetic spectrum. Our eyes have a resolution of 200 micrometres and we cannot observe events that occur within a time period of less than 0.01 seconds. Hence our own physical limitations may limit our intuition.

■ Determination of the Avogadro constant and molar volume from physical measurement

In 1914 William Bragg used X-ray crystallography to determine the Avogadro constant. X-ray crystallography involves passing X-rays through very pure crystals and analysing the scattering patterns to determine the arrangement of particles in the crystal.

■ **Figure 1.32** One mole of various ionic substances: copper(II) sulfate (blue), nickel sulfate (green), potassium dichromate(VI) (orange), sodium chloride (white) and copper(I) oxide (brown)

General approach

■ The spacing of particles in a crystal is first determined.

■ Knowing the distance between atoms (or ions) in the crystal, it is then possible to find the volume occupied by one atom.

■ The volume of one mole of the substance is then determined. This is known as the molar volume (Figure 1.32).

■ Finally, the volume of one mole is divided by the volume of one atom to obtain the Avogadro constant.

Example calculation

Figure 1.33 shows a unit cell of sodium metal, which has a body-centred cubic structure. The unit cell is the simplest arrangement of atoms which, when repeated, will reproduce the same structure.

The central atom is located inside the unit cell. The eight atoms at the corners are equally shared between eight unit cells. This means the unit cell effectively contains a total of $(1 + 8 \times \frac{1}{8})$, that is, two atoms.

X-ray diffraction methods show that the width of the sodium unit cell (shown as a in Figure 1.33) is 0.429 nm, or 0.429×10^{-7} cm (1 nm = 10^{-9} m).

Thus, the volume of the unit cell (that is, two atoms)

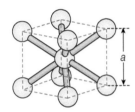

■ **Figure 1.33**
Unit cell of sodium metal

$$= (0.429 \times 10^{-7})^3 \, cm^3$$

$$= 0.0790 \times 10^{-21} \, cm^3$$

Therefore, the volume occupied by one sodium atom is $0.0395 \times 10^{-21} \, cm^3$. The relative atomic mass of sodium is 22.99 and the density of sodium is $0.97 \, g \, cm^{-3}$.

Using the equation volume = $\dfrac{mass}{density}$, the volume of one mole of sodium atoms is given by:

$$volume = \frac{22.99 \, g}{0.97 \, g \, cm^{-3}} = 23.70 \, cm^3$$

$$\text{The Avogadro constant} = \frac{\text{volume of one mole of atoms}}{\text{volume of one atom}}$$

$$= \frac{23.70 \, cm^3}{0.0395 \times 10^{-21} \, cm^3}$$

$$= 6 \times 10^{23}$$

14 Under your teacher's supervision fill a bowl with water and sprinkle some fine powder such as talcum powder over the surface. Place a small drop of pure oil on the surface of the water. It will spread out and form an approximately circular area clear of powder. It is assumed to be a monolayer, meaning it is one molecule thick and the molecules are assumed to be cubes. The volume of one drop of oil can be measured by counting how many drops it takes to fill a micro measuring cylinder. If the oil's density is known an easier method would be to find the mass of a certain number of drops. The surface area of the film can be calculated from measuring its diameter. The thickness of the film is given by the expression volume (cm^3) ÷ area (cm^2). Your value should be in the region of 1.4×10^{-7} cm. If you know the density and molar mass of the pure oil then extend the calculation to determine the Avogadro constant.

■ Formulas

Relative atomic mass, relative formula mass and molar mass

It is very difficult to determine directly the actual masses of individual atoms. However, it is relatively simple to compare the mass of one atom of a chemical element with the mass of atoms of other elements. The relative masses of atoms are determined by the use of a mass spectrometer (Chapter 2). The concept of relative masses of atoms is shown in Figure 1.34.

The relative atomic mass of an element is how many times greater the average mass of atoms of that element is than one-twelfth the mass of a carbon-12 atom. The weighted average mass is used since the majority of elements exist as mixtures of isotopes whose masses vary slightly (Chapter 2):

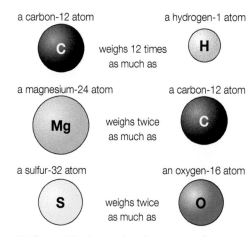

■ **Figure 1.34** Comparing the masses of atoms

$$\text{relative atomic mass} = 12 \times \frac{\text{average mass of one atom of the element}}{\text{mass of one atom of carbon-12}}$$

For example, the average mass of one atom of hydrogen from a large sample of hydrogen atoms is 1.01. (More than 99% of hydrogen atoms have a mass of exactly 1; less than 1% have a mass of exactly 2.)

$$\text{relative atomic mass of hydrogen} = 12 \times \frac{1.01}{12} = 1.01$$

The relative atomic mass expresses masses of atoms as relative values using the carbon-12 atomic mass scale. Relative atomic masses (symbol A_r) are simply pure numbers and do not have units.

Figure 1.35 illustrates the concept of relative atomic mass applied to some isotopes of common elements. Atoms of magnesium-24 are twice as heavy as carbon-12 atoms. Therefore, the relative atomic mass of magnesium-24 atoms is 24. Three helium-4 atoms have the same mass as one carbon-12 atom. Therefore, the relative atomic mass of helium-4 atoms is 4.

■ **Figure 1.35** Diagrams illustrating the concept of relative atomic mass applied to carbon, magnesium and helium atoms

Relative atomic masses of all the chemical elements are listed on page 6 of the IB *Chemistry data booklet*, but data for the first 20 elements are listed in Table 1.8 on the next page. The relative atomic masses are reported to two decimal places.

■ **Table 1.8** Atomic data for the first 20 chemical elements

Atomic number	Name	Symbol	Relative atomic mass
1	Hydrogen	H	1.01
2	Helium	He	4.00
3	Lithium	Li	6.94
4	Beryllium	Be	9.01
5	Boron	B	10.81
6	Carbon	C	12.01
7	Nitrogen	N	14.01
8	Oxygen	O	16.00
9	Fluorine	F	19.00
10	Neon	Ne	20.18
11	Sodium	Na	22.99
12	Magnesium	Mg	24.31
13	Aluminium	Al	26.98
14	Silicon	Si	28.09
15	Phosphorus	P	30.97
16	Sulfur	S	32.07
17	Chlorine	Cl	35.45
18	Argon	Ar	39.95
19	Potassium	K	39.10
20	Calcium	Ca	40.08

15 Deduce how much more massive, to the nearest integer, is a chlorine atom compared to a beryllium atom.

With elements, especially the common gaseous elements, it is important to differentiate between the relative atomic mass and the relative molecular mass. Thus oxygen, for example, has a relative atomic mass of 16.00 but a relative molecular mass of 32.00 because it exists as diatomic molecules (O_2).

The **relative molecular mass** is the sum of the relative atomic masses of all the atoms in one molecule. Relative molecular masses (symbol M_r) are pure numbers and do not have units.

$$\text{relative molecular mass} = 12 \times \frac{\text{average mass of one molecule of the element}}{\text{mass of one atom of carbon-12}}$$

The **relative formula mass** is the sum of the relative atomic masses of all the atoms (in the form of ions) in one formula unit of an ionic compound. Relative formula masses are again pure numbers and do not have units.

■ Molar mass

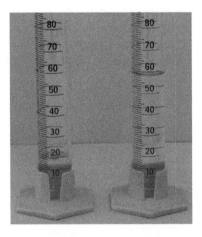

■ **Figure 1.36** (*right*) One mole of ethanol (C_2H_5OH, molar mass = 46 g mol⁻¹) and (*left*) one mole of water (H_2O, molar mass = 18 g mol⁻¹) in separate measuring cylinders. One mole of different liquids may have very different masses and volumes

The **molar mass** (symbol M) is the mass of one mole (Figure 1.36) of any substance (atoms, molecules, ions or formula units) where the carbon-12 isotope is assigned a value of *exactly* 12 g mol⁻¹. It is a particularly useful concept since it can be applied to any chemical entity. It has units of grams per mol (g mol⁻¹). It must be distinguished from the relative atomic/molecular/formula mass, which is a ratio and hence has no units, although both have the same numerical value.

The equation below describes the relationship between the amount of a substance, its mass (in grams) and its molar mass (g mol⁻¹):

$$\text{amount of substance (mol)} = \frac{\text{mass (g)}}{\text{molar mass (g mol}^{-1})}$$

From this relationship it can be deduced that the mass of one mole of any substance will be equal to its molar mass in grams (Table 1.9).

■ Table 1.9 Some examples of molar masses

Formula	Molar mass/g mol⁻¹	Number of particles	Type of particles
H	1.01	6.02×10^{23}	Atoms
C	12.01	6.02×10^{23}	Atoms
CH_4	16.05	6.02×10^{23}	Molecules
H_2O	18.02	6.02×10^{23}	Molecules
NaCl [Na⁺Cl⁻]	58.85	$2 \times 6.02 \times 10^{23}$	Ions
$CaCO_3$ [Ca²⁺CO₃²⁻]	100.09	$2 \times 6.02 \times 10^{23}$	Ions

The molar mass of an atom or ion is equal to its relative atomic mass expressed in grams per mole. The molar mass is the mass per amount of a substance. It is a derived SI unit. The base SI unit for mass is the kilogram and that for the amount of a substance is the mole. Thus the derived unit for molar mass is kg mol⁻¹. However, for both practical and historical reasons, molar masses are almost always quoted in grams per mole, especially in chemistry.

For example, the molar mass of sodium atoms is 22.99 g mol⁻¹ and the relative atomic mass of sodium is 22.99. The molar mass of iron(II) ions, Fe^{2+}, is 55.85 g mol⁻¹ and the relative atomic mass of iron is 55.85. The molar mass of chloride ions, Cl⁻, is 35.45 g mol⁻¹ and the relative atomic mass of chlorine is 35.45. The removal or gain of electrons has no effect on the calculations. The mass of the electrons is negligible and is ignored.

The molar mass of molecules or formula units is calculated by adding together the relative atomic masses of the elements in the molecule.

For example, the molar mass of sulfuric acid molecules, H_2SO_4 is 98.08 g mol⁻¹. This is 2 atoms of hydrogen each of mass 1.01 = 2.02 g mol⁻¹, 1 atom of sulfur of mass 32.06 = 32.06 g mol⁻¹ and 4 atoms of oxygen of mass 16.00 = 64.00 g mol⁻¹.

The molar mass of lead(II) nitrate, $Pb(NO_3)_2$ is 331.21 g mol⁻¹. This formula mass has two nitrate groups. This formula unit contains 1 atom of lead of mass of 207.19 g mol⁻¹, 2 atoms of nitrogen of mass 14.01 = 28.02 g mol⁻¹ and 6 atoms of oxygen of mass 16.00 = 96.00 g mol⁻¹.

16 Deduce the molar mass of magnesium carbonate, $MgCO_3$.

17 Deduce the relative molecular mass of carbon dioxide, CO_2.

18 Deduce the relative formula mass of hydrated iron(II) sulfate crystals, $FeSO_4.7H_2O$.

Nature of Science

Concepts – the concept of the mole developed from earlier related ideas

John Dalton's table of elements shown in Figure 1.37 include 'equivalent masses' or gram equivalent masses. It is the mass of one equivalent, that is the mass of a substance which will react with one gram of hydrogen. Equivalent masses were a useful generalization of the law of definite proportions.

■ Figure 1.37 Dalton's symbols for the chemical elements. Note that some of his 'elements' are compounds, for example, magnesia is magnesium oxide

ELEMENTS

		w⁰			w⁰
⊙	Hydrogen	1	⊕	Strontian	46
◑	Azote	5	✪	Barytes	68
●	Carbon	5,4	Ⓘ	Iron	50
○	Oxygen	7	Ⓩ	Zinc	56
⊗	Phosphorus	9	Ⓒ	Copper	56
⊕	Sulphur	13	Ⓛ	Lead	90
◐	Magnesia	20	Ⓢ	Silver	190
⊖	Lime	24	ⓖ	Gold	190
◑	Soda	28	Ⓟ	Platina	190
⦀	Potash	42	✪	Mercury	167

One of the greatest problems was the reaction of hydrogen with oxygen to produce water: 1 gram of hydrogen reacts with 8 grams of oxygen to form 9 grams of water, so the equivalent mass of oxygen was defined as 8 grams; 35.5 grams of chlorine react with 1 gram of hydrogen so the equivalent mass of chlorine was 35.5 grams.

However, expressing the reaction in terms of gas volumes following Gay Lussac's law, *two* volumes of hydrogen react with one volume of oxygen to produce two volumes of water, suggesting that the mass equivalent should be 16. Dalton and Gay-Lussac did not see that their laws of combining masses and combining volumes could be reconciled.

However, the work of Cannizzaro (1826–1910) helped explain this and many similar problems. At the Karlsruhe conference in 1860 he promoted the work of Avogadro and his concept that many gases, such as oxygen and hydrogen, were diatomic molecules. The equivalent mass of oxygen was then accepted as 16. The concept of relative atomic mass and mole is related to the concept of equivalent mass.

The SI system (Système International d'Unités)

The international system of units (in French *le Système International d'Unités*, abbreviated as SI) was established by the 11th general conference on weights and measures (CGPM). The CGPM is an inter-governmental organization created by a diplomatic treaty known as the Metre Convention which was signed in Paris in 1875. The metric system was found to be more convenient as it was based on the decimal system. The fundamental units of the metric system are the gram for mass, the metre for length and the litre for the volume of fluids.

In 1960, the international committee of weights and measures recommended the use of an international system of units, abbreviated as SI units. SI units are largely a modification of the metric system. The seven units in the SI system are given in Table 1.10.

■ **Table 1.10** The international system of units (SI)

Physical quantity	Abbreviation	Name of unit	Symbol	Detail
Length	*l*	metre	m	The metre is the length of the path travelled by light in vacuum during a time interval of 1/299 792 458 of a second. It is also defined as a length equal to 650 763.73 wavelengths of a particular orange-red light emitted by a lamp containing krypton-86 gas
Mass	*m*	kilogram	kg	The kilogram is the unit of mass; it is equal to the mass of the international prototype kilogram, which is a certain platinum–iridium cylinder kept at the International Bureau of Weights and Measures near Paris
Time	*t*	second	s	The second is the duration of 9 192 631 770 periods of radiation corresponding to the transition between the two hyperfine levels of the ground state of the caesium-33 atom
Electric current	*I*	ampere	A	The ampere is defined as the constant current which when maintained in two parallel straight wires one metre apart in a vacuum, produces a force between the wires equal to 2×10^{-7} newtons
Thermodynamic temperature	*T*	kelvin	K	The kelvin unit of thermodynamic temperature is the fraction 1/273.16 of the thermodynamic temperature of the triple point of water, i.e. the temperature at which liquid water, ice and water vapour co-exist
Luminous intensity	I_v	candela	cd	The candela is the luminous intensity, in a given direction, of a source that emits monochromatic radiation of frequency 540×10^{12} hertz and that has a radiant intensity in that direction of 1/683 watt per steradian
Amount of substance	*n*	mole	mol	The mole is the amount of substance of a system which contains as many elementary entities as there are atoms in 0.012 kilogram of carbon-12; its symbol is mol. When the mole is used, the elementary entities must be specified and may be atoms, molecules, ions, electrons, other particles or specified groups of such particles

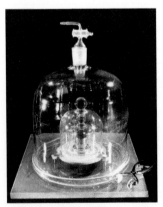

■ **Figure 1.38** The international prototype kilogram at the BIPM

The mass standard has been defined as the mass of a platinum–iridium cylinder (Figure 1.38) that is stored in an air-tight container at the International Bureau of Weights and Measures (BIPM) in Sèvres, France. An alloy of platinum and iridium was chosen for this standard because it is highly resistant to chemical attack and its mass will not change for a very long time. Scientists are in search of a new standard of mass via accurate determination of the Avogadro constant.

Calculating quantities

The equation relating the amount of substance in moles, mass and molar mass can be used to calculate any quantity given the values of the other two:

$$\text{amount of substance (mol)} = \frac{\text{mass (g)}}{\text{molar mass (g mol}^{-1})}$$

Determining the amount from mass and molar mass

In order to determine the amount of substance (in moles) the equation is used in the form shown above.

19 Calculate the approximate amount of water molecules present in 54 g of water, H_2O.

20 Calculate the approximate amount of calcium present in 0.500 kg of calcium.

21 Calculate the approximate amount of water present in a drop with a mass of 180 mg.

22 Calculate the approximate mass of 0.40 mol of calcium carbonate, $CaCO_3$.

23 0.00200 mol of a substance weighs 1.00 g. Calculate the molar mass of the substance.

Determining the mass from amount and molar mass

To determine the mass from the other two quantities the equation is rearranged to:

$$\text{mass (g)} = \text{molar mass (g mol}^{-1}) \times \text{amount (mol)}$$

Determining the molar mass from mass and amount

To determine the molar mass from the other two quantities the following form is used:

$$\text{molar mass (g mol}^{-1}) = \frac{\text{mass (g)}}{\text{amount (mol)}}$$

Calculating the mass of a single atom or molecule

If the mass of a given number of atoms or molecules is known, then the mass of a single atom or molecule can be calculated.

Worked example

Calculate the mass of a single atom of carbon.

$$\text{Mass of a single carbon atom} = \frac{12\,\text{g mol}^{-1}}{6 \times 10^{23}\,\text{mol}^{-1}} = 2 \times 10^{-23}\,\text{g}$$

24 Calculate the mass (in kg) of a single molecule of carbon dioxide, CO_2. Use the IB values for the Avogadro constant and relative atomic masses.

Calculating the number of atoms of a specific element in a given mass of a molecular compound

The total number of atoms and the number of atoms of a specific chemical element in a given mass of a molecular compound may also be calculated.

Figure 1.39 is a summary showing how to interconvert between mass (in g), amount (in mol) and number of particles using molar mass and Avogadro's constant.

■ **Figure 1.39** Summary of interconversions between amount, mass and number of particles

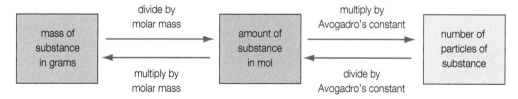

25 Calculate the approximate numbers of carbon and hydrogen atoms and the total number of atoms in 22 g of propane, C_3H_8.

Molecular and empirical formula

The mole concept can be used to calculate the formula of a substance from experimental results. The formula obtained is the simplest possible formula (involving integers) for that compound. It is known as the empirical formula of the substance and can be applied to ionic and covalent compounds.

Worked example

Use the experimental result that 32 g of sulfur reacts with 32 g of oxygen to calculate the empirical formula of this oxide of sulfur.

	Sulfur	*Oxygen*
Combining masses (found from experiment)	32 g	32 g
Amount of atoms	$\dfrac{32\,g}{32\,g\,mol^{-1}}$	$\dfrac{32\,g}{16\,g\,mol^{-1}}$
Ratio of moles	1 :	2
The empirical formula is therefore SO_2.		

The **molecular formula** represents the actual number of atoms in a molecule of a simple covalent substance. The empirical formula and molecular formula may be identical for a molecule or they may be different. The empirical formula may be found by dividing the coefficients in the molecular formula by the highest common factor.

For example, the empirical and molecular formulas of water are both H_2O; the molecular formula of hydrogen peroxide is H_2O_2, but the empirical formula is HO. The molecular formula of benzene is C_6H_6 and the empirical formula is CH.

Since ionic compounds exist as giant ionic structures (Chapter 4) the concept of a molecule *cannot* be applied. The formula of an ionic compound is therefore an empirical formula, representing the ions present in their simplest ratio.

Experimental determination of empirical formula

The empirical formula may also be determined from the composition data of the compound. This data is obtained experimentally. Frequently the composition will be expressed as percentages rather than as masses. The method of working is exactly the same because with percentages we are considering the mass of each element in 100 grams of the compound.

26 Calculate the empirical formula of a compound with following percentage composition by mass: carbon 39.13%, oxygen 52.17% and hydrogen 8.700%.

Worked example

Determine the empirical formula of a compound containing 85.7% by mass of carbon and 14.3% hydrogen.

These percentage figures apply to any chosen amount of substance. If you choose 100 grams, then the percentages are simply converted to masses.

	Carbon	*Hydrogen*
Percentages by mass	85.7%	14.3%
Combining masses in 100 g	85.7 g	14.3 g
Amount of atoms	$\dfrac{85.7\,g}{12\,g\,mol^{-1}}$	$\dfrac{14.3\,g}{1\,g\,mol^{-1}}$
Ratio of moles of atoms	7.14 :	14.3
Ratio of moles of atoms	1 :	2
The empirical formula is therefore CH_2.		

■ **Figure 1.40**
Apparatus for determining the empirical formula of magnesium oxide (by gravimetric analysis)

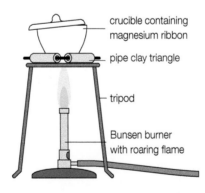

crucible containing magnesium ribbon

pipe clay triangle

tripod

Bunsen burner with roaring flame

Empirical formulas can often be determined by direct determination, for example by chemically converting a weighed sample of one element to the chosen compound and then weighing the compound to find the mass of the second element that chemically combined with the first (Figure 1.40). An alternative method is to decompose a weighed sample of a compound containing only two elements, so that only one element remains, measure the mass of the remaining element, and then calculate the mass of the element that was originally combined. The change in mass can be monitored and measured by a data-logger.

27 44.6 grams of an oxide of lead produced 41.4 grams of lead on reduction with hydrogen (to form water). Deduce the empirical formula of the oxide of lead.

Scientific evidence must be empirical, meaning that it is dependent on evidence (raw data) that is observable by the senses. In a related sense 'empirical' in science is synonymous with 'experimental'. Hence, the term 'empirical formula' refers to a formula that is derived from experimental results, often involving weighing of masses. This approach is known as gravimetric analysis.

A similar approach can be used to determine the empirical formula of a hydrated salt (Figure 1.41) whose water of crystallization can be removed without the anhydrous salt undergoing decomposition. In the calculation the water and the anhydrous salt are treated as formula units and divided by their molar masses.

■ **Figure 1.41** Blue hydrated copper(II) sulfate crystals and almost colourless anhydrous copper(II) sulfate crystals

> **Worked example**
>
> 12.3 grams of hydrated magnesium sulfate, $MgSO_4.xH_2O$, gives 6.0 grams of anhydrous magnesium sulfate, $MgSO_4$, on heating to constant mass. Deduce the value of x.
>
> Mass of water driven off = 12.3 g − 6.0 g = 6.3 g
>
> | | $MgSO_4$ | H_2O |
> |---|---|---|
> | Combining masses | 6.0 g | 6.3 g |
> | Amount of atoms | $\dfrac{6 g}{120 g mol^{-1}}$ | $\dfrac{6.3 g}{18 g mol^{-1}}$ |
> | Ratio of moles | 0.05 : | 0.35 |
> | Dividing through by the smallest number | = 1 : | = 7 |
>
> The empirical formula is therefore $MgSO_4.7H_2O$.

The percentage composition of a hydrocarbon is usually found by combusting a known mass of the pure compound in excess air or oxygen, then finding the masses of both the carbon dioxide (formed from the carbon in the compound) and the water (formed from the hydrogen).

> **Worked example**
>
> 5.6 grams of a pure hydrocarbon forms 17.6 grams of carbon dioxide and 7.20 grams of water when it undergoes complete combustion. Determine its empirical formula.
>
> Amount of carbon dioxide = $\dfrac{17.6 g}{44.0 g mol^{-1}}$ = 0.400 mol
>
> Hence, the amount of carbon atoms is 0.400 mol, since every carbon dioxide molecule contains one carbon atom.
>
> Amount of water = $\dfrac{7.20 g}{18.0 g mol^{-1}}$ = 0.400 mol
>
> Hence the amount of hydrogen atoms is 0.800 mol, since every water molecule contains two hydrogen atoms.
>
> The ratio of carbon to hydrogen atoms is 0.400 : 0.800, that is, 1 : 2. Hence the empirical formula is CH_2.

28 0.50 g of an organic compound containing carbon, hydrogen and oxygen gives 0.6875 g of carbon dioxide and 0.5625 g of water on combustion. Determine the empirical formula of the compound.

Determining the identity of an element in an empirical formula from percentage by mass data

> **Worked example**
>
> Determine the identity of element X in a compound XCO_3 which has 40% by mass of X and 12% by mass of carbon.
>
> > In a sample of 100 g of XCO_3 there will be 40 g of element X, 12 g of carbon atoms and 48 g of oxygen (100 g – 40 g – 12 g).
> >
> > Amount of carbon atoms = $\dfrac{12\,g}{12\,g\,mol^{-1}}$ = 1 mol
> >
> > Amount of oxygen atoms = $\dfrac{48\,g}{16\,g\,mol^{-1}}$ = 3 mol
> >
> > Since the empirical formula is XCO_3, the amounts of the three elements must be in a 1 : 1 : 3 ratio. Hence, 40 g of element X contains one mole of that element and the element is therefore calcium, since it has a molar mass of 40 g mol^{-1}.

Determining the number of atoms of an element in a molecule given its molar mass and the percentage by mass of the element

> **Worked example**
>
> An iron-containing protein has a molar mass of 136 000 g mol^{-1}. 0.33% by mass is iron. Calculate the number of iron atoms present in one molecule of the protein.
>
> > The combined molar mass of all the iron atoms = 0.0033 × 136 000 = 448.8 g mol^{-1}
> >
> > $\dfrac{448\,g\,mol^{-1}}{56\,g\,mol^{-1}}$ = 8 (to 1 s.f.)
> >
> > There are eight iron atoms in each molecule of the protein.

29 Calculate the percentage composition by mass of methane, CH_4 (M = 16 g mol^{-1}).

30 Calculate the percentage composition by mass of hydrated sodium sulfate, $Na_2SO_4.10H_2O$ (M = 322 g mol^{-1}).

Determining the percentage by mass of an element in a compound of known formula

The experimentally determined percentage composition by mass of a compound is used to calculate the empirical formula of a compound. The reverse process can also be applied and the percentage by mass of a specific element in a compound of known formula can be calculated.

The method may be divided into three steps:

1 Determine the molar mass of the compound from its formula.
2 Write down the fraction by mass of each element (or water of crystallization) and convert this to a percentage.
3 Check to ensure that the percentages sum to 100.

Determining the molecular formula

Since the molecular formula is a multiple of the empirical formula, the following relationship holds:

molecular formula = empirical formula × n, where n represents a small integer

Therefore in order to calculate the molecular formula of a compound it is necessary to know its molar mass. Molar masses can be determined by a variety of physical measurements, including back titrations (for weak acids and bases) and weighing gases. Mass spectrometry is frequently used to determine the molar masses of molecular substances (Chapter 2). Automated instruments for determining the empirical and molecular formulas of organic compounds are available.

31 A compound contains 73.47% carbon, 10.20% hydrogen and 16.33% by mass of oxygen. The compound has a molar mass of 196 g mol^{-1}. Calculate the molecular formula.

■ Stoichiometry in electrolysis

Balanced half-equations (with equal numbers of electrons) can be used to establish the mole ratio of products in electrolysis. Half equations are used to describe redox reactions. These reactions involve the transfer of electrons (Chapter 9).

For example, if molten sodium chloride is electrolysed then the mole ratio of sodium atoms to chlorine molecules is 2 : 1.

2 mol of sodium ions accept 2 mol of electrons to form 2 mol of sodium atoms:

$$2Na^+ + 2e^- \rightarrow 2Na$$

2 mol of chloride ions release 2 mol of electrons to form 1 mol of chlorine molecules:

$$2Cl^- \rightarrow Cl_2 + 2e^-$$

A mole of electrons is known as a Faraday. 1 Faraday or 1 mole of electrons carries a charge of 96 500 coulombs (C). The quantity of charge carried by a single electron is known from experiments to be 1.60×10^{-19} C.

If it can be determined how many of these charges are needed to make up the number of coulombs in 1 Faraday, then you will know how many electrons there are in a mole of electrons, that is, the Avogadro constant.

$$\frac{96\,500\,C\,mol^{-1}}{1.60 \times 10^{-19}\,C} = 6 \times 10^{23}\,mol^{-1}$$

The Avogadro constant can be experimentally obtained by an electroplating experiment. Consider the electrolysis of silver nitrate using silver electrodes. The reaction at the cathode (negative electrode) is:

$$Ag^+(aq) + e^- \rightarrow Ag(s)$$

An experiment showed that electrolysing silver nitrate solution, $AgNO_3(aq)$, using a current of 0.100 amperes for 30 minutes resulted in the cathode gaining a mass of 0.201 g.

The quantity of charge is given by the product of the time (in seconds) and the current in amperes, so

quantity of charge (C) = $(30 \times 60)\,s \times 0.100\,A = 180\,C$

The half-equation shows that 1 mol of silver atoms is formed from 1 mol of silver ions.

Amount of silver atoms = $\dfrac{0.201\,g}{107.87\,g\,mol^{-1}} = 0.00186\,mol$

That means that there were 0.00186 moles of electrons in the 180 coulombs passed through the circuit.

The number of coulombs of charge can be calculated from 180 C/0.00186 mol = 96 774 C mol^{-1}. This is close to the literature value of 96 500 C mol^{-1}.

The Avogadro constant can be calculated from dividing the charge on the electron by the experimentally determined value for the Faraday constant:

$$\frac{96\,500\,C\,mol^{-1}}{1.60 \times 10^{-19}\,C} = 6.025 \times 10^{23}\,mol^{-1}$$

1.3 Reacting masses and volumes *– mole ratios in chemical equations can be used to calculate reacting ratios by mass and gas volume*

■ Calculating theoretical yields

Almost all stoichiometric problems can be solved in just four simple steps (Figure 1.42):
1 If necessary, provide a balanced equation.
2 Convert the mass (or volume) units of a given reactant to an amount (in moles).
3 Using the mole ratio from the coefficients in the equation, calculate the amount of the required product.
4 Convert the amount of the product to the appropriate units of mass (or volume).

■ **Figure 1.42**
Graphical summary of interconversion of mass relationships in a chemical reaction

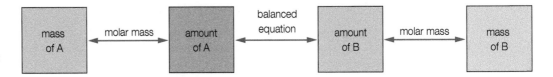

Determining the mass of a product (from a single reaction)

Worked example

Calculate the mass of calcium oxide that could be obtained by heating 2.5 grams of calcium carbonate, $CaCO_3$. (Assume that the calcium carbonate is pure and that complete decomposition occurs.)

Step 1 – Balanced equation: $CaCO_3(s) \rightarrow CaO(s) + CO_2(g)$

Step 2 – Convert to moles: Amount of calcium carbonate $= \dfrac{2.5\,g}{100\,g\,mol^{-1}} = 0.025\,mol$

Step 3 – Use the mole ratio: The coefficients in the equation indicate that one mole of calcium carbonate, $CaCO_3$, decomposes to give one mole of carbon dioxide, CO_2, and one mole of calcium oxide, CaO.

Consequently, 0.025 mol of calcium carbonate, $CaCO_3$, decomposes to give 0.025 mol of carbon dioxide, CO_2, and 0.025 mol of calcium oxide, CaO.

Step 4 – Convert to mass or volume: Mass of calcium oxide $= 0.025\,mol \times 56\,g\,mol^{-1} = 1.4\,g$

Determining the mass of a product (from consecutive reactions), where the product of a reaction is the reactant of a subsequent reaction

Worked example

Calculate the mass of nitric acid that can be produced from 56 grams of nitrogen gas.

$N_2 + 3H_2 \rightarrow 2NH_3$

$4NH_3 + 5O_2 \rightarrow 4NO + 6H_2O$

$2NO + O_2 \rightarrow 2NO_2$

$2H_2O + 4NO_2 + O_2 \rightarrow 4HNO_3$

The coefficients in the equations indicate that: 1 mol of N_2 produces 2 mol of NH_3; 4 mol of NH_3 produces 4 mol of NO; 2 mol of NO produces 2 mol of NO_2; and 4 mol of NO_2 produces 4 mol of HNO_3. So overall, 1 mol of N_2 produces 2 mol of HNO_3.

Amount of nitrogen, $N_2 = \dfrac{56\,g}{28\,g\,mol^{-1}} = 2\,mol$

Amount of nitric acid produced $= 2 \times 2\,mol = 4\,mol$

Hence, mass of nitric acid produced $= 4\,mol \times 63\,g\,mol^{-1} = 252\,g$

Utilization: Stoichiometric calculations in industry

Stoichiometric calculations are fundamental to chemical processes in a wide variety of industries including the food, pharmaceutical and manufacturing industries.

For example, the blast furnace is involved in the production of iron from iron(III) oxide according to the following equation:

$$Fe_2O_3(s) + 3CO(g) \rightarrow 2Fe(l) + 3CO_2(g)$$

The principles of stoichiometry can be used to calculate the approximate mass of iron that can be produced from 10 tonnes of iron(III) oxide.

$$\text{Amount of } Fe_2O_3 = \frac{1 \times 10^7\,g}{160\,g} = 62\,500\,mol$$

and hence the approximate mass of iron is

$$2 \times 62\,500\,mol \times 56\,g\,mol^{-1} = 7\,000\,000\,g = 7.0\,\text{tonnes}$$

■ The limiting reactant and the reactant in excess

Frequently during chemical reactions, one of the reactants is present in excess. This means that once the reaction is complete, some of that reactant will be left over. For example, consider the reaction between hydrogen and oxygen to form water:

$$2H_2(g) + O_2(g) \rightarrow 2H_2O(l)$$

Suppose there is a reaction where two moles of hydrogen and two moles of oxygen are available for reaction. The coefficients in the equation indicate that only one mole of oxygen is required to react with two moles of hydrogen. This means that one mole of oxygen will be left over when the reaction is complete.

The amount of water obtained is determined by the amount of reactant that is completely consumed during the reaction. This reactant is termed the limiting reactant. The reactant which is not completely consumed is referred to as the reactant in excess.

Worked example

Calculate the mass of magnesium that can be obtained from the reaction between 4.8 grams of magnesium and 4.8 grams of sulfur. Identify the limiting reactant and calculate the mass of the unreacted element present in excess.

$Mg(s) + S(s) \rightarrow MgS(s)$

Amount of magnesium atoms $= \dfrac{4.8}{24} = 0.20\,mol$

Amount of sulfur atoms $= \dfrac{4.8}{32} = 0.15\,mol$

The coefficients in the equation indicate that one mole of magnesium atoms reacts with one mole of sulfur atoms to form one mole of magnesium sulfide. The amounts indicate that sulfur is the limiting reactant and magnesium is present in excess.

Mass of magnesium sulfide formed $= 0.15\,mol \times 56\,g\,mol^{-1} = 8.4\,g$

Amount of magnesium unreacted $= 0.20\,mol - 0.15\,mol = 0.05\,mol$

Mass of magnesium unreacted $= 0.050\,mol \times 24\,g\,mol^{-1} = 1.2\,g$

ToK Link

Assigning numbers to the masses of the chemical elements has allowed chemistry to develop into a physical science. Why is mathematics so effective in describing the natural world?

Assigning values of the relative masses of the atoms of chemical elements allowed chemistry to develop into a physical science. The concepts of relative atomic mass and the law of conservation of mass allowed quantitative chemistry (stoichiometry) to develop. Aristotle wrote, 'Mathematics is the study of quantity' and Descartes wrote, 'Mathematics is the science of order and measurement'. The deepest philosophical and scientific mysteries are often those that we take for granted. It is quite possible that you have never reflected on the fact that chemists uses mathematics to describe and explain the physical world. Mathematical concepts, such as differential equations and logarithms, that were developed for purely abstract reasons turn out to explain real chemical phenomena. Their utility (usefulness), as physicist Eugene Wigner once wrote, 'is a wonderful gift which we neither understand nor deserve'. Is mathematics 'invented' (a creation of the human mind) or 'discovered' (something that exists independently of human thought) or both? What is beyond doubt is the astonishing power, precision and conciseness of mathematics. For example, James Clerk Maxwell's four equations of electromagnetism summarized the field of electromagnetism in the 1860s; they also predicted the existence of radio waves two decades before the German physicist Hertz detected them. Radio waves are now widely used in MRI scanners in hospitals and in mobile phones.

■ Percentage and experimental yields

The quantity of product that is calculated to be formed when all the limiting reactant reacts is termed the theoretical yield. The mass, volume or amount of a product actually obtained in a chemical reaction is termed the experimental yield.

The experimental yield is always less than the theoretical yield for one or more of the following reasons:

- side or competing reactions
- the reaction is reversible and reaches equilibrium (Chapter 7)
- mechanical losses/physical loss of the reactants or products – these are the small amounts of product that are lost when they remain stuck to glassware or filter paper as they are transferred in the lab
- impurities present in the reactants.

Competing reactions

In certain circumstances, the same two chemicals can react to give different products. For example, when carbon burns in a plentiful supply of oxygen, it reacts to produce carbon dioxide, $CO_2(g)$, as expected in the presence of a plentiful supply of oxygen (air), according to the following chemical equation:

$$C(s) + O_2(g) \rightarrow CO_2(g).$$

In fact, carbon monoxide, $CO(g)$, is also produced to a small extent even when carbon burns with an excess of oxygen available:

$$2C(s) + O_2(g) \rightarrow 2CO(g)$$

This is an example of a competing reaction. Since some of the carbon reacts to form carbon monoxide in the competing reaction, the experimental yield of carbon dioxide is always less than predicted.

The percentage yield can be calculated from the following expression:

$$\text{percentage yield} = \frac{\text{experimental yield}}{\text{theoretical yield}} \times 100$$

Percentage yields are of particular importance in organic chemistry (Chapter 10) because there are significant side reactions and many organic reactions are reversible.

---

32 In an experiment to produce a sample of hex-1-ene, 20.4 grams of hexan-1-ol was heated with an excess of phosphoric(v) acid. The phosphoric(v) acid acted as a dehydrating agent, removing water from the alcohol to form hex-1-ene.

$$CH_3CH_2CH_2CH_2CH_2CH_2OH \rightarrow CH_3CH_2CH_2CH_2CH=CH_2 + H_2O$$
$$\text{hexan-1-ol} \qquad\qquad\qquad \text{hex-1-ene}$$

After purification of the hex-1-ene, 10.08 grams was produced. Calculate the percentage yield.

Utilization of percentage yield: Monitoring the efficiency of industrial processes

Achieving high percentage yields in industry is very important because chemical reactions often form by-products as well as the intended product. In most reactions, not all of the reactants actually react. What is left at the end of a reaction is typically a mixture of product and impurities (by-products and starting reactants). Achieving high percentage yields is especially important in industries that rely on organic synthesis, such as the pharmaceutical industry. It may require ten steps to synthesize a drug molecule and if each step has a percentage yield of 90%, the overall yield is only 35%:

$$0.9 \times 0.9 \times 0.9 \times 0.9 \times 0.9 \times 0.9 \times 0.9 \times 0.9 \times 0.9 \times 0.9 = 0.35$$

In reactions such as the Haber process, the reactants (nitrogen and hydrogen) can be recycled, in which case high yields are less of an issue.

■ Percentage purity

The percentage purity is the percentage of a specified compound or element in an impure sample. The percentage purity of a substance is often determined by a titration or a back titration.

The percentage purity of a sample of a chemical substance can be calculated from the following relationship:

$$\text{percentage purity} = \frac{\text{mass of pure substance in a sample}}{\text{mass of sample}} \times 100$$

Worked example

When 12 grams of impure carbon was burnt in excess oxygen, 33 grams of carbon dioxide was obtained. Calculate the percentage purity of the carbon.

The balanced equation for the reaction is:

$$C(s) \; + \; O_2(g) \rightarrow CO_2(g)$$
$$1 \text{ mol} \quad 1 \text{ mol} \quad 1 \text{ mol}$$

Amount of carbon dioxide formed $= \dfrac{33\,g}{44\,g\,mol^{-1}} = 0.75\,mol$

Since 1 mole of carbon dioxide is obtained from 1 mole of carbon (in the presence of excess oxygen), the amount of carbon in the original sample must be 0.75 mol.

Therefore, the mass of carbon in the original sample $= 0.75\,mol \times 12\,g\,mol^{-1} = 9.0\,g$.

Hence, the percentage purity $= \dfrac{9.0\,g}{12\,g} \times 100 = 75\%$

■ Reacting volumes of gases

A French chemist called Gay-Lussac studied chemical reactions between gases. He discovered that in such reactions, the volumes of the reacting gases (measured at the same temperature and pressure) were in a simple whole number ratio to one another and the volumes of the gaseous products. This is known as Gay-Lussac's law. For example, he found that one volume of hydrogen always reacted with exactly the same volume of chlorine to form two volumes of hydrogen chloride (Figures 1.43 and 1.45), and one volume of oxygen always reacted with two volumes of hydrogen to form two volumes of steam (Figure 1.44).

The Italian chemist Avogadro explained Gay-Lussac's results by suggesting that equal volumes of gases, measured at the same temperature and pressure, contain the same number of molecules. This suggestion is now called Avogadro's law. Mathematically, it can be expressed as:

$$V \propto n$$

where V represents the volume of gas and n represents the amount of gas (in moles). For example, if the number of molecules of a mass of gas is doubled, then the volume (at constant temperature and pressure) of the gas is doubled.

Using Avogadro's law, Gay-Lussac's observations on the formation of steam by direct synthesis can be interpreted as shown below:

2 volumes of hydrogen + 1 volume of oxygen → 2 volumes of steam

means

2 mol of hydrogen molecules + 1 mol of oxygen molecules → 2 mol of steam (water molecules)

and

2 hydrogen molecules + 1 oxygen molecule → 2 steam (water) molecules

Avogadro's law is a consequence of the large intermolecular distances between molecules in the gaseous state: a gas is mainly *empty space*.

■ **Figure 1.43**
Molecular models showing the reaction between hydrogen and chlorine

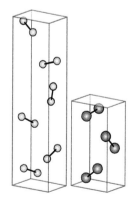

■ **Figure 1.44**
Two volumes of hydrogen molecules and one volume of oxygen molecules (an illustration of Avogadro's law)

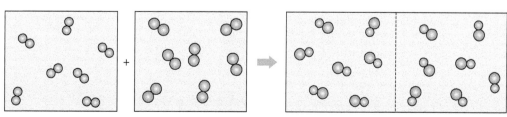

■ **Figure 1.45** A diagrammatic illustration of Avogadro's law for the formation of hydrogen chloride from hydrogen and chlorine

Calculating the volumes of reactants used

> **Worked example**
>
> Calculate the volume of oxygen needed to burn 200 cm³ of propane.
>
> $C_3H_8(g) + 5O_2(g) \rightarrow 3CO_2(g) + 4H_2O(l)$
>
> This equation indicates that one mole of propane reacts with five moles of oxygen to produce three moles of carbon dioxide and four moles of water. Applying Avogadro's law means that one volume of propane reacts with five volumes of oxygen to produce three volumes of carbon dioxide.
>
> (Note that Avogadro's law only applies to gases. Since liquid water is formed you cannot make a statement about its volume.)
>
> The volumes of propane and oxygen must be in a 1 : 5 ratio, hence the volume of oxygen needed is 5 × 200 cm³ = 1000 cm³.

> **Worked example**
>
> Calculate the volume of air needed to burn 200 cm³ of propane. Air is 20% by volume oxygen.
>
> $C_3H_8(g) + 5O_2(g) \rightarrow 3CO_2(g) + 4H_2O(l)$
>
> The volume of oxygen required is 1000 cm³. However, air is only $\frac{1}{5}$ oxygen and so you need five times as much air as oxygen. Hence, the volume of air required is 5 × 1000 cm³ = 5000 cm³.

Calculating the volumes of products produced

> **Worked example**
>
> Calculate the volume of carbon dioxide produced by the combustion of 0.500 dm³ of butane, C_4H_{10}.
>
> $2C_4H_{10}(g) + 13O_2(g) \rightarrow 8CO_2(g) + 10H_2O(l)$
>
> This equation indicates that 2 volumes of butane react with 13 volumes of oxygen to form 8 volumes of carbon dioxide.
>
> The amounts of butane and carbon dioxide are in a 2 : 8 ratio, hence the volume of carbon dioxide formed is 0.500 dm³ × 4 = 2.00 dm³.

Deducing the molecular formula

> **Worked example**
>
> When 20 cm³ of a gaseous hydrocarbon is reacted with excess oxygen the gaseous products consist of 80 cm³ of carbon dioxide, CO_2, and 80 cm³ of steam, H_2O, measured under the same conditions of pressure and temperature (above 100 °C).
>
> Deduce the molecular formula of the hydrocarbon.
>
>   20 cm³ hydrocarbon + excess oxygen → 80 cm³ CO_2 + 80 cm³ H_2O
>
>   1 molecule of hydrocarbon → 4 molecules of CO_2 + 4 molecules of H_2O
>
> Each molecule of the hydrocarbon must contain four carbon atoms and eight hydrogen atoms. The molecular formula is therefore C_4H_8.

Calculating reacting volumes using Avogadro's law

The foul smell that skunks spray is due to a number of thiols, one of which is methanethiol, CH_3SH. A 10.00 cm³ sample of methanethiol was exploded with 60.00 cm³ of oxygen. Apply Avogadro's law and determine the final volume of the resultant mixture of gases when cooled to room temperature.

$$CH_3SH(g) + 3O_2(g) \rightarrow CO_2(g) + SO_2(g) + 2H_2O(l)$$

The oxygen is in excess and hence the methanethiol is the limiting reagent. The volume of the oxygen left = $60.00\,cm^3 - 30.00\,cm^3 = 30.00\,cm^3$. The volume of carbon dioxide = $10.00\,cm^3$, volume of sulfur dioxide = $10.00\,cm^3$ and the total volume is $30.00\,cm^3 + 10.00\,cm^3 + 10.00\,cm^3 = 50.00\,cm^3$.

Utilization of gas volume changes during chemical reactions

Gas volume changes during chemical reactions are responsible for the inflation of air bags in vehicles. Sodium azide is made for use in car air bags. When this compound is heated to $300\,°C$ it rapidly decomposes into its elements according to the following equation:

$$2NaN_3(s) \rightarrow 2Na(s) + 3N_2(g)$$

The molar mass of sodium azide is $65.02\,g\,mol^{-1}$. This means that $65.02\,g$ (1 mol) of it will release $1.5\,mol$ of nitrogen gas. At STP (273 K and 100 kPa) this will occupy a volume of $34.05\,dm^3$.

The explosive known as TNT (trinitrotoluene) is very useful because it works without the presence of a separate oxidizing agent. Basically, all of the energy is stored in the TNT, so the explosion can occur even if there is no oxygen present. The explosion of TNT is a decomposition reaction and large volumes of hot and expanding gases are formed:

$$2C_7H_5N_3O_6(s) \rightarrow 7C(s) + 7CO(g) + 5H_2O(g) + 3N_2(g)$$

■ Molar volume of a gas

It follows from Avogadro's law that the volume occupied by one mole of molecules must be the same for all gases (Figure 1.46). It is known as the gas molar volume and has an approximate value of $22.7\,dm^3$ at $0\,°C$ (273 K) and 1 atmosphere (100 kPa). These conditions are known as standard temperature and pressure (STP).

This relationship, together with Avogadro's constant ($6.02 \times 10^{23}\,mol^{-1}$), allows us to solve some types of stoichiometry problems.

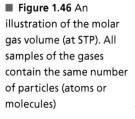

33 Calculate the volume of oxygen in dm^3 at STP that contains $1.35\,mol$ of molecules.

34 Calculate the amount of hydrogen gas in $175\,cm^3$ at STP.

35 Calculate the number of molecules present in $2.85\,dm^3$ of carbon dioxide at STP.

36 Calculate the density (in grams per cubic decimetre, $g\,dm^{-3}$) of argon gas at STP. The relative atomic mass (from the periodic table) of argon is 39.95. Hence, $22.7\,dm^3$ (1 mol) of argon gas weighs $39.95\,g$.

37 20.8 grams of a gas occupies $7.44\,dm^3$ at STP. Determine the molar mass of the gas.

38 When 3.06 grams of potassium chlorate(v), $KClO_3$, is heated it produces $840\,cm^3$ of oxygen (at STP) and leaves a residue of solid potassium chloride, KCl. Deduce the balanced equation. The molar mass of potassium chlorate(v) is $122.5\,g\,mol^{-1}$.

■ Figure 1.46 An illustration of the molar gas volume (at STP). All samples of the gases contain the same number of particles (atoms or molecules)

■ Figure 1.47 Summary of interconversions between the amount of gas and volume (at STP)

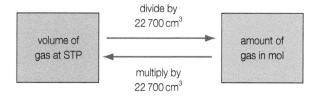

■ Figure 1.48 Caricature of Amedeo Avogadro

Making careful observations and obtaining evidence for scientific theories – Avogadro's hypothesis

Amedeo Avogadro (1776–1856) was an Italian physicist who made many early contributions to the concepts of molecular behaviour and relative molecular mass (formerly known as molecular weight) (Figure 1.48). His most critical contribution was making the distinction between atoms and molecules. His hypothesis was based on the careful experimental work by Gay-Lussac and John Dalton's atomic theory. He trained and practised as a lawyer, but later became Professor of Physics at Turin University. As a tribute to him, the number of particles in one mole of a substance is known as the Avogadro constant (formerly known as the Avogadro number).

■ Relationship between temperature, pressure and volume of a gas

In a gas the molecules are completely free to move in all directions and travel in straight lines until they collide with other gas molecules or atoms or bounce off the walls of the container. The *overall* resulting movement is completely random (Figure 1.49).

Forces of attraction between molecules or between single molecules and molecules of the walls of the container are usually so small that they can be neglected. However, when molecules approach close to one another, or to molecules of the walls, their kinetic energy brings them close enough for these forces to become repulsive and no longer negligible – hence they rebound.

When a gas is heated, the particles move faster and therefore collide more often with each other and the walls of the container. Gases are very compressible because of the large interatomic or intermolecular spaces between the particles. This also causes the density of gases to be very low compared to those of solids and liquids.

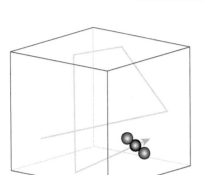

■ **Figure 1.49** The overall random movement of a gas molecule

Effect of pressure on volume of a gas

The effect of pressure on a fixed volume of gas can be demonstrated (in a qualitative manner) by trapping some air inside a sealed gas syringe connected to a pressure gauge and pushing in the plunger (Figure 1.50): the pressure of the gas increases as the volume decreases. The temperature remains constant during this change (if it is performed slowly, so that the air can remain in temperature equilibrium with the syringe and the surroundings).

■ **Figure 1.50** A syringe of air connected to a pressure gauge

The increase in the pressure of the gas is due to the increase in the frequency of collisions between the gas particles and the container walls. Since the volume is smaller, and the number of particles is constant, they hit the walls more often. There are a number of very useful simulations of the various gas laws on the internet. For example, see http://group.chem.iastate.edu/Greenbowe/sections/projectfolder/flashfiles/gaslaw/boyles_law_graph.html.

Effect of temperature on volume of a gas

This can be easily demonstrated (in a qualitative manner) by trapping some air inside a sealed gas syringe and placing it in a beaker of hot water: the volume of the gas increases as the temperature increases (Figure 1.51). The pressure remains constant during this change.

Heating the gas makes the particles move (on average) faster so that they hit the walls of the container more frequently and with greater momentum. This pushes the plunger of the syringe outwards, increasing the volume of the gas until this reduces the collision frequency to compensate for the increased speed and the pressure in the trapped gas is equal to the pressure of the atmosphere on the other side of the syringe.

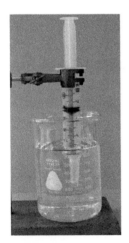

■ **Figure 1.51**
A sealed syringe of air in a beaker of hot water

Effect of temperature on pressure of a gas

If a sealed container is heated with gas inside, then once the temperature is sufficiently high the lid will fly off or the container will explode. This shows that gas pressure (at constant volume) increases with temperature.

The effects of changing one of these variables (pressure, temperature and volume) on a fixed mass of gas, while keeping the other one constant, are summarized in Table 1.11.

■ **Table 1.11** Summary of the behaviour of gases

a At constant temperature

Pressure	Volume
Increase	Decrease
Decrease	Increase

b At constant volume

Temperature	Pressure
Increase	Increase
Decrease	Decrease

c At constant pressure

Temperature	Volume
Increase	Increase
Decrease	Decrease

Gas density

The density of a gas is defined as the mass of the gas divided by its volume. The volume of the gas changes with temperature and pressure. Specifically, if the pressure on a gas is increased its volume decreases, resulting in an increase in density. If the temperature of a gas is increased, the volume increases and the density is reduced.

Units of gas pressure

Gases exert outward force on the walls of the container in which they are enclosed. The outward force experienced by the walls is due to bombardment of gas molecules on the walls. This outward force per unit area of the walls is termed as gas pressure.

$$\text{Pressure} = \frac{\text{force}}{\text{area}}$$

By definition,

$$\text{force} = \text{mass} \times \text{acceleration}$$

$$= \text{mass} \times \frac{\text{velocity}}{\text{time}}$$

$$= \text{mass} \times \frac{\text{distance}}{\text{time} \times \text{time}}$$

Thus, the SI unit of force has units of $kg\,m\,s^{-2}$ which is called the newton (N). $1\,N = 1\,kg\,m\,s^{-2}$.

Putting the SI units of force (N) and area (m^2) together, we get the SI unit of pressure as N/m^2 or $N\,m^{-2}$.

This SI unit of pressure is called the pascal (Pa) in the honour of the French mathematician and physicist Blaise Pascal. $1\,Pa = 1\,N\,m^{-2}$ and $1000\,Pa = 1$ kilopascal, abbreviated as kPa.

For gases, this unit of pressure is very small. Hence pressure is generally expressed in terms of a larger unit named the bar. One bar represents 100 kilopascal. Thus $1\,bar = 100\,kPa = 10^5\,Pa$. It may be noted that the older unit of pressure of gases was the atmosphere, which was abbreviated as atm. The relationship between these units is as given below:

$$1\,atm = 1.01325\,bar = 1.01325 \times 10^5\,Pa \qquad or \qquad 1\,bar = 0.987\,atm$$

An older non-SI unit is the pound per square inch (psi). It is the pressure resulting from a force of one pound applied to an area of one square inch. Pressure gauges often have two scales that read in psi and kPa. $1\,psi = 6894.757\,Pa$ and $1\,atm = 14.696\,psi$.

The atmospheric pressure can be measured by a simple device called a barometer. A simple barometer can be made by filling mercury in a tube (longer than 76 cm) closed at one end and inverting it in an open vessel containing mercury. The mercury level in the tube adjusts itself and stands approximately 76 cm above the level of mercury in the open vessel.

The weight of the mercury column held in the tube gives a measure of atmospheric pressure. The height of the column decreases when the pressure of the atmosphere decreases whereas the height of the column increases with increases in the atmospheric pressure.

■ Kinetic theory of gases

The behaviour of gases is explained by the kinetic theory of gases, which makes the following assumptions about the behaviour and properties of particles in a gas:

■ The individual molecules or atoms of a gas each have a negligible volume compared to the container.

■ There are no attractive or repulsive forces operating between the atoms or molecules of the gas, except at collisions between molecules and between individual molecules and the walls of the container (Figure 1.52).

■ The collisions between the molecules or atoms with themselves and the walls of the container are perfectly elastic and give rise to gas pressure.

■ The mean kinetic energy of the molecules or atoms of a gas is directly proportional to its absolute temperature on the thermodynamic scale. The kinetic energy of a gaseous molecule or atom is given by the expression $\frac{1}{2}mv^2$, where m represents the mass of the particle and v represents its speed.

enlargement of square showing bombardment by atoms or molecules in air

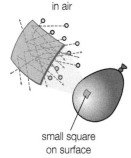

small square on surface

■ **Figure 1.52** The generation of gas pressure on the inner surface of a balloon

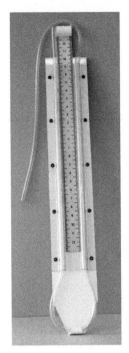

■ **Figure 1.53**
Manometer to
measure gas pressure

This model of a gas is known as the ideal gas model and is a good description of the behaviour of most gases, especially at high temperatures and low pressures. However, an ideal gas is a *hypothetical state* since the first two assumptions of the ideal gas model cannot be precisely true. No gas behaves absolutely perfectly as an ideal gas.

The pressure of a gas can be measured using a manometer (Figure 1.53). In its simplest form the manometer is a U-tube about half-filled with liquid. With both ends of the tube open, the liquid is at the same height in each leg. When positive pressure is applied to one leg, the liquid is forced down in that leg and up in the other. The difference in height indicates the pressure.

The temperature scale used in kinetic theory is the absolute or thermodynamic (Kelvin) scale. The thermodynamic scale of temperature uses units of kelvins (K), which have the same size as the more familiar degrees Celsius (°C) but whose 'zero' is absolute zero (–273.15 °C) (Figure 1.54). Hence, a temperature change of 1 K is the same as a temperature change of 1 °C. Unlike the Celsius scale, negative numbers are not used in the absolute scale.

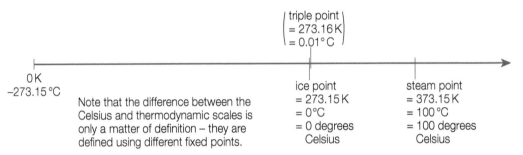

■ **Figure 1.54** The defining temperatures on the absolute or thermodynamic (Kelvin) and Celsius scales

Conversion between the Celsius and thermodynamic scales is governed by the equation:

$$t = T - 273.15$$

where t is the temperature in degrees Celsius and T is the absolute temperature in Kelvin. So, for example:

$$60.00\,°C = 333.15\,K - 273.15$$

hence 60.00 °C is equivalent to 333.15 K.

Chemistry, like all the scientific disciplines, has its own specialized vocabulary. However, the greatest problems tend to arise not from specially invented names, but from widely used words whose meaning does not match their usage in chemistry. For example the word 'ideal' is used to describe a state of perfection. However, an ideal or perfect gas is a simplified or imperfect mathematical model of a gas. 'Ideal laws' simplify the problem of describing phenomena by ignoring the less important features of a system.

■ The gas laws

Boyle's law

Boyle found that (at constant temperature), the volume of a fixed mass of gas is inversely proportional to its pressure. In other words, if the pressure on a sample of gas is increased, then the volume decreases. This can be expressed mathematically as:

$$P \propto \frac{1}{V} \quad \text{or as} \quad P \propto V^{-1}$$

where P represents the pressure and V represents the volume.

Alternatively Boyle's law can be expressed as $P \times V = K$, where K represents a constant that varies with the gas and temperature.

■ **Figure 1.55** Boyle's law apparatus

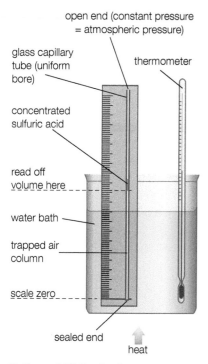

open end (constant pressure
= atmospheric pressure)

glass capillary
tube (uniform
bore)

thermometer

concentrated
sulfuric acid

read off
volume here

water bath

trapped air
column

scale zero

sealed end

heat

■ **Figure 1.56** Charles' law apparatus

Boyle's law (Figure 1.55) can be used to calculate the new pressure or volume if a fixed mass of gas (at constant temperature) undergoes a change in pressure or volume:

$$P_1 \times V_1 = P_2 \times V_2$$

where P_1 represents the initial pressure, V_1 represents the initial volume, P_2 represents the final pressure and V_2 represents the final volume.

> ### Worked example
>
> A sample of gas collected in a 350 cm³ container exerts a pressure of 103 kPa. Calculate the volume of this gas at a pressure of 150 kPa. (Assume that the temperature remains constant.)
>
> Boyle's law: $P_1 \times V_1 = P_2 \times V_2$
>
> $103 \text{ kPa} \times 350 \text{ cm}^3 = 150 \text{ kPa} \times V_2$
>
> $103 \text{ kPa} \times \dfrac{350 \text{ cm}^3}{150 \text{ kPa}} = 240 \text{ cm}^3$

Charles' law

If the absolute temperature of a gas is doubled then the volume (at constant pressure) doubles. Conversely, if the absolute temperature of a gas is halved (at constant pressure), the volume halves.

This behaviour is known as Charles' law (Figure 1.56) and can be expressed mathematically as $V \propto T$, where V represents the volume and T represents the absolute temperature in Kelvin. Alternatively Charles' law can be expressed as $V = K \times T$ (where K represents a constant that varies with the gas and pressure).

Note that a doubling of the temperature in degrees Celsius is *not* a doubling of the absolute temperature, for example a doubling of the temperature from 200 to 400 °C is only a rise from (200 + 273) = 473 K to (400 C + 273) = 673 K, that is, a ratio of 673/473 or 1.42.

Charles' law can be used to calculate the new temperature or volume if a fixed mass of gas (at constant pressure) undergoes a change in temperature or volume. It can be expressed as:

$$\frac{V_1}{T_1} = \frac{V_2}{T_2}$$

where V_1 represents the initial volume, T_1 represents the initial absolute temperature, V_2 represents the final volume and T_2 is the final absolute temperature.

39 A 4.50 dm³ sample of gas is warmed at constant pressure from 300 K to 350 K. Calculate its final volume.

The pressure law

The pressure law states that for a fixed mass of gas (at constant volume) its absolute temperature is directly proportional to pressure. This behaviour can be expressed mathematically as $P \propto T$, where P represents the pressure and T represents the absolute temperature in Kelvin. Alternatively the pressure law can be expressed as $P = K \times T$ or $P/T = K$ (where K represents a constant that varies with the gas).

The pressure law can be used to calculate the new pressure or temperature if a fixed mass of gas (at constant volume) undergoes a change in temperature or pressure. This is done using the following equation:

$$\frac{P_1}{T_1} = \frac{P_1}{T_2}$$

where P_1 represents the initial pressure, T_1 represents the initial absolute temperature, P_2 represents the final pressure and T_2 represents the final absolute temperature.

40 10 dm³ of a gas is found to have a pressure of 97 000 Pa at 25.0 °C. What would be the temperature required (in degrees Celsius) to change the pressure to 101 325 Pa?

41 The temperature of a gas sample is changed from 27 °C to 2727 °C at constant volume. What is the ratio of the final pressure to the initial pressure?

Equation of state ('combined gas law')

The equation of state is formed by combining Boyle's law ($P \times V$ = constant) and Charles' law (V/T = constant):

$$\frac{PV}{T} = \text{constant, for a fixed mass of gas}$$

This equation is sometimes called the combined gas law, but it is properly termed the equation of state (for an ideal gas).

This relationship is often written as:

$$\frac{P_1 \times V_1}{T_1} = \frac{P_2 \times V_2}{T_2}$$

Gas volumes are usually compared at STP. As with Charles' law, all temperatures must be expressed as absolute temperatures in Kelvin.

42 At 60 °C and 1.05 × 10⁵ Pa the volume of a sample of gas collected is 60 cm³. What would be the volume of the gas at STP?

The ideal gas equation

We have seen that Boyle's law (PV = constant) and Charles' law (V/T = constant) can be combined together to give a combined gas law known as the equation of state:

$$\frac{PV}{T} = \text{constant, for a fixed mass of gas}$$

It follows from Avogadro's law that for one mole of gas (V_m) the constant will be the same for all gases. It is called the gas constant and given the symbol R:

$$\frac{P \times V_m}{T} = R$$

This can be rearranged as $PV_m = RT$.

This equation is called the ideal gas equation and, for n moles of gas, the equation becomes:

$$PV = nRT$$

where P represents the pressure in pascals (Pa), V represents the volume in cubic metres (m³), n represents the amount of gas (mol), R represents the gas constant (8.31 J K⁻¹ mol⁻¹) and T represents the absolute temperature (Kelvin). (The ideal gas equation is printed on page 1 of the IB *Chemistry data booklet*.)

It is vital that volumes expressed in dm³ and cm³ are converted to cubic metres if the value of the gas constant R given above is used, and that the pressure is expressed in pascals. 1 dm³ = 0.001 or 10⁻³ m³ and 1 cm³ = 0.000001 or 10⁻⁶ m³.

The ideal gas equation can be used to determine the relative molecular masses of gases (Figure 1.57) or volatile liquids (Figure 1.58).

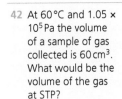
connect to vacuum pump and then supply of gas X

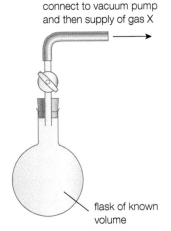
flask of known volume

Figure 1.57 Apparatus for determining the relative molecular mass of a gas

Figure 1.58 Apparatus for determining the relative molecular mass of a volatile liquid

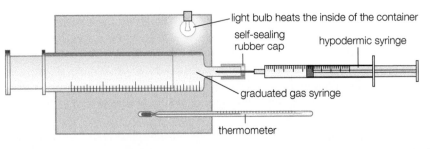
light bulb heats the inside of the container
self-sealing rubber cap
hypodermic syringe
graduated gas syringe
thermometer

43 At 273 K and 101 325 Pa, 12.64 grams of a gas occupy 4.00 dm³. Calculate the relative molecular mass of the gas.

Calculations may also involve measurements involving the density of gas, which should be expressed or converted to SI units of kg m⁻³. However, note that g dm⁻³ and kg m⁻³ are equivalent – no conversion is required.

44 Calculate the relative molecular mass of a gas which has a density of 2.615 g dm⁻³ at 298 K and 101 325 Pa.

Another method of solving this type of problem is to combine the ideal gas equation with the expression for density (*d*) and the relationship between the number of moles (*n*), the mass (*m*), the pressure (*P*) in kilopascals (kPa) and the relative molecular mass (M_r):

$$PV = nRT = \frac{mRT}{M_r} \qquad \text{so} \qquad M_r = \frac{mRT}{PV}$$

$$d = \frac{m}{V} \qquad \text{so} \qquad V = \frac{m}{d}$$

Substituting for V in the equation for M_r:

$$M_r = \frac{dRT}{P}$$

The gas constant can be experimentally determined using relatively available laboratory equipment. Magnesium and hydrochloric acid can be used to generate hydrogen gas. The gas can collected in a eudiometer, a glass tube with a volume scale, closed at one end. Then gas will be collected in the closed end of the tube via the technique of water displacement. Once collected, the volume of the gas, the temperature of the gas, the amount of gas and the pressure of gas can be directly measured or indirectly determined. By substituting these values into the ideal gas law and solving for *R*, an experimental value for the gas constant can be determined. Data-loggers can be used to measure temperature, pressure and volume changes during experiments involving gases.

ToK Link

The ideal gas equation can be deduced from a small number of assumptions of ideal behaviour. What is the role of reason, perception, intuition and imagination in the development of scientific models?

'What are substances made from?' is a question that has been asked for thousands of years since the time of the Ancient Greek philosophers. Gradually scientists began to believe that all substances are made up of particles (atoms, molecules and ions). They are too small to be seen, but many simple experiments suggest that matter must be made of particles.

Observations (using sense perception as a way of knowing) involving the diffusion of coloured gases, such as bromine, and the serial dilution of a highly coloured substance such as potassium manganate(VII), can only be explained if the substances are assumed to be composed of large numbers of moving particles.

The development of the kinetic molecular theory was a direct consequence of the intuition, imagination and reasoning (logic) of various scientists involved in the development of the theory. These included Maxwell, Brown and Einstein.

The various gas laws were developed at the end of the 18th century, when scientists began to realize that relationships between the pressure, volume and temperature of a sample of gas could be obtained which would describe the behaviour of all gases. Gases and mixtures of gases behave in a similar way over a wide variety of physical conditions because (to a good approximation) they all consist of molecules or atoms which are widely spaced: a gas is mainly empty space. The ideal gas equation can be derived from kinetic molecular theory. The gas laws are now considered as special cases of the ideal gas equation, with one or more of the variables (pressure, volume and absolute temperature) held constant.

Graphs relating to the ideal gas equation

A gas that obeys the ideal gas equation (and all the gas laws) under all conditions is said to behave as an ideal gas, or to behave ideally. No gas behaves ideally: all gases deviate to some extent from ideal behaviour and are described as real gases. The deviation from ideal gas behaviour can be shown by plotting *PV/RT* against *P* or *PV* against *P*. For a gas behaving ideally, these plots would give straight lines (Figure 1.59).

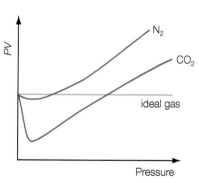

■ **Figure 1.59** Deviation from ideal behaviour at high pressure

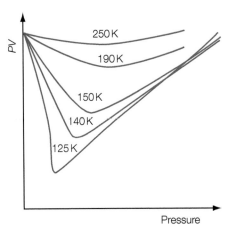

■ Figure 1.60 Deviation from ideal behaviour at low temperature

The greatest deviation from ideal behaviour occurs when the gas is subjected to a low temperature and high pressure (Figure 1.60). A real gas deviates from ideal behaviour considerably at high pressures. This is because when gases are put under pressure and compressed, the molecules or atoms come sufficiently close together for intermolecular forces (Chapter 4) to operate and the particles to be attracted to each other. In other gases, for example ammonia, stronger hydrogen bonds operate and the deviation from ideal behaviour is even greater.

One of the assumptions of the ideal gas model is that the volume of molecules is negligible compared with the volume occupied by the gas. This is no longer true in a highly compressed gas where the actual volume of the gas molecules becomes significant. At low temperatures, deviation from ideal behaviour occurs because the molecules are moving slowly, which significantly strengthens the intermolecular forces operating between neighbouring molecules or atoms.

■ Solutions

Water dissolves a wide range of different chemical substances. Water is a solvent and the substances dissolved in the water are termed solutes. The mixture of solvent and solute is termed a solution.

When one mole of a solute is dissolved in water and the volume of solution made up to $1000\,cm^3$ ($1\,dm^3$), the resulting solution is termed a molar solution ($1\,mol\,dm^{-3}$). If two moles of a solute are made up to $1000\,cm^3$ of solution (or one mole to $500\,cm^3$), the solution is described as $2\,mol\,dm^{-3}$ (Figure 1.61). Concentration is often depicted with square brackets around the solute of interest; for example, the concentration of hydrogen ion is depicted as $[H^+]$.

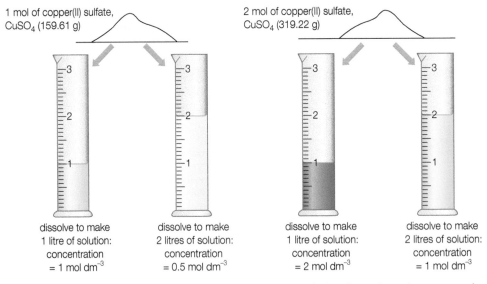

■ Figure 1.61 A diagram showing how the concentration of a solution depends on the amount of solute and the volume of solvent

The concentration of a solution is the amount of solute (in moles) contained within one cubic decimetre. The concentration of a solution is given by the following expression:

$$\text{concentration of solution } (mol\,dm^{-3}) = \frac{\text{amount of solute (mol)}}{\text{volume of solution } (dm^3)}$$

45 Calculate the concentration of the solution formed when 0.5 mol of glucose is dissolved in 5.0 dm³ of water.

46 Determine the concentration of the solution when 4.00 grams of sodium hydroxide (molar mass 40.0 g mol⁻¹) is dissolved in 200 cm³ of water.

47 Calculate the mass of hydrated copper(II) sulfate, $CuSO_4.5H_2O$ (molar mass 249.7 g mol⁻¹) present in 25.0 cm³ of a 0.500 mol dm⁻³ solution.

48 Calculate the concentration (in mol dm⁻³) of a solution of hydrochloric acid containing 14.6 grams of hydrogen chloride in 100 cm³ of solution.

Soluble ionic compounds dissociate into their component ions when dissolved in an excess of water. The concentrations of the individual ions will depend on the amounts of these ions when the substance (salt, base or alkali) dissolves. In a 4.0 mol dm⁻³ aqueous solution of aluminium nitrate, for example, the concentration of the aluminium ions is 4.0 mol dm⁻³, but the concentration of the nitrate ions is 12.0 mol dm⁻³.

$$Al(NO_3)_3(aq) \rightarrow Al^{3+}(aq) + 3NO_3^-(aq)$$
$$1\,mol \qquad\qquad 1\,mol \qquad\quad 3\,mol$$

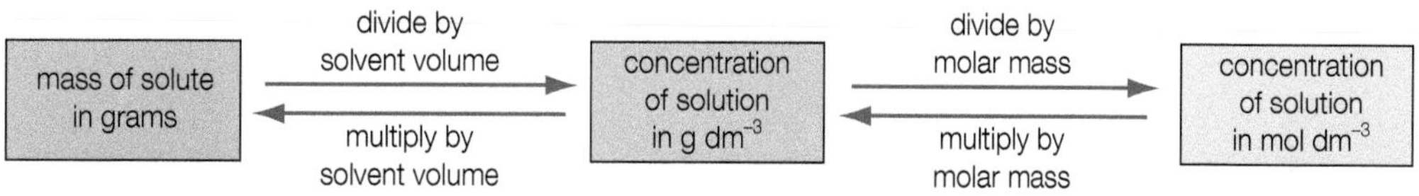

■ **Figure 1.62** Summary of the interconversion between concentration (in moles per cubic decimetre of solution) and concentration (in grams per cubic decimetre of solution)

Parts per million

The concentration of very dilute solutions is often expressed in parts per million (ppm). Parts per million is defined as:

$$ppm\ of\ component = \frac{mass\ of\ component\ in\ solution}{total\ mass\ of\ solution} \times 10^6$$

A solution whose concentration is 1 ppm contains 1 g of solute for each million (10^6) grams of solution or, equivalently, 1 mg of solute per kilogram of solution. Because the density of water is almost 1 g cm⁻³, 1 kg of a dilute aqueous solution has a volume very close to 1 dm³. Thus 1 ppm also corresponds to 1 mg of solute per cubic decimetre of aqueous solution.

> ### Worked example
>
> A 2.5 g sample of ground water was found (by atomic absorption spectroscopy) to contain 5.4 μg of cadmium ions. Determine the concentration of Cd^{2+} in parts per million.
>
> 5.4 μg = 5.4 × 10⁻⁶ g. Concentration of Cd^{2+} (in ppm) = $\dfrac{5.4 \times 10^{-6}\,g}{2.5\,g \times 10^6}$ = 2.2 ppm.

Dilution of acids

Acids are supplied as concentrated acids. The solutions required in the laboratory are prepared by diluting the concentrated solutions with water. For safety reasons the dilution is carried out by slowly adding the concentrated acid to the water. Water should *never* be added to concentrated acids. When a concentrated solution is diluted with water, the amount of solute in the solution remains unchanged.

This can be expressed by the following relationship:

$$M_1 \times V_1 = M_2 \times V_2$$

where M_1 represents the initial concentration, M_2 represents the concentration after dilution, V_1 represents the initial volume and V_2 represents the volume after dilution.

49 Calculate the volume to which 25.0 cm³ of 5.0 mol dm⁻³ hydrochloric acid must be diluted to produce a concentration of 1.5 mol dm⁻³.

Figure 1.63
A selection of apparatus used in a titration: pipette filler, burette and pipette

Volumetric chemistry

A solution of known concentration is called a standard solution. In volumetric chemistry a series of titrations is carried out, frequently with an acid and a base. In each titration (Figure 1.63) a solution is added in small measured quantities, from a burette, to a fixed volume of another solution, measured with a pipette, in the presence of an indicator. The addition of the solution is continued until the indicator just changes colour. At this stage, termed the end-point, the two substances are present in stoichiometric quantities.

Acid–base titrations

In these titrations acid and base are reacted in the presence of a suitable acid–base indicator (Chapter 18). Uses of acid–base titrations include:

- determining the concentrations of solutions
- determining the percentage purity or molar mass of an acid or base
- deducing the equation for a neutralization reaction
- determining the amount of water of crystallization in a hydrated salt.

Worked example

Sodium hydroxide reacts with hydrochloric acid according to the following equation:

$$NaOH(aq) + HCl(aq) \rightarrow NaCl(aq) + H_2O(l)$$

Calculate the volume of $0.0500\,mol\,dm^{-3}$ sodium hydroxide solution to react exactly with $25\,cm^3$ of $0.20\,mol\,dm^{-3}$ hydrochloric acid.

Amount of hydrochloric acid $= \dfrac{25.0}{1000}dm^3 \times 0.200\,mol\,dm^{-3} = 5.00 \times 10^{-3}\,mol$

The equation's stoichiometry indicates that the alkali and acid react in a 1 : 1 molar ratio. Hence the amount of sodium hydroxide is $5.00 \times 10^{-3}\,mol$.

Volume of sodium hydroxide $= \dfrac{1000 \times 5.00 \times 10^{-3}\,mol}{0.0500\,mol\,dm^{-3}} = 100\,cm^3$

---

50 0.558 grams of a monobasic aromatic carboxylic acid, HX, was dissolved in distilled water. A few drops of phenolphthalein indicator was added and the mixture was titrated with $0.100\,mol\,dm^{-3}$ sodium hydroxide solution. It took $41.0\,cm^3$ of the alkali to obtain the end-point (with a permanent pink colour). Calculate the molar mass of the organic acid.

51 $17.5\,cm^3$ of $0.150\,mol\,dm^{-3}$ potassium hydroxide solution react with $20.0\,cm^3$ of phosphoric(v) acid, H_3PO_4 of concentration $0.0656\,mol\,dm^{-3}$. Deduce the equation for the reaction.

The results of a titration with a solution of known concentration can be used to determine the concentration of the other solution.

---

52 A $50.0\,cm^3$ sample of concentrated sulfuric acid was diluted to $1.00\,dm^3$. A sample of the diluted sulfuric acid was analysed by titrating with aqueous sodium hydroxide. In the titration, $25.00\,cm^3$ of $1.00\,mol\,dm^{-3}$ aqueous sodium hydroxide required $20.0\,cm^3$ of the diluted sulfuric acid for neutralization. Determine the concentration of the original concentrated sulfuric acid solution through the following steps:

a Construct the equation for the complete neutralization of sulfuric acid by sodium hydroxide.
b Calculate the amount of sodium hydroxide that was used in the titration.
c Calculate the concentration of the diluted sulfuric acid.
d Calculate the concentration of the original concentrated sulfuric acid solution.

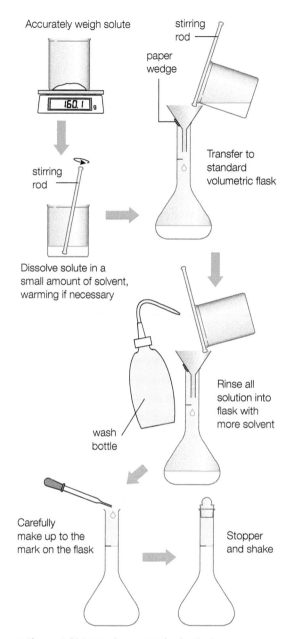

Accurately weigh solute

stirring rod

paper wedge

Transfer to standard volumetric flask

stirring rod

Dissolve solute in a small amount of solvent, warming if necessary

wash bottle

Rinse all solution into flask with more solvent

Carefully make up to the mark on the flask

Stopper and shake

■ **Figure 1.64** Preparing a standard solution

Primary standard solutions

Titrations often involve a primary standard solution. Its concentration may have been determined by titration with another primary standard solution or by weighing the solute and preparing a solution of known volume (Figure 1.64). The concentrations of primary standard solutions do not change with time. Few chemical substances are suitable for use as primary standards. If a substance is to be weighed accurately enough for use in preparing a primary standard solution, the following criteria must be met:

■ The substance must be available in a high state of purity or be easily purified.
■ The substance must not be volatile, or some of it would be lost during the weighing process.
■ The substance must not react with oxygen, water or carbon dioxide.

Compounds suitable as primary standards are:

■ strong acid – ethanedioic acid (oxalic acid)
■ strong base – anhydrous sodium carbonate
■ oxidizing agent – potassium dichromate(VI)
■ reducing agent – iron(II) sulfate (in the form of hydrated ammonium iron(II) sulfate).

A number of solutions when freshly prepared are used as alternative primary standards, for example sodium and potassium hydroxides, sulfuric and hydrochloric acids, and potassium manganate(VII). These cannot be stored since their concentrations change with time due to a chemical reaction (usually with oxygen and/or water in the storage vessel).

Back titration

In the technique known as back titration, a known excess of one reagent A is allowed to react with an unknown amount of a reagent B. At the end of the reaction, the amount of A that remains unreacted is found by titration. A simple calculation gives the amount of A that has reacted with B and also the amount of B that has reacted.

In a typical acid–base back titration, a quantity of a base is added to an excess of an acid (or vice versa). All the base and some of the acid react. The acid remaining is then titrated with a standard alkali and its amount determined. From the results, the amount of acid which has reacted with the base can be found and the amount of base can then be calculated. The principle of this type of titration is illustrated in Figure 1.65.

Back titrations are usually used when the determination of the amount of a substance poses some difficulty in the direct titration method, for example with insoluble solid substances where the end-point is difficult to detect and volatile substances where inaccuracy arises due to loss of substance during titration.

■ **Figure 1.65**
Illustration of the principle of an acid–base back titration

Amount of standard acid (**calculated** from its volume and concentration)	
Amount of acid reacting with sample (**unknown**)	Amount of acid reacting with the standard solution of alkali used in the titration (**calculated** from its volume and concentration)

53 Magnesium oxide is not very soluble in water, and is difficult to titrate directly. Its purity can be determined by use of a 'back titration' method. 4.08 g of impure magnesium oxide was completely dissolved in 100 cm³ of 2.00 mol dm⁻³ aqueous hydrochloric acid. The excess acid required 19.7 cm³ of 0.200 mol dm⁻³ aqueous sodium hydroxide for neutralization. Work through the following steps to find out what the purity of the impure magnesium oxide is.

a Construct equations for the two neutralization reactions.
b Calculate the amount of hydrochloric acid added to the magnesium oxide.
c Calculate the amount of excess hydrochloric acid titrated.
d Calculate the amount of hydrochloric acid reacting with the magnesium oxide.
e Calculate the mass of magnesium oxide that reacted with the initial hydrochloric acid, and hence determine the percentage purity of the magnesium oxide.

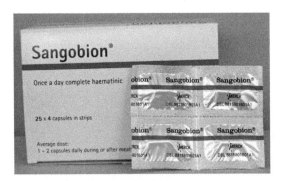

■ **Figure 1.66** Redox titrations can be performed in company laboratories to ensure that materials such as these iron tablets, bleach (sodium chlorate(I)) and vitamin C (ascorbic acid) contain the stated amounts or concentrations of substances in them

Redox titrations

Calculations involving redox titrations (Figure 1.66) are identical to those involving acids and bases. Uses of redox titrations include:

■ determining the concentration of a solution

■ determining the percentage purity of a salt or other substances, for example an alloy

■ determining the charge and relative atomic mass of an ion

■ deducing the ionic equation for a reaction

■ determining the amount of water of crystallization in a hydrated salt.

Chapter 9 shows how ionic equations for redox titrations can be constructed and examines the principles underlying several types of redox titrations.

54 Hydrated iron(II) sulfate has the formula $FeSO_4.xH_2O$. An experiment was performed to determine x, the amount of water of crystallization in hydrated iron(II) sulfate. 50.60 grams of hydrated iron(II) sulfate were dissolved in distilled water to make 500.00 cm³ of solution. 20.00 cm³ of this solution reacted completely with 24.00 cm³ of 0.100 mol dm⁻³ potassium dichromate(VI) solution. Use this data to determine the value of x and hence the formula of hydrated iron(II) sulfate.

$$6Fe^{2+}(aq) + 14H^+(aq) + Cr_2O_7^{2-}(aq) \rightarrow 2Cr^{3+}(aq) + 7H_2O(l) + 6Fe^{3+}(aq)$$

55 Potassium manganate(VII), $KMnO_4$, oxidizes potassium iodide, KI, to iodine, I_2. The iodine liberated is titrated with aqueous sodium thiosulfate, $Na_2S_2O_3$.

$$16H^+(aq) + 2MnO_4^-(aq) + 10I^-(aq) \rightarrow 2Mn^{2+}(aq) + 8H_2O(l) + 5I_2(aq)$$
$$2S_2O_3^{2-}(aq) + I_2(aq) \rightarrow S_4O_6^{2-}(aq) + 2I^-(aq)$$

The iodine produced from 25.00 cm³ of potassium manganate(VII) solution required 26.40 cm³ of 0.500 mol dm⁻³ sodium thiosulfate solution for complete reaction. Calculate the concentration of the potassium manganate(VII) solution.

56 Sodium nitrite, $NaNO_2$ is used as a preservative in meat products such as frankfurters. In an acidic solution, nitrite ions are converted to nitrous acid, HNO_2, which reacts with the manganate(VII) ion. A 1.00 g sample of a water-soluble solid containing $NaNO_2$ was dissolved in dilute H_2SO_4, and titrated with 0.0100 mol dm⁻³ aqueous $KMnO_4$ solution. In the reaction, NO_2^- is oxidized to NO_3^-. The titration required 12.15 cm³ of the $KMnO_4$ solution. Calculate the percentage by mass of $NaNO_2$ in the 1.00 g sample.

$$5NO_2^- + 6H^+ + 2MnO_4^- \rightarrow 5NO_3^- + 2Mn^{2+} + 3H_2O$$

Precipitation titrations

A common type of precipitation titration uses silver nitrate to determine the concentration of chloride ions. Silver nitrate solution is added to a chloride solution in the presence of potassium chromate(VI), which acts as an 'indicator'.

The net ionic equation for a silver nitrate titration is:

$$Ag^+(aq) + Cl^-(aq) \rightarrow AgCl(s)$$

If a chloride solution is acidic, calcium carbonate powder is added to neutralize the acid. One use of silver nitrate titrations is to determine the formulas of chlorides.

Worked example

0.010 mol of an ionic chloride was dissolved in water and found to react completely with 20.00 cm^3 of 1.00 mol dm^{-3} silver nitrate solution. Determine the formula, using M to represent the metal.

Amount of silver nitrate $= \dfrac{20}{1000}$ dm$^3 \times 1.00$ mol dm$^{-3} = 0.020$ mol of silver ions

These react with chloride ions in the molar ratio of 1 : 1.

$$Ag^+(aq) + Cl^-(aq) \rightarrow AgCl(s)$$

This means that 0.010 mol of the chloride contains 0.020 mol of chlorine, Cl. Hence the formula is MCl_2.

■ *Examination questions – a selection*

Paper 1 IB questions and IB style questions

Q1 What is the total number of oxygen atoms in 0.200 mol of glucose, $C_6H_{12}O_6$?

A	1.20	**C**	1.20×10^{23}
B	6.00	**D**	7.22×10^{23}

Q2 Which sample has the greatest mass?

A	1.0 mol of N_2H_4	**C**	3.0 mol of NH_3
B	2.0 mol of N_2	**D**	25.0 mol of H_2

Standard Level Paper 1, Nov 2013, Q1

Q3 Which of the following samples contains the smallest number of atoms?

A	1 g H_2	**C**	1 g S_8
B	1 g O_2	**D**	1 g Br_2

Q4 Which changes of state are endothermic processes?

    I freezing   **III** subliming
    II boiling

A	I and II only	**C**	II and III only
B	I and III only	**D**	I, II and III

Q5 Hydrogen peroxide, H_2O_2, reacts with manganate(VII) ions, MnO_4^-, in basic solution according to the following equation:

$$2MnO_4^-(aq) + 3H_2O_2(aq)$$
$$\rightarrow 2MnO_2(s) + 3O_2(g) + 2OH^-(aq) + 2H_2O(l)$$

How many moles of hydrogen peroxide would be needed to produce eight moles of water?

A	one	**C**	three
B	two	**D**	twelve

Q6 What are the coefficients of $H_2SO_4(aq)$ and $H_3PO_4(aq)$ when the following equation is balanced using the smallest possible whole numbers?

$$—Ca_3(PO_4)_2(s) + —H_2SO_4$$
$$\rightarrow —CaSO_4(s) + —H_3PO_4(aq)$$

	Coefficient of $H_2SO_4(aq)$	Coefficient of $H_3PO_4(aq)$
A	1	2
B	2	3
C	3	1
D	3	2

Standard Level Paper 1, May 2013, Q3

Q7 A certain compound has a molecular mass of 56 g mol^{-1}. Which of the following cannot be an empirical formula for this compound?

A	BH_3	**C**	MgN_2H_4
B	C_3H_4O	**D**	HCl

Q8 Which of the following is an empirical formula?

A	N_2F_2	**C**	C_2H_4O
B	$C_2H_4O_2$	**D**	C_2N_2

Q9 What mass of carbon dioxide, $CO_2(g)$, in g, is produced when 5.0 g of calcium carbonate, $CaCO_3(s)$, reacts completely with hydrochloric acid, HCl(aq)?

A	0.050	**C**	4.4
B	2.2	**D**	5.0

Higher Level Paper 1, May 2013, Q2

Q10 Which one of the following equations is **not** correctly balanced?

A $Ca(s) + 2H^+(aq) \rightarrow Ca^{2+}(aq) + H_2(g)$
B $Mg(s) + 2H_2O(l) \rightarrow Mg(OH)_2(aq) + H_2(g)$
C $Fe^{2+}(aq) + Ag^+(aq) \rightarrow Fe^{3+}(aq) + Ag(s)$
D $Fe^{2+}(aq) + Cl_2(g) \rightarrow Fe^{3+}(aq) + 2Cl^-(aq)$

Q11 32.0 grams of sulfur (atomic mass of 32.0) combine with a metal M (atomic mass of 40.0) to give a product which weighs 52.0 g. What is the empirical formula of the sulfide formed?

A MS   C M_2S

B MS_2 D M_2S_5

Q12 An unknown element M combines with oxygen to form the compound MO_2. If 36.0 g of element M combines exactly with 16.0 g of oxygen, what is the atomic mass of M in grams?

A 12.0   C 24.0

B 16.0   D 72.0

Q13 When 16.00 grams of hydrogen gas reacts with 64.0 grams of oxygen gas in a reaction (atomic masses are H = 1.00, O = 16.00), what will be present in the resulting mixture?

A H_2, H_2O, and O_2 C O_2, H_2O

B H_2, H_2O D H_2, O_2

Q14 One molecule of a small protein contains 63 atoms of carbon. The mass percentage of carbon in the protein is 55.74%. What is the molar mass of the protein?

A $1357 \, g \, mol^{-1}$ C $821.3 \, g \, mol^{-1}$

B $421.7 \, g \, mol^{-1}$ D $756.6 \, g \, mol^{-1}$

Q15 Which one of the following is an incorrect assumption of the kinetic theory of gases?

A Atoms or molecules travel in straight lines between collisions but are in overall random motion.

B Atoms or molecules of a gas are much smaller than the average distances between them.

C Collisions between atoms or molecules of a gas and the containing vessel are perfectly elastic and no loss of kinetic energy occurs.

D In a given gas, all particles have the same kinetic energy at a given temperature.

Q16 $1000 \, cm^3$ of hydrogen gas (hydrogen molecules, H_2) contains Z molecules at room temperature and pressure. What will be the number of atoms in $500 \, cm^3$ of radon gas (radon atoms) at the same temperature and pressure? (Assume both gases behave ideally.)

A Z   C Z/2

B 2Z   D Z/4

Q17 Under what conditions of temperature and pressure will a real gas behave most like an ideal gas?

Temperature	Pressure
A Low	Low
B High	Low
C High	High
D Low	High

Q18 When compared at the same pressure and temperature, which one of the following physical properties has the same value for H_2, and for D_2? [D = $\frac{2}{1}$H].

A average molecular speed

B relative molecular mass

C collision rate between molecules

D average kinetic energy of molecules

Q19 A $350 \, cm^3$ sample of helium gas is collected at 22.0 °C and 99.3 kPa. What volume would this gas occupy at STP?

A $318 \, cm^3$ C $477 \, cm^3$

B $450 \, cm^3$ D $220 \, cm^3$

Q20 A 27.0 g sample of an unknown carbon–hydrogen compound was burned in excess oxygen to form 88.0 g of CO_2 and 27.0 g of H_2O. What is the possible molecular formula of the hydrocarbon?

A CH_4 C C_2H_6

B C_4H_6 D C_6H_6

Q21 $1000 \, cm^3$ of ammonia gas combines with $1250 \, cm^3$ of oxygen to produce two gaseous compounds with a combined volume of $2500 \, cm^3$, all volumes being measured at 200 °C and 0.500 atm pressure. Which of the following equations fits these facts?

A $4NH_3 + 7O_2 \rightarrow 4NO_2 + 6H_2O$

B $4NH_3 + 5O_2 \rightarrow 4NO + 6H_2O$

C $4NH_3 + 5O_2 \rightarrow 2N_2O_2 + 6H_2O$

D $4NH_3 + 3O_2 \rightarrow 2N_2 + 6H_2O$

Q22 In order to dilute $40.0 \, cm^3$ of $0.600 \, mol \, dm^{-3}$ HCl(aq) to $0.100 \, mol \, dm^{-3}$, what volume of water must be added?

A $60 \, cm^3$ C $200 \, cm^3$

B $160 \, cm^3$ D $240 \, cm^3$

Q23 How many grams of AgCl would be precipitated if an excess of $AgNO_3$ solution were added to $55.0 \, cm^3$ of $0.200 \, mol \, dm^{-3}$ KCl solution? [Molar mass of silver chloride = $143.32 \, g \, mol^{-1}$]

A 1.58 g   C 6.43 g

B 1.11 g   D 7.80 g

Q24 The temperature of an ideal gas sample is changed from 100 °C to 200 °C at constant pressure. What is the ratio of the final volume to the initial volume?

A 1 : 2   C 1.27 : 1

B 4 : 1   D 1 : 1.27

Q25 At STP (i.e. 0 °C and 1 atm pressure (101 kPa)), it was found that $1.15 \, dm^3$ of a gas weighed 3.96 g. What is its molar mass?

A $77 \, g \, mol^{-1}$ C $47 \, g \, mol^{-1}$

B $39 \, g \, mol^{-1}$ D $4 \, g \, mol^{-1}$

Q26 A sample of argon gas in a sealed container of fixed volume is heated from 50 to 250 °C. Which quantity will remain constant?
  A average speed of the atoms
  B pressure of the gas
  C average kinetic energy of the atoms
  D density of the argon

Paper 2 IB questions and IB style questions

Q1 10 cm³ of ethene, C_2H_4, is burned in 40 cm³ of oxygen, producing carbon dioxide and some liquid water. Some oxygen remained.
  a Write the equation for the complete combustion of ethene. [2]
  b Calculate the volume of carbon dioxide and the volume of oxygen remaining. [2]

Q2 **a** Write an equation for the formation of zinc iodide from zinc and iodine. [1]
  b 100.0 g of zinc is allowed to react with 100.0 g of iodine producing zinc iodide. Calculate the amount (in moles) of zinc and iodine, and hence determine which reactant is in excess. [3]
  c Calculate the mass of zinc iodide that will be produced. [1]

Higher Level Paper 2, May 2004, Q3

Q3 A balloon, which can hold a maximum of 1000 cm³ of nitrogen before bursting, contains 955 cm³ of nitrogen at 5 °C.
  a Determine whether the balloon will burst if the temperature is increased to 30 °C. [3]
  b Use the kinetic theory to explain what happens to the molecules of nitrogen inside the balloon as the temperature is increased to 30 °C. [2]

Q4 Hydrated sodium carbonate has the formula $Na_2CO_3.nH_2O$. An experiment was performed to determine n, the amount of water of crystallization. A sample of 50.00 grams of hydrated sodium carbonate was dissolved in 250 cm³ of water. 20.00 cm³ of this solution reacted completely with 13.95 cm³ of 2.00 mol dm⁻³ hydrochloric acid.

$Na_2CO_3(aq) + 2HCl(aq)$
$$\rightarrow 2NaCl(aq) + CO_2(g) + H_2O(l)$$

  a Calculate the amount of hydrochloric acid reacted. [1]
  b Calculate the amount of sodium carbonate in the 20 cm³ of the solution used in the reaction. [1]
  c Calculate the concentration of sodium carbonate in the sample. [1]
  d Calculate the molar mass of the hydrated sodium carbonate. [1]
  e Calculate the value of n. [2]

Q5 **a** Aqueous XO_4^{3-} ions form a precipitate with aqueous silver ions. Write a balanced equation for the reaction, including state symbols. [1]
  b When 41.18 cm³ of a solution of aqueous silver ions with a concentration of 0.2040 mol dm⁻³ is added to a solution of ions, 1.172 g of the precipitate is formed.
    i Calculate the amount (in moles) of Ag^+ ions used in the reaction. [1]
    ii Calculate the amount (in moles) of the precipitate formed. [1]
    iii Calculate the molar mass of the precipitate. [2]
    iv Determine the relative atomic mass of X and identify the element. [2]

Higher Level Paper 2, Nov 2003, Q2

Q6 11 mg of sulfuric acid are added to 2 kg of water. Determine the concentration of sulfuric acid in ppm. [2]

Q7 A 0.6125 g sample of potassium iodate(v), KIO_3, is dissolved in distilled water and made up to 250.00 cm³ in a volumetric flask. A 25.00 cm³ portion of the solution is added to an excess of acidified potassium iodide solution. The iodine formed requires 24.50 cm³ of sodium thiosulfate solution for titration.

Determine the concentration of the sodium thiosulfate solution.

$IO_3^-(aq) + 5I^-(aq) + 6H^+(aq) \rightarrow 3I_2 + 3H_2O(l)$ [4]

2 Atomic structure

ESSENTIAL IDEAS

- The mass of an atom is concentrated in its minute, positively charged nucleus.
- The electron configuration of an atom can be deduced from its atomic number.

2.1 The nuclear atom – *the mass of an atom is concentrated in its minute, positively charged nucleus*

Atomic structure

Atoms are composed of three sub-atomic particles: protons, neutrons and electrons. Each atom consists of two regions: the nucleus and the electron shells. The nucleus is a very small dense positively charged region located at the centre of the atom. The nucleus contains protons and neutrons. These are known as nucleons since they are found in the nucleus. Virtually all of the mass of an atom is due to the protons and neutrons. The electrons occupy the empty space around the nucleus and are arranged in shells. Each shell can hold a specific maximum number of electrons. This simple model of the atom is illustrated in Figure 2.1.

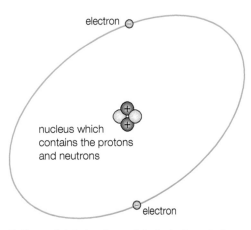

■ **Figure 2.1** A simple model of a helium-4 atom

Nature of Science

Paradigm shifts – the sub-atomic particle theory of matter

Atomism, the concept that matter is composed of atoms, is thousands of years old. The idea was founded in philosophical reasoning rather than experimentation. The earliest references to atomism date back to India in the sixth century BCE. The earliest references in the Western World emerged a century later in Ancient Greece, from Leucippus and his student Democritus.

In 1803, the British chemist John Dalton (1766–1844) developed an atomic theory to explain why chemical elements react in simple proportions by mass. He proposed that each chemical element consisted of identical atoms and that these atoms could bond together to form chemical compounds. It is not clear whether Dalton was aware of previous ancient ideas about atoms, but his interest in atoms was strongly influenced by the experiments he performed on gases. He did not prove the existence of atoms; he simply demonstrated that his atomic theory was consistent with experimental data.

Unfortunately, some of Dalton's assumptions were later shown to be incorrect. For example, by assuming the formula for water was OH he calculated the relative atomic mass of oxygen to be 7 (where the atomic mass of hydrogen was assigned a value of 1). The critical distinction between atoms and molecules, for example, O and O_2, was not made until 1811, by Avogadro (Chapter 1), but it remained ineffective until clarified by Cannizzaro in 1858. Dalton's atomic theory had to be modified in the twentieth century, following the discovery of radioactivity, isotopes and sub-atomic particles, but it is still a useful model for explaining chemical composition and chemical changes.

Dalton's chemical theory is often used as an example of a paradigm shift, or revolution in 'scientific thinking'. In the nineteenth century, the prevalent scientific thought (supported by influential scientists, such as Kelvin and Mach) did not accept the idea of Dalton's atoms. As evidence for Dalton's theory increased, more and more scientists found value in using Dalton's ideas and gradually a shift in thinking about atoms in this manner became more acceptable. This acceptance of a new approach towards viewing a phenomenon is called a 'paradigm shift'.

■ Relative masses and relative charges of protons, neutrons and electrons

Protons have a positive charge and neutrons have no electrical charge and hence are neutral. These particles have almost exactly the same mass. Electrons have a negative charge. The opposite charges of the proton and electron (through electrostatic forces of attraction) hold the atom together. Electrons have a very small mass compared with protons and neutrons. A summary of the characteristics of the sub-atomic particles is given in Table 2.1.

■ **Table 2.1**
Characteristics of protons, neutrons and electrons

Sub-atomic particle	Symbol	Relative mass	Relative charge	Nuclide notation
Proton	p	1	+1	$_1^1p$
Neutron	n	1	0	$_0^1n$
Electron	e	5×10^{-4} (negligible)	−1	$_{-1}^{0}e$

The charge is measured relative to that of a proton; the mass is measured relative to that of the proton or neutron (as they have nearly the same mass). Atoms are electrically neutral because they contain equal numbers of protons and electrons.

Neutrons help to stabilize the nucleus. They separate the protons, reducing the electrostatic repulsion, and also attract each other and protons (via the strong nuclear force). However, if too many or too few neutrons are present, the nucleus is unstable and will undergo radioactive decay.

Although electrons are the smallest of the three sub-atomic particles, they control the chemical properties of the chemical elements. Different elements have different chemical properties because they have different numbers of electrons and hence different arrangements in their electron shells. Figure 2.2 gives an idea of the scale of an atom.

■ **Figure 2.2**
A series of diagrams illustrating the size of atoms

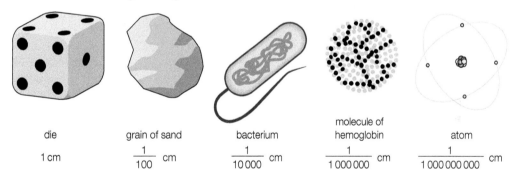

die	grain of sand	bacterium	molecule of hemoglobin	atom
1 cm	$\frac{1}{100}$ cm	$\frac{1}{10\,000}$ cm	$\frac{1}{1\,000\,000}$ cm	$\frac{1}{1\,000\,000\,000}$ cm

1   Refer to the section on fundamental particles on page 3 of the IB *Chemistry data booklet*. Calculate the mass (in kilograms) and charge (in coulombs) of one mole of electrons.

2   An atom has a radius of 0.1 nm and the nucleus a radius of 10^{-16} m. The formula for the volume of a sphere is given by the expression $\frac{4}{3}\pi r^3$, where r is the radius.
Calculate the volumes of the atom and the nucleus and deduce the percentage of the atom that is occupied by the nucleus.

3   Use the data in the IB *Chemistry data booklet* to calculate how many times heavier a hydrogen atom is compared to an electron.

Nature of Science

Evidence and improvements in instrumentation, and paradigm shifts – use of alpha particles in the development of the nuclear model that was first proposed by Rutherford

Around the beginning of the twentieth century, physicists started to find evidence that atoms are made up of smaller particles. These are known as sub-atomic particles. Sir William Crookes was experimenting in 1895 on the discharge and conduction of electricity through samples of gases at low pressure. He discovered that a beam of rays (waves) was emitted by the cathode (negative electrode). Crookes termed these rays cathode rays. Crookes clearly showed that cathode rays behave like a stream of negatively charged particles.

J.J. Thomson (Figure 2.3) measured the ratio of the charge to the mass of the particles in the beam by noting their trajectory under the influence of magnetic and electric fields (Figure 2.4) and found it to be over 1000 times less than that of a hydrogen ion (H^+). In further experiments Thomson demonstrated that a hydrogen atom had only one electron. From his measurement he calculated that the ratio of charge to mass, e/m, was $-1.76 \times 10^{11}\,C\,kg^{-1}$. The coulomb (C) is the SI unit of charge. Since he obtained the same value, regardless of the nature of the gas and its pressure, he concluded that these negatively charged particles are present in all atoms. They were named electrons and recognized as the charge carriers in an electric current. Thomson's apparatus for determining the value of the charge-to-mass ratio of the electron led to the development of the mass spectrometer. This instrument separates gaseous positive ions according to the value of e/m. The development of the mass spectrometer allowed the discovery of isotopes.

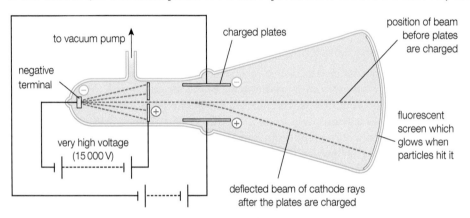

■ **Figure 2.4** Deflection of cathode rays by an electric field

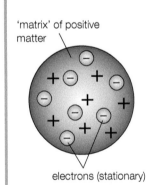

■ **Figure 2.5** Thomson's 'plum pudding' model of the internal structure of the atom

In 1904 J.J. Thomson (Nobel Prize in Physics in 1906) surveyed the experimental evidence suggesting that atoms consist of charged particles. He described the atom as a uniform (always the same) sphere of positive electricity and mass, in which negative electrons are embedded. This model was known as the 'plum pudding' model of atomic structure (Figure 2.5).

If this atomic model is correct, then a thin metal foil is a film of positive electricity containing electrons. A beam of alpha particles fired at it should pass straight through. Alpha particles are positively charged particles composed of two protons and two neutrons. In 1909 Ernest Rutherford and his two students, Geiger and Marsden, tested this prediction (Figure 2.6). A zinc sulfide detector (spinthariscope) was moved around the gold foil to determine the directions in which the alpha particles travelled after striking the foil.

They found, as they predicted, that alpha particles readily penetrated the thin gold foil. However, to their surprise, a small fraction (about 1 in 8000) of particles were deflected through large angles. Rutherford concluded that the mass and positive charge must be concentrated in a small region of the atom, termed the nucleus. Figure 2.7 shows his graphical interpretation of the results. Rutherford's results were supported by theoretical calculations from classical physics that predicted almost identical scattering results to those he observed. He was able to calculate approximate values for the radii of the gold atom and its nucleus.

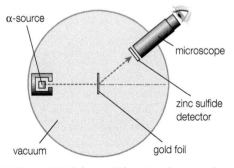

■ **Figure 2.6** Alpha particle scattering experiment

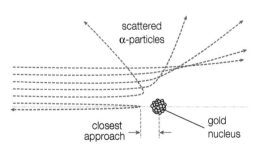

■ **Figure 2.7** Possible trajectories of the alpha particles from Rutherford's gold foil experiment

Thomson's model could explain the electrical neutrality of the atom, but could not be reconciled with the Rutherford scattering of alpha particles from thin metal foils. Rutherford's nuclear model was another paradigm shift ('scientific revolution') in thinking about atomic structure and Thomson's model was abandoned.

The classical model of the nuclear atom was proposed by Rutherford in 1909 (see Figure 2.1). The protons (large and positively charged) are located in the nucleus and the electrons (much lighter and negatively charged) are located in energy levels known as shells. They occupy this space by repelling the electrons of neighbouring atoms. If another atom approaches very closely, its electrons experience severe repulsion.

Rutherford was awarded the Nobel Prize in Chemistry in 1908. He famously remarked: 'It was quite the most incredible event that has ever happened to me in my life. It was almost as incredible as if you fired a 15-inch shell at a piece of tissue paper and it came back and hit you.'

It should be noted that Rutherford's work depended on improvements in instrumentation. The spinthariscope is a simple instrument that visually shows individual alpha particles by means of the scintillations ('flashes of light') they produce when hitting a phosphorescent screen. It was first demonstrated in 1903 by William Crookes but improved in 1908 by Erich Regener, who devised a method of counting scintillations by observing them with a microscope. It was by means of counting scintillations that Rutherford and Geiger clarified the nature of the alpha particle (helium nucleus), and it was also the method they used in measuring the scattering of alpha particles from a thin gold foil that in 1909 led to the discovery of the atomic nucleus.

ToK Link

No sub-atomic particles can be (or will be) directly observed. Which ways of knowing do we use to interpret indirect evidence, gained through the use of technology? Do we believe or know of their existence?

Strong indirect proof for the existence of atoms and molecules came from the kinetic theory of gases (Chapter 1), which assumes that gases consist of many millions of atoms or molecules in rapid random motion. However, the existence of atoms was doubted by a number of notable scientists up until 1900. In 1905, Einstein provided a very convincing mathematical explanation for Brownian motion. This is the random movement of pollen grains or smoke particles visible under a light microscope (Figure 2.8).

Einstein explained this phenomenon by invoking their constant bombardment by gas molecules (Figure 2.9).

Atoms and molecules are too small to see under a light microscope, but now atoms and molecules can be directly visualized as fuzzy dots using a scanning tunnelling microscope (STM). This instrument uses a very fine probe containing a tungsten tip to scan a solid surface. A small potential difference is applied between the probe and the surface. Tiny changes in current are recorded when the surface is uneven.

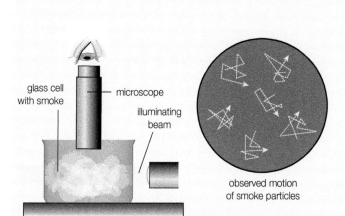

■ **Figure 2.8** Observing Brownian motion in smoke

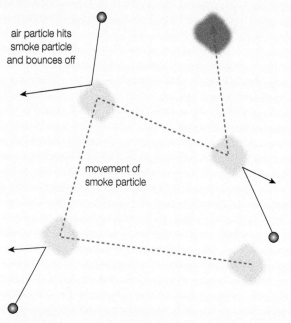

■ **Figure 2.9** A molecular explanation for Brownian motion

■ **Figure 2.10**
John Dalton

A computer then generates a contour map of the surface and the outline of individual atoms can be detected. The atoms resemble the hard spheres proposed by Dalton (Figure 2.10), but the STM images are in fact showing the electrons. The fuzziness occurs because the electrons move in a 'cloud' and are not in fixed energy levels or orbits. Previous generations of chemists believed in atoms, but the STM provides empirical evidence for the existence of atoms.

All of the sub-atomic particles are smaller than the wavelength of visible light and therefore cannot be directly observed (using sense perception) using a light microscope (although a sophisticated visible light microscope can involve a certain amount of computer processing before an image is displayed on a screen).

There is no 'atomic microscope' that allows scientists to look inside atoms. Understanding of the structure of the atom was only gradually built up and refined through a series of experiments using reason as a way of knowing. Key experiments were Thomson's discovery of cathode rays (electrons), Rutherford's alpha particle scattering experiment (nuclear model of the atom), and the discovery by Davisson and Germer that electrons could undergo diffraction (de Broglie's dual nature of matter).

However, electrons do not have to be observed as particles. The quantum corral (Figure 2.11) shows that electrons can move across a copper surface but they are trapped by a ring of iron atoms, put in place (at low temperature) using an STM (Chapter 12). The electrons behave as standing waves and are observed as 'ripples'. The agreement between the experimental results and the predictions based on these models is what constitutes scientific proof.

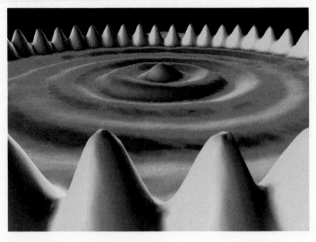

■ **Figure 2.11** Quantum corral

Deflection of sub-atomic particles

Additional Perspectives

Moving charged particles such as protons, electrons (cathode rays) and ions are deflected by electric and magnetic fields in an evacuated vacuum tube. These deflections are shown in Figure 2.12. The deflections of positive ions in a magnetic field is a key feature of the mass spectrometer used to study atoms.

Charged sub-atomic particles and ions that enter a magnetic field are deflected from a straight line to follow an arc of a circle, the radius of which depends on their mass-to-charge ratio (m/z). Positively charged ions with a lower mass-to-charge ratio will be deflected more than those with a higher mass-to-charge ratio. For example, the lighter ion $^{20}Ne^+$ is deflected more than the heavier $^{21}Ne^+$, which in turn is deflected more than the even heavier $^{22}Ne^+$ (Figure 2.13). This is a reflection of *increasing* mass-to-charge ratio. These three ions are derived from three isotopes of neon.

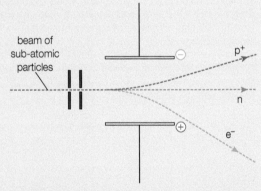

■ **Figure 2.12** The behaviour of protons, neutrons and electrons in an electric field

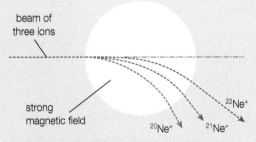

■ **Figure 2.13** Deflection of unipositive ions in a mass spectrometer

ToK Link

Richard Feynman: *'If all of scientific knowledge were to be destroyed and only one sentence passed on to the next generation, I believe it is that all things are made of atoms.'* Are the models and theories which scientists create accurate descriptions of the natural world, or are they primarily useful interpretations for prediction, explanation and control of the natural world?

One of the most commonly used constructs used in chemistry and science is a model. A scientific model is a simple way of describing, explaining and predicting scientific results. Models might be simple mathematical descriptions, for example the various gas laws (Chapter 1) and the Schrödinger wave function model of the hydrogen atom, or completely non-mathematical, for example the simple electrostatic model of a hydrogen atom with a single electron orbiting a single proton (though this was developed into a quantitative model based on classical physics by Bohr).

Many chemical models are known to be incorrect, for example, the Lewis theory of bonding, or an incomplete description of chemical phenomena, for example, the octet rule (Chapter 4). For the purposes of teaching chemistry it is often preferable to use simple approximate bonding models that give correct predictions for the majority of cases, than to use a more accurate but complicated model, such as the quantum mechanical model (Chapter 12), which is based on the electron's wave properties.

Light behaves in a way that is difficult to comprehend, so physical models are used to provide a picture to help us understand what is going on. We say that light is like a wave in some situations, and like a particle in others. Light is actually not like either a wave or a particle, but the models help us to understand why the light is behaving in a particular way.

Models are very important in the study of the atom. Being smaller than the wavelength of visible light, an atom cannot be seen with the eye, and so physical models must be useful, they must help explain phenomena and they should be able to predict further patterns of behaviour. These patterns can then be looked for in experiments and, if found, the model is deemed useful.

---

4 Find out and explain the use of probability density functions to describe the behaviour of electrons in the orbitals of atoms. A probability distribution function is any function whose integral over a set gives the probability that a random variable has a value in that set. Use diagrams to illustrate your answer.

The Maxwell–Boltzmann distribution curve is a probability density function. State the assumptions underlying the Maxwell–Boltzmann distribution curve and explain why it is a probability function.

■ Mass number, atomic number and isotopes

The **atomic number** (symbol Z) is the number of protons in the nucleus. The atomic number is the same for every atom of a particular element and no two different elements have the same atomic number.

Neutrons and protons have an almost identical mass but electrons have very little mass, so the mass of an atom depends on the number of protons and neutrons in its nucleus. The total number of protons and neutrons is called the **mass number** (symbol A).

Nuclides of a chemical element are described by the notation $^A_Z X$, where X represents the symbol of the chemical element, Z represents the atomic number and A represents the mass number. For example:

$$\begin{array}{l}\text{mass number } (A) \rightarrow 27 \\ \text{atomic number } (Z) \rightarrow 13\end{array} \text{Al}$$

The number of neutrons in an atom can be found from the following relationship:

number of neutrons = mass number (A) – atomic number (Z)

So in the example above, an atom of aluminium-27 would contain 13 protons, 13 electrons and 14 neutrons (27 – 13).

Not all of the atoms in a naturally occurring sample of a chemical element are identical. Atoms of the same element that have different mass numbers are called **isotopes**. Because they are the same element, they will have the same atomic number, but they have different numbers of neutrons. Examples of isotopes are carbon-12, $^{12}_6 C$, and carbon-13, $^{13}_6 C$.

The notation for a specific nuclide can be written if the mass number and atomic number are given. For example, the notation for a sodium atom with a mass number of 23 is written in the following way:

$$^{23}_{11}Na$$

Chemical elements (names and symbols) and their atomic numbers are listed on pages 4 and 5 of the IB *Chemistry data booklet*.

An element forms an **ion** when one or more electrons are added to or removed from the atom. A positive ion is formed by the removal of electrons and a negative ion is formed by the addition of electrons. Thus in an ion the number of protons and neutrons remains the same as in the atom – only the number of electrons changes. The number of protons, neutrons and electrons in an atom or ion can therefore be calculated from the mass number, atomic number and charge, as shown by the following examples.

Worked examples

Deduce the number of electrons, protons and neutrons in $^{31}_{15}P^{3-}$.

The subscript number in the nuclide notation is the atomic number. Hence an atom of phosphorus contains 15 protons and therefore 15 electrons. However, since the ion has a net charge of −3 the ion contains 18 (15 + 3) electrons. The difference between the subscript number (atomic number) and the superscript number (mass number) is equal to the number of neutrons, which in this example is 16 (31 − 15).

Deduce the number of electrons in $^{24}_{12}Mg^{2+}$.

Since the atomic number of magnesium is 12, an atom of magnesium contains 12 electrons. However, since the ion has a net charge of +2 the ion contains 10 (12 − 2) electrons. The difference between the subscript number (atomic number) and the superscript number (mass number) is equal to the number of neutrons, which in this example is 12 (24 − 12).

Calculate the total number of electrons in four moles of beryllium atoms.

The atomic number of beryllium is 4, hence each atom of beryllium contains 4 protons and 4 electrons. The total number of electrons in four moles of beryllium atoms is therefore

$$4 \times 4 \text{ mol} \times 6 \times 10^{23} \text{ mol}^{-1} = 9.6 \times 10^{24}$$

A common mistake is to misread the question and give the answer 16, namely the total number of electrons in four beryllium atoms.

 ### Using the nuclear symbol $^A_Z X$ to deduce the number of protons, neutrons and electrons in atoms and ions

Deduce the numbers of protons, neutrons and electrons present in the following sulfur species: $^{32}_{16}S$, $^{33}_{16}S$ and $^{36}_{16}S^{2-}$.

The subscript numbers are the atomic numbers, which are the numbers of protons. The superscript numbers are the mass numbers or nucleon numbers, which are the numbers of protons and neutrons. The differences between the subscript and superscript numbers are the numbers of neutrons.

Species	Number of protons	Number of neutrons	Number of electrons
$^{32}_{16}S$	16	16	16
$^{33}_{16}S$	16	17	16
$^{36}_{16}S^{2-}$	16	20	18

Table 2.2 gives further examples of common nuclides and their symbols and the numbers of their sub-atomic particles.

■ **Table 2.2**
Selected nuclides

Name of ion or atom	Symbol of particle	Number of protons	Number of neutrons	Number of electrons
Beryllium atom	$^{9}_{4}Be$	4	5	4
Oxygen atom	$^{16}_{8}O$	8	8	8
Neon atom	$^{20}_{10}Ne$	10	10	10
Fluorine atom	$^{19}_{9}F$	9	10	9
Oxygen atom	$^{18}_{8}O$	8	10	8
Magnesium ion	$^{24}_{12}Mg^{2+}$	12	12	10
Chloride ion	$^{37}_{17}Cl^{-}$	17	20	18
Aluminium ion	$^{27}_{13}Al^{3+}$	13	14	10
Calcium ion	$^{40}_{20}Ca^{2+}$	20	20	18

5 Deduce the number of protons, neutron and electrons in the following hydrogen species: $^{3}_{1}H^{-}$, $^{3}_{1}H^{+}$, $^{2}_{1}H^{-}$ and $^{1}_{1}H_{2}^{+}$

Properties of isotopes

Many elements exist as a mixture of isotopes. Figure 2.14 shows the isotopes of carbon, chlorine and hydrogen as nuclide symbols. Isotopes of the same element all have the same element symbol and atomic number. Figure 2.15 shows the three isotopes of hydrogen as Bohr diagrams.

Carbon:
Carbon-12 ($^{12}_{6}C$)
Carbon-13 ($^{13}_{6}C$)

Chlorine:
Chlorine-35 ($^{35}_{17}Cl$)
Chlorine-37 ($^{37}_{17}Cl$)

Hydrogen:
Hydrogen-1 ($^{1}_{1}H$)
Hydrogen-2 ($^{2}_{1}H$)
Hydrogen-3 ($^{3}_{1}H$)

■ **Figure 2.14** Stable isotopes of carbon, chlorine and hydrogen

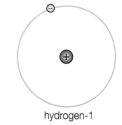
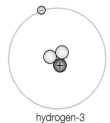

hydrogen-1   hydrogen-2   hydrogen-3

■ **Figure 2.15** The three isotopes of hydrogen: protium, deuterium and tritium

Isotopes of the same chemical element have identical chemical properties but slightly different physical properties. For example, the lighter isotope will always diffuse more rapidly.

Additional Perspectives

Isotopes in compounds

Compounds will often exist as a mixture of molecules with different relative molecular masses. For example, a sample of carbon consists of the isotopes carbon-12 and carbon-13. A sample of oxygen consists of the isotopes oxygen-16 and oxygen-17. This means that there will be six types of carbon dioxide molecules:

$$^{12}C^{16}O_2 \quad ^{12}C^{16}O^{17}O \quad ^{12}C^{17}O_2 \quad ^{13}C^{16}O_2 \quad ^{13}C^{16}O^{17}O \quad \text{and} \quad ^{13}C^{17}O_2$$

Isotope enrichment

Enriched uranium is a type of uranium in which the percentage composition of uranium-235 has been increased through a process of isotope separation. Enriched uranium is a critical step in preparing uranium for nuclear power generation or nuclear weapons. Isotope separation is a very difficult and energy-intensive process. Uranium-235 and uranium-238 have identical chemical properties, and their physical properties are only very slightly different. An atom of uranium-235 is only 1.26% lighter than an atom of uranium-238, which forms 99.3% of natural uranium.

The first technique to be developed for uranium enrichment was gaseous diffusion. The uranium was reacted with fluorine to form uranium hexafluoride molecules, UF_6. The uranium hexafluoride was vaporized and the gaseous molecules were then forced through a series of semi-permeable membranes. The rate of diffusion of a gas is proportional to the square root of $1/M$, where M represents the molar mass. Hence, the lighter UF_6 molecules, which contain U-235, diffuse faster than those containing U-238. As a consequence, the front of the diffusing gas becomes enriched in $^{235}UF_6$. The process is repeated many times to achieve a partial separation. The currently preferred method of isotope separation by centrifugation also uses UF_6.

Radioactivity and the uses of radioisotopes

In 1896 the French chemist Henri Becquerel (1852–1908) discovered that uranium salts released radiation which passed through the wrapping paper around a photographic plate, exposing it (turning it black). The phenomenon was investigated by Pierre (1859–1906) and Marie Curie (1867–1934), who named it radioactivity. Henri Becquerel and the Curies were awarded the Nobel Prize in Physics in 1903. Marie Curie's death may have been caused by prolonged exposure to radiation. At the time its damaging effects were not known and most of her work had been carried out with no safety measures. Her husband died in 1906 in a tragic accident in Paris involving a horse-drawn carriage. Marie Curie was born in Poland but later became a French citizen. The Curies discovered two new elements, radium and polonium, the latter named after Marie's birthplace, Poland.

A number of chemical elements contain unstable nuclides. The nuclei of these chemical elements break up spontaneously with the emission of ionizing radiation (Table 2.3). These unstable nuclides are described as radioactive and are called radionuclides. The radiation is of three distinct types and their properties are summarized in Table 2.3. Radiation can be detected and measured using a Geiger–Müller tube (Figure 2.16).

■ **Figure 2.16**
Geiger–Müller tube
(radiation counter)

Radiation	Relative charge	Relative mass	Nature	Penetration	Deflection by electric field
Alpha particles	+2	4	2 protons and 2 neutrons (He^{2+} ion)	Stopped by a few sheets of paper	Low
Beta particles	−1	$\frac{1}{1837}$	Electron	Stopped by a few mm of plastic or aluminium	High
Gamma rays	0	0	Electromagnetic radiation of very high frequency	Stopped by a few cm of lead	None

■ **Table 2.3** Summary of the properties of alpha and beta particles and gamma rays

■ **Figure 2.17** Stainless steel surgical blades are sterilized by gamma radiation

When the nucleus of a radionuclide releases an alpha or beta particle, an atom of a new element is formed. For example, carbon-14 and iodine-131 both undergo beta-decay, which can be described by the following nuclear equations:

$$^{14}_{6}C \rightarrow {}^{14}_{7}N + {}^{0}_{-1}e \qquad {}^{131}_{53}I \rightarrow {}^{131}_{54}Xe + {}^{0}_{-1}e$$

Cobalt-60 is another beta emitter, but iodine-125 is a pure gamma emitter. Iodine-131 and cobalt-60 are both gamma emitters (Figure 2.17).

The rate at which nuclei undergo radioactive decay varies between chemical elements. Radioactive decay is an exponential process (Figure 2.18). The rates of radioactive decay are compared using the half-life, which is the time taken for half of the radioactive nuclei to undergo decay. During alpha and beta radioactive decay a more stable isotope is formed.

Each radionuclide has its own unique half-life which is unaffected by temperature or pressure. For example, iodine-131 has a half-life of 8 days (Figure 2.19). This means that after every 8 days the number of radioactive atoms present is half that of the number present 8 days previously.

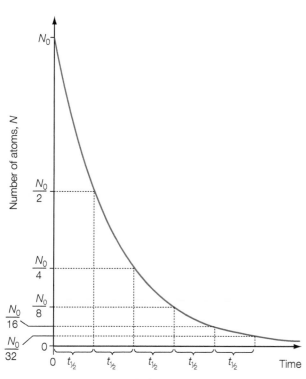

■ **Figure 2.18** Idealized half-life curve for radioactive decay

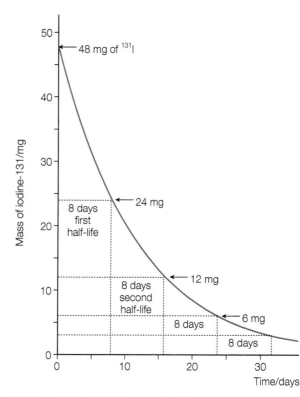

■ **Figure 2.19** A half-life curve for iodine-131

■ Utilization: uses of radioisotopes

Medical uses of radioactivity

The first use of radioactivity in medicine was the use of radium in the treatment of cancers. Ionizing radiation from radium (or other radionuclide) is focused on the tumour (cancer), and the energy that the radiation carries is used to kill the cancer cells. Sources of fast neutrons have also been used to treat some cancers. Ionizing radiation also kills healthy tissue so it is important that narrow and controlled beams are used. Another technique is to directly inject a radionuclide into the body. This can be done to study the biochemical reactions in the body or for the radionuclide to be concentrated in a particular part of the body and irradiate cancerous tissue.

For example, iodine is an essential element to the body and collects in the thyroid gland where it is used to synthesize the hormone thyroxine. By feeding patients with radioactive iodine-131 it is possible to discover whether the thyroid gland is functioning properly or whether it has a growth. This method relies on the fact that isotopes of the same element have the same chemical properties.

Archaeological dating

Carbon-12 atoms are found in living organisms as organic compounds and in the atmosphere as carbon dioxide. Cosmic rays from the Sun can cause carbon-14 atoms to be produced in the upper edge of the atmosphere. If a high speed neutron (from the cosmic rays) with sufficient kinetic energy collides with a nitrogen-14 atom, the following nuclear reaction (known as a natural transmutation) takes place:

$$^{14}_{7}N + ^{1}_{0}n \rightarrow ^{14}_{6}C + ^{1}_{1}H$$

The half-life of the carbon-14 atom formed is 5730 years (Figure 2.20). If the Earth is assumed to be bombarded with cosmic rays at a constant rate then the rate of production of carbon-14 atoms will be constant. Consequently, the ratio of carbon-12 to carbon-14 atoms should be constant. Plants absorb carbon dioxide and use to it synthesize glucose during the process of photosynthesis. Hence, carbon-14 atoms will be incorporated into plants and then animals, including humans.

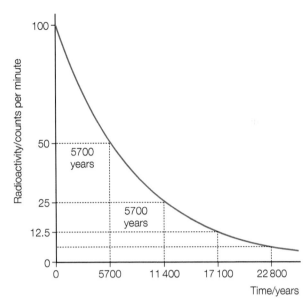

Figure 2.20 The radioactive decay curve of carbon-14

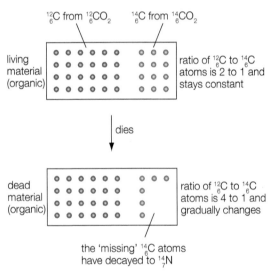

Figure 2.21 Illustration of the principle of radiocarbon dating (the ratios of carbon-12 to carbon-14 are out of proportion to show the change)

However, when the living organism dies no more carbon atoms will enter the organism. The proportion of carbon-14 in the dead material begins to decrease because of the beta decay of carbon-14 atoms:

$$^{14}_{6}C \rightarrow {}^{14}_{7}N + {}^{\ 0}_{-1}e$$

If a scientist measures the relative proportions of carbon-12 and carbon-14, the smaller the amount of carbon-14, the further back in time the uptake of radionuclide stopped. The proportion of carbon-14 can be used to estimate the age of the sample and is the basis for radiocarbon dating (Figure 2.21).

Geological dating: the age of Earth

When uranium-238 decays it undergoes a series of 14 alpha and beta decays. This series of steps is known as the uranium radioactive decay series. Helium gas is released (due to the eight beta decays) and the final product is stable lead-206. For every uranium-238 atom that decays, one atom of lead-206 is produced at the end of the decay series.

Since the half-lives of all the isotopes in the decay series of uranium-238 are known, this means that if the number of lead atoms in a sample of uranium can be counted, then it is possible to calculate how long the uranium-238 has been undergoing decay (assuming that the lead or helium has not been formed as the product of other decay schemes).

Rocks can also be dated by comparing the amounts of various other radionuclides, for example lead-206 and lead-204, potassium-40 and argon-40, rubidium-87 and strontium-87. Using isotope dating methods, the oldest rocks on the Earth are 3.7×10^9 years old which means that the Earth is at least this old, because the isotope method can only work from the time that the rocks became solid. For example, any helium atoms formed while the rocks were still liquid would have boiled off as gas. Rocks from the Moon and meteorites appear to be around 4.6×10^9 years old.

Tracer experiments

Isotopes can be of great use in chemical research and are often used in tracer experiments; that is, where the use of an isotope can help to trace the course of a reaction.

For example, lead(II) chloride, $PbCl_2$, is a white insoluble solid whereas lead(II) nitrate, $Pb(NO_3)_2$, is easily soluble in water. Naturally occurring lead is a mixture of the isotopes lead-206, lead-207 and lead-208, all of which are stable (towards decay) and not radioactive. However, the isotope lead-212 is radioactive and a beta emitter with a half-life of around 11 hours.

Suppose the lead(II) chloride is prepared from radioactive lead-212. The lead(II) chloride has been labelled, and we can show the labelled radioactive lead ion in a formula by using a star: *$PbCl_2$. Consider the situation when *$PbCl_2$ is added to a solution of $Pb(NO_3)_2$, left for a number hours to reach equilibrium, and then the solution separated from the solid. The solution can be crystallized, and the lead(II) nitrate collected. The crystals are radioactive because some of the nitrate is in the form of *$Pb(NO_3)_2$. This result is explained by realizing that an 'insoluble' substance is not 100% insoluble, but slightly or partially soluble. Some of the labelled lead(II) ions must have left the lattice of the *$PbCl_2$ crystals and dissolved in the water. There they became mixed with the ordinary isotopes of lead. When the solution was separated, some of the radioactive lead was left in the solution, and some of the non-radioactive lead found its way into the lead(II) chloride. This is known as an exchange reaction.

Nuclear medicine

Nuclear medicine is the use of radioactive materials in medicine, both for diagnosis and for therapy (usually cancer therapy). In therapy, the aim is to localize the radioactive material in cancerous (malignant) cells so they are killed by the ionizing radiation. Since the healthy cells surrounding the diseased tissue must not be killed, short-range ionizing radiations (alpha and beta radiations) are used.

In nuclear diagnosis, radioactive materials are used to study the function of human organs. These are radiopharmaceuticals which combine a pharmaceutical (medicine) and a radionuclide. The pharmaceutical used will depend on the organ to be studied, for example iodine-131, ^{131}I, is used to study the thyroid gland. The radionuclide allows doctors to monitor the passage of the radiopharmaceutical through parts of the human body.

The radionuclide needs to be a gamma emitter (long-range ionizing radiation) that can be monitored from outside the patient's body. It should have a relatively short half-life to limit the radiation dose to the patient. The radionuclide most commonly used is technetium-99m, ^{99m}Tc. The 'm' indicates that this is a metastable isotope, that is, that its half-life is considerably longer than most isotopes that undergo gamma decay.

Positron emission tomography (PET)

Certain radionuclides undergo radioactive decay by emitting positrons (positively charged electrons, a form of antimatter). In diagnosis positron-emitting isotopes, such as oxygen-15 and carbon-11, are used to label compounds that are introduced into the human body, often in the form of a drink. The compounds chosen are those which tend to collect and concentrate in certain parts of the body. The positrons collide with electrons and annihilate each other, emitting a pair of gamma rays. Annihilation involves the masses of a particle and its anti-particle being converted into electromagnetic energy.

The patient is surrounded by gamma photon detectors whose output is used to construct 'real-time' artificially coloured images (Figure 2.22). This technique is known as positron emission tomography (PET) and is especially useful for imaging delicate organs, such as the brain. It can be used to give three-dimensional images of radioactive tracer concentrations in the body and can be used to detect cancer.

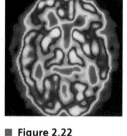

■ **Figure 2.22** A PET scan of the brain following the ingestion of a beta-emitting radioactive substance in a drink

■ Operation of a mass spectrometer

A **mass spectrometer** (Figure 2.23) allows chemists to determine accurately the relative atomic masses of atoms. It can also be used to determine the relative molecular masses of molecular compounds and establish their structure.

The operation of the mass spectrometer is not required by the syllabus but is described below since the processes rely upon electrostatics and electromagnetism, which are important concepts in many areas of chemistry.

■ **Figure 2.23** Diagram of a single beam mass spectrometer in cross-section

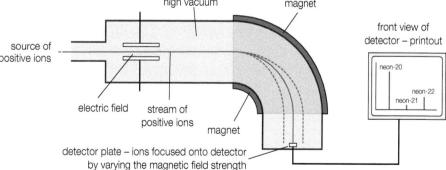

Inside a mass spectrometer there is a vacuum. A sample of the element is vaporized, then introduced into an ionization chamber where it is bombarded with electrons travelling at high speeds. The energetic collisions that take place cause the gaseous atoms to lose one of their electrons and form unipositive ions:

$$M(g) + e^- \xrightarrow{\text{bombarding electron}} M^+(g) + e^- + e^-$$

The beam of positive ions is accelerated by an electric field and then deflected by a powerful magnetic field. The degree of deflection depends on the mass-to-charge ratio of the positive ions. However, since the charge on each ion is the same, the deflection only depends on their masses. The lighter ions which are formed from the lighter isotope atoms are deflected more than the heavier ones.

A detector counts the numbers of each of the different ions that impact upon it, giving a measure of the percentage abundance of each isotope. The counter functions by releasing an electron for every ion it detects; this signal is then amplified. A mass spectrum for chlorine atoms is shown in Figure 2.24. The two peaks are due to detection of $^{35}Cl^+$ and $^{37}Cl^+$ ions. The mass spectrum shows that chlorine is composed of two isotopes: chlorine-35 and chlorine-37 in a 3 : 1 or 75% : 25% ratio by abundance.

■ **Figure 2.24**
Mass spectrum of a sample of naturally occurring chlorine atoms

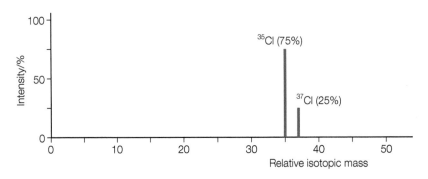

The horizontal axis for a mass spectrum is actually mass-to-charge ratio (m/z). However, since all the ions are unipositive, the scale is equivalent to mass since the charge on all the ions is +1.

Atomic number	10
Element	**Ne**
Relative atomic mass	20.18

■ **Figure 2.25**
The representation of elements in the periodic table of the IB *Chemistry data booklet*; 20.18 is the relative atomic mass of neon. The nuclide notation for neon-20 is $^{20}_{10}Ne$

Using mass spectrometry to determine relative atomic mass

The chemical elements are listed in a special arrangement called the periodic table (Chapter 3). The periodic table can be found on page 6 of the IB *Chemistry data booklet*. Each chemical element is placed in a box with its chemical symbol (Chapter 1), its atomic number (written above) and its **relative atomic mass** (written below) (Figure 2.25).

The majority of chemical elements in nature exist as a mixture of isotopes in fixed proportions. For example, the mass spectrum of chlorine reveals that a natural sample of chlorine atoms consists of 75% chlorine-35 and 25% chlorine-37.

The relative atomic mass (symbol A_r) is the *weighted average* mass of a sample of naturally occurring atoms on the carbon-12 scale. The relative atomic mass of an element is the weighted average of its isotopes compared to one-twelfth of the mass of one atom of carbon-12:

$$\text{relative atomic mass} = \frac{\text{weighted average mass of the isotopes of the chemical element}}{\frac{1}{12} \times \text{the mass of one atom of carbon-12}}$$

However, since one-twelfth the mass of one atom of carbon-12 is 1, then relative atomic mass of a chemical element is effectively the weighted average isotopic mass divided by 1.

Relative atomic masses can be calculated from a mass spectrum of a chemical element by multiplying the relative isotopic mass of each isotope by its percentage abundance and adding all the values together.

Using chlorine as an example:

$$\text{relative atomic mass of chlorine} = \left(\frac{75}{100} \times 35\right) + \left(\frac{25}{100} \times 37\right) = 35.5$$

Worked example

Rubidium exists as a mixture of two isotopes, ^{85}Rb and ^{87}Rb. The percentage abundances are 72.1% and 27.9%, respectively. Calculate the relative atomic mass of rubidium.

Relative atomic mass of rubidium $= \left(\frac{72.1}{100} \times 85\right) + \left(\frac{27.9}{100} \times 87\right) = 85.6$

The use of simple algebra allows the percentage abundance of one isotope to be calculated given the relative atomic mass of the chemical element and the atomic mass of the other isotope.

Worked example

The relative atomic mass of gallium is 69.7. Gallium is composed of two isotopes: gallium-69 and gallium-71. Calculate the percentage abundance of gallium-69.

Let %Ga-69 = x. Then %Ga-71 = $(100 - x)$, since the two isotopic percentages must sum to 100.

$69.7 = \dfrac{69x + 71(100 - x)}{100}$

$6970 = 69x + 71(100 - x)$

Expanding the bracket (multiplying all the terms inside by 71):

$6970 = 69x - 71x + 7100$

$6970 = -2x + 7100$ (subtract 71x from 69x)

$-130 = -2x$ (subtract 7100 from 6970)

$x = \dfrac{-130}{-2} = 65$

Hence, the percentage abundance of gallium-69 is 65%.

Calculations involving non-integer relative atomic masses and abundance of isotopes from given data, including mass spectra

The relative abundances of the isotopes of magnesium are shown below. Calculate the relative atomic mass of magnesium.

Isotope	Magnesium-24	Magnesium-25	Magnesium-26
Relative abundance (%)	78.6	10.1	11.3

Relative atomic mass of magnesium $= \dfrac{(24 \times 78.6) + (25 \times 10.1) + (26 \times 11.3)}{100} = 24.3$

Analysis using a mass spectrometer shows that the element boron consists of two isotopes: ^{10}B and ^{11}B. Calculate the relative percentage abundances of each of the two isotopes, given that the relative abundance for the two isotopes is:

^{10}B/^{11}B = 0.23

The relative abundance of 10B = 0.23/(1 + 0.23) × 100 = 18.7%

The relative abundance of 11B = (100 − 18.7) = 81.3%

The mass spectrum of the element X is given on the right. Deduce the element.

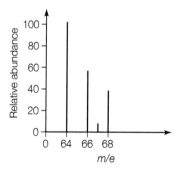

There are four peaks in the mass spectrum at m/z values of 64, 66, 67 and 68. The relative atomic mass is hence given by the following expression:

$\dfrac{(64 \times 100) + (66 \times 56) + (67 \times 8) + (68 \times 38)}{100 + 56 + 8 + 38} = 65.42$ (zinc).

---

6   Iridium has a relative atomic mass of 192.22. Its isotopes are ^{191}Ir and ^{193}Ir. Calculate the percentage abundances of the two isotopes.

7   Find out how mass spectrometry was used in the discovery of carbon-60.

2.2 Electron configuration – *the electron configuration of an atom can be deduced from its atomic number*

■ Light as waves and particles

Light is an important form of energy and is often described using a wave model. According to this theory, light is transmitted in the form of **electromagnetic waves**. These consist of an oscillating electric wave and a magnetic wave which travel together in a sinusoidal pattern (Figure 2.26). The two waves are arranged perpendicularly, that is, at right angles.

■ **Figure 2.26**
Oscillating electric and magnetic fields in an electromagnetic wave

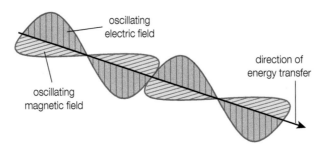

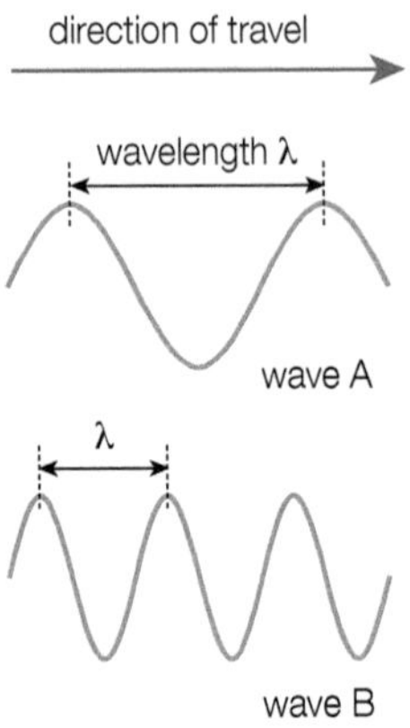

Light waves and other waves are described by the following terms:

- **Wavelength**
  The wavelength (symbol Greek letter lambda, λ) is defined as the distance between two neighbouring crests or troughs of a wave (Figure 2.27).
- **Frequency**
  The frequency (symbol Greek letter nu, ν) is defined as the number of waves that pass a point in one second. Its units are **hertz** (Hz). If one wave passes a point every second, then it has a frequency of 1 Hz.
- **Speed**
  The speed is the distance travelled by a wave in one second. It is denoted by c and is measured in metres per second (m s^{-1}).

The frequency (ν) and wavelength (λ) are related to the speed by the **wave equation**:

$$c = \nu\lambda \qquad \text{or} \qquad \nu = c/\lambda$$

where c is the speed of light. Light travels in a vacuum at a speed of 3.00×10^8 metres per second.

Different colours in visible light correspond to electromagnetic waves of different wavelengths and frequencies (Figure 2.28). In addition to visible light there are other types of electromagnetic radiation, such as X-rays, ultraviolet rays, infrared rays, microwaves and radio waves. Figure 2.29 shows the electromagnetic spectrum. It is an arrangement of all the types of electromagnetic radiation in order of wavelength or frequency. The electromagnetic spectrum can be found on page 3 of the IB *Chemistry data booklet*.

direction of travel

wavelength λ

wave A

λ

wave B

■ **Figure 2.27**
Wave A has twice the wavelength of wave B

■ **Figure 2.28**
A helium–neon laser (632.8nm wavelength)

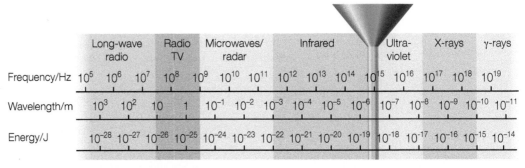

■ **Figure 2.29** The electromagnetic spectrum

■ **Figure 2.30**
Light and other
electromagnetic
radiation can be
described in two
ways: as a wave or as
a stream of packets of
energy called photons

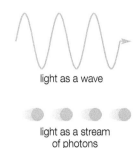

light as a wave

light as a stream
of photons
(packets of energy)

Light can also be described by a particle model (Figure 2.30) that treats light as a stream of photons or tiny 'packets' of light energy. The two models of light are linked by Planck's equation:

$$E = h\nu$$

where E represents the energy of a photon (in joules), ν represents the frequency of the light (in hertz, Hz, or s^{-1}) and h represents Planck's constant (6.63×10^{-34} J s). Planck's equation is given on page 1 of the IB *Chemistry data booklet* and Planck's constant is given on page 2 of the booklet.

Describing the relationship between colour, wavelength, frequency and energy across the electromagnetic spectrum

The electromagnetic spectrum in Figure 2.31 arranges electromagnetic radiation from high frequency and energy on the left to low frequency and low energy on the right. Energy and frequency have a directly proportional relationship: $E = h\nu$. However, wavelength increases from left to right across the electromagnetic spectrum because there is an inverse relationship between frequency and wavelength: $c = \nu \times \lambda$. In the visible region the colours gradually change from blue to red with decreasing frequency.

8 Compare the relative frequencies, wavelengths, energies and wave numbers (reciprocal of wavelength [in cm]) of ultraviolet and infrared radiations.

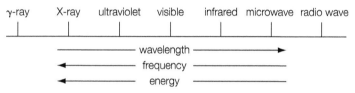

γ-ray   X-ray   ultraviolet   visible   infrared   microwave   radio wave

———————→ wavelength ——————————→
←————————— frequency ———————————
←————————— energy ——————————

■ **Figure 2.31** The electromagnetic spectrum

■ Spectra

If sunlight or light from an electric bulb is formed into a beam by a slit and passed through a prism on to a screen, a rainbow of separated colours is observed. The spectrum of colours formed from white light is composed of visible light of a certain range of wavelengths and is called a **continuous spectrum** (Figure 2.32). A rainbow is an example of a continuous spectrum: there is an infinite number of colours that vary smoothly.

If gaseous atoms are excited they emit light of certain wavelengths. Excitation occurs when electrons in the atom are raised to a higher energy level, and light is emitted as they return to the unexcited state. The process of electron excitation may be thermal or electrical. Thermal excitation occurs when a substance is vaporized and a flame is formed (Figure 2.33). Electrical excitation occurs when a high voltage is passed across a tube containing a gaseous sample of the element at low pressure. Molecules will be dissociated by the high voltage. Sodium street lamps (Figure 2.34), neon advertising signs (Figure 2.35) and exploding fireworks are all examples of electron excitation.

If the light from atoms with excited electrons is passed through a prism, an emission spectrum is formed. Emission spectra consist of a number of separate sets, or series, of narrow coloured lines on a black background. Hence emission spectra are often called **line spectra**. Each chemical element has its own *unique* line spectrum that can be used to identify the chemical element.

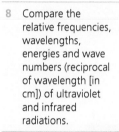

white light

slits

prism

screen

■ **Figure 2.32**
Production of a
continuous spectrum

■ **Figure 2.33** Flame test colours

■ **Figure 2.34** A sodium street lamp

■ **Figure 2.35** Advertising signs use noble gases

The emission spectrum for hydrogen atoms in the visible region is shown in Figure 2.36. This series of lines is called the Balmer series, after Johann Balmer, who first observed these lines. Similar sets of lines are observed in the ultraviolet (Lyman series) and infrared regions of the electromagnetic spectrum (Figure 2.37). An emission or line spectrum (Figure 2.38) differs from a continuous spectrum in two important ways:

1   An emission spectrum is made up of separate lines (coloured if they are in the visible region), that is, it is discontinuous.
2   The lines converge, becoming progressively closer as the frequency or energy of the emission lines increases.

■ **Figure 2.36**
The Balmer series
of hydrogen

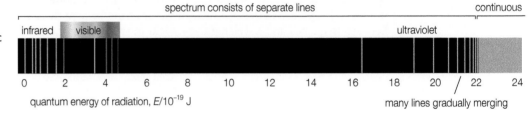

■ **Figure 2.37** The
complete emission or
line spectrum of atomic
hydrogen

■ **Figure 2.38**
a Continuous spectrum
of white light;
b emission or line
spectrum of sodium
atoms; and **c** emission
or line spectrum of
cadmium atoms

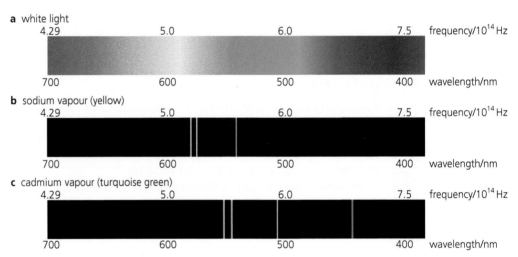

Distinguishing between a continuous spectrum and a line spectrum

In a continuous spectrum, the radiations corresponding to all wavelengths (within a certain range) are present. There are no lines or bands present in a continuous spectrum. The emission spectrum of incandescent (white hot) solids is continuous. A line spectrum is produced by a luminous gas and appears as distinct lines characteristic of the various elements constituting the gas. A line spectrum may result from an emission or an absorption process.

Utilization: Fireworks

The gunpowder used in fireworks (Figure 2.39) is a mixture of powdered graphite (carbon), sulfur and an oxidizing agent, such as potassium nitrate(v), KNO_3 or potassium chlorate(vii), $KClO_4$. The carbon and sulfur are oxidized to their oxide products. A binder may be present to hold together the powdered mixture of chemicals.

■ **Figure 2.39** Fireworks

Metals or metal compounds are added to the gunpowder to produce coloured light when the gunpowder burns:

- Intense white light from burning magnesium or aluminium
- Yellow light from sodium salts (often Na_3AlF_6)
- Orange light from calcium chloride, $CaCl_2$
- Red light from strontium salts, such as $SrCO_3$, or lithium salts, such as Li_2CO_3
- Green light from barium salts, such as $Ba(NO_3)_2$
- Blue light from copper(II) salts, such as $CuCO_3$; blue is the most difficult colour to produce in fireworks
- A purple colour can be produced from a mixture of strontium (red) and copper (blue) compounds.

These flame colours can be observed in the laboratory if flame tests are carried out on volatile metal salts. At the high temperature of the flame, electrons are promoted to higher energy levels. The colours observed arise from these excited metal atoms or ions. When the electrons return to the ground state, the atoms emit light of characteristic frequencies.

Additional Perspectives

Absorption spectra

If white light is passed through a sample of gaseous atoms and the emerging light is analysed, the light beam will be found to be missing certain wavelengths of light. This is because certain wavelengths have been absorbed by the gaseous atoms. The absorbed energy has caused electron excitation. These absorptions are observed as black lines against the coloured background of the visible spectrum. Figure 2.40 shows the relationship between the absorption spectrum and the emission spectrum of an excited atom.

■ **Figure 2.40** Relationship between an absorption spectrum and the emission spectrum of the same element: **a** continuous spectrum of white light; **b** absorption spectrum of an element; **c** emission or line spectrum of the same element

---

Utilization: Determining metal concentrations

The technique of atomic emission spectroscopy makes use of these principles to analyse samples for the presence of elements. For example, a sample of water from an industrial plant might be analysed for polluting heavy metals, or the composition of steel may be monitored during manufacture. The emission spectrum for each metal is unique and characteristic as the spacings or energy gaps between atomic energy levels are different for each element. This is due to differing nuclear charge and differing electron–electron repulsion. The intensity of light emitted at particular frequencies is measured and used (via the Beer–Lambert law, see Chapter 21) to determine the concentration of metals in the sample.

Utilization: Studying stars

The glowing regions of stars emit light of all frequencies between the infrared and ultraviolet regions of the electromagnetic spectrum. Some stars, like the Sun, emit mainly visible light; others, with a higher temperature, emit mainly ultraviolet radiation. The surface of a star is known as the photosphere.

Outside the star's photosphere is a region called the chromosphere that contains ions, atoms and, in cooler stars, small molecules. These particles absorb some of the light that is emitted from the glowing photosphere. So when researchers analyse the light that reaches the Earth from the star, they observe that certain frequencies are missing – the ones which have been absorbed.

Beta-Centauri is a B-type star (a type of very hot star). The spectrum of the visible light from Beta-Centauri, the star's visible absorption spectrum, is shown in Figure 2.41. The absorption lines can be clearly observed. Because these correspond to the frequencies that are missing, they appear as black lines on the bright background of light emitted from the star. The absorption lines in Beta-Centauri's spectrum arise only from excited hydrogen and helium atoms. These are the only atoms that are able to absorb visible light at the very high temperature of Beta-Centauri.

■ **Figure 2.41**
The absorption spectra of a B-type star and the Sun

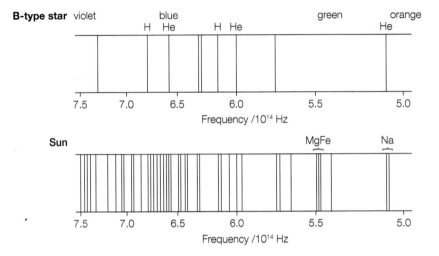

For comparison, the Sun's absorption spectrum is also shown Figure 2.41. Because the Sun is at the lower temperature, different particles are able to absorb visible light. For example, lines from sodium, iron and magnesium can be seen. The Sun's chromosphere consists mainly of hydrogen and helium but, at the temperature of the Sun, these do not absorb visible light.

During a total solar eclipse, the glow of the Sun's photosphere is completely blocked out by the Moon. The light being emitted by the chromosphere is all that can be seen, and it is then that the presence of hydrogen and helium is revealed. Hydrogen atoms dominate the chromosphere's emission spectrum, but helium emission lines can also be seen. Helium gets its name from *helios*, the Greek word for the Sun. The previously unknown element was first detected in the chromosphere during the eclipse of 1868.

■ Energy levels and spectra

All the elements release a characteristic mixture of lights when a sample is placed into a high voltage discharge tube (Figure 2.42). Bohr was the first to produce a theory that could account for the complete emission spectrum of hydrogen. He suggested that electrons in atoms moved in energy levels known as **orbits**, where they had certain fixed amounts of potential energy. The further the orbit was away from the nucleus, the greater the amount of potential energy the electron contained. This is analogous to raising an object above the Earth's surface – the higher it is, the greater the amount of gravitational potential energy it contains.

According to Bohr's theory an electron moving in one of these orbits does not emit energy. In order to move to an orbit further away from the nucleus, the electron must absorb energy (electrical or thermal energy) to do work against the attraction of the positively charged nucleus. The atom or electron is now said to be in an excited state.

The emission or line spectrum is formed when electrons that have been excited drop back from orbits of high energy to an orbit of lower energy. They emit light of a particular wavelength (Figure 2.43). The energy of the light is equal to the difference between the two energy levels (ΔE) and the frequency of the light is related to the energy difference by Planck's equation:

$$\Delta E = h\nu$$

■ **Figure 2.42** A high voltage discharge tube containing neon gas at low pressure

Bohr labelled his energy levels or orbits with the letter n and a number. An electron in the lowest energy level (nearest the nucleus) was labelled as $n = 1$; an electron in this orbit is in its ground state, the most stable state for a hydrogen atom. The next orbit or energy level is labelled as $n = 2$, and so on. The energy levels or orbits correspond to electron shells (page 73).

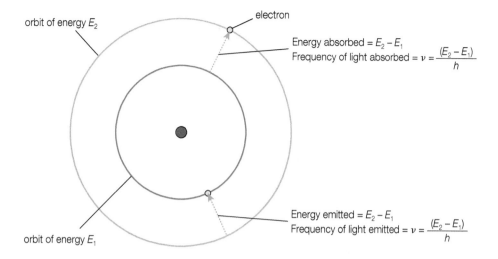

■ **Figure 2.43**
The origin of spectral lines

If an electron receives enough energy to remove it completely from the attraction of the nucleus, the atom is ionized. The energy required to ionize the electron is known as the ionization energy (Chapter 3). It is equivalent to the transition from $n = 1$ to $n = \infty$. The n used in Bohr's notation to represent energy levels is known as the **principal quantum number**. It is effectively the 'shell number'.

Figure 2.44 shows how Bohr's ideas can be used to explain the origin of the Lyman series. The circles represent the energy levels that the electron in a hydrogen atom can occupy. The distances between the circles represent the energy differences between the energy levels. The lines shown in Figure 2.44 are all part of the Lyman series. They are formed as excited electrons from higher energy levels 'fall' from higher energy levels ($n = 2, 3, 4, 5$, etc.) to the ground state ($n = 1$). The Balmer series of lines is formed when excited electrons fall from higher energy levels to the second energy level ($n = 2$).

Figure 2.44 shows that the energy levels become more closely spaced until they converge at high potential energy. This is known as the convergence limit and corresponds to the electron being completely free of the influence of the nucleus of the hydrogen atom. A hydrogen atom that has lost its electron is said to be ionized. The difference between the convergence limit and the ground state is the ionization energy (Figure 2.45).

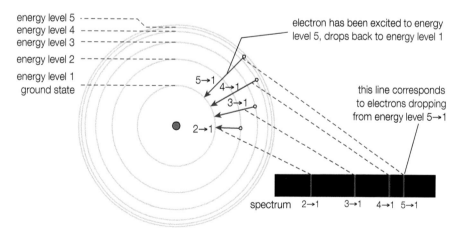

■ **Figure 2.44** How the energy levels in the hydrogen atom give rise to the Lyman series

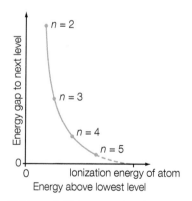

■ **Figure 2.45** A graph showing how the value of ionization energy can be estimated by extrapolation

The diagram in Figure 2.46 (overleaf) is similar to Figure 2.44 except the energy levels have been drawn as straight lines, rather than as circles. In addition, the electron transitions that give rise to the other spectral series have been added.

■ **Figure 2.46**
The origin of all the
major spectral series in
the hydrogen emission
spectrum

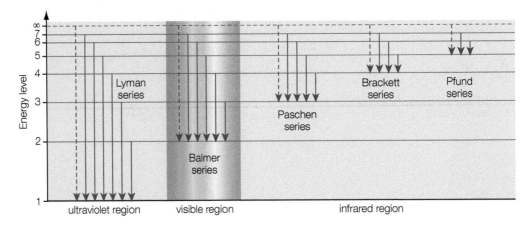

■ **Figure 2.46**
The origin of all the
major spectral series in
the hydrogen emission
spectrum

9 Figure 2.37 shows a simplified diagram of the visible emission spectrum of atomic hydrogen (gaseous
hydrogen atoms at low pressure).
a Identify three physical measurements about light that might be represented along the horizontal axis.
b State whether these measurements are increasing or decreasing from left to right.
c Explain why the emission spectrum of hydrogen consists of a series of spectral lines that converge.
d To which energy level do the electron transitions corresponding to the visible lines in the
emission spectrum of hydrogen relate to?
e Outline why the emission spectrum of an element is sometimes compared to the 'fingerprint of a criminal'.
f Find out how the element helium was discovered and use the internet to find and draw its emission and
absorption spectra.
g Explain the difference between a continuous spectrum, for example the colours observed on a thin oil
film on water, and an emission (line) spectrum.

Nature of Science | **Using theories to explain natural phenomena – line spectra and the Bohr model**

Niels Bohr (1885–1962) was a Danish physicist who was awarded the Nobel Prize in Physics
in 1922 for major contributions to our understanding of atomic structure and in developing
quantum mechanics. He was also part of the team that worked on the Manhattan Project,
which developed the first atomic bomb. Bohr studied under Rutherford and J.J. Thomson.
The Bohr model (1913) of atomic structure is a simple quantum mechanical model: electrons
can only have certain values or quantities of energy. The Bohr model was also quantitative
and accounted for Balmer's formula. However, Bohr's original theory was flawed and could not
account for the spectra of atoms other than the hydrogen atom (or related species, for example
He$^+$) and has been replaced by Schrödinger's quantum mechanical model. 'Anyone who is not
shocked by quantum theory has not understood it', is a saying attributed to Bohr.

■ Particle physics

Physicists continue to study the sub-atomic particles,
using particle accelerators to study collisions between
charged particles. Protons and neutrons have been
found to be made up of smaller particles called quarks
(Figure 2.47) which are held together by gluons. Quarks
have non-integral (fractional) charges.

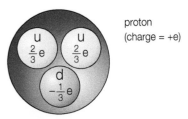

proton
(charge = +e)

In Europe, collaborative teams of scientists and
support staff from different countries work on experiments
using particle accelerators at the European laboratory for
particle physics (CERN, for *Organisation Européenne pour
la Recherche Nucléaire*) in Geneva, Switzerland. There are
currently 20 member countries, which contribute money
to its operating budget in proportion to their national
income. Large amounts of electricity are consumed by
the particle accelerators. A number of countries, such as

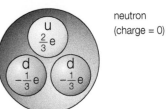

neutron
(charge = 0)

■ **Figure 2.47** Quark structure of
proton and neutron

India, the United States and China have observer status at CERN. CERN also collaborates with other centres that carry out particle physics, such as the facility at Brookhaven.

CERN (Figure 2.48) was established in 1954 and has been involved in a number of important discoveries including the discovery of the Higgs boson in 2013 and the first creation of anti-hydrogen atoms in 1995. CERN is also a major networking hub and a pioneer of internet technology. The Large Hadron Collider is the world's largest and most powerful particle accelerator.

■ **Figure 2.48** CERN

■ The electron arrangement for atoms and ions

The electrons in atoms are arranged in energy shells. Hydrogen has an atomic number of 1 and therefore one electron. This electron enters the shell nearest the nucleus. This is the first shell (first energy level). The first shell ($n = 1$) can hold a maximum of two electrons, so in the lithium atom (atomic number 3) the third electron enters the second shell (second energy level). The second ($n = 2$) shell can hold a maximum of eight electrons. Hence sodium, with an atomic number of 11, is the first chemical element to have electrons in the third shell (third energy level).

The maximum number of electrons each shell (main energy level) can hold is given by the expression $2n^2$. Hence the first, second, third and fourth shells can hold up to a maximum of 2, 8, 18 and 32 electrons.

Chemists often use a shorthand notation to describe the arrangement of electrons in shells. It indicates the number of electrons in each shell without drawing the shells. It is known as the electron arrangement. Hydrogen has an electron arrangement of 1; lithium has an electron arrangement 2,1 or 2.1 and sodium has an electron arrangement of 2,8,1 or 2.8.1. Table 2.4 lists electron arrangements for the first 20 chemical elements; Figure 2.49 shows the shell structures for selected elements.

■ **Table 2.4** Electron arrangements for the first 20 chemical elements

Element	Atomic number	Energy shell 1st	2nd	3rd	4th
Hydrogen	1	1			
Helium	2	2			
Lithium	3	2	1		
Beryllium	4	2	2		
Boron	5	2	3		
Carbon	6	2	4		
Nitrogen	7	2	5		
Oxygen	8	2	6		
Fluorine	9	2	7		
Neon	10	2	8		

Element	Atomic number	Energy shell 1st	2nd	3rd	4th
Sodium	11	2	8	1	
Magnesium	12	2	8	2	
Aluminium	13	2	8	3	
Silicon	14	2	8	4	
Phosphorus	15	2	8	5	
Sulfur	16	2	8	6	
Chlorine	17	2	8	7	
Argon	18	2	8	8	
Potassium	19	2	8	8	1
Calcium	20	2	8	8	2

■ **Figure 2.49** Electron arrangements of hydrogen, lithium, sodium, argon and potassium, shown as shell structures

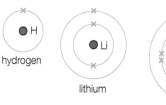
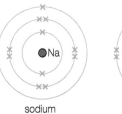

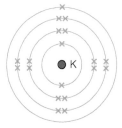

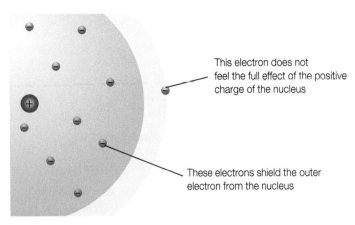

This electron does not feel the full effect of the positive charge of the nucleus

These electrons shield the outer electron from the nucleus

■ **Figure 2.50** Electron shielding

The third shell can hold a maximum of 18 electrons. However, when there are eight electrons in the third shell there is a degree of stability and the next two electrons enter the fourth shell. For the transition metals beyond calcium the additional electrons enter the third shell until it contains the maximum of 18 electrons. In addition, the second and subsequent shells are divided into a number of sub-shells. Atoms (other than hydrogen) also rearrange their electrons before they can form chemical bonds with other atoms.

This process is called hybridization (Chapter 14). An important concept introduced in Chapter 3 and also in Chapter 12 is electron shielding (Figure 2.50). The electrons in the different shells experience different attractive forces due to the presence of other electrons. The outer electrons experience the most shielding.

ToK Link

Jacob Bronowski: 'One aim of the physical sciences has been to give an exact picture of the material world. One achievement... has been to prove that this aim is unattainable'. What are the implications of this claim for the aspirations of natural sciences in particular and for knowledge in general?

This claim is probably related to 'modern' (approximately 100 years old) physics such as Einstein's theory of special relativity and quantum physics, including the Uncertainty Principle. An exact description (picture) of the material or physical world is impossible. Quantum mechanics means that the world is 'fuzzy' at the atomic and molecular level, and there are limits of experimental precision dictated by the Uncertainty Principle. Matter on the atomic level is 'schizophrenic' due to its wave–particle duality. The material world is described by a series of scientific models, all of which are limited and incomplete as descriptions of physical phenomena.

There is no absolute knowledge in science and the scientific method assumes that there is a material world of objects and phenomena existing out there that is independent of the observers, the scientists. However, some physicists might question the assertion that the material world is independent of the observers. Thus, Schrödinger's cat is both alive and dead until the observation is made, i.e. the box is opened, the wave function is collapsed, and one of the eventualities – alive or dead – is manifested.

10 Find out about the thought experiment 'Schrödinger's Cat'

Niels Bohr wrote, 'It is wrong to think that the task of physics is to find out how nature is. Physics concerns what we can say about nature.'

ToK Link

Heisenberg's Uncertainty Principle states that there is a theoretical limit to the precision with which we can know the momentum and the position of a particle. What are the implications of this for the limits of human knowledge?

In 1927 the German physicist Heisenberg stated the Uncertainty Principle, which is the consequence of the dual behaviour of matter and radiation (de Broglie's hypothesis). It states that it is impossible to determine *simultaneously* the exact position and exact momentum (or velocity) of an electron (or any sub-atomic particle) along a given direction.

Mathematically, it can be described by the equation:

$$\Delta x \times \Delta p \geq \frac{h}{4\pi}$$

where Δx is the uncertainty in position and Δp is the uncertainty in momentum (or velocity) of the particle. The momentum of the electron is the product of its mass (m) and velocity (v). If the position of the electron is known with a high degree of accuracy (Δx is small), then the velocity of the electron will be uncertain. However, if the velocity of the electron is known precisely, then the position of the electron will be uncertain (Δx will be large).

For an electron whose mass is 9.110×10^{-31} kg,

$$\Delta v \times \Delta x \geq \frac{h}{4\pi m} = \frac{6.63 \times 10^{-34}\,\text{J}\,\text{s}}{4 \times 3.1416 \times 9.110 \times 10^{-31}\,\text{kg}} \approx 10^{-4}\,\text{m}^2\,\text{s}^{-1}$$

If the electron was located to an absolute uncertainty of 10^{-8} m then the uncertainty in its average velocity would be

$$\frac{10^{-4}\ \text{m}^2\text{s}^{-1}}{10^{-8}\ \text{m}} = 10^4\ \text{m s}^{-1}$$

Hence if some physical measurement is recorded of the electron's position or velocity, the outcome will always be a fuzzy or blurred 'picture'. One of the important implications of Heisenberg's Uncertainty Principle shown by this calculation is that it rules out the existence of definite paths (trajectories) of electrons.

Heisenberg sometimes explained the Uncertainty Principle as a problem of making measurements. He used a thought experiment 'photographing' an electron. To take the 'picture' a scientist might imagine bouncing a photon (a light particle) off the electron. That would reveal its position, but it would also give kinetic energy to the electron, causing it to move. Knowing about the electron's position would create uncertainty in its velocity. Heisenberg's Uncertainty Principle does not propose 'everything is uncertain'. Rather it indicates very exactly where the limits of uncertainty lie when measurements of atomic events are recorded.

It is questionable in quantum mechanics as to whether the physical world is independent of the observer. The actual observation (measurement) could reveal a position while changing the momentum. Quantum mechanics can posit that an electron has a spin that is either 'clockwise' or 'anticlockwise' – but it is not until the measurement that it has one or the other. In this sense, objects and phenomena are certainly not independent of the observers.

■ Orbitals and energy levels

Electrons are arranged in shells (energy levels) around the nucleus of an atom. The shells are usually numbered 1 (first), 2 (second), 3 (third) etc., starting from the nucleus.

Each shell consists of a number of sub-shells (sub-levels), labelled s, p, d or f. The existence of sub-shells is confirmed experimentally by the fine structure present in successive ionization energy data.

The number of sub-shells is equal to the shell number. Hence, the first shell is composed of one sub-shell, the second shell is composed of two sub-shells, and so on. The sub-shell composition of the first four shells is summarized in Table 2.5.

■ **Table 2.5** Structure of the first four electron shells

Shell (energy level) number	Number of sub-shells in the shell	Sub-shells (sub-levels)
1	1	1s
2	2	2s and 2p
3	3	3s, 3p and 3d
4	4	4s, 4p, 4d and 4f

■ **Figure 2.51** Representations of a 1s orbital, a 2p orbital and 3d orbital, each containing one electron

Each sub-shell contains a number of orbitals in which the electrons are placed (Figure 2.51). The number of orbitals in each sub-shell depends on the type of sub-shell. Table 2.6 summarizes the numbers of orbitals and electrons in the four common types of sub-shell. Each orbital can be represented by a 'square box'. Each orbital can hold a maximum of two electrons. An electron is represented by an arrow: ↑.

■ **Table 2.6** Number of orbitals in the four types of sub-shells

Type of sub-shell (sub-level)	Number of orbitals	Maximum number of electrons in the sub-shell (sub-level)
s	1	2
p	3	6
d	5	10
f	7	14

Figure 2.52 shows how the energy shells are split into sub-shells (not applicable to hydrogen). The structure of these shells is summarized in Table 2.7.

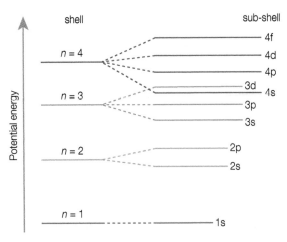

■ **Figure 2.52** Energy levels of electron sub-shells

■ **Table 2.7** Structure of sub-shells (not hydrogen)

Shell (energy level)	Sub-shell	Number of electrons in sub-shell	Maximum number of electrons in the shell (energy level)
$n = 1$	s	2	2
$n = 2$	s	2	
	p	6	8
$n = 3$	s	2	
	p	6	18
	d	10	
$n = 4$	s	2	
	p	6	
	d	10	
	f	14	32

Figure 2.53 shows the energy levels of the atomic orbitals (except hydrogen). Note that the 4s sub-shell (sub-level) has a lower energy than the 3d sub-shell and hence electrons fill the 4s sub-shell before they occupy the 3d sub-shell. This sub-shell overlap (Figure 12.54) first occurs with the first row of the d-block metals (Chapter 13). However, the 3d sub-shell is then stabilized across the first row of the d-block metals.

■ **Figure 2.53** Orbital structure of atoms

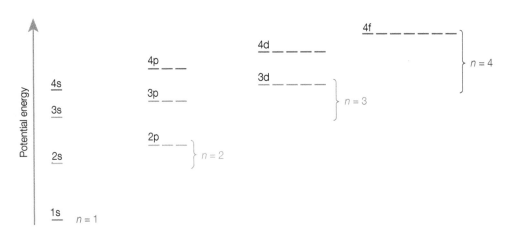

■ **Figure 2.54** The 3d–4s sub-shell overlap

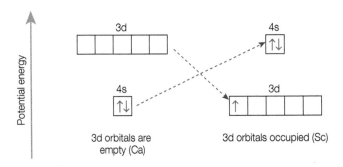

Additional Perspectives

Energy levels in hydrogen

In a hydrogen atom the sub-shells all have the same energy. For example, the 2s and 2p sub-shells have the same energy. In helium the two sub-shells have different energies. This is because of electron–electron repulsion in the helium atom between the two electrons. (This type of repulsion occurs in all atoms except hydrogen.)

■ Shapes of orbitals

Electrons do not occupy fixed positions within an atom, nor do they follow orbits in the shells. Electrons occupy volumes or regions of space called orbitals (Figure 2.55). The four types of orbitals, s, p, d and f, all have different shapes. (The shapes and energies of atomic orbitals are obtained by solving the Schrödinger wave equation.)

■ **Figure 2.55** Shapes of s and p orbitals

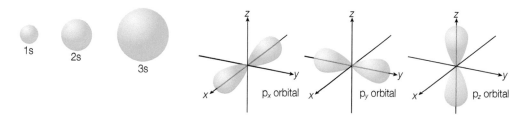

All s orbitals can be represented as spheres. They differ only in size and energy. The 3s orbital is larger than the 2s orbital, which is larger than the 1s orbital. The larger orbitals are described as being *diffuse* since the electron density is less.

The p orbitals have two lobes forming a 'dumb-bell' shape and have different orientations in space. They are arranged at right angles to each other and are labelled p_x, p_y and p_z to reflect their orientation. The three p orbitals all have the same energy – the orbitals are said to be degenerate. The 3p orbitals have the same shape as the 2p orbitals but are larger.

(Knowledge of the shapes of the 3d orbitals is not required by the IB *Chemistry guide*, but they are described in Chapter 13.)

The most important orbitals are those in the outer shells, which are involved in the formation of chemical bonds. Covalent bonds are formed when atomic orbitals overlap and merge to form molecular orbitals (Chapter 14).

Recognizing the shape of an s orbital and the p_x, p_y and p_z orbitals

An s atomic orbital is always spherical with a nucleus located at the centre. The radii of the s orbitals increases with principal quantum number (n). Figure 2.56 shows the 1s and 2s orbitals. Note that the 2s orbital is larger and hence the electron density is less than the 1s orbital.

The p orbitals have a dumb-bell shape. The three p orbitals are arranged along the x, y and z axes in space. Figure 2.57 shows three p orbitals of an atom. The sizes of the p orbitals are 2p < 3p < 4p. There is no 1p orbital.

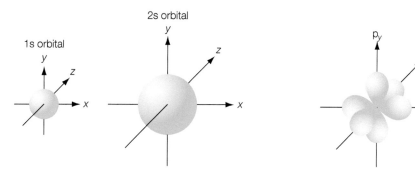

■ **Figure 2.56** Shapes of the 1s and 2s orbitals   ■ **Figure 2.57** Three p orbitals

Quantum mechanical model

The quantum mechanical model is a *probability* model (which uses a wave function to describe mathematically the location of the electron). The orbitals described previously are drawn as volumes of space where electrons spend 95% of their time. A more accurate description of

■ **Figure 2.58**
Quantum mechanical
'electron cloud'
model of a 1s orbital
in a hydrogen atom

boundary within which
there is a 95% chance
of finding an electron

the 1s orbital in a hydrogen atom is shown in Figure 2.58. It is a computer-generated image showing the positions of the electron in a hydrogen atom over a very short interval of time. The boundary of the 1s orbital is clearly visible, but it is seen to be 'fuzzy' owing to the existence of some electron density outside the boundary surface of the orbital.

It is also helpful to compare and contrast Bohr's concept of an *orbit* with Schrödinger's concept of an *orbital*. The differences are summarized in Table 2.8. Schrödinger's quantum mechanical model has superseded Bohr's model, but chemists still use it because it is simple and useful in describing the hydrogen atom.

■ **Table 2.8** Summary
of the differences
between an orbit and
an orbital

Orbit	Orbital
A well-defined circular orbit followed by an electron revolving around the nucleus.	A region of space where an electron is likely to be located.
It represents planar motion.	It represents three-dimensional motion.
Orbits are non-directional and hence cannot account for the shapes of molecules.	Orbitals have different shapes.
The maximum number of electrons in an orbit is $2n^2$, where n represents the number of the orbit.	An orbital cannot accommodate more than two electrons.
The electron is viewed as a localized particle.	The electron is viewed as a mathematical wave function, indicating the probability of finding an electron in a particular region of space.

■ Filling atomic orbitals

The electrons are arranged in atomic orbitals according to certain principles:

■ Each orbital can hold up to a maximum of two electrons. This, in simplified form, is the Pauli exclusion principle.

■ Electrons enter and occupy an empty atomic orbital with the lowest energy. This is known as the Aufbau principle (see Figures 2.59 and 2.60).

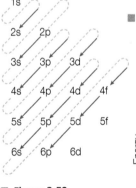

■ **Figure 2.59**
The Aufbau principle
for filling atomic
orbitals with electrons

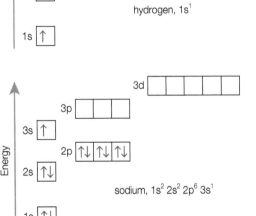

■ **Figure 2.60** Electrons
in energy levels or
orbitals to show the
application of the
Aufbau or building-up
principle

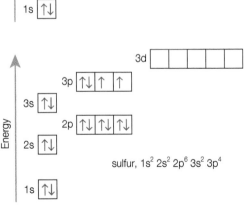

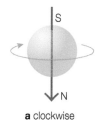

a clockwise

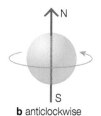

b anticlockwise

■ **Figure 2.61**
Electron spin

- Within a sub-shell, electrons experience repulsion and hence enter two different orbitals of the same energy. This is known as Hund's rule.
- Electrons behave as particles and hence possess a classical property known as spin. An electron can spin in two different directions: clockwise and anticlockwise, shown by the symbols ↑ or ↓. Two electrons in the same orbital must have *opposite* spins, i.e. ↑↓ and not ↑↑.
- Single electrons in the same sub-shell must have the *same* (parallel) spin, i.e. ↑ ↑ and not ↑ ↓.

When a charged particle spins on its axis, a magnetic field is produced (Figure 2.61). Thus, electrons have magnetic properties. Protons show similar behaviour to electrons and also produce a magnetic field. This property is exploited in the technique of nuclear magnetic resonance (NMR).

■ Electron configurations of atoms

The detailed electron configuration of the hydrogen atom (atomic number 1) is:

1s
↑

It can be written as $1s^1$. The large number represents the shell number (principal quantum number), the letter represents the sub-shell and the superscript number represents the number of electrons in the sub-shell.

The detailed electron configuration of the helium atom (atomic number 2) is:

1s
↑↓

It can be written as $1s^2$. The two electrons must form a spin pair.

The lithium atom (atomic number 3) has three electrons. Two electrons enter the 1s orbital (as a spin pair). The 1s orbital is now full; so the third electron enters the 2s orbital (the next orbital with the lowest energy). This is in accordance with Hund's rule. The detailed electron configuration is:

1s 2s
↑↓ ↑

It can be written as $1s^2 2s^1$.

The beryllium atom (atomic number 4) has the detailed electron configuration shown below.

1s 2s
↑↓ ↑↓

It can be written as $1s^2 2s^2$.

The boron atom (atomic number 5) has five electrons. The first four electrons occupy the 1s and 2s orbitals. The fifth electron occupies the 2p orbital. The correct detailed electron configuration is:

1s 2s 2p
↑↓ ↑↓ ↑

It can be written as $1s^2 2s^2 2p^1$.

The carbon atom (atomic number 6) has six electrons and the correct detailed electron configuration is:

1s 2s 2p
↑↓ ↑↓ ↑ ↑

It can be written as $1s^2 2s^2 2p^2$.

Note that the following detailed electron configurations are *not allowed* (i.e. are forbidden) for a carbon atom in its ground state.

Detailed electron configuration	Reason for error (principle violated)
1s 2s 2p $\uparrow\downarrow$ $\uparrow\downarrow$ $\uparrow\downarrow$ ☐	The 2p electrons should occupy different orbitals. Hund's rule has been violated.
1s 2s 2p $\uparrow\downarrow$ $\uparrow\downarrow$ $\uparrow$ $\downarrow$	The single electrons in the same sub-shell should have the same spin.
1s 2s 2p $\uparrow\downarrow$ $\uparrow$ $\uparrow$ $\uparrow$ $\uparrow$	The 2s orbital can accept one more electron, so it should contain two electrons. The Aufbau principle has been violated.

■ Division of the periodic table into blocks

The long form of the periodic table is divided into four blocks: the s-, p-, d- and f-blocks (Chapter 3). This division reflects the filling of the outermost orbitals with electrons (Figure 2.62).

The detailed electron configurations of the first 37 elements are shown in Table 2.9. These are the ground state (lowest energy) configurations of the atoms.

Two elements in the first row of the d-block have unexpected electron configurations (highlighted in Table 2.9) that do not obey the Aufbau principle. The outer electron configuration of the chromium atom is $4s^1 3d^5$ and not $4s^2 3d^4$ as expected. The outer configuration of the copper atom is $4s^1 3d^{10}$ and not $4s^2 3d^9$. A *simplified explanation* for these observations is that a half-filled or completely filled 3d sub-shell is a particularly stable electron configuration. The outer electron configurations for copper and chromium atoms can also be written as $3d^5 4s^1$ and $3d^{10} 4s^1$ so that the 3d sub-shell is placed into the third shell.

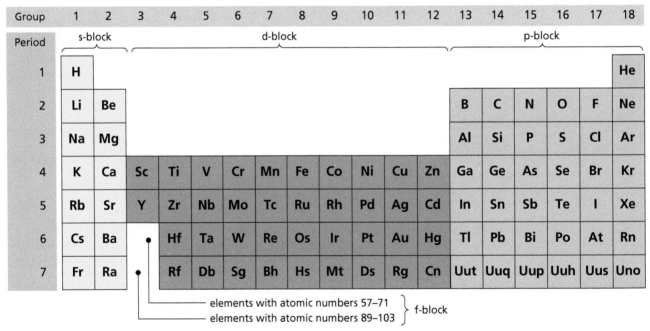

■ **Figure 2.62** Long form of the periodic table marked into s-, p-, d- and f-blocks

You will *not* be expected to know the electron configurations of elements 39 to 48 (the second row of the d-block). However, their atoms behave like the first row – they ionize via loss of the 5s and then the 4d electrons. A number of other elements, in addition to copper and chromium, have anomalous configurations.

Atomic number	Chemical symbol of element	Electron configuration	Atomic number	Chemical symbol of element	Electron configuration	Atomic number	Chemical symbol of element	Electron configuration
1	H	$1s^1$	13	Al	$[Ne]3s^23p^1$	25	Mn	$[Ar]4s^23d^5$
2	He	$1s^2$	14	Si	$[Ne]3s^23p^2$	26	Fe	$[Ar]4s^23d^6$
3	Li	$[He]2s^1$	15	P	$[Ne]3s^23p^3$	27	Co	$[Ar]4s^23d^7$
4	Be	$[He]2s^2$	16	S	$[Ne]3s^23p^4$	28	Ni	$[Ar]4s^23d^8$
5	B	$[He]2s^22p^1$	17	Cl	$[Ne]3s^23p^5$	29	**Cu**	$\mathbf{[Ar]4s^13d^{10}}$
6	C	$[He]2s^22p^2$	18	Ar	$[Ne]3s^23p^6$	30	Zn	$[Ar]4s^23d^{10}$
7	N	$[He]2s^22p^3$	19	K	$[Ar]4s^1$	31	Ga	$[Ar]4s^23d^{10}4p^1$
8	O	$[He]2s^22p^4$	20	Ca	$[Ar]4s^2$	32	Ge	$[Ar]4s^23d^{10}4p^2$
9	F	$[He]2s^22p^5$	21	Sc	$[Ar]4s^23d^1$	33	As	$[Ar]4s^23d^{10}4p^3$
10	Ne	$[He]2s^22p^6$	22	Ti	$[Ar]4s^23d^2$	34	Se	$[Ar]4s^23d^{10}4p^4$
11	Na	$[Ne]3s^1$	23	V	$[Ar]4s^23d^3$	35	Br	$[Ar]4s^23d^{10}4p^5$
12	Mg	$[Ne]3s^2$	24	**Cr**	$\mathbf{[Ar]4s^13d^5}$	36	Kr	$[Ar]4s^23d^{10}4p^6$
						37	Rb	$[Kr]5s^1$

■ **Table 2.9** Detailed electron configurations of gaseous isolated atoms in the ground state (the electron configurations of the atoms in bold are discussed on page 80).

Additional Perspectives

Electron configurations of excited species

When one or more electrons absorb thermal or electrical energy, they are promoted into higher energy orbitals. The atoms and electrons are in an excited state.

A specific example of an excited sodium atom is shown below in Figure 2.63. The return of the excited electron to the ground state will give rise to emission of electromagnetic radiation corresponding to a specific line in the emission spectrum of sodium atoms.

■ **Figure 2.63** Orbital notation for sodium atoms in ground and excited states

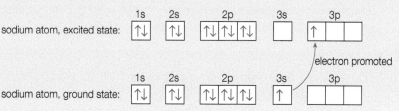

■ Electronic configuration of ions

Hund's rule, the Pauli exclusion principle and the Aufbau principle also apply when extra electrons are added to form negative ions (anions). The fluoride ion (Figure 2.64) is formed when a fluorine atom ($1s^22s^22p^5$) gains an additional electron.

To deduce the electron configuration of positive ions (cations), electrons are removed in reverse order (that is, the last electron is removed first). (An exception to this 'rule' occurs with the transition metals – see Chapter 13.)

For example, the $O^+(g)$ ion is formed by the removal of one electron from an oxygen atom ($1s^22s^22p^4$) (Figure 2.65). This ionization process can be made to occur inside a mass spectrometer. The electron removed is the last electron from the 2p sub-shell.

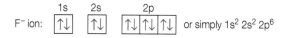

■ **Figure 2.64** Orbital notation and detailed electron configuration for a fluoride ion, F⁻

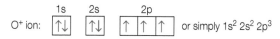

■ **Figure 2.65** Orbital notation and detailed electron configuration for an O⁺(g) ion

■ The octet rule

The electron arrangements of noble gases are relatively stable and their atoms do not lose or gain electrons to form ions. Atoms of noble gases, with the exception of helium, have eight electrons in their outer shells. This arrangement is known as an octet.

According to the octet rule, atoms usually form stable ions by losing or gaining electrons to attain an octet (Chapter 4). For example, the nitrogen atom gains three electrons to attain the stable electron arrangement of neon, the nearest noble gas (Figure 2.66). The calcium atom loses two electrons to attain the electron arrangement of the noble gas, argon (Figure 2.67). Lithium and beryllium atoms lose electrons to attain the electronic arrangement of a helium atom, with two electrons. The lithium atom loses one electron to form the lithium ion, Li^+ (Figure 2.68).

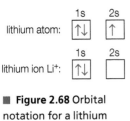

Figure 2.68 Orbital notation for a lithium atom and the lithium ion, Li^+

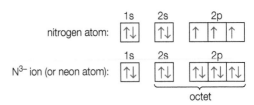

■ **Figure 2.66** Orbital notation for a nitrogen atom and the nitride ion, N^{3-}

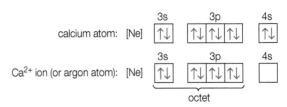

■ **Figure 2.67** Orbital notation for a calcium atom and the calcium ion, Ca^{2+}

Applying of the Aufbau principle, Hund's rule and the Pauli exclusion principle to write electron configurations for atoms and ions up to $Z = 36$

The electron configuration of any atom or ion ($Z < 36$) can be predicted by applying the Aufbau principle, Hund's rule and the Pauli exclusion principle. The two exceptions are copper and chromium.

11 Write full electron configurations and orbital diagrams for the following Ti^{3+}, Cr^{2+}, Cu, P^{3-}, Cl and Ga. Assume all atoms are gaseous and in the ground state.

12 For each of the following, decide whether the full or condensed electronic configuration shown represents
   a an atom, a positive ion (cation) or a negative ion (anion) of the element shown,
   b in the ground state or an excited state.
   i   Li $1s^2 2p^1$
   ii H $1s^2$
   iii S [He] $2s^2 2p^6 3s^2 3p^4$
   iv N $1s^2 2s^1 2p^3$
   v   F [He] $2s^2 2p^5 3s^1$

13 Find out about the use of quantum numbers to describe electrons in atoms.

■ *Examination questions – a selection*

Paper 1 IB questions and IB style questions

Q1 Which statement is correct about the isotopes of an element?
   A They have the same mass number.
   B They have the same numbers of protons and neutrons in the nucleus.
   C They have more protons than neutrons.
   D They have the same electron arrangement or configuration.

Q2 A chemical element with the symbol X has the electron arrangement 2,8,6. Which chemical species is this chemical element most likely to form?
   A the ion X^{3+}
   B the ion X^{6+}
   C the compound H_2X [$2H^+X^{2-}$]
   D the compound XF_8 [$X^{8+}8F^-$]

Q3 Which of the following particles contains more electrons than neutrons?
   I ^1_1H **II** $^{35}_{17}Cl^-$ **III** $^{39}_{19}K^+$

   A I only   **C** I and II only
   B II only   **D** II and III only

Standard Level Paper 1, May 2000, Q6

Q4 What information about the structure of a helium atom can be gained from its emission spectrum?
A Most of the mass of the atom is in its nucleus.
B A helium atom contains two electrons and two protons.
C The electrons in the helium atom are held near the nucleus.
D The electrons may exist in any of several energy levels.

Q5 An element has the electron arrangement 2,8,6. What is the element?
A C   **B** S   **C** P   **D** Ar

Q6 Which is an incorrect statement about the atomic emission spectrum of hydrogen?
A The frequency of each line depends on the difference in energy between the higher and lower energy levels.
B The spectrum consists of several series of lines.
C Electronic transitions to the level $n = 2$ give rise to lines in the visible region.
D It is a continuous spectrum.

Q7 What is the correct number of each particle in a fluoride ion, $^{19}F^-$?

	Protons	Neutrons	Electrons
A	9	10	8
B	9	10	9
C	9	10	10
D	9	19	10

Standard Level Paper 1, Nov 2003, Q5

Q8 Which one of the following atoms has the greatest number of unpaired electrons in the ground state?
A Mn   **B** Fe   **C** Ni   **D** Sc

Q9 Why was the Bohr theory of the atom developed?
A To account for changes in gas volumes with temperature.
B To account for the ratios by mass of elements in compounds.
C To account for the emission or line spectrum of hydrogen atoms.
D To account for chemical formulas.

Q10 A particular element consists of two isotopes: 72% of mass number 85 and 28% of mass number 87. What is the expected range of the relative atomic mass?

A less than 85   **C** between 85 and 86
B between 86 and 87   **D** more than 88

Q11 How many valence electrons (electrons in the outermost shell) are present in the element of atomic number 14?

A 4   **B** 3   **C** 2   **D** 1

Q12 Which one of the following atoms will have the same number of neutrons as an atom of $^{88}_{38}Sr$?
A $^{91}_{39}Y$ **B** $^{87}_{37}Rb$ **C** $^{89}_{38}Sr$ **D** $^{84}_{36}Kr$

Q13 Which statement is correct for the emission spectrum of the hydrogen atom?
A The lines converge at lower energies.
B The lines are produced when electrons move from lower to higher energy levels.
C The lines in the visible region involve electron transitions into the energy level closest to the nucleus.
D The line corresponding to the greatest emission of energy is in the ultraviolet region.
Standard Level Paper 1, Nov 2003, Q6

Q14 Naturally occurring chlorine consists of the isotopes chlorine-35 and chlorine-37. The relative atomic mass of chlorine is 35.5. Which one of the following statements is true?
A The chlorine-35 and chlorine-37 atoms are present in equal amounts.
B The ratio of chlorine-37 atoms to chlorine-35 atoms is 2 : 1.
C The ratio of chlorine-37 to chlorine-35 atoms is 37/35.
D There are three times as many chlorine-35 atoms as chlorine-37 atoms.

Q15 Which statement is correct about a line emission spectrum?
A Electrons neither absorb nor release energy as they move from low to high energy levels.
B Electrons absorb energy as they move from high to low energy levels.
C Electrons release energy as they move from low to high energy levels.
D Electrons release energy as they move from high to low energy levels.
Standard Level Paper 1, Nov 2005, Q6

Q16 Which electronic transition within a hydrogen atom requires the greatest energy?

A $n = 1 \rightarrow n = 2$ **C** $n = 2 \rightarrow n = 3$
B $n = 3 \rightarrow n = 5$ **D** $n = 5 \rightarrow n = \infty$

Q17 How many unpaired electrons are present in an atom of element with a proton number (Z) of 23 in its ground state?

A 3   **B** 1   **C** 7   **D** 5

Q18 The atomic numbers and mass numbers for four different nuclei are given in the table below. Which two are isotopes?

	Atomic number	Mass number
I	101	258
II	102	258
III	102	260
IV	103	259

A I and II   **C** III and IV
B II and III   **D** I and IV

Standard Level Paper 1, Nov 1998, Q6

Q19 All isotopes of uranium have the same:

   I   number of protons
   II number of neutrons
   III mass number

  A I only   **C** III only
  B II only   **D** I and III only

Q20 Which elements are characterized by the filling of d orbitals?

  A Halogens
  B Rare earths (lanthanides)
  C Actinides
  D First row transition series

Q21 What does an atomic orbital in an atom represent?

  A A circular path followed by an electron moving around the nucleus of an atom.
  B A point of zero electron density.
  C A region of space in which there is high probability of finding an electron.
  D A fixed distance from the nucleus where an electron is always found with a specific energy.

Q22 Which one of the following atomic orbital descriptions is not allowed under modern orbital theory?

  A 2d   **B** 4s   **C** 5p   **D** 4f

Paper 2 IB questions and IB style questions

Q1 The element bromine exists as the isotopes ^{79}Br and ^{81}Br, and has a relative atomic mass of 79.90.

  a Copy and complete the following table to show the numbers of sub-atomic particles in the species shown. [3]

	An atom of ^{79}Br	An ion of ^{81}Br$^-$
Protons		
Neutrons		
Electrons		

  b State and explain which of the two isotopes ^{79}Br and ^{81}Br is more common in the element bromine. [1]

Standard Level Paper 2, Nov 2005, Q3

Q2 The element silver has two isotopes, $^{107}_{47}$Ag and $^{109}_{47}$Ag, and a relative atomic mass of 107.87.

  a Define the term *isotope*. [1]

  b State the number of protons, electrons and neutrons in $^{107}_{87}$Ag$^+$. [2]

  c State the name and the mass number of the isotope relative to which all relative atomic masses are measured. [1]

Q3 The diagram below (not to scale) represents some of the electron energy levels in the hydrogen atom.

  a Draw an arrow on a copy of the diagram to represent the lowest energy transition in the visible emission spectrum. Label this arrow B. [2]

  b Draw an arrow on a copy of the diagram to represent the electron transition for the ionization of hydrogen. Label this arrow A. [2]

Higher Level Paper 2, May 2003

Q4 Describe the emission or line spectrum of gaseous hydrogen atoms and explain how this is related to the energy levels in the atom. [3]

Q5 **a** Define the term relative atomic mass (A_r). [1]

  b Relative atomic masses of elements are obtained using a mass spectrometer. Draw in cross section a simple annotated diagram of the mass spectrometer. [5]

  c The relative atomic mass of naturally occurring copper is 63.55. Calculate the abundances of ^{63}Cu and ^{65}Cu in a sample of naturally occurring copper atoms. [2]

  d The isotopes of some elements are radioactive. State a radionuclide used in medicine. [1]

Periodicity

- The arrangement of elements in the periodic table helps to predict their electron configuration.
- Elements show trends in their physical and chemical properties across periods and down groups.

3.1 Periodic table – *the arrangement of elements in the periodic table reflects their electron configuration*

Nature of Science

Scientists organize subjects based on structure and function

Chemists in the nineteenth century had a problem. Over sixty elements had been discovered and many of their compounds synthesized and studied. There was a large amount of data, but this was not classified and organized. The elements had to be grouped together in some way so that similarities between elements could be noted and patterns and trends could be observed. Only when chemists had managed to organize their facts could the study of chemistry advance. Further advances in chemistry followed the development of the periodic table, which was initially based on the properties of the elements.

■ The arrangement of elements in the periodic table

The chemical elements in the periodic table (Figure 3.1) are arranged in order of increasing atomic number. This arrangement leads to periodicity – repeating patterns of chemical and physical properties. These are a reflection of repeating changes in electron configuration. Physical properties such as melting and boiling points, atomic properties such as ionization energy, and chemical properties such as rate of reaction with water, all show periodicity.

A horizontal row of elements in the periodic table is called a period. There are seven main periods in the periodic table (six are shown in Figure 3.1). Across a period the chemical properties gradually change from those of reactive metals to those of reactive non-metals, ending with an unreactive non-metal (Table 3.1).

A column of chemical elements in the periodic table is known as a group. There are eighteen groups in the periodic table: 1 to 18. The members of group 1 are known as the alkali metals and the elements in group 17 are known as the halogens. The members of group 18 are all unreactive gases known as the noble gases. The noble gases are monatomic, existing as atoms. They are very unreactive and very few compounds of noble gases have been prepared.

The transition metals are a block of elements between groups 2 and 13. The transition metals all have very similar chemical and physical properties. Unlike groups 1 and 2, in the transition metals there are similarities both across and down the block.

The properties of transition metals are summarized below:

- relatively high melting points, high boiling points and high densities
- fairly unreactive towards water, but some react slowly with steam (Chapter 9)
- form more than one stable cation (Chapter 4) and covalently bonded complex ions (Figure 3.3) (Chapter 13)
- often have coloured compounds (Figure 3.4) and coloured solutions (Chapter 13)
- often act as catalysts (Chapters 6 and 7)
- can be combined with other transition metals (and also with other metals) to form a variety of metallic mixtures known as alloys (Figure 3.5) (Chapter 22 on the accompanying website).

(Chapter 13 contains further information about transition metals and their compounds.)

Group

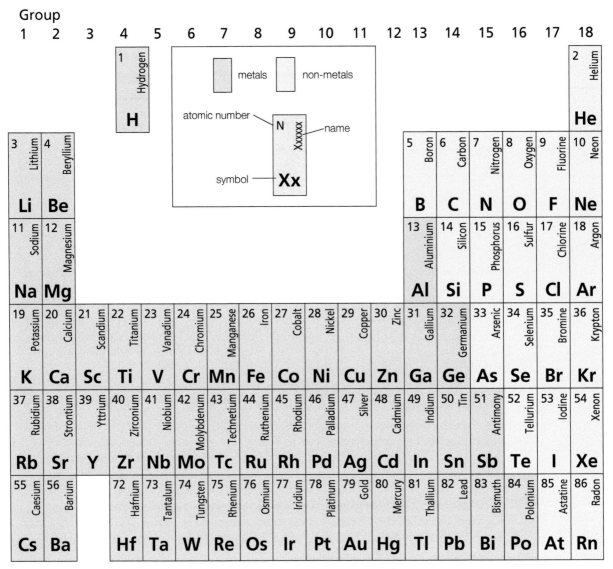

■ **Figure 3.1** The periodic table, showing the division into metals and non-metals

Element	Sodium	Magnesium	Aluminium	Silicon	Phosphorus (white)	Sulfur	Chlorine	Argon
Appearance	Silvery metal	Silvery metal	Silvery metal	Silvery solid	White solid	Yellow solid	Greenish gas	Colourless gas
Electron arrangement	2,8,1	2,8,2	2,8,3	2,8,4	2,8,5	2,8,6	2,8,7	2,8,8
Bonding and structure	Giant metallic lattice	Giant metallic lattice	Giant metallic lattice	Giant covalent (three-dimensional)	Simple molecular (P_4)	Simple molecular (S_8)	Simple molecular (Cl_2)	Monatomic (Ar)
Ion formed	Na^+	Mg^{2+}	Al^{3+}	—	P^{3-}	S^{2-}	Cl^-	—

■ **Table 3.1** Properties of elements in period 3

■ **Figure 3.2** Samples of the period 3 elements: sodium, magnesium, aluminium, silicon, phosphorus, sulfur, chlorine and argon

■ **Figure 3.3** From left to right: thiocyanate ions, iron(III) ions and complex ions formed by the reaction between iron(III) and thiocyanate ions

■ **Figure 3.4** A sample of hydrated nickel chloride, $NiCl_2.6H_2O$; nickel is a transition metal

■ **Figure 3.5** British £2 coin showing an outer gold-coloured nickel-brass ring made from 76% copper, 20% zinc and 4% nickel and an inner silver-coloured cupro-nickel disc made from 75% copper and 25% nickel

■ Electron arrangement and the periodic table

It is the electrons in the outer or valence shell that determine the chemical and physical properties of the chemical element. The position of a chemical element in the periodic table is related to its electron arrangement. The period number indicates the number of shells in the atom of the element. All chemical elements in the same period have the same number of shells. In groups 1 and 2, the number of valence electrons is equal to the group number. In groups 13 to 18, the number of valence electrons is equal to the group number minus 10.

Figure 3.6 shows how the electron arrangement of a chemical element is related to its group and period number. This so-called 'short form' of the periodic table omits the transition elements.

■ **Figure 3.6** The short form of the periodic table, showing the first 20 chemical elements and their electron arrangements

Group	1	2	13	14	15	16	17	18
Period 1	1 **H** 1							2 **He** 2
2	3 **Li** 2,1	4 **Be** 2,2	5 **B** 2,3	6 **C** 2,4	7 **N** 2,5	8 **O** 2,6	9 **F** 2,7	10 **Ne** 2,8
3	11 **Na** 2,8,1	12 **Mg** 2,8,2	13 **Al** 2,8,3	14 **Si** 2,8,4	15 **P** 2,8,5	16 **S** 2,8,6	17 **Cl** 2,8,7	18 **Ar** 2,8,8
4	19 **K** 2,8,8,1	20 **Ca** 2,8,8,2						

Based on the electron arrangements of the elements (Chapter 12), the periodic table can be divided into four blocks of elements (Figure 3.7):

- ■ s-block elements
- ■ p-block elements
- ■ d-block elements
- ■ f-block elements.

■ **Figure 3.7** A diagram showing electron sub-shell filling in periods 1 to 7

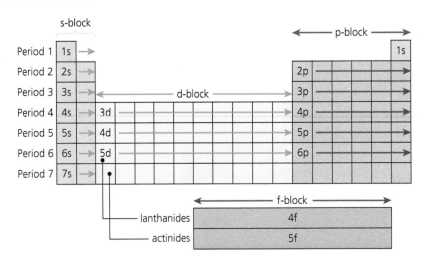

■ **Figure 3.8** Simple three-dimensional periodic table

The s-block consists of hydrogen, helium and groups 1 (alkali metals) and 2. All the s-block elements have a half-filled s orbital (s^1) or a completely filled s orbital (s^2) in the outermost shell.

The p-block consists of groups 13 to 18. The s- and p-blocks are collectively called the main group elements. Each p-block element has an outer electron configuration that varies from s^2p^1 (group 13), s^2p^2 (group 14) through to s^2p^6 (the noble gases in group 18).

The d-block (Chapter 13) consists of three series of metals. Each series of d-block metals contains ten metals with outer electron configurations ranging from d^1s^2 to $d^{10}s^2$.

There are two series of metals at the bottom of the periodic table known as the f-block metals because they contain f orbitals that are being filled. The two rows of the f-block series, known as the lanthanoids and actinoids, each contain 14 elements.

The block classification of elements is emphasized in a simple three-dimensional periodic table (Figure 3.8).

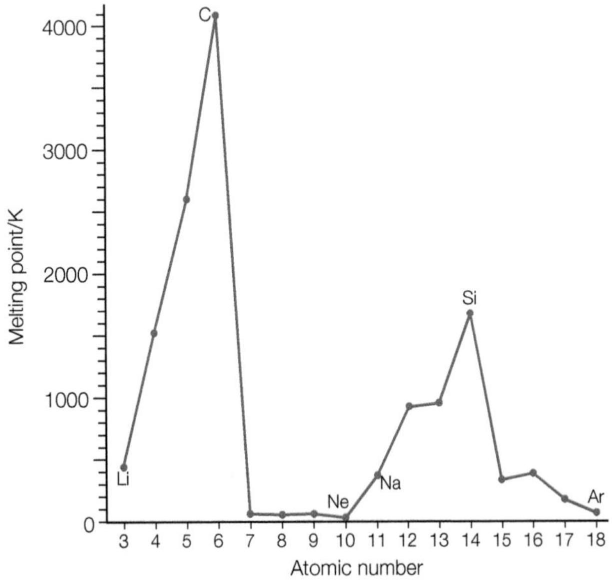

The periodic table is said to show periodicity of physical and chemical properties. Periodicity is a general term that refers to an event that happens at regular intervals. For example, a freely swinging pendulum exhibits periodicity. The periodic table shows chemical periodicity in both the groups (columns) and the periods (rows). The periodic table was generated from the periodic law which states that many of the physical and chemical properties, for example melting points of the elements (Figure 3.9), vary in a regular manner with increasing atomic number. Moving from the lowest atomic number to the highest atomic number atoms, the properties of the elements are similar at regular intervals of 2, 8, 18 and 32. These numbers correspond to the filling of the first four shells of electrons. The term 'periodic trend' describes the way in which a property increases or decreases along a series of elements in the periodic table. This can refer to the changes in properties down a group or across a period.

■ **Figure 3.9** A graph showing periodicity in the melting points of elements

Obtaining evidence for scientific theories by making and testing predictions based on them

Döbereiner's triads

In 1829 the German chemist Johann Döbereiner (1780–1849) noticed that, where groups of three similar chemical elements occurred, the relative atomic mass of the middle element came about half-way between those of the other two. Two of Döbereiner's triads are shown in Figure 3.10.

Newlands' octaves

In 1864 the British chemist John Newlands (1837–1898) found that if the elements were arranged in order of increasing relative atomic mass then a pattern appeared (Figure 3.11). Starting at any given element, the eighth one from it was, as he phrased it, 'a kind of repetition of the first'. Because of the similarity to a musical scale he called it the 'law of octaves'. Newlands' octaves place some very different elements in the same column, for example phosphorus and manganese, and iron and sulfur. The pattern breaks down if the list of elements is extended. It was widely ridiculed at the time but laid the foundations for later work by Mendeleev.

Li lithium 6.9	Cl chlorine 35.5
Na sodium 23.0	Br bromine 79.9
K potassium 39.1	I iodine 126.9

■ **Figure 3.10** Two of Döbereiner's triads

H	Li	Be	B	C	N	O
F	Na	Mg	Al	Si	P	S
Cl	K	Ca	Cr	Ti	Mn	Fe

■ **Figure 3.11** Newland's octaves

■ **Figure 3.12** Miniature set including a stamp (in the middle part) commemorating the publication of Mendeleev's first periodic table in 1869

Mendeleev's periodic table

Dimitri Mendeleev (1834–1907) (Figure 13.12) was a Russian chemist who arranged the known chemical elements into a table in order of increasing relative atomic mass (then known as atomic weight) in a similar manner to Newlands *but*, in order to obtain better chemical periodicity, he left gaps for undiscovered elements. He made predictions for the chemical and physical properties of five 'missing' chemical elements based upon the properties of neighbouring elements. These predictions were later proved to be accurate, following the discovery of germanium (Table 3.2), gallium, scandium, francium and technetium.

■ **Table 3.2** A selection of predictions about germanium made by Mendeleev

	Predicted properties of *eka*-silicon, Es (predicted by Mendeleev in 1871)	Properties of germanium, Ge (discovered by Winkler in 1886)
Relative atomic mass	72	72.6
Density	$5.5\,g\,cm^{-3}$	$5.47\,g\,cm^{-3}$
Appearance	Dirty grey metal	Lustrous (shiny) grey metal
With air	Will form a white powder, EsO_2, on heating	Gives a white powder, GeO_2, on heating
With acids	Slight reaction only	No reaction with dilute sulfuric or hydrochloric acid
Properties of oxide, MO_2	Very high melting point, 4.7 times denser than water	Very high melting point, 4.7 times denser than water
Properties of chloride, MCl_4	Liquid, boiling point less than 100 °C	Liquid, boiling point 86 °C

ToK Link

Mendeleev is a good example of a 'risk-taker'; he invited chemists to test and potentially falsify his predictions. The requirement that a scientific hypothesis be falsifiable was proposed by the philosopher Karl Popper to be the 'criterion of demarcation' of the empirical sciences because it sets apart scientific knowledge from other forms of knowledge. A hypothesis that is not subject to the possibility of empirical falsification does not belong in the realm of science. Mendeleev's periodic table (Figure 3.13) is known as the 'short form' and is still used in Russia and former communist countries. His table is divided into eight groups and, with the exception of the eighth, each group is divided into two sub-groups A and B. This form of the periodic table suffers from some drawbacks, for example manganese is classified with the halogens, with which it has little in common. It should be noted that the structure of atoms was not known at this time and many elements had not been discovered, most notably the noble gases. Mendeleev also had to correct some relative atomic masses which had been determined incorrectly.

Group	1		2		3		4		5		6		7		8
Sub-group	A	B	A	B	A	B	A	B	A	B	A	B	A	B	
1st period	H														
2nd period	Li		Be			B	C		N		O		F		
3rd period	Na		Mg			Al	Si		P		S		Cl		
4th period	K	Cu	Ca	Zn	–	–	Ti	*	V	As	Cr	Se	Mn	Br	Fe Co Ni
5th period	Rb	Ag	Sr	Cd	Y	In	Zr	Sn	Nb	Sb	Mo	Te	–	I	Ru Rh Pd
6th period	Cs	Au	Ba	Hg	La	Tl	–	Pb	Ta	Bi	W	–	–	–	Os Ir Pt
7th period	–		–		–		Th		–		U				

■ **Figure 3.13** Mendeleev's periodic table (modernized form)

■ **Figure 3.14**
A commemorative version of Mendeleev's periodic table

The periodic table shown in Figure 3.14 is on the end wall of the four storey building in which Mendeleev worked from 1893 onwards. It was erected in 1934 to celebrate the centenary of Mendeleev's birth. The title is written in Russian Cyrillic script and reads *'Periodic System of Elements, D.I. Mendeleev'*. The elements whose symbols are blue were discovered between Mendeleev's death in 1907 and 1934. Blanks were left for francium and astatine, still to be discovered. J represents iodine and A represented argon until 1958. At the bottom of the periodic table are the group formulas for the hydrides and oxides, emphasizing that the table is based on *chemical* properties.

18	19
Ar	**K**
39.95	39.10

52	53
Te	**I**
127.60	126.90

■ **Figure 3.15** Atomic data for argon and potassium and for tellurium and iodine

Mendeleev's periodic table was based on relative atomic masses and the chemical properties of the elements. His work was done prior to knowledge about the electronic structure of atoms. In 1869 two elements had to be listed in the *wrong* order according to their relative atomic masses so they could be fitted into the correct group based on their chemical properties (Figure 3.15).

Iodine has a lower relative atomic mass than tellurium and hence should be placed in Mendeleev's group 6. However, Mendeleev placed it in his group 7 since it clearly has similar properties to the other halogens. The discovery of the noble gases introduced a similar reversal of relative atomic mass between argon and potassium.

■ **Figure 3.16** Henry Moseley

A new basis for the order of elements in the periodic table was established by the English chemist Henry Moseley (1887–1915) (Figure 3.16), who studied the X-rays released when atoms of different metallic elements were bombarded by electrons. He discovered a simple relationship between the frequency of the X-rays and the atomic (proton) number (Figure 3.17).

From these results Moseley suggested that one proton (and therefore one electron) was added to the atom on going from one element to the next. Atomic number was therefore a more fundamental property of atoms than relative atomic mass. When the elements are arranged in order of atomic number the problems of elements being in the 'wrong order', for example iodine and tellurium, are removed. Moseley published his findings in 1914, but died in the First World War.

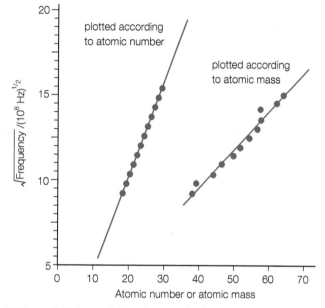

■ **Figure 3.17** Some of Moseley's results for the X-ray spectra of various metals

 ■ **Development of the periodic table**

The development of the periodic table took many years and involved many scientists from different countries building upon the foundations of each other's work and ideas. The first attempts to categorize the elements were by Döbereiner ('law of triads') and Newlands ('law of octaves'). Mendeleev was the first chemist to devise a periodic table with all the known elements that he used to predict properties of undiscovered elements. Mendeleev's periodic table has been modified in the light of work carried out by Rutherford and Moseley. Discoveries about sub-atomic properties led them to realise that elements should be arranged by atomic number.

ToK Link

What role did inductive and deductive reasoning play in the development of the periodic table?

Inductive reasoning involves proceeding from many special cases to a general rule. Deductive reasoning proceeds from a general assumption. Science often involves both deductive and inductive reasoning.

When chemists studied the properties of the elements they found that many conduct electricity in the solid state and are shiny (when polished) and malleable. This is an empirical definition of the elements that are now called metals. This is a simple example of inductive reasoning.

Mendeleev arranged the elements by atomic mass and was able to accurately predict the chemical and physical properties of elements that were not discovered yet. This was made possible by looking at the properties of elements that came before and after them within a group. This is a simple example of deductive reasoning.

ToK Link

The predictive power of Mendeleev's periodic table illustrates the 'risk-taking' nature of science. What is the demarcation between scientific and pseudoscientific claims?

Karl Popper was the first philosopher of science to identify 'the demarcation problem' of finding a criterion to distinguish between empirical science and pseudoscience. Popper's most important contribution to the philosophy of science was his concept that a scientific claim must be potentially falsifiable.

A clear example of empirical science is the falsifying of Thomson's 'plum pudding' model by Rutherford's gold foil experiment. One issue is that some so-called scientific theories are non-falsifiable, for example string theory.

Science can be demarcated from pseudoscience less by what science is, and more by what scientists do. Science is a set of methods aimed at testing hypotheses and developing theories. If the theory is adopted by the scientific community, then the chances are it is science.

Utilization: Use of the periodic table in other disciplines

The periodic table of the elements has had a profound influence on the development of modern chemistry and physics, including quantum mechanics. Physicists are often interested in nuclear structure and nuclear reactions. The periodic table can be used to establish the numbers of protons (atomic number) and neutrons (via the relative isotopic mass) in a specific isotope of an element.

A biologist can use the periodic table in same way as a chemist. It can be used to find elements with similar chemical properties, predict chemical formulas, predict charges on simple ions, predict electron structures of atoms and ions, find simple ions of similar ionic radius, predict physical and chemical properties, and relative atomic masses can be used in calculations involving the mole concept.

1   Find out about alternative forms of the periodic table including spiral forms.

■ The period number

The period number indicates the outer energy level (shell) that is occupied by electrons. There are seven periods in the periodic table.

The short periods

In period 1 the 1s orbital ($n = 1$) is being filled. Period 1 consists of hydrogen ($1s^1$) and helium ($1s^2$).

In period 2 the $n = 2$ shell of orbitals is being filled. Period 2 consists of eight elements from lithium ($1s^2\,2s^2$) to neon ($1s^2\,2s^2\,2p^6$). The 2s orbital is filled first, followed by the 2p orbital.

In period 3 ($n = 3$) the 3s orbital is filled first, followed by the 3p orbitals. Period 3 consists of eight elements from sodium ($1s^2\,2s^2\,2p^6\,3s^1$) to argon ($1s^2\,2s^2\,2p^6\,3s^2\,3p^6$).

The long periods

In period 4 elements, the 4s, 3d and 4p orbitals are involved. Period 4 consists of 18 elements from potassium ($1s^2\,2s^2\,2p^6\,3s^2\,3p^6\,4s^1$) to krypton ($1s^2\,2s^2\,2p^6\,3s^2\,3p^6\,3d^{10}\,4s^2\,4p^6$). Among the period 4 elements are a set of the d-block elements (transition metals).

In the outer energy level (shell) of period 5 elements, the 5s, 4d and 5p orbitals are involved. Period 5 consists of 18 elements from rubidium to xenon.

In the outer energy level (shell) of period 6 elements, the 6s, 4f, 5d and 6p orbitals are involved. Period 6 consists of 32 elements. One series of 15 elements, known as the lanthanoids, is removed from this period and placed at the bottom of the periodic table. The lanthanoids are also known as the rare earth elements and have a wide range of industrial uses.

The lanthanoids are chemically very similar since they have the same electron configurations in the two outermost energy levels. The differences occur in the next further-in energy level. For example, the electron configuration of cerium (Ce) is:

$$1s^2\,2s^2\,2p^6\,3s^2\,3p^6\,4s^2\,3d^{10}\,4p^6\,5s^2\,4d^{10}\,5p^6\,6s^2\,4f^2$$

and that of praseodymium (Pr) is:

$$1s^2\,2s^2\,2p^6\,3s^2\,3p^6\,4s^2\,3d^{10}\,4p^6\,5s^2\,4d^{10}\,5p^6\,6s^2\,4f^3$$

The only difference between these two configurations is in the number of 4f electrons. Both the fifth and sixth energy levels contain electrons.

In the outer energy level (shell) of period 7 elements, the 7s, 5f, 6d and 7p orbitals are involved. Period 6 consists of 32 elements. The number of elements in period 7 has been slowly increasing due to the discovery of new radioactive elements.

One series of 15 elements, known as the actinoids, is removed from this period and placed at the bottom of the periodic table. Uranium is an actinide element.

The relationship between principal energy level and period on the periodic table is simple: the number of a period on the periodic table is the same as the number of the highest principal energy level (n) for the atoms on that row (i.e. the principal energy level occupied by its valence electrons). Thus, elements on period 4 have a highest principal energy level of 4, whereas the valence electrons of elements on period 7 are at principal energy level 7.

The number of valence electrons of an atom can be deduced from its position on the periodic table. For the s-block (groups 1 and 2), the number of valence electrons equals the group number. In the p-block (groups 13 to 18), the number of valence electrons equals the number minus 10. In the d-block (group 3 to 12), the number of electrons equals the group number (this includes both s and d electrons). For the f-block this includes all of the s, d and f electrons.

For example, sodium is in group 1 with a [Ne] $3s^1$ configuration and has one valence electron; selenium is in group 16 with the configuration [Ar] $3d^{10}$ $4s^2$ $4s^4$ and has six valence electrons; and cobalt is in group 9, with the configuration [Ar] $3d^7$ $4s^2$ and has nine valence electrons.

Worked example

Deduce the number of valence electrons in an atom of lead, and the number of electron shells (energy levels) in an atom of strontium. Explain your answer in terms of the positions of these elements in the periodic table.

Lead is an element in group 14 of the periodic table. Hence there are $14 - 10 = 4$ electrons in the valence shell.

Strontium is an element in period 5 of the periodic table. Hence, there are five electron shells (energy levels) in an atom of strontium.

Deducing the electronic configuration from the element's position on the periodic table, and vice versa

The elements in the periodic table are arranged into groups where the elements have similar electronic configurations. For example, all the elements in group 1 are metals and the outer or valence shell (with the highest value of n) of each element has one electron only:

Na: $1s^2\ 2s^2\ 2p^6\ 3s^1$

K: $1s^2\ 2s^2\ 2p^6\ 3s^2\ 3p^6\ 4s^1$

Hence, the general electronic configuration of the valence shell for group 1 elements is ns^1. Similarly, all the elements in group 13 have three electrons in their outermost or valence shell.

Al: $1s^2\ 2s^2\ 2p^6\ 3s^2\ 3p^1$

Ga: $1s^2\ 2s^2\ 2p^6\ 3s^2\ 3p^6\ 3d^{10}\ 4s^2\ 4p^1$

Hence the general electron configuration of the valence shell for the group 13 elements is $ns^2\,np^1$. The electrons in the outermost energy level are the valence electrons and involved in bonding. The position of an element in the periodic table can be deduced from its outermost electron configuration.

Worked examples

The electronic configuration of the magnesium atom is $1s^2\ 2s^2\ 2p^6\ 3s^2$. Deduce its position in the periodic table.

The outermost or valence configuration is $3s^2$. Hence magnesium is an s-block element. The principal quantum number, or shell number, of 3 ($n = 3$) gives the period and the number of valence electrons, 2, indicates the group. Thus magnesium is in period 3 and group 2 of the periodic table.

Element X is in group 2 and period 3 of the periodic table. Deduce the electronic configuration of this element.

X has the valence configuration $3s^2$ and hence the full electronic configuration, $1s^2\ 2s^2\ 2p^6\ 3s^2$.

Deduce the electronic configurations of the valence shells in atoms of gallium and lead.

Gallium is an element in group 13 and period 4 of the periodic table. Hence the electronic configuration of the valence shell is $4s^2\ 4p^1$. Lead is an element in group 14 and period 6 of the periodic table. Hence the electronic configuration of the valence shell is $6s^2\ 6p^2$.

2   Deduce the electronic configurations of the following elements: X is in group 2 and period 3, Y is in group 15 and period 2, and Z is in group 18 and period 3.

3   Identify the position of the elements P ($... 3s^2\ 3p^6$), Q ($... 4s^2\ 4p^5$) and R ($... 3s^2\ 3p^6\ 4s^2$) in the periodic table.

■ Types of elements

Metals

It is useful to classify the elements into three categories: metals, non-metals and metalloids. The chemical properties of metals depend on the ability of an atom to lose one or more electrons to form positive ions. This occurs during chemical reactions involving metals. Physical properties such as hardness and melting point vary considerably among metals. Group 1 metals are soft with low melting points, but transition metals are hard with high melting points. Other physical properties are characteristic of all metals in general. For example, all metals are lustrous (shiny when polished), malleable (can be hammered into thin sheets) and ductile (can be drawn into thin wires). All metals are excellent conductors of electricity and heat (thermal energy). The electrical conductivity slowly decreases with temperature.

Non-metals

Non-metallic elements have the opposite physical properties: they are dull (not shiny), brittle (they snap under tension) and they cannot be drawn into wires (they are non-ductile) and cannot be hammered into thin sheets (they are non-malleable). Non-metals, with the exception of graphite, are non-conductors of electricity (insulators).

Metalloids

There are a few elements that have the properties of both metals and non-metals. These elements are known as metalloids. Metalloids are poor conductors of electricity. The conductivity of a metalloid increases as the temperature rises and is greatly affected by the presence of small amounts of impurities. Silicon and germanium are good examples of metalloids. They are used in semi-conducting devices, such as silicon chips for microprocessors.

Figure 3.18 shows the positions of metals, non-metals and metalloids in the periodic table. Note that the cell for carbon has been shaded less heavily because carbon's two most common allotropes, diamond and graphite, have different electrical conductivities. Graphite is a moderate conductor of electricity and is classified as a metalloid. Diamond is a non-conductor (insulator) of electricity and is classified as a non-metal.

One criterion for classifying an element as a metal, a non-metal or a metalloid is the acid–base behaviour of the oxide. In general metals form basic oxides, non-metals form acidic oxides and metalloids form amphoteric oxides. Basic oxides react with acid, acidic oxides react with bases and amphoteric oxides react with both acids and bases.

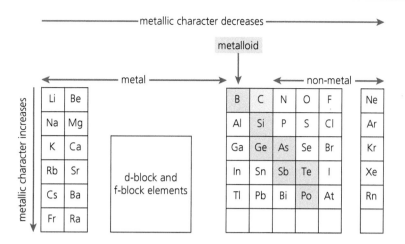

■ Figure 3.18
The positions of metals, non-metals and metalloids in the periodic table

Nature of Science

Looking for patterns – synthesizing new substances based on the reactivity of elements

The noble gases have completely filled s and p sub-shells. All the members of group 18 have large first ionization energies. They show the expected decrease as we move down the group as the increase in the shielding effect outweighs the increase in nuclear charge. Because the noble gases have stable electron configurations they were originally termed inert gases.

In 1962 Neil Bartlett hypothesized that the ionization energy of xenon, the largest non-radioactive noble gas, might be low enough for it to form compounds. Bartlett chose to react xenon with fluorine, the element with the highest electronegativity, which gives it a strong affinity for electrons. In 1962 Bartlett synthesized the first noble gas compound by reacting xenon with the fluorine-containing compound, PtF_6. The compound had the formula $XePtF_6$ [$Xe^+ PtF_6^-$]. He also showed that xenon could combine directly to form the molecular compounds XeF_2, XeF_4 and XeF_6.

■ Making predictions about an element's properties

Because there are patterns in the way the elements are arranged in the periodic table, it can be used to predict their properties and interpret data.

Reactivity

At the top of group 17, fluorine is the most reactive and astatine at the bottom is the least reactive. Astatine is rare and radioactive, but predictions about its reactions and physical properties are possible. Astatine should not replace any of the other halogens from their compounds.

Astatine should be replaced from sodium astatide solution by fluorine, chlorine, bromine or iodine. For example:

bromine + sodium astatide → sodium bromide + astatine

$Br_2(aq) + NaAt(aq) \rightarrow NaBr(aq) + At_2(aq)$

Physical properties

Table 3.3 shows the melting points of group 17 elements, with one value missing.

■ Table 3.3 Melting points of the halogens

Group 17 element (halogen)	Boiling point/°C
Fluorine	−188
Chlorine	−34
Bromine	59
Iodine	184
Astatine	—

The melting points show a pattern, or trend, down the group. It is therefore possible to predict that the melting point of astatine is approximately 380 °C. The same can be done with other physical properties, such as the melting points, and atomic properties, such as first ionization energy.

4   Use graphs to plot the melting points, electron affinity values and first ionization energies for the halogens fluorine, chlorine, bromine and iodine (group 17 elements). Extrapolate the smooth curves to estimate the values for astatine. Compare your values with the values on the pages 7 and 8 of the *IB Chemistry data booklet*.

3.2 Periodic trends – *elements show trends in their physical and chemical properties across periods and down groups*

First ionization energy

The first ionization energy is the minimum energy required to remove one mole of electrons from one mole of gaseous atoms (under standard thermodynamic conditions of 25 °C and 1 atm).

In general: $X(g) \rightarrow X^+(g) + e^-$

For example, the first ionization energy of hydrogen is given by the following equation:

$H(g) \rightarrow H^+(g) + e^-$ $\Delta H = +1310 \, kJ \, mol^{-1}$

The amount of energy required to carry out this process for a mole of hydrogen atoms is 1310 kilojoules.

Atoms of each element have different values of first ionization energy.

Electronegativity

The electronegativity of an atom is the ability or power of an atom in a covalent bond to attract shared pairs of electrons to itself. The greater the electronegativity of an atom, the greater its ability to attract shared pairs of electrons to itself.

Electronegativity values are usually based on the Pauling scale. A value of 4.0 is given to fluorine, the most electronegative atom. The least electronegative element, francium, has an electronegativity value of 0.7. The values for all the other elements lie between these two extremes. Note that electronegativity values are pure numbers with no units.

■ Trends in the properties of the elements in group 1 and group 17

Trends in atomic and ionic radii

At the right of the periodic table, the atomic radius is defined as half the distance between the nuclei of two covalently bonded atoms (Figure 3.19). For example, the bond length in a chlorine molecule (the distance between two chlorine nuclei) is 0.199 nm. Therefore the atomic radius of chorine is ½ × 199 = 99 pm (1 picometre [pm] = 10^{-12} m; 1 nanometre [nm] = 10^{-9} m). At the left of the periodic table, the atomic radius is that of the atom in the metal lattice (the metallic radius). For the noble gases the atomic radius is that of an isolated atom (the van der Waals' radius).

In general the atomic radius of an atom is determined by the balance between two opposing factors:

■   the shielding effect by the electrons of the inner shell(s) – this makes the atomic radius larger. The shielding effect is the result of repulsion between the electrons in the inner shell and those in the outer or valence shell.

■   the nuclear charge (due to the protons) – this is an attractive force that pulls all the electrons closer to the nucleus. With an increase in nuclear charge, the atomic radius becomes smaller.

However, when moving down a group in the periodic table, there is an *increase* in the atomic radius as the nuclear charge increases (Tables 3.4 and 3.5 and Figures 3.20 and 3.21). This is the result of two factors:

■   the increase in the number of complete electron shells between the outer (valence) electrons and the nucleus

■   the increase in the shielding effect of the outer electrons by the inner electrons.

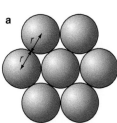

a

r
r

metallic radius

b

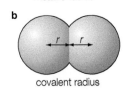

r   *r*

covalent radius

c

r

van der Waals' radius
(for group 18)

■ **Figure 3.19**
Atomic radius

Atom	Atomic number	Atomic radius/pm
Li	3	152
Na	11	186
K	19	231
Rb	37	244
Cs	55	262
Fr	87	270

■ **Table 3.4** The variation of atomic radii in group 1

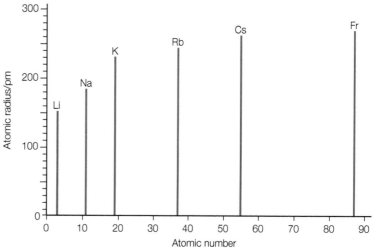

■ **Figure 3.20** Bar chart showing the variation of atomic radii in group 1

Atom	Atomic number	Atomic radius/pm
F	9	58
Cl	17	99
Br	35	114
I	53	133
At	85	140

■ **Table 3.5** The variation of atomic radii in group 17

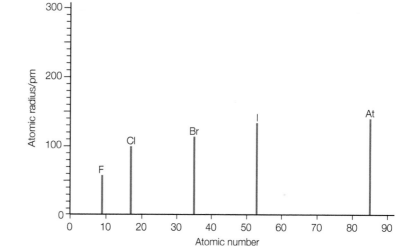

■ **Figure 3.21** Bar chart showing the variation of atomic radii in group 17

Moving down a group, both the nuclear charge and the shielding effect increase. However, the outer electrons enter new shells. So, although the nucleus gains protons, the electrons are not only further away, but also more effectively screened by an additional shell of electrons (Figure 3.22).

■ **Figure 3.22**
Summary of trends in periodicity in atomic radii in the periodic table

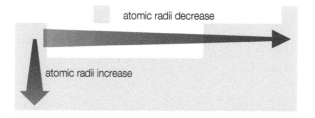

atomic radii decrease

atomic radii increase

Ionic radii for ions of the same charge also increase down a group for the same reason (Tables 3.6 and 3.7). Ionic radii are the radii for ions in a crystalline ionic compound (Figure 3.23).

Ion	Atomic number	Ionic radius/pm
Li⁺	3	68
Na⁺	11	98
K⁺	19	133
Rb⁺	37	148
Cs⁺	55	167
Fr⁺	87	No data

■ **Table 3.6** The variation of ionic radii in group 1

Ion	Atomic number	Ionic radius/pm
F⁻	9	133
Cl⁻	17	181
Br⁻	35	196
I⁻	353	219
At⁻	85	No data

■ **Table 3.7** The variation of ionic radii in group 17

■ **Figure 3.23**
The relative sizes of the atoms and ions of group 1 metals

 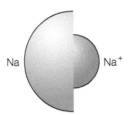 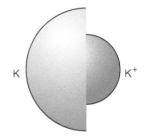

Trends in first ionization energy

On moving down a group, the atomic radius increases as additional electron shells are added. This causes the shielding effect to increase. The further the outer or valence shell is from the nucleus, the smaller the attractive force exerted by the protons in the nucleus. Hence, the more easily an outer electron can be removed and the lower the ionization energy. So, within each group, the first ionization energies decrease down the group. This is shown in Table 3.8 and Figure 3.24.

Atom	Atomic number	First ionization energy/kJ mol⁻¹
Li	3	519
Na	11	494
K	19	418
Rb	37	402
Cs	55	376

■ **Table 3.8** The variation of first ionization energy in group 1

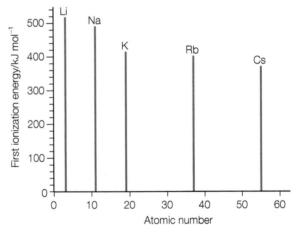

■ **Figure 3.24** Bar graph showing the variation of first ionization energy in group 1

Additional Perspectives

Effective nuclear charge

An alternative way to account for differences in ionization energy is to use the concept of effective nuclear charge.

Trends in electronegativity

Electronegativity values generally decrease down a group. Clear decreasing trends in electronegativity can be found in group 1 (the alkali metals, Table 3.9) and group 17 (the halogens, Table 3.10). Electronegativity can be interpreted as a measure of non-metallic or metallic character. Decreasing electronegativity down a group indicates a decrease in non-metallic character and an increase in metallic character.

The decrease in electronegativity down groups 1 and 17 can be explained by the increase in atomic radius. There is therefore an increasing distance between the nucleus and shared pairs of electrons. Hence the attractive force is decreased. Although the nuclear charge increases down a group, this is counteracted by the increased shielding due to additional electron shells.

The trends in electronegativity can be used to explain the redox properties of groups 1 and 17. Reducing power decreases down group 1; oxidizing power increases up group 17 (Chapter 9).

Atom	Atomic number	Electronegativity
Li	3	1.0
Na	11	0.9
K	19	0.8
Rb	37	0.8
Cs	55	0.8
Fr	87	0.7

■ **Table 3.9** The variation of electronegativity in group 1

Atom	Atomic number	Electronegativity
F	9	4.0
Cl	17	3.2
Br	35	3.0
I	53	2.7
At	85	2.2

■ **Table 3.10** The variation of electronegativity in group 17

Trends in melting point and boiling point

Group 1

The melting points of the alkali metals decrease down the group (Table 3.11 and Figure 3.25). Metals are held together in the solid and liquid states by metallic bonding (Chapter 4). Metals are composed of a lattice of positive ions surrounded by delocalized electrons which move between the ions. The delocalized electrons are valence electrons shed by the metal atoms as they enter the lattice.

The melting points decrease down the group because the strength of the metallic bonding decreases. This occurs because the attractive forces between the delocalized electrons and the nucleus decrease owing to the increase in distance. The increase in nuclear charge is counteracted by the increase in shielding.

Atom	Atomic number	Melting point/K
Li	3	454
Na	11	371
K	19	337
Rb	37	312
Cs	55	302
Fr	87	300

■ **Table 3.11** The variation of melting point in group 1

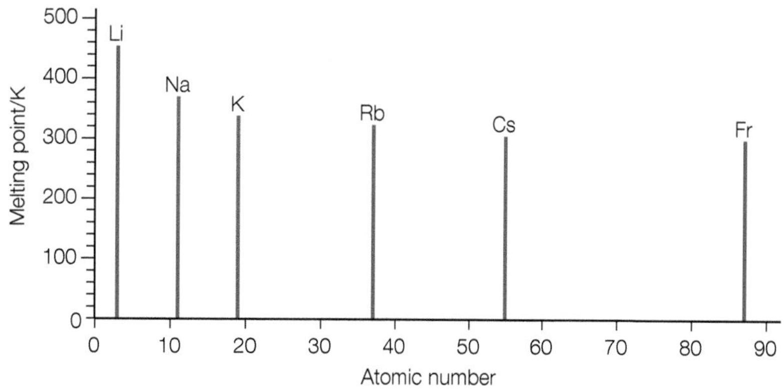

■ **Figure 3.25** The melting points of the alkali metals

Group 17

In contrast to the alkali metals, the melting and boiling points of the halogens *increase* down the group (Table 3.12 and Figure 3.26). This is because as the molecules become larger, the attractive forces between them increase. These shorter-range attractive forces are known as London or dispersion forces and increase with the number of electrons in atoms or molecules (Chapter 4).

Atom	Atomic number	Melting point/K
F	9	54
Cl	17	172
Br	35	266
I	53	387
At	85	575

■ **Table 3.12** The variation of melting point in group 17

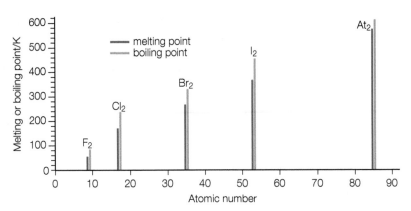

■ **Figure 3.26** Melting and boiling points of the halogens

■ Trends in properties of elements across period 3

Trends in atomic radii

There is a gradual decrease in atomic radius across period 3 from left to right (Table 3.13 and Figure 3.27). When moving from group to group across a period, the number of protons and the number of electrons increases by one. Since the electrons are added to the same shell, there is only a slight increase in the shielding effect across the period. At the same time additional protons are added to the nucleus, increasing the nuclear charge. The effect of the increase in nuclear charge more than outweighs the small increase in shielding and consequently all the electrons are pulled closer to the nucleus. Hence, atomic radii decrease across period 3. The same effect is observed in other periods.

■ **Table 3.13**
The atomic radii in period 3

Atom	Atomic radius/pm
Na	186
Mg	160
Al	143
Si	117
P	110
S	104
Cl	99
Ar	No data

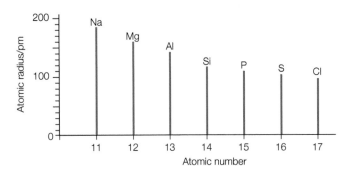

■ **Figure 3.27** Bar graph of the atomic radii in period 3

Trends in ionic radii

The data in Table 3.14 shows the following trends in ionic radii across period 3:

■ The radii of positive ions decrease from the sodium ion, Na^+ to the aluminium ion, Al^{3+}.

■ The radii of negative ions decrease from the phosphide ion, P^{3-} to the chloride ion, Cl^-.

■ The ionic radii increase from the aluminium ion, Al^{3+} to the phosphide ion, P^{3-}.

■ **Table 3.14**
The ionic radii in period 3

Element	Sodium	Magnesium	Aluminium	Silicon	Phosphorus	Sulfur	Chlorine
Ion	Na^+	Mg^{2+}	Al^{3+}	(Si^{4+} and Si^{4-})	P^{3-}	S^{2-}	Cl^-
Ionic radius/pm	98	65	45	(42 and 271)	212	190	181

The data for the silicon ions are theoretical values, but they fit the same trends. Silicon does not form simple ions (Si^{4+} or Si^{4-}) and its bonding is covalent.

Isoelectronic species

Isoelectronic species are atoms and ions that have the same number of electrons. For a specific number of electrons, the higher the nuclear charge, the greater the forces of attraction between the nucleus and the electrons. Hence, the smaller the atomic or ionic radius.

Ions of sodium, magnesium and aluminium are isoelectronic species (Table 3.15). The nuclear charge increases from the sodium ion to the aluminium ion. The higher nuclear charge pulls all the electron shells closer to the nucleus. Hence, the ionic radii decrease.

Similarly, the nuclear charge increases from the phosphide ion to the chloride ion. The higher nuclear charge causes the electron shells to be pulled closer to the nucleus. Again, the ionic radii decrease (Table 3.16).

Species	Na^+	Mg^{2+}	Al^{3+}
Nuclear charge	+11	+12	+13
Number of electrons	10	10	10
Ionic radius/pm	98	65	45

■ **Table 3.15** Atomic data for sodium, magnesium and aluminium ions

Species	P^{3-}	S^{2-}	Cl^-
Nuclear charge	+15	+16	+17
Number of electrons	18	18	18
Ionic radius/pm	212	190	181

■ **Table 3.16** Atomic data for phosphide, sulfide and chloride ions

The large increase in size from the aluminium ion to the phosphide ion is due to the presence of an additional electron shell. This causes a large increase in the shielding effect and as a result the ionic radius increases.

Trends in first ionization energy

The first ionization energies of the elements in period 3 are listed in Table 3.17. The general trend is an increase in first ionization energy across the periodic table. When moving across a period from left to right the nuclear charge increases but the shielding effect only increases slightly (since electrons enter the same shell). Consequently, the electron shells are pulled progressively closer to the nucleus and as a result first ionization energies increase.

■ **Table 3.17** First ionization energies for the elements in period 3

Element	Sodium	Magnesium	Aluminium	Silicon	Phosphorus	Sulfur	Chlorine
First ionization energy/ kJ mol⁻¹	494	736	577	786	1060	1000	1260

However, the increase in first ionization energy is not uniform and there are two *decreases* – between magnesium and aluminium and between phosphorus and sulfur. These decreases can only be explained by reference to sub-shells and orbitals.

The first ionization energy of aluminium is lower than that of magnesium, even though aluminium has a smaller atomic radius. The decrease in first ionization energy from magnesium ($1s^2\ 2s^2\ 2p^6\ 3s^2$) to aluminium ($1s^2\ 2s^2\ 2p^6\ 3s^2\ 3p^1$) occurs because the electrons in the filled 3s orbital are more effective at shielding the electron in the 3p orbital than they are at shielding each other. Therefore less energy is needed to remove a single 3p electron than to remove a paired 3s electron.

The first ionization energy of sulfur ($1s^2\ 2s^2\ 2p^6\ 3s^2\ 3p^2\ 3p^1\ 3p^1$) is less than that of phosphorus ($1s^2\ 2s^2\ 2p^6\ 3s^2\ 3p^1 3p^1\ 3p^1$) because less energy is required to remove an electron from the $3p^4$ orbitals of sulfur than from the half-filled 3p orbitals of phosphorus. The presence of a spin pair of electrons results in greater electron repulsion compared to two unpaired electrons in separate orbitals.

■ Trends in electronegativity values

The electronegativities of the elements in period 3 are listed in Table 3.18. The general trend is an increase in first ionization energy across the periodic table. When moving across a period from left to right the nuclear charge increases but the shielding effect only increases slightly (since electrons enter the same shell). Consequently, the electron shells are pulled progressively closer to the nucleus and as a result electronegativity values increase.

■ **Table 3.18** Electronegativity values for the elements in period 3

Element	Sodium	Magnesium	Aluminium	Silicon	Phosphorus	Sulfur	Chlorine
Electronegativity	0.9	1.3	1.6	1.9	2.2	2.6	3.2

Generally, the electronegativity values of chemical elements increase across a period and decrease down a group (Figure 3.28). This observation can be used to compare the relative electronegativity values of two elements in the periodic table. To do this, find the positions of the elements in the periodic table. Then simply see which one is further up and to the right; that is the more electronegative element (Figure 3.29). The further apart the two elements are in the periodic table, the larger the difference will be in their electronegativities. This is important in determining the type of bonding between the two elements (Chapter 4).

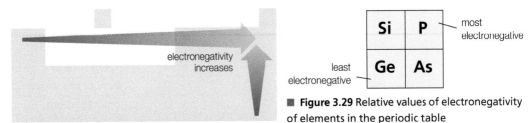

■ **Figure 3.28** Trends in electronegativity for s- and p-block elements

electronegativity increases

most electronegative

least electronegative

Si	P
Ge	As

■ **Figure 3.29** Relative values of electronegativity of elements in the periodic table

■ Trends in electron affinity

Electron affinity

The ionization energy is a measure of the tendency of an atom of an element to form a positive ion. In a similar way, the tendency of a gaseous atom to form a negative ion is described by its electron affinity.

The first electron affinity can be defined as the enthalpy change that occurs when one mole of isolated gaseous atoms accepts a mole of electrons to form a mole of gaseous negative ions with a charge of −1:

$$X(g) + e^- \rightarrow X^-(g)$$

Depending on the element, the process of adding an electron can be either exothermic or endothermic. In an exothermic process heat is released – the ion is more stable than the atom. In an endothermic process heat is absorbed and the ion is less stable than the atom. The more negative the value, the greater the tendency for an atom of that element to accept electrons.

Factors affecting electron affinity

The greater the nuclear charge, the greater the attraction for the incoming electron and hence the more negative the value of the first electron affinity. The larger the size of the atom the greater the distance between the nucleus and the incoming electron entering the valence shell. If an atom has completely filled sub-shells in the valence shell then the electron configuration is relatively stable and hence the atoms of these elements will have positive values of first electrons affinity.

Variation across a period and down a group

5 Plot a bar chart showing electron affinity plotted next to electronegativity. Comment on the relationship between the two atomic properties.

On moving across a period, the atomic size decreases and the nuclear charge increases. Both these factors result in greater attraction for the incoming electron. Hence first electron affinities tend to become negative across a period (left to right).

On moving down a group, the atomic size as well as nuclear charge increases. However, the effect of the increase in atomic size is much greater than that of the increase in nuclear charge. Hence the values of first electron affinity becomes less negative moving down a group.

■ Metallic character

In general metallic character decreases across a period and increases down a group. The metallic character of elements can be compared in terms of first ionization energies. The first ionization energy of an element increases across a period and decreases down a group. In general, reactive metals have low ionization energies but reactive non-metals have high ionization energies. From left to right across a period there is a decrease in metallic character and an increase in non-metallic character. Going down a group, the metallic character increases and the first ionization energy decreases. The more reactive the metal, the greater the metallic character of the metal.

Thus metals are grouped on the left-hand side, whereas non-metals are grouped on the right. The most reactive metals are on the left and at the bottom of the periodic table. The most reactive non-metals are on the right and at the top of the periodic table. From left to right across a period, there is a decrease in metallic character and an increase in non-metallic character (Table 3.19).

Group	1	2	13	14	15	16	17	18
Symbol	Na	Mg	Al	Si	P	S	Cl	Ar
Name	Sodium	Magnesium	Aluminium	Silicon	Phosphorus	Sulfur	Chlorine	Argon
Character	Metallic	Metallic	Metallic	Metalloid	Non-metallic	Non-metallic	Non-metallic	Non-metallic

■ **Table 3.19** Classification of period 3 elements

Periodic trends in properties can be studied with the use of online computer databases. These contain large amounts of data related to atomic, physical and chemical properties. These can be extracted and analysed by a spreadsheet or displayed graphically by the database. Figure 3.30 shows the front page of WebElements (www.webelements.com) developed by Professor Mark Winter at Sheffield University.

■ **Figure 3.30** WebElements

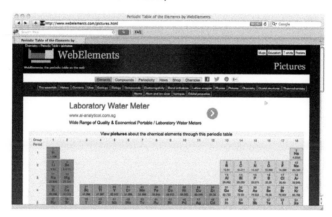

Predicting and explaining the behaviour of an element based on its position in the periodic table

Predict and explain the likely metallic behaviour of caesium and selenium based on their position in the periodic table.

Caesium is on the left-hand side and towards the bottom of the periodic table. Metallic character increases (from right to left) across the periodic table and down the periodic table. This means that caesium will be very reactive towards water, oxygen and the halogens (and other non-metals).

This behaviour is explained by low first ionization energy, low electronegativity and low electron affinity and large atomic radius. Reactive metals form very basic oxides. So caesium oxide is expected to react with water to form caesium hydroxide, which is expected to be fully soluble and completely ionized in water.

Selenium is on the right-hand side and towards the middle of the periodic table. Non-metallic character increases across the periodic table (left to right) and decreases down a group. It is predicted to be a moderately reactive non-metallic element with little metallic behaviour.

This behaviour is explained by moderate values of first ionization energy, electronegativity, electron affinity and atomic radius. Non-metallic oxides are often acidic and react with water. So the oxides of selenium, SeO_2 and SeO_3, are expected to react with water to form acidic solutions of H_2SeO_3 and H_2SeO_4.

6 Predict and explain the expected properties of the element indium.

ToK Link

The periodic table is an excellent example of classification in science. How does classification and categorization help and hinder the pursuit of knowledge?

Classification and categorization are very important in the pursuit of knowledge since they provide a common and agreed medium of communication between scientists. However, they can simultaneously limit what may be considered knowledge in their new field. For example, biology is the study of living organisms. These are often defined as those that are cellular and carry out certain processes, such as respiration, nutrition etc. However, this categorization excludes viruses (Chapters 23 and 25, on the accompanying website), which meet some of the criteria, such as heredity and reproduction. This categorization and classification may hinder the pursuit of knowledge, since without the inclusion of viruses as 'living' organisms, the biological model may be incomplete.

■ Similarities and differences in the properties of the elements in group 1 and group 17

The alkali metals

The alkali metals are a group of very reactive metals. The first three members of the group are lithium, sodium and potassium. Their atomic and physical properties are summarized in Table 3.20. The electrode potentials are a measure of reducing strength (Chapter 19). The more negative the value, the greater the tendency for the atom to lose an electron (in aqueous solution).

■ **Table 3.20**
The atomic and physical properties of three alkali metals

Element	Lithium	Sodium	Potassium
Electron arrangement	2,1	2,8,1	2,8,8,1
Electron configuration	$1s^2\,2s^1$	$1s^2\,2s^2\,2p^6\,3s^1$	$1s^2\,2s^2\,2p^6\,3s^2\,3p^6\,4s^1$
Chemical symbol	Li	Na	K
First ionization energy/kJ mol^{-1}	519	494	418
Atomic radius/nm	0.152	0.186	0.231
Melting point/K	454	371	337
Boiling point/K	1600	1156	1047
Density/g cm^{-3}	0.53	0.97	0.86
Standard electrode potential, $E^{\ominus}$M$^+$(aq) | M(s)/V	−3.03	−2.71	−2.92

Sodium

Sodium is a soft silvery-white metal and an excellent conductor of heat and electricity. It rapidly corrodes in moist air, initially to form sodium oxide, Na_2O. When placed in water sodium floats but immediately reacts with the water (Figure 3.31) to form a solution of sodium hydroxide and hydrogen gas:

$$2Na(s) + 2H_2O(l) \rightarrow 2NaOH(aq) + H_2(g)$$

The heat energy produced by this exothermic reaction (Chapter 5) is sufficient to melt the sodium, but not usually to ignite the hydrogen (unless the sodium is not allowed to move). The sodium burns with a brilliant golden-yellow flame.

Sodium hydroxide is a strong alkali (Chapter 8). It is completely ionized in water and forms a strongly alkaline solution of sodium hydroxide with a high pH:

$$2Na(s) + 2H_2O(l) \rightarrow 2Na^+(aq) + 2OH^-(aq) + H_2(g)$$

This reaction is an example of a redox reaction (Chapter 9), in which the sodium acts as a reducing agent.

■ **Figure 3.31** Reaction between sodium and water

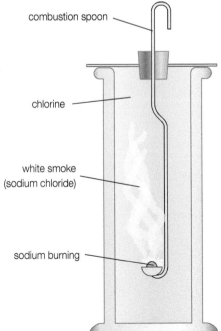

combustion spoon

chlorine

white smoke (sodium chloride)

sodium burning

■ **Figure 3.32** Sodium burning in chlorine

When a piece of hot sodium is lowered into a gas jar of chlorine, the metal continues to burn, forming a white smoke of sodium chloride (Figure 3.32).

$$2Na(s) + Cl_2(g) \rightarrow 2NaCl(s)$$

Similar reactions occur with bromine and iodine to form sodium bromide and sodium iodide, but the reactions are slower and less heat is released.

Potassium and lithium

Potassium is a soft silvery metal that, like sodium, is a good conductor of heat and electricity. The reactions of potassium are less vigorous than corresponding reactions of sodium (partly due to its lower first ionization energy), but the reactions are otherwise identical. Its reaction with water is sufficient to raise the temperature of the hydrogen to its ignition point; the metal burns with a lilac (pale purple) flame.

Lithium is a hard silver metal that has identical reactions to sodium, but slower (partly due to its higher first ionization energy). Lithium and potassium also react with chlorine: the reaction with potassium is faster and more exothermic (compared to sodium); the reaction with lithium is slower and less exothermic (compared to sodium).

The halogens

The halogens are a group of very reactive non-metals. The first three members of the group are chlorine, bromine and iodine. Their atomic and physical properties are summarized in Table 3.21.

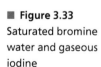

■ **Table 3.21** The atomic and physical properties of the halogens

Element	Chlorine	Bromine	Iodine
Chemical formula	Cl_2	Br_2	I_2
Structure	Cl–Cl	Br–Br	I–I
Electron arrangement	2,8,7	2,8,18,7	2,8,18,18,7
Detailed outer shell arrangement	$3s^2 3p^5$	$4s^2 4p^5$	$5s^2 5p^5$
State at room temperature and pressure	Gas	Liquid	Solid
Colour	Pale green	Red-brown	Black
Melting point/K	172	266	387
Boiling point/K	239	332	458 (sublimes)
Standard electrode potential, $E^\ominus$ $X_2(aq)/X^-(aq)/V$	1.36	1.09	0.54

All the halogens have an outer or valence shell with seven electrons. A full shell or noble gas configuration is obtained by the addition of one extra electron (from a metal) to form a **halide** ion, or by the sharing of electrons to form covalent bonds and hence molecules.

■ **Figure 3.33** Saturated bromine water and gaseous iodine

All the halogens exist as diatomic molecules where two halogen atoms are held together by a single covalent bond (a shared pair of electrons). Diatomic molecules are present in all three physical states.

All the halogens are coloured, with the colour becoming progressively darker as you move down the group (Figure 3.33). The volatility of the halogens decreases down the group as boiling and melting points increase. This decrease correlates with an increase in the strength or extent of London or dispersion forces operating between molecules (Chapter 4). These are weak attractive forces that operate between neighbouring molecules in the liquid and solid states.

Properties of the halogens

Solubility

Halogens are absorbed into organic solvents, such as tetrachloromethane ('carbon tetrachloride') or hexane. In these non-polar solvents chlorine is colourless, bromine is red and iodine is violet. In polar organic solvents such as ethanol ('alcohol') and propanone ('acetone'), bromine and iodine give brownish solutions.

Chlorine is moderately soluble in water, forming a solution known as chlorine water. It contains a mixture of hydrochloric and chloric(I) acids in equilibrium with chlorine molecules. The position of the equilibrium is pH dependent and a low pH (acidic conditions) favours chlorine molecules (Chapter 7).

$$Cl_2(aq) + H_2O(l) \rightleftharpoons HCl(aq) + HOCl(aq)$$
$$\text{chloric(I) acid}$$

Chlorine gas turns moist blue litmus paper red and then decolorizes it (Figure 3.34). The bleaching properties of chlorine water are due to the presence of chlorate(I) ions:

$$HCl(aq) \rightarrow H^+(aq) + Cl^-(aq) \quad HOCl(aq) \rightleftharpoons H^+(aq) + OCl^-(aq)$$
$$\text{chlorate(I) ion}$$

Bromine undergoes a similar reaction to form bromine water. Iodine is slightly soluble in water, but readily soluble in ethanol (Figure 3.35). This is an illustration of the 'like dissolves like' principle (Chapter 4): iodine is non-polar and so is more soluble in ethanol than in water, due to the lower polarity of ethanol.

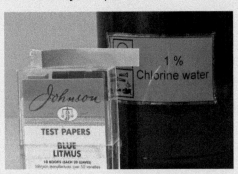

■ **Figure 3.34** The reaction between blue litmus paper and chlorine gas

■ **Figure 3.35** Iodine added to ethanol (on the left) and water (on the right)

Household 'chlorine bleach' is a dilute solution of sodium chlorate(I) (sodium hypochlorite). It is prepared by absorbing chlorine gas into cold sodium hydroxide solution. More concentrated solutions are used to disinfect drinking water and swimming pools. Bleach should never be mixed with other household cleaners. With bleach, acid-based cleaners produce chlorine and ammonia-based products produce toxic chloramines, for example NH_2Cl.

Standard electrode potential

The standard electrode potential (Chapter 19) is a measure of how much tendency a chemical species in solution has to lose or gain electrons. Positive numbers indicate a chemical species (molecule, ion or atom) which is an oxidizing agent – a species which has a high tendency to accept electrons. Negative numbers indicate a chemical species (molecule, ion or atom) which is a reducing agent – a species which has a high tendency to donate electrons.

The decrease in standard electrode potentials indicates that the halogens become progressively less powerful as oxidizing agents as you move down the group, that is, they have a decreasing tendency to accept electrons:

$$X_2(aq) + 2e^- \rightarrow 2X^-(aq)$$

This correlates with the trend for electronegativity, but note that standard electrode potentials are about redox behaviour in solution whereas electronegativity is a bond property.

■ Reactions of the halogens

Replacement reactions

When chlorine water is added to an aqueous solution of potassium bromide, KBr, the solution becomes yellow-orange owing to the formation of bromine:

$$Cl_2(aq) + 2Br^-(aq) \rightarrow Br_2(aq) + 2Cl^-(aq)$$

Chlorine also reacts with potassium iodide solution to form a brown solution of iodine:

$$Cl_2(aq) + 2I^-(aq) \rightarrow I_2(aq) + 2Cl^-(aq)$$

The two reactions shown above for chlorine are known as replacement reactions and involve a more reactive halogen, chlorine, replacing or 'pushing out' a less reactive halogen from its salt.

These are redox reactions – the halogen acts as an oxidizing agent and the halide ion acts as a reducing agent (Chapter 9). There is a transfer of electrons from the iodide ions and bromide ions to the chlorine molecules. Going down group 17 the halogens become more weakly oxidizing and the halide ions become more strongly reducing.

Bromine water will give a replacement reaction with a solution of an iodide:

$$Br_2(aq) + 2I^-(aq) \rightarrow I_2(aq) + 2Br^-(aq)$$

However, as bromine is less reactive than chlorine, it is unable to replace chloride ions and no reaction occurs. Iodine, being the most unreactive halogen, is unable to replace bromide or chloride ions and no reaction occurs.

Additional Perspectives

Explaining trends in the behaviour of the halogens

The trends in oxidizing and reducing power for the halogens and the halide ions can be easily explained in terms of the relative sizes of the halogen atoms and halide ions (Figure 3.36). A halide ion is oxidized by the removal of one of its outer eight electrons. In a large halide ion, the outer electrons are more easily removed as they are further from the nucleus and more effectively shielded from its attraction by the inner electrons. Small halide ions have their outer electrons located closer to the nucleus and less effective shielding occurs, hence their affinity for electrons is higher. A similar argument explains why a small halogen atom can attract an extra electron with a greater affinity than a larger halogen atom.

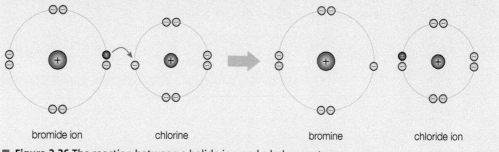

bromide ion   chlorine   bromine   chloride ion

■ **Figure 3.36** The reaction between a halide ion and a halogen atom

Reactions of the halide ions

The term halide ions collectively refers to fluoride, F^-, chloride, Cl^-, bromide, Br^- and iodide, I^-, ions which are present in metal salts, for example sodium chloride, NaCl [Na^+ Cl^-].

Halide ions are colourless, but the four halide ions may be distinguished from each other in solution by the use of silver nitrate solution (acidified with nitric acid).

With a solution of a chloride salt, silver nitrate gives a white precipitate of silver chloride (Figure 3.37), for example:

$$NaCl(aq) + AgNO_3(aq) \rightarrow NaNO_3(aq) + AgCl(s)$$

or ionically:

$$Cl^-(aq) + Ag^+(aq) \rightarrow AgCl(s)$$

The silver chloride rapidly turns purple in sunlight due to photodecomposition:

$$2AgCl(s) \rightarrow 2Ag(s) + Cl_2(g)$$

Bromides and iodides give cream and yellow precipitates of silver bromide and silver iodide (Figure 3.38), respectively:

$$Br^-(aq) + Ag^+(aq) \rightarrow AgBr(s)$$
$$I^-(aq) + Ag^+(aq) \rightarrow AgI(s)$$

(Fluorides do not give any precipitate with acidified silver nitrate solution since silver fluoride is soluble.)

■ **Figure 3.37**
The precipitation of silver chloride

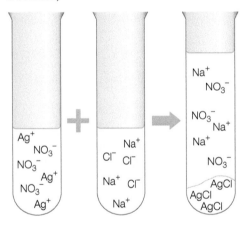

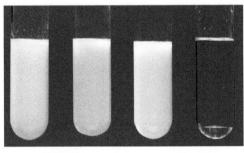

■ **Figure 3.38** The colours of the silver halides – from left to right, silver iodide, silver bromide, silver chloride and silver fluoride

Trends in properties of the oxides in period 3

Metallic oxides tend to be ionic and hence basic. The more reactive metals form oxides that react with water to form alkaline solutions:

$$Na_2O(s) + H_2O(l) \rightarrow 2NaOH(aq)$$
$$MgO(s) + H_2O(l) \rightarrow Mg(OH)_2(aq)$$

Non-metallic oxides tend to be covalent and **acidic**. The more reactive non-metals (Figure 3.39) form oxides that react with water to form acidic solutions.

$$P_4O_{10}(s) + 6H_2O(l) \rightarrow 4H_3PO_4(aq)$$
$$SO_3(g) + H_2O(l) \rightarrow H_2SO_4(aq)$$

or

$$SO_3(g) + H_2O(l) \rightarrow H_2SO_4(aq) \rightleftharpoons H^+(aq) + HSO_4^-(aq)$$

■ **Figure 3.39**
Partially hydrolysed phosphorus(v) oxide, P_4O_{10}

Aluminium oxide

Unlike sodium and magnesium oxides, aluminium oxide does not react with water, although it does react slowly with warm, dilute aqueous solutions of dilute acids to form salts, for example:

$$Al_2O_3(s) + 6HCl(aq) \rightarrow 2AlCl_3(aq) + 3H_2O(l)$$

$$Al_2O_3(s) + 6H^+(aq) \rightarrow 2Al^{3+}(aq) + 3H_2O(l)$$

Aluminium oxide also reacts with warm concentrated solutions of strong alkalis to form aluminates, for example:

$$Al_2O_3(s) + 2NaOH(aq) + 3H_2O(l) \rightarrow 2NaAl(OH)_4(aq)$$

$$Al_2O_3(s) + 2OH^-(aq) + 3H_2O(l) \rightarrow 2Al(OH)_4(aq)$$

Aluminium oxide is amphoteric since it reacts with both acids and bases. Amphoteric oxides are likely to be formed by metals near the division between metals and non-metals.

Table 3.22 summarizes the formulas and properties of the oxides of period 3 elements.

■ **Table 3.22** Formula and properties of the oxides of period 3 elements

Formula	Na_2O	MgO	Al_2O_3	SiO_2	P_4O_6 and P_4O_{10}	SO_2 and SO_3	Cl_2O and Cl_2O_7
Physical state under standard conditions	Solid	Solid	Solid	Solid	Solids	Gas and volatile solid	Gas and solid
Bonding	Ionic	Ionic	Ionic (with covalent character)	Giant covalent	Simple covalent	Simple covalent	Simple covalent
Acid–base nature	Basic	Basic	Amphoteric	Weakly acidic	Weakly acidic	Strongly acidic	Strongly acidic

Constructing the equations to explain the pH changes in reactions of Na_2O, MgO, P_4O_{10}, and the oxides of nitrogen and sulfur with water

Sodium oxide

Sodium oxide is a simple strongly basic oxide. It is basic because it contains the oxide ion, O^{2-}, which is a very strong base with a high tendency to combine with hydrogen ions.

Sodium oxide reacts exothermically (heat is released) with cold water to produce sodium hydroxide solution. Depending on its concentration, this will have a pH around 14. This is a chemical reaction with water and is known as a hydrolysis reaction.

■ Unbalanced (conversion of reactants to products):

$$Na_2O(s) + H_2O(l) \rightarrow NaOH(aq)$$

■ Balanced:

$$Na_2O(s)(aq) + H_2O(l) \rightarrow 2NaOH(aq)$$

■ Ionically:

$$O^{2-}(aq) + H_2O(l) \rightarrow 2OH^-(aq)$$

Magnesium oxide

Magnesium oxide is a simple basic oxide, because it also contains oxide ions. However, it is not as strongly basic as sodium oxide because the ionic bonding is stronger.

In the case of sodium oxide, the solid is held together by electrostatic attractions between 1+ and 2− ions. In the magnesium oxide, the electrostatic attractions are between 2+ and 2−. It takes more energy to break this ionic bonding.

As a result, reactions involving magnesium oxide will always be less exothermic than those of sodium oxide. In addition the reaction with water is reversible, which lowers the pH to 9.

■ Balanced:

$$MgO(s) + H_2O(l) \rightleftharpoons Mg(OH)_2(aq)$$

■ Ionically:

$$O^{2-}(aq) + H_2O(l) \rightleftharpoons 2OH^-(aq)$$

Oxides of sulfur

Sulfur dioxide is fairly soluble in water, reacting with it to give a solution of sulfurous acid (sulfuric(IV) acid), H_2SO_3. This only exists in solution, and any attempt to isolate it just causes sulfur dioxide to be given off again.

$$SO_2(g) + H_2O(l) \rightarrow H_2SO_3(aq)$$

Sulfur trioxide reacts violently with water to form a solution of sulfuric(VI) acid:

$$SO_3(g) + H_2O(l) \rightarrow H_2SO_4(aq)$$

Phosphorus(v) oxide

Phosphorus(v) oxide reacts violently with water to form a solution of phosphoric(v) oxide, a weak acid. This is another example of hydrolysis, where water is involved in a chemical reaction.

■ Unbalanced (conversion of reactants to products):

$$P_4O_{10}(s) + H_2O(l) \rightarrow H_3PO_4(aq)$$

■ Balanced:

$$P_4O_{10}(s) + 6H_2O(l) \rightarrow 4H_3PO_4(aq)$$

Oxides of nitrogen

Nitrogen dioxide, NO_2, is a brown gas produced from the reaction of nitrogen and oxygen gases in the air during combustion, especially at high temperatures. In areas of high motor vehicle traffic, such as in large cities, the amount of nitrogen oxides emitted into the atmosphere as air pollution can be significant.

The following chemical reaction occurs when nitrogen dioxide (nitrogen(IV) oxide) reacts with water:

$$2NO_2(g) + H_2O(l) \rightarrow HNO_2(aq) + HNO_3(aq)$$

Nitric(III) acid (nitrous acid) then decomposes as follows:

$$3HNO_2(aq) \rightarrow HNO_3(aq) + 2\,NO(g) + H_2O(l)$$

and the nitrogen monoxide will oxidize to form nitrogen dioxide that again reacts with water, ultimately forming nitric acid:

$$4NO(g) + 3O_2(g) + 2H_2O(l) \rightarrow 4HNO_3(aq)$$

 Utilization: Acid rain

Pure rain water is slightly acidic and has a pH of about 5.6. This acidity is caused by carbon dioxide in the atmosphere reacting with rain droplets to form carbonic acid. Rain water with a pH of less than 5.6 is termed acid rain. The main acids present in acid rain are sulfuric acid (H_2SO_4) and nitric acid (HNO_3).

The sulfuric acid in acid rain is formed from sulfur dioxide in the atmosphere. Sulfur dioxide is released from volcanoes, but the majority comes from the burning of sulfur-containing fuels, primarily coal in power stations. Car exhaust emissions and the smelting of metals, such as zinc, also contribute to sulfur dioxide pollution. The sulfur dioxide undergoes oxidation to form sulfur trioxide which reacts with water to form sulfuric acid. Sulfur dioxide also reacts with water to form sulfurous acid, H_2SO_3.

The nitric acid present in acid rain is formed from oxides of nitrogen, nitrogen monoxide, NO, and nitrogen dioxide, NO_2. These two oxides are produced during combustion processes, especially those in car engines and in power stations. Nitrogen monoxide is rapidly oxidized by air to nitrogen dioxide, which reacts with water in the presence of oxygen to form nitric acid.

Acid rain causes direct and indirect damage to the environment. In lakes it can directly kill a variety of organisms, such as young fish and insect larvae. Acidic water releases aluminium ions from rocks and soil which are washed into lakes. Aluminium ions are toxic and interfere with the gills of fish, preventing them from extracting dissolved oxygen from the water.

Trees, especially, those at high altitudes, are prone to damage by both acid rain and gaseous sulfur dioxide. The trees drop their leaves and can no longer photosynthesize. Ozone at this level near the ground also plays a role in damaging trees and in catalysing the formation of sulfur trioxide from sulfur dioxide.

Acid rain can also cause damage to building materials and historical monuments (Figure 3.40). This is because the sulfuric acid in the rain chemically reacts with the calcium carbonate ($CaCO_3$) in limestone or marble to create calcium sulfate, which then flakes off.

$$CaCO_3(s) + H_2SO_4(aq) \rightarrow CaSO_4(aq) + CO_2(g) + H_2O(l)$$

Acid rain also reacts with iron and promotes its oxidation to soluble iron(II) ions.

Sulfur dioxide is just one example of a product that has caused global problems when released into the environment. Acid rain is a problem in a number of countries, such as the United Kingdom, China, India, South Africa and some European countries. Acid rain is also a trans-boundary problem since acid rain produced in one country can be blown by the prevailing winds into a neighbouring country (Figure 3.41).

Heavy metals, such as mercury, and certain organic compounds have long life-times in water and cause global pollution. CFC production and emission of greenhouse gases, such as carbon dioxide, are responsible for the global problems of ozone depletion and global warming.

■ **Figure 3.40** Gravestones eroded by carbonic acid and acid rain

■ **Figure 3.41** Trees from the Czech Republic damaged by acid rain

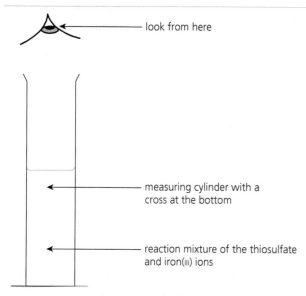

— look from here

— measuring cylinder with a cross at the bottom

— reaction mixture of the thiosulfate and iron(III) ions

■ **Figure 3.42** Investigating catalysis in the reaction between thiosulfate and iron(III) ions

7 Transition metals and their compounds often act as catalysts and increase the rates of reactions, without undergoing a permanent chemical change.

Manganese compounds are being developed as catalysts to absorb sulfur dioxide from power stations and convert it directly to sulfuric acid in one step.

The reaction between sodium thiosulfate and iron(III) nitrate is catalysed by copper(II), nickel(II), cobalt(II) and iron(II) ions.

$$2Fe^{3+}(aq) + 2S_2O_3^{2-}(aq) \rightarrow 2Fe^{2+}(aq) + S_4O_6^{2-}(aq)$$

A cross is drawn on a piece of paper and put underneath a measuring cylinder so it can be seen when looking down the cylinder from the top (Figure 3.42). Iron(III) nitrate and sodium thiosulfate solutions are poured in and the time recorded until the cross cannot be seen. The experiment can then be treated with a few drops of each catalyst. The most effective catalyst is the one with the shortest reaction time.

Design an investigation that controls the variables, to allow you to establish the most effective catalyst in this reaction.

■ *Examination questions – a selection*

Paper 1 IB questions and IB style questions

Q1 Which element shows chemical behaviour similar to calcium?
- **A** strontium
- **B** chlorine
- **C** sodium
- **D** boron

Q2 The following are three statements concerning the periodic table.
- **I** The horizontal rows are called periods and the vertical columns are called groups.
- **II** Electronegativity decreases down any group and across a period from left to right.
- **III** Reactivity increases down all groups.

Which of the above is/are true?
- **A** I, II and III
- **B** I and II only
- **C** II and III only
- **D** I only

Q3 Which is the correct trend (left to right) across period 3 for the oxides?
- **A** basic to acidic
- **B** acidic to basic
- **C** increasingly basic
- **D** neutral to acidic

Q4 What happens when chlorine water is added to an aqueous solution of potassium iodide?
- **A** No reaction occurs because chlorine is less reactive than iodine.
- **B** Chlorine molecules are oxidized to chloride ions.
- **C** Iodide ions are oxidized to iodine molecules.
- **D** A purple precipitate of iodine is formed.

Q5 Which of the following best determines the order in which the elements are arranged in the modern form of the periodic table?
- **A** relative atomic mass
- **B** mass number
- **C** atomic number
- **D** chemical reactivity

Q6 Which is a correct statement about the element with an atomic number of 20?
- **A** It is in group 14.
- **B** It is in group 2.
- **C** It is a transition metal.
- **D** It is in group 17 and is a halogen.

Q7 In general, atomic radii decrease:
- **A** within a group from lower to higher atomic number
- **B** within a period from lower to higher atomic number
- **C** with an increase in the number of isotopes of an element
- **D** with an increase in the shielding of the nuclear charge

Q8 When the elements are listed in order of increasing reactivity with air, the correct order is:
- **A** Na, K, Cs
- **B** Cs, K, Na
- **C** Cs, Na, K
- **D** K, Cs, Na

Q9 For which type of isoelectronic ions do ionic radii decrease with increasing nuclear charge?
- **A** positive ions only
- **B** negative ions only
- **C** neither positive or negative ions
- **D** both positive and negative ions

Q10 Which properties are typical of most non-metals in period 3 (Na to Ar)?
- **I** They form ions by gaining one or more electrons.
- **II** They are poor conductors of heat and electricity.
- **III** They have high melting points.

- **A** I and II only
- **B** I and III only
- **C** II and III only
- **D** I, II and III

Standard Level Paper 1, Nov 2005, Q7

Q11 On the periodic table, groups of elements show similarities in their chemical properties. This can be best explained by the:
- **A** differences in the number of protons in the nucleus of the atoms
- **B** similarities in the results of emission spectrum analysis of gaseous samples of a group
- **C** similarities in the electronic structures of the atoms
- **D** differences in the number of neutrons in the nucleus of the atoms

Q12 Which atom has the smallest atomic radius?
- **A** $_{31}Ga$
- **B** $_{20}Ca$
- **C** $_{35}Br$
- **D** $_{37}Rb$

Q13 Which one of the following series represents the correct size order for the various iodine species?
- **A** $I < I^- < I^+$
- **B** $I < I^+ < I^-$
- **C** $I^+ < I < I^-$
- **D** $I^- < I < I^+$

Q14 Which one of the following will be observed as the atomic number of the elements in a single group of elements on the periodic table increases?
- **A** an increase in atomic radius
- **B** an increase in ionization energy and hence decrease in reactivity
- **C** a decrease in ionic radius
- **D** an increase in electronegativity

Q15 Which of the following properties of the halogens increase from F to I?
- **I** atomic radius
- **II** melting point
- **III** electronegativity

- **A** I only
- **B** I and II only
- **C** I and III only
- **D** I, II and III

Standard Level Paper 1, Nov 2003, Q7

Q16 In general, how do ionization energies vary as the periodic table is crossed from left to right?
- **A** They remain constant.
- **B** They increase.
- **C** They increase to a maximum and then decrease.
- **D** They decrease.

Q17 0.01 mol samples of the following oxides were added to separate 1 dm³ portions of water. Which will produce the most acidic solution?

A $Al_2O_3(s)$ **C** $Na_2O(s)$
B $SiO_2(s)$ **D** $SO_3(g)$

Q18 Which property increases with increasing atomic number for both the alkali metals and the halogens?

A melting points   **C** electronegativities
B first ionization energies   **D** atomic radii

Q19 Which one of the following elements has the lowest first ionization energy?

A Li   **C** B
B Na   **D** Mg

Q20 Barium, with an atomic number of 56, is an element in group 2 of the periodic table (below strontium with atomic number 38). Which of the following statements about barium is not correct?

A Its first ionization energy is lower than that of strontium.
B It has two electrons in its outermost energy level.
C Its atomic radius is smaller than that of strontium.
D It forms a chloride with the formula $BaCl_2$.

Q21 Which element is in the f-block of the periodic table?

A Ba   **C** Sn
B Gd   **D** W

Q22 Element X is in group 5 and period 4 of the periodic table. Which statement is correct?

A X has 5 occupied energy levels.
B X can form ions with 3⁻ charge.
C X is a transition element.
D X has 4 valence electrons.

Higher Level Paper 1, Nov 2013, Q6

Q23 Which statements are correct for the alkali metals Li to Cs?

I Melting point increases
II First ionization energy decreases
III Ionic radius increases

A I and II only   **C** II and III only
B I and III only   **D** I, II and III

Higher Level Paper 1, Nov 2013, Q7

Q24 An element has the following successive ionization energies (kJ mol⁻¹): 967, 1951, 2732, 4852, 6020, 12 400, 15 450 and 18 900. In which group of the periodic table is this element most likely to be found?

A Group 1   **C** Group 13
B Group 2   **D** Group 15

Paper 2 IB questions and IB style questions

Q1 **a** **i** Define the term ionization energy. [2]
     ii Write an equation, including state symbols, for the process occurring when measuring the first ionization energy of aluminium. [1]
   b Explain why the first ionization energy of magnesium is greater than that of sodium. [3]
   c Lithium reacts with water. Write an equation for the reaction and state two observations that could be made during the reaction. [3]

Standard Level Paper 2, Nov 2005, Q4

Q2 **a** **i** Explain why the ionic radius of bromine is less than that of selenium. [2]
     ii Explain what is meant by the term electronegativity and explain why the electronegativity of fluorine is greater than that of chlorine. [3]
   b For each of the following reactions in aqueous solution, state one observation that would be made, and deduce the equation.
     i The reaction between chlorine and potassium iodide. [2]
     ii The reaction between silver ions and bromide ions. [2]
   c Deduce whether or not each of the reactions in **b** is a redox reaction, giving a reason in each case. [4]

Q3 **a** What factors determine the size of an atom or ion? [3]
   b **i** Explain why the ionic radius of sodium is much smaller than its atomic radius. [2]
     ii Explain why the cations of group 1 increase in size with increasing atomic number. [2]
   c Explain why the ionic radius of Mg^{2+} is less than that of Na^+. [2]
   d Arrange the following species in order of increasing size:
     i N, N^{3-} [1]
     ii Fe, Fe^{2+} and Fe^{3+} [1]

Q4 Describe and explain the variation in ionic radius of the elements across period 3 from sodium to chlorine. [6]

Q5 For the elements of period 3 (Na to Ar), state and explain:
   a the general trend in ionization energy [2]
   b any exceptions to the general trend. [4]

Q6 Describe the acid–base character of the oxides of the period 3 elements Na to Ar. [3]

Chemical bonding and structure

4.1 Ionic bonding and structure – *ionic compounds are held together in lattice structures by ionic bonds*

■ Ionic bonding

Ionic bonding occurs when one or more electrons are transferred from the outer shell of one atom to the outer shell of another atom. The atom losing an electron or electrons forms a positively charged ion (cation) and the atom gaining an electron or electrons forms a negatively charged ion (anion). Ionic bonding is the electrostatic attraction between oppositely charged ions (Figure 4.1).

■ **Figure 4.1** Electron rearrangement during **a** covalent bonding and **b** ionic bonding

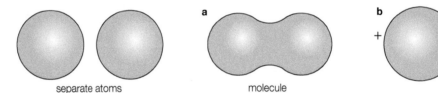

separate atoms   molecule   ions

Ionic bonding is described as non-directional since each ion is attracted to every other ion of opposite charge, though the attraction decreases with distance. In contrast, covalent bonding involves the sharing of electron pairs between atoms and is directional.

■ Formation of ions by electron transfer

The formation of an ionic compound typically involves the reaction between a metal and a non-metal. An example of ionic bond formation involves the reaction between sodium and chlorine to form sodium chloride.

The electron arrangements of the sodium and chlorine atoms are:

sodium atom, Na	2,8,1
chlorine atom, Cl	2,8,7

The ionic bonding in sodium chloride occurs when the valence electron from the third shell of the sodium atom is transferred to the chlorine atom.

The electron arrangements of the sodium and chloride ions are:

sodium ion, Na^+	2,8
chloride ion, Cl^-	2,8,8

These ions have stable noble gas electron arrangements: the sodium ion has the electron arrangement of neon and the chloride ion has the electron arrangement of argon.

The ionic bonding in sodium chloride can also be described in terms of electron configurations. The sodium atom has the configuration $1s^2\, 2s^2\, 2p^6\, 3s^1$ and the chlorine atom is $1s^2\, 2s^2\, 2p^6\, 3s^2\, 3p^5$. In the formation of sodium chloride, the electron in the 3s orbital of sodium is transferred to the half-filled 3p orbital of the chlorine atom. The sodium ion has the configuration $1s^2\, 2s^2\, 2p^6$ and the chloride ion has the configuration $1s^2\, 2s^2\, 2p^6\, 3s^2\, 3p^6$.

Lewis diagrams can be used to represent the transfer of electrons that occurs during the formation of ionic bonds. For example, the reaction between sodium and chlorine atoms is described in Figure 4.2 using Lewis diagrams.

■ Figure 4.2
Ionic bonding in sodium chloride, NaCl showing **a** all electrons and **b** only the outer or valence electrons. The curved arrow indicates the transfer of an electron from the sodium atom to the chlorine atom

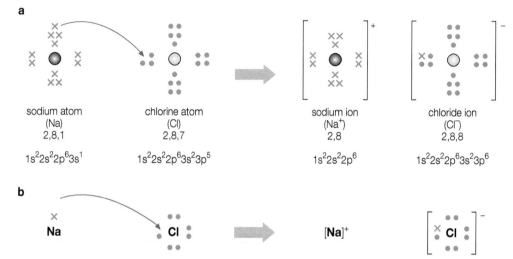

a

sodium atom
(Na)
2,8,1
$1s^22s^22p^63s^1$

chlorine atom
(Cl)
2,8,7
$1s^22s^22p^63s^23p^5$

sodium ion
(Na$^+$)
2,8
$1s^22s^22p^6$

chloride ion
(Cl$^-$)
2,8,8
$1s^22s^22p^63s^23p^6$

b

Na   Cl   [Na]$^+$ [× Cl :]$^-$

The ions will be arranged into a regular arrangement (Figure 4.3) known as a lattice. Within the lattice, oppositely charged ions attract and ions of the same charge repel each other. However, there is an overall, or net, attractive force. The strength of an ionic lattice is measured by its lattice enthalpy. The lattice enthalpy is the energy required to decompose one mole of an ionic lattice into gaseous ions (Chapter 15).

A sodium atom and a sodium ion have *very different* properties. For example, sodium ions dissolve in water without a chemical reaction. In contrast, sodium atoms react with water to form sodium ions. These differences occur because the sodium ion is charged and has a stable electron arrangement. A sodium

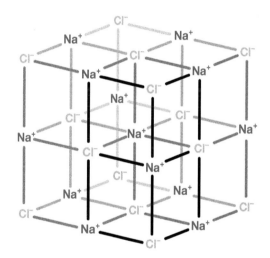

■ Figure 4.3 Ionic lattice for sodium chloride

ion has the same electron arrangement as an argon atom, but they have different properties because the sodium ion is charged and has a different number of protons in its nucleus.

Figure 4.4 shows the electron transfer that takes place during the formation of calcium fluoride. A calcium atom (2,8,8,2) obtains a full outer shell by losing two electrons. These are transferred, one to each of the fluorine atoms (2,7). A compound is formed containing two fluoride ions, F$^-$, for each calcium ion, Ca^{2+}. The formula of the compound is CaF$_2$. Ionic compounds are always electrically neutral.

1 Describe the formations of calcium fluoride, sodium oxide and aluminium oxide in terms of electron configurations of the atoms involved and the ions formed after electron transfer.

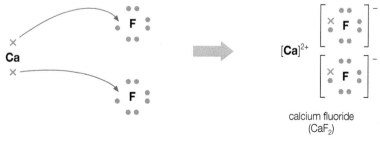

calcium fluoride
(CaF$_2$)

■ Figure 4.4 Simplified diagram of the ionic bonding in calcium fluoride, CaF$_2$

Positive ions are often referred to as cations because they move towards the cathode (negative electrode) when placed in an electric field. Negative ions move towards the anode (positive electrode), so they are termed anions (Chapter 9).

Formation of ions by elements in groups 1, 2 and 13

The elements in groups 1, 2 and 13 have only 1, 2 or 3 electrons in their outer shell. These elements at the beginning of a period *lose* electrons to form positive ions (cations). The resulting simple ions obey the octet rule (eight electrons in the outer shell) and have an electron arrangement like the noble gas at the end of the previous period.

Examples: $Na \rightarrow Na^+ + e^-$ Na^+, Mg^{2+} and Al^{3+} all have
            $Mg \rightarrow Mg^{2+} + 2e^-$ the same electronic
            $Al \rightarrow Al^{3+} + 3e^-$ structure as Ne.

Formation of ions by elements in groups 15, 16 and 17

The elements in groups 15, 16 and 17 have 5, 6 or 7 electrons in their outer shell. These elements near the end of the period *gain* electrons to form negative ions (anions). The resulting simple ions obey the octet rule and have an electron arrangement like the noble gas at the end of the period.

Examples: $P + 3e^- \rightarrow P^{3-}$ P^{3-}, S^{2-} and Cl^- all have the
            $S + 2e^- \rightarrow S^{2-}$ same electronic structure
            $Cl + e^- \rightarrow Cl^-$ as Ar.

Elements in groups 14 and 18

The elements in group 18 have full outer shells of electrons. This is a stable electron arrangement and these elements only form compounds with the most reactive elements, notably fluorine. The first two elements in group 14, carbon and silicon, have outer shells which are half full. These two elements generally do not form simple ions but instead form covalent bonds. (However, carbon reacts with metals to form a number of metal carbides.)

Table 4.1 shows the electron arrangements of the atoms and simple ions of the elements in period 3 of the periodic table.

2   Prepare a similar table for the elements in period 2.

Group	1	2	13	14	15	16	17	18
Element	Sodium	Magnesium	Aluminium	Silicon	Phosphorus	Sulfur	Chlorine	Argon
Electron arrangement	2,8,1	2,8,2	2,8,3	2,8,4	2,8,5	2,8,6	2,8,7	2,8,8
Electron configuration	$1s^2\,2s^2\,2p^6$ $3s^1$	$1s^2\,2s^2\,2p^6$ $3s^2$	$1s^2\,2s^2\,2p^6$ $3s^2\,3p^1$	$1s^2\,2s^2\,2p^6$ $3s^2\,3p^2$	$1s^2\,2s^2\,2p^6$ $3s^2\,3p^3$	$1s^2\,2s^2\,2p^6$ $3s^2\,3p^4$	$1s^2\,2s^2\,2p^6$ $3s^2\,3p^5$	$1s^2\,2s^2\,2p^6$ $3s^2\,3p^6$
Number of electrons in outer shell	1	2	3	4	5	6	7	8
Common simple ion	Na^+	Mg^{2+}	Al^{3+}	–	P^{3-} (phosphide)	S^{2-} (sulfide)	Cl^- (chloride)	–
Electron arrangement of ion	2,8	2,8	2,8	–	2,8,8	2,8,8	2,8,8	–
Electron configuration of ion	$1s^2\,2s^2\,2p^6$	$1s^2\,2s^2\,2p^6$	$1s^2\,2s^2\,2p^6$		$1s^2\,2s^2\,2p^6$ $3s^2\,3p^6$	$1s^2\,2s^2\,2p^6$ $3s^2\,3p^6$	$1s^2\,2s^2\,2p^6$ $3s^2\,3p^6$	–

■ **Table 4.1** Electron arrangements of the atoms and simple ions of the elements in period 3

The octet rule

All noble gas atoms (except helium) have eight valence electrons. Around 1920 the American chemist Gilbert Lewis observed that atoms of elements in groups 1 to 2 and 13 to 17 tended to gain, lose or share electrons so that they are surrounded by eight valence electrons. This is because the electronic configurations of the noble gas atoms are very stable. The tendency of many atoms in compounds to achieve noble gas configurations is termed the 'octet rule'. An octet of electrons is four pairs of valence electrons arranged around the atom. The octet rule applies to both ionic and covalent bonds. However, the octet rule is not observed for elements beyond the second period of the periodic table as these elements have more than four valence orbitals available for bonding. Lewis made many contributions to physical chemistry. In 1916 he proposed the idea that a covalent bond consisted of a shared pair of electrons. In 1923 he formulated the electron pair theory of acid–base reactions, now known as Lewis theory (Chapter 8). He also made contributions to thermodynamics and was the first scientist to prepare 'heavy water', $^2_1H_2O$.

ToK Link

General rules in chemistry (like the octet rule) often have exceptions. How many exceptions have to exist for a rule to cease to be useful?

There are a number of general exceptions to the octet rule: electron deficient compounds in which the central atom has an incomplete octet, free radicals (with an unpaired electron), molecules whose central atom is surrounded by more than eight electrons (an expanded octet) and compounds of hydrogen and the transition metals (d-block) and lanthanoids (f-block).

However, the octet rule is useful for describing the bonding in the majority of familiar compounds. It is useful in introducing a simple

(although flawed) model of chemical bonding based on pairing of electrons and achieving noble gas configurations.

Chemistry is a subtle and complicated subject and hence has many empirical 'rules' (sometimes without any firm theoretical foundation) but very few 'laws' – most of which are strongly grounded in physics. 'Rules' are meant to be 'broken', but 'laws' are meant to be 'obeyed'.

There is no definite number of exceptions for a rule in chemistry to cease to be useful and to be discarded. This is decided by an active dialogue within the chemical community.

Ions of the transition elements

Most of the transition elements form more than one stable positive ion. For example, copper forms copper(I), Cu^+, and copper(II), Cu^{2+}, and iron forms iron(II), Fe^{2+}, and iron(III), Fe^{3+}. The Roman number indicates the oxidation number of the transition metal (Chapter 9). It is helpful if the charges on the simple positive ions are learnt, and those most commonly encountered are summarized in Table 4.2. A charge of +2 is the most common charge on a transition metal simple ion.

Name of transition metal	Simple positive ions
Silver	Ag^+
Iron	Fe^{2+}, Fe^{3+}
Copper	Cu^+, Cu^{2+}
Manganese	Mn^{2+}, Mn^{3+} and Mn^{4+}
Chromium	Cr^{3+} and Cr^{2+} (not stable in air)

■ **Table 4.2** Charges on selected transition element ions

The formulas of ionic compounds are *empirical* formulas (Chapter 1). For example, sodium chloride consists of a lattice containing a large number of sodium and chloride ions in a 1 : 1 ratio. Each sodium ion is attracted to every chloride ion; each chloride ion is attracted to every sodium ion. However, no molecules are present and thus only an empirical formula, NaCl, can be written. If the ionic nature is to be emphasized, then the formula may be written as $[Na^+Cl^-]$.

Additional Perspectives

Electron configurations of selected atoms and ions

Gallium is a group 13 metal with the following electron configuration:

$1s^2\,2s^2\,2p^6\,3s^2\,3p^6\,3d^{10}\,4s^2\,4p^1$

The gallium(III) ion is formed by the loss of three valence electrons. The electron configuration of the gallium(III) ion, Ga^{3+}, is:

$1s^2\,2s^2\,2p^6\,3s^2\,3p^6\,3d^{10}$

A noble gas core with an outer d^{10} configuration is known as a pseudo-noble gas configuration. A d^{10} cation is stable because the third shell is completely filled with 18 electrons, with 10 electrons in the d sub-shell.

The iron(II) ion (Fe^{2+}) is unstable in solution, whereas the iron(III) ion (Fe^{3+}) is stable. Iron(II) compounds are readily oxidized to iron(III) compounds. In contrast, the manganese(II) ion (Mn^{2+}) is stable, whereas the manganese(III) ion (Mn^{3+}) is unstable.

Fe^{2+}	$1s^2\,2s^2\,2p^6\,3s^2\,3p^6\,3d^6$
Fe^{3+}	$1s^2\,2s^2\,2p^6\,3s^2\,3p^6\,3d^5$
Mn^{2+}	$1s^2\,2s^2\,2p^6\,3s^2\,3p^6\,3d^5$
Mn^{3+}	$1s^2\,2s^2\,2p^6\,3s^2\,3p^6\,3d^4$

The iron(III) and manganese(II) ions are stable because of the special stability associated with the half-filled 3d sub-shell (d^5 configuration) (Chapter 13).

Why ionic compounds form

It should be emphasized that ionic bonding is *not* driven by the transfer of electrons in order for ions to achieve stable noble gas configurations. The electron affinities of some atoms are exothermic and release energy, but the removal of electrons from atoms and ions requires energy, so ionization is always an endothermic process (Chapter 3). The driving force for the formation of ionic compounds is that when ions are brought close together in an ionic crystal the favourable electrostatic forces of attraction more than outweigh the energy changes required for ion formation (in the gas phase) (see Chapter 15 for a discussion of lattice enthalpy and the Born–Haber cycle).

Physical state of ionic compounds under standard conditions

Ionic compounds are usually solids at room temperature and pressure. They form crystals and melt at relatively high temperatures. This is due to the presence of very strong attractive forces operating between oppositely charged ions. Consequently, large amounts of thermal energy are required to overcome the strong inter-ionic forces. The strong ionic bonding means that ionically bonded substances have low volatility. This means they have high melting and boiling points and undergo negligible evaporation at temperatures below their boiling point.

Utilization: Ionic liquids as solvents

Ionic liquids are salts that are liquids at room temperature. They have a number of advantages over the organic solvents traditionally used in industry. Ionic liquids are not volatile and so they do not evaporate and escape into the atmosphere. They dissolve a range of polar organic compounds, are stable to heating to fairly high temperatures and are non-flammable. They can also be easily recovered from reaction mixtures and re-used. Ionic liquids are also known as designer solvents because different combinations of positive and negative ions produce ionic liquids with different properties. Chemists are now investigating the possibility of using ionic liquids instead of the toxic and volatile organic solvents currently used in many industrial processes. This is an example of green chemistry.

Figure 4.5 shows the structure of an ionic liquid that contains an organic positive ion and an inorganic negative ion. Ionic liquids are also being explored as heat exchange substances in power generation. They may be suitable for transforming the heat from comparatively low temperature sources, including solar, geothermal, combustion waste heat and bottom cycling of existing power plants, into high value power generation.

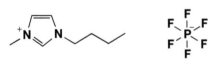

■ **Figure 4.5** Structure of ([BMIM] [PF$_6$])

■ Predicting the type of bonding from electronegativity values

Ionic bonding between two elements typically occurs when a metal is chemically bonded with a non-metal. Hence, the bonding in the compound barium fluoride, BaF$_2$, is predicted to be ionic since barium is a metal and fluorine a non-metal.

Ionic bonding is favoured if the metal and non-metal elements are reactive. The reactivity of metals and non-metals can be assessed using electronegativity values (Chapter 3). Ionic bonding is most likely when there is a large difference in electronegativity values between the two elements.

The electronegativity (Table 4.3) of an atom is the ability or power of an atom in a covalent bond to attract shared pairs of electrons to itself. The greater the electronegativity of an atom, the greater its ability to attract shared pairs of electrons to itself. The most electronegative elements are highly reactive non-metals and the least electronegative elements are the reactive metals.

Electronegativity generally increases on passing across a period, because of the increasing nuclear charge and decreasing atomic radius. Electronegativity decreases on moving down a group since the combined effects of increasing atomic size and the shielding effect outweigh the increase in nuclear charge (Chapter 3).

■ Table 4.3
Electronegativity
values (Pauling scale)

												H 2.2							He
Li 1.0	Be 1.6												B 2.0	C 2.6	N 3.0	O 3.4	F 4.0	Ne	
Na 0.9	Mg 1.3												Al 1.6	Si 1.9	P 2.2	S 2.6	Cl 3.2	Ar	
K 0.8	Ca 1.0	Sc 1.4	Ti 1.5	V 1.6	Cr 1.7	Min 1.6	Fe 1.8	Co 1.9	Ni 1.9	Cu 1.9	Zn 1.6	Ga 1.8	Ge 2.0	As 2.2	Se 2.6	Br 3.0	Kr	
Rb 0.8	Sr 1.0	Y 1.2	Zr 1.3	Nb 1.6	Mo 2.2	Tc 2.1	Ru 2.2	Rh 2.3	Pd 2.2	Ag 1.9	Cd 1.7	In 1.8	Sn 2.0	Sb 2.0	Te 2.1	I 2.7	Xe	
Cs 0.8	Ba 0.9	La 1.1	Hf 1.3	Ta 1.5	W 1.7	Re 1.9	Os 2.2	Ir 2.2	Pt 2.2	Au 2.4	Hg 1.9	Tl 1.8	Pb 1.8	Bi 1.9	Po 2.0	At 2.2	Rn	
Fr 0.7	Ra 0.9	Ac 1.1																

There are some general rules for predicting the type of chemical bond based upon the electronegativity differences:

■ If the difference in electronegativity values is greater than 1.8, then the bond is ionic.

■ If the difference in electronegativity values is 0, then the bond is non-polar covalent.

■ If the difference in electronegativity values is greater than 0 but less than 1.8, then the bond is polar covalent.

Polar covalent bonds are covalent bonds with ionic character (partial electron transfer). Ionic and covalent bonding are extremes forms of bonding: polar bonds are intermediate in nature. The larger the difference in electronegativity between the atoms, the greater the polarity of the bond and the greater the ionic character (Figure 4.6).

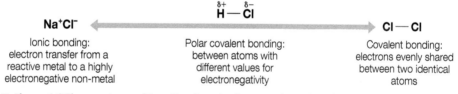

■ **Figure 4.6** The spectrum of bonding from ionic to covalent via polar covalent. The delta symbols shown for polar covalent bonding represent fractional charges on the two atoms

Worked example

Using electronegativity values from Table 4.3, predict the type of bonding in fluorine molecules (F_2), hydrogen iodide (HI) and lithium fluoride (LiF).

Using the values in the table:

Fluorine, F_2	Difference in electronegativity = 4.0 – 4.0 = 0 Non-polar covalent bond, F–F
Hydrogen iodide, HI	Difference in electronegativity = 2.7 – 2.2 = 0.5 Polar covalent bond, $^{\delta+}H–I^{\delta-}$
Lithium fluoride, LiF	Difference in electronegativity = 4.0 – 1.0 = 3.0 Ionic bond, Li^+F^-

3 Deduce the difference in electronegativity in the following bonds and predict the type of bonding: chlorine–chlorine, hydrogen–fluorine, carbon–chlorine, beryllium–chlorine and carbon–hydrogen.

■ Polyatomic ions

Many ions contain more than one atom. These types of ions are known as polyatomic ions. Table 4.4 summarizes the names, formulas and structures of commonly encountered polyatomic ions. A number of these ions are stabilized by resonance (π delocalization; see page 134).

In compounds such as magnesium sulfate, $MgSO_4$ or $[Mg^{2+} SO_4^{2-}]$, the bonding within the sulfate ions is covalent, but it is ionic between the sulfate and magnesium ions.

Name of ion	Formula	Structure of polyatomic ion	Example of compound
Ammonium	NH_4^+		NH_4Cl, ammonium chloride
Oxonium or hydroxonium	H_3O^+		$H_3O^+Cl^-$, hydrochloric acid (Chapter 8)
Sulfate(VI)	SO_4^{2-}		$MgSO_4$, magnesium sulfate
Hydrogen-carbonate	HCO_3^-		$KHCO_3$, potassium hydrogen-carbonate

Name of ion	Formula	Structure of polyatomic ion	Example of compound
Nitrate(V)	NO_3^-		$AgNO_3$, silver nitrate(V)
Phosphate(V)	PO_4^{3-}		K_3PO_4, potassium phosphate(V)
Hydroxide	OH^-		$NaOH$, sodium hydroxide
Carbonate	CO_3^{2-}		Na_2CO_3, sodium carbonate

■ **Table 4.4** Common polyatomic ions

■ Naming ionic compounds

Naming the cation

Ionic compounds are composed of positive ions and negative ions. The cation is always named first, and then the negative ion. Naming of the positive ion depends on whether the positive ion is monatomic. If not, special Stock names are used. If the positive ion is monatomic, the name depends on whether the element forms more than one positive ion.

For example, potassium always forms the same positive ion, K^+, in all its compounds. However, copper forms two positive ions: copper(I), Cu^+, and copper(II), Cu^{2+}. Hence the name copper is ambiguous. The names of copper compounds should start with either copper(I) or copper(II). These Roman numbers actually represent the oxidation state (Chapter 9) but this is related to the charge. The elements that form just one positive ion are the alkali metals (Group 1 metals) and the alkaline earth metals (Group 2 metals). The transition metals often form a range of stable positive ions. For example, iron forms iron(II), Fe^{2+}, and iron(III), Fe^{3+}.

For example, consider $CoCl_2$ and $BaCl_2$. Cobalt is a transition metal and likely to form two or more stable positive ions. Hence the name is cobalt(II) chloride. However, since barium is in group 2, the charge in its compounds is always +2, so there is no need to specify the oxidation state ('charge'). The compound is simply barium chloride. There is one common polyatomic positive ion, the ammonium ion, NH_4^+. Hence, ammonium chloride has the formula NH_4Cl [NH_4^+ Cl^-].

Naming the anion

If the anion is monatomic (has one atom), the name of the element is changed by changing the ending to *-ide*. This ending is used for binary metal–non-metal compounds. All monatomic ions have names ending in *-ide*, for example, chloride, Cl^-, oxide, O^{2-}, and nitride, N^{3-}. However, there are a few negative ions that consist of more than atom which also end in *-ide*, for example cyanide, CN^-, and hydroxide, OH^-.

Oxyanions

Oxyanions consist of an atom of an element plus a number of oxygen atoms covalently bonded to it. The name of the oxyanion is given by the name of the element changed to either *-ate* or *-ite*. If the element has a number of oxidation states then it is necessary to add a Roman number to show the oxidation state. Examples of this nomenclature include sodium nitrate(v), $NaNO_3$ [$Na^+ NO_3^-$] and sodium nitrate(III), $NaNO_2$ [$Na^+ NO_2^-$] and potassium sulfate(IV), K_2SO_3 [$2K^+ SO_3^{2-}$] and potassium sulfate(VI), K_2SO_4 [$2K^+ SO_4^{2-}$]. There are a number of other oxyanions that are commonly found in compounds. These include chromate(VI), CrO_4^{2-}, dichromate(VI), $Cr_2O_7^{2-}$, ethanoate, CH_3COO^-, and peroxide, O_2^{2-}.

Deducing the formula and name of an ionic compound from its ions

Table 4.5 gives examples of ionic compounds, including those with polyatomic ions and with elements showing variable oxidation states. These examples will allow you to deduce formulas and names from the ions present.

■ **Table 4.5** Examples of ionic compounds including those with polyatomic ions

Name	Formula	Ions	Ions present
Sodium oxide	Na_2O	[$2Na^+ O^{2-}$]	Sodium and oxide
Cobalt(III) fluoride	CoF_3	[$Co^{3+} 3F^-$]	Cobalt(III) and fluoride
Magnesium nitride	Mg_3N_2	[$3Mg^{2+} 2N^{3-}$]	Magnesium and nitride
Potassium ethanoate	CH_3COOK	[$CH_3COO^- K^+$]	Ethanoate and potassium
Potassium manganate(VII)	$KMnO_4$	[$K^+ MnO_4^-$]	Potassium and manganate(VII)
Potassium dichromate(VI)	$K_2Cr_2O_7$	[$2K^+ Cr_2O_7^{2-}$]	Potassium and dichromate(VI)
Calcium phosphate(v)	$Ca_3(PO_4)_2$	[$3Ca^{2+} 2PO_4^{3-}$]	Calcium and phosphate
Calcium hydrogencarbonate	$Ca(HCO_3)_2$	[$Ca^{2+} 2HCO_3^-$]	Calcium and hydrogen

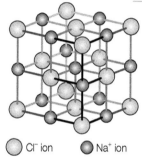

◯ Cl⁻ ion ● Na⁺ ion

■ **Figure 4.7** Ionic lattice for sodium chloride

■ Structure of giant ionic compounds

In an ionic substance, oppositely charged ions attract each other and ions of the same charge repel each other. Hence, each cation in a lattice is surrounded by a number of anions as its closest neighbours, and each anion is surrounded by a number of cations. Two cations, or two anions, are never located next to each other. A single ionic crystal contains a huge number of ions in regular repeating units, known as unit cells. Hence, ionic solids are said to possess a giant structure.

One of the simplest ionic lattices is the lattice adopted by sodium chloride (Figure 4.7). It is a simple cubic lattice, also referred to as the rock salt structure. Each sodium ion is surrounded by six chloride ions; each chloride ion is surrounded by six sodium ions. The structure of ionic lattices was established from X-ray diffraction studies (Chapter 22, on the accompanying website).

Coordination number

The number of ions that surround another of the opposite charge in an ionic lattice is called the coordination number. The sodium chloride lattice is known as a 6 : 6 lattice since each ion is surrounded by six oppositely charged ions (Figure 4.8). The coordination number of an ionic lattice depends on the relative sizes of the ions and their relative charges (Chapter 15).

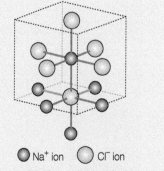

● Na⁺ ion ◯ Cl⁻ ion

■ **Figure 4.8** The sodium chloride lattice showing 6 : 6 coordination

Analysis of crystals by X-ray diffraction

Many solids are crystalline solids and consist of a regular three-dimensional arrangement of atoms, molecules or ions, known as a lattice. The wavelengths of X-rays and the distances between the particles in a crystal are of a similar size. Hence X-rays are diffracted (scattered) if they strike the crystal lattice at a shallow angle (Figure 4.9).

■ **Figure 4.9** Strong X-ray reflections from a set of crystal planes will occur if the waves arrive and leave in phase

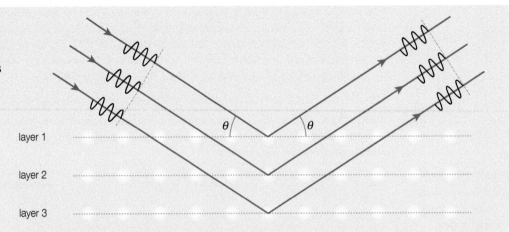

The X-ray diffraction pattern is photographed and computer software is used to calculate the positions of the particles within the lattice. This can be used to generate an electron density map (Figure 4.10) of the molecule in a molecular lattice. Each contour line connects points of the same electron density. Bond lengths and bond angles of the molecule may be obtained from the electron density map.

■ **Figure 4.10** The structure of the 4-methyl benzoic acid molecule superimposed on its electron density map

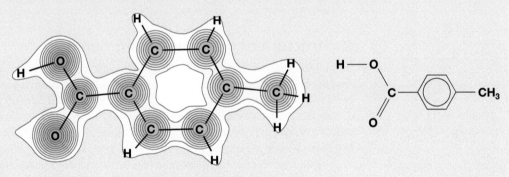

■ Physical properties of ionic compounds

The brittle nature of an ionic crystal, and its ability to be cleaved along planes, results from the mutual repulsion between layers when ions are displaced as seen in Figure 4.11.

■ **Figure 4.11** Cleavage in ionic solids: a layer of ions **a** before and **b** after cleavage

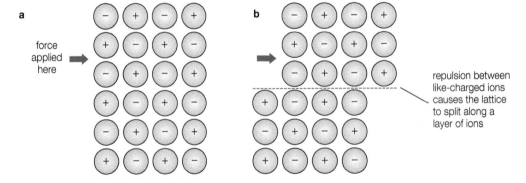

■ **Figure 4.12** An impure sample of corundum: a very hard, crystalline form of the ionic compound aluminium oxide

The attraction between oppositely charged ions is much greater than the repulsive forces operating between ions of the same charge. Hence, the lattice is relatively strong and large amounts of heat energy are needed to break it up and separate the ions. Ionic solids are therefore hard (Figure 4.12) and have high melting and boiling points. The strong electrostatic attractive forces operating between ions of opposite charge remain when the solid melts to form a liquid, so boiling points are relatively high.

Since the ions are held rigidly in the lattice by electrostatic forces of attraction, the solids cannot conduct electricity when a voltage is applied. However, when molten or dissolved in water to form an aqueous solution (if the compound is soluble), the lattice is broken up and the ions are free to move, and the substances do conduct electricity. When an ionic solid dissolves in water, the mobile water molecules interact with the ions on the surface of the lattice and bond to the ions (Figure 4.13). This process is known as hydration and the ions are said to be hydrated.

■ **Figure 4.13**
An ionic solid dissolving in water

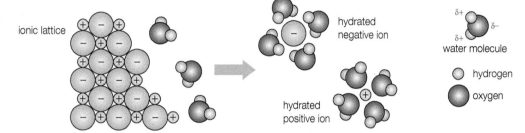

Additional Perspectives

Ion–dipole interactions

The bonds formed between the ions and water molecules are known as ion–dipole interactions. Energy is released during the hydration process and hence hydration is an exothermic process. The hydrated ions are no longer attracted to the oppositely charged ions so they enter the water. Eventually, provided water is present in significant excess, the lattice is completely broken down and all the ions are hydrated (see Chapter 15). The hydrated cations and anions are not attracted to each other owing to the presence of the water molecules.

There are two types of ion–dipole interactions: ion–dipole bonds and dative covalent bonds.

Ion–dipole bonds

These are the electrostatic forces of attractions which exist between an ion and the oppositely charged region of a water molecule. Ion–dipole forces are formed between simple metal ions from groups 1 and 2 and anions.

Dative covalent bonds

If a metal ion has empty low energy 3d and 4s orbitals it can form dative covalent bonds with water molecules, and a complex ion is formed. The d-block metals and metals from period 3 onwards, for example lead ions, aluminium ions (Figure 4.14) and tin ions, can all form complex ions with water (Chapter 13). A lone pair of electrons on the oxygen atom is used to form a dative bond with the central metal ion.

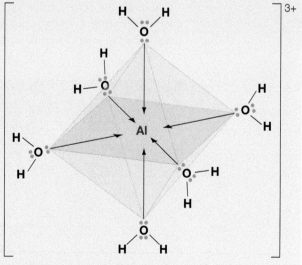

■ **Figure 4.14** Structure of the hexaaquaaluminium ion

Investigating and explaining the physical properties of ionic compounds

There are a number of observations that provide empirical evidence that a compound is ionic. Ionic compounds do not conduct electricity in the solid state, but become conducting if molten.

The inference from this observation is that the heating disrupts the lattice, releasing mobile ions. Often, just below the melting point of an ionic solid the ions can move sufficiently well within the crystal lattice to allow some conduction to occur. Another possible inference from this observation is that ions are formed from the atoms during the melting process. The ions could be the product of the reaction, rather than being present in the solid before the reaction.

If an ionic compound is soluble it will dissolve in water to form a conducting solution. Again the inference is that conductivity is due to the presence of ions, which are present in the solid state. Evidence that ionic solids contain ions is derived from X-ray diffraction studies and calculations involving lattice energies.

Many ionic compounds are soluble in water. Water is a good solvent for ionic crystals because it consists of polar molecules with a positive end that can attract negative ions and a negative end that can attract positive ions. It is the ability of water to surround both types of ions that makes it such a good solvent for ionic crystals. This layer of water molecules is known as the hydration sphere. Many dissolving processes are also accompanied by an increase in entropy (disorder, see Chapter 15) owing to the mixing that occurs during dissolving.

Some ionic compounds are insoluble in water. This observation can be explained by inferring that the ionic bonding within the lattice is stronger than the ion–dipole bonds formed when the ionic solid dissolves and hydrates. The increase in entropy is insufficient to make the process favourable. Insoluble ionic compounds usually have small and highly charged ions and high lattice energies.

All common ionic compounds are non-volatile solids at room temperature and pressure. They generally do not undergo sublimation or significant evaporation when heated.

■ Extraction of sodium chloride

Sodium chloride is a very important chemical. It is used as a seasoning in food and is an essential part of our diets. It is also an important raw material used to make other chemicals, for example solvents, the plastic PVC and the chlorine used to disinfect water. The oldest way of obtaining sea water is by solar evaporation of sea water (Figure 4.15). The sea water is contained within trenches and the water allowed to slowly evaporate in the sunlight.

However, most salt is dug out of the ground in the form of rock salt or brought to the surface by solution mining (Figure 4.16). Water is pumped underground and the salt dissolves in it, forming a concentrated solution known as brine. The brine is pumped up to the surface as it is needed. The water can be removed by heating or by solar evaporation.

■ **Figure 4.15** Solar evaporation of sea water

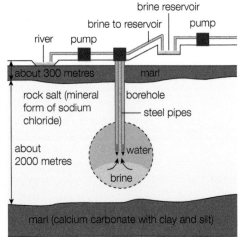

■ **Figure 4.16** Extraction of rock salt by solution mining

■ Evidence for ions

ToK Link

What evidence do you have for the existence of ions? What is the difference between direct and indirect evidence?

The best experimental evidence for ions in compounds, such as sodium chloride, comes from X-ray diffraction studies that can both locate the positions of the nuclei and also map the electron density between them. Such studies show that the sodium and chloride ions are arranged in a regular lattice and that the electron density between adjacent sodium and chlorine nuclei falls to almost zero. These observations are consistent with the complete transfer of the sodium atom's valence electron to chlorine.

■ Figure 4.17 Electrolysis of aqueous copper(II) chromate(VI)

Other experimental evidence for the existence of ions is derived from electrolysis. Opposite charges repel and unlike charges attract, and the results observed during electrolysis can only be explained by invoking mobile ions that can lose or gain electrons in reactions on the electrode surfaces. Ions are also formed by electron bombardment in a mass spectrometer. Their charged nature is shown by their deflection from straight line paths in a vacuum when they encounter an electric or magnetic field.

Indirect evidence for ions is that the concept of electrically charged particles is consistent with the properties of ionic compounds (i.e. high melting temperatures, showing strong forces of attraction between ions, solubility in polar solvents and conducting electricity when molten or in aqueous solution).

Perhaps the most convincing empirical evidence is the migration of ions in electrolysis (Figure 4.17). For example, electrolysis of green aqueous copper(II) chromate(VI) gives rise to a yellow colour (chromate(VI) ions) at the anode and a blue colour (copper(II) ions) at the cathode.

Nature of Science

Using theories to explain natural phenomena

Many substances are easily classified into one of three groups: metals, compounds containing non-metals, and compounds containing metals and non-metals. These substances often have clear and well-defined chemical and physical properties that can be described by a bonding model. These different groups of substances behave differently because of the different types of bonding operating between their particles. These differences can all be explained with reference to the electronic structure of the atoms involved in the bonding.

4.2 Covalent bonding – *covalent compounds form by the sharing of electrons*

■ Covalent bond formation

The simplest covalently bonded molecule is the hydrogen molecule, H_2. The two hydrogen atoms are held together because their nuclei are both attracted to the electron pair which is shared between them. Both the atoms are identical so the electrons are shared equally – a single non-polar covalent bond is formed. This simple electrostatic model is summarized in Figure 4.18.

However, very often the two atoms bonded will have different sizes. The smaller atom will attract the shared pair(s) of electrons more strongly since its nucleus will be closer to the electrons and will experience less shielding (Figure 4.19). The smaller atom is more electronegative. The resulting covalent bond is a single polar covalent bond.

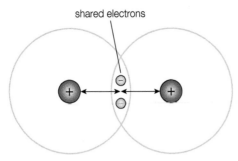

Both nuclei are attracted to the same pair of shared electrons. This holds the nuclei together.

■ **Figure 4.18** A simple electrostatic model of the covalent bond in the hydrogen molecule, H_2

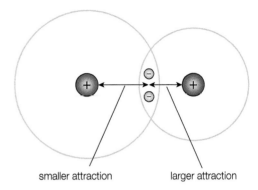

smaller attraction   larger attraction

■ **Figure 4.19** The unequal sharing of electrons in a polar covalent bond

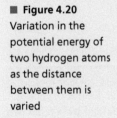

Additional Perspectives

A simple model of covalent bonding

Consider the energy changes involved when a single covalent bond is formed from two hydrogen atoms (Figure 4.20). As the two hydrogen atoms approach each other, each nucleus starts to electrostatically attract the other atom's electron. The covalent bond starts to form and energy is released. However, if the two hydrogen atoms came too close together, there would be considerable repulsion between the nuclei and the potential energy of the system would rise. The covalent bond in the hydrogen molecule represents a position of equilibrium or balance, in which the forces of attraction between the nuclei and the bonding electrons exactly match the repulsive forces between the two nuclei. This simple 'spring model' of covalent bonds is used in infrared spectroscopy (Chapter 11). The distance between the two bonded hydrogen nuclei is known as the bond length and the energy per mole required to separate the atoms in the bond is known as the bond dissociation enthalpy (Chapter 5).

■ **Figure 4.20** Variation in the potential energy of two hydrogen atoms as the distance between them is varied

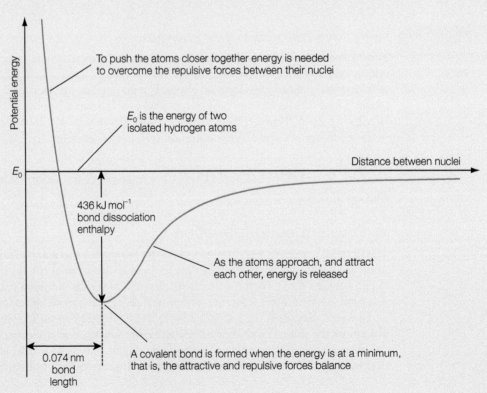

To push the atoms closer together energy is needed to overcome the repulsive forces between their nuclei

E_0 is the energy of two isolated hydrogen atoms

Distance between nuclei

E_0

$436\,kJ\,mol^{-1}$ bond dissociation enthalpy

As the atoms approach, and attract each other, energy is released

0.074 nm bond length

A covalent bond is formed when the energy is at a minimum, that is, the attractive and repulsive forces balance

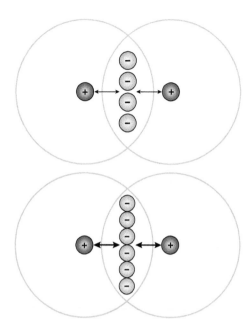

■ **Figure 4.21** A simple electrostatic model of the covalent bonds in the oxygen molecule, O_2, and the nitrogen molecule, N_2

■ Multiple bonding

Sometimes a stable electronic arrangement can only be achieved if more than one pair of electrons are shared between the two nuclei. When two pairs of electrons are shared, a double bond is formed. A double bond is represented by two lines. The oxygen molecule, O_2, contains a double bond and is represented by O=O. A triple bond corresponds to the sharing of three pairs of electrons, each atom contributing three electrons. This occurs, for example, in the nitrogen molecule. Each triple bond is represented by a triple line. The nitrogen molecule, N_2, contains a triple bond and is represented by N≡N. Figure 4.21 shows simple electrostatic models of the oxygen and nitrogen molecules.

Bond strength

Double bonds are stronger than single bonds (for the same pair of atoms) because there are more pairs of shared electrons between the two nuclei. Triple bonds are stronger than double bonds (for the same pair of atoms). This observation can be accounted for by the increase in attraction by the nuclei for the shared pairs of electrons (based on the simple classical model of covalent bonding).

Consequently, bond strengths (as measured by bond enthalpies) *increase* and bond lengths *decrease* from single to double to triple bonds (for the same pair of atoms). This is illustrated in Table 4.6 for the element carbon. This relationship is typically observed for atoms in other covalent bonds. For example, ethanoic acid, CH_3–COOH, contains two carbon–oxygen bonds, one single and one double. The double bond, C=O (length 0.122 nm), is significantly shorter than the single bond, C–O (0.143 nm).

■ **Table 4.6** The bond enthalpies and bond lengths of carbon–carbon bonds

Bond type	Bond enthalpy/kJ mol^{-1}	Bond length/nm
Single (C–C)	348	0.154
Double (C=C)	612	0.134
Triple (C≡C)	837	0.120

The benzene molecule has carbon–carbon bond lengths and strengths intermediate between carbon–carbon single and carbon–carbon double bonds. This indicates that the molecule is a resonance hybrid.

Nature of Science Using theories to explain natural phenomena

Ionic bonding and covalent bonding are treated and described separately, but in practice there are many examples of substances with bonding that has both ionic and covalent character. The simple and extreme models of ionic and covalent bonding described in this chapter are very useful in describing the structures and properties of compounds.

When a compound has strong covalent character then we expect it to be molecular with all the typical properties associated with simple molecular structures, such as relatively low melting and boiling points and non-electrolyte behaviour in water. This means that the solution will contain molecules and be non-conducting. Simple molecular substances are also non-conducting in the solid and liquid states. However, some molecular substances react with water to release ions. This is known as hydrolysis. An example is anhydrous aluminium chloride, which reacts with water in a hydrolysis reaction to form aluminium hydroxide and hydrochloric acid.

When the bonding is essentially ionic then the compounds are expected to be crystalline, brittle, high melting point solids and to show electrolyte behaviour in water. This means that the solution will be a good conductor due to the presence of mobile ions. There are of course exceptions, for example, there is a group of ionic compounds that are liquids under standard conditions.

The simplest approach to predicting bond type is to assume that the bonding between a metal and non-metal is ionic and that between two non-metals is covalent. This 'rule' makes many accurate predictions, but there are a number of exceptions. For example, $AlCl_3$ and $PbCl_4$ are essentially covalent. A more sophisticated approach is to use the difference in electronegativity as the main criterion for determining whether the bonding will be mainly ionic or mainly covalent.

■ Bond polarity

We have seen how electronegativity values can be used to predict whether a bond is ionic or covalent. The relative polarities of covalent bonds can also be predicted from electronegativity values. The larger the difference between the electronegativities of the atoms forming the covalent bond, the more unequal the sharing will be and the more polar the bond.

The electronegativities of selected elements are shown in Table 4.7.

■ **Table 4.7**
Electronegativity
values of six elements

Element	F	O	N	Cl	C	H
Electronegativity	4.0	3.4	3.0	3.2	2.6	2.2

The values quoted show that C–Cl and C–O bonds are both polar. However, the C–O bond (electronegativity difference of 0.8) is more polar than the C–Cl bond (electronegativity difference of 0.6). The N–Cl bond, however, is non-polar because the electronegativity difference between nitrogen and chlorine is zero. The C–H bond (electronegativity difference of 0.4) has very low polarity.

■ Bond polarity and dipole moment

Non-polar and covalent bonds

Diatomic molecules of elements, such as hydrogen, oxygen, nitrogen and the halogens, consist of two identical atoms covalently bonded together. The bonding electrons are symmetrically arranged around the two nuclei and are attracted equally to both nuclei. This is because the two atoms in the bond are identical and have the same electronegativity values. This type of bond is called a non-polar bond.

When two atoms with *different* electronegativity values form a covalent bond, the shared pairs of bonding electrons will be attracted more strongly by the more electronegative element. This results in an asymmetrical distribution of the bonding electrons.

For example, in the hydrogen chloride molecule, the more electronegative chlorine atom attracts the bonding pair more strongly than the hydrogen atom does. Consequently, the chlorine atom has a partial or fractional negative charge and the hydrogen atom has a partial or fractional positive charge. The hydrogen chloride molecule is described as being polar and the bond in the hydrogen chloride molecule is described as polar covalent.

In polar molecules, the centres of the positive and negative charges do not coincide. One end of a polar molecule has a partial positive charge, and the other a partial negative charge. The degree of bond polarity depends on the difference in the electronegativity values of the two elements.

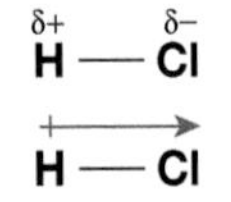

The polarity of the hydrogen chloride molecule can be indicated in two ways (Figure 4.22). By convention the arrow always points from the positive charge to the negative charge. The symbols 'δ+' and 'δ–' represent the partial positive and negative charges on the hydrogen and chlorine atoms. The arrow denotes the shift in electron density towards the more electronegative chlorine atom. The crossed end of the arrow represents a plus sign that designates the positive end (the less electronegative atom).

The separation of charge in a polar bond is termed polarization. When two electrical charges of opposite sign are separated by a small distance, a dipole is established. The size of a dipole is measured by its dipole moment.

hydrogen chloride

■ **Figure 4.22** Bond
polarity in the
hydrogen chloride
molecule

Deducing the polar nature of a covalent bond from electronegativity values

The difference in electronegativity values between two non-metallic atoms in a covalent bond gives an approximate indication of the polar nature of the covalent bond. The greater the difference in electronegativity, the greater the polar nature of the covalent bond. For example, the H–F bond is very polar since the difference in the two electronegativity values is 1.8. Fluorine has an electronegativity value of 4.0 and hydrogen has an electronegativity value of 2.2. However, the N–O bond will be less polar because the difference in electronegativity values is only 0.4. Oxygen has an electronegativity value of 3.4 and nitrogen 3.0.

Utilization: Cooking with polar molecules using microwaves

Microwaves are a form of electromagnetic radiation with wavelengths ranging from as long as one metre to as short as one millimetre, or equivalently, with frequencies between 300 MHz (0.3 GhZ) and 300 GHz. They have energies in the range $0.0100–1.00 kJ mol^{-1}$.

Microwave ovens (Figure 4.23) operate by irradiating the food with microwaves of frequency 2.45 GHz. The energy of these microwaves is absorbed by the bonds in the water and other polar molecules. The energy absorbed is distributed as a result of molecular collisions and is converted into molecular vibrations and rotations – so the food heats up. This is the principle behind microwave cooking.

■ Naming inorganic compounds

4 Name the following molecules: PBr_3, PCl_5, $PbCl_2$, $PbCl_4$, ICl and SF_6.

For compounds containing two non-metal atoms, the actual number of atoms of the element or the oxidation number is stated, for example carbon monoxide, CO, where *mon-* means one, and carbon dioxide, CO_2, where *di-* means two. Sulfur dioxide is SO_2, but could also be named sulfur(IV) oxide, where IV (4) is the oxidation number of sulfur. Sulfur trioxide, SO_3, where *tri-* means three, could also be named sulfur(VI) oxide. There are a small number of simple molecules that do not follow these rules. For example, water, H_2O, ammonia, NH_3 and methane, CH_4.

Nature of Science

Using theories to explain natural phenomena

The American chemist Gilbert Lewis (1875–1946) suggested a simple way of showing the valence electrons in an atom and tracking them during bond formation. These diagrams are known as Lewis structures (Table 4.8) and emphasize the importance of bond pairs in molecules and the attainment of a stable noble gas arrangement of electrons. This is known as the octet rule; although there are exceptions to it, it is a useful model for introducing many important concepts of bonding.

■ **Table 4.8** The Lewis structures of some elements in period 2 and 3

Group	Electronic configuration	Lewis diagram	Electronic configuration	Lewis diagram
1	Li $1s^2 2s^1$	Li•	Na [Ne] $3s^1$	Na•
2	Be $1s^2 2s^2$	•Be•	Mg [Ne] $3s^2$	•Mg•
13	B $1s^2 2s^2 2p^1$	•B̤•	Al [Ne] $3s^2 3p^1$	•A̤l•
14	C $1s^2 2s^2 2p^2$	•C̈•	Si [Ne] $3s^2 3p^2$	•S̈i•
15	N $1s^2 2s^2 2p^3$	•N̈•	P [Ne] $3s^2 3p^3$	•P̈•
16	O $1s^2 2s^2 2p^4$	•Ö•	S [Ne] $3s^2 3p^4$	•S̈•
17	F $1s^2 2s^2 2p^5$	⦂F̈•	Cl [Ne] $3s^2 3p^5$	⦂C̈l•

A quantity termed electronegativity is used to estimate whether a bond is non-polar, polar or strongly ionic. It is defined as the ability of an atom in a molecule to attract a pair of electrons towards itself. The electronegativity is often measured on the Pauling scale and is related to the atom's ionization energy and electron affinity. The American chemist Linus Pauling (1901–1994) developed the first and most widely used scale (0 to 4).

4.3 Covalent structures *– Lewis (electron dot) structures show the electron domains in the valence shell and are used to predict molecular shape*

■ Using Lewis structures to describe the formation of covalent bonds

In a single bond, each atom contributes one electron to the shared pair of electrons. Through the sharing of a pair of electrons, each atom now achieves the configuration of a noble gas. When two or more atoms are joined by covalent bonds, the particle or chemical species that results is known as a molecule. Covalent compounds are composed of molecules and each molecule is a group of bonded atoms held together by covalent bonds. Covalent bonds are usually formed between non-metallic elements.

A diatomic molecule is a molecule that consists of two identical atoms joined together by covalent bonds. For example, hydrogen gas exists as diatomic molecules, H_2. The structure of a hydrogen molecule, H_2, can be shown by using a Lewis structure (electron dot diagram) (Figure 4.24). A pair of electrons can be represented by dots, crosses, a combination of dots and crosses or by a line. Many chemists prefer to use a combination of dots and crosses so that it is clear which atom contributed the electrons.

■ **Figure 4.24** Lewis structures (electron dot diagrams) for the hydrogen molecule, H_2

H $\overset{\bullet}{\underset{\times}{}}$ H   H $\overset{\bullet}{\underset{\bullet}{}}$ H   H $\overset{\times}{\underset{\times}{}}$ H   H — H

Lewis structures (electron dot diagrams) are shown in Figure 4.25 for the chlorine molecule, Cl_2. Note that the lone (unshared) pairs of electrons must be represented and that Cl–Cl is *not* a Lewis structure since it does not display the lone pairs of the two chlorine atoms. Lewis structures only include the outer or valence electrons since these are the electrons involved in bonding.

■ **Figure 4.25** Lewis structures (electron dot diagrams) for the chlorine molecule, Cl_2

Cl Cl   Cl Cl   Cl Cl |Cl — Cl|

In the case of the elements oxygen and nitrogen, two and three pairs of electrons respectively must be shared between the two atoms of their molecules to achieve a stable noble gas electron arrangement. The oxygen molecule has a double bond and the nitrogen molecule has a triple bond (Figure 4.26).

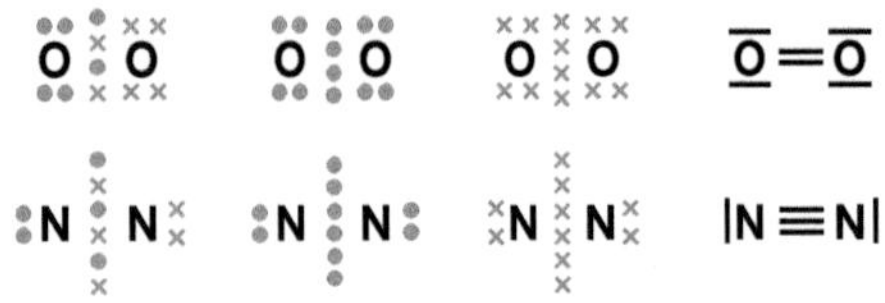

■ **Figure 4.26** Lewis structures (electron dot diagrams) for oxygen and nitrogen molecules

O O   O O   O O   O̅ = O̅

N N   N N   N N |N ≡ N|

Electron dot diagrams may also be drawn for molecules of compounds. Figure 4.27 gives the electron dot diagrams for hydrogen chloride, methane, water, ammonia, ethane, ethene and carbon dioxide molecules. All the diagrams represent molecules in which the bonded atoms have achieved the electron arrangement of a noble gas.

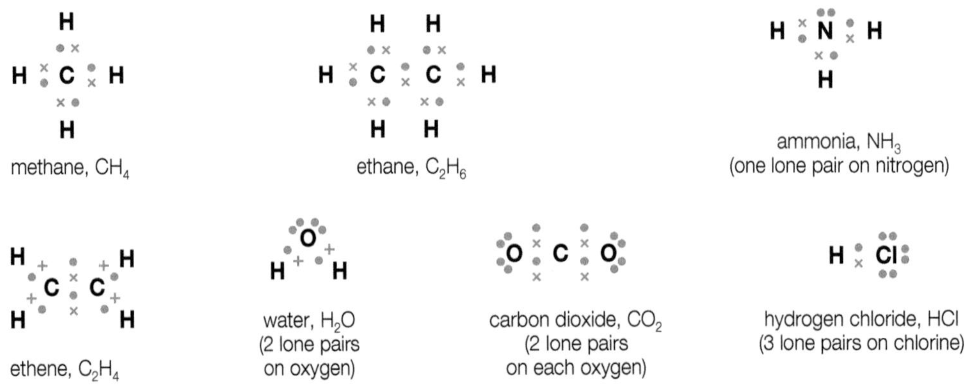

■ **Figure 4.27** Lewis structures (electron dot diagrams) for a selection of simple covalent compounds

methane, CH_4

ethane, C_2H_6

ammonia, NH_3 (one lone pair on nitrogen)

ethene, C_2H_4

water, H_2O (2 lone pairs on oxygen)

carbon dioxide, CO_2 (2 lone pairs on each oxygen)

hydrogen chloride, HCl (3 lone pairs on chlorine)

Lewis structures (electron dot diagrams) may also be drawn to show the formation of ions in ionic compounds (Figure 4.28).

■ **Figure 4.28** Lewis structures (electron dot diagrams) for lithium fluoride, LiF, and sodium sulfide, Na_2S

lithium fluoride

sodium sulfide

The only difference between Lewis structures (electron dot diagrams) of polyatomic ions (Figure 4.29) and molecules is that with ions you must consider the charge when counting valence electrons. Since electrons are negative, ions with a negative charge have extra electrons (sometimes denoted by a square); ions with a positive charge are short of electrons. A number of polyatomic ions have dative bonds, where both electrons in the covalent bond are donated by *one* of the two atoms that form the bond.

■ **Figure 4.29** Lewis structures (electron dot diagrams) for the hydroxide, cyanide and carbonate ions

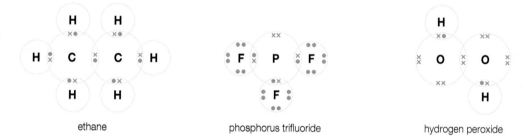

hydroxide ion   cyanide ion

carbonate ion

Lewis structures may also be drawn with dots and crosses including Venn diagrams (Figure 4.30). This approach is used for complicated molecules, as it allows an easy check to be made of exactly which bonds the electrons are in.

■ **Figure 4.30** Lewis structures including Venn diagrams for the ethane, phosphorus trifluoride and hydrogen peroxide molecules

ethane   phosphorus trifluoride   hydrogen peroxide

Drawing Lewis structures for molecules and ions

In general the following steps are followed when writing Lewis structures for molecules and ions:

- Calculate the total number of valence electrons for all the atoms in the molecule or ion. The number of valence electrons is deduced from each atom's group in the periodic table.
- Arrange all the atoms surrounding the central atom by using a pair of electrons per bond. The central atom is most often the atom which is least electronegative. Hydrogen is never a central atom.
- Assign the remaining electrons to the terminal atoms so that each terminal atom has eight electrons. However, if hydrogen is the terminal atom, then it can only hold two electrons.
- Place any electrons left over on the central atom. In the case of period 3 elements, such as sulfur and phosphorus, the central atom may have more than eight electrons.

> **Worked example**
>
> Draw the Lewis structure (electron dot diagram) for hydrogen cyanide, HCN.
>
> - The total number of valence electrons is 10: one from the hydrogen atom, four electrons from the carbon atom and five electrons from the nitrogen atom.
> - The bonds around the central atom use four electrons:
>
> **H ⦂C⦂N**
>
> - There are six electrons left to place. The hydrogen cannot take any more in its outer shell, as it already has two electrons, so these can be placed around the nitrogen atom, which can accommodate eight electrons in its outer shell. There are no more electrons for the central carbon atom.
>
> **H ⦂C⦂N⦂**
>
> - The central carbon does not have enough electrons to form an octet, so move two lone pairs of electrons from the nitrogen atom to the carbon atom to form a triple bond between the two atoms.
>
> **H ⦂C⦂N⦂**

The octet rule

When an atom forms a chemical bond by gaining, losing or sharing valency electrons, its electronic configuration becomes the same as that of a noble gas either at the end of the same period or at the end of the previous period in the periodic table. With the exception of helium, noble gases in group 18 have a stable octet (that is, eight electrons) in the outer or valence shells of their atoms. The formation of chemical bonds to achieve a stable noble gas configuration is known as the octet rule. It applies to both ionic and covalent bonds, but there are a number of exceptions.

Molecules that do not obey the octet rule

There are a number of molecules that do not obey the octet rule. There are three types of exceptions:

- molecules in which a central atom has an incomplete octet
- molecules in which a central atom has an expanded octet
- molecules with an odd number of electrons.

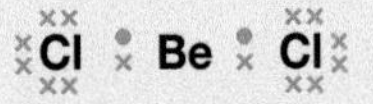

Incomplete octet

In the beryllium chloride molecule ($BeCl_2(g)$), the beryllium atom has only four electrons in its valence shell (Figure 4.31). The molecule is described as electron deficient. The boron trichloride molecule is also electron deficient: the central boron atom has only six electrons in its valence shell (Figure 4.32). A related example of an electron-deficient molecule is aluminium trichloride, $AlCl_3$. The aluminium atom has only six electrons in its valence shell. All these molecules have incomplete octets.

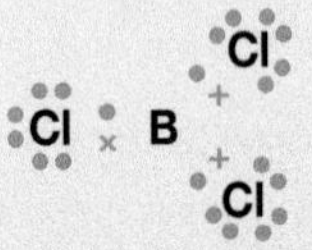

Expanded octet

Molecules with an expanded octet have a central atom which has more than eight electrons in its valence shell (Figure 4.33). Examples are phosphorus pentafluoride, PF_5 and sulfur hexafluoride, SF_6 (both in Chapter 14). In phosphorus pentafluoride, there are five covalent bonds (that is, 10 electrons around the phosphorus atom) and in sulfur hexafluoride, SF_6, there are six covalent bonds (that is, 12 electrons around the sulfur atom).

Figure 4.31 Lewis diagram of the beryllium chloride molecule

Figure 4.32 Lewis diagram of the boron trichloride molecule

boron trichloride

Figure 4.33 Lewis structures (electron dot diagrams) of sulfur hexafluoride, SF_6, phosphorus pentafluoride, PF_5, and PCl_6^-

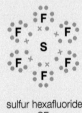
sulfur hexafluoride
SF_6

phosphorus pentafluoride
PF_5

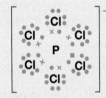
phosphorus hexachloride ion
PCl_6^-

The outer shells of the elements phosphorus and sulfur in period 3 of the periodic table can hold up to 18 electrons. The elements in period 2 do not form compounds with more than eight electrons in the outer shell because the second shell can only hold up to eight electrons. Hence, nitrogen trifluoride, NF_3, is a stable species but nitrogen pentafluoride, NF_5, is unknown. However, phosphorus trifluoride, PF_3, and phosphorus pentafluoride, PF_5, are both stable molecules.

nitrogen monoxide

nitrogen dioxide

■ **Figure 4.34** Lewis structures (electron dot diagrams) of nitrogen monoxide and nitrogen dioxide molecules

Odd-electron molecules

In most stable molecules, the number of electrons is even and complete pairing of electrons occurs. However, a small number of molecules and ions contain an odd number of valence electrons. Most odd-electron molecules have a central atom from an odd-numbered group, such as nitrogen and chlorine. Nitrogen monoxide, •NO, and nitrogen dioxide, •NO$_2$, are examples of odd-electron molecules (Figure 4.34). The oxy-chlorine radical •OCl is an intermediate formed during the destruction of ozone by chlorofluorocarbons.

Molecules and ions with an unpaired electron are known as free radicals; their existence can be explained by the molecular orbital (MO) theory of bonding (Chapter 14). Both nitrogen monoxide and nitrogen dioxide exist as resonance hybrids (see pages 134–135) of two Lewis structures.

---

5   Draw Lewis structures for the following species: $^+CH_3$, $^-CH_3$ and •CH$_3$.

Coordinate (dative) bonding

In some molecules and polyatomic ions, both electrons to be shared come from the same atom. The covalent bond formed is known as a coordinate or dative covalent bond. In Lewis structures (electron dot diagrams), a coordinate or dative bond is often denoted by an arrow pointing from the atom which donates the lone pair to the atom which receives it.

For example, the carbon monoxide molecule, CO (Figure 4.35), contains one dative bond. Once formed, the dative bond is indistinguishable from the other two single covalent bonds.

■ **Figure 4.35** Lewis structure for the carbon monoxide molecule, CO

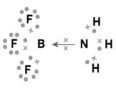

carbon monoxide

Dative bonding may also be found in molecular addition compounds (or adducts), such as boron trifluoride ammonia, BF$_3$.NH$_3$ (Figure 4.36). The boron atom in boron trifluoride has only six electrons in its outer shell and so can accept an additional two electrons to fill the shell and obey the octet rule. The nitrogen atom on the ammonia molecule donates its lone pair of electrons to form the dative bond between the nitrogen and the boron atom.

■ **Figure 4.36** Lewis structure for the boron trifluoride ammonia, BF$_3$.NH$_3$, molecule

boron trifluoride ammonia

The formation of dative bonds between a pair of reacting chemical species is the basis of a theory of acidity known as Lewis theory (Chapter 18). Dative bonds are also involved in the formation of transition metal complex ions (Chapter 13). Dative bond formation is often part of organic reaction mechanisms (Chapter 20). Aqueous solutions of acids contain the oxonium ion, H$_3$O$^+$, a datively bonded species (Chapter 8).

Dative bonding is also present in some common polyatomic ions. Three examples are shown in Figure 4.37. Ammonia and hydrogen chloride react together rapidly to form ammonium chloride. This is a white ionic solid with the formula NH$_4$Cl [NH$_4{}^+$ Cl$^-$]. When a fluoride ion shares a lone pair with the boron atom in boron trifluoride, a tetrafluoroborate ion, BF$_4{}^-$, is formed. In the nitrate ion, NO$_3{}^-$, the nitrogen atom achieves an octet by forming a dative bond with one of the oxygen atoms.

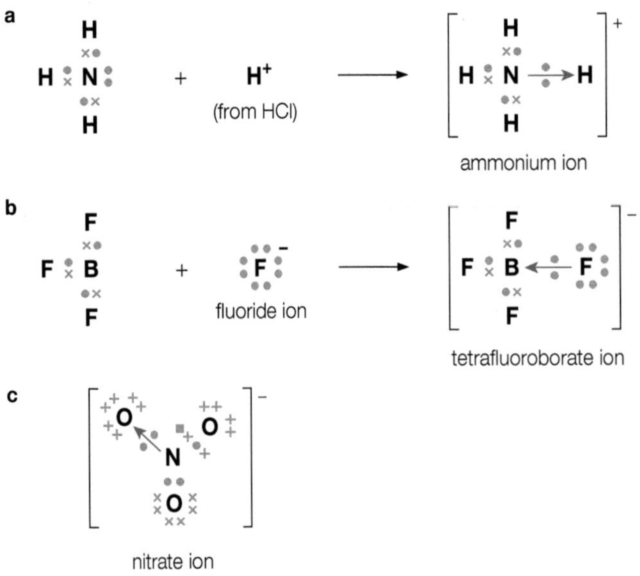

■ **Figure 4.37**
Formation of the
a ammonium and
b tetrafluoroborate
ions; **c** structure of the
nitrate ion

a

ammonium ion

b

tetrafluoroborate ion

c

nitrate ion

Bonding and electron orbitals

The Lewis model (electron dot model) is a very useful but simplistic approach to chemical bonding. However, a deeper understanding of chemical bonding and chemical reactions is obtained if atomic orbitals are considered (Chapter 12). Covalent bonds are formed when orbitals overlap to form molecular orbitals (Chapter 14). In hydrogen, the two 1s atomic orbitals overlap and merge to form a σ (sigma) bond (Figure 4.38). All single bonds are σ bonds. The second bond of a double bond, known as a π (pi) bond (Figure 4.39), is formed by the sideways overlap of p orbitals. The π bond is weaker than the single bond. This explains why ethene, which has a carbon–carbon double bond, is relatively reactive (Chapter 20).

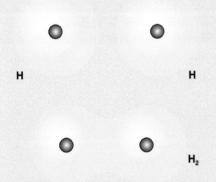

■ **Figure 4.38** The formation of a covalent bond by the overlap of 1s atomic orbitals

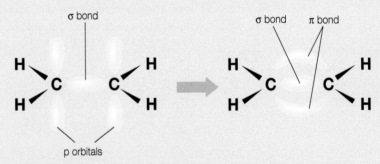

■ **Figure 4.39** The formation of the first bond (σ bond) and the second bond (π bond) in the ethene molecule

Resonance structures

Some molecules and ions have structures that cannot be represented by one Lewis structure (electron dot diagram) only. For example, the gas trioxygen (ozone), O_3, consists of molecules that can be represented by two Lewis (electron dot) structures as shown in Figure 4.40. The double-headed arrow represents resonance and the curly arrows show movement of electron pairs.

■ **Figure 4.40** Lewis structures for ozone

The two Lewis structures I and II are known as the resonance structures for the ozone molecule. The two alternative Lewis structures for ozone are equivalent except for the position of valence electrons. The term resonance refers to a molecule or polyatomic ion in which two or more possible Lewis structures can be drawn, but not the actual structure.

For example, structures I and II do not represent the real structure of ozone because they show the ozone molecule as having two types of bonds: a double bond, O=O, bond length 0.121 nm and a single bond, O–O, with a bond length of 0.132 nm. The double bond is shorter than the single bond, O–O. However, X-ray analysis shows that both bonds in the ozone molecule have the same length, which is, 0.128 nm. In other words, the bonds in the ozone molecule are intermediate between a single and a double bond. It can be concluded the two Lewis structures cannot by themselves accurately represent the ozone molecule. The ozone molecule exists as a resonance hybrid of the two (Figure 4.41). The dotted lines indicate that the bonds have partial double bond character and have pi electrons delocalized (spread out) over the molecule.

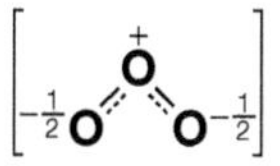

There are a number of other molecules and ions that show resonance and exist as resonance hybrids, for example, the carbonate ion (Figure 4.42) and the benzene molecule (Figure 4.43). Resonance and the concept of formal charge are discussed in detail in Chapter 14.

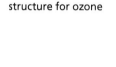

■ **Figure 4.41**
Resonance hybrid structure for ozone

■ **Figure 4.42**
Resonance structures and hybrid for the carbonate ion

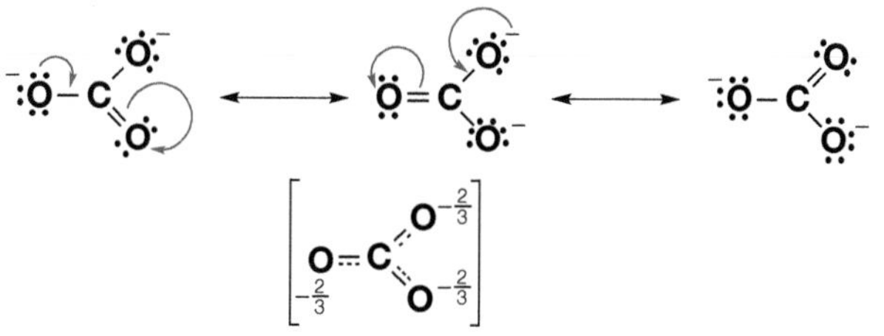

■ **Figure 4.43**
Resonance structures and hybrid for the benzene molecule

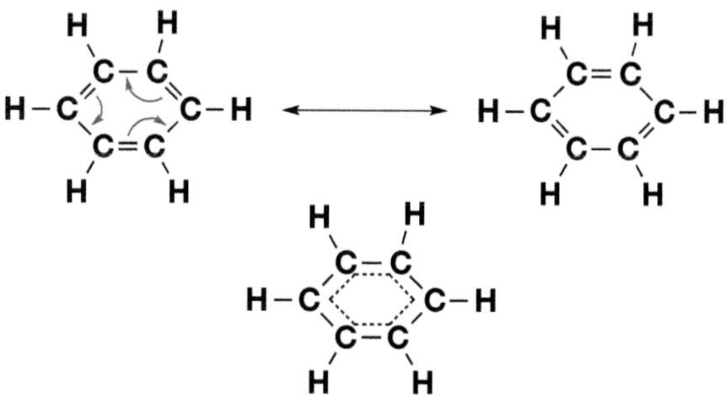

6   Draw resonance structures for the ethanoate ion, CH_3COO^- and the cyanate ion, NCO^-. Both ions are resonance hybrids of two resonance structures.

ToK Link

Does the need for resonance structures decrease the value or validity of Lewis (electron dot) theory?

Lewis theory was a pre-quantum theory and based on the simple idea that stable electron structures were those where the atoms could get a noble gas configuration by sharing or transferring electrons. The ideas of covalent and ionic bonds came from this model. Resonance structures were introduced because no unique bonds could be defined for some molecules, for example, benzene and some oxyanions, such as sulfate(VI) and nitrate(V), and were therefore an extension of Lewis ideas to such cases.

It could be argued that the need for resonance structures does not decrease the validity of Lewis theory since it extends the usefulness of the theory and overcomes its limitations. However, if you take the view that Lewis theory means that every molecule and ion should have its own unique structure then you have to accept that the existence of resonance structures diminishes its validity. But then every scientific theory, especially chemical theory, has its limitations.

Resonance structures extend the utility of Lewis theory in explaining electron delocalization in certain structures. Resonance structures are an integral part of Lewis theory that allows rationalization of chemical and physical properties in a simple and predictive manner. Lewis theory follows the idea of electron pair bonds, and a typical example where resonance is used is for describing the cyclic structure of benzene, C_6H_6, in which all the C–C bond lengths are the same. Using electron pair bonding and incorporating pi bonds, then the Lewis structure has alternating single and double bonds.

However, in this case, swapping the single for double bonds and *vice versa* leads to an alternative arrangement for the Lewis structure, and the resonance model uses the idea that the real structure is made up of a combination of the two resonance structures, which is represented by a double-headed arrow. By extension, the more resonance forms that can be drawn, the more thermodynamically stable is the system.

The success of this model (valence bond) is demonstrated both in chemical reactivity and in explaining physical properties. For example:

- the use of the 'curly arrow' to devise a reaction mechanism follows from using one of the resonance forms in say a substitution reaction on a benzene ring (Chapter 20).

- the relative acidities of acids containing a benzene ring, where the conjugate base with the highest number of resonance structures is the most acidic.

There are also 'inorganic' examples. For example, in the nitrate(v) ion, NO_3^-, all the N–O bonds are identical, and a Lewis structure has two single bonds and one double bond between oxygen and nitrogen, the two singly bonded oxygen atoms carry a negative charge and the nitrogen atom carries a positive charge. Two other resonance structures can be drawn, in which each oxygen atom in turn has the double bond to nitrogen, demonstrating that all N–O bonds are the same length.

What criteria do we use when assessing different explanations?

There are a number of criteria that chemists use when assessing different explanations (chemical theories). There are a number of factors that lead to a 'good' chemical theory, in other words, one that is long-lasting and resilient to experimental falsification.

These include predictive accuracy, internal consistency (this means that the theory should not need to be continually modified to make it work in different situations), external consistency (theory should not disagree with other fundamental chemical or physical theories), simplicity (the theory should be as simple as possible), unifying (it should bring together different branches of chemistry, as Maxwell's electromagnetic theory brought together electricity and magnetism) and fertility (the theory can be applied in situations where it was not originally intended).

■ Valence shell electron pair repulsion theory

The shapes of molecules and ions can be predicted by the valence shell electron pair repulsion theory (VSEPR). If the Lewis structure is drawn for a molecule or a polyatomic ion, the shape of this molecule or ion can be predicted using this theory.

The VSEPR theory states that:

- the electron pairs around the central atom repel each other

- bonding pairs and lone pairs of electrons arrange themselves to be as far apart as possible.

Bonding (shared) and lone (unshared) pairs are termed electron domains (historically, in some systems, negative charge centres).

The molecule or polyatomic ion adopts the shape that minimizes the repulsion between the bonding and lone pairs of electrons. The shapes of the molecules and polyatomic ions are therefore determined by the electron pairs rather than by the atoms.

Basic molecular shapes

Three of the five basic molecular shapes are linear, trigonal planar and tetrahedral. Table 4.9 shows the arrangement of the electron pairs (charge centres) that results in minimum repulsion and the basic shapes of the molecules. The two other basic shapes adopted by molecules, trigonal bipyramidal and octahedral, are discussed in Chapter 14.

■ **Table 4.9** Basic
molecular shapes

Molecule shape	Number of electron pairs	Description
	2	Linear
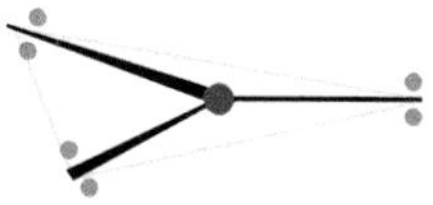	3	Triangular planar (trigonal planar)
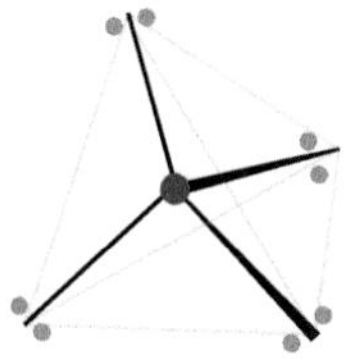	4	Tetrahedral
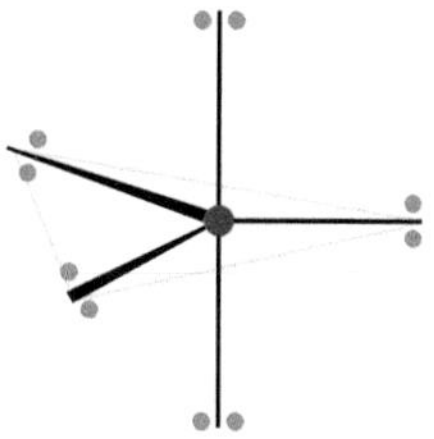	5	Triangular bipyramidal (trigonal bipyramidal)
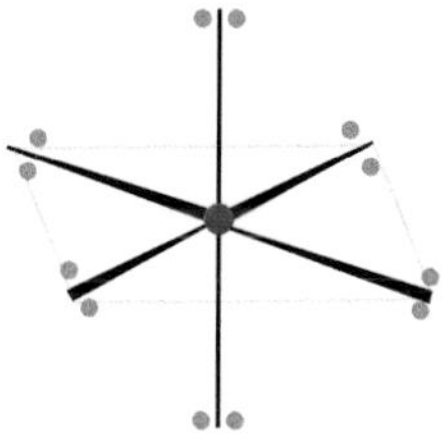	6	Octahedral

Shapes of molecules and bond angles

The shapes and bond angles of molecules and ions are primarily determined by the number of electron pairs. However, the number of electron pairs alone does not account completely for the shapes and bond angles. In the VSEPR theory, a lone pair of electrons repels other electron pairs more strongly than a bonding pair. This is because the region in space occupied by a lone pair of electrons is closer to the nucleus of an atom than a bonding pair. Bonding pairs of electrons are spread out between the nuclei of the atoms which they bind together. Thus, a lone pair can exert a greater repelling effect than a bonding pair. The order of the repulsion strength of lone pairs and bond pairs of electron is:

lone pair–lone pair repulsion > lone pair–bond pair repulsion > bond pair–bond pair repulsion
strongest   weakest

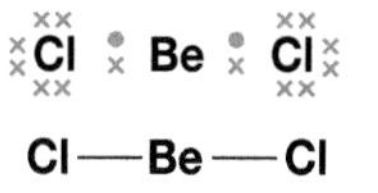

Cl——Be——Cl

beryllium chloride

■ **Figure 4.44**
Lewis structure and
molecular shape of
beryllium chloride

Two electron pairs

Consider the gaseous beryllium chloride molecule, $BeCl_2(g)$. The Lewis structure of the molecule shows there are only two electron pairs (two electron domains) in the valence shell of the beryllium atom (Figure 4.44). These two pairs of electrons try to separate as far as possible from each other so as to minimize electron repulsion. Thus, the beryllium chloride molecule adopts a linear shape with a bond angle of 180°, because the electron pairs are farthest apart when they are on opposite sides of the beryllium atom.

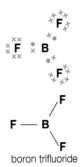

boron trifluoride

■ **Figure 4.45**
Lewis structure and
molecular shape of
boron trifluoride

■ **Figure 4.46**
Lewis structure and
molecular shape of the
methane molecule

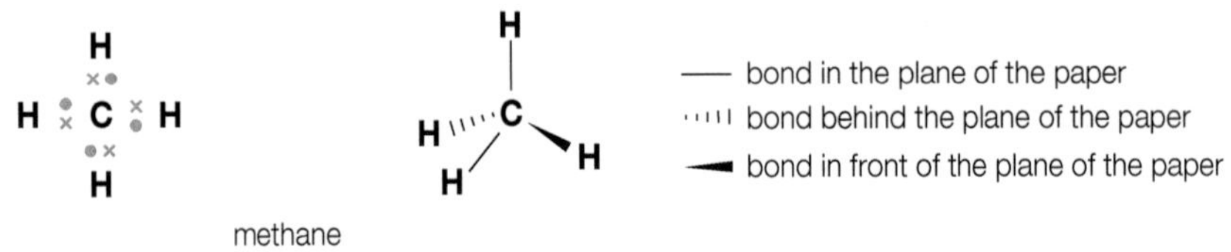

Three electron pairs

Boron is an element in group 13 of the periodic table. Therefore, it has three valence electrons. The Lewis structure (Figure 4.45) of the boron trifluoride molecule, BF_3, shows there are only three electron pairs (three electron domains) in the valence shell of the boron atom. These three bonding pairs repel each other equally, with the result that the boron trifluoride molecule is a trigonal planar (flat) molecule. The three boron–fluorine bonds point towards the three corners of an equilateral triangle. The bond angles are all equal at 120°.

Four electron pairs

The methane molecule, CH_4, has four bonding pairs of electrons (four electron domains) located in the valence shell of the central carbon atom. The repulsion between the bonding pairs of electrons is minimized when the angle between the electron pairs is 109.5° (the tetrahedral angle). Wedges and tapers are used to show the directions of the bonds (Figure 4.46).

methane

—— bond in the plane of the paper
····· bond behind the plane of the paper
▬◄ bond in front of the plane of the paper

It is important to distinguish between the orientation or arrangement of electron pairs in the outer shell and the shapes of molecules. The shape of a molecule or ion refers to the positions of the atoms or groups of atoms around the central atom and not the orientation of the electron pairs. The shape of a molecule or ion depends not only on the number of electron pairs, but also on whether these electron pairs are bonding pairs of electrons or lone pairs of electrons.

Therefore, there are three molecular shapes corresponding to four electron pairs that are arranged tetrahedrally around the central atom. These molecular shapes are described as tetrahedral, pyramidal and V-shaped/non-linear or bent. For example the methane molecule, CH_4, is tetrahedral in shape; the ammonia molecule, NH_3, is trigonal pyramidal; and the water molecule, H_2O, is V-shaped/non-linear or bent (Figure 4.47) – even though all of these molecules have four pairs of electrons arranged tetrahedrally around the central atom (carbon, nitrogen and oxygen, respectively).

■ **Figure 4.47** Lewis
structures and
molecular shapes of
the ammonia and
water molecules

ammonia

water

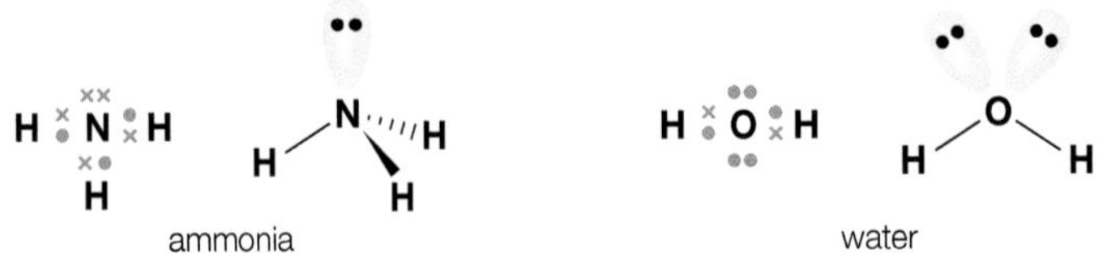

The bond angles of the methane, ammonia and water molecules are shown in Table 4.10. The bond angles decrease as the number of lone pairs of electrons increases (Figure 4.48).

Molecule	Number of lone pairs	Bond angles
Methane, CH_4	0	109.5°
Ammonia, NH_3	1	107.0°
Water, H_2O	2	104.5°

■ **Table 4.10** Number of lone pairs and bond angles for methane, ammonia and water molecules

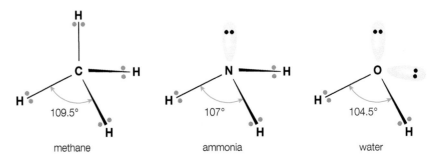

■ **Figure 4.48** The shapes and bond angles of the methane, ammonia and water molecules

■ **Figure 4.49** Models of hydrogen fluoride (three lone pairs), water (two lone pairs) and ammonia molecules (one lone pair)

The bond angles of H–C–H bonds in the methane molecule are 109.5°. The predicted bond angles of H–N–H bonds in ammonia would be 109.5°, *if* all the electron pairs repelled each other equally as they do in methane. However, the experimentally determined bond angles (via X-ray diffraction) in the ammonia molecule are 107°, which is 2.5° smaller than the predicted tetrahedral angle. An even smaller bond angle is shown by the water molecule.

The progressive decrease in the bond angle is caused by the lone pair electron repulsion being greater than the bonding pair electron repulsion. This is because the electrons of a lone pair are closer to the nucleus than a bonding pair. This greater repulsive effect tends to push the bonding pairs in the ammonia molecule closer together, so that the ammonia molecule is a slightly distorted tetrahedron with a smaller than expected bond angle. The effect is even greater in the water molecule, where the additional repulsion between the two lone pairs causes a greater deviation in bond angle from the tetrahedral bond angle (Figure 4.49).

Multiple bonds

VSEPR theory can also be used to explain the shapes of molecules or ions that contain a double or triple bond. A double or triple bond has the same effect as a single bond because all the bonding pairs of electrons are located between the two atoms forming a covalent bond. A double or triple bond is therefore counted as one bonding pair (one electron domain) when predicting the shapes of molecules and ions.

Thus the carbon dioxide molecule, CO_2, has a linear structure like the beryllium chloride molecule (Figure 4.50), and the ethene molecule, C_2H_4, is trigonal planar around each of the two carbon atoms (Figure 4.51). It is a planar molecule.

carbon dioxide

■ **Figure 4.50** Lewis structure and molecular shape of the carbon dioxide molecule

ethene

■ **Figure 4.51** Lewis structure and molecular shape of the ethene molecule

Effect of electronegativity on molecular shape

The shapes of molecules and ions are determined mainly by the number of electron pairs located around the central atom of the molecule or ion, and the effects of any lone pairs of electrons on the bond angles. Another factor that affects the bond angle is the electronegativity of the central atom.

7 Deduce the molecular shapes of the following species: $^+CH_3$, $^-CH_3$, PH_3, AsH_5 and NH_2^-.

Polarity of molecules

Diatomic molecules that contain two atoms of different electronegativities are described as polar molecules. However, the polarity of a molecule containing more than two atoms depends on both the polarities of the bonds and the shape of the molecule. Molecules that are very polar have large dipole moments. Non-polar molecules have a zero dipole moment (Table 4.11).

A molecule containing more than two atoms of different electronegativities may be non-polar even though there are polar bonds in the molecule. Molecules with polar bonds are non-polar because these molecules are symmetrical, that is, the central atom is symmetrically surrounded by identical atoms.

Bond dipoles and dipole moments are vector quantities, which means they have both a magnitude (size) and direction. The overall dipole moment of a polyatomic molecule is the sum of its bond dipoles. In the carbon dioxide molecule the

Name of molecule	Formula	Polarity of molecule
Hydrogen chloride	HCl	Polar
Water	H_2O	Polar
Ammonia	NH_3	Polar
Benzene	C_6H_6	Non-polar
Boron trichloride	BCl_3	Non-polar
Methane	CH_4	Non-polar
Bromobenzene	C_6H_5Br	Polar
Carbon dioxide	CO_2	Non-polar
Sulfur dioxide	SO_2	Polar
Tetrachloromethane	CCl_4	Non-polar

■ **Table 4.11** Polarity of some molecules

two bond dipoles, although equal in magnitude, are exactly opposite in direction. Hence, the dipoles vectorially cancel each other and the overall dipole moment is zero (Figure 4.52).

■ **Figure 4.52** The polarity of carbon dioxide, water and tetrachloromethane molecules

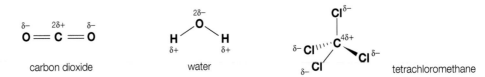

carbon dioxide   water   tetrachloromethane

■ **Figure 4.53** The effect of a charged polyethene rod on water

The water molecule has a bent shape. The two polar bonds are identical, so the bond dipoles are equal in magnitude. However, the bond dipoles are not directly opposite one another and therefore do not cancel each other. Consequently, the water molecule is a polar molecule (Figure 4.52) because it has an overall dipole moment.

The tetrachloromethane molecule is non-polar. Based on the electronegativity difference between carbon and chlorine, the carbon–chlorine bonds are polar. The resultant dipole moment is zero, which means that the dipoles must be oriented in such a way that they cancel each other. The tetrahedral arrangement of the four chlorine atoms around the central carbon atom provides the symmetrical distribution of bond dipoles that leads to this vectorial cancellation (Figure 4.52). Consequently, the tetrachloromethane molecule is non-polar.

One simple way to test whether a liquid is polar or non-polar is to use a charged rod, as shown in Figure 4.53. When a charged rod is brought close to the stream of a liquid running from the jet of a burette, a polar liquid will be deflected from its vertical path towards the charged rod but a non-polar liquid will not be affected. The greater the polarity of the liquid, the greater the deflection (under the same experimental conditions).

When polar molecules are placed in an electric field (Figure 4.54) the electrostatic forces will line up the molecules with the electric field. However, the order is disrupted by random movements due to the kinetic energy of the molecules.

■ **Figure 4.54** Polar molecules in an electric field

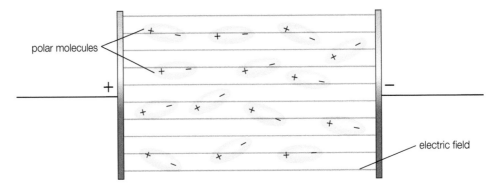

Importance of molecular shape

Additional Perspectives

The three-dimensional shape of drug molecules (Figure 4.55) is a very important issue in drug design and in drug–receptor interaction (binding). The biological activity of a drug depends mainly on its interaction with biological drug targets, such as proteins inside or on cells (receptors, enzymes), nucleic acids (DNA and RNA) and membranes (phospholipids and glycolipids). All these have complex three-dimensional structures which are capable of recognizing and interacting (binding) specifically to the drug molecule in only one of the many possible arrangements in the three-dimensional space. It is the three-dimensional structure of the drug target that determines which of the potential drug candidate molecules is bound within its cavity and with what affinity (strength).

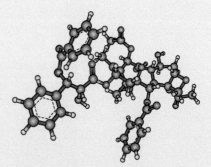

■ **Figure 4.55** A computer-generated model of Taxol, a natural anti-cancer drug from the Pacific yew tree

Using models as representations of the real world

The original VSEPR theory (Figure 4.56) is a classical theory that accounts for the shapes of most main group molecules. Lewis structures are simple representations of molecules and ions that emphasize the importance of electron pairs (represented by dots and/or crosses). VSEPR theory proposes that the favoured molecular shape is that which minimizes the repulsion between electron pairs in the valence shell of the central atom.

The detailed molecular shapes are based upon recognizing that bonding pairs and lone pairs do not lead to the same extent of electron pair repulsion. The strength of the repulsions between the electron pairs in a valence shell decreases in the order:

lone pair–lone pair > lone pair–bonding pair > bonding pair–bonding pair.

VSEPR theory, like all representations of the world, has its limitations. VSEPR theory works well for main group (non-transitional) compounds but is less useful for transition metal compounds. Lone pairs in transition metal complexes do not occupy directional orbits like those in the main group compounds. The shape of a complex ion can usually be deduced by counting the electron pair donors (ligands) and placing them as far apart from each other around the central metal ion.

VSEPR theory fails for very strongly ionic systems, such as the molecule $Li_2O(g)$, which is formed when solid lithium oxide is vaporized $Li_2O(g)$ is linear with repulsion of positively charged lithium atoms being the dominant factor. It is more correctly regarded as $2Li^+ O^{2-}$, because the oxide ion is not very polarisable. If lithium oxide (Li–O–Li) were covalent then VSEPR theory would predict a bent shape (as in H_2O) since the oxygen atom is surrounded by two bonding and two non-bonding pairs of electrons.

■ **Figure 4.56** VSEPR model of methane molecule

■ Giant covalent lattices

Giant covalent lattices usually consist of a three-dimensional lattice of covalently bonded atoms. These atoms can be either all of the same type, as in silicon and carbon (diamond and graphite), or of two different elements, as in silicon dioxide.

Diamond and graphite

Pure carbon exists in three allotropic forms: diamond (Figure 4.57), graphite and a family of related molecules known as the fullerenes. Allotropes are two (or more) crystalline forms of the same element, in which the atoms (or molecules) are bonded differently.

The properties of diamond, graphite and the fullerene carbon-60 (C_{60}) are summarized in Table 4.12. The differences in physical properties are due to the large differences in the bonding between the carbon atoms in the three allotropes.

■ **Figure 4.57** Model of a diamond lattice

■ **Table 4.12**
The physical properties of diamond, graphite and carbon-60

Allotrope	Diamond	Graphite	Carbon-60 (C_{60})
Colour	Colourless and transparent	Black and opaque	Black (in large quantities)
Hardness	Very hard	Very soft and slippery	Soft
Electrical conductivity	Very poor – a good insulator	Good – along the plane of the layers	Very poor – a good insulator
Density	$3.51\,g\,cm^{-3}$	$2.23\,g\,cm^{-3}$	$1.72\,g\,cm^{-3}$
Melting point/K	3823	Sublimation point 3925–3970	Sublimation point 800
Boiling point/K	5100	Sublimation point 3925–3970	Sublimation point 800

In diamond (Figure 4.58), each carbon atom is tetrahedrally bonded to four other carbon atoms by single, localized covalent bonds. A very rigid three-dimensional network is formed. In diamond the bond angles are 109° and each carbon atom has a coordination number of four because there are four neighbouring carbon atoms near to it.

In graphite, each carbon atom is covalently bonded to only three other carbon atoms. A two-dimensional network is formed consisting of hexagonal rings of carbon atoms. A graphite crystal (Figure 4.59) is composed of many layers of hexagonally arranged carbon atoms, stacked

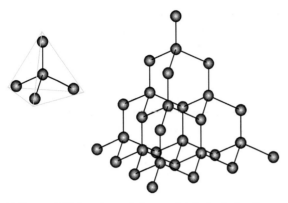

■ **Figure 4.58** Structure of diamond: tetrahedral unit and lattice

■ **Figure 4.59** Sample of graphite crystals and a model of graphite

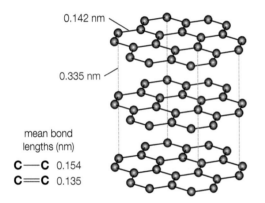

0.142 nm

0.335 nm

mean bond lengths (nm)

C——C 0.154
C══C 0.135

■ **Figure 4.60** Structure of graphite

on top of one another (Figure 4.60). Each sheet can be regarded as a single molecule of carbon. There is no covalent bonding between the layers of carbon atoms, but extensive London (dispersion) forces operate due to the relatively large surface area.

Each carbon atom has a spare electron which becomes delocalized along the plane, resulting in two-dimensional metallic bonding (Figure 4.61). The presence of delocalized electrons accounts for the ability of graphite to conduct electricity along the plane of the crystal when a voltage is applied.

Within the graphite layers, the carbon–carbon bond length is in between that of a single and a double carbon–carbon bond, suggesting that there is a partial double bond character between carbon atoms in the layers.

■ **Figure 4.61**
The structure of graphite showing the delocalization of electrons between the layers

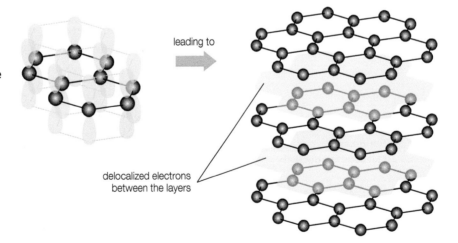

leading to

delocalized electrons
between the layers

Fullerenes

In 1985 a new allotropic form of pure carbon, known as carbon-60, was discovered. It is a simple molecular form of carbon and was first prepared by very rapidly condensing vapour consisting of carbon atoms, produced from graphite using a high power laser. The synthesis of carbon-60 was performed in an inert atmosphere of helium maintained at low pressure.

The atoms in a molecule of carbon-60 are arranged into the shape of a truncated icosahedron (Figure 4.62). This is the mathematical name given to the football or soccer ball. This structure has 60 vertices (corners) and 32 faces: 12 pentagons and 20 hexagons. The pentagons are 'isolated' – no pentagons are adjacent.

The bonding in a molecule of carbon-60 is shown in Figure 4.63. This is a series of alternating carbon–carbon double and single bonds. This arrangement of bonds is known as a conjugated system and would be expected to give carbon-60 similar chemical properties to benzene. However, the p orbital overlap inside and outside the curved surface is poor (Figure 4.64). Inside, the orbital lobes are too close and repulsion occurs; outside, the orbital lobes are too far away from each other for effective overlap. The molecule's carbon–carbon double bonds therefore behave like those of an alkene and it undergoes a variety of addition reactions, for example, bromination. Freshly prepared samples dissolve in methylbenzene and other non-polar solvents to yield a purple solution.

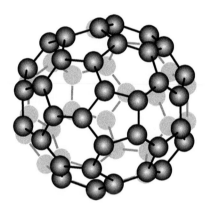

■ **Figure 4.62** Structure of carbon-60 (C_{60})

■ **Figure 4.63**
The structure of carbon-60 (showing the alternating single and double carbon–carbon bonds)

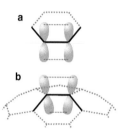

■ **Figure 4.64** Simplified diagrams showing p orbital overlap in **a** benzene (planar) and **b** carbon-60 (non-planar)

Carbon-60 is the most abundant member of a family of related closed carbon cages (C_{32} upwards), known as fullerenes. Each of the fullerenes has an even number of carbon atoms and contains 12 five-membered rings and a variable number of six-membered rings. Related to the fullerenes are nanotubes, which can be regarded as a sheet of rolled-up graphite capped at each end by 'half' a fullerene.

In September 1985 British chemist Harold Kroto (Figure 4.65) of the University of Sussex collaborated with Americans Richard E. Smalley, Robert F. Curl, James R. Heath and Sean C. O'Brien at Rice University in Houston, Texas in some experiments on graphite. Kroto had an interest in molecules found in interstellar space and had wanted to show that molecules containing long chains of carbon atoms could be formed under the conditions believed to be typical of the outer atmospheres of stars known as red giants. Smalley had developed a cluster beam apparatus which could vaporize small samples of solid graphite into carbon atoms which could be rapidly cooled and analysed.

Using mass spectrometry (Chapter 2) they detected long chains of carbon atoms, but in addition all the mass spectra showed the presence of a stable C_{60} species. After building some models prompted by Kroto's recollection of the geodesic dome at Expo 67 in Montreal, they proposed the truncated icosahedron as its structure. In 1990 American physicist Donald Huffman and his German colleague Wolfgang Krätschmer found that soot enriched in carbon-60 could be readily formed by passing a large electric current through graphite rods in helium. The carbon-60 could be extracted from the soot by dissolving it in methylbenzene and then filtering to remove the insoluble soot.

Kroto, Smalley and Curl were awarded the Nobel Prize in Chemistry in 1996.

■ **Figure 4.65** Professor Sir Harry Kroto standing in front of a carbon-60 arc generator

■ **Figure 4.66** Graphene showing its atomic-scale honeycomb lattice formed of carbon atoms

Graphene

Graphene (Figure 4.66) is a newly discovered form of carbon that consists of single layers of graphite. These layers are stabilized by mobile pi electrons. Graphite itself can be regarded as an allotrope of carbon formed by a stacking of graphene sheets interacting through weak London (dispersion) forces. Indeed graphene was first isolated in experiments to see how thin a piece of graphite could be made by polishing it down. However, thinner material was obtained by cleaning graphite with 'sticky tape' for surface science experiments. This led to an investigation by Geim and Novoselov into just how thin these layers peeled from the surface of graphite with tape could be made, and to the first isolation of graphene flakes in 2004. Graphene is also the structural element of fullerenes and nanotubes. It can be viewed as a very large aromatic molecule formed from many fused benzene molecules.

High-quality graphene is strong, light, nearly transparent and an excellent conductor of heat and electricity (some 300 times better than copper). Its interactions with other materials and with light, and its inherently two-dimensional nature, produce unique properties.

Graphene is prepared by removing monolayers from a sample of graphite as described above or by heating a sample of silicon carbide (SiC) to remove the silicon. Recently, a method has been devised using a blender and a suspension of graphite powder. This offers the potential to find a means of producing graphene in large-scale amounts for use in industry.

8 Predict the properties of silicon carbide (SiC). It has a giant covalent structure based on diamond. Find out about the uses of silicon carbide.

Graphene has many interesting properties, for example, its tensile strength is 1000 times greater than steel and behaves as a semi-metal, making it very suitable for electronic devices. The introduction of about 1% content of graphene into plastics could make them electrically conducting. Graphene is the most chemically reactive form of carbon due to the presence of carbon atoms on the edges with dangling bonds. This reactivity has potential, as compounds of graphene may have important uses. Membranes of graphene oxide, for instance, have been shown to be preferentially permeable to water, suggesting possible uses in water purification and desalination.

Silicon and silicon dioxide

Silicon is another element that exists as a giant covalent structure. The most common form of silicon dioxide (silica) is quartz, which has a structure similar to diamond in which tetrahedral SiO_4 groups are bonded together by Si–O–Si bonds (Figure 4.67). Silicon dioxide has physical properties that are very similar to diamond. It is hard, transparent and has high melting and boiling points. A common impure form of silicon dioxide is sand, which is coloured yellow by the presence of iron(III) oxide.

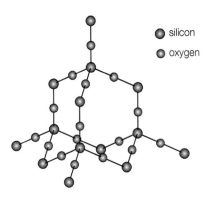

○ silicon
○ oxygen

■ **Figure 4.67** Structure of quartz (silicon dioxide)

4.4 Intermolecular forces – *the physical properties of molecular substances result from different types of forces between their molecules*

Obtaining evidence for scientific theories and testing predictions based on them

The noble gas helium will only turn to a liquid at the very low temperature of 4 K. An important question is why does helium liquefy at low temperatures, but at higher temperatures forms a gas. Helium is an extreme example in terms of the very low temperature at which it liquefies, but many other non-metallic elements and simple covalent substances show similar behaviour. For example, iodine is a solid up to 456 K, but above this temperature it sublimes and a vapour containing molecules is formed. These observations are explained by invoking weak intermolecular and interatomic forces that are significantly greater than those caused by gravity. These are distinct from the electrostatic forces that exist between oppositely charged ions and the sharing of electron pairs in covalent bonds.

Fritz London (1900–1954) was a German-born American theoretical physicist. He made fundamental contributions to the theories of chemical bonding and intermolecular forces. London dispersion forces are postulated to operate between atoms, such as helium, and non-polar molecules, such as iodine, I_2. Linus Pauling (1901–1994) was an American chemist who developed the concept of a hydrogen bond to explain the properties and trends observed in polar molecules containing bonds between hydrogen and nitrogen, oxygen or fluorine. The term van der Waals' forces includes all types of intermolecular forces: London (dispersion) forces, hydrogen bonding and dipole–dipole forces.

The term van der Waals' forces includes three types of intermolecular forces: London (dispersion) forces, permanent dipole–dipole forces (sometimes referred to as Keesom forces) and permanent–induced dipole interactions (Debye forces). In 1910, van der Waals was awarded the Nobel Prize for his work on 'the equation of state for gases and liquids' concerned with the reasons for non-ideal behaviour in real gases. His equation introduced compensatory terms to account for the non-zero size of the particles and the inter-particle forces between them. This broader definition of van der Waals' forces runs contrary to the use of the term in many current textbooks, but is consistent with its use in the IB syllabus.

■ London (dispersion) forces

Substances composed of non-polar molecules, such as oxygen, carbon dioxide, nitrogen, the halogens and the noble gases, can all be liquefied and then solidified by cooling. This observation suggests that there are attractive forces operating between molecules and atoms in the liquid and solid states. These short-range attractive forces are known as London (dispersion) forces and are due to the formation of temporary dipoles (Figure 4.68).

Temporary dipoles are caused by the temporary and random fluctuations in the electron density in a molecule or an atom. Over an averaged period of time, the electron density is spread evenly around the nucleus or nuclei. However, at a given instant, the electron density distribution may be asymmetrical, giving the atom or molecule a temporary dipole (Figure 4.69). A dipole is a separation of charge.

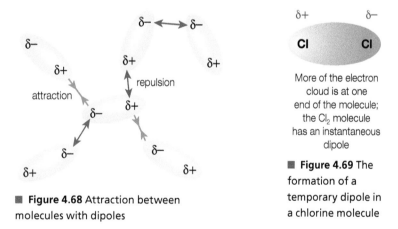

■ **Figure 4.68** Attraction between molecules with dipoles

■ **Figure 4.69** The formation of a temporary dipole in a chlorine molecule

The formation of a temporary dipole in one atom or molecule causes electrons in a neighbouring atom or molecule to be displaced, resulting in the formation of another temporary dipole. This process is termed induction, and the newly formed dipole an induced dipole. The formation of induced dipoles is rapidly transmitted through the liquid or solid. The forces of attraction between temporary or induced dipoles (Figure 4.70) are known as London (dispersion) forces.

■ **Figure 4.70** An instantaneous dipole–induced dipole attraction

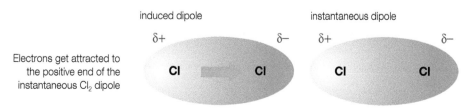

London (dispersion) forces are generally small, but the exact size or extent depends on the polarizability of the atom. This is a measure of the ease with which the electron density of an atom or molecule can be distorted by an electric field. The larger the molecule or atom, the greater the volume occupied by the electrons and the greater the polarization and the larger the size of the temporary or induced dipole (Figure 4.71). Hence, London (dispersion) forces increase with relative atomic or relative molecular mass.

■ **Figure 4.71**
The polarization of xenon atoms leads to production of induced dipole forces between atoms

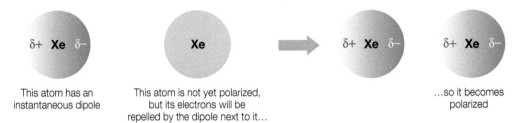

This atom has an instantaneous dipole

This atom is not yet polarized, but its electrons will be repelled by the dipole next to it...

...so it becomes polarized

Factors which influence London (dispersion) forces

The strength of London (dispersion) forces is influenced by two factors:

■ molecular size

■ molecular shape.

Table 4.13 shows the boiling points of the halogens. The molecules increase in size and contain a greater number of electrons as group 17 is descended. In addition, the electrons become located further away from the nucleus and hence are less strongly attracted. Consequently, the electron cloud can be distorted increasingly easily. In other words, the polarizability of the bond increases, together with the size of the induced dipole. This results in stronger and more extensive London (dispersion) forces. Therefore, the boiling points increase from fluorine to bromine. A similar trend is observed in the noble gases (Figure 4.72).

Molecule	Boiling point/K	Molar mass/g mol^{-1}
F_2	85	38
Cl_2	239	71
Br_2	332	160

■ **Table 4.13** The boiling points of the halogens

Note that it is the number of electrons that control London (dispersion) forces, not the force of gravity, which is negligible.

■ **Figure 4.72**
The boiling points of the noble gases

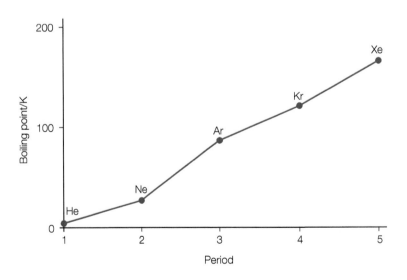

Molecular shape is also important in determining the size or extent of London (dispersion) forces of attraction. Molecules with a large surface area allow a closer contact between molecules. This gives rise to greater or more extensive London (dispersion) forces of attraction than in molecules of similar molecular mass but with more compact shapes due to branching.

For example, pentane has a higher boiling point than its isomer 2,2-dimethylpropane. Both molecules have the same molecular formula, but they have different structures. The London (dispersion) forces between pentane molecules in the liquid or solid states are stronger because the linear molecules have a larger surface area for interaction. In contrast, its isomer, 2,2-dimethylpropane, is more compact (adopting a roughly spherical shape) owing to its extensive branching, and hence has a smaller surface area for interaction (Figure 4.73).

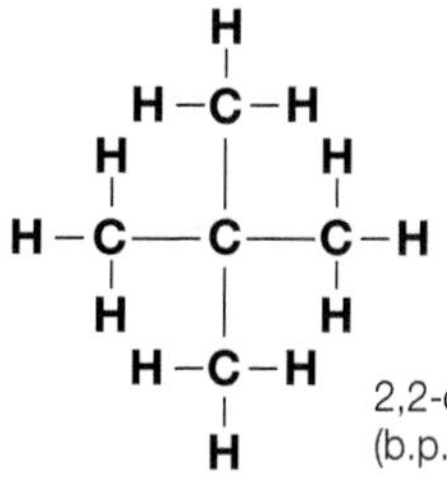

2,2-dimethylpropane (b.p. 283 K)

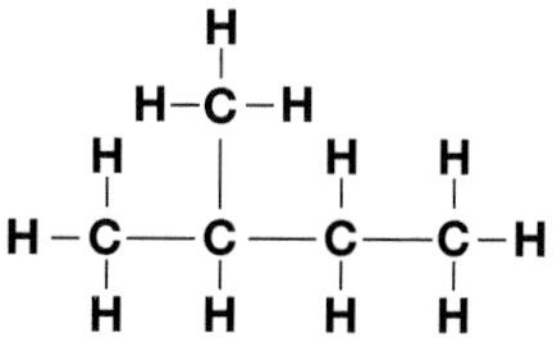

2-methylbutane (b.p. 301 K)

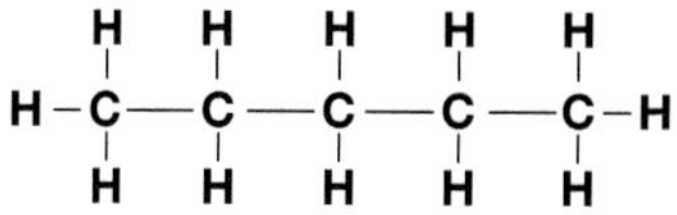

pentane (b.p. 309 K)

■ **Figure 4.73** Branched-chain alkanes have lower boiling points than straight-chain isomers

In comparing the relative strengths of intermolecular forces, the following generalizations are useful:

■ When molecules have very different molecular masses, London (dispersion) forces are more significant than dipole–dipole forces. The molecule with the largest relative molecular mass has the strongest intermolecular attractions.

■ When molecules have similar molecular masses, dipole–dipole forces are more significant. The most polar molecule has the strongest intermolecular attractions.

Table 4.14 shows the increase in melting and boiling points of the hydrogen halides from hydrogen chloride to hydrogen iodide. All the molecules have a linear shape.

■ **Table 4.14**
The melting and boiling points of the hydrogen halides

Molecule	Molecular mass	Melting point/K	Boiling point/K
Hydrogen chloride, HCl	36.5	159	188
Hydrogen bromide, HBr	81.0	186	207
Hydrogen iodide, HI	128.0	222	238

The hydrogen chloride molecule is the most polar molecule since chlorine is the most electronegative of the three halogen atoms considered. However, hydrogen chloride has the lowest boiling and melting points of these three hydrogen halides. The data shows that the intermolecular forces of attraction are strongest in hydrogen iodide molecules. Thus the influence of London (dispersion) forces is more significant than dipole–dipole forces when comparing molecules of very different molecular masses.

London (dispersion) forces are responsible for the soft and slippery properties of graphite. London (dispersion) forces of attraction also account for the deviations of the noble gases and the halogens from ideal gas behaviour (Chapter 1). They are also partly responsible for the solubility of covalent compounds, especially organic compounds, in organic solvents.

■ Dipole–dipole forces

A molecule that contains polar bonds may be polar or non-polar, depending on the shape of the molecule. In a polar molecule, there is a permanent dipole moment. A dipole–dipole force exists between polar molecules because the positive end of the dipole of one molecule will electrostatically attract the negative end of the dipole of another molecule (Figure 4.74).

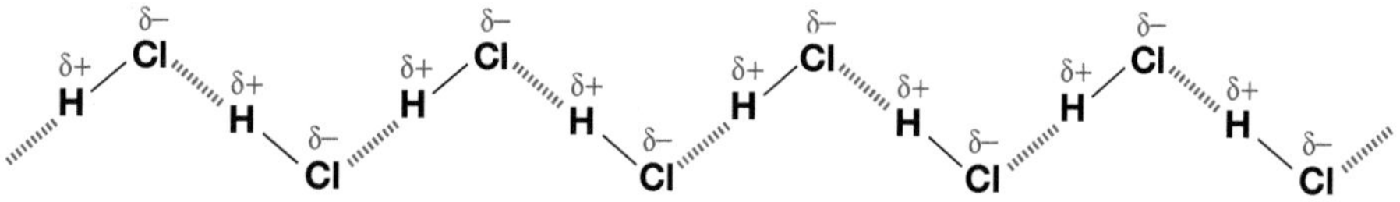

■ **Figure 4.74**
Dipole–dipole forces in solid hydrogen chloride

Dipole–dipole forces are often called permanent dipole–dipole forces because they only occur between molecules with permanent dipole moments. Dipole–dipole forces are only effective when the polar molecules are very close together, in the solid and liquid states. They are very weak in comparison to ionic or covalent bonds.

The strength of a dipole–dipole force depends on the size of the dipole moment of the molecule involved. The larger the dipole moment, the more polar the molecules of the substance and the greater the strength of the dipole–dipole force. For polar substances with similar relative molecular masses, the higher the dipole moment, the stronger the dipole–dipole attractions and the higher the boiling point, as shown in Table 4.15.

■ **Table 4.15** Dipole moments and boiling points for molecules having similar relative molecular masses

Name of substance	Formula	Relative molecular mass	Dipole moment/D	Boiling point/K
Propane	$CH_3CH_2CH_3$	44	0.1	231
Methoxymethane	CH_3OCH_3	46	1.3	249
Ethanenitrile	CH_3CN	41	3.9	355

■ Hydrogen bonding

If two molecules of hydrogen fluoride are close to one another, the hydrogen atom of one molecule will be attracted to the fluorine atom of the other molecule (Figure 4.75). This occurs because of the electrostatic attraction between the partial positive charge on the hydrogen atom and the partial negative charge on the fluorine atom. This charge separation or dipole exists because fluorine is more electronegative than hydrogen. The electrostatic attraction that holds the hydrogen atom of one molecule to the fluorine atom of another molecule is an example of a hydrogen bond. Hydrogen bonds are often represented by long dotted (or dashed) lines, as shown in Figure 4.75. In the solid and liquid states, hydrogen fluoride consists of zigzag chains of hydrogen fluoride molecules. The neighbouring hydrogen fluoride molecules are held together by hydrogen bonds.

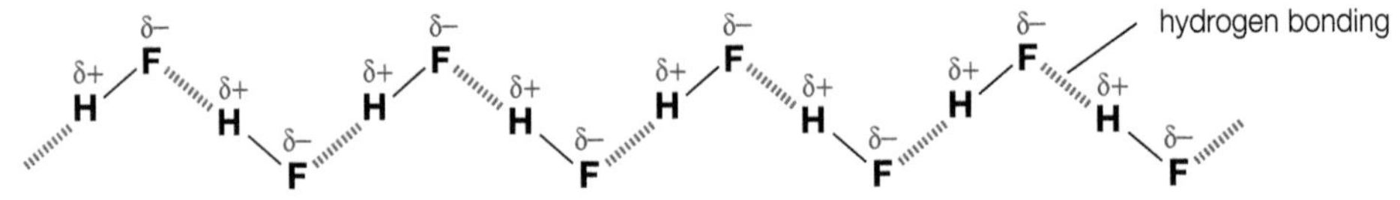

■ **Figure 4.75** Hydrogen bonding in liquid hydrogen fluoride

Hydrogen bonding is a strong permanent dipole–dipole attraction between molecules which contain a hydrogen atom covalently bonded to a fluorine, oxygen or nitrogen atom. These three atoms are small and highly electronegative. The essential requirements for the formation of a hydrogen bond are a hydrogen atom directly attached to oxygen, nitrogen or fluorine and a lone pair of electrons on the electronegative atom.

In the ammonia molecule, the nitrogen atom has one lone pair of electrons. This means that each ammonia molecule can form one hydrogen bond (Figure 4.76). Nitrogen is larger and less electronegative than fluorine and hence the resulting hydrogen bonding in ammonia is weaker than the hydrogen bond formed by hydrogen fluoride.

Each water molecule has two lone pairs which can form hydrogen bonds with two other water molecules. This helps to explain the three-dimensional lattice structure in ice.

If we consider the overall effect of the hydrogen bonds in water and hydrogen fluoride, the collective strength of the hydrogen bonds in water is greater than the strength of the hydrogen bonds in hydrogen fluoride. This is because each oxygen atom (with two lone pairs) in the water molecule can form two hydrogen bonds with two other water molecules, whereas each fluorine atom in the hydrogen fluoride molecule can form only one hydrogen bond with another hydrogen fluoride molecule.

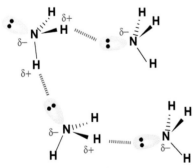

■ **Figure 4.76** Hydrogen bonding in ammonia

■ Effects of hydrogen bonding on physical properties

Hydrogen bonding affects:

- the boiling points of water, ammonia, hydrogen fluoride and other molecules
- the solubility of simple covalent molecules such as ammonia, methanol and ethanoic acid in water
- the density of water and ice
- the viscosity of liquids, for example the alcohols.

Effect of hydrogen bonding on boiling point

■ **Figure 4.77**
The boiling points of the hydrides of elements in groups 14 to 17

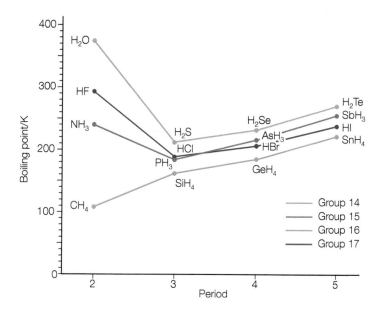

Figure 4.77 compares the boiling points of the hydrides of elements in groups 14 to 17 and allows the following conclusions to be drawn:

- The hydrides of group 14 elements (methane, CH_4, silane, SiH_4, germane, GeH_4 and stannane, SnH_4) display 'normal' behaviour, that is, the boiling points increase regularly when the relative molecular mass increases. This is because the London (dispersion) forces of attraction increase as the molecular size increases.
- With the exception of ammonia, water and hydrogen fluoride, hydrogen bonds are not present in the hydrides of elements in groups 15, 16 and 17. The increase in the boiling points for the hydrides of each periodic group is therefore due to the increase in London (dispersion) forces as the molecular size increases.
- The boiling points of ammonia, water and hydrogen fluoride are anomalously high compared to those of the hydrides of other elements in groups 15, 16 and 17 of the periodic table. This is evidence for the existence of hydrogen bonds which are appreciably stronger than the London (dispersion) forces that exist between molecules.

9 Iodine monochloride, I–Cl has a very similar molar mass to bromine, Br_2, but has a higher boiling point. Explain.

Effect of hydrogen bonding on the solubility of simple covalent compounds

Water is a good solvent for liquids and gases consisting of small polar molecules that can form hydrogen bonds with water molecules. For example, ammonia is a simple covalent compound. In general, simple covalent compounds are insoluble in water. Ammonia and amines are soluble in water because ammonia and amine molecules can form hydrogen bonds with water molecules. Similarly, alcohols and carboxylic acids are soluble in water because the alcohol groups in the organic compounds can form hydrogen bonds with water molecules.

However, not all organic compounds that contain primary amine groups, $-NH_2$, or alcohol groups, $-OH$, are totally soluble in water. As the relative molecular mass increases, the polar amine or alcohol functional group represents a progressively smaller portion of the molecule, but the hydrocarbon-based portion of the molecule becomes increasingly larger. Since hydrocarbons are insoluble in water, the solubility decreases as the relative molecular mass of the amine, phenol or alcohol increases.

Phenol, C_6H_5OH, is slightly soluble in water and slightly soluble in non-polar solvents at room temperature. Phenol has a polar hydroxyl group, –OH, which allows it to hydrogen bond to water molecules when dissolved in water (Figure 4.78). However, the solubility is limited by the bulky non-polar benzene ring, which interacts with molecules of non-polar solvents, for example, benzene.

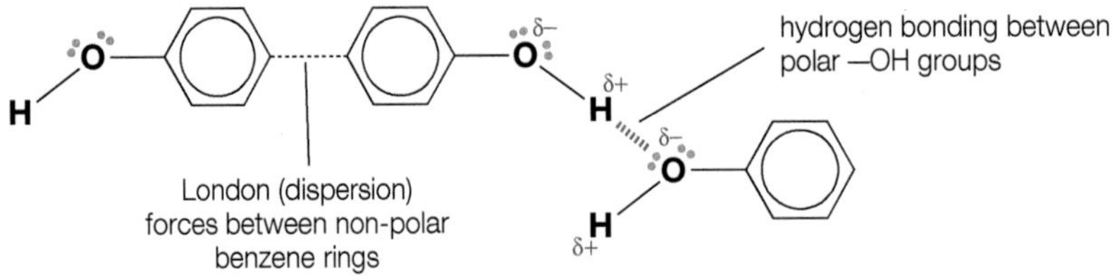

■ **Figure 4.78**
Accounting for the solubility of phenol in polar and non-polar solvents

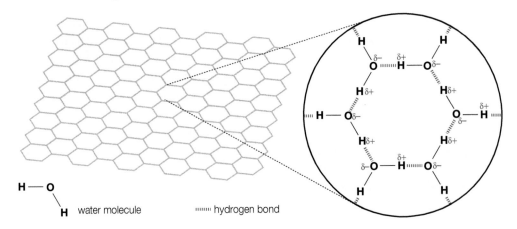

Hydrogen bonding is responsible for many of the characteristic properties of water and ice. For example, hydrogen bonding is responsible for the high boiling point of water and the low density of ice. Hydrogen bonding is also responsible for the high surface tension of water (Figure 4.79). Surface tension – the 'skin' on the surface of water – arises because the molecules on the surface are pulled in to the bulk of the liquid strongly but there is no force pulling them out so the surface tends to adopt a minimum area.

■ **Figure 4.79**
Through hydrogen bonding, molecules on the surface of water form very temporary hexagonal arrays which are responsible for the high surface tension

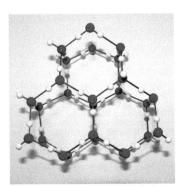

■ **Figure 4.80** The structure of ice

Hydrogen bonding is responsible for the unusual relative densities of water and ice. Water is one of the few substances that is less dense as a solid than it is as a liquid. In ice, each water molecule is surrounded tetrahedrally by four other water molecules joined by intermolecular hydrogen bonding. The water molecules arrange themselves into a lattice (similar to that of diamond) to *maximize* the number of hydrogen bonds and hence *minimize* the energy. The lattice (Figure 4.80) has a relatively large amount of space between the molecules. The 'open' structure of ice accounts for the fact that ice is less dense than water at 0 °C.

When ice melts, some of the hydrogen bonds are broken, which allows some of the water molecules to be packed closer together, resulting in a decrease in volume. Hence, water has a higher density than ice. With further heating, additional hydrogen bonds are broken as more free water molecules are produced, so that just above the melting point, the density of water increases with temperature but at the same time, water expands as it is heated (due to increased molecular movement) and this causes its density to decrease. These two processes – the reduction in volume due to melting and the thermal expansion – act in opposite directions. From 0 to 4 °C, the process of reduction in volume predominates, and water becomes progressively denser. Beyond 4 °C, the thermal expansion predominates, and the density of water decreases with increasing temperature. Figure 4.81 shows the variation in density with temperature for water.

■ Hydrogen bonding in biological molecules

Proteins are polymers with long chains consisting of repeating units with the structure –RCCONH–. Hydrogen bonding can occur between the carbonyl groups (>C=O) and the amine groups (H–N<). Hydrogen bonding can occur between the chains or within the chain to form secondary structures known as the β-sheet and the α-helix.

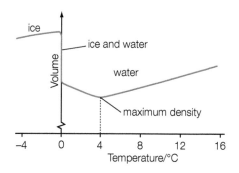

■ **Figure 4.81** The volume of water versus temperature

In chromosomal DNA the four bases form pairs with specific partners by hydrogen bonding (Figure 4.82), allowing DNA replication to occur. The hydrogen bonds are relatively weak and can be broken by appropriate enzymes. Thymine always hydrogen bonds to adenine; cytosine always hydrogen bonds to guanine. These are known as base pairs.

■ **Figure 4.82**
Base pairing in DNA

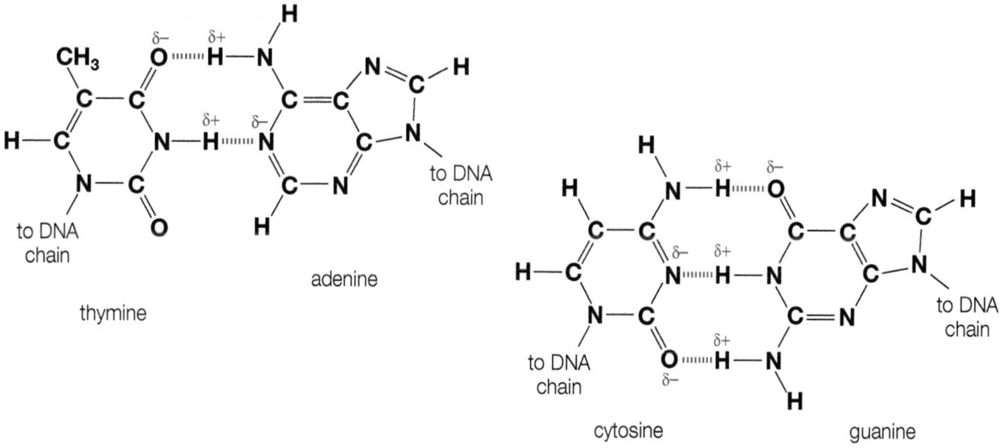

thymine   adenine

cytosine   guanine

Hydrogen bonding in ethanoic acid

When dissolved in non-polar solvents or heated to just above its boiling point, ethanoic acid has an apparent molar mass of $120\,\text{g mol}^{-1}$ instead of the $60\,\text{g mol}^{-1}$ that would be expected from its molecular formula of CH_3COOH. These observations can be accounted for by the formation of a hydrogen-bonded dimer (Figure 4.83).

■ **Figure 4.83**
The formation of a hydrogen-bonded dimer of ethanoic acid

$$2\ \textbf{CH}_3\textbf{COOH} \longrightarrow (\textbf{CH}_3\textbf{COOH})_2$$

M_r 60   120

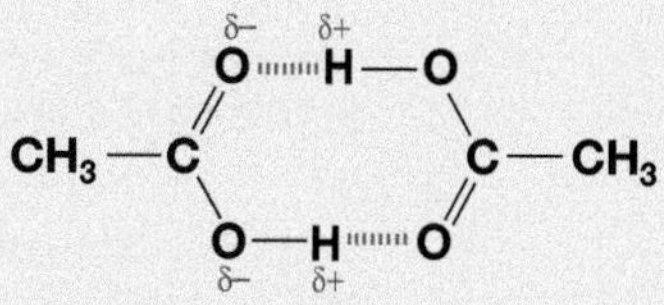

When dissolved in water, such an association cannot occur because the ethanoic acid molecules will be hydrogen bonded to the water molecules instead. At high temperature (well above its boiling point), the dimer will dissociate into individual ethanoic molecules.

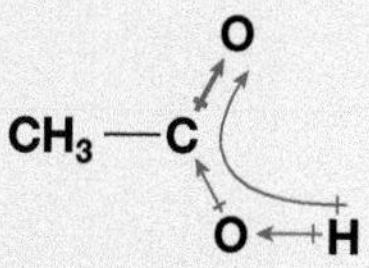

The hydrogen bonding between the ethanoic molecules is relatively strong owing to the electron-withdrawing effect (Figure 4.84) of the carbonyl group, which increases the size of the positive charge on the hydrogen atom of the –OH group. This effect is not present in alcohols and hence carboxylic acids form stronger hydrogen bonds compared to alcohols (of similar molar mass).

■ **Figure 4.84**
The effect of introducing a carbonyl group into an alcohol molecule

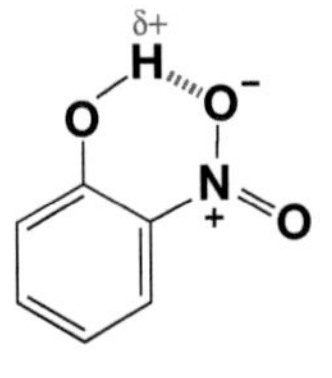

■ **Figure 4.85**
Hydrogen bonding in
2-nitrophenol

■ Intramolecular hydrogen bonding

Hydrogen bonding that occurs between atoms of the same molecule is termed *intramolecular* hydrogen bonding. This is exemplified by 2-nitrophenol. In 2-nitrophenol, the hydrogen atom of the alcohol group, –OH, can form an intramolecular hydrogen bond with the oxygen atom of the nitro group, –NO$_2$ (Figure 4.85).

In 4-nitrophenol, the hydrogen atom of the alcohol group, –OH, cannot form an intramolecular hydrogen bond with the oxygen atom in the nitro group, –NO$_2$, because they are too far apart. In contrast, 4-nitrophenol forms *intermolecular* hydrogen bonds (Figure 4.86). Consequently, the melting point of 4-nitrophenol is higher than that of 2-nitrophenol, which is mainly associated via London (dispersion) forces.

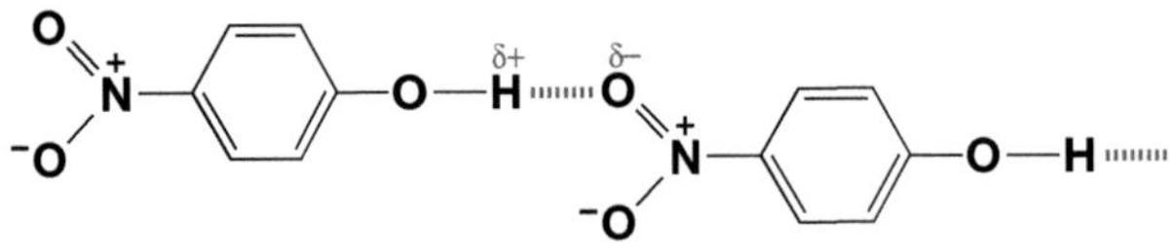

■ **Figure 4.86** Hydrogen bonding in 4-nitrophenol

---

10 Explain why CS$_2$ has a higher boiling point than CO$_2$. Explain why H$_2$O has a lower boiling point than H$_2$O$_2$.

ToK Link

The nature of the hydrogen bond is the topic of much discussion and the current definition from the IUPAC gives six criteria which should be used as evidence for the occurrence of hydrogen bonding. How does a specialized vocabulary help and hinder the growth of knowledge?

The IB syllabus defines hydrogen bonds as occurring when hydrogen is covalently bonded to one of the three atoms, fluorine, oxygen or nitrogen. These three atoms have relatively small atomic radii and relatively high values of electronegativity. The IB syllabus invokes boiling point data of hydrides to reinforce this categorization.

However, there is nothing 'special' or unusual about hydrogen bonds; they can be simply regarded as an especially strong dipole–dipole interaction. Chlorine is slightly more electronegative than nitrogen but its larger atomic radius prevents the formation of an intermolecular force as strong as nitrogen.

This misconception is reinforced by use of the apparently very different terms: hydrogen bond and dipole–dipole force. Both are permanent dipole forces. The difference is their relative strength and *not* their nature.

The electrostatic ('ionic') nature of hydrogen bonds is stressed by the IB syllabus, which emphasizes the attraction between the partial positive charge on the hydrogen and the partial negative charge on the nitrogen, fluorine or oxygen. However, quantum mechanical calculations also suggest partial covalent character and some sharing of a lone pair on the nitrogen, fluorine or oxygen atom. The strength of the hydrogen bond is maximized when the three atoms are arranged in a linear manner.

However, the IUPAC has a broader definition of the hydrogen bond: 'The hydrogen bond is an attractive interaction between a hydrogen atom from a molecule or molecular fragment X–H in which X is more electronegative than H, and an atom or group of atoms in the same or a different molecule, in which there is still evidence of bond formation'.

For an intermolecular force to be classified as a hydrogen bond some experimental criteria must ideally be met. Experimental evidence for hydrogen bonding is obtained from nuclear magnetic resonance (NMR), X-ray diffraction, infrared spectroscopy (IR) and enthalpy change measurements, often performed in the gas phase.

According to the IUPAC definition, hydrogen bonding is not restricted to the atoms fluorine, nitrogen and oxygen, but the interactions with these atoms are usually an order of magnitude stronger than those with the heavier elements, such as chlorine and sulfur. And so in the solid state weak hydrogen bonds with these elements are observed. It is also permissible to invoke hydrogen bonding between A–H and an anion. In fact the strongest known hydrogen bond occurs in the HF$_2^-$ anion: F–H....F$^-$.

■ Physical properties

Table 4.16 compares the properties of solid crystalline substances with different types of bonding.

Type of bonding	Metallic	Giant covalent	Simple molecular	Ionic
Examples	Sodium, aluminium, iron, mercury and brass (copper and zinc)	Diamond, polyethene, nylon, silicon dioxide and graphite	Iodine, methane, hydrogen chloride, water, benzoic acid, ethanol, ammonia and fullerenes	Sodium chloride, magnesium oxide, calcium fluoride and sodium carbonate
Composition	Metal atoms	Non-metallic atoms	Molecules	Ions
Nature of bonding	Cations attracted to delocalized valence electrons	Atoms bonded by strong covalent bonds	Covalently bonded molecules held together by weak intermolecular forces	Strong electrostatic attraction between oppositely charged ions
Physical state at room temperature and pressure	Solids (except mercury)	Solids	Gases, liquids and solids	Solids
Hardness	Usually hard (but group 1 metals are soft)	Extremely hard	Soft (if solids)	Hard and brittle; undergo cleavage
Melting point	Usually high (except group 1 and mercury)	Very high	Very low or low	High
Electrical conductivity (in molten state)	Conductors	Non-conductors (except graphite)	Usually non-conductors	Conductors
Solubility	Insoluble, but dissolve in other metals to form alloys	Totally insoluble in all solvents	Usually soluble in non-polar solvents; usually less soluble in polar solvents	Usually soluble in polar solvents; insoluble in non-polar solvents

■ **Table 4.16** Comparing and contrasting the properties of solid crystalline substances

Solubility of solids

When a solution is formed, the particles from the simple molecular solid mix freely with those from the liquid. The process of dissolution may be thought of as occurring in three stages:

1 The solid's lattice must be broken. This process will be endothermic, that is, heat is absorbed.
2 The intermolecular forces in the liquid, whether London (dispersion) forces, hydrogen bonds or dipole–dipole attractions, must be disrupted to some extent. Again, this is an endothermic process, as attractive forces are being broken and this requires energy.
3 New bonds are formed between the molecules in the solid and the liquid. This is an exothermic process.

Generally, a solid is more likely to dissolve in a liquid if the overall enthalpy change is exothermic. High solubility is therefore *more likely* if:

strength of the attraction between the molecular solid and liquid molecules in the solution	>	combined strengths of the attractions between molecules in the pure solid and between molecules in the pure liquid

Although the thermodynamics of solubility are rather more complex than this (involving a consideration of *entropy changes* as described in Chapter 15), this simple 'rule of thumb' often helps us to account for patterns in solubility. It can be summarized in the phrase 'like dissolves like'.

Worked example

Account for the observation that iodine is soluble in hexane but not in water (Figure 4.87).

Iodine and hexane are non-polar substances. When mixed together a solution is formed because:

| strength of the iodine–hexane attraction in solution (London (dispersion) forces) | > | combined strengths of the attractions in iodine solid (London (dispersion) forces) and hexane liquid (London (dispersion) forces) |

Also, water is a polar solvent, with its molecules forming hydrogen bonds. When mixed with non-polar iodine molecules, nearly all of the water molecules continue to hydrogen bond with each other. Thus, the resulting iodine–water attractions are extremely weak in comparison to the combined strength of the hydrogen bonds in water and the London (dispersion) forces in iodine. Consequently, iodine is virtually insoluble in water.

■ **Figure 4.87** Iodine introduced to hexane and water

Solubility of liquids

The dissolving of one liquid in another may be explained in a similar way to the dissolving of a solid in a liquid. For example, water will mix with polar liquids such as ethanol (C_2H_5OH) and propanone ((CH_3)$_2$CO). The oppositely charged ends of the different molecules attract one another and hydrogen bonds are formed (Figure 4.88). The hydrogen bonds formed between the water and ethanol molecules are stronger than the hydrogen bonds formed between the molecules in the pure liquids. Entropy also plays an important role in determining the solubility of liquids in liquids.

■ **Figure 4.88**
A mixture of water and ethanol

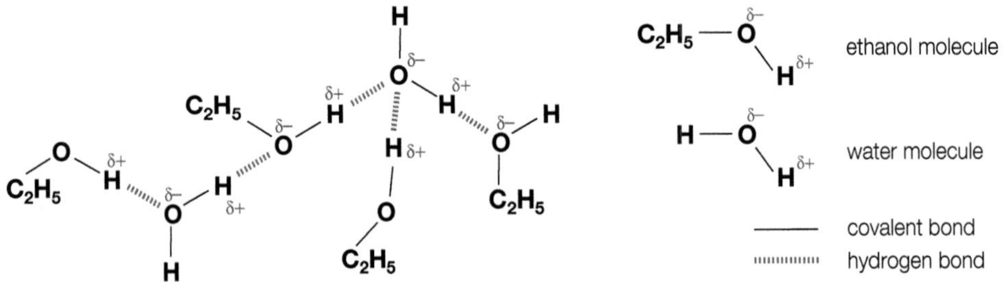

C₂H₅ — O ... H ($\delta-$) ethanol molecule

H — O ... H ($\delta-$, $\delta+$) water molecule

——— covalent bond
.... hydrogen bond

However, when water is added to an unreactive and non-polar liquid, such as tetrachloromethane, CCl_4, two layers separate out. The water molecules attract each other strongly, via hydrogen bond formation, but have no tendency to mix with the molecules of tetrachloromethane (Figure 4.89). It is not energetically favourable to replace the strong hydrogen bonds formed between water molecules with the weaker London (dispersion) forces formed between water and tetrachloromethane molecules. The 'like dissolves like' principle holds.

■ **Figure 4.89**
The interface between water and tetrachloromethane

Cl — C — Cl with Cl above and Cl below
tetrachloromethane molecule

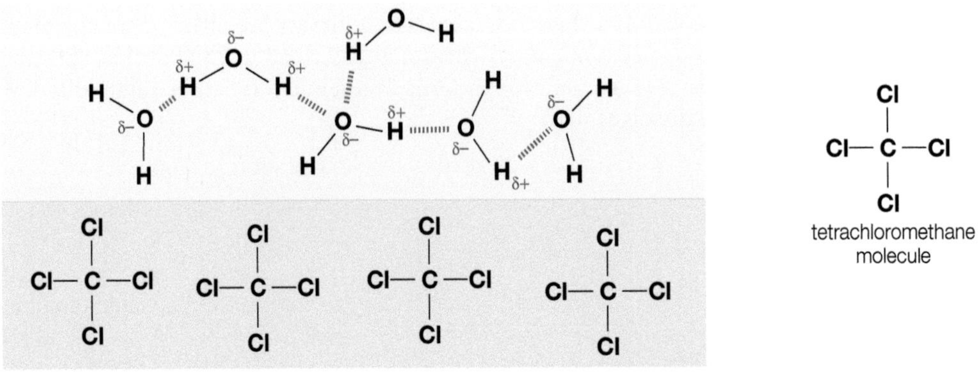

Solubility of gases

Gases are generally only slightly soluble in water. Examples of gases in this category include oxygen, hydrogen, nitrogen and the noble gases. A small number of gases are highly soluble in water because they react with water to release ions. Of course, it can be argued that the solubility is a property of the new ions, not the original gas. A chemical change has taken place.

For example, sulfur dioxide, SO_2, reacts with water to form a solution of hydrogen and hydrogen sulfate ions:

$$SO_2(g) + H_2O(g) \rightleftharpoons H^+(aq) + HSO_3^-(aq)$$

This solution is known as sulfurous (sulfuric(IV)) acid and is a major component of acid rain.

Hydrogen chloride reacts with water to form hydrochloric acid. The force of attraction between the negatively charged oxygen atoms of the water molecules and the positively charged hydrogen atoms of the hydrogen chloride molecules is sufficient that the hydrogen–chlorine bond is polarized and broken. The chlorine atom retains both electrons of this bond, while the oxygen atom of the water molecule uses one of its lone pairs to form a dative bond with the hydrogen ion (Figure 4.90). Virtually all of the hydrogen chloride molecules ionize in this way and therefore the hydrochloric acid solution is a strong acid (Chapter 8).

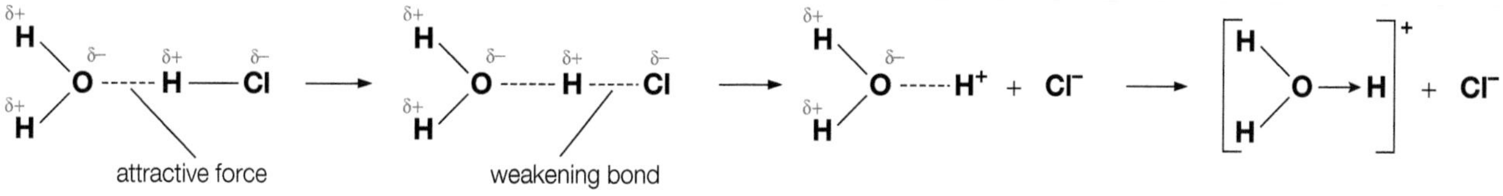

■ **Figure 4.90** The reaction between water and hydrogen chloride molecules

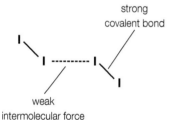

■ **Figure 4.91** Strong covalent and weak intermolecular forces (London (dispersion) forces)

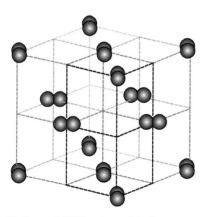

■ **Figure 4.92** Structure of iodine: a simple molecular substance

Physical properties of simple molecular compounds

Simple molecular compounds are formed by the covalent bonding of a relatively small number of atoms. The bonds holding the atoms together in molecules are relatively *strong* covalent bonds. However, the molecules are associated together in the solid and liquid states by relatively *weak* intermolecular forces (Figure 4.91). Therefore, under standard conditions, simple molecular compounds are either gases or liquids, or soft solids with low melting points. The melting points are low because of the weak intermolecular attractions that exist between molecules in the liquid and solid states.

Melting points of simple molecular compounds are greatly affected by the presence of impurities. Impurities lower the melting point and cause it to become a melting range. The melting point of the impure solid is no longer sharp, but a range of values. This occurs because the presence of even small amounts of impurities affects the regular packing of molecules into a lattice.

Most simple covalent compounds whose intermolecular forces are London (dispersion) forces, for example iodine (Figure 4.92) and the halogenoalkanes, are poorly soluble in water, but are soluble in less polar or non-polar solvents. Simple covalent compounds whose intermolecular forces are hydrogen bonds are often soluble in water, for example amines, carboxylic acids, amides and sugars, provided they have relatively low molar mass or can form multiple hydrogen bonds.

Generally, simple molecular compounds do not conduct electricity when molten. This is because they do not contain ions but molecules. Molecules are electrically neutral and are not attracted to charged electrodes.

However, a number of simple molecular compounds are soluble in water and undergo a chemical reaction with water (hydrolysis) to release ions. The molecular substance is completely or partially converted into ions. Examples of such substances include chlorine, Cl_2, ammonia, NH_3, and hydrogen chloride, HCl. The first two reactions are equilibrium reactions, but the last reaction goes to completion.

$$Cl_2(g) + H_2O(l) \rightleftharpoons HCl(aq) + HOCl(aq)$$

$$NH_3(g) + H_2O(l) \rightleftharpoons NH_4^+(aq) + OH^-(aq)$$

$$HCl(g) + H_2O(l) \rightarrow H_3O^+(aq) + Cl^-(aq)$$

In the last reaction H_3O^+ is the oxonium ion, present in aqueous solutions of acid. It is formed when a water molecule forms a dative bond to a proton.

Physical properties of polymers

Addition polymers

Addition polymers are formed from alkenes and are discussed in Chapter 10. Alkenes can be made to join together in the presence of high pressure and a suitable catalyst. The π-bond breaks and the molecules join together by covalent bonds. No other product is formed, and so this is known as addition polymerization. Since the polymers are made from alkenes they are also known as polyalkenes. The product of this addition process is a very long hydrocarbon chain. Addition polymers can be made from any alkene, including the simplest, ethene (Figure 4.93).

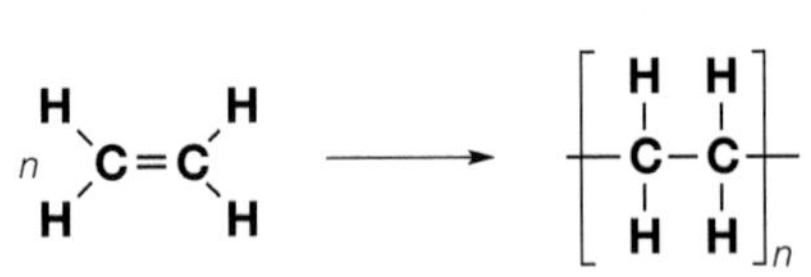

ethene → polyethene

■ **Figure 4.93** The formation of polyethene

Addition polymers (polyalkenes) are long-chain hydrocarbons that are saturated and non-polar. Their structure results in their having a number of characteristic properties:

■ Since the hydrocarbon chains are often very long, the London (dispersion) forces between the chains are often very strong and the polymers have relatively high melting and boiling points.

■ Since the chain length is variable, most polymers contain chains of a variety of different lengths. Thus the London (dispersion) forces are of variable strength and these polymers tend to melt gradually over a range of temperatures rather than sharply at a fixed temperature.

■ As the chains are not rigidly held in place by each other, the polymers tend to be relatively soft.

■ Since the chains are non-polar, addition polymers are insoluble in water.

■ Since the intermolecular forces between the molecules are strong and the chains are often tangled, they are generally insoluble in non-polar solvents as well.

■ In fact, the long hydrocarbon chains result in polyalkenes being very unreactive generally.

Biodegradable polymers

Synthetic polymers are highly stable and although it is this property that makes them so useful it has created a problem in their disposal. Waste polymers are normally disposed of in landfill sites but because they do not readily break down or degrade in the environment, these landfill sites are rapidly reaching capacity. Recycling and incineration (burning) of polymers are possible solutions but another approach in dealing with the plastic industry's environmental problems is to make biodegradable polymers.

Biopolymers are natural polymers and many have properties similar to synthetic polymers. Unlike synthetic polymers, however, they can be broken down by micro-organisms present in the environment, that is, they are biodegradable.

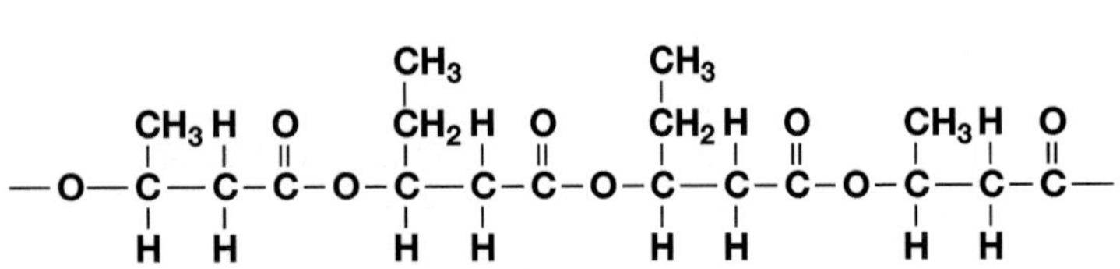

Figure 4.94 shows the structure of Biopol, a biodegradable synthetic polymer manufactured by certain strains of bacteria. Although relatively expensive, it has found use as a packaging material for cosmetics and motor oils although its main intended applications were medical – for surgical stitches and in the controlled release of medicines into the body.

■ **Figure 4.94** Structure of Biopol

Deducing the types of intermolecular force present in substances, based on their structure and chemical formula

The flow chart in Figure 4.95 can be used to identify the type of intermolecular force(s) present in a molecular substance. Knowledge of its molecular formula, structure and its shape and hence its polarity is required before the intermolecular force can be identified.

■ **Figure 4.95**
Identifying
intermolecular forces

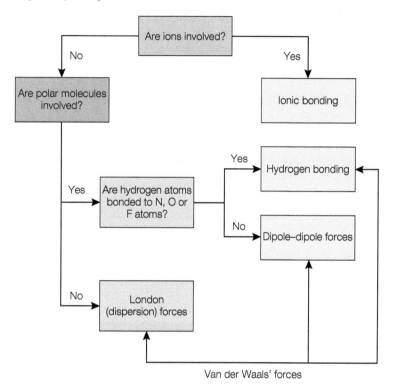

For example, consider the interhalogen, bromine monochloride, BrCl. The compound is composed of two non-metals and hence likely to be covalent. It is a polar molecule with a partial negative charge on the chlorine and a partial positive charge on the bromine. There is no hydrogen atom present so dipole–dipole forces and London (dispersion) forces are operating between the molecules.

Now consider the molecule hydrazine, N_2H_4. The compound is composed of two non-metals and hence likely to be covalent. It is a polar molecule with a partial negative charge on the nitrogen atoms and a partial positive charge on the hydrogen atoms. It is polar because it is pyramidal around both nitrogen atoms. There are hydrogen atoms bonded to the nitrogen atoms so hydrogen bonds and London (dispersion) forces are operating between the molecules.

Worked example

Predict and explain the properties of phosphine, PH_3.

Phosphorus(III) hydride, PH_3, is a simple molecular substance with pyramidal shaped molecules. Phosphorus is less electronegative than nitrogen. Hence, only weak London (dispersion) forces with dipole–dipole forces, and not hydrogen bonding, are present in PH_3. As a consequence PH_3 is predicted to be relatively volatile and have relatively low melting and boiling points. Small amounts of thermal energy are required to break the London (dispersion) and dipole–dipole forces acting between molecules in the solid and liquid states. Since PH_3 is simple molecular it will not be an electrolyte in the molten state. PH_3 will be a non-conductor in both the solid and liquid states – no mobile ions will be present. It is expected to be only slightly soluble in water since it is unable to form hydrogen bonds with water. There may be some hydrolysis reaction with water (similar to ammonia):

$$PH_3(g) + H_2O(l) \rightleftharpoons PH_4^+ + OH^-(aq)$$

4.5 Metallic bonding – *metallic bonds involve a lattice of cations with delocalized electrons*

Nature of Science **Using theories to explain the distinctive properties of metals**

The properties of metals are very different from those of ionic and covalent compounds. Many metals are strong and can be bent without breaking; many are malleable (can be beaten into thin sheets) and ductile (can be drawn into wires). They are shiny when cut or polished and are excellent electrical and thermal conductors. Any theory of metallic bonding must account for all these physical properties and any differences or trends in these properties observed for metals.

The properties of metals can be explained by the simple 'electron sea' model which views metals as consisting of cations in fixed positions surrounded by a 'sea' of moving delocalized valence electrons.

This theory of metallic bonding explains the physical properties of metals. If a stress is applied to the metal, the structure can change shape without the crystal fracturing. This is in contrast to the effect of stress on an ionic crystal, which will shatter.

The high thermal conductivity of metals is explained. When heat is supplied to a metal, the kinetic energy of the electrons is increased and this is transmitted through the system of delocalized electrons to the cooler regions of the metal.

The 'electron sea' model also explains the high electrical conductivity of metals. If a potential difference (voltage) is applied between the ends of a metal sample, the delocalized electrons (electron cloud) will flow towards the positive electrode.

The shiny appearance can only be explained with the band theory model of metallic bonding. The metal contains a large number of molecular orbitals at different energy levels. When light is absorbed by a metal, electrons are excited. A large number of electron transitions is possible, with a whole range of frequencies absorbed. As electrons return to lower energy levels, light is emitted and this makes the metal surface shine.

■ Metallic bonding

In metals, the valence electrons are no longer associated with a particular metal atom, but are free to move throughout the metal. The mobile valence electrons are described as delocalized. Hence, the metal atoms are effectively ionized. This description is confirmed by X-ray analysis (Figure 4.96) which shows that metal crystals are composed of positive ions (cations) surrounded by the delocalized valence electrons.

Metallic bonding (Figure 4.97) is the electrostatic attraction between the metal ions and the delocalized electrons. Metallic bonding is *non-directional*: all of the valence electrons are attracted to the nuclei of all the metal ions. The presence of delocalized electrons accounts for the physical properties of metals. This model of metallic bonding is often known as the electron-sea model, where the delocalized electrons form the 'sea'.

■ **Figure 4.96**
An electron density map of aluminium

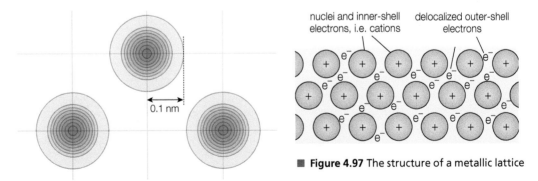

■ **Figure 4.97** The structure of a metallic lattice

Explaining the physical properties of metals

Metals are ductile and malleable and are excellent conductors of heat and electricity. In a metal, the valence electrons do not belong to any particular atom. Hence, if sufficient force is applied to the metal, one layer of metal atoms can slide over another without disrupting the metallic bonding (Figure 4.98). The metallic bonding in a metal is strong and flexible and so metals can be hammered into thin sheets (malleability) or drawn into long wires (ductility) without breaking.

■ **Figure 4.98** The application of a shear force to a metal lattice: adjacent layers can slide over each other

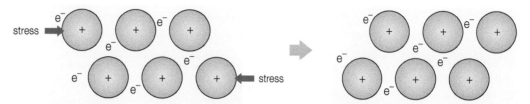

However, if atoms of other elements are added by alloying, the layers of ions will not slide over each other so readily. The alloy is thus less malleable and ductile and consequently harder and stronger.

When a voltage (potential difference) is applied across a metal, the delocalized electrons are repelled from the negative electrode and move towards the positive electrode. This orderly flow of electrons constitutes an electric current.

The delocalized electrons can also conduct heat by carrying kinetic energy (in the form of vibrations) from a hot part of the metal lattice to a colder part of the lattice. The presence of delocalized electrons in metals accounts for the thermal and electrical conductivity of metals.

The melting points of metals

The melting point is an approximate measure of the strength of the metallic bonding in a metal lattice. The higher the melting point, the stronger the metallic bonding.

The delocalized electrons in the valence shell of the metal atoms are responsible for the metallic bond, and therefore for its strength. The other factor controlling the strength of metallic bonding is the size of the metal ion. The smaller the ionic radius, the stronger the metallic bonding. Thus:

$$\text{strength of metallic bond} \propto \frac{\text{number of valence electrons per atom}}{\text{metallic radius}}$$

The strength of metallic bonding therefore increases in period 3 from sodium, through magnesium, to aluminium (Figure 4.99) as the number of valence electrons per atom increases from one, to two and then three. The ionic radius decreases from sodium to aluminium, as the large increase in nuclear charge outweighs the small increase in shielding (Chapter 3). Consequently, the melting points increase from sodium to aluminium (Table 4.17). The same trend is exhibited by the metallic elements in period 2.

■ **Figure 4.99** Metals with small highly charged ions form stronger metallic bonds (metallic bond strength increases A < B < C)

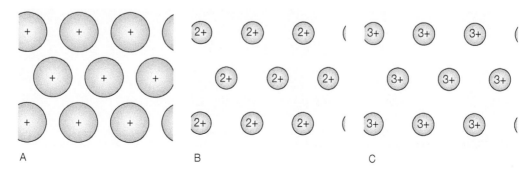

■ **Table 4.17** Melting and boiling points of period 3 metals

Element	Sodium	Magnesium	Aluminium
Melting point/K	371	922	936
Boiling point/K	1156	1363	2740
Metallic radius (10^{-12} m)	98	65	45

On descending groups 1 and 2 in the s-block, the boiling and melting points generally decrease (Table 4.18) as the metallic bonding becomes longer and weaker. This is due to the increase in atomic and ionic radii, the increase in shielding (due to greater electron–electron repulsion) and the greater distance between the nuclei and the delocalized valence electrons. Any 'breaks' in the trends will be due to a change in the packing of ions (lattice structure).

■ **Table 4.18** Melting and boiling points of s-block metals

Group 1 metal	Boiling point	Group 2 metal	Boiling point
Lithium	1342	Beryllium	2468
Sodium	882.9	Magnesium	1090
Potassium	759	Calcium	1484
Rubidium	688	Strontium	1377
Caesium	671	Barium	1845

The boiling points of metals are considerably higher than their melting points. This implies that most of the metallic bonding still exists in the liquid state. However, when the liquid changes into a gas (vapour), the atoms must be separated to large distances, which involves breaking the metallic bonds.

■ Alloys

An alloy is typically a homogeneous mixture of metals or a mixture of a metal and a non-metal, usually carbon but sometimes phosphorus. Alloys usually have different properties from those of the component elements, and melt over a range of temperature. Alloys are generally made by mixing the metal with the other elements in molten form, and allowing the mixture to cool and the alloy to solidify.

Alloys are usually divided into ferrous and non-ferrous alloys. Ferrous alloys include the steels, which are alloys of iron containing up to 2% carbon. The majority of non-ferrous alloys are based on copper. Familiar alloys of copper are brass (copper and zinc) and bronze (copper and tin). Bronze is an alloy that people have used considerably over long periods of history. It is still used to produce statues and sculpted artwork.

Explaining the properties of alloys

Most pure metals are not used in engineering because they do not have the required properties. For example, the pure metal may readily undergo corrosion or be too soft. However, the properties of a metal may be improved by the formation of an alloy. Alloys are often harder than the original metals because the irregularity in the structure helps to stop rows of metal atoms from slipping over each other (Figure 4.100).

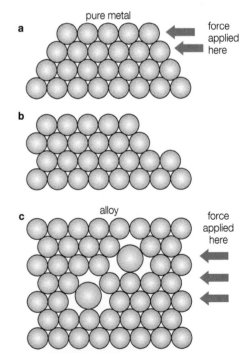

■ **Figure 4.100 a** The position of the atoms in a pure metal before a force is applied; **b** after the force is applied, slippage has taken place; **c** in an alloy, slippage is prevented because the atoms of different size cannot easily slide over each other

For example, brass is stronger than copper and is more easily worked because of its higher malleability – brass is also more resistant to corrosion. Duralumin (an alloy of aluminium with magnesium and copper) is much stronger than aluminium, but the presence of copper makes it prone to corrosion. Stainless steel contains iron with chromium, nickel and a small amount of carbon. It is extremely hardwearing and resistant to corrosion even when heated – its resistance to corrosion can be improved by increasing the chromium content.

 ## Metal resources

The majority of metals occur as mineral resources in rock enriched in one or more metals. Some minerals are used as they are found in the ground, i.e. they require no further processing or very little processing, for example, gold. Most minerals must be processed before they are used. Iron is found in abundance in minerals, but the process of extracting iron from different minerals varies in cost depending on the mineral. It is most cost-effective to extract the iron from oxide minerals like hematite (Fe_2O_3) or magnetite (Fe_3O_4). Although iron also occurs in other minerals, the concentration of iron in these minerals is less, and the cost of extraction is increased because strong bonds between iron, silicon and oxygen must be broken.

Because such variables as extraction costs, labour costs and energy costs vary with time and from country to country, what determines an economically viable deposit of minerals varies considerably with time and place. In general, the higher the concentration of the substance, the more economical it is to mine.

An ore is a body of material from which one or more valuable substances can be extracted economically. An ore deposit will consist of ore minerals that contain the valuable substance, usually a metal. Since economics controls what concentration (grade) of the substance in a deposit makes it profitable to mine, different substances require different concentrations to be profitable. However, the concentration that can be economically mined changes due to economic conditions such as demand for the substance and the cost of extraction.

Supplies of metal are finite and must be carefully conserved and recycled as the global population increases and demand increases. Supplies of metals are one factor that determines national wealth. For example, mining is an important primary industry in Australia, which has been supplying iron ore, zinc, uranium, copper, gold, bauxite (aluminium ore) and rare earth elements (lanthanoids).

■ Band theory

The 'electron sea' model of metallic bonding is a simple model of metallic bonding, but a more detailed and realistic way of describing metallic bonding is band theory (Chapter 24 on the accompanying website). This is based on molecular orbital theory (Chapter 14), which describes bond formation via the overlapping and merging of atomic orbitals.

 When the electron clouds of two atomic orbitals of two metal atoms overlap and merge, two molecular orbitals are formed. When the atomic orbitals of four adjacent metal atoms overlap, four molecular orbitals are formed. The molecular orbitals of highest and lowest energy result from the overlap of adjacent metal atoms, while the intermediate energy levels arise from the overlap of the atomic orbitals of metal atoms further away.

In a solid containing n metal atoms, n molecular orbitals are formed with a range of energies. These form a band with a virtually continuous range of energy levels (Figure 4.101). Each molecular orbital can contain two electrons of opposite spin (Chapter 2), so an energy band formed from n metal atoms is able to contain $2n$ electrons.

For a solid to be able to conduct electricity and show metallic behaviour, an energy band must be partially filled with electrons. If the energy band is empty, there are no electrons to flow

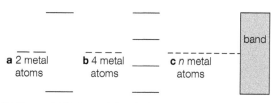

■ **Figure 4.101** The origin of a band of molecular orbitals from metal atoms in a lattice

and form a current when a voltage is applied across the metal. If the energy band is empty, there are no electrons to form the current; if the energy band is full and its orbitals fully occupied, there are no empty orbitals for the electrons to move into.

■ The structure of metals

Metals atoms (cations) pack closely together in a regular structure to form crystals. Arrangements in which the gaps are kept to a minimum are known as close-packed structures. X-ray diffraction studies have revealed that there are three main types of metallic structure: hexagonal close packed, face-centred cubic close packed and body-centred cubic.

■ **Figure 4.102**
Face-centred cubic
close-packed structure

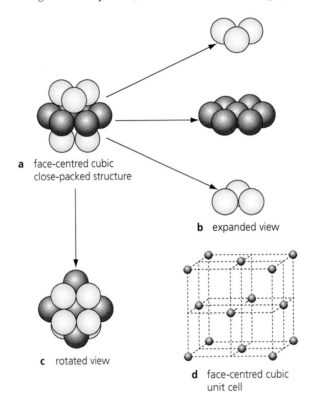

a face-centred cubic
close-packed structure

b expanded view

c rotated view

d face-centred cubic
unit cell

Figure 4.102 is a diagram of the face-centred cubic structure, showing every metal atom (cation) touching 12 others, six in the same layer (plane), three in the layer above and three in the layer below. The metal atoms (cations) have a coordination number of 12. The high coordination number in these close-packed metal structures is due to the non-directional nature of metallic bonding. The unit cell is the smallest repeating unit of the metal crystal (Figure 4.103).

■ **Figure 4.103**
Polished metal crystals

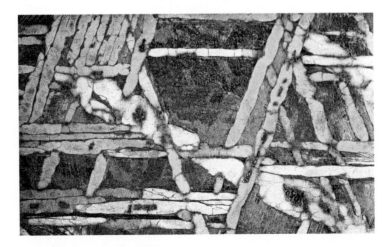

Examination questions – a selection

Paper 1 IB questions and IB style questions

Q1 Which compound contains ionic bonds?
- **A** magnesium chloride, $MgCl_2$
- **B** dichloroethane, CH_2Cl_2
- **C** ethanoic acid, CH_3COOH
- **D** silicon tetrabromide, $SiBr_4$

Q2 When CH_4, NH_3, H_2O are arranged in order of **decreasing bond angle**, what is the correct order?
- **A** CH_4, NH_3, H_2O
- **C** NH_3, CH_4, H_2O
- **B** NH_3, H_2O, CH_4
- **D** H_2O, NH_3, CH_4

Q3 In which of the following pairs does the second substance have the lower boiling point?
- **A** Cl_2, Br_2
- **C** C_3H_8, C_4H_{10}
- **B** H_2O, H_2S
- **D** CH_3OCH_3, CH_3CH_2OH

Q4 According to VSEPR theory, which molecule would be expected to have the smallest bond angle?
- **A** H_2O
- **C** SiH_4
- **B** H_2CO
- **D** NH_3

Q5 In which of the following substances would hydrogen bonding be expected to occur?
-     **I** C_2H_6 **II** CH_3CH_2COOH **III** CH_3OCH_3
- **A** II only
- **C** II and III only
- **B** I and III only
- **D** I, II and III

Q6 Why is the boiling point of ethane greater than that of neon?
- **A** The ethane molecule is polar.
- **B** Hydrogen bonds form between ethane molecules but are not present in liquid neon.
- **C** More electrons are present in ethane than in neon.
- **D** A molecule of ethane has a greater mass than a neon atom.

Q7 Which is the best description of ionic bonding in sodium chloride?
- **A** Electrostatic attraction between sodium and chlorine nuclei
- **B** Electrostatic attraction of sodium and chlorine nuclei towards shared electrons in the bond between the chlorine and sodium nuclei
- **C** Electrostatic attraction between sodium cations and electrons
- **D** Electrostatic attraction between oppositely charged sodium and chloride ions

Q8 Which compound is the most soluble in water?
- **A** ethane
- **C** propan-1-ol
- **B** propane
- **D** hexan-1-ol

Q9 Element X is in group 13 and element Y is in group 16 of the periodic table. Which is the most likely formula of the compound formed when X and Y react together?
- **A** XY
- **C** X_3Y_2
- **B** X_2Y_3
- **D** XY_2

Q10 Which molecule contains a multiple bond?
- **A** H_2
- **C** C_2F_4
- **B** H_2O
- **D** C_2F_6

Q11 Which is **not** present in $C_2H_5OC_2H_5$ in the liquid state?
- **A** covalent bonding
- **B** London (dispersion) forces
- **C** dipole–dipole attractions
- **D** hydrogen bonding

Q12 Chlorine has a lower boiling point than bromine. Which property of the two elements is responsible for this observation?
- **A** ionization energies
- **C** bond polarities
- **B** bond enthalpies
- **D** number of electrons

Q13 Which of the following molecules is planar?
- **A** NCl_3
- **C** C_3H_6
- **B** C_2H_4
- **D** SF_6

Q14 A solid has a high melting point, does not conduct electricity as a solid, but does when it is dissolved in water. What type of substance is the solid?
- **A** ionic
- **C** giant molecular
- **B** simple molecular
- **D** metallic

Q15 When the Lewis structure for $HCOOCH_3$ is drawn, how many bonds and how many lone pairs of electrons are present?
- **A** 8 and 4
- **C** 5 and 5
- **B** 7 and 5
- **D** 7 and 4

Q16 The angle between the two carbon–carbon bonds in CH_3CHCF_2 is closest to:
- **A** 180°
- **C** 109°
- **B** 120°
- **D** 90°

Q17 The molar masses of C_2H_6, CH_3OH and CH_3F are similar. How do their boiling points compare?
- **A** $C_2H_6 < CH_3OH < CH_3F$
- **B** $CH_3F < CH_3OH < C_2H_6$
- **C** $CH_3OH < CH_3F < C_2H_6$
- **D** $C_2H_6 < CH_3F < CH_3OH$

Q18 Which intermolecular forces exist in dry ice, $CO_2(s)$?
- **A** dipole–dipole interactions
- **B** covalent bonds
- **C** London (dispersion) forces
- **D** hydrogen bonds

Q19 Which one of the following molecules would be expected to be linear?
- **A** H_2O_2
- **C** SO_3
- **B** NO_2
- **D** CO_2

Q20 Which of the compounds H_2O, H_2S, H_2Se and HCl has the highest boiling point?
- **A** H_2O
- **B** H_2S
- **C** H_2Se
- **D** HCl

Q21 Which is an incorrect statement about carbon-60 (C_{60})?
- **A** It is a giant molecular substance.
- **B** It is a soft powder.
- **C** The surface of its molecules is composed of rings of five and six carbon atoms.
- **D** London (dispersion) forces of attraction hold the molecules in a lattice.

Q22 Given the following electronegativity values:

H: 2.2   N: 3.0   O: 3.4   F: 4.0

which bond has the greatest polarity?
- **A** O–H in H_2O
- **B** N–F in NF_3
- **C** N–O in NO_2
- **D** N–H in NH_3

Q23 Which one of the following species has a triangular pyramidal geometry?
- **A** BCl_3
- **B** NCl_3
- **C** H_2Se
- **D** C_2H_2

Q24 According to IUPAC which of the following interactions are included under the term van der Waals' forces?
- **I** London dispersion forces
- **II** Dipole–dipole forces (permanent dipole forces)
- **III** Dipole–induced dipole forces
- **A** I, II and III
- **B** II and III only
- **C** I and III only
- **D** I and II only

Q25 Which substance is hard, with a high melting point and does not conduct electricity in any physical state?
- **A** silicon(IV) oxide
- **B** magnesium chloride
- **C** cobalt
- **D** lead(II) fluoride

Q26 Which statements about the structure and bonding of silicon dioxide are correct?

	Structure	Bonding
A	Silicon dioxide forms a giant covalent network	Each oxygen atom is covalently bonded to two silicon atoms.
B	Silicon dioxide molecules are V-shaped or bent	Each silicon atom is covalently bonded to two oxygen atoms
C	Silicon dioxide molecules are linear	A double covalent bond exists between silicon and oxygen atoms
D	Silicon dioxide forms a giant covalent network	Each oxygen atom is covalently bonded to four silicon atoms

Higher Level Paper 1, May 2013, Q10

Q27 Which of the following species does not exhibit resonance?
- **A** hydroxide ion, OH^-
- **B** benzene, C_6H_6
- **C** nitrate ion, NO_3^-
- **D** ozone, O_3

Q28 Which compound contains both covalent and ionic bonds?
- **A** sodium carbonate, Na_2CO_3
- **B** magnesium fluoride, MgF_2
- **C** dichloromethane, CH_2Cl_2
- **D** propanoic acid, CH_3CH_2COOH

Paper 2 IB questions and IB style questions

Q1 Describe the variation in melting points and electrical conductivities of the elements sodium to argon, and explain these variations in terms of their structures and bonding. [6]

Q2
- **a** Draw electron dot structures for N_2 and F_2 and explain why F_2 is much more reactive than N_2. [3]
- **b** Compare the polarity of the bonds N–F and C–F. Are the molecules NF_3 and CF_4 polar or non-polar? In all your answers give your reasons. [5]

Standard Level Paper 2, May 1999, Q5

Q3 Explain at the molecular level why ethanol (C_2H_5OH) is soluble in water, but cholesterol ($C_{27}H_{45}OH$) and ethane (C_2H_6) are not. [4]

Standard Level Paper 2, May 2001, Q6

Q4 The elements potassium and fluorine and the compound potassium fluoride can be used to show the connection between bonding, structure and physical properties.
- **a** Describe the type of bonding in potassium metal and explain why potassium is a good conductor of electricity. [4]
- **b** Draw a Lewis structure for fluorine. Name and describe the bonding within and between the molecules in liquid fluorine. [4]
- **c** Write the electronic structures of both potassium and fluorine and describe how the atoms combine to form potassium fluoride. [4]
- **d** Explain why potassium fluoride does not conduct electricity until it is heated above its melting point. [1]

Q5
- **a** Boron trifluoride, BF_3, and aluminium fluoride, AlF_3, differ markedly in their physical properties.

Compound	Melting point/°C
BF_3	−144
AlF_3	1291

Deduce the type of bonding present in each of these compounds and draw 'dot and cross' diagrams to illustrate this bonding. [6]
- **b** Boron trifluoride forms a compound with ammonia. The reaction occurs in the gas phase.
  - **i** Describe the type of covalent bond that is formed during this reaction. [2]
  - **ii** Draw the Lewis diagram and structural formula for the compound (adduct) formed in this reaction. [2]

5 Energetics/thermochemistry

ESSENTIAL IDEAS

■ The enthalpy changes from chemical reactions can be calculated from their effect on the temperature of their surroundings.
■ In chemical transformations energy can neither be created nor destroyed (the first law of thermodynamics).
■ Energy is absorbed when bonds are broken and is released when bonds are formed.

5.1 Measuring energy changes – *the enthalpy changes from chemical reactions can be calculated from their effect on the temperature of their surroundings*

■ Heat

If you touch a hot surface, thermal energy will enter your hand because the surface is warmer than your hand. But if you touch ice, thermal energy will leave your hand and pass into the colder ice. The direction of spontaneous energy transfer is always from a warmer substance to a cooler substance. The thermal energy that is transferred from an object to another because of a temperature difference between them is called heat. The term 'heat' is best regarded as a description of a process rather than the name of a form of energy. We say heat is transferred between a system and its surroundings if the transfer of energy occurs as a result of a temperature difference between them.

When heat flows from one object to another object, they are said to be in thermal contact. During thermal contact, heat will flow from the hotter object to the cooler object until they are both at the same temperature. This is known as thermal equilibrium and the rates of heat flow between the two bodies are the same. Heat can never flow on its own from a cooler object to a hotter object. This is against the laws of thermodynamics.

Physicists use the concept of internal energy, which is the sum of all types of energies inside a substance, including potential energy due to forces between molecules. A substance does not contain heat but it does contain internal energy.

■ Temperature

All three states of matter – solids, liquids and gases – are made of atoms, ions or molecules. These particles are vibrating in solids and in liquids, and moving around in gases (translational motion). Because of these random motions at all temperatures above absolute zero (0 K or −273 °C), the particles in matter have kinetic energy. The average kinetic energy of these individual particles causes what we perceive through sense perception as warmth. Whenever a substance becomes warmer, the average kinetic energy of its particles has increased.

The random kinetic energy of particles in matter can be increased in a number of ways. For example, solar energy from the Sun being absorbed by sea water, striking a piece of metal with a hammer many times, compressing the air in a tyre pump for a bicycle or simply using a flame.

Temperature is directly related to the random motion of particles in substances at temperatures above absolute zero. In the case of an ideal gas, the absolute temperature (in Kelvin) is directly proportional to the average kinetic energy of translational motion (from one place to another). In liquids and solids there is still a similar relationship. So the warmth you feel when you touch a hot surface is the kinetic energy transferred by molecules in the hot surface to your colder fingers.

Be aware that temperature is not a measure of the total kinetic energy of all the molecules in a substance. There is twice as much molecular kinetic energy (in joules) in $2\,dm^3$ of boiling water as in $1\,dm^3$ of boiling water at the same temperature. However, the temperatures of both cubic decimetres (litres) of water are the same because the average kinetic molecular energy is the same.

The Fahrenheit scale

The physical quantity that tells us how hot a sample of a substance is, is temperature. Temperature is expressed by a number that corresponds to a degree mark on a chosen scale. The Celsius and Fahrenheit scales are based on the physical properties of water but the absolute or thermodynamic scale of temperature is not based on the physical properties of any substance. The kelvin is the SI unit of temperature and is based on absolute zero (approximately −273 °C) – the temperature at which the particles of a substance have no random kinetic energy. The kelvin has the same incremental scaling as the degree Celsius. So a change of 1 K is the same as a change of 1 °C.

Nearly all matter expands when its temperature increases and contracts when its temperature decreases. A mercury or alcohol thermometer measures temperature by showing the expansions and contractions of a liquid in a sealed glass tube using a calibrated scale.

The Fahrenheit scale of temperature (Figure 5.1) is widely used in the United States. The number 32 indicates the temperature at which water freezes and the number 212 indicates the temperature at which water boils. The Fahrenheit scale is not part of the metric system. It is named after the German physicist Gabriel Fahrenheit (1686–1736).

---

1   Find out how to convert temperatures between Fahrenheit and Celsius.

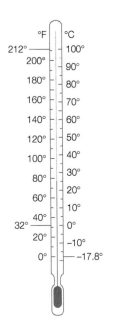

■ **Figure 5.1**
Fahrenheit and
Celsius scales on
a thermometer

■ Conservation of energy

Energy is conserved during chemical reactions. The amount of energy in the Universe at the end of the chemical reaction is the same as at the beginning. This is known as the law of conservation of energy. This implies that the amount of energy in the Universe remains constant and energy is neither created nor destroyed. Energy can be converted from one form to another, from potential or chemical energy to internal energy and heat energy, but the total energy within the Universe remains fixed.

---

2   Find out about perpetual motion machines.

Nature of Science

Fundamental principle – conservation of energy is a fundamental principle of science

The law of conservation of energy states that energy cannot be created or destroyed and that it is simply changed from one form to another. Hence, whenever one form of energy disappears, an equal amount of energy in some other form appears. When the Universe is taken into consideration, there is one quantity that does not change: energy.

The law of conservation of energy is also represented in the first law of thermodynamics, the study of energy changes during chemical reactions and physical changes. The first law of thermodynamics includes the principle that the amount of energy in an isolated system is constant: when one form of energy disappears, an equal amount of energy in another form is produced.

It is now known that energy can be produced by the loss of mass during a nuclear reaction. Energy and mass are related by Einstein's mass–energy equivalence relationship $E = mc^2$, where c is the velocity of light. The modified law, therefore, states that the total mass and energy of an isolated system remain constant.

■ Exothermic and endothermic reactions

Enthalpy changes

Chemical reactions involve a transfer of energy. Chemical substances contain chemical energy, a form of potential energy. Many chemical reactions involve a transfer of chemical energy into heat.

■ **Figure 5.2**
A burning magnesium sparkler (an exothermic reaction)

■ **Figure 5.3**
Burning Camping Gaz (compressed butane)

For example, when methane (the major component of natural gas) burns in excess oxygen, chemical energy is transferred to the surroundings as heat. The products of this combustion reaction are water and carbon dioxide:

$$CH_4(g) + 2O_2(g) \rightarrow CO_2(g) + 2H_2O(l)$$

The majority of chemical reactions release heat energy to their surroundings (Figures 5.2 and 5.3). This type of reaction is known as an exothermic reaction. A few chemical reactions absorb heat energy from their surroundings: these reactions are known as endothermic reactions. An example of an endothermic reaction is the thermal decomposition of calcium carbonate to form calcium oxide and carbon dioxide:

$$CaCO_3(s) \rightarrow CaO(s) + CO_2(g)$$

When an exothermic reaction transfers heat energy to the surroundings the chemical reactants lose potential energy. The products have less potential energy than the reactants. This potential energy stored in the chemical bonds is known as enthalpy and is given the symbol H. The transfer of heat energy that occurs (*at constant pressure*) during a chemical reaction from the reaction mixture (known as the system) to the surroundings is known as the enthalpy change, ΔH, where the Greek letter delta means 'change in'.

The negative and positive signs in enthalpy changes do *not* represent 'positive' and 'negative' energy. They simply indicate the direction of the flow of heat energy (Figure 5.4). Enthalpy changes are usually measured in units of kilojoules per mole ($kJ\,mol^{-1}$). The value of the enthalpy change for a particular reaction will vary with the conditions, especially concentration of chemicals.

Hence, standard enthalpy changes, $\Delta H^{\oplus}$, are measured under standard conditions:

- a pressure of 1 atmosphere or $100\,kPa$
- a temperature of $25\,°C$ ($298\,K$) (though in theory any temperature can be specified)
- concentrations of $1\,mol\,dm^{-3}$.
- If carbon involved, then it is assumed to be in the form of graphite (unless diamond is specified).

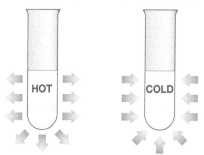

Exothermic reactions give out heat. This warms the mixture and then heat is lost to the surroundings

Endothermic reactions take in heat. This cools the mixture at first and then heat is gained from the surroundings

■ **Figure 5.4** The directions of heat flow during exothermic and endothermic reactions

Further points about enthalpy changes

In a reversible reaction (Chapter 7), if the forward reaction is exothermic, then the reverse reaction is endothermic, for example:

$$N_2(g) + 3H_2(g) \rightleftharpoons 2NH_3(g) \qquad \Delta H^{\oplus} = -92\,kJ\,mol^{-1}$$
$$2NH_3(g) \rightleftharpoons N_2(g) + 3H_2(g) \qquad \Delta H^{\oplus} = +92\,kJ\,mol^{-1}$$

Similarly, if the forward reaction is endothermic, the reverse reaction is exothermic.

The enthalpy change depends on the amounts of reactants used. If the coefficients of the thermochemical equation are multiplied or divided by a common factor, the value of the enthalpy change is changed by the same factor. For example:

$$\text{if} \quad CO(g) + \tfrac{1}{2} O_2(g) \rightarrow CO_2(g) \quad \Delta H^{\oplus} = -283\,kJ\,mol^{-1}$$

$$\text{then} \quad 2CO(g) + O_2(g) \rightarrow 2CO_2(g) \quad \Delta H^{\oplus} = 2 \times -283 = -566\,kJ\,mol^{-1}$$

Thermochemical equations are often manipulated according to these rules when solving problems using Hess's law.

■ Calculation of enthalpy changes

Specific heat capacity

When a substance is heated, the temperature of the substance increases. The size of the increase depends on the heat capacity of the substance. The heat capacity of the substance is the amount of heat energy required to raise the temperature of a substance by one degree Celsius or one kelvin. Heat capacity has units of joules per degree Celsius ($J\,°C^{-1}$) or joules per kelvin ($J\,K^{-1}$).

The specific heat capacity (Figure 5.5) is the amount of heat required to raise the temperature of a unit mass of the substance by one degree Celsius or one kelvin. Specific heat capacity, c, often has units of joules per gram per degree Celsius ($J\,g^{-1}\,°C^{-1}$). The lower the specific heat capacity of a substance, the greater its temperature rise for the same amount of heat absorbed:

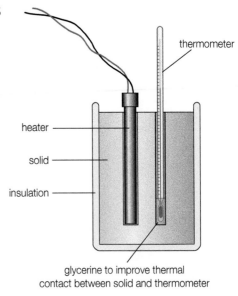

■ **Figure 5.5** Measuring the specific heat capacity of a solid

heat energy (q) = mass of object (m) × specific heat capacity (c) × temperature rise (ΔT)

i.e. $\qquad q = mc\Delta T$

Worked examples

Calculate the heat capacity of 80.0 grams of water. The specific heat capacity of water is $4.18\,J\,g^{-1}\,°C^{-1}$.

Heat capacity = $80.0\,g × 4.18\,J\,g^{-1}\,°C^{-1} = 334.4\,J\,°C^{-1}$

How much heat energy is required to increase the temperature of 20 grams of nickel (specific heat capacity $440\,J\,kg^{-1}\,°C^{-1}$) from 50 °C to 70 °C?

$q = mc\Delta T$

$q = 0.02\,kg × 440\,J\,kg^{-1}\,°C^{-1} × 20\,°C = 176\,J$

Using $q = mc\Delta T$ to calculate the heat change when the temperature of a pure substance is changed

A 10.0 g piece of pure iron has its temperature changed from 25 °C to 500 °C. The specific heat capacity of iron is $0.45\,J\,g^{-1}\,°C^{-1}$. Calculate the amount of heat energy in joules required to bring about this change.

$q = 10.0\,g × 0.45\,J\,g^{-1}\,°C^{-1} × 475\,C = 2137.7\,J$

Calculate the mass of gold (specific heat capacity $0.13\,J\,g^{-1}\,°C^{-1}$) that can be heated through the same temperature difference when supplied with the same amount of thermal energy.

$m = \dfrac{q}{c}\,\Delta T$

$m = \dfrac{2137.7\,J}{0.13\,J\,g^{-1}\,°C^{-1} × 475\,°C} = 34.61\,g$

■ Evaluating the results of a laboratory calorimetry experiment to determine an enthalpy change

The amount of thermal energy (heat) required to convert a solid to a liquid at constant temperature and pressure depends on the amount of substance present. However, the amount of heat needed to melt a specific amount, known as the heat of fusion, is always the same. It is often useful to refer to the amount of heat needed per gram or per mole of substance (molar heat of fusion). The molar heat of fusion is therefore the energy needed to change one mole of a solid into liquid at the melting point and it is specific to that substance. The involvement of thermal energy can be shown in equation form as follows:

$$H_2O(s) \rightarrow H_2O(l)$$

An excess amount of ice is placed in a calorimeter (polystyrene cup) with a known amount of hot water. Enough time is allowed for the ice to melt to bring the temperature of the ice-water to the melting point of ice, approximately 0 °C. At this time the extra ice is removed. The volume of the melted ice and water in the cup will be used with temperature data for the calorimeter to calculate the molar heat of fusion of ice. The density of water ($1.00\,\text{g cm}^{-3}$) will be used to convert volume to mass where needed.

Sample calculation (with no random errors or uncertainties, to simplify the calculation)

Results from the experiment

Volume of hot water = $90.4\,\text{cm}^3$
Final minimum temperature (water and ice) = 0.70 °C
Temperature of hot water = 53.6 °C
Volume (hot water and melted ice) = $151.9\,\text{cm}^3$

Steps in calculating the enthalpy change

1 Calculate the change in temperature of the original hot water in the calorimeter. The water cooled from 53.6 °C to 0.7 °C.

$$\Delta T = 53.6\,°C - 0.70\,°C = 52.9\,°C \approx 53\,°C$$

2 Calculate the heat lost by this water (q_w) in joules. Since the density of water is $1.00\,\text{g cm}^{-3}$, the mass of $90.4\,\text{cm}^3$ of hot water is 90.4 g.

$$q_w = mc\Delta T = (90.4\,\text{g}) \times (4.18\,\text{J g}^{-1}\,°C^{-1}) \times (53\,°C) = 20027\,\text{J}$$

3 Calculate the heat used to melt the ice (q_i). Assume that all of the heat lost by the water went into melting the ice.
Therefore, $q_i = q_w = 20027\,\text{J}$

4 Calculate the volume of water that is from melted ice. The difference between the final volume and the initial volume is due to melted ice.

$$V_i = 151.9\,\text{cm}^3 - 90.4\,\text{cm}^3 = 61.5\,\text{cm}^3$$

5 Calculate the mass of melted ice. The melted ice is now liquid water. Use the volume you just calculated. With a density of $1.00\,\text{g cm}^{-3}$, $61.5\,\text{cm}^3$ of water has a mass of 61.5 g.

6 Calculate the amount (mol) of melted ice. Use the molar mass to convert. Ice has the formula H_2O.

$$\frac{61.5\,\text{g}}{1} \times \frac{1\,\text{mole ice}}{18.02\,\text{g}} = 3.41\,\text{mol}$$

7 Calculate the enthalpy of fusion.

$$\text{Enthalpy of fusion} = \frac{\text{heat to melt ice}}{\text{amount of ice}} = \frac{q_i}{\text{moles}} = \frac{20027\,\text{J}}{3.41\,\text{mol}} = 5873\,\text{J mol}^{-1}$$

The literature value for the enthalpy of fusion of ice is $5660 \, J \, mol^{-1}$.

An evaluation of this experiment would include a calculation of the percentage error and a comparison to the total percentage error due to the all measurements. Likely systematic errors should be identified, discussed and suggestions made for ways of reducing them and the random errors. Any assumptions and limitations should be discussed.

■ Measuring enthalpy changes

Enthalpy changes are usually measured by their effect on a known volume of water in a container known as a calorimeter. A chemical reaction involving known amounts of chemicals dissolved in the water may be performed and the temperature increase or decrease measured. Alternatively, a combustion reaction may be performed and the temperature increase in the water bath recorded.

The heat produced or absorbed may be calculated from the following expression:

$$\text{heat change} = \begin{array}{c} \text{total mass of water} \\ \text{or solution} \end{array} \times \begin{array}{c} \text{specific heat capacity} \\ \text{of water} \end{array} \times \begin{array}{c} \text{temperature} \\ \text{change} \end{array}$$

In symbols:

$$q \, (J) = m \, (g) \times c \, (J \, g^{-1} \, °C^{-1}) \times \Delta T \, (°C)$$

The calculations of heat transferred to the water are based on the following assumptions:

■ The reaction is assumed to occur sufficiently rapidly for the maximum temperature to be reached before the reaction mixture begins to cool to room temperature. This occurs if the next condition is completely fulfilled.

■ There is no heat transfer between the solution, thermometer, the surrounding air and the calorimeter.

(In practice neither of these conditions is completely fulfilled, but the rate of heat transfer in or out of the calorimeter is tracked and extrapolated back to the moment the reaction began.)

■ The solution is sufficiently dilute that its density and specific heat capacity are taken to be equal to those of water, namely, $1 \, g \, cm^{-3}$ and $4.18 \, J \, g^{-1} \, °C^{-1}$.

The heat change is for the specific amount of chemicals used in the reaction. This is usually less than one mole, so by simple proportion or 'scaling up' the heat change is then calculated for the amounts of chemicals shown in the chemical equation.

Worked example

$50.00 \, cm^3$ of $0.100 \, mol \, dm^{-3}$ silver nitrate solution was put in a calorimeter and $0.200 \, g$ of zinc powder added. The temperature of the solution rose by $4.3 \, °C$. Deduce which reagent was in excess and then calculate the enthalpy change for the reaction (per mole of zinc that reacts). Assume that the density of the solution is $1.00 \, g \, cm^{-3}$ and the specific heat capacity of the solution is $4.18 \, J \, g^{-1} \, °C^{-1}$. Ignore the heat capacity of the metals and dissolved ions.

$$q = 50.00 \, g \times 4.18 \, J \, g^{-1} \, °C^{-1} \times 4.3 \, °C = 898.7 \, J$$

$$\text{Amount of silver nitrate} = \frac{50.0}{1000} dm^3 \times 0.100 \, mol \, dm^{-3} = 0.00500 \, mol$$

$$\text{Amount of zinc} = \frac{0.200 \, g}{65.37 \, g \, mol^{-1}} = 0.0031 \, mol$$

$$2AgNO_3(aq) + Zn(s) \rightarrow Zn(NO_3)_2(aq) + 2Ag(s)$$

Zinc is the *excess* reactant (Chapter 1) and hence the temperature change and the enthalpy change are determined by the *limiting* reactant, the silver nitrate. Therefore:

$$\Delta H = \frac{-0.8987 \, kJ}{0.00500 \, mol} = -180 \, kJ \, mol^{-1}$$

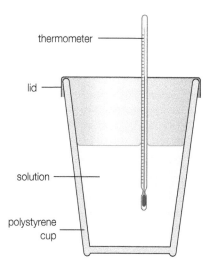

■ **Figure 5.6** A simple calorimeter: polystyrene cup, lid and thermometer

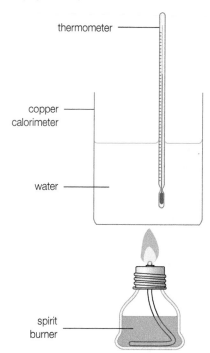

■ **Figure 5.7** Simple apparatus used to measure enthalpy changes of combustion of liquids

The enthalpy changes of reactions in solution can be easily measured with the simple apparatus shown in Figure 5.6. A lid may be fitted to minimize heat transfer. More accurate measurements could be performed in a calorimeter based around a Thermos or vacuum flask.

Problems with calorimetry

There are three problems associated with the use of calorimeters:

- The desired reaction does not (fully) occur. This is relevant to enthalpies of combustion where incomplete combustion occurs.

- Loss of heat to the surroundings (exothermic reactions); absorption of heat from the surroundings (endothermic reactions). This unwanted flow of heat can be reduced by 'lagging' the calorimeter to ensure it is well insulated.

- Using an incorrect specific heat capacity in the calculation of the heat change. If a copper can is used as a calorimeter (Figure 5.7) during an enthalpy change of combustion investigation, then its specific heat capacity needs to be taken into account in the calculation. For example:

heat transferred = mass of water × specific heat capacity of water × temperature change
+ mass of copper × specific heat capacity of copper × temperature change

Temperature corrections

Accurate results can be obtained by using simple calorimeters (e.g. a polystyrene cup fitted with a lid) for fast reactions, such as neutralizations or precipitations. However, for slower reactions such as metal ion replacement, the results will be less accurate with the same apparatus. This is because there is heat loss to the surroundings; this will increase if the reaction is slow because the heat will be lost over a longer period of time. Consequently, the temperature rise observed in the calorimeter is not as great as it should be. However, an allowance can be made for this by plotting a temperature–time graph (or cooling curve). The method is described below.

One reagent is placed in the polystyrene cup and its temperature recorded at, say, 1 minute intervals for, say, 4 minutes, stirring continuously. At a known time, say 4.5 minutes from the start, the second reagent is added, stirring continuously, and the temperature recorded until the maximum temperature is reached. As the reaction mixture starts to cool, temperature recording and stirring are continued for at least 5 minutes. A graph of temperature against time is then plotted. Data-loggers can be used to record temperature changes in solutions.

The lines are extrapolated to the time of mixing to determine the temperature change that would have occurred had mixing of the reagents been instantaneous with no heat loss to the surroundings. Graphs are given for an exothermic (Figure 5.8) and an endothermic reaction (Figure 5.9).

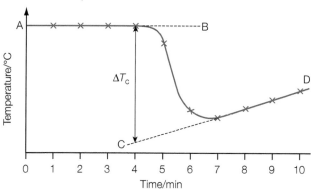

■ **Figure 5.8** A temperature correction curve for an exothermic reaction

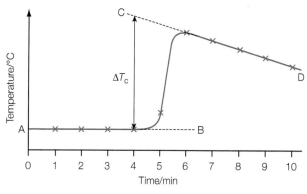

■ **Figure 5.9** A temperature correction curve for an endothermic reaction

ToK Link

What criteria do we use in judging discrepancies between experimental and theoretical values?

It is important to recognize the distinction between a theoretical value and a literature value: discrepancies between an experimentally determined value and a literature value are due to random and systematic errors, but a discrepancy between an experimental value and a theoretical value may be indicative of inappropriate assumptions in the theoretical model. For example, calculated lattice enthalpies usually assume a purely ionic model and therefore a discrepancy with experiment may indicate a covalent character in the bonding.

Which ways of knowing do we use when assessing experimental limitations and theoretical assumptions?

Sense perception, reason and emotion are certainly all important here. Sometimes reason and emotion can conflict with one another. Classic examples of the influence of emotion are cold fusion and the recently reported 'faster than light' neutrinos. It is an emotional response to rush to publish a scientific paper with a result that runs counter to a well-tested prevailing theory, whereas it would have been preferable to ensure that all variables had been accounted for, before making the results public.

■ Enthalpy change of combustion

The standard enthalpy change of combustion for a substance is the heat energy released when one mole of the pure substance is completely burnt in excess oxygen under standard conditions.

An example of the enthalpy change of combustion is the combustion of methane. The reaction can be described by the following thermochemical equation:

$$CH_4(g) + 2O_2(g) \rightarrow CO_2(g) + 2H_2O(l) \qquad \Delta H_c^{\oplus} = -698\,kJ\,mol^{-1}$$

Enthalpy changes of combustion are always negative as heat is released during combustion processes.

Measuring enthalpy changes of combustion of fuels

Enthalpy changes for the combustion of liquids can be measured in a flame combustion calorimeter (Figure 5.10). The investigation is carried out as follows:

1 Place a known volume and hence known mass of water into the calorimeter.
2 Stir and record the temperature of the water.
3 Record the mass of the spirit burner.
4 Turn on the pump so that there is steady flow of air and hence oxygen through the copper coil.
5 Use the electrically operated heating coil to light the wick.
6 Slowly stir the water throughout the experiment.
7 Allow the spirit burner to heat up the water.
8 Record the maximum temperature of the water.
9 Re-weigh the spirit burner to determine the mass of liquid fuel combusted.

■ **Figure 5.10**
Measuring the enthalpy change of combustion of a liquid fuel using a flame combustion calorimeter

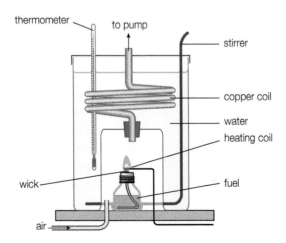

Worked example

Some example results are given below for the combustion of methanol.

Volume of water = 100 cm³

Temperature rise = 34.5 °C

Mass of methanol burned = 0.75 g

Specific heat capacity of water = 4.18 J g⁻¹ °C⁻¹

Use these results to calculate the molar enthalpy change of combustion. Compare the value with the literature value.

Heat energy transferred = 100 g × 4.18 J °C⁻¹ g⁻¹ × 34.5 °C = 14 421 J

Amount of methanol burnt = $\frac{0.75 \, g}{32 \, g \, mol^{-1}}$ = 0.023 mol

Amount of energy released per mole of methanol = $\frac{14\,421 \, J}{0.023 \, mol}$ = 627 000 J mol⁻¹

Hence the enthalpy change of combustion of methanol is −627 kJ mol⁻¹.

The experimental literature value for the standard enthalpy change of combustion of methanol is −726 kJ mol⁻¹. The absolute error is (726 − 627), that is, 99 kJ mol⁻¹. The percentage error is (726 − 630)/726 × 100, that is 14% (Chapter 11).

The error is due to the large heat losses that occur during the use of the flame combustion calorimeter. Heat losses to the surrounding air are relatively large, despite the use of heat shields. Also, heat energy from the flame heats up the material of the calorimeter itself, as well as the water. A correction can be made for the heat losses to the calorimeter if the specific heat capacity of copper is known or if the apparatus is standardized using a substance of known enthalpy change of combustion.

Utilization: Determining the energy content in food and fuels using a bomb calorimeter

The experimental literature values for standard enthalpy changes of combustion are obtained using a more accurate bomb calorimeter. These can be obtained for fuels as well as energy contents of dried foodstuffs.

This technique involves combusting a known mass of dried food in the presence of excess oxygen and recording the change in temperature of water. This apparatus gives accurate readings because heat losses to the surroundings are minimized. Strictly speaking, the bomb calorimeter measures internal energy changes, but these can be converted to enthalpies.

A sample of dried bread with a mass of 1.48 g was completely combusted (in a bomb calorimeter) and was found to raise the temperature of 100 g of water by 71 °C. The quantity of heat transferred, q, is given by the expression:

$$q = mc\Delta T; \quad q = 100 \, g \times 4.18 \, J \, g^{-1} \, °C^{-1} \times 71 \, °C = 29\,678 \, J$$

Hence the energy content of the dried bread is 29 678 J/1.48 g = 20 052 J g⁻¹.

Additional Perspectives

The energy values of food

Although the cells of our body do not burn digested food (nutrients) in the same way as fossil fuels are burnt, the outcome is the same. Molecular oxygen is still required and the energy obtained from compounds is similar as if they were combusted in a calorimeter. When glucose is respired ('burnt') in the cells of our body there are a series of enzyme-controlled steps, each catalysed by an enzyme. The enthalpy change of combustion is its energy value and for ease of comparison, values are usually given for 100 g of dried food. Some typical values of food from a database are given in Table 5.1.

Food	Energy content (kJ/100 g)
Apple	200
Milk	270
Potatoes	370
White bread	900
Bacon	1470
Cheddar cheese	1700
Butter	3040

■ **Table 5.1** The energy values of selected food

When food is consumed some of its energy context is lost through our faeces in the form of fibre. If we consume more energy than we expend, the surplus is stored as fat. Most of the energy we consume is used up by our bodies. The exact amount we use depends on our age, sex, height, weight and the amount of activity we do. For men, the range is usually between 9200 kJ and 12 100 kJ per day although for manual workers it can be more. For women, the range is 6700 to 8800 kJ per day. Energy is needed for the enzyme-controlled chemical changes that occur inside our body cells. This termed metabolism. For example, energy is needed to metabolize the food we consume and to keep us warm in cold weather.

■ Enthalpy change of neutralization

The standard enthalpy change of neutralization is the enthalpy change that takes place when one mole of hydrogen ions is *completely* neutralized by an alkali under standard conditions.

An example of the enthalpy change of neutralization is from the reaction between sodium hydroxide solution and hydrochloric acid. The reaction can be described by the following thermochemical equation:

$$NaOH(aq) + HCl(aq) \rightarrow NaCl(aq) + H_2O(l) \qquad \Delta H^\circ = -57 \text{ kJ mol}^{-1}$$

The enthalpy change of neutralization of a strong acid with a strong alkali is almost the same for all strong acids and strong alkalis. This is because strong acids and strong alkalis undergo complete ionization or dissociation in water:

$$NaOH(s) + (aq) \rightarrow Na^+(aq) + OH^-(aq)$$
$$HCl(g) + (aq) \rightarrow H^+(aq) + Cl^-(aq)$$

The reaction between a strong base and a strong acid is the combination of hydrogen and hydroxide ions to form water molecules. The other ions are spectator ions (they take no part in the reaction). The reaction can be described by the following ionic equation:

$$H^+(aq) + OH^-(aq) \rightarrow H_2O(l) \qquad \Delta H^\circ = -57 \text{ kJ mol}^{-1}$$

For sulfuric acid, a dibasic acid, the enthalpy of neutralization equation is

$$\tfrac{1}{2}H_2SO_4(aq) + KOH(aq) \rightarrow \tfrac{1}{2}K_2SO_4(aq) + H_2O(l) \qquad \Delta H^\circ = -57 \text{ kJ mol}^{-1}$$

and *not*

$$H_2SO_4(aq) + 2KOH(aq) \rightarrow K_2SO_4(aq) + 2H_2O(l)$$

This is because during the neutralization process each sulfuric acid molecule releases two hydrogen ions:

$$H_2SO_4(aq) \rightarrow 2H^+(aq) + SO_4^{2-}(aq)$$

However, where neutralizations involve a *weak* acid, a *weak* base, or both, then the enthalpy of neutralization will be *smaller* in magnitude than −57 kJ mol^{-1}, that is, slightly less exothermic.

For example, the enthalpy of neutralization for ethanoic acid and sodium hydroxide is $-55.2\,kJ\,mol^{-1}$ because some of the energy released on neutralization is used to ionize or dissociate the acid:

$$CH_3COOH(aq) + NaOH(aq) \rightarrow CH_3COONa(aq) + H_2O(l)$$

$$CH_3COOH(aq) \rightarrow CH_3COO^-(aq) + H^+(aq)$$

This can be shown in the form of an enthalpy level cycle (Figure 5.11).

■ **Figure 5.11** Enthalpy level cycle for the neutralization of ethanoic acid

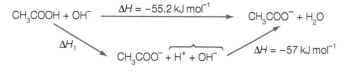

■ **Figure 5.12** A graph of temperature versus volume of acid for an investigation to determine the enthalpy change of neutralization for an acid

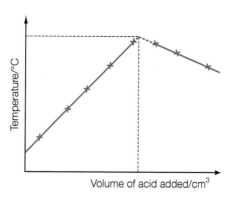

A simple method for determining the enthalpy change of neutralization involves mixing equal volumes of dilute solutions of a strong acid and a strong base of known concentration and measuring the temperature rise. A thick plastic cup fitted with a lid makes a cheap and effective calorimeter.

The maximum temperature can be deduced from the graph (see Figure 5.12) by extrapolating both lines back to find out where they intersect.

Worked example

$50.00\,cm^3$ of $1.0\,mol\,dm^{-3}$ hydrochloric acid was added to $50.00\,cm^3$ of $1.0\,mol\,dm^{-3}$ sodium hydroxide solution. The temperature rose by $6.8\,°C$. Calculate the enthalpy change of neutralization for this reaction. Assume that the density of the solution is $1.00\,g\,cm^{-3}$ and the specific heat capacity of the solution is $4.18\,J\,g^1\,°C^{-1}$.

$$q = mc\Delta T$$

$$q = 100\,g \times 4.18\,J\,g^1\,°C^{-1} \times 6.8\,°C = 2842\,J$$

$$NaOH(aq) + HCl(aq) \rightarrow NaCl(aq) + H_2O(l)$$

$$\text{Amount of hydrochloric acid} = \frac{50.00}{1000}\,dm^3 \times 1.0\,mol\,dm^{-3} = 0.050\,mol$$

$$\text{Amount of sodium hydroxide} = \frac{50.00}{1000}\,dm^3 \times 1.0\,mol\,dm^{-3} = 0.050\,mol$$

$$\text{Enthalpy change of neutralization} = \frac{-2.842\,kJ}{0.050\,mol} = 56.8\,kJ\,mol^{-1} \approx 57\,kJ\,mol^{-1}$$

(The answer is expressed to two significant figures because $6.8\,°C$ has only two significant figures.)

Additional Perspectives

Enthalpy change of solution

The standard enthalpy change of solution is the enthalpy change that occurs when one mole of a solute dissolves in a large excess of water, so that no further heat change occurs when more water is added to the solution.

For example, the enthalpy change of solution when dissolving sodium chloride in water is the enthalpy change of the following reaction:

$$NaCl(s) + (aq) \rightarrow Na^+(aq) + Cl^-(aq) \qquad \Delta H^{\ominus} = +3.9\,kJ\,mol^{-1}$$

This enthalpy change of solution is positive, that is, the reaction is endothermic. This reaction proceeds because a large positive entropy change occurs during the dissolving process (Chapter 15). Many ionic compounds have enthalpies of solution that are negative, that is, the reactions are exothermic.

Worked example

0.848 grams of anhydrous lithium chloride, LiCl, are added to 36.0 grams of water at 25 °C in a polystyrene cup acting as a calorimeter. The final temperature of the solution was 29.8 °C. Calculate the enthalpy change of solution for one mole of lithium chloride.

Amount of lithium chloride $= \dfrac{0.848\,g}{42.4\,g\,mol^{-1}} = 0.0200\,mol$

Amount of water $= \dfrac{36.0\,g}{18.02\,g\,mol^{-1}} = 2.00\,mol$

Therefore, $\dfrac{\text{amount of LiCl}}{\text{amount of }H_2O} = \dfrac{1}{100}$

$\Delta H = 36.0\,g \times 4.18\,J\,g^{-1}\,°C^{-1} \times 4.8\,°C = -0.72\,kJ$

'Scaling up' to molar quantities:

$\Delta H = -0.72\,kJ \times \dfrac{1\,mol}{0.020\,mol} = -36\,kJ$

Therefore:

$LiCl(s) + (aq) \rightarrow LiCl(aq)$ $\Delta H_{sol}^{\ominus} = -36\,kJ\,mol^{-1}$ (to two significant figures)

■ Enthalpy change of formation

The **enthalpy change of formation**, $\Delta H_f^{\ominus}$, of a substance is the heat change (at constant pressure) on production of one mole of the pure substance from its elements in their standard states under standard thermodynamic conditions (298 K and 1 atm pressure).

The **standard state** is *generally* the most thermodynamically stable form of the pure element that exists under standard thermodynamic conditions. For carbon it is graphite and for phosphorus it is white phosphorus, $P_4(s)$. (However, red phosphorus is more stable than white phosphorus.)

The enthalpy change of formation of silver bromide, AgBr, is the enthalpy change for the reaction:

$$Ag(s) + \tfrac{1}{2}Br_2(l) \rightarrow AgBr(s) \qquad\qquad \Delta H_f^{\ominus} = -99.5\,kJ\,mol^{-1}$$

The following balanced equations do *not* represent enthalpy changes of formation:

$2Ag(s) + Br_2(l) \rightarrow 2AgBr(s)$ two moles of silver bromide are formed

$Ag(s) + \tfrac{1}{2}Br_2(g) \rightarrow AgBr(s)$ bromine is *not* in its standard state

Enthalpy changes of formation are often difficult to measure in practice due to competing side reactions and slow rates of reaction. For example, methane and potassium manganate(VII) *cannot* be prepared from their elements via the following thermochemical equations:

$C(s) + 2H_2(g) \rightarrow CH_4(g)$ $\Delta H_f^{\ominus} = -75\,kJ\,mol^{-1}$

$K(s) + Mn(s) + 2O_2(g) \rightarrow KMnO_4(s)$ $\Delta H_f^{\ominus} = -813\,kJ\,mol^{-1}$

The IB *Chemistry data booklet* tabulates enthalpies of formation for selected organic compounds on page 12. Note that enthalpy changes of formation for elements (in their standard states) are zero since the thermochemical equation representing the formation of an element is a *null* reaction: no reaction is involved in their formation. For example, the standard enthalpy change of formation of oxygen is represented by:

$$O_2(g) \rightarrow O_2(g) \qquad\qquad \Delta H_f^\ominus = 0\,kJ\,mol^{-1}$$

However, the enthalpy changes of formation for ozone ($O_3(g)$) and diamond (C(s, diamond)) are *not* zero since these are *not* the standard states of the elements oxygen and carbon.

A number of enthalpies of formation can be directly determined, for example the enthalpy of formation of water:

$$H_2(g) + \frac{1}{2}O_2(g) \rightarrow H_2O(l) \qquad\qquad \Delta H_f^\ominus = -286\,kJ\,mol^{-1}$$

This enthalpy change is also equivalent to the enthalpy of combustion of hydrogen. The **enthalpy of combustion** is the enthalpy change (at constant pressure) when one mole of a pure substance undergoes complete combustion under standard thermodynamic conditions.

For example, the standard enthalpies of combustion of hydrogen, methane and ethanol are represented by:

$$H_2(g) + \frac{1}{2}O_2(g) \rightarrow H_2O(l) \qquad\qquad \Delta H_c^\ominus = -286\,kJ\,mol^{-1}$$

$$CH_4(g) + 2O_2(g) \rightarrow CO_2(g) + 2H_2O(l) \qquad\qquad \Delta H_c^\ominus = -890\,kJ\,mol^{-1}$$

$$CH_3CH_2OH(l) + 3O_2(g) \rightarrow 2CO_2(g) + 3H_2O(l) \qquad \Delta H_c^\ominus = -1370\,kJ\,mol^{-1}$$

Enthalpies of formation are usually calculated indirectly from other enthalpy changes of reaction including bond enthalpies. Enthalpy changes of formation are commonly used to calculate enthalpy changes of reaction, using Hess's law.

Enthalpy changes of formation are usually negative, that is, the corresponding reactions are exothermic. However, some compounds have positive enthalpies of formation, for example benzene and nitrogen monoxide:

$$6C(s) + 3H_2(g) \rightarrow C_6H_6(l) \qquad\qquad \Delta H_f^\ominus = +49\,kJ\,mol^{-1}$$

$$\frac{1}{2}N_2(g) + \frac{1}{2}O_2(g) \rightarrow NO(g) \qquad\qquad \Delta H_f^\ominus = +90\,kJ\,mol^{-1}$$

These compounds are energetically unstable relative to their elements. The Gibbs free energy change of formation, $\Delta G_f^\ominus$, is the criterion that determines the *thermodynamic* stability of a compound relative to its elements (Chapter 15). Both benzene and nitrogen monoxide are *kinetically* stable – there is a large activation energy barrier to decomposition at room temperature. However, nitrogen monoxide does undergo significant decomposition in the presence of a platinum catalyst, as the catalyst lowers the activation energy barrier to the reaction (Chapter 6).

The normal 'rules' for manipulating enthalpy changes apply to enthalpies of formation. If a thermochemical equation is reversed, then the sign of the enthalpy change is reversed. If the balanced thermochemical equation is multiplied (or divided) by a constant, the enthalpy change is multiplied (or divided) by the same constant.

Nature of Science

Making careful observations – measuring energy transfers between system and surroundings

The measurement of accurate enthalpy changes relies upon the accurate measurement of temperature changes due to an exchange of heat between the system and surroundings.

When analysing energy changes, chemists need to focus on a limited and well-defined part of the Universe to keep track of the heat energy changes that occur. The part chosen for study is the system; everything else is termed the surroundings. When you study the heat energy changes that accompany a chemical reaction in the laboratory, the reactants and products form the system. The container or calorimeter and everything beyond it are the surroundings.

Systems may be open, closed or isolated (Figure 5.13). An open system is one where energy and matter can be interchanged with the surroundings. A beaker of boiling water over a Bunsen burner is an open system. Heat energy can enter the system from the flame, and water is slowly released into the surroundings as steam.

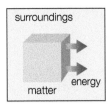

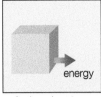

a open system   **b** closed system   **c** isolated system

energy can enter or leave the system as heat or as work is done on the piston

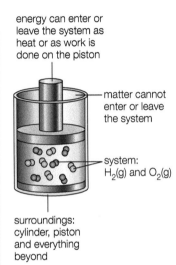

matter cannot enter or leave the system

system: $H_2(g)$ and $O_2(g)$

surroundings: cylinder, piston and everything beyond

■ **Figure 5.14**
A closed system containing a mixture of hydrogen and oxygen gases

Most chemical systems studied in energetics or thermochemistry are closed systems that can exchange energy but not matter with their surroundings. Consider a mixture of hydrogen and oxygen gas in a cylinder fitted with a friction-less piston (Figure 5.14). The system is the oxygen and hydrogen gases; the cylinder, piston and everything else in the Universe are the surroundings.

If the gases react to form water, heat energy is released. There is no change in mass but the system can exchange energy with its surroundings in the form of work and heat. If the piston is moved up then the system has done work. This is orderly motion. If the surrounding air outside the piston is heated, then the random movement of particles in the air increases. This is due to the absorption of heat.

An isolated system is one in which neither energy nor matter can be exchanged with the surroundings. An insulated vacuum flask containing hot coffee approximates to an isolated system. However, the hot coffee eventually cools and enters into state of thermal equilibrium with the surroundings.

A characteristic of a system is called a property. Intensive properties do not directly depend on the amount of matter in the system (for example temperature and pressure). Extensive properties, for example mass and volume, do directly depend on the number of particles. The ratio of two extensive properties becomes intensive in nature.

A system in equilibrium experiences no changes when it is isolated from its surroundings. A system is in thermal equilibrium if the temperature is the same throughout the system. It is in mechanical equilibrium if the pressure stays constant.

5.2 Hess's law – *in chemical transformations energy can neither be created or destroyed (the first law of thermodynamics)*

■ Hess's law and enthalpy change

Hess's law states that if a reaction consists of a number of steps, the overall enthalpy change is equal to the sum of the enthalpy changes for all the individual steps. Hess's law (Figure 5.15) states that the overall enthalpy change in a reaction is constant and not dependent on the pathway taken.

When reactant A is converted directly into product D by route 1, or indirectly by route 2 (via intermediates B and C), then according to Hess's law the enthalpy change in route 1 will equal the enthalpy changes of the reactions in route 2.

In symbols:

$$\Delta H_1 = \Delta H_2 + \Delta H_3 + \Delta H_4$$

Route 1
ΔH this way ...

ΔH_1

A → D

Route 2
... is the same as
ΔH this way

ΔH_2 ΔH_4

B → C

ΔH_3

■ **Figure 5.15** An illustration of the principle of Hess's law

Using Hess's law to calculate the enthalpy change of a reaction

Hess's law can be used to calculate the enthalpy change of a reaction. Consider the following reaction:

$$C(s) + \frac{1}{2}O_2(g) \rightarrow CO(g)$$

The enthalpy change of this reaction *cannot* be found directly by experiment because carbon dioxide is always formed when carbon reacts with even a limited amount of oxygen. This is an unavoidable reaction. However, the enthalpy changes of combustion of carbon and carbon monoxide *can* be found experimentally.

The reactions and their enthalpy changes of reaction can be linked using Hess's law, as shown in Figure 5.16. There are two pathways from carbon to carbon dioxide: a *direct* pathway (route 1) and an *indirect* pathway (route 2), where the carbon is burnt to form carbon monoxide and then burnt to produce carbon dioxide.

Route 1: $\quad C(s) + O_2(g) \rightarrow CO_2(g) \qquad \Delta H_1^\ominus = -394 \text{ kJ mol}^{-1}$

Route 2: $\quad C(s) + \frac{1}{2}O_2(g) \rightarrow CO(g) \qquad \Delta H_2^\ominus = ?$

$\qquad\qquad CO(g) + \frac{1}{2}O_2(g) \rightarrow CO_2(g) \qquad \Delta H_3^\ominus = -283 \text{ kJ mol}^{-1}$

■ **Figure 5.16** An example of Hess's law

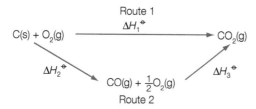

Applying Hess's law, the enthalpy change in route 1 equals the enthalpy change in route 2. In symbols:

$$\Delta H_1 = \Delta H_2 + \Delta H_3$$

$$\Delta H_2 = \Delta H_1 - \Delta H_3 = -394 - (-283) = -111 \text{ kJ mol}^{-1}$$

So the enthalpy change for the combustion of carbon to form carbon monoxide is -111 kJ mol^{-1}.

Nature of Science

Hypothesis – testing Hess's law

Germain Hess deduced his law of heat summation (later known as Hess's law) during three years of calorimetric measurements, from 1839 to 1842. In his words, 'the heat developed in a chemical change is constant, whether the change occurs directly, or indirectly in several stages.' That is, the total heat involved in a chemical change depends solely upon the beginning reactants and the end products, no matter how many reactions are involved in getting from the beginning to the end. The enthalpy change is independent of the path taken from reactants to products. This is an example of what is termed a state function in thermodynamics. It follows that the enthalpy changes for chemical reactions must be additive, just as the chemical reactions themselves are additive. Hess's hypothesis has been tested with a very large number of chemical reactions and has not been falsified, and its status has been converted from a tentative hypothesis to a well-supported law.

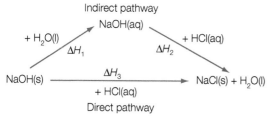

■ **Figure 5.17** A further example of Hess's law

Reactions in aqueous solutions

The conversion of solid sodium hydroxide into sodium chloride solution illustrates the use of a Hess's law energy cycle for reactions in aqueous solution. Figure 5.17 shows two pathways for this reaction.

The first pathway (indirect pathway) involves two steps.

Step 1: solid sodium hydroxide is dissolved in water:

$$NaOH(s) + (aq) \rightarrow NaOH(aq) \qquad \Delta H_1 = -43\,kJ\,mol^{-1}$$

Step 2: sodium hydroxide solution is neutralized by hydrochloric acid:

$$NaOH(aq) + HCl(aq) \rightarrow NaCl(aq) + H_2O(l) \qquad \Delta H_2 = -57\,kJ\,mol^{-1}$$

The second pathway (direct pathway) involves one step.

Step 3: solid sodium hydroxide is added directly to hydrochloric acid.

$$NaOH(s) + HCl(aq) \rightarrow NaCl(aq) + H_2O(l)$$

$$\Delta H_3 = \Delta H_1 + \Delta H_2 = (-43) + (-57) = -100\,kJ\,mol^{-1}$$

Decomposition of calcium carbonate

Hess's law can be used to determine the value of an endothermic reaction, for example the thermal decomposition of calcium carbonate:

$$CaCO_3(s) \rightarrow CaO(s) + CO_2(g)$$

The reaction is slow and a high temperature is required to bring it to completion. Direct measurement of the temperature is therefore not practical. Instead, two reactions that take place readily at room temperature are carried out and their enthalpy changes used to find the enthalpy of decomposition of calcium carbonate. These reactions are the reactions of calcium carbonate and calcium oxide with dilute hydrochloric acid:

$$CaCO_3(s) + 2HCl(aq) \rightarrow CaCl_2(aq) + H_2O(l)$$
$$\Delta H^\ominus = -17\,kJ\,mol^{-1}$$

$$CaO(s) + 2HCl(aq) \rightarrow CaCl_2(aq) + H_2O(l)$$
$$\Delta H^\ominus = -195\,kJ\,mol^{-1}$$

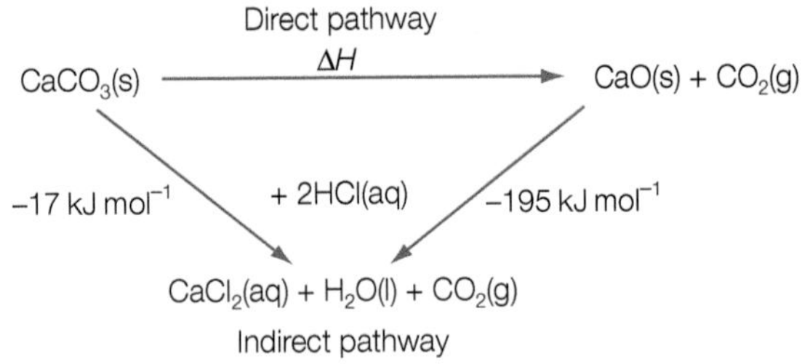

■ **Figure 5.18** Hess's law cycle for the decomposition of calcium carbonate

A Hess's law cycle (Figure 5.18) can be drawn to indicate the direct and indirect routes or pathways. $\Delta H^\ominus + (-195) = -17$ so $\Delta H^\ominus = -17 - (-195) = +178\,kJ\,mol^{-1}$.

Enthalpy of hydration of an anhydrous salt

Hess's law can also be used to determine the enthalpy of hydration of an anhydrous salt. For example, anhydrous copper(II) sulfate:

$$CuSO_4(s) + 5H_2O(l) \rightarrow CuSO_4.5H_2O(s)$$

The enthalpy of hydration of anhydrous copper(II) cannot be found directly. This is because if five moles of water are added to anhydrous copper(II) sulfate, hydrated copper(II) sulfate is not produced in a controlled way. It can only be produced by crystallization from a solution. The enthalpy change can be found indirectly by determining the enthalpy of solution of both anhydrous and hydrated copper(II) sulfates (Figure 5.19).

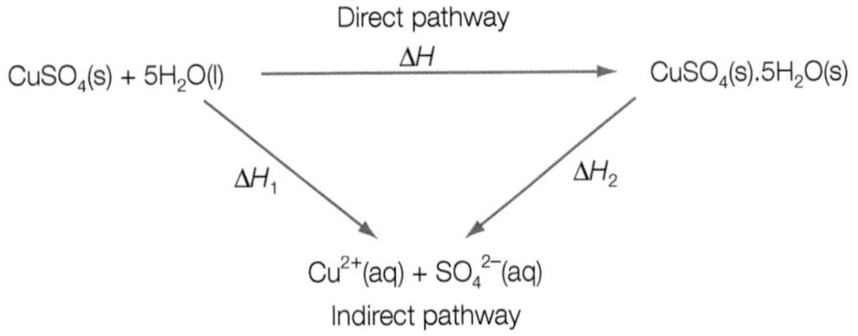

■ **Figure 5.19** Hess's law cycle to find the enthalpy change when anhydrous copper(II) sulfate crystals are hydrated

An algebraic method

Hess's law problems do not have to be solved by drawing enthalpy cycles (although they are preferred for complicated energetic calculations). They can also be solved by an 'algebraic method' that involves manipulating the equations so that when added together they give the required enthalpy change.

Worked example

From the following data at 25 °C and 1 atmosphere pressure:

Equation 1: $2CO_2(g) \rightarrow 2CO(g) + O_2(g)$ $\Delta H^{\ominus} = 566 \, kJ \, mol^{-1}$

Equation 2: $3CO(g) + O_3(g) \rightarrow 3CO_2(g)$ $\Delta H^{\ominus} = -992 \, kJ \, mol^{-1}$

calculate the enthalpy change calculated for the conversion of oxygen to one mole of ozone (O_3), i.e. for the reaction:

$\frac{3}{2} O_2(g) \rightarrow O_3(g)$

O_2 is required in the reactant side and O_3 is required on the product side. Reversing equation 1 and multiplying it by $\frac{3}{2}$ gives:

$\frac{3}{2} O_2(g) + 3CO(g) \rightarrow 3CO_2(g)$ $\Delta H^{\ominus} = -849 \, kJ \, mol^{-1}$

(Equation 3)

Reversing equation 2 gives:

$3CO_2(g) \rightarrow 3CO(g) + O_3(g)$ $\Delta H^{\ominus} = +992 \, kJ \, mol^{-1}$

(Equation 4)

Adding equations 3 and 4 gives the desired reaction (as the CO and CO_2 molecules cancel out), and adding the ΔH values which gives the desired final ΔH.

$\frac{3}{2} O_2(g) \rightarrow O_3(g)$ $\Delta H^{\ominus} = -849 + 992 = +143 \, kJ \, mol^{-1}$

One of the most important uses of Hess's law is to calculate enthalpy changes that are difficult to measure experimentally.

Worked example

Calculate the enthalpy change for the conversion of graphite to diamond under standard thermodynamic conditions.

$C(s, graphite) + O_2(g) \rightarrow CO_2(g)$ $\Delta H_1^{\ominus} = -393 \, kJ \, mol^{-1}$

$C(s, diamond) + O_2(g) \rightarrow CO_2(g)$ $\Delta H_2^{\ominus} = -395 \, kJ \, mol^{-1}$

The problem may be solved via use of an energy cycle (Figure 5.20) or via algebraic manipulation.

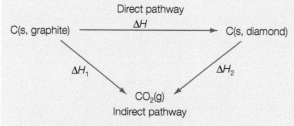

■ **Figure 5.20** Energy cycle showing direct conversion of graphite to diamond and indirect conversion via carbon dioxide

Using an energy cycle

$\Delta H = \Delta H_1 - \Delta H_2 = (-393) - (-395)$ $\Delta H^{\ominus} = +2 \, kJ \, mol^{-1}$

Using an algebraic method

$C(s, graphite) + O_2(g) \rightarrow CO_2(g)$ $\Delta H^{\ominus} = -393 \, kJ \, mol^{-1}$

Then reversing the original second equation, also reversing the sign of the enthalpy change:

$CO_2(g) \rightarrow C(s, diamond) + O_2(g)$ $\Delta H^{\ominus} = +395 \, kJ \, mol^{-1}$

The two equations are added together and the oxygen and carbon dioxide molecules cancelled:

$C(s, graphite) \rightarrow C(s, diamond)$ $\Delta H^{\ominus} = +2 \, kJ \, mol^{-1}$

It should also be noted that the value and sign of the enthalpy change (ΔH) do *not* indicate whether a reaction occurs or not. There are spontaneous exothermic and endothermic reactions. The Gibbs free energy change (ΔG) determines whether a reaction occurs or not (under standard conditions) (Chapter 15). In addition, the size and sign of the enthalpy change do *not* give any indication of the rate of reaction: the rate of reaction is determined by the activation energy barrier.

■ Enthalpy changes of reaction from enthalpy changes of formation

The enthalpy change of any reaction can be determined by calculation, from the enthalpy changes of formation of all the substances in the chemical equation, using Hess's law.

In words:

$$\begin{array}{ccc} \text{enthalpy change} & = & \text{sum of enthalpies of} & - & \text{sum of enthalpies of} \\ \text{of a reaction} & & \text{formation of products} & & \text{formation of reactants} \end{array}$$

In symbols:

$$\Delta H \quad = \quad \Sigma \Delta H_f^{\ominus}[\text{products}] \quad - \quad \Sigma \Delta H_f^{\ominus}[\text{reactants}]$$

As we saw, the calculation can be carried out using an energy level diagram, a Hess's law cycle (Figure 5.21) or with algebra.

■ **Figure 5.21**
Hess's law cycle for calculating the standard enthalpy of a reaction from standard enthalpies of formation

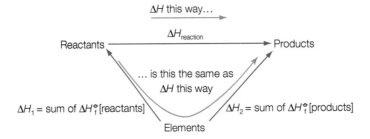

Worked example

Calculate the enthalpy change of the following reaction:

$$3CuO(s) + 2Al(s) \rightarrow 3Cu(s) + Al_2O_3(s)$$

$\Delta H_f^{\ominus}[CuO] = -155\,kJ\,mol^{-1}$

$\Delta H_f^{\ominus}[Al_2O_3] = -1669\,kJ\,mol^{-1}$

This is a redox reaction (Chapter 9) and involves a more reactive metal replacing a less reactive metal from its oxide.

Figure 5.22 shows there are two routes for forming the products of the reaction from their elements. Route 1 is the direct route and route 2 is the indirect route where the reactants are formed from their elements and then the reactants are converted to products.

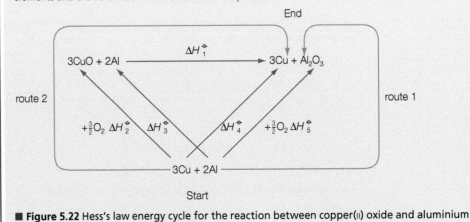

■ **Figure 5.22** Hess's law energy cycle for the reaction between copper(II) oxide and aluminium

Applying Hess's law:

enthalpy change in route 1 = enthalpy change in route 2

Hence:

$$\Delta H_2^{\ominus} + \Delta H_3^{\ominus} + \Delta H_1^{\ominus} = \Delta H_4^{\ominus} + \Delta H_5^{\ominus}$$

$$\Delta H_1^{\ominus} = \Delta H_4^{\ominus} + \Delta H_5^{\ominus} - \Delta H_2^{\ominus} - \Delta H_3^{\ominus}$$

$$\Delta H_1^{\ominus} = (0\,kJ\,mol^{-1}) + (-1669\,kJ\,mol^{-1}) - 3 \times (-155\,kJ\,mol^{-1}) - (0\,kJ\,mol^{-1})$$

$$= -1204\,kJ\,mol^{-1}$$

(i.e. $\Delta H = \sum \Delta H_f^{\ominus}$ [products] $- \sum \Delta H_f^{\ominus}$ [reactants])

■ Enthalpy changes of reaction from enthalpy changes of combustion

An enthalpy change can also be calculated from enthalpy changes of combustion. However, this can only be done for reactions in which the substances on both sides of the equation can be burnt in oxygen (Figure 5.23). This method is widely used for organic compounds.

■ **Figure 5.23**
Hess's law cycle for calculating the standard enthalpies of formation from standard enthalpies of combustion

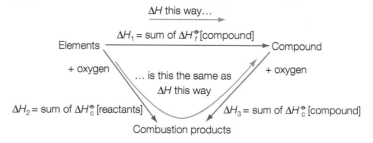

Worked example

Calculate the enthalpy change of reaction for the hydrogenation of propene to form propane.

$$CH_3-CH{=}CH_2(g) + H_2(g) \rightarrow CH_3-CH_2-CH_3(g)$$

$$\Delta H_c^{\ominus}[C_3H_6(g)] = -2509\,kJ\,mol^{-1}$$

$$\Delta H_c^{\ominus}[H_2(g)] = -286\,kJ\,mol^{-1}$$

$$\Delta H_c^{\ominus}[C_3H_8(g)] = -2220\,kJ\,mol^{-1}$$

The diagram in Figure 5.24 shows two routes for the combustion of propene and hydrogen into carbon dioxide and water. In route 1 the reactants are burnt directly in oxygen. In route 2 the reactants are first converted to propane, which is then burnt completely.

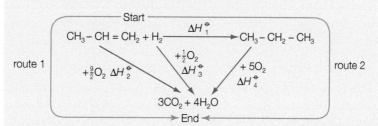

■ **Figure 5.24** Hess's law energy cycle for calculating the enthalpy of hydrogenation of propene from the enthalpies of combustion of propene, hydrogen and propane

Applying Hess's law:

enthalpy change in route 1 = enthalpy change in route 2

$$\Delta H_2^{\ominus} + \Delta H_3^{\ominus} = \Delta H_1^{\ominus} + \Delta H_4^{\ominus}$$

$$\Delta H_1^{\ominus} = \Delta H_2^{\ominus} + \Delta H_3^{\ominus} - \Delta H_4^{\ominus}$$

$$\Delta H_1^{\ominus} = (-2509\,kJ\,mol^{-1}) + (-286\,kJ\,mol^{-1}) - (-2220\,kJ\,mol^{-1})$$

$$= -575\,kJ\,mol^{-1}$$

Additional Perspectives

Enthalpy changes during changes of state

It is essential to specify the physical states of the substances involved when writing thermochemical equations to represent an enthalpy change. This is because any change in physical state (Chapter 1) has its own enthalpy change (Figure 5.25).

■ Figure 5.25
Changes of state and energy changes

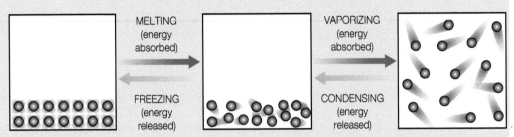

The enthalpy of fusion of ammonia would be the enthalpy change for the reaction:

$$NH_3(s) \rightarrow NH_3(l)$$

and the enthalpy of vaporization of ammonia would be the enthalpy change for the reaction:

$$NH_3(l) \rightarrow NH_3(g)$$

Enthalpies of vaporization and sublimation are always endothermic since intermolecular forces of attraction need to be overcome. The enthalpy of sublimation for iodine would be the enthalpy change for the reaction:

$$I_2(s) \rightarrow I_2(g)$$

The values of these enthalpy changes will vary with the strength of intermolecular forces (Chapter 4).

Additional Perspectives

Dissolving of ionic compounds

When an ionic compound dissolves in water, the process may be exothermic or endothermic, depending on the substance concerned. The value for the enthalpy change, ΔH, for such a reaction is the sum of two factors:

$$\Delta H = + \begin{bmatrix} \text{energy to overcome the} \\ \text{electrostatic forces of attraction} \\ \text{between ions in the lattice} \end{bmatrix} - \begin{bmatrix} \text{energy released when the} \\ \text{ions attract water molecules} \\ \text{around themselves} \end{bmatrix}$$

The sign of the enthalpy change, ΔH, for the reaction depends on which of these two quantities is larger. The dissolving of ionic solids is discussed in Chapters 4 and 15.

Applying Hess's Law to calculate enthalpy changes

Use the following thermochemical data to calculate the enthalpy of formation of sulfur trioxide. The enthalpy of formation of sulfur dioxide is $-297.4\,\text{kJ}\,\text{mol}^{-1}$ and the enthalpy of combustion of sulfur dioxide is $-97.9\,\text{kJ}\,\text{mol}^{-1}$.

Thermochemical equations can be written to describe these two enthalpy changes:

$$S(s) + O_2(g) \rightarrow SO_2(g) \qquad \Delta H^\oplus = -297.4\,\text{kJ}\,\text{mol}^{-1}$$

$$SO_2(g) + \tfrac{1}{2}O_2(g) \rightarrow SO_3(g) \quad \Delta H^\oplus = -97.7\,\text{kJ}\,\text{mol}^{-1}$$

Summing these two equations and cancelling sulfur dioxide gives an equation for the enthalpy of formation of sulfur trioxide:

$$S(s) + \tfrac{3}{2}O_2(g) \rightarrow SO_2(g) \qquad \Delta H^\oplus = -297.4 + (-97.7) = -95.3\,\text{kJ}\,\text{mol}^{-1}$$

Calculating the enthalpy change of reactions using $\Delta H_f^{\ominus}$ data

The enthalpies of formation of carbon monoxide, carbon dioxide, dinitrogen monoxide and dinitrogen tetroxide are −110, −393, 81 and 9.7 kJ mol⁻¹. Determine the value of the enthalpy of reaction for the following reaction:

$$N_2O_4(g) + 3CO(g) \rightarrow N_2O(g) + 3CO_2(g)$$

$$\Delta H = \Sigma\Delta H_f^{\ominus}[\text{products}] - \Sigma\Delta H_f^{\ominus}[\text{reactants}]$$

$$\Delta H = [3\Delta H_f^{\ominus}(CO_2(g) + \Delta H_f^{\ominus}(N_2O(g))] - [3\Delta H_f^{\ominus}(CO(g)) + \Delta H_f^{\ominus}(N_2O_4(g))]$$

$$\Delta H = [(3 \times -393) + 81] - [(3 \times -110) + (-9.78)] = 1437.7 \text{ kJ mol}^{-1}$$

Determining the enthalpy change of a reaction that is the sum of multiple reactions with known enthalpy changes

Calculate the enthalpy of combustion of glucose from the following thermochemical data:

Equation 1:	$C(s) + O_2(g) \rightarrow O_2(g)$	$\Delta H^{\ominus} = -395.0 \text{ kJ}$
Equation 2:	$H_2(g) + \frac{1}{2}O_2(g) \rightarrow H_2O(l)$	$\Delta H^{\ominus} = -269.4 \text{ kJ}$
Equation 3:	$6C(s) + 6H_2(g) + 3O_2(g) \rightarrow C_6H_{12}O_6(l)$	$\Delta H^{\ominus} = -269.4 \text{ kJ}$

The enthalpy of combustion for glucose is described by the following equation:

$$C_6H_{12}O_6(s) + 6O_2(g) \rightarrow 6CO_2(g) + 6H_2O(l)$$

It can be obtained by multiplying equations 1 and 2 by 6 and summing them:

$$6C(s) + 6H_2(g) + 9O_2(g) \rightarrow 6CO_2(g) + 6H_2O(l) \qquad \Delta H^{\ominus} = -3986.4 \text{ kJ}$$

Subtracting equation 3 from equation 4 gives the enthalpy of combustion for glucose:

$$C_6H_{12}O_6(s) + 6O_2(g) \rightarrow 6CO_2(g) + 6H_2O(l) \qquad \Delta H^{\ominus} = -2816.6 \text{ kJ}$$

■ Utilization: Relevance of Hess's law in wider areas

Hess's law is relevant when discussing the energy content of foods. If a bomb calorimeter is used to measure the amount of energy present in a food sample by converting it to carbon dioxide, water and nitrogen, then you obtain a certain amount of thermal energy in joules.

However, the body will not break down food to this extent and so this overestimates the amount of energy available to the body in food. Normally, any nitrogen present in food ends up in urea, which is excreted in the urine. Therefore, a more accurate measure of how much energy is present in food would be to measure how much energy would be released if all the nitrogen present ended up in urea, rather than the total nitrogen. This cannot be measured in the laboratory, but if a bomb calorimeter was used to measure the amount of energy present in urea, then that could be compared with the total amount of energy present in food to get the amount of available energy. This illustrates how the principles of Hess's law can be used to determine more accurate calorific values of food.

Hess's law has significance in carrying out processes in the production plant. For example, a specific chemical reaction in an organic synthesis may be exothermic and release a large amount of thermal energy which would be considered too risky since the resulting temperature rise might result in decomposition of the chemicals and the risk of a runaway reaction. In the research laboratory, this is less likely to happen because cooling a small-scale reaction is more efficient than a larger scale reaction.

The solution to this issue is to identify the different thermodynamic stages in the reaction, such as the heat of solvation of the different reagents and the heat emitted by the reaction itself. Dissolving the reagents, then allowing these solutions to cool before they are mixed, means that the heat emitted during the reaction itself is less and the reaction is safer.

Another aspect of Hess's law would be in the measurement of the binding affinities of drugs to a protein target. Stability is obtained due to the binding interactions formed between the drug and the binding site (hydrogen bonds, London (dispersion) forces, ionic interactions and so on), but there are also 'energy penalties' such as the energy required to dehydrate both the drug and the target binding site. Dehydrate means to remove the surrounding water molecules (the hydration sphere) and is an example of desolvation – removal of the solvent molecules.

The measured binding affinity of drugs to their protein receptors is the sum of both these opposing effects. To get a better idea of the strength of the binding interactions, researchers could dissolve each drug in water and measure its enthalpy of hydration, then use the negative value of those figures to get a measure of the energy penalty involved in dehydration. However, this would really only be valid for rigid drugs since the effects of any entropy changes when the drug binds are not being taken into account. Measuring the dehydration energy penalty of the protein is not so easy, but if the study compares different drugs, then it would be reasonable to assume that is a constant and it should be possible to get results that would show which drugs are binding most effectively without the complication of different desolvation penalties.

ToK Link

Hess's Law is an example of the application of the conservation of energy. What are the challenges and limitations of applying general principles to specific instances?

Hess's law is always valid since the conservation of energy is a universal truth for all practical purposes. It yields an enthalpy value, $\Delta H^{\ominus}$, but this is only related to heat if the reaction is at constant pressure and no expansion work (Figure 5.26) is done. Work is the amount of energy transferred by a force: expansion work $(w) = -p\Delta V$, where p is the external pressure and ΔV is the change in volume.

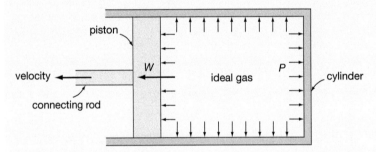

■ **Figure 5.26** Expansion work

An example from kinetics is simple collision theory developed from the kinetic theory of gases to account for the influence of concentration and temperature on reaction rates. The theory is based on several postulates: (i) the reactant particles behave as hard spheres, (ii) there is no interaction between the reactant particles until they collide, and (iii) only collisions with a combined minimum kinetic energy greater than the activation energy, E_a, will lead to reaction. The collision theory is usually able to predict, satisfactorily, the rate of reaction involving simple molecules. However, difficulties arise with reactions that involve complicated molecules. The observed rates tend to be lower than what the collision theory predicts, sometimes by a factor of 10^5 or more. Therefore, another factor, called the steric factor, has to be introduced; this may be interpreted as a preference for a particular orientation (e.g. direction, angle of approach) of the reacting molecules.

Even in its more complex form, collision theory does not accurately predict the reaction between metal atoms such as sodium or potassium and halogen molecules such as bromine, for example $K(g) + Br_2(g) \rightarrow KBr(g) + Br(g)$. As the alkali metal atom approaches the bromine molecule its valence electron moves to the bromine molecule (thus providing a 'harpoon'). There are then two ions with an electrostatic attraction between them. As a result the ions move together and the reaction takes place. This mechanism, which has been worked out quantitatively, explains why the reaction occurs far more readily than might be expected taking into account only mechanical collisions between the alkali metal atoms and halogen molecules.

■ Recycling

The resources on the Earth are limited and it is important that the actions we take now help future generations. To achieve sustainable development, there needs to be a balance between the need for economic development, where standards of living improve, and respect for the environment and the resources it provides for us. Recycling is an important way to help achieve sustainable development and many resources including glass, paper and especially metals can be recycled.

Glass is easily recycled. It can be melted and re-moulded to make new objects, such as bottles. The energy needed to do this is less than the energy needed to make new glass from its raw materials.

Paper is broken up into small pieces and re-formed to make new sheets of paper. This takes less energy to do than making paper from trees. However, paper can only be recycled a few times before its fibres become too short to be useful, and the recycled paper is often only good enough for toilet paper or cardboard. But it can be used as a fuel or compost instead.

Metals are very important non-renewable resources, and the supplies of metals will eventually run out unless extensive recycling is practised. Table 5.2 gives some approximate recent figures about selected metals.

■ **Table 5.2** Recent data about selected metals

Metal	Mass of metal used up each year (10^6 tonnes)	Approximate number of years before the metal is used up (depleted)
Iron	100	110
Aluminium	15	350
Copper	8	40
Zinc	5	60
Lead	5	20
Tin	0.50	15

These are approximate figures from the past but they clearly demonstrate the need to recycle metals – that is, to melt down used metals – rather than throw them away. There is also a need to reduce the environmental impact of mining, for example contamination of soil and water, as well as acid rain production and global warming. A metal company will recycle metal only if it is economical. The company has to work out the costs of collecting the scrap, transporting it, melting it down, getting rid of impurities and paying the workers' wages. In future, as metals get scarcer and more expensive, recycling will become a more important process but it varies in its efficiency in energy terms in different countries.

5.3 Bond enthalpies *– energy is absorbed when bonds are broken and is released when bonds are formed*

■ Bond enthalpies

The bond enthalpy (bond energy) is the amount of energy required to break one mole of a specific covalent bond between two atoms in one mole of gaseous molecules. Measurement of bond enthalpies can be performed using a mass spectrometer (Chapter 2). The concept of bond enthalpy is illustrated in Figure 5.27 using the hydrogen molecule.

For the hydrogen molecule, the thermochemical equation describing the bond dissociation enthalpy is:

$$H_2(g) \rightarrow 2H(g) \qquad \Delta H^\ominus = +436\,kJ\,mol^{-1}$$

The bond enthalpy for hydrogen is $436\,kJ\,mol^{-1}$. Because energy is required to overcome or break the attractive forces between the shared pair of electrons and the nuclei, the bond breaking process is endothermic (that is, heat energy is absorbed from the surroundings). It should be noted that if the H–H bond had been formed, then 436 kilojoules of heat energy would have been released to the surroundings. This is a simple application of Hess's law. Bond breaking is *always* an endothermic process; bond formation is *always* an exothermic process.

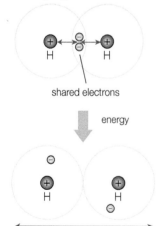

Both nuclei are attracted to the same pair of electrons

hydrogen molecule

shared electrons

energy

pull atoms apart against the force of electrostatic attraction

■ **Figure 5.27** To break a covalent bond the attractive forces between the shared pair or pairs of electrons and the nuclei of the two atoms need to be overcome

The strength of a covalent bond is indicated by the size of the bond enthalpy. The larger the bond enthalpy, the stronger the covalent bond. Also, bond enthalpy is inversely proportional to bond length.

Average bond enthalpies

Many bond enthalpies are *average* bond enthalpies. For example, the C–H bond enthalpy is based upon the average bond energies in methane, alkanes and other hydrocarbons.

Because bond enthalpies are often average values it means that enthalpy changes calculated using bond enthalpies will *not* be exactly equal to an accurate experimentally determined value.

A selection of bond enthalpies and bond lengths is given in Table 5.3. A more extensive table of bond enthalpies is given on page 11 of the IB *Chemistry data booklet*.

■ **Table 5.3** A selection of average bond enthalpies (at 298 K)

Bond	$\Delta H^{\ominus}$ /kJ mol^{-1}	Bond length/Pm
H–H	436	74
C–C	346	154
C=C	614	134
C≡C	839	120
N–N	158	146
N=N	470	125
O–O	144	148
O=O	498	121
F–F	159	142
Cl–Cl	242	199
Br–Br	193	228
I–I	151	267
C–H	414	108
O–H	463	97
C≡N	890	116
H–F	567	92
N–H	391	101
O–H	463	97
C=O	804	122

Factors affecting average bond enthalpies

■ **Effect of bond length**

The larger the atoms joined by a particular bond, the longer the bond length. Large atoms have more electrons than smaller atoms and this results in an increase in repulsion between the electron shells of each atom. In addition, the nucleus of each atom is more effectively shielded (Chapter 12). Both of these effects lead to a weakening of the bond. For example, in the halogens the bond strength weakens in the order: chlorine, bromine and iodine. Fluorine, however, has a surprisingly low bond enthalpy, which is accounted for by lone pair–lone pair repulsion.

■ **Effect of number of bonding electrons**

The more electrons present in a bond, the greater the strength of the bond. This is because an increasing number of electrons leads to an increase in electrostatic forces of attraction. Hence triple bonds are expected to be stronger than double bonds, which should be stronger than single bonds (for the same element). This can clearly be observed with carbon (Table 5.3).

■ **Effect of bond polarity**

Bonds become more polar as the difference in electronegativity (Chapter 3) between the two bonded atoms increases (Chapter 4). This increases the ionic character of the bond and increases the strength of polar covalent bonds. This can be observed with N–H, O–H and F–H where bond strength increases with increasing polarity.

■ Using bond dissociation enthalpies to calculate enthalpy changes of reaction

Bond enthalpies can be used to determine the enthalpy change for a particular reaction involving molecules in the gaseous state, for example the combustion of methane:

$$CH_4(g) + 2O_2(g) \rightarrow CO_2(g) + 2H_2O(g)$$

The reaction can be regarded as occurring in two steps: first, all of the bonds in the reactants have to be broken to form atoms. This is an endothermic process and heat energy has to be absorbed from the surroundings. In the second step, bond formation occurs. This is an exothermic process and releases heat energy to the surroundings. The overall reaction is exothermic since the energy released during bond formation is greater than the energy absorbed during bond breaking (Figure 5.28).

■ **Figure 5.28** Breaking and forming of bonds during the combustion of methane

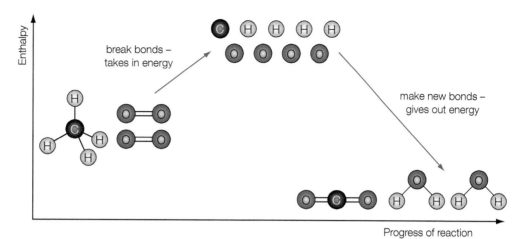

Bond enthalpy data can be used to calculate the enthalpy change for this reaction.

Bond breaking:

Breaking 4 C—H bonds in a methane molecule = 4 × 412 = 1648 kJ
Breaking 2 O=O bonds in two oxygen molecules = 2 × 496 = 992 kJ
Total amount of energy required to break all these bonds = (1648 + 992) = 2640 kJ

Bond making:

Making 2 C—O bonds in a carbon dioxide molecule = 2 × 743 = 1486 kJ
Making 4 O=H bonds in two water molecules = 4 × 463 = 1852 kJ
Total amount of energy released to surroundings when these bonds are formed
= (1486 + 1852) = 3338 kJ

The enthalpy change for this reaction is:

$$\Delta H = \Sigma \left(\begin{array}{c} \text{energy required} \\ \text{to break bonds} \end{array} \right) - \Sigma \left(\begin{array}{c} \text{energy released when} \\ \text{bonds are formed} \end{array} \right)$$

$$= (2640 - 3338)$$

$$= -698 \, \text{kJ mol}^{-1}$$

Since more energy is released when the new bonds in the products are formed than is needed to break the bonds in the reactants to begin with, there is an overall release of energy in the form of heat. The reaction is exothermic. In a reaction which is endothermic, the energy absorbed by bond breaking is greater than the energy released by bond formation.

The bond breaking and making processes can be represented by a Hess's law cycle (see Figure 5.29). This calculated value is slightly different from the real value because the bond enthalpies are averages. In addition, the water that is produced (in the calculation) is *not* in its standard state, as a liquid. The gaseous state is always used when performing bond enthalpy calculations.

■ **Figure 5.29** Using a Hess's law cycle to represent the bond breaking and bond making processes for the complete combustion of methane

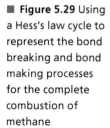
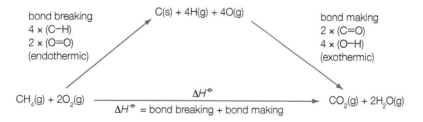

Average bond enthalpies can be used to calculate the enthalpy change for any reaction involving molecules in the gaseous state. This is done by assuming that an alternative route for all reactions can be achieved theoretically via the gaseous atoms involved in the compounds (Figure 5.30).

■ **Figure 5.30**
Generalized energy
cycle to determine an
enthalpy change from
bond energies

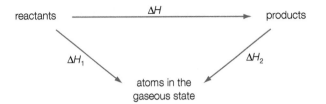

ΔH_1 = sum of the average bond enthalpies of the reactants

ΔH_2 = sum of the average bond enthalpies of the products

Applying Hess's law gives:

$$\Delta H = \Delta H_1 - \Delta H_2$$

This leads to the expression:

$$\Delta H = \Sigma(\text{average bond enthalpies of the reactants}) - \Sigma(\text{average bond enthalpies of the products})$$

i.e. $\Delta H = \Sigma(\text{bonds broken}) - \Sigma(\text{bonds made})$

Bond enthalpy data can also be used to determine an unknown bond enthalpy provided that the enthalpy change and all the other bond enthalpies are known.

Worked example

The bond enthalpies for $H_2(g)$ and $HCl(g)$ are $435\,kJ\,mol^{-1}$ and $431\,kJ\,mol^{-1}$, respectively, for the reaction

$$H_2(g) + Cl_2(g) \rightarrow 2HCl(g)$$

and the enthalpy change of reaction is $-184\,kJ\,mol^{-1}$. Calculate the bond enthalpy of chlorine.

Enthalpy change = $\Sigma(\text{bonds broken}) - \Sigma(\text{bonds made})$

$-184 = (435 + Cl-Cl) - (2 \times 431)$

$-184 = (435 + Cl-Cl) - 862$

$Cl-Cl = 243\,kJ\,mol^{-1}$

■ Potential energy profiles

Enthalpy changes can be shown using **potential energy profiles** (Figures 5.31 and 5.32).

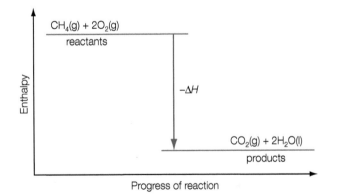

■ **Figure 5.31** Enthalpy level diagram for an exothermic reaction – the combustion of methane

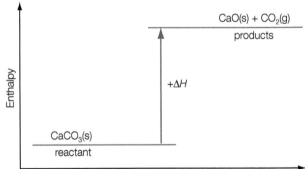

■ **Figure 5.32** Enthalpy level diagram for an endothermic reaction – the thermal decomposition of calcium carbonate

Thermochemical equations are equations which show the associated enthalpy changes.

$$CH_4(g) + 2O_2(g) \rightarrow CO_2(g) + 2H_2O(l) \qquad \Delta H^\ominus = -890\,kJ\,mol^{-1}$$

$$CaCO_3(s) \rightarrow CaO(s) + CO_2(g) \qquad \Delta H^\ominus = +180\,kJ\,mol^{-1}$$

For an exothermic reaction the enthalpy change, ΔH, is described as negative because potential energy has been lost from the reaction mixture to the surroundings, in the form of heat. The products are at a lower energy or enthalpy level than the reactants.

Endothermic reactions absorb heat energy from the surroundings. The products of an endothermic reaction contain more potential energy or enthalpy than the reactants. For this type of reaction the enthalpy change is positive, because the chemical reactants gain heat from their surroundings.

Additional Perspectives

Activation energy

All chemical reactions, both endothermic and exothermic, have an activation energy barrier (Chapter 6). The activation energy of a reaction is usually denoted by E_a, and is given in units of kilojoules per mole. The activation energy barrier (Figure 5.33) controls the rate of the reaction: the smaller the value of the activation energy, the greater the rate of the reaction.

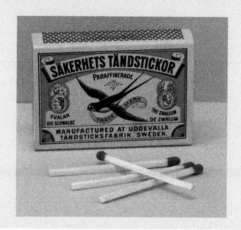

■ **Figure 5.33** Matches and match box. The match head consists of potassium chlorate(v), sulfur and phosphorus trisulfide; the frictional heat when the match is struck against the side of the box is sufficient to give the reactants enough combined kinetic energy to overcome the activation energy barrier

 ## Sketching potential energy profiles

Sketch a potential energy profile for the following thermochemical equation:

$$H_2(g) + \frac{1}{2}O_2(g) \rightarrow H_2O(l) \qquad \Delta H = -242\,kJ\,mol^{1}$$

State and explain if the reaction is exothermic or endothermic, and whether the reactants or the products are more stable.

The negative sign in front of the enthalpy change indicates that thermal energy (heat) flows from the system (chemicals) to the surroundings. This implies that the reactants have less potential energy than the reactants and hence are more stable (Figure 5.34).

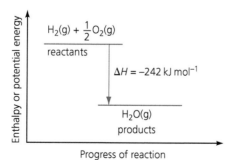

■ **Figure 5.34** Potential energy profile for $H_2(g) + \frac{1}{2}O_2(g) \rightarrow H_2O(l)$; $\Delta H = -242\,kJ\,mol^{-1}$

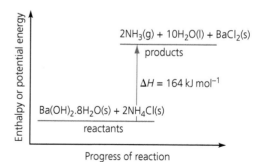

■ **Figure 5.35** Potential energy profile for $Ba(OH)_2.8H_2O(s) + 2NH_4Cl(s) \rightarrow 2NH_3(g) + 10H_2O(l) + BaCl_2(s)$; $\Delta H = +164\,kJ\,mol^{-1}$

Sketch a potential energy profile for the following thermochemical equation:

$$Ba(OH)_2.8H_2O(s) + 2NH_4Cl(s) \rightarrow 2NH_3(g) + 10H_2O(l) + BaCl_2(s)$$
$$\Delta H = +164\,kJ\,mol^{-1}$$

State and explain if the reaction is exothermic or endothermic, and whether the reactants or the products are more stable.

The positive sign sign in front of the enthalpy change indicates that thermal energy (heat) flows from the surroundings to the system (chemicals). This implies that the products have more potential energy than the reactants and hence are less stable (Figure 5.35).

For the sake of simplicity the activation energy barrier has not been drawn on the potential energy profiles.

■ Ozone depletion

The chlorofluorocarbons (CFCs) have almost ideal properties for use as aerosol propellants and refrigerant heat-transfer fluids. They are chemically and biologically inert (and hence safe to use and handle) and they can be easily liquefied by pressure slightly above atmospheric pressure. Although fairly expensive to produce (compared to other refrigerants like ammonia), they rapidly replaced fluids that had been used before. In the early 1970s, however, concern was expressed that their very inertness was a global disadvantage.

Once released to the environment, CFCs remain chemically unchanged for years in the atmosphere. Due to their volatile nature, they diffuse upwards through the atmosphere and eventually find their way into the stratosphere (about 20 km above the Earth's surface). Here they are exposed to the stronger ultraviolet rays of the Sun. Although the carbon–fluorine bond is very strong, the carbon–chlorine bond is weak enough to be split by ultraviolet light. This forms chlorine atoms (also known as radicals) which upset the delicately balanced equilibrium between ozone formation and ozone breakdown. It is believed that a variety of biological consequences such as increases in skin cancer, cataracts in the eye, damage to plants, and reduction of plankton populations in the oceans may result from the increased ultraviolet exposure due to ozone depletion. The social consequences involve the reduction of outdoor activities in the regions of the world most heavily affected by the two ozone holes located at the two poles and the increased need for people to use sunscreen.

It has been estimated that one chlorine atom can catalytically destroy over 10^5 ozone molecules before it eventually diffuses back into the lower atmosphere. There it can react with water vapour to produce hydrogen chloride, which can be flushed out by rain, as dilute hydrochloric acid. Once the 'ozone hole' (Figure 5.36) above the Antarctic was discovered in 1985, global agreements were signed in Montreal (1989) and London (1990). As a result, the global production of CFCs has been drastically reduced. In many of their applications they can be replaced by hydrocarbons such as propane. It will still take several decades for natural regeneration reactions to allow the ozone concentration to recover, but there is recent evidence that is occurring. Other stratospheric pollutants such as nitrogen monoxide, NO, from high flying aircraft also destroy ozone.

Stratospheric ozone depletion raises a number of ethical issues. Ozone depletion can harm humans, animals, plants and ecosystems. Yet the harm caused by ozone-depleting chemicals was initially unknown, unintentional and indirect. Producers of ozone-depleting chemicals were at first unaware that their products could harm the environment and/or people, and they had no intention to cause harm. The harm was indirect because it was not the chemicals themselves, but rather the effects of the chemicals on stratospheric ozone, that caused damage. Lastly, the harm was diffuse in that it was not the action of a single individual, but rather the cumulative effects of many corporations and individuals producing and using ozone-depleting chemicals, that caused the problem.

For example, should people be held responsible for harm that they did not know they were causing? Do corporations and nations have the same moral responsibilities as individuals? What obligations exist when the nature and size of the harm of CFCs were initially unknown? When harm is caused by the joint actions of many parties, how should responsibility be allocated?

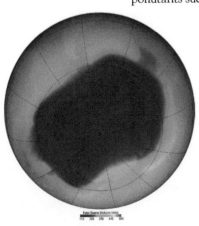

■ **Figure 5.36** The ozone hole

The bond strength in ozone relative to oxygen in its importance to the atmosphere

The Sun radiates a wide spectrum of radiation, ranging from the infrared to the ultraviolet (UV) region and including the visible region. Part of this range of radiations corresponds to the energy required to break covalent bonds, including those in molecules such as DNA. This can damage genes and lead to skin cancer, and also damage the proteins in connective tissue and lead to wrinkles.

The most damaging region is the ultraviolet region whose radiation has photons with the highest frequency and therefore the highest energy. Some chemicals absorb this radiation, for example glass and manufactured chemicals such as sunscreens, but the best protection is the atmosphere itself. The ultraviolet region is divided into three regions: UV A (wavelength 400–320 nm), UV B (wavelength 320–280 nm) and UV C (wavelength below 280 nm). UV A radiation is needed by humans for the synthesis of vitamin D but UV B and UV C are harmful.

Atmospheric gases in the stratosphere absorb ultraviolet radiation very well ('strongly'). Ozone, O_3, absorbs especially strongly. In the stratosphere the ultraviolet radiation breaks covalent bonds in molecules to give reactive fragments called radicals. The bonds in the ozone molecule absorb the harmful radiation present in UV B and UV C. This leads to the destruction of the ozone:

$$O_3(g) + hv \rightarrow O(g) + O_2(g)$$
$$O_3(g) + O(g) \rightarrow 2O_2(g)$$

A dynamic equilibrium is established in these reactions. The ozone concentration varies due to the amount of radiation received from the Sun. The bonds in ozone are slightly weaker than those in the oxygen molecule due to the presence of resonance or delocalization. This means that the oxygen–oxygen bonds have partial double bond character and will have a bond energy intermediate between a double bond and a single bond. The bond energy of the oxygen–oxygen bonds present in ozone is 445 kJ mol^{-1} while the bond energy of the double bond present in the oxygen molecule is 498 kJ mol^{-1}. Because the bonds in the O_3 molecule are weaker than those in the O_2 molecule, photolysis ('splitting by light') is achieved with lower-energy photons.

Oxygen molecules also absorb ultraviolet radiation. When an oxygen molecule absorbs a photon of the appropriate energy it will undergo photolysis and dissociate into oxygen atoms:

$$O_2(g) + hv \rightarrow O(g) + O(g)$$
$$O_2(g) + O(g) \rightarrow O_3(g)$$

The last reaction requires a third molecule to take away the energy associated with the free radical O and O_2, and the reaction can be represented by

$$O_2(g) + O(g) + M \rightarrow O_3(g) + M*$$

The principle of the conservation of energy can be used to calculate the maximum wavelength of the photon that has enough energy to break (cleave) a specific bond, for example, the O=O bond present in oxygen, O_2.

The energy per O=O bond is:

$$\frac{498\,000 \, \text{J mol}^{-1}}{6.022 \times 10^{23} \, \text{bonds mol}^{-1}} = 8.27 \times 10^{-19} \, \text{J bond}^{-1}$$

The wavelength, λ, of the photons can be calculated using the expression $E = hc/\lambda$:

$$\lambda = \frac{6.626 \times 10^{-34} \, \text{J s} \times 3.00 \times 10^8 \, \text{m s}^{-1}}{8.27 \times 10^{-19} \, \text{J}} = 2.403 \times 10^{-7} \, \text{m or } 240 \, \text{nm}$$

Only photons of wavelengths less than 240 nm can photolyze the O_2 molecule. Such high-energy photons are present in the solar spectrum at high altitude.

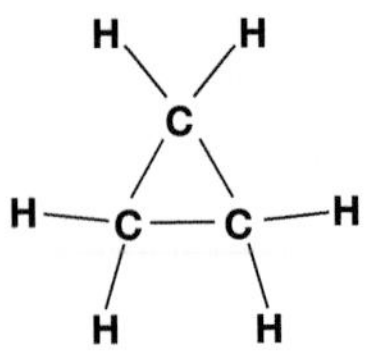

■ **Figure 5.37**
Structure of
cyclopropane

Models and theories

Measured energy changes can be explained based on the model of bonds broken and bonds formed. Since these explanations are based on a model, agreement with empirical data depends on the sophistication of the model, and data obtained can be used to modify theories where appropriate.

Calculations involving bond enthalpies generally give values of enthalpy changes that are close to experimentally determined values. However, with a small number of molecules the calculated enthalpy change is *significantly* different from the real value.

For example, cyclopropane (see Figure 5.37) is much *less* energetically stable than a bond energy calculation predicts. This is due to the 'strain energy' placed into the molecule during its formation. The angles between the carbon–carbon bonds forming the ring are 60°, whereas the *preferred* bond angle is 109° (Chapter 4).

In contrast, the benzene molecule is *more* energetically stable than a bond energy calculation would suggest. This is because the molecule is a hybrid (Chapter 14) of the two resonance structures shown in Figure 5.38. Its carbon–carbon bonds are *intermediate* between single and double bonds, but because the π electrons (Chapter 14) move around the ring they stabilize the molecule.

The benzene molecule is a cyclic or ring system, like cyclopropane, but does *not* suffer from strain energy.

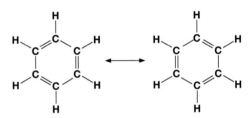

■ **Figure 5.38** Resonance structures of the benzene molecule

Calculating enthalpy changes from known bond enthalpy values and comparing these to experimentally measured values

Calculate the expected value of the enthalpy of formation for dinitrogen monoxide and comment on the calculated value compared to its experimental value. Assume N_2O has one N=N bond and one O=O bond.

The enthalpy of formation of dinitrogen monoxide is described by the following equation:

$$N_2(g) + \frac{1}{2}O_2(g) \rightarrow N_2O(g)$$

Enthalpy change $= \sum(\text{bonds broken}) - \sum(\text{bonds made})$

$$= (946 + \frac{1}{2} \times 498) - (418 + 607) = 170\,\text{kJ mol}^{-1}$$

The experimental value for the enthalpy of formation for dinitrogen monoxide is $82\,\text{kJ mol}^{-1}$. This is a significant difference and indicates that dinitrogen monoxide is resonance stabilized. The difference between the expected and observed values of the enthalpy of formation is the resonance energy ($88\,\text{kJ mol}^{-1}$).

Enthalpies of combustion of alkanes

Bond energies are by and large additive, which means that the specific bond energies are approximately constant for a range of related molecules, for example the alkanes and alcohols.

Consider the alkanes, a group of hydrocarbons that are derived from methane, CH_4, by progressively adding methylene, $-CH_2-$ units (Figure 5.39).

■ **Figure 5.39**
The formation
of alkanes by the
progressive addition of
methylene, $-CH_2-$ units

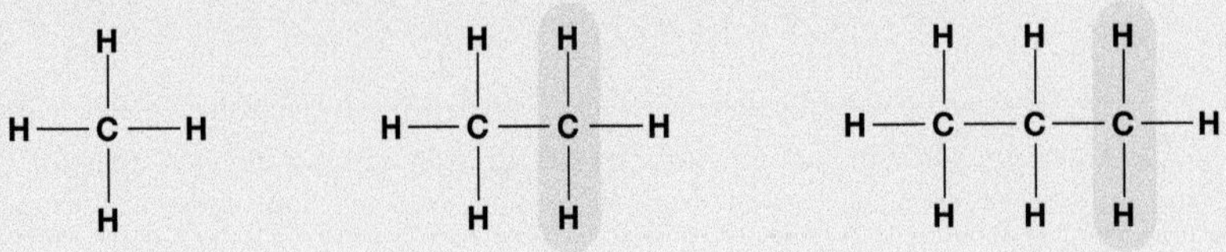

If a series of hydrocarbons is combusted, the addition of each extra methylene group will be responsible for an additional enthalpy change:

$$-CH_2- + 1\frac{1}{2}O_2(g) \rightarrow CO_2(g) + H_2O(l)$$

The enthalpy change, ΔH, for this process can be calculated using bond enthalpies:

Breaking bonds: $1 \times$ C—C, $2 \times$ C—H, $1\frac{1}{2} \times$ O=O
Making bonds: $2 \times$ C=O, $2 \times$ O–H

Using the values from page 11 of the IB *Chemistry data booklet*:

Breaking bonds:	$1 \times$ C—C	346
	$2 \times$ C—H	2×414
	$1\frac{1}{2} \times$ O=O	$1\frac{1}{2} \times 498$
Total energy		1921 kJ
Making bonds:	$2 \times$ C=O	2×804
	$2 \times$ O—H	2×463
Total energy		2534 kJ

Enthalpy change = $\sum$(bonds broken) − $\sum$(bonds made) = (1921) + (−2534) = −613 kJ mol^{-1}

Hence the additional enthalpy of combustion for each additional methylene unit, $-CH_2-$, is −613 kJ mol^{-1}. This type of simple calculation predicts that there should be an approximate linear relationship between the enthalpy change of combustion of an alkane and the number of carbon atoms (Figure 5.40). Experimental values confirm this prediction.

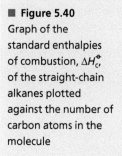

■ **Figure 5.40**
Graph of the standard enthalpies of combustion, $\Delta H_c^\ominus$, of the straight-chain alkanes plotted against the number of carbon atoms in the molecule

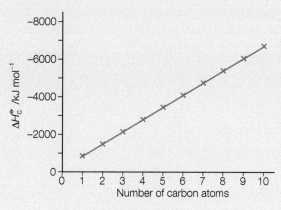

Utilization: Fossil fuels as energy sources

A fuel is a substance that releases thermal energy (heat) that can do work. Most fuels release this energy during combustion with molecular oxygen. An ideal chemical fuel should have a number of properties, including a high value of enthalpy of combustion. Table 5.4 gives the standard enthalpies of combustion of some fuel alternatives to petrol. There is no standard enthalpy change of combustion for petrol because it is a complex homogenous mixture of about 100 compounds, mainly hydrocarbons, of which the majority are alkanes. However, the standard enthalpy change of combustion of octane, the major component of petrol, is −5470 kJ mol^{-1}. Its high enthalpy of combustion is one reason why it has desirable chemical properties to be a good fuel.

■ **Table 5.4** Enthalpies of combustion of fuels

Fuel	Main component	Formula and standard state	$\Delta H^{\ominus}_c$ of main component/kJ mol^{-1}
Hydrogen	Hydrogen	$H_2(g)$	−286
Compressed natural gas (CNG)	90% methane	$CH_4(g)$	−890
Liquid petroleum gas (LPG)	95% propane	$C_3H_8(g)$	−2219
Methanol	Methanol	$CH_3OH(l)$	−726
Alcohol	Ethanol	$C_2H_5OH(l)$	−1367

Another relevant property of fuels is the energy density of the fuel (Table 5.5). This is the amount of thermal energy (heat) released by 1 kilogram of the fuel. The energy density is calculated from the standard enthalpy of combustion of the fuel and the mass of one mole of the fuel. Petrol has an energy density of approximately 46000 kJ kg^{-1} which makes it a very concentrated energy source. Liquid hydrogen has a higher density than petrol, but currently storage problems on board a vehicle are one reason why its use is limited, along with the very low temperatures required to keep it as a liquid.

■ **Table 5.5** Energy densities of fuels

Fuel	Formula	$\Delta H^{\ominus}_c$	Mass of one mole/g	Energy density/kJ kg^{-1}
Hydrogen	$H_2(g)$	−286	2	143000
Methane	$CH_4(g)$	−890	16	27800
Methanol	$CH_3OH(l)$	−2219	32	22700
Ethanol	$C_2H_5OH(l)$	−1367	46	30000

Additional Perspectives

Feasibility of reactions

There are many examples of reactions which are spontaneous. The vast majority of these reactions are exothermic. Hence it appears that the enthalpy change, ΔH, is a reliable guide to which direction a reaction will go. However, there are examples of endothermic reactions that occur without the need for heat to initiate the reaction, for example, the reaction between citric acid and a solution of sodium hydrogencarbonate. Some salts dissolve endothermically in water. Chapter 15 introduces a factor, known as entropy, that, in conjunction with enthalpy and temperature, determines whether or not reactions occur at a specified temperature.

■ *Examination questions – a selection*

Paper 1 IB questions and IB style questions

Q1 When 0.3205 g of methanol is completely combusted under a water filled flame combustion calorimeter, the temperature of 1×10^3 cm^3 of water is raised by 1.5°C. (Molar mass of methanol = 32.05 g mol^{-1}; specific heat capacity of water = 4.18 J g^{-1}°C^{-1}.)

What is the expression for the molar enthalpy of combustion of methanol?

A $-\dfrac{1\times10^3 \times 4.18 \times 1.5 \times 32.05}{0.3205}$

B $-\dfrac{1\times10^3 \times 4.18 \times (273.00 + 1.5) \times 32.05}{0.3205 \times 1 \times 10^3}$

C $-\dfrac{1\times10^3 \times 4.18 \times 1.5 \times 32.05}{0.3205 \times 1 \times 10^3}$

D $-\dfrac{0.3205 \times 1 \times 10^3}{1 \times 10^3 \times 4.18 \times 1.5 \times 32.05}$

Q2 Which of the following reactions would you expect to provide the largest amount of heat?
A $C_2H_6(l) + 7O_2(l) \rightarrow 4CO_2(g) + 6H_2O(g)$
B $C_2H_6(l) + 7O_2(g) \rightarrow 4CO_2(g) + 6H_2O(g)$
C $C_2H_6(g) + 7O_2(g) \rightarrow 4CO_2(g) + 6H_2O(g)$
D $C_2H_6(g) + 7O_2(g) \rightarrow 4CO_2(g) + 6H_2O(l)$

Q3 Why does the temperature of boiling water remain constant even though heat is supplied at a constant rate?
A Heat is lost to the surroundings.
B The heat is used to break the covalent bonds in the water molecules.
C Heat is also taken in by the container.
D The heat is used to overcome the intermolecular forces of attraction between water molecules.

Standard Level Paper 1, Nov 2005, Q14

Q4 When 0.050 mol of nitric acid is reacted with 0.050 mol of potassium hydroxide in water, the temperature of the system increases by 13.7 °C.

Calculate the enthalpy of reaction in $kJ\,mol^{-1}$.

$$HNO_3(aq) + KOH(aq) \rightarrow KNO_3(aq) + H_2O(l)$$

Assume that the heat capacity of the system was $209.2\,J\,°C^{-1}$.

A $+57.3\,kJ\,mol^{-1}$ **C** $-2.87\,kJ\,mol^{-1}$
B $+2.87\,kJ\,mol^{-1}$ **D** $-57.3\,kJ\,mol^{-1}$

Q5 What can be deduced about the relative stability of the reactants and products and the sign of ΔH, from the enthalpy level diagram below?

Relative stability	**Sign of ΔH**
A products more stable	–
B products more stable	+
C reactants more stable	–
D reactants more stable	+

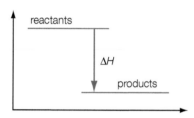

Standard Level Paper 1, May 1999, Q16

Q6 The specific heat capacities of some metals are given below.

Metal	**Specific heat capacity ($J\,g^{-1}\,K^{-1}$)**
copper	0.385
magnesium	1.020
mercury	0.138
platinum	0.130

If $100\,kJ$ of heat is added to $10.0\,g$ samples of each of the metals above, which are all at $25\,°C$, which metal will have the lowest temperature?

A copper   **C** mercury
B magnesium   **D** platinum

Q7 The bond energy for the H–F bond is equal to the enthalpy change for which process?

A $H^+(g) + F^-(g) \rightarrow HF(g)$

B $HF(g) \rightarrow H(g) + F(g)$

C $\frac{1}{2}F_2(g) + \frac{1}{2}H_2(g) \rightarrow HF(g)$

D $HF(g) \rightarrow \frac{1}{2}F_2(g) + \frac{1}{2}H_2(g)$

Q8 When a sample of a pure hydrocarbon (melting point $85\,°C$) cools, the temperature is observed to remain constant as it solidifies. Which statement accounts for this observation?

A The heat released in the change of state equals the heat loss to the surroundings.

B The temperature of the system has fallen to room temperature.

C The solid which forms insulates the system, preventing heat loss.

D Heat is gained from the surroundings as the solid forms, maintaining a constant temperature.

Q9 Consider the following equation:

$$6CO_2(g) + 6H_2O(l) \rightarrow C_6H_{12}O_6(s) + 6O_2(g)$$
$$\Delta H = 2824\,kJ\,mol^{-1}$$

What is the enthalpy change associated with the production of $100.0\,g$ of $C_6H_{12}O_6$?

A $157\,kJ$ **C** $508\,kJ$
B $282\,kJ$ **D** $1570\,kJ$

Q10 $N_2(g) + O_2(g) \rightarrow 2NO(g)$ $\Delta H = 180.4\,kJ\,mol^{-1}$
$N_2(g) + 2O_2(g) \rightarrow 2NO_2(g)$ $\Delta H = 66.4\,kJ\,mol^{-1}$

Use the enthalpy values to calculate ΔH for the reaction:

$$NO(g) + \frac{1}{2}O_2(g) \rightarrow NO_2(g)$$

A $-57\,kJ\,mol^{-1}$ **C** $57\,kJ\,mol^{-1}$
B $-114\,kJ\,mol^{-1}$ **D** $114\,kJ\,mol^{-1}$

Standard Level Paper 1, May 2000, Q18

Q11 The heating curve for $10\,g$ of a substance is given below. How much energy would be required to melt completely $40\,g$ of the substance that is initially at $10\,°C$?

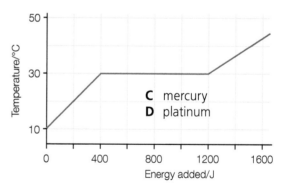

A $4800\,J$ **C** $1600\,J$
B $2400\,J$ **D** $800\,J$

Q12 The bond energies for H_2, I_2 and HI are 432, 149 and $295\,kJ\,mol^{-1}$, respectively. From these data, what is the enthalpy change (in kJ) for the reaction below?

$$H_2(g) + I_2(g) \rightarrow 2HI(g)$$

A $+9$ **C** -286
B $+286$ **D** -9

Q13 The specific heat capacity of aluminum is $0.900 \, J \, g^{-1} \, K^{-1}$. What is the heat energy change, in J, when 10.0 g of aluminum is heated and its temperature increases from 15.0 °C to 35 °C?

A +180 C +1800
B +315 D +2637

Higher Level Paper 1, May 2013, Q14

Q14 Which reaction represents the average bond enthalpy of the Si–H bond in silane, SiH_4?

A $\frac{1}{4} SiH_4(g) \rightarrow \frac{1}{4} Si(g) + \frac{1}{2} H_2(g)$

B $\frac{1}{4} SiH_4(g) \rightarrow \frac{1}{4} SiH_2(g) + \frac{1}{4} H_2(g)$

C $\frac{1}{4} SiH_4(g) \rightarrow \frac{1}{4} Si(g) + H(g)$

D $\frac{1}{4} SiH_4(g) \rightarrow \frac{1}{4} Si(s) + H(g)$

Q15 Which of the following is the correct equation for the standard enthalpy change of formation of carbon monoxide?

A $C(s) + \frac{1}{2} O_2(g) \rightarrow CO(g)$

B $C(g) + \frac{1}{2} O_2(g) \rightarrow CO(g)$

C $C(g) + O(g) \rightarrow CO(g)$

D $2C(s) + O_2(g) \rightarrow 2CO(g)$

Q16 The bond enthalpies for $H_2(g)$ and HF(g) are $435 \, kJ \, mol^{-1}$ and $565 \, kJ \, mol^{-1}$, respectively. For the reaction $\frac{1}{2} H_2(g) + \frac{1}{2} F_2(g) \rightarrow HF(g)$, the enthalpy of reaction is $-268 \, kJ \, mol^{-1}$ of HF produced. What is the bond energy of F_2 in $kJ \, mol^{-1}$?

A 464 C 243
B 138 D 159

Q17 The standard enthalpy change of formation values of two oxides of phosphorus are:

$P_4(s) + 3O_2(g) \rightarrow P_4O_6(s) \quad \Delta H_f^\ominus = -1600 \, kJ \, mol^{-1}$

$P_4(s) + 5O_2(g) \rightarrow P_4O_{10}(s) \quad \Delta H_f^\ominus = -3000 \, kJ \, mol^{-1}$

What is the enthalpy change, in $kJ \, mol^{-1}$, for the reaction below?

$P_4O_6(s) + 2O_2(g) \rightarrow P_4O_{10}(s)$

A +4600 C −1400
B +1400 D −4600

Paper 2 IB questions and IB style questions

Q1 a i Define the term average bond enthalpy. [3]
ii Explain why the fluorine molecule, F_2, is not suitable as an example to illustrate the term average bond enthalpy. [1]

b i Using values from page 11 of the IB *Chemistry data booklet*, calculate the enthalpy change for the following reaction:
$CH_4(g) + F_2(g) \rightarrow CH_3F(g) + HF(g)$ [3]
ii Sketch an enthalpy diagram for the reaction. [2]
iii Without carrying out a calculation, suggest, with a reason, how the enthalpy change for the following reaction compares with that of the previous reaction.
$CH_3F(g) + F_2(g) \rightarrow CH_2F_2(g) + HF(g)$ [2]

Q2 In aqueous solution, lithium hydroxide and hydrochloric acid react as follows.

$LiOH(aq) + HCl(aq) \rightarrow LiCl(aq) + H_2O(l)$

The data below are from an experiment to determine the standard enthalpy change of this reaction.

$50.0 \, cm^3$ of a $0.500 \, mol \, dm^{-3}$ solution of LiOH was mixed rapidly in a glass beaker with $50.0 \, cm^3$ of a $0.500 \, mol \, dm^{-3}$ solution of HCl.
Initial temperature of each solution = 20.6 °C
Final temperature of the mixture = 24.1 °C

a State, with a reason, whether the reaction is exothermic or endothermic. [1]
b Explain why the solutions were mixed rapidly. [1]
c Calculate the enthalpy change of this reaction in $kJ \, mol^{-1}$. Assume that the specific heat capacity of the solution is the same as that of water. [4]
d Identify the major source of error in the experimental procedure described above. Explain how it could be minimized. [2]
e The experiment was repeated but with an HCl concentration of $0.520 \, mol \, dm^{-3}$ instead of $0.500 \, mol \, dm^{-3}$. State and explain what the temperature change would be. [2]

Q3 a Define the term standard enthalpy change of formation. [2]
b Define the term standard enthalpy change of combustion. [2]
c State Hess's law. [1]
d Calculate the standard enthalpy change of formation of propane, C_3H_8, given the following standard enthalpies of combustion:
$\Delta H_c^\ominus [C_3H_8(g)] = -2220 \, kJ \, mol^{-1}$
$\Delta H_c^\ominus [C_{graphite}(s)] = -393 \, kJ \, mol^{-1}$
$\Delta H_c^\ominus [H_2(g)] = -286 \, kJ \, mol^{-1}$

Draw an energy cycle and use Hess's law to produce an equation for the enthalpy change of formation. [4]

6 Chemical kinetics

ESSENTIAL IDEA

■ The greater the probability that molecules collide with sufficient energy and proper orientation, the higher the rate of reaction.

Chemical reactions are key to our way of life. Two significant reactions, both involving oxidation, are illustrated in Figure 6.1. They differ significantly in the rate at which they take place; thankfully rusting is a relatively slow process.

■ **Figure 6.1**

a The reaction taking place in the cylinder of a petrol engine; **b** the corroding wreck of the Titanic, where the rusting reaction is encouraged by sea water

The reactions in a petrol engine require a spark to ignite them, but in a diesel engine similar hydrocarbon fuels are ignited without a spark. Increased compression is enough to generate the reaction. These considerations show us the complexity of the factors involved in controlling the rate of a chemical reaction.

6.1 Collision theory and rates of reaction – *the greater the probability that molecules collide with sufficient energy and proper orientation, the higher the rate of reaction*

The branch of chemistry concerned with reaction rates and the sequence of elementary steps by which a chemical reaction occurs is called reaction kinetics or chemical kinetics. The study of kinetics allows chemists to:

■ determine how quickly a reaction will take place

■ determine the conditions required for a specific reaction rate

■ propose a reaction mechanism.

Nature of Science   The confluence of ideas and the principle of Occam's razor

We cannot see the reactions taking place between atoms and molecules but we can build a theory of the interactions taking place based on our overall model of the nature of substance.

Having developed the atomic theory of matter as our working model of how materials are made up, it is a relatively straightforward step to think through the essential steps that need to take place for a reaction to happen. The most obvious requirement is that the particles – whether they are atoms, molecules or ions – must actually meet (or collide).

If we then accept that during the course of a reaction the atoms involved 'change partners' to form new substances, then we must accept that initially some bonds must be broken for the new couplings to take place. Given that bond breaking needs energy, we arrive at the beginnings of the concept of activation energy.

These considerations illustrate how ideas in science converge to develop an increasingly sophisticated model of the nature of the sub-microscopic world. In the development of a scientific theory the principle of Occam's razor, with its emphasis on looking for the simplest option or explanation, can be useful. It can certainly be seen to apply to the model we have developed as the basis of reaction kinetics. However, we need to be careful in applying the 'razor' as it cannot be the only consideration. Indeed the very basis of our ideas here, Dalton's atomic theory, was initially rejected by Ernst Mach and the logical positivists on the grounds that it was too complex. It took observations such Brownian motion and the explanations of this phenomenon put forward by Einstein to generate acceptance of the theory.

■ Collision theory

Simple **collision theory** states that before a chemical reaction can occur, the following requirements must be met:

■ The reactants (ions, atoms or molecules) must physically collide and come into direct contact with each other (Figure 6.2).

■ For many reacting molecules **steric factors** are involved: the molecules must collide in the correct relative positions so their reactive atoms or functional groups are aligned. The molecules must be orientated properly so that they can react. This is known as collision geometry (Figure 6.3).

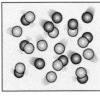

no reaction   reaction

low concentration =   high concentration =
few collisions   more collisions

■ **Figure 6.2** For a reaction to take place the particles must collide. Any factor that increases the frequency of collision will increase the rate of reaction

■ **Figure 6.3** Two nitrogen dioxide molecules approaching with sufficient kinetic energy to overcome the activation energy barrier must collide in the correct orientation in order to form dinitrogen tetroxide

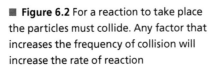

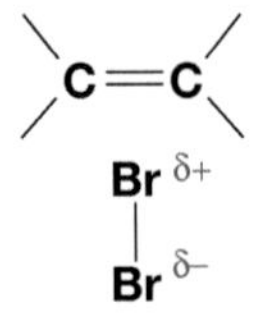

■ **Figure 6.4**
A bromine molecule undergoing polarization as it approaches an ethene molecule

An example of the influence of steric factors is provided by the bromination of ethene (Figure 6.4), where the bromine molecule has to approach the pi bond of the double bond 'sideways on' (Chapter 20).

Another example from organic chemistry (Chapter 20) is provided by the reaction between 1-bromobutane molecules and hydroxide ions. This mechanism is known as an S_N2 mechanism and a successful collision involves the hydroxide ion approaching the carbon atom from behind. This is known as backside attack (Figure 6.5).

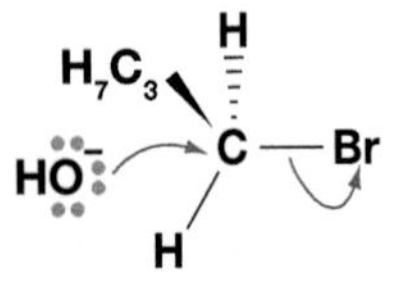

■ Not all collisions are successful even if the particles are properly oriented. For a reaction to happen some bonds must be broken and this requires energy. Each of the colliding particles must be travelling at sufficient velocity so that when they collide there is enough kinetic energy to enable the reaction to occur. This fixed amount of kinetic energy that the particles need is required to overcome an endothermic 'energy barrier' (see Figure 6.6) whose value is the **activation energy** (E_a).

■ **Figure 6.5**
Backside attack on the carbon atom of a 1-bromobutane molecule by a hydroxide ion

The activation energy is the minimum amount of kinetic energy that colliding particles must possess for a collision to result in a reaction. It is the energy required to overcome repulsion, to start rearranging the bonds to produce the product molecules.

Values of barrier heights vary widely between chemical reactions. They control how rapidly reactions take place and how their rates respond to changes in temperature. (Most reactions involve a number of steps and the activation energy may not correspond to the height of any individual activation energy barrier. It is a concept best applied to the individual elementary steps of a multi-step reaction.)

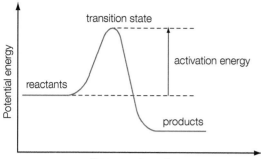

■ Figure 6.6
Concept of barrier
height and activation
energy (for an
exothermic reaction)

Fast reactions are associated with low values for their energy barriers (and hence activation energies) and slow reactions are associated with high values of their energy barriers (and activation energies).

If the colliding species do not possess sufficient kinetic energy to surmount the energy barrier and/or have the correct collision geometry then the collision will be ineffective and the reacting species will not undergo a chemical reaction.

1 Figure 6.6 shows an energy diagram for an exothermic reaction. Sketch the energy profile for an endothermic reaction.

2 Figure 6.7 shows some possible orientations for collisions between ethene and hydrogen chloride molecules. Only one of the possibilities shown (collision 1) results in a successful or effective collision. Discuss why this is and the reasons for the other collisions being unsuccessful. (You should consider the orientation and polarization of the interacting molecules.)

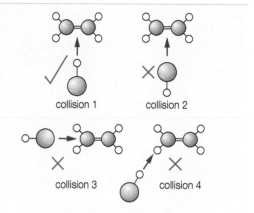

■ Figure 6.7 Some possible different orientations for collisions between ethene and hydrogen chloride molecules

■ Factors affecting the rate of reaction

As we have discussed and established the basic ideas involved in the collision theory, we can begin to deduce those factors that would affect the rate of any given reaction. Essentially, any change in conditions that would increase the collision frequency would result in a higher rate of reaction. What changes would mean that particles collide more often and with more energy? Here we consider changes in concentration (or pressure, if dealing with gases), temperature, light, the particle size of any solids involved, and the possible introduction of a catalyst.

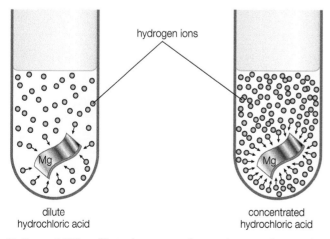

■ Figure 6.8 The effect of concentration on the rate of a reaction between magnesium and hydrochloric acid (hydrogen ions)

Concentration

The term concentration refers to the numbers of particles present in a particular volume of solution. It is usually expressed in moles per cubic decimetre ($mol\,dm^{-3}$) (Chapter 1).

It is *generally* found that the greater the concentration of the reactants (A and B), the greater the rate of reaction. This is because increasing the concentration of the reactants (A and B) increases the number of collisions between particles of A and B and, therefore, increases the rate of reaction (Figures 6.2 and 6.8). In particular, a doubling in the concentration of one of the reactants *often* doubles the rate of reaction. This is because the rate of collisions involving that reactant has been doubled.

This also explains why we observe the greatest rate of reaction as soon as the reacting solutions are mixed, that is, when they are at their highest concentrations.

As the reaction proceeds the concentrations of the reactants present decrease and the rate of reaction will decrease because there are fewer collisions. This experimental prediction is what we observe in practice, as we shall see later in this chapter.

Pressure

When one or more of the reactants are gases an increase in pressure can lead to an increase in the rate of reaction (provided the order – see Chapter 16 – is positive). The increase in pressure forces the particles closer together, which causes an increase in the collision rate and hence an increase in the rate of reaction.

An increase in pressure can be regarded as an increase in 'concentration' since more gas molecules will be present in a particular volume of space (Figure 6.9). Since liquids and solids undergo little change in volume when the pressure is increased (Chapter 1), their reaction rates are little affected by changes in pressure.

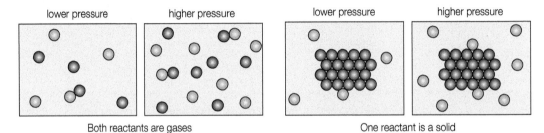

■ **Figure 6.9** The effect of pressure on gaseous reactions and between a gas and a solid

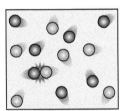
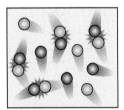

cold – slow movement, few collisions, little kinetic energy

hot – fast movement, more collisions, more kinetic energy

■ **Figure 6.10** The effect of temperature on gaseous molecules

Temperature

When particles in gases, liquids or solutions are heated, they move with higher velocities. This has two consequences: firstly, they travel a greater distance in a given time and so will be involved in more collisions and hence cause an increase in rate (Figure 6.10). Thus the particles will collide more often; however, more importantly, at a higher temperature a larger proportion of the colliding species will have kinetic energies equal to or exceeding the energy barrier.

Frequently, a rise of 10 °C approximately doubles the initial rate of reaction. This relationship is a simplification. It holds generally true for reactions that have an activation energy of around 50 kJ mol^{-1} and are being carried out at temperatures near room temperature. However, it does not hold for all reactions over all temperatures (Chapter 16).

Particle size

When one of the reactants is a solid, the reaction takes place on the surface of the solid. If the solid is broken up into smaller pieces or particles, the surface area is increased, giving a greater area over which collisions can occur (see Figure 6.11). The effect is similar to an increase in concentration as there is a greater reactive surface exposed for the same mass of solid.

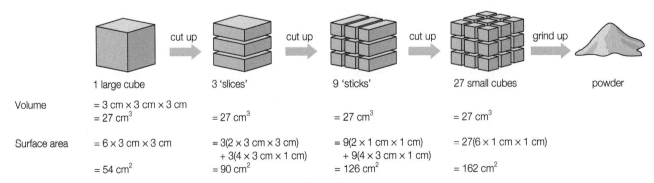

■ **Figure 6.11** The effect of particle size on the surface area of a solid reactant

We will see that this idea is not just important for a solid reactant, but also for the effectiveness of a solid catalyst. A number of important industrial catalysts are solids and the reactions they catalyse occur on the surface of the catalyst.

ToK Link

What role does inductive reasoning have in science?

How do we step from the findings of some particular experiments to suggest a general rule? For instance, how do we know that for a new reaction, one that we have not previously met, that the rate of reaction will increase if we raise the temperature at which it is carried out? This comes through inductive reasoning. Inductive reasoning is a fundamental tool of the scientist and allows us to generalize from the specific. If we carry out a series of experiments where the result is that increased temperature results in a higher rate of reaction, then we postulate a general law that this is the case for all reactions. The general law remains valid until falsified by further experiment.

Empiricist philosophers such as David Hume argued that we cannot generalize from the particular – just because the Sun has risen each day in the past does not prove that it will necessarily rise tomorrow. But we accept that there is a uniformity to nature and cannot imagine a normal situation where it would not be true.

Light

Interestingly, the rates of some reactions are greatly increased by exposure to sunlight. This occurs because the visible or ultraviolet light energy breaks bonds in the reactant molecule(s). For example, the silver halides (Chapter 3), silver nitrate, hydrogen peroxide and nitric acid are all photosensitive and undergo partial decomposition (to form radicals, often in the form of reactive atoms) in the presence of sunlight.

$$2AgX(s) \rightarrow 2Ag(s) + X_2(g), \text{ where X represents a halogen}$$
$$2AgNO_3(s) \rightarrow 2Ag(s) + 2NO_2(g) + O_2(g)$$
$$2H_2O_2(aq) \rightarrow 2H_2O(l) + O_2(g)$$
$$4HNO_3(aq) \rightarrow 2H_2O(l) + 4NO_2(g) + O_2(g)$$

Mixtures of hydrogen and bromine, or of methane and chlorine (Chapter 10), do not react in the dark, but in the presence of light a very rapid reaction takes place.

$$H_2(g) + Br_2(g) \rightarrow 2HBr(g)$$
$$CH_4(g) + Cl_2(g) \rightarrow CH_3Cl(g) + HCl(g)$$

Table 6.1 summarizes the effects of different factors on reaction rate.
The concept of reaction order is discussed in Chapter 16.

Factor	Reactions affected	Change made in conditions	Usual effect on the initial rate of reaction
Temperature	All	Increase	Increase
		Increase by 10 K	Approximately doubles
Concentration	All	Increase	Usually increases (unless zero order)
		Doubling of concentration of one of the reactants	Usually exactly doubles (if first order)
Light	Generally those involving reactions of mixtures of gases, including the halogens	Reaction in sunlight or ultraviolet light	Very large increase
Particle size	Reactions involving solids and liquids, solids and gases or mixtures of gases	Powdering the solid, resulting in a large increase in surface area	Very large increase

■ **Table 6.1** Summary of the factors affecting rates of reaction

Utilization: Catalysts

A catalyst is a substance that can increase the rate of a reaction but remains chemically unchanged at the end of the reaction. Catalysts are important in many industrial processes, where they are frequently transition metals or their compounds (see Chapters 3, 13 and 23). Catalysts increase the rate of reactions by providing a new alternative pathway or mechanism for the reaction that has a lower energy than the uncatalysed pathway (Figure 6.12a). (This statement is simplistic since most reactions consist of a number of steps, each of which has its own associated activation energy.) There are two types of catalysts: homogeneous and heterogeneous (Chapter 16).

Be careful when defining the action of a catalyst. It is important to stress that a catalyst provides an alternative pathway with a lower activation energy. The catalyst does *not* lower the activation energy of the uncatalysed reaction. The mountain pass analogy (Figure 6.12 b) helps to illustrate this point – taking the alternative route does not lower the mountain!

Catalysts increase the rates of both reversible and irreversible reactions. Catalysts do *not* alter the position of equilibrium (Chapter 7), they only increase the rate at which equilibrium is achieved. In other words, the presence of a catalyst does not increase the yield of products but increases the rate of their production. This is because a catalyst lowers the activation energy barrier, E_a, for both the forward and reverse reactions, increasing the rates of both forward and reverse reactions to the same degree. (This effect of a catalyst on forward and reverse energy barriers is known as the principle of microscopic reversibility.) Hence, to find a good catalyst for a particular reaction it is sufficient to look for a good catalyst for the reverse reaction.

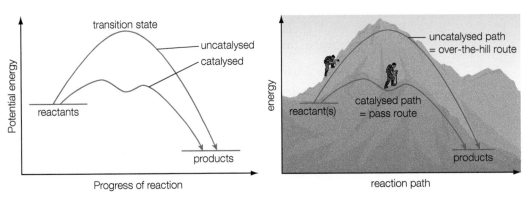

■ **Figure 6.12 a** General enthalpy level diagram for uncatalysed and catalysed reactions of an exothermic reaction. **b** The 'mountain pass' analogy for the mechanism of catalytic action stressing the idea of the creation of an alternative reaction pathway

However, catalysts have no effect on reactions that are not thermodynamically spontaneous; in other words, they are not able to catalyse reactions that are not energetically favourable. This is because catalysts do *not* alter the enthalpy change, ΔH, or the Gibbs free energy change, ΔG (Chapter 15), which occurs during the reaction.

Biological catalysts are known as enzymes (Chapter 23 on the accompanying website) and consist of proteins, often associated with metal ions. A substance that decreases the rate of a reaction is called an inhibitor. An example of an inhibitor is the 'anti-knock' compound, tetraethyl lead(IV), which was used to prevent pre-ignition in 'leaded' petrol vapour but has now been banned in practically all countries (Chapter 10). There are many specific and general inhibitors known for enzymes: many nerve gases and poisons, for example cyanides, operate as enzyme inhibitors, often by interacting with the active site of the enzyme (Figure 6.13).

Catalysts are widely used in the chemical industry: examples include finely divided iron in the Haber process for making ammonia and platinum in the Contact process (Chapter 7). A complex organometallic catalyst, known as a Ziegler–Natta catalyst, is used in the production of polymers synthesized from alkenes (Chapter 22 on the accompanying website). The search for new catalysts for industrial and commercial processes has gathered pace in recent years with the modern emphasis on 'green chemistry'. Part of the significance of enzymes in biological systems

■ **Figure 6.13**
A computer model showing a small molecule entering the active site of a protein molecule

is that they allow chemical reactions to take place under mild conditions. The same is true industrially. Using catalysts, reactions can be carried out under milder conditions which are therefore economically more viable and intrinsically safer.

Aqueous hydrogen peroxide decomposes to water and oxygen. Solid manganese(IV) oxide ('manganese dioxide') acts as a catalyst (Figure 6.14):

$$2H_2O_2(aq) \rightarrow 2H_2O(l) + O_2(g)$$

The insoluble manganese dioxide can be filtered off, washed and dried before being re-used as a catalyst. The decomposition of hydrogen peroxide can also be demonstrated using finely chopped pieces of fresh liver or blood that release the enzyme catalase (Chapter 23 on the accompanying website).

■ **Figure 6.14** The production of an oxygen-filled foam from the manganese(iv) oxide catalysed decomposition of hydrogen peroxide (note that the demonstrator should be wearing a lab coat)

Another example of catalysis involves the oxidation of potassium sodium tartrate (potassium sodium 2,3-dihydroxybutanedioic acid) by hydrogen peroxide solution to give a mixture of oxygen and carbon dioxide gases. The reaction is catalysed by cobalt(II) chloride. As the experiment proceeds, the pink colour of the aqueous cobalt(II) ions changes to green, revealing the presence of a cobalt(III) complex intermediate, before reverting to the original pink colour, indicating 'regeneration' of the catalyst (Figure 6.15). These two reactions demonstrate the two types of catalysis: homogeneous and heterogeneous catalysis (Chapter 16).

■ **Figure 6.15** The reaction between tartrate ions and hydrogen peroxide in the presence of cobalt(II) ions, acting as a catalyst. The pink solution on the left contains cobalt(II) ions, the green solution in the middle contains a temporary green intermediate containing cobalt(III) ions, and the pink solution on the right contains regenerated cobalt(II) ions

The role of CFCs in atmospheric ozone depletion

One example of a catalytic cycle that has had serious environmental consequences is the role that chlorofluorocarbons (CFCs) play in the phenomenon of ozone depletion in the upper atmosphere, particularly over the Earth's poles. Concern grew following the detection of the Antarctic 'ozone hole' and the identification of the chlorofluorocarbons used in aerosols, refrigerators and air-conditioning plants as mediators of this depletion.

Chlorofluorocarbons are highly stable compounds and their release into the lower atmosphere means that they can survive intact into the upper atmosphere. Here, under the influence of powerful UV radiation they decompose to produce chlorine free radicals (energized chlorine atoms) (Chapter 5):

$$CF_2Cl_2 \rightarrow \bullet CF_2Cl + Cl\bullet$$
$$\text{chlorine free radical}$$

These highly reactive chlorine free radicals catalyse the breakdown of ozone to diatomic oxygen molecules. The catalytic cycle is represented by the following equations (see Figure 6.16).

$$Cl\bullet + O_3 \rightarrow ClO\bullet + O_2$$
$$ClO\bullet + O \rightarrow Cl\bullet + O_2$$

The free oxygen atoms are present because of the action of UV radiation on molecular oxygen and are part of the normal generation of ozone in the upper atmosphere.

■ **Figure 6.16**
The catalytic cycle involved in the depletion of the ozone layer

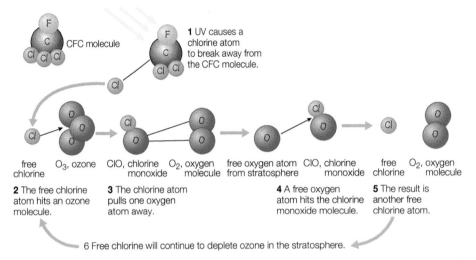

1 UV causes a chlorine atom to break away from the CFC molecule.

free chlorine   O₃, ozone   ClO, chlorine monoxide   O₂, oxygen molecule   free oxygen atom from stratosphere   ClO, chlorine monoxide   free chlorine   O₂, oxygen molecule

2 The free chlorine atom hits an ozone molecule.

3 The chlorine atom pulls one oxygen atom away.

4 A free oxygen atom hits the chlorine monoxide molecule.

5 The result is another free chlorine atom.

6 Free chlorine will continue to deplete ozone in the stratosphere.

Note that the chlorine free radical is regenerated in this cycle. It is a catalytic cycle, also called a chain reaction, in which it is estimated that a single chlorine free radical can eliminate about 1 million ozone molecules. The overall reaction is:

$$O_3 + O \rightarrow 2O_2$$

The detection of the depletion of the ozone layer by compounds such as chlorofluorocarbons led to the signing of the Montreal Protocol in 1987. This led to the freezing of the production of CFCs and the search for substitutes. This follow-up can be viewed as the most successful example of international cooperation in response to an environmental problem yet seen. Predictions are that the ozone layer may be beginning to recover, though estimates now suggest that it will not be completely recovered until 2060–2070. This example of international cooperation is a positive model for the steps required in tackling other, more major and significant global environmental problems.

3   The Haber process used in industry to make ammonia uses an exothermic reaction.
    $$N_2(g) + 3H_2(g) \rightleftharpoons 2NH_3(g)$$
    a Sketch the enthalpy profile for the Haber process in the absence of a catalyst.
    b On the same diagram, sketch the enthalpy profile for the process in the presence of a catalyst.
    c Label the activation energy on one of the profiles.

4   The activation energy for the uncatalysed decomposition of ammonia to its elements is $+335\,kJ\,mol^{-1}$.
    a The enthalpy of reaction for this decomposition is $+92\,kJ\,mol^{-1}$. Calculate the activation energy for the uncatalysed formation of ammonia from nitrogen and hydrogen. Include a sketch of the energy profile in your answer.
    b If a catalyst, such as iron or tungsten, is introduced the activation energy is altered. Explain how it will change.

5   The 'traditional' method of nitrating benzene involves the use of concentrated nitric acid and concentrated sulfuric acid at around 55 °C. The product is nitrobenzene.

    A 'green chemistry' method of nitration uses dilute nitric acid and a catalyst of MoO_3 and SiO_2 at 140 °C to give the same product.

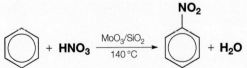

a What are the systematic names for the two chemicals forming the catalyst in the second method?
b Suggest two reasons why the second method is 'greener' than the traditional method, and one way in which using the MoO_3/SiO_2 catalyst is less 'green'.

■ The Maxwell–Boltzmann distribution

Theoretical calculations and experimental measurements both suggest that the kinetic energies of gas molecules in an ideal gas are distributed over a range known as a Maxwell–Boltzmann distribution (see Figure 6.17). Similar distributions of kinetic energies are present in the particles in solutions and liquids. Consideration of the features of this analysis of the energies possessed by particles adds further weight to the reasoning behind the collision theory. The key is to remember that activation energy, E_a, is defined as the minimum amount of kinetic energy which colliding molecules require in order to react.

The total area under the curve is directly proportional to the total number of molecules and the area under any portion of the curve is directly proportional to the number of molecules with kinetic energies in that range. When the temperature of a gas, liquid or solution is increased, a number of changes occur in the shape of the Maxwell–Boltzmann distribution (see Figure 6.18):

- The peak of the curve moves to the right so the most likely value of kinetic energy for the molecules increases.

- The curve flattens so the total area under it and, therefore, the total number of molecules remains constant.

- The area under the curve to the right of the activation energy, E_a, increases. This means that at higher temperatures, a greater percentage of molecules have energies equal to or in excess of the activation energy, E_a.

Temperature is a measure of the average kinetic energy of the particles of a substance. When the temperature is increased, the collision rate increases because the average speeds of particles in the gas, liquid or solution are increased. However, this has only a very minor effect on the rate of reaction and cannot account for the rapid increase in reaction rate as the temperature increases. For many reactions when the temperature of the reactants is increased by 10 °C, the collision rate increases by about 2%, but the rate of reaction increases by about 100% because of the increased number of molecules that possess energies in excess of the activation energy.

Consideration of the Maxwell–Boltzmann distribution of the kinetic energies of the particles in a sample also helps us interpret the action of a catalyst in speeding up a chemical reaction (Figure 6.19). A catalyst acts by allowing a reaction to take place by an alternative reaction pathway that has a lower activation energy. This means that a greater proportion of the sample particles have sufficient energy to react on collision.

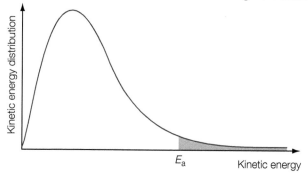

■ **Figure 6.17** Maxwell–Boltzmann distribution of kinetic energies in an ideal gas

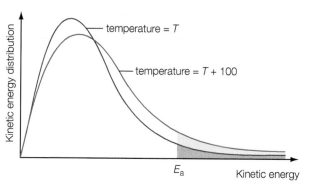

■ **Figure 6.18** Maxwell–Boltzmann distribution of kinetic energies in a solution or gas at two different temperatures

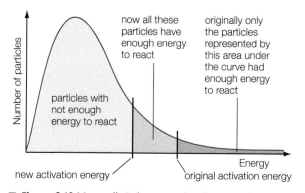

■ **Figure 6.19** Maxwell–Boltzmann distribution of kinetic energies showing the effect of the lower activation energy of the new catalysed pathway on the proportion of particles with sufficient energy to react

ToK Link

Testing the theory

The collision theory is a useful one not only in the sense that it has provided insight into the nature of chemical reactions, but also because it is a theory that can be readily tested. The mark of a scientific theory is that it can be tested and falsified. So far, collision theory has been supported by experimental evidence, but if new data were produced that could not be explained using the collision theory then it would need to be modified or dismissed in favour of a new theory that did explain all the evidence. Currently collision theory is the best explanation of the experimental data produced so far (at this working level). It should be noted here that we have not begun to distinguish between elementary and complex, multi-step reactions. That discussion is developed in Chapter 16 with the introduction of the idea of the rate-determining step in a sequence of stages. This is an example of how the theory is modified to explain more complex situations. Note that unimolecular reactions are an apparent exception which require special treatment.

Simple collision theory can, in fact, be modified and extended to reactions in solution. In solutions, which contain solvated molecules and ions rather than simple molecules or atoms, interactions are known as encounters rather than collisions. It would be expected that encounter rates should be smaller than collision frequencies because the solvent molecules reduce the collision rate between reactants. However, encounters may be more likely than collisions where molecules are trapped in a temporary 'cage' of solvent molecules (Figure 6.20).

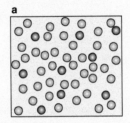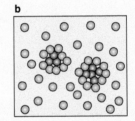

■ **Figure 6.20** The effect of a solvent 'cage' on the rate of reaction in a solvent

6 a Sketch a graph to show the Maxwell–Boltzmann distribution of molecular energies in a sample of a gas. Make sure that you have labelled the axes.
   b What meant by the activation energy of a reaction?
   c Shade an area on your graph to show the proportion of molecules capable of reacting.
   d Mark on your graph a possible value for the activation energy for the same reaction in the presence of a catalyst.
   e Shade an area on your graph showing the additional number of molecules capable of reacting because of the catalyst.
   f Draw on your graph a second curve showing the distribution of energies for the same sample at a slightly higher temperature.

7 a Explain why gases react together faster at a higher pressure.
   b Explain why reactants in solution react faster at higher concentration.
   c Explain why finely divided solids react more quickly than lumps of the same mass of solid.
   d Explain why raising the temperature increases the rate of reaction.

ToK Link

Absolute temperature and temperature scales

The concept of **absolute zero** is a very useful one as it gives us a reference point where the translational kinetic energy of particles is zero (the origin on the *x*-axis of the Maxwell–Boltzmann distribution curves). At absolute zero a substance has no transferable heat energy, it is the point at which the motion of particles is minimal. It is the point at which an ideal gas at constant pressure would reach zero volume (see Chapter 1). The **Kelvin scale** of temperature, which begins by assigning the value of nought (0) to absolute zero, therefore gives us a convenient numerical measure of the level of kinetic energy in a sample. The Kelvin scale is an absolute, thermodynamic temperature scale measured in kelvins (K). Being an absolute unit of measure means that the values can be manipulated algebraically: twice the value on this scale indicates that the mean energy of the particles is doubled for the sample. The average kinetic energy of the particles is proportional to the absolute temperature. For this reason the Kelvin scale is universally used in science as the standard measure of temperature.

Other temperature scales are used in everyday situations – the Celsius and Fahrenheit scales for example. These are both arbitrary scales based on the number of increments, or degrees, decided between the two fixed points – the freezing point and boiling point of water at atmospheric pressure. The size of the increments on the Kelvin and Celsius scales is identical (one kelvin, 1 K = one degree Celsius, 1 °C) and 'degrees Celsius' are often used in science experiments. Conversion between the two is straightforward, simply involving the addition or subtraction of 273 (or more precisely, 273.15). Figure 6.21 illustrates the parallels and interconversions between these two temperature scales.

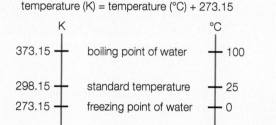

temperature (K) = temperature (°C) + 273.15

K		°C
373.15	boiling point of water	100
298.15	standard temperature	25
273.15	freezing point of water	0
0	absolute zero	−273.15

■ **Figure 6.21** A comparison of the Kelvin and Celsius temperature scales used in science experimentation

The Celsius and Fahrenheit scales are entirely valid as convenient measures of relative warmth in everyday situations. The Fahrenheit scale, where absolute zero is −459.7 °F, is not used in scientific experiments. However, where the phenomenon of temperature as a physical measurement of the level of kinetic energy in a sample is required then the Kelvin scale is the standard.

8 a Which of the following samples of gas has the highest value of mean kinetic energy?
 A He at 25 °C
 B He at 50 °C
 C He at 0 °C
 D He at −124 °C
   b Which of samples A, B or C will have double the mean kinetic energy of sample D?

Nature of Science

The interaction of science and technology

Absolute zero, 0 K, has not been achieved experimentally, although new technologies are enhancing attempts to reach ever closer to this minimum value. Improved laser cooling methods and the use of magnets to help contain gases are helping in such experiments. Currently the lowest temperature achieved was set in 1999 when researchers in Finland reached 100 picokelvin (1×10^{-10} K) by cooling the nuclear spins of a piece of rhodium metal. The average temperature of the Universe is estimated at 2.73 K, while the lowest natural temperature ever recorded was 1 K in the Boomerang nebula (recorded in 2003).

At very low temperatures close to absolute zero matter exhibits many unusual properties, including superconductivity and superfluidity. Advances in technology allow the scientific exploration of previously uncharted areas. Together, the findings permit the link in thinking between the microscopic world, here described by the Maxwell–Boltzmann distribution, and macroscopic properties, temperature in this case.

■ Reaction rates

Some reactions are very fast, for example neutralization and precipitation reactions (Chapter 1). Other reactions are slow, for example the enzymatic browning of fruits (Chapter 26), and some very slow, for example rusting (see Figure 6.1b, and Chapter 9).

The **rate** of a chemical reaction is a measure of the 'speed' of the reaction: those reactions that are complete in a relatively short space of time are said to have high rates. The rate refers to the change in the amount (if it is a liquid or solid) or concentration (if it is a gas or in solution) of a reactant or product in unit time. The rate is defined as the change in concentration or amount of a reactant or product with time, t:

$$\text{rate} = \frac{\text{change in concentration}}{\text{change in time}} \quad \text{or rate} = \frac{(\text{concentration at time } t_2 - \text{concentration at time } t_1)}{(\text{time } t_2 - \text{time } t_1)}$$

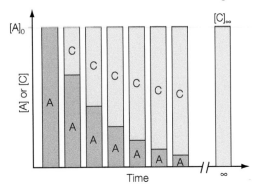

■ **Figure 6.22** The relationship between reactant and product concentrations

Figure 6.22 shows a graphical method of visualizing how reactant and product concentrations are related to time. Symbolically [A] represents reactant concentrations and [C] represents product concentrations. A 1:1 molar ratio exists between the amount of A consumed and the amount of C formed. $[C]_\infty$ represents the concentration of the product after infinite time has passed and the reaction has stopped.

In experiments we can follow the progress of a reaction by measuring the disappearance of a reactant or by the appearance of a product. If we follow the disappearance of reactant A, then using calculus notation:

$$\text{rate} = -\frac{d[A]}{dt}$$

where [A] represents the concentration or amount of a reactant, t_2 is greater than t_1 and d, the first differential, indicates a small change in a quantity. The negative sign is there because reactant A is disappearing. The usual units for reaction rate are moles per cubic decimetre per second ($mol\,dm^{-3}\,s^{-1}$).

Worked example

During a reaction, 0.04 mol of a substance is produced in a 2.5 dm³ vessel in 20 seconds. What is the rate of reaction?

Determine the amount produced in 1.0 dm³:

$$\text{concentration} = \frac{0.04\ \text{mol}}{2.5\ \text{dm}^3} = 0.016\ \text{mol dm}^{-3}$$

Determine the amount produced per second:

$$\text{rate} = \frac{0.016\ \text{mol dm}^{-3}}{20\ \text{s}} = 8 \times 10^{-4}\ \text{mol dm}^{-3}\,\text{s}^{-1}$$

9 A reaction produces 22 g of carbon dioxide in 15 seconds in a vessel of capacity 4 dm³. What is the rate of reaction?

10 Acidified hydrogen peroxide and aqueous potassium iodide react according to the following equation:

$$2H^+(aq) + H_2O_2(aq) + 2I^-(aq) \rightarrow I_2(aq) + 2H_2O(l)$$

It was found that the concentration of iodine was 0.06 mol dm⁻³ after allowing the reactants to react for 30 seconds. Calculate the average rate of formation of iodine during this time.

The rates of change in concentration of all reactants and products expressed in molar units are related to each other via the coefficients in the balanced equation (Chapter 1).

Any reaction can be represented by the following general equation:

$$aA \quad + \quad bB \quad \rightarrow \quad cC \quad + \quad dD$$
reactants products

The relative rates of reaction are given by the following expression:

$$\text{rate} = -\frac{1}{a}\frac{d[A]}{dt} = -\frac{1}{b}\frac{d[B]}{dt} = +\frac{1}{c}\frac{d[C]}{dt} = +\frac{1}{d}\frac{d[D]}{dt}$$

Again the *negative* sign indicates that the concentrations of the reactants A and B *decrease* with time, whereas the *positive* sign indicates that the concentrations of the products C and D *increase* with time.

In the reaction between acidified hydrogen peroxide and aqueous potassium iodide (question 10 above) the average rate of appearance of water will be twice the average rate of appearance of iodine. This is because two water molecules are formed for every iodine molecule formed.

$$2H^+(aq) + H_2O_2(aq) + 2I^-(aq) \rightarrow I_2(aq) + 2H_2O(l)$$

In symbols:

$$\text{rate} = \frac{1}{2}\frac{d[I_2(aq)]}{dt} = \frac{d[H_2O(l)]}{dt}$$

Again referring to the equation, the rate of disappearance or consumption of hydrogen peroxide will be the same as the rate of appearance of iodine.

In symbols:

$$\text{rate} = \frac{-d[H_2O_2(aq)]}{dt} = \frac{d[I_2(aq)]}{dt}$$

This is because one molecule of iodine is formed for every hydrogen peroxide molecule consumed. The negative sign in this expression indicates a decrease in the peroxide concentration with time.

Figure 6.23 shows a graph of the amount or concentration of a reactant against time. (This form of graph is obtained in most reactions, with the exception of autocatalysis or zero order reactions (Chapter 16).) You can see that the gradient of the graph continually decreases with time and, hence, the rate of reaction decreases with time. The reaction rate is zero when the reactants are all consumed and the reaction stops.

Figure 6.24 shows a graph of the concentration or amount of product against time. The gradient of the graph decreases progressively with time because the rate of reaction decreases with time as the reactants are consumed. The instantaneous rate is the rate of a reaction at a particular time, unlike the average rate, which is the average rate over a particular time interval.

The graphs show that rate of a reaction is not constant but varies with time due to changes in the concentrations of reactants (Figure 6.25). As the reaction progresses the reactants are continually being used up. Since the rate of a reaction varies with time, it is usually necessary to express the rate at a particular time instead of averaging over a time period.

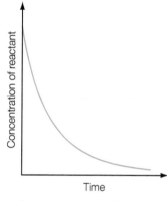

■ **Figure 6.23** Graph of concentration or amount of reactant against time

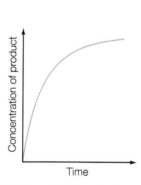

■ **Figure 6.24** Graph of concentration or amount of product against time

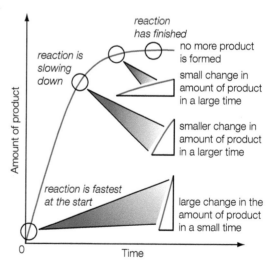

■ **Figure 6.25** The variation in the rate of a reaction as the reaction progresses

The instantaneous rate of reaction can be determined graphically (see Figures 6.26 and 6.27) from a graph of product or reactant concentration or amount against time.

The instantaneous rate of reaction at any time is equal to the gradient or slope of the graph at that time. The rate will either be positive or negative, depending on whether the y-axis shows the concentration of a product or a reactant.

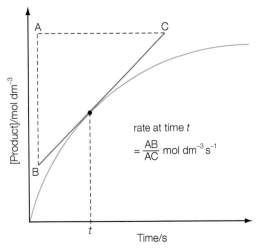

Figure 6.26 Concentration–time graph for the formation of a product. The rate of formation of product at time *t* is the gradient (or slope) of the curve at this point

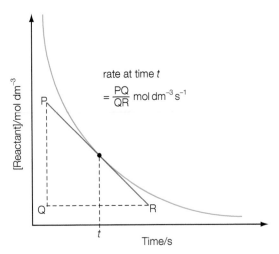

Figure 6.27 Concentration–time graph for the disappearance of a reactant. The rate of loss of reactant at time *t* is the gradient (or slope) of the curve at this point

The steeper the gradient of the graph, the faster the reaction, and the higher its rate. When the graph is horizontal (i.e. the gradient is zero) the rate of reaction is zero, indicating the reaction has finished.

In practical situations, raw data is typically collected for some property that changes with time. This raw data may be directly proportional to the reactant concentration, for example absorbance, or may have a more complicated relationship, for example pH, which is a logarithmic function. This raw data can be converted into a rate expressed in moles per cubic decimetre ($mol\,dm^{-3}$).

It is important in kinetics to discover how the rate of reaction varies with concentration of the reactants. It allows chemists to deduce the order and the rate expression for the reaction (Chapter 16). One simple, but not very precise, approach is to draw a number of tangents on a concentration–time graph (Figure 6.28) and then plot a graph of the rates (the numerical value of the gradients) against concentration. Many reactants show a directly proportional relationship between concentration and rate (reactions in which this is the case are said to be first order for that reactant (Chapter 16)).

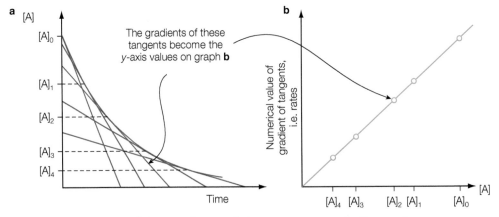

Figure 6.28 a Concentration versus time graph; **b** rate versus concentration graph

Time/min	0	0.5	1.0	1.5	2.0	2.5	3.0	3.5	4.0	4.5	5.0
Volume of oxygen gas/cm³	0	18	35	48	58	66	72	78	81	84	87
Hydrogen concentration mol dm⁻³	0.159	0.129	0.101	0.080	0.063	0.050	0.040	0.030	0.025	0.020	0.018

■ **Table 6.2** The catalysed decomposition of hydrogen peroxide solution

■ **Figure 6.29** A graph of concentration of hydrogen peroxide against time

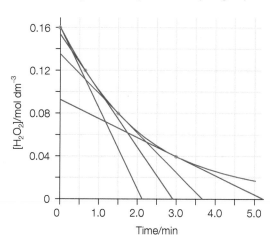

Table 6.2 shows data for the catalysed decomposition of hydrogen peroxide solution into oxygen gas and water. A graph of the concentration of hydrogen peroxide solution against time (Figure 6.29) allows the gradients at various points on the curve to be calculated. For example, at the start of the reaction the gradient is given by:

$$\text{gradient} = -\frac{0.16\,\text{mol dm}^{-3}}{2.1\,\text{min}}$$
$$= -0.076\,\text{mol dm}^{-3}\,\text{min}^{-1}$$

Thus the rate of decomposition at the start of the reaction is $0.076\,\text{mol dm}^{-3}\,\text{min}^{-1}$. Similar graphical calculations at other points produce additional rate values (Table 6.3).

Hydrogen peroxide concentration/mol dm⁻³	0.16	0.12	0.08	0.04
Rate/mol dm⁻³ min⁻¹	0.076	0.049	0.033	0.019

■ **Table 6.3** Hydrogen peroxide concentrations and corresponding values of instantaneous rate of decomposition

■ **Figure 6.30** A graph of rate of hydrogen peroxide decomposition against concentration

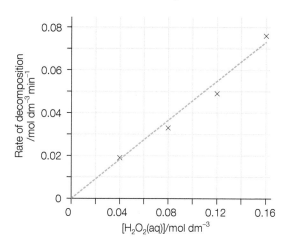

The relationship between the concentration and the rate of decomposition of hydrogen peroxide is illustrated in the graph of rate versus concentration in Figure 6.30. The dotted line of best fit shows that, within the limits of experimental error, the rate of decomposition of hydrogen peroxide is directly proportional to its concentration.

The importance of initial rates

Measuring rates from a concentration–time graph involves drawing a graph and measuring the gradients to the curve at a number of points, at least five. This can be an inaccurate process at any point, but especially towards the end of the reaction when it is slowing down and the change in rate is relatively small. This problem can be avoided by measuring the initial rates in a series of investigations where the initial concentration of the reactant under investigation is varied (Chapter 16). In this approach the amount of a product (or loss of a reactant) is measured over a small period of time. Since the reactant concentration changes very slightly, the rate will be approximately constant and the initial rate is calculated by dividing the change in concentration by the time taken.

■ Measuring rates of reaction

To measure the rate of reaction the reactants need to be mixed so that the reaction begins. The concentration of one of the reactants (or products) is then measured against time. The temperature (and for gaseous reactions, the pressure) must be controlled and kept constant.

There are many different ways in which the rate of reaction can be measured for a particular reaction. All of them measure either directly or indirectly a change in the concentration of either a reactant or product. Suitable changes include:

- colour
- formation of a precipitate
- change in mass, for example a gas produced, causing a loss of mass
- volume of gas produced
- time taken for a given mass of a product to appear
- pH
- temperature.

Reactions that produce gases

Reactions that produce gases are most easily investigated by collecting and measuring the volume of gas produced in a gas syringe. The volume of gas collected will increase as the concentration of the reactants decreases. (The rate of increase of volume of gas (tangent to the volume–time curve) can be used as a measure of reaction rate.)

Figure 6.31 shows apparatus suitable for investigating the reaction between calcium carbonate and dilute hydrochloric acid. This arrangement ensures the two reactants are kept separate while the apparatus is set up so that the start time can be accurately recorded.

■ **Figure 6.31**
Apparatus used to study the rate of a reaction that releases a gas

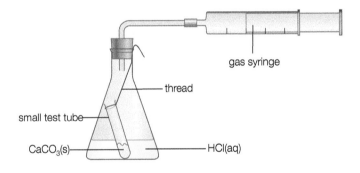

■ **Figure 6.32**
A graph of total volume of carbon dioxide collected against time

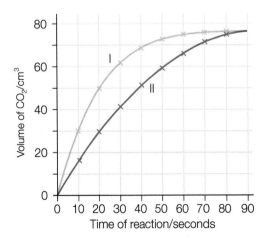

Figure 6.32 shows a typical graph (line II) of the results, where total volume of carbon dioxide gas is plotted against time. The reaction is fastest when the graph is steepest at the beginning of the reaction. The reaction finishes when the graph becomes horizontal, that is, when there is no further production of hydrogen.

The other line (line I) indicates data from a second similar experiment using the same amounts of calcium carbonate and hydrochloric acid but with conditions changed so the reaction is faster. This might be done by using acid at a higher temperature, using acid of a higher concentration or using powdered calcium carbonate rather than lumps.

■ **Figure 6.33** Following the rate of reaction between marble chips (calcium carbonate) and hydrochloric acid

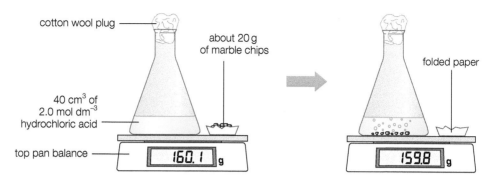

■ **Figure 6.34** The effect of chip size on a graph of mass of flask and contents versus time for the reaction between calcium carbonate and hydrochloric acid

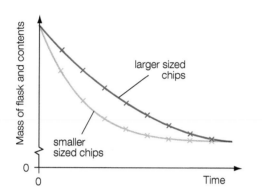

Alternatively, a reaction producing a gas can be performed in an open flask placed on an electronic balance. The reaction can then be investigated by recording the loss of mass as the gas is produced. This is shown in Figure 6.33 for the reaction between calcium carbonate and hydrochloric acid. Figure 6.34 shows the effect of chip size on a graph of mass of flask and contents versus time.

Reactions that produce a colour change

If one of the reactants or products of a reaction is highly coloured, the intensity of the colour can be used to measure the rate of reaction. If a reactant is coloured, the colour of the reaction mixture will fade during the reaction. If a product is coloured, then reaction mixture will gradually become more intensely coloured as the reaction proceeds. An instrument known as a colorimeter can measure the colour intensity. Later, experiments can be done to find the relationship between the colour intensity and the concentration of either the reactant or product.

In a colorimeter (see Figure 6.35), a narrow beam of light passes through the reaction mixture towards a sensitive photocell. The current generated within the photocell depends on the intensity of light that was transmitted through the reaction mixture, which in turn depends on the concentration of the coloured product or reactant. The colorimeter is used to measure absorbance against time (Figure 6.36) because absorbance is directly proportional to the concentration of the coloured species (provided the concentration is relatively low) (Chapter 21).

■ **Figure 6.35** Block diagram of a colorimeter or spectrometer

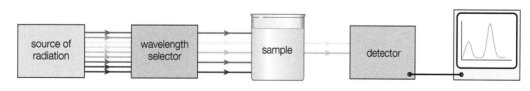

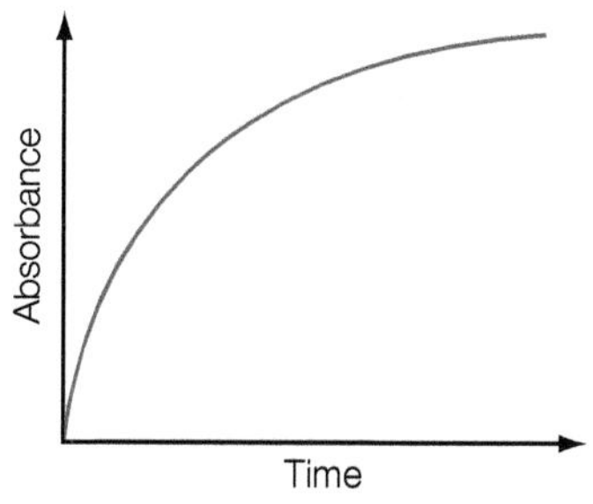

■ **Figure 6.36** A typical graph of absorbance against time. This is equivalent to the volume-against-time graph in Figure 6.32

An example of a reaction that can be investigated using a colorimeter is the iodination of propanone in the presence of dilute acid. In this reaction the iodine is the only coloured species and its colour varies from a pale yellow to a darker orange or brown colour, depending upon its concentration. The lower the light absorbance, the further the reaction has progressed. Data logging may be used to investigate this reaction.

$$CH_3COCH_3(aq) + I_2(aq) \rightarrow CH_3COCH_2I(aq) + HI(aq)$$

Reactions that involve a change in ion concentration

If one of the reactants or products in a reaction is either hydroxide ions, $OH^-(aq)$ or hydrogen ions, $H^+(aq)$ (oxonium ions $H_3O^+(aq)$), then there will be a change in pH (Chapter 8). This can be followed with a pH probe and meter. One interesting example of this is the study of the kinetics of reactions involving the enzyme urease. Since one of the products of enzyme action is ammonia, the reaction can be followed by monitoring the increased alkalinity of the solution. Note also that this type of reaction could also be followed by the sample removal/titration method mentioned below.

If there is an overall change in the number of ions during a reaction, then there will be a change in conductivity that can be measured using a conductivity probe and meter (Figure 6.37). Conductivity increases in the reaction mixture if there is an overall increase in the number of ions during a reaction; it decreases if there is an overall decrease in the number of ions. The conductivity also varies with the size of the ions: generally, smaller ions move faster and have higher conductivities than larger, slower moving ions.

■ **Figure 6.37**
A conductivity cell and meter

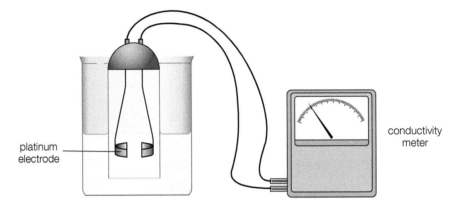

For example, the alkaline hydrolysis of bromoethane can be followed using conductivity measurements. As this reaction proceeds, the small and fast moving hydroxide ions are consumed and replaced by slower moving bromide ions. Therefore, the electrical conductivity decreases as the reaction proceeds.

$$C_2H_5Br(l) + OH^-(aq) \rightarrow C_2H_5OH(aq) + Br^-(aq)$$

Pressure and volume changes

Some reactions involving liquids show a small change in volume that can be measured and recorded. Reactions between gases are often investigated by measuring and recording changes in volume (at constant pressure) (Figure 6.38) or pressure (at constant volume). This technique can only be used if the number of moles of reactants is different from the number of moles of products, for example:

$$2NO(g) + O_2(g) \rightarrow 2NO_2(g)$$

However, if the number of moles of reactants is equal to the number of moles of products, there will be no change in volume and hence pressure, for example:

$$H_2(g) + I_2(g) \rightarrow 2HI(g)$$

It is important to ensure that temperature is kept constant during these reactions so that pressure and volume changes are not, in part, due to temperature changes.

■ **Figure 6.38**
Apparatus for measuring changes in gas volume in a reaction maintained at constant pressure

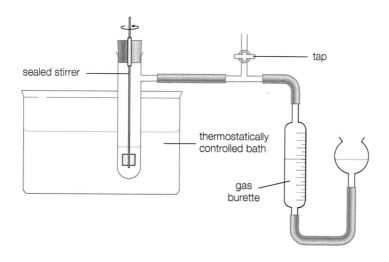

Withdrawal of samples and titration

For some reactions small samples of the reaction mixture can be removed and then analysed by performing an acid–base or redox titration (Chapter 1) with a standard solution (Figure 6.39). This will allow the amount of a particular reactant remaining to be determined. The small sample of the reaction mixture is usually added to a large volume of cold water so the reaction is stopped, or at least slowed down. It suffers from being a destructive technique. This method can be used to measure the rate of saponification (alkaline hydrolysis) of ethyl ethanoate (Chapter 1):

$$C_2H_5COOC_2H_5(l) + NaOH(aq) \rightarrow C_2H_5COO^-Na^+(aq) + C_2H_5OH(l)$$

At regular intervals during the reaction, a sample of the reaction mixture is taken and titrated against hydrochloric acid using a suitable indicator (Figure 6.39). This allows the concentration of the sodium hydroxide remaining in the reaction mixture to be calculated (Chapter 1). The smaller the volume of hydrochloric acid solution required for neutralization, the further the reaction has progressed.

■ **Figure 6.39**
Following the course of an acid-catalysed reaction via sampling and titration with alkali

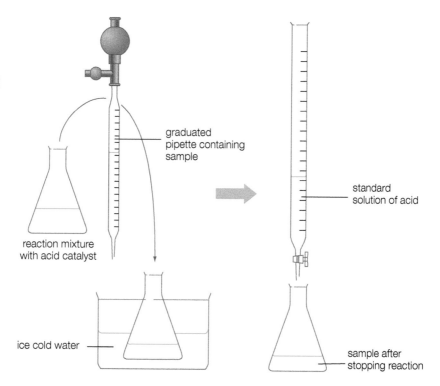

$$NaOH(aq) + HCl(aq) \rightarrow NaCl(aq) + H_2O(l)$$

The reaction between iodine and propanone can also be followed by chemical analysis. At regular time intervals, samples of the reaction mixture are quenched with sodium hydrogencarbonate solution to remove the acid catalyst and stop the reaction. The iodine in the quenched mixture is then titrated with sodium thiosulfate using starch as the indicator.

$$I_2(aq) + 2S_2O_3^{2-}(aq) \rightarrow 2I^-(aq) + S_4O_6^{2-}(aq)$$

Rotation of the plane of polarized light

Some organic molecules, particularly sugars and amino acids, rotate the plane of polarized light. The direction of rotation and the angle can be measured with a polarimeter. Changes in the concentrations of these optically active molecules cause a change in the amount of rotation.

For example, sucrose is hydrolysed in acidic solution:

$$\underset{\text{sucrose}}{C_{12}H_{22}O_{11}(aq)} + \underset{\text{water}}{H_2O(l)} \rightarrow \underset{\text{glucose}}{C_6H_{12}O_6(aq)} + \underset{\text{fructose}}{C_6H_{12}O_6(aq)}$$

During this reaction a change in the optical rotation of the solution occurs. Although both the reactant and the two products are optically active, the sizes and directions in which they rotate plane-polarized light differ. The overall change in optical activity can therefore be measured by means of a polarimeter (Chapter 20).

Using time as a measure of rate

In some reactions it is easy to measure the time it takes for a particular stage of a reaction to be reached. For example, in the reaction between sodium thiosulfate solution and dilute acid, a very fine precipitate of sulfur is produced.

$$S_2O_3^{2-}(aq) + 2H^+(aq) \rightarrow SO_2(g) + H_2O(l) + S(s)$$

The effect of changing the temperature or the concentrations of the two reactants can be investigated by carrying out the reaction in a conical flask placed on a cross drawn on a piece of paper (Figure 6.40). The time from the start of the reaction until there is sufficient sulfur to hide the cross when it is looked at from above the solution is recorded. The same total volume of solutions and the same cross have to be used in each experiment.

The graphs in Figures 6.41 and 6.42 summarize the results of kinetic investigations into the rate of reaction between sodium thiosulfate and hydrochloric acid. The volume of sodium thiosulfate used is proportional to its concentration and so the reciprocal of the time ($\frac{1}{t}$ or t^{-1}) or 'rate' taken for the obscuring of the cross is directly proportional to the initial rate in $mol\,dm^{-3}\,s^{-1}$.

■ Figure 6.40
a The production of a colloidal suspension of sulfur by the reaction between thiosulfate and hydrogen ions
b Diagram of the approach used to monitor the time of production of sufficient sulfur to hide the cross

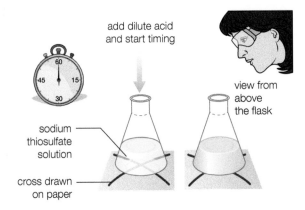

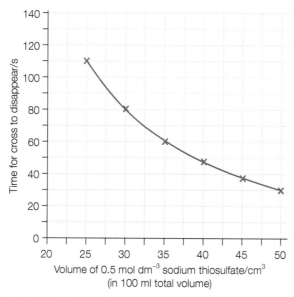

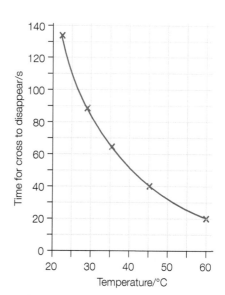

■ **Figure 6.41** Sample raw data for the reaction between sodium thiosulfate and acid at different concentrations of sodium thiosulfate

■ **Figure 6.42** Sample raw data for the reaction between sodium thiosulfate and acid at different temperatures

The reaction between sodium thiosulfate is perhaps the most used of a type of investigation in which the time to reach a particular point in measured as an indicator of the rate of a reaction. It is effectively a type of 'clock reaction'.

More generally clock reactions are reactions in solution that can be followed by a particular technique in which the time at which a certain amount of product is exceeded by reaction with an indicator is recorded. Suppose a particular reaction gives products A and B. Two substances P and Q are added. P reacts with and removes A; only a defined, relatively small amount of P is added. Q interacts with A to produce a colour change, and so once all the P is consumed and excess A is produced there is a sharp colour change. Clearly, it is vital that neither P nor Q interferes with the reaction being studied.

Probably the most famous clock reaction is an iodine clock reaction, a redox reaction involving hydrogen peroxide and acidified iodide ions. The iodine is not seen when the reactants are first mixed because it is being converted to colourless iodide ions in a reaction with another reactant. The reaction of the acidified iodide ions with hydrogen peroxide is:

$$H_2O_2(l) + 2I^-(aq) + 2H^+(aq) \rightarrow I_2(aq) + 2H_2O(l)$$

In kinetic investigations of this reaction, sodium thiosulfate (*substance P*) of known concentration together with a little starch solution (*substance Q*) are added to the mixture of hydrogen peroxide and acidified iodide ions. The iodine produced by the main reaction immediately reacts with thiosulfate ions:

$$I_2(aq) + 2S_2O_3^{2-}(aq) \rightarrow 2I^-(aq) + S_4O_6^{2-}(aq)$$

■ **Figure 6.43** An iodine clock reaction

When all the thiosulfate has been used up, the iodine will be produced very rapidly and the reaction mixture suddenly turns blue-black (Figure 6.43) if starch is present (or brown if the starch is absent). In this clock reaction, if A were iodine then P would be thiosulfate and Q would be starch.

The time t (known as the induction period) from mixing the reactants to the appearance of the blue-black colour of the starch–iodine complex is the time for a fixed amount of iodine to be formed. The appearance of the iodine indicates when a particular amount of iodine has been formed, regardless of the time required for this to occur. We can therefore simply use $1/t$ as a measure of the initial rate of reaction.

Another common version of the iodine clock is the reaction between peroxodisulfate(VI) and iodide ions:

$$S_2O_8^{2-}(aq) + 2I^-(aq) \rightarrow 2SO_4^{2-}(aq) + I_2(aq)$$

Investigations are carried out by adding solutions of thiosulfate ions of different concentrations to reaction mixtures containing peroxodisulfate and iodide ions. Some starch solution is also added. The time from mixing to the appearance of the blue-black starch–iodine complex is again measured and $1/t$ is used as a measure of the initial reaction rate.

11 Magnesium reacts with hydrochloric acid to produce hydrogen gas. A series of experiments was carried out to measure the volume of gas produced under different conditions using a gas syringe.

The first experiment used 0.10g of magnesium ribbon reacting with 30cm³ of 0.50mol dm⁻³ HCl solution. This reaction was carried out at 20°C. The results for this experiment are given in the following table.

Time/s	0	15	30	45	60	75	90	105	120	135	150	165	180
Volume of gas/cm³	0.0	18.6	32.3	44.3	54.8	62.7	68.4	72.6	74.9	75.4	75.6	75.6	75.6

a Sketch a diagram of the apparatus used for this experiment. Give the balanced equation for the reaction.
b Draw a graph of this data and use your graph to calculate the initial rate of reaction. Include the units for the rate of reaction.
c Interpret the shape of the graph and the variation in rate of reaction using the collision theory.
d Calculate the average rate of reaction over the first 150s.
e Why does the volume of gas collected not change after 150s?
f This experiment was repeated using 0.05g of magnesium ribbon. On the same axes used previously, sketch the graph that would be obtained. Label this graph B.
g The experiment was repeated under the same conditions but using 0.10g of powdered magnesium. On the same axes, sketch the graph that would be obtained. Label this graph C.
h The original experiment was repeated at 10°C. Again using the same axes, sketch the graph that would be obtained and label it graph D.
i Sketch the Maxwell–Boltzmann distribution for the first experiment and the experiment at 10°C. Use this to explain the effect of changing the temperature on the rate of this reaction.

12 The reaction between dilute hydrochloric acid and sodium thiosulfate solution produces a fine yellow precipitate that clouds the solution. This means that the rate of this reaction can be found by measuring the time taken for a cross (×) under the reaction to become hidden.

Below are the results of tests carried out at five different temperatures. In each case, 50cm³ of aqueous sodium thiosulfate was poured into a flask. 10cm³ of hydrochloric acid was added to the flask. The initial and final temperatures were measured.

Experiment	Initial temperature/°C	Final temperature/°C	Average temperature/°C	Time for cross to disappear/s
A	24	24		130
B	33	31		79
C	40	38		55
D	51	47		33
E	60	54		26

a Work out the average temperature at which each experiment was carried out.
b Plot a graph of the time taken for the cross to disappear against the average temperature for the experiment.
c In which experiment was the rate of reaction fastest?
d Explain why the rate was fastest in this experiment.
e Why were the same volumes of sodium thiosulfate and hydrochloric acid solutions used in each experiment? Why do the conical flasks used in each test run need to be of the same dimensions?
f Deduce from the graph the time it would take for the cross to disappear if the experiment was repeated at 70°C. Show on the graph how you found your estimate.
g Sketch on the graph the curve you would expect if all the experiments were carried out with 50cm³ of more concentrated sodium thiosulfate solution.
h Explain what you would do to obtain a temperature of around 0 to 5°C.

■ *Examination questions – a selection*

Paper 1 IB questions and IB style questions

Q1 Which statements explain the increase in the rate of reaction when the temperature is increased?
 I More particles have energy greater than the activation energy.
 II The frequency of collisions increases.
 III The activation energy decreases.
 A I and II only   **C** II and III only
 B I and III only   **D** I, II and III

Standard Level Paper 1, May 2013, Q17

Q2 Which piece of equipment could not be used in an experiment to measure the rate of this reaction?

$$CH_3COCH_3(aq) + I_2(aq) \rightarrow CH_3COCH_2I(aq) + H^+(aq) + I^-(aq)$$

 A a colorimeter   **C** a stopwatch
 B a gas syringe   **D** a pH meter

Standard Level Paper 1, November 2012, Q16

Q3 Which of the following changes in the experimental conditions would increase the rate of this reaction?

Note that other conditions remain constant.

$$CaCO_3(s) + 2HCl(aq) \rightarrow CaCl_2(aq) + H_2O(l) + CO_2(g)$$

 I Larger lumps of calcium carbonate are used
 II The temperature of the reaction mixture is increased
 III The concentration of hydrochloric acid is increased
 A I and II only   **C** II and III only
 B I, II and III only   **D** I and III

Q4 Which of the graphs below show the Maxwell–Boltzmann distribution of kinetic energies for the same amount of gas at two temperatures, where T_2 is greater than T_1?

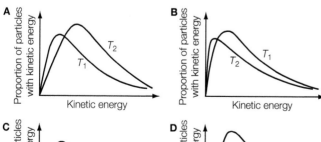

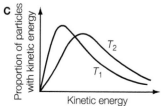

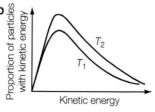

Q5 In which flask will the reaction between 2.0 g of magnesium carbonate and 25 cm³ 1.0 mol dm⁻³ hydrochloric acid occur most rapidly?

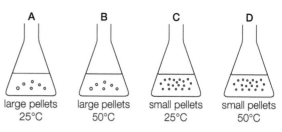

Standard Level Paper 1, November 2012, Q18

Q6 Which combination in the table correctly states the value and units of the gradient?

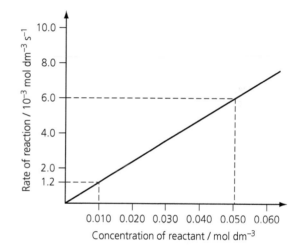

	Value	Units
A	$\dfrac{6.0 \times 10^{-3} - 1.2 \times 10^{-3}}{0.050 - 0.010}$	s^{-1}
B	$\dfrac{6.0 \times 10^{-3} - 1.2 \times 10^{-3}}{0.050 - 0.010}$	s
C	$\dfrac{0.050 - 0.010}{6.0 \times 10^{-3} - 1.2 \times 10^{-3}}$	s^{-1}
D	$\dfrac{0.050 - 0.010}{6.0 \times 10^{-3} - 1.2 \times 10^{-3}}$	s

Q7 Which statement is correct for a collision between reactant particles leading to a reaction?
 A Colliding particles must have different energies.
 B All reactant particles must have the same energy.
 C Colliding particles must have a kinetic energy higher than the activation energy.
 D Colliding particles must have the same velocity.

Standard Level Paper 1, November 2005, Q19

Paper 2 IB questions and IB style questions

Q1 The graph below was obtained when calcium carbonate reacted with dilute hydrochloric acid, under two different conditions, X and Y.

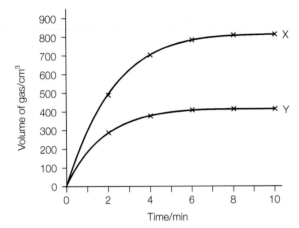

a i Name the gas produced in the reaction. [1]

ii Write a balanced equation for the reaction occurring. [2]

b Identify the volume of gas produced and the time taken for the reaction under condition X to be complete. [2]

c i Explain the shape of curve Y in terms of collision theory. [2]

ii Suggest two possible reasons for the differences between curves X and Y. [2]

Q2 The following results were obtained when 0.0800 grams of magnesium ribbon were added to a large excess of dilute hydrochloric acid while the temperature was kept constant (by means of a water bath). The hydrogen gas was collected in a 100 cm³ gas syringe.

$$Mg(s) + 2HCl(aq) \rightarrow MgCl_2(aq) + H_2(g)$$

Time/s	Volume of hydrogen gas evolved/cm³
0	0
20	30
40	49
60	58
80	65
100	70
120	75
140	75

a What was the volume of gas produced in

i the first 20 second interval (from 0 seconds to 20 seconds) [1]

ii the second 20 second interval (from 20 seconds to 40 seconds) [1]

iii the third 20 second interval (from 40 seconds to 60 seconds)? [1]

b Explain why the volume of hydrogen gas changes in each of these 20 second intervals. [2]

c Why is the volume the same after 140 seconds and 120 seconds? [1]

d Plot a graph of the volume of hydrogen produced against time. From the graph, estimate the rate of reaction at [3]

i 30 seconds [2]

ii 50 seconds [2]

e How would the initial rate of production of gas change if

i the temperature were increased [1]

ii the acid were diluted with an equal volume of water [1]

iii the same mass of magnesium powder were used instead of magnesium ribbon? [1]

f How would the final volume of gas change if

i a greater mass of magnesium were used with the same volume of acid [1]

ii a larger volume of acid were used with the same mass of magnesium? [1]

g Various data-logging sensors are available for linking to a computer to measure the following: gas pressure, light, motion, and change in mass by direct connection to a balance.

i Which of these could most usefully be used to monitor the rate of this reaction, and which not? [3]

ii Briefly explain why in each case. [3]

Q3 a A solution of hydrogen peroxide, H_2O_2, is added to a solution of sodium iodide, NaI, acidified with hydrochloric acid, HCl. The yellow colour of the iodine, I_2, can be used to determine the rate of reaction.

$$H_2O_2(aq) + 2NaI(aq) + 2HCl(aq) \rightarrow$$
$$2NaCl(aq) + I_2(aq) + 2H_2O(l)$$

The experiment is repeated with some changes to the reaction conditions. For each of the changes that follow, predict, stating a reason, its effect on the rate of reaction.

i The concentration of H_2O_2 is increased at constant temperature. [2]

ii The solution of NaI is prepared from fine powder instead of from large crystals. [2]

b Explain why the rate of reaction increases when the temperature of the system increases. [3]

Standard Level Paper 2, November 2009, Q2

7 Equilibrium

ESSENTIAL IDEA

- Many reactions are reversible. These reactions will reach a state of equilibrium when the rates of the forward and reverse reaction are equal. The position of equilibrium can be controlled by changing the conditions.

Figure 7.1 Fireworks at the New Year celebrations over Sydney Harbour

There are some chemical reactions that very obviously go virtually to completion. For example, spectacular firework displays involve a range of colourful and eye-catching reactions that help us to celebrate significant occasions (Figure 7.1). However, there are a significant number of reactions that do not go even close to completion. In these cases a reverse reaction is set up that runs in 'competition' with the forward reaction.

Such reversible reactions are key to certain industrially important processes such as the synthesis of ammonia and the production of sulfuric acid. They are also crucial in our body chemistry. The reversible nature of so many metabolic reactions in our biochemistry means that these reactions can be controlled by subtle changes in conditions. For instance, reversible effects control how oxygen binds to, and is released from, the hemoglobin in red blood cells as they flow through our lungs and other tissues of our body. The complexity of our body chemistry is dependent on the fine control that is possible where the metabolic pathways consist of sequences of reversible reactions.

7.1 Equilibrium – *many reactions are reversible; these reactions will reach a state of equilibrium when the rates of the forward and reverse reaction are equal; the position of equilibrium can be controlled by changing the conditions*

■ Dynamic equilibrium

Some of the essential features of a dynamic equilibrium are best illustrated by considering physical systems. Such systems can give clear-cut examples of basic dynamic changes taking place while the overall properties of different parts, or components, of the system remain constant.

Physical equilibria

We are all familiar with the phenomenon of evaporation. Puddles of water disappear after a rain shower. Propanone disappears from the cupped palm of your hand even as you watch, and your hand feels cold as the liquid evaporates. These are open systems: once evaporated, the molecules in the vapour escape and mix with the air. Evaporation continues as the molecules gain enough kinetic energy from the surroundings to escape the surface of the liquid and enter the atmosphere. Eventually all the liquid disappears into the air. This process has many uses, including the evaporation of water from salt pans (Figure 7.2).

Figure 7.2 The Inca salt pans at Maras Ollantaytambo, Peru

If you place some water in a sealed container a different situation arises. To start with, water will still vaporize. However, the air in the container will become saturated with water vapour until it can hold no more water. Equilibrium will be established between the liquid water and the water-saturated air above it. Some water molecules will still have sufficient kinetic energy to escape the surface and enter the vapour phase. Simultaneously some molecules in the vapour will condense back into the liquid.

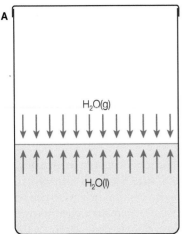
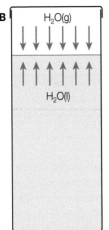

■ **Figure 7.3** The effect of surface area on the evaporation of water in a closed container

At equilibrium, the rate of vaporization is equal to the rate of condensation.

$$H_2O(l) \rightleftharpoons H_2O(g)$$

Experiments can be carried out on this type of system. Figure 7.3 represents two containers (A and B) with the same amount of water in them, but the surface area in A is twice that in B. The rates of evaporation and condensation are both twice as fast in A as in B, but the position of equilibrium is unchanged. The vapour pressure of water in the two systems is the same.

This type of physical liquid–vapour equilibrium can be visually demonstrated using bromine. Bromine is the one non-metallic element that is a liquid at room temperature. It is a volatile liquid (boiling point 332 K). When placed in a sealed container, the orange-brown vapour collects over the deep red-brown liquid. As the liquid slowly evaporates over a period of time, the colour of the vapour becomes more intense. Eventually, the intensity of colour of the vapour as it sits over the liquid remains constant (Figure 7.4).

The unchanging colour of the vapour in the flask suggests that a position of balance has been reached. Some of the bromine has formed a vapour and some of the bromine remains as a liquid. A position of equilibrium has been reached between bromine liquid and bromine gas. This equilibrium can be summarized as:

$$Br_2(l) \rightleftharpoons Br_2(g)$$

■ **Figure 7.4** A sealed flask containing bromine demonstrates a physical equilibrium between the liquid and its vapour

At this point the rate of evaporation and the rate of condensation are the same. There is no net change in the amounts of bromine liquid and vapour present.

The equilibrium sign ($\rightleftharpoons$) is used to show that both bromine liquid and bromine gas are present in the flask. Do all the liquid bromine molecules remain in the liquid while all the gaseous molecules stay as vapour (a static equilibrium)? Or is there an exchange of molecules, with some liquid molecules entering the vapour state while an equal number of vapour molecules condense to liquid (a dynamic equilibrium)? Experiments show that liquid and gas molecules move around rapidly and randomly, giving rise to our ideas of the kinetic theory of matter (Chapter 1). Given these ideas, it seems likely that a dynamic rather than a static equilibrium is set up in the flask. In which case, the rate at which molecules leave the liquid surface and enter the vapour is equal to the rate at which other molecules in the vapour return to the liquid. Random molecular activity occurs even after all the obvious visual signs of change have disappeared.

The solubility of gases in water extends these ideas to another physical situation. There are many fizzy drinks that involve carbon dioxide dissolved under pressure, forming $CO_2(aq)$ (Figure 7.5). The pressure needs to be maintained if the carbon dioxide is to stay dissolved as $CO_2(aq)$. This is done by keeping the lid screwed on tightly. Once we release the pressure by slightly unscrewing the lid the carbon dioxide begins to come out of solution. A stream of bubbles is produced which can be slowed down by re-tightening the cap on

■ **Figure 7.5** Dynamic equilibrium in a sealed bottle of fizzy drink. The bottle on the left has had its cap slightly opened, and then closed again

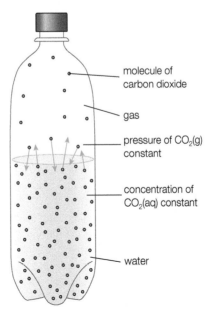

molecule of carbon dioxide

gas

pressure of $CO_2(g)$ constant

concentration of $CO_2(aq)$ constant

water

the bottle (Figure 7.5). This process is said to be a reversible reaction, which means it can go in either direction.

$$CO_2(g) + (aq) \underset{\text{decrease pressure}}{\overset{\text{increase pressure}}{\rightleftharpoons}} CO_2(aq)$$

Again the double-headed arrow symbol ($\rightleftharpoons$) represents a dynamic equilibrium or a 'balanced state'. This can be explained in the following way. In the bottle of fizzy drink, the concentration of the carbon dioxide molecules dissolved in water and the concentration of carbon dioxide molecules in the gas phase are constant. If you examined the situation further then you would see that carbon dioxide molecules are constantly moving back and forth between the liquid and the gas phase (Figure 7.5). The rate of movement of carbon dioxide molecules from the liquid to the gas phase is the same as the rate of movement of carbon dioxide from the gas phase to the water. So even though molecules of carbon dioxide are moving between the two environments, no apparent change is taking place.

ToK Link

The language of chemistry

The sciences involve a precision of language that is often more detailed and precise than everyday conversation. Some words, such as *volatile* for instance, have precise meanings that are particular to a scientific context. Such words become part of a specialized scientific vocabulary in addition to their normal usage.

The terms 'gas' and 'vapour' are often used interchangeably and in most circumstances this is quite acceptable. The term 'vapour' has the more limited and exact meaning and refers to gases formed by evaporation of substances that are usually liquids or solids at room temperature. Thus, in the case we looked at just now, the orange-brown bromine 'gas' is more usually referred to as bromine vapour; it is directly in contact with bromine liquid. Physicists will use the term 'vapour' to refer to any substance in the gas phase under conditions where it can be liquefied simply by increasing the pressure. In these cases they are gases below their critical temperature (Chapter 17).

A further example of a specialized term is that of a closed system, meaning one where no matter is exchanged with the external surroundings. Figure 7.6 shows clearly the difference between a closed and open system in terms of the outcome of the reaction involved.

Many chemical reactions can be studied without placing them in closed containers. They can reach equilibrium in open flasks if the reaction takes place entirely in solution and no gas is lost.

■ **Figure 7.6 a** A closed system where no carbon dioxide escapes and an equilibrium is established. **b** An open system; here the calcium carbonate is continually decomposing as the carbon dioxide is lost. The reaction goes to completion

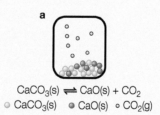

a

$CaCO_3(s) \rightleftharpoons CaO(s) + CO_2$
○ $CaCO_3(s)$ ● $CaO(s)$ ○ $CO_2(g)$

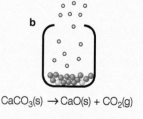

b

$CaCO_3(s) \rightarrow CaO(s) + CO_2(g)$

'Dynamic' is a key word in our understanding of what is happening in the chemical or physical equilibria that can be set up in a closed system. It implies continuous activity. Except at the beginning and end of the day, a busy store is often at dynamic equilibrium, with the number of customers arriving matching the number leaving. Dynamic equilibrium is quite unlike the 'static equilibrium' of a ball at rest at the foot of a hill (where 'static' indicates an absence of activity). A store is at static equilibrium before it opens for business.

A further example of a dynamic equilibrium is a fish swimming upstream at the same speed as the stream is flowing down. The fish appears to be static (not moving), but it is in dynamic equilibrium with the stream (Figure 7.7).

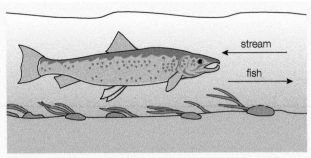

■ **Figure 7.7** Dynamic equilibrium: the fish appears to be still. However, it is swimming upstream at the same velocity as the stream is flowing in the opposite direction

These examples illustrate the stress placed on clear thinking in the sciences and the importance of the use of language in defining the ideas talked of. However, does such precision also impose restrictions on our thinking? Does it restrict subtlety in grappling with complex ideas; and are there, in fact, aspects of our lives and knowing that are beyond the language of science?

Chemical equilibria

A chemical equilibrium can only occur when the chemical system is closed. One reaction that gives a visual demonstration of aspects of a chemical equilibrium is based on a chemical test for iron(III) ions (Fe^{3+} ions) in solution. Aqueous iron(III) ions react with thiocyanate ions (SCN^- ions) to produce a blood red colour (Figure 7.8). The red colour is due to the soluble complex ion, $[Fe(SCN)]^{2+}$.

$$Fe^{3+}(aq) + SCN^-(aq) \rightleftharpoons [Fe(SCN)]^{2+}(aq)$$
pale yellow colourless   deep red

The system forms an equilibrium mixture containing unreacted Fe^{3+} ions, unreacted SCN^- ions and the complex ion product $[Fe(SCN)]^{2+}$.

It is possible to study the nature of the equilibrium set up by this reaction at room temperature by looking at the effect of adding various ions on the intensity of the red colour of the solution. Provided sufficiently dilute solutions are used, this can be done using a colorimeter. In this way we avoid any bias involved in simply using our own eyesight. If a few drops of a solution containing a soluble iron(III) salt are added to an equilibrium solution, the colour of the solution becomes darker. A new state of equilibrium has been quickly achieved in which the concentration of $[Fe(SCN)]^{2+}$ is greater than before. Increasing the concentration of $Fe^{3+}(aq)$ has increased the concentration of the complex ion.

In a similar way, the concentration of $[Fe(SCN)]^{2+}(aq)$ can also be increased when a few drops of potassium thiocyanate solution are added to the equilibrium solution. The red colour again intensifies. In this way we can see that an equilibrium mixture has been set up by a chemical reaction. This dynamic balance between the ions in the mixture can be disturbed by some simple additions to the mixture.

Reversible chemical reactions reach this balanced state of equilibrium when the rates of both the forward and reverse reactions are equal. If this is true then, under given conditions, the same equilibrium mixture should be reached whether we start with the chemicals on one side of the equation or the other. For instance, the gas phase reaction

$$H_2(g) + I_2(g) \rightleftharpoons 2HI(g)$$

has been studied under various conditions. The reaction can be stopped quickly (quenched) by cooling, and the amount of iodine present in the equilibrium mixture found by titration with

■ **Figure 7.8** The equilibrium between $Fe^{3+}(aq)$ ions and $SCN^-(aq)$ ions can be studied by colorimetry. A soluble blood red coloured complex is formed between the two ions

sodium thiosulfate. Figure 7.9 illustrates the type of results obtained in studies of this kind. Note that the same equilibrium concentrations of $H_2(g)$, $I_2(g)$ and $HI(g)$ are reached whichever direction the equilibrium is approached from.

■ **Figure 7.9 a** Graph of the concentration of reactants and products with time when reacting equal amounts of hydrogen gas and iodine vapour **b** Graph showing the achievement of the same equilibrium state by decomposition of hydrogen iodide vapour at the same temperature

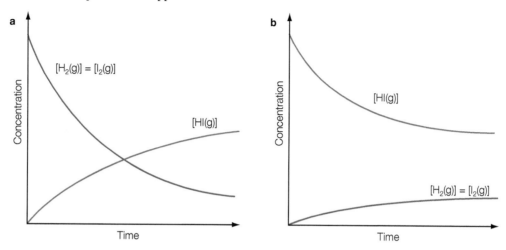

1 a What are the characteristics of a reversible reaction in a state of dynamic equilibrium?
  b What conditions are necessary before equilibrium can be achieved?

2 When the gases dinitrogen tetroxide and nitrogen monoxide are mixed in a 1 : 2 ratio, the two gases slowly react to form the blue compound dinitrogen trioxide according to the following equation:

$$N_2O_4(g) + 2NO(g) \rightleftharpoons 2N_2O_3(g)$$

  a Sketch the graph showing how the concentrations of the reactants and products change from the time of mixing until equilibrium is achieved. At equilibrium the concentration of product is less than that of the starting reactants.
  b Sketch a graph showing how the rates of reaction of the forward and reverse reactions change as the reaction progresses to equilibrium.

ToK Link

Size matters

By its very nature the essential features of a physical or chemical equilibrium state are at a sub-microscopic level beyond our sight. In order to make sense of what we understand is happening at this level it is often necessary to use analogies or thought experiments to create mental 'pictures' of what is occurring in these situations.

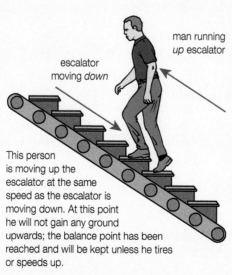

This person is moving up the escalator at the same speed as the escalator is moving down. At this point he will not gain any ground upwards; the balance point has been reached and will be kept unless he tires or speeds up.

■ **Figure 7.10** One useful analogy of dynamic equilibrium is that of a person trying to go up the down escalator

Various analogies have been suggested to describe dynamic equilibria at the molecular level (see Figure 7.7 earlier). One of the most frequently used is that of a person walking or running up a 'down' escalator at the same rate as the moving staircase is descending. The person is moving, the escalator is moving too, but the overall effect is that the person remains at the same point up the incline (Figure 7.10). A similar analogy from the fitness club would be a person running or walking on a treadmill set at an appropriate speed.

Such analogies always have their weaknesses but they do try to convey the idea of continuous change producing a stable situation where certain overall properties do not alter. One 'thought experiment' that you can try is to imagine that you are one of the atoms in a chemical mixture at equilibrium, a nitrogen atom in an ammonia molecule, for instance. Imagine that you detach yourself from the ammonia molecule and become part of a nitrogen molecule, N_2 – but only if another nitrogen atom comes the other way, from the nitrogen molecule to the ammonia molecule. Then you can imagine being part of a dynamic equilibrium.

Probing the sub-microscopic world – isotopic labelling

The equivalent of such thought experiments can be carried out using radioactive or 'heavy' isotopes (Chapter 2) of an element involved in the reaction. In this way we can 'tag' certain atoms and show that movement continues to occur even though a system is in equilibrium. An experiment can be set up to show that there is dynamic exchange of atoms between the molecules in an equilibrium mixture. A heavy isotope is one having an extra neutron or neutrons in the nucleus of the atom. For example, deuterium ($_1^2H$), sometimes given the symbol D, is an isotope of hydrogen in which the nucleus of each atom contains a neutron as well as a proton. In studies on the ammonia equilibrium, some of the hydrogen is replaced by an equal amount of 'heavy hydrogen', D_2. The D_2 molecules behave chemically in exactly the same way as H_2 molecules and will take part in the reaction (Figure 7.11). When the new equilibrium mixture is subsequently analysed using a mass spectrometer (Chapter 2) some NH_2D, NHD_2, ND_3 and HD will be detected. This finding can only occur if there is an exchange of atoms between the molecules of ammonia, hydrogen and deuterium in the equilibrium mixture.

■ **Figure 7.11** Incorporation of deuterium into ammonia within the ammonia, hydrogen and deuterium equilibrium mixture

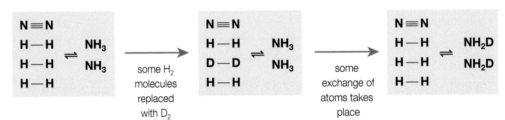

■ The position of equilibrium

From the discussion so far, the basic features of dynamic equilibria can be summarized as follows:

- A dynamic equilibrium can only be established in a closed system. There can be no loss or gain of material to or from the surroundings.
- At equilibrium, macroscopic properties such as the amounts of the various substances involved are unchanging under the given conditions. The amounts of reactants and products remain constant.
- The equilibrium is dynamic, not static. At the sub-microscopic level the particles present continue to take part in the forward and reverse processes.
- At equilibrium the rates of the forward and reverse reactions are equal so that no net change takes place.
- Under given conditions the equilibrium position can be achieved from either direction. A mixture of a given equilibrium composition can be made starting with either the substances on the left-hand or the right-hand side of the equation for the reversible reaction.
- The dynamic nature of these equilibria means that they are stable under fixed conditions but sensitive to alterations in these conditions. This immediate sensitivity to changes in conditions, such as alterations in temperature, pH or the concentration of a reactant, can be taken as an indication that the system was indeed at equilibrium.
- The chemical equilibria we will study in these chapters are all examples of homogeneous equilibria. The reactants and products are all in the same physical phase – either in the gaseous or liquid state, or in aqueous solution.

■ The equilibrium constant

The quantitative study of many chemical equilibria has shown that the following equilibrium law applies to such systems. The position of the equilibrium for a particular reversible reaction can be defined by a constant which has a numerical value found by relating the equilibrium concentrations of the products to those of the reactants. This constant is known as the equilibrium constant, K_c, for the reaction.

We can write an equilibrium expression for K_c for a general reaction:

$$aA + bB \rightleftharpoons cC + dD$$

where a, b, c and d represent the coefficients [the amounts of each substance (in moles)] in the equation, as:

$$K_c = \frac{[C]^c_{eqm}\,[D]^d_{eqm}}{[A]^a_{eqm}\,[D]^b_{eqm}}$$

It is important to note that the concentration values fed into the expression *must* be those that occur at equilibrium, not the starting values. For this reason the terms $[C]_{eqm}$ etc. are used, and strictly speaking this is how the expression should be written. However, this can make the expression look rather cluttered and generally the expression is written as summarized below:

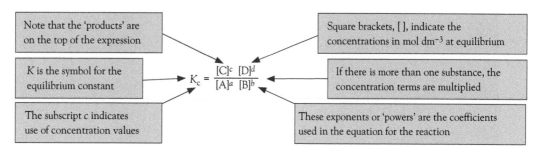

Note that the 'products' are on the top of the expression

K is the symbol for the equilibrium constant

The subscript c indicates use of concentration values

$$K_c = \frac{[C]^c\,[D]^d}{[A]^a\,[B]^b}$$

Square brackets, [ ], indicate the concentrations in mol dm^{-3} at equilibrium

If there is more than one substance, the concentration terms are multiplied

These exponents or 'powers' are the coefficients used in the equation for the reaction

It should be noted that the equilibrium constant, K_c, is constant for a given temperature. If the temperature changes, then the value of K_c will change. This is a general expression of the equilibrium law. The general expression is then adapted to the particular reaction being studied.

Worked example

Use the figures given in Table 7.1 to demonstrate that using this type of relationship and the equilibrium concentrations for a particular reaction produces a constant value.

$$N_2(g) + 3H_2(g) \rightleftharpoons 2NH_3(g) \quad K_c = \frac{[NH_3]^2}{[N_2][H_2]^3}$$

■ **Table 7.1** Results from three experiments on the ammonia synthesis reaction at 500 °C

	[N$_2$]/mol dm^{-3}	[H$_2$]/mol dm^{-3}	[NH$_3$]/mol dm^{-3}
Experiment 1	0.922	0.763	0.157
Experiment 2	0.399	1.197	0.203
Experiment 3	2.59	2.77	1.82

Substituting values from Table 7.1:

Experiment 1: $K_c = \dfrac{(0.157)^2}{0.922 \times (0.763)^3} = 0.0602$

Experiment 2: $K_c = \dfrac{(0.203)^2}{0.399 \times (1.197)^3} = 0.0602$

Experiment 3: $K_c = \dfrac{(1.82)^2}{2.59 \times (2.77)^3} = 0.0602$

This is a constant value for all three experiments.

■ Different values for the equilibrium constant for the same reaction

Reversing the direction

In applying the equilibrium law to a particular reaction it is important to first write down the equation for the reaction studied. Using an example we looked at earlier:

$$H_2(g) + I_2(g) \rightleftharpoons 2HI(g)$$

The concentrations of the substances on the right-hand (product) side of the equation are written in the numerator (the upper part of the fraction), while the concentrations of those substances on the left-hand (reactant) side are placed as the denominator (the lower part of the fraction). So the equilibrium expression for this reaction is:

$$K_c = \frac{[HI]^2}{[H_2][I_2]}$$

It is important to always quote K_c with the relevant chemical equation for the reaction being considered. The value of K_c is a number that indicates the extent to which the equilibrium lies to the right-hand side of the equation we have written. It is crucial to be clear about the equation to which a K_c applies. Suppose the value for K_c above was X at a particular temperature, what would be the value of K_c for the reaction written as the decomposition of hydrogen iodide?

$$2HI(g) \rightleftharpoons H_2(g) + I_2(g)$$

For this reverse reaction, the equilibrium constant, K_c', at the same temperature is:

$$K_c' = \frac{[H_2][I_2]}{[HI]^2} = \frac{1}{X}$$

In general, the values, at the same temperature, for the forward and reverse equations for an equilibrium system are related as follows:

$$K_c' = \frac{1}{K_c} \quad \text{or} \quad K_c^{-1}$$

i.e. the value of the equilibrium constant for the reverse reaction is the reciprocal of that for the forward reaction.

The equilibrium law is very much an experimentally determined one. The basic structure of the expression for a particular reaction is confirmed by the value of K_c remaining constant for a series of experiments at a given temperature. Table 7.2a shows the values for K_c obtained in such a series of experiments when hydrogen and iodine are reacted in a sealed container at 700 K. These results show that a constant value of 54 is obtained when the equilibrium concentrations are fed into the expression:

$$K_c = \frac{[HI]^2}{[H_2][I_2]}$$

The results for further experiments where the equilibrium at 700 K is approached from the other direction are given in Table 7.2b. These results demonstrate the reciprocal relationship of the equilibrium constants found from the two sets of experiments.

■ **Table 7.2a**
The results for a series of experiments on the reaction
$H_2(g) + I_2(g) \rightleftharpoons 2HI(g)$

	$[H_2]_{eqm}/$ 10^{-3} mol dm^{-3}	$[I_2]_{eqm}/$ 10^{-3} mol dm^{-3}	$[HI]_{eqm}/$ 10^{-3} mol dm^{-3}	K_c
Experiment 1	4.56	0.74	13.49	54
Experiment 2	3.56	1.25	15.50	54
Experiment 3	2.25	2.34	16.86	54

■ **Table 7.2b** The
experimental results
for the reaction
$2HI(g) \rightleftharpoons H_2(g) + I_2(g)$

	$[H_2]_{eqm}/$ 10^{-3} mol dm^{-3}	$[I_2]_{eqm}/$ 10^{-3} mol dm^{-3}	$[HI]_{eqm}/$ 10^{-3} mol dm^{-3}	K_c'	K_c $(1/K_c')$
Experiment 4	0.48	0.48	3.52	0.0186	54
Experiment 5	0.50	0.50	3.67	0.0186	54

We can see that when discussing a reversible reaction it is important to give the equation for the reaction clearly. Even though the reaction is reversible, the species on the right of the equation are often referred to as 'products', while those on the left are still termed the 'reactants'. The structure of the equilibrium expression depends on the direction in which the equation is written, as does the value of K_c that we derive from it. We will shortly see that this is also important when predicting the adjustments that take place in an equilibrium mixture when conditions change.

Changing the stoichiometry

As a further example of why it is important to always quote the equation upon which the value of K_c is based, we can look at the reaction between hydrogen and iodine again. It is possible to write the equation for the reactions as follows:

$$\tfrac{1}{2}H_2(g) + \tfrac{1}{2}I_2(g) \rightleftharpoons HI(g)$$

The equilibrium expression derived from this equation is:

$$K_c'' = \frac{[HI]}{[H_2]^{\frac{1}{2}}\ [I_2]^{\frac{1}{2}}}$$

and the value of the constant at 700 K is 7.3. Compare this value with the one of 54 given in Table 7.2a for the equation $H_2(g) + I_2(g) \rightleftharpoons 2HI(g)$ at 700 K. We can see that

$$K_c'' = \sqrt{K_c}$$

Reactions in sequence

The reactions between the oxides of nitrogen are of interest in demonstrating how the overall K_c value for a sequence of reactions relates to the individual values for the different steps.

Worked example

Show that the K_c value for the reaction

$$N_2(g) + 2O_2(g) \rightleftharpoons 2NO_2(g) \qquad \text{Reaction 3 } (K_{c3})$$

is given by $K_{c3} = K_{c1} \times K_{c2}$ where reactions 1 and 2 are as follows:

$$N_2(g) + O_2(g) \rightleftharpoons 2NO(g) \qquad \text{Reaction 1 } (K_{c1})$$
$$2NO(g) + O_2(g) \rightleftharpoons 2NO_2(g) \qquad \text{Reaction 2 } (K_{c2})$$

Reactions 1 and 2 are sequential reactions that added together give the overall equation for reaction 3:

$$N_2(g) + O_2(g) \rightleftharpoons 2NO(g)$$
$$2NO(g) + O_2(g) \rightleftharpoons 2NO_2(g)$$
$$N_2(g) + 2O_2(g) \rightleftharpoons 2NO_2(g)$$

Now we need to establish the expressions for K_{c1}, K_{c2} and K_{c3}, respectively.

$$K_{c1} = \frac{[NO]^2}{[N_2][O_2]} \qquad K_{c2} = \frac{[NO_2]^2}{[NO]^2[O_2]} \qquad K_{c3} = \frac{[NO_2]^2}{[N_2][O_2]^2}$$

Now we need to work out the expression for $K_{c1} \times K_{c2}$.

$$K_{c1} \times K_{c2} = \frac{[NO]^2}{[N_2][O_2]} \times \frac{[NO_2]^2}{[NO]^2[O_2]} = \frac{[NO_2]^2}{[N_2][O_2]^2}$$

This is the expression for K_{c3}.

Therefore $K_{c3} = K_{c1} \times K_{c2}$

In general, for reactions that take place in sequence, the overall K_c value is equal to the product of the individual K_c values for each of the individual reaction steps. 'Coupled' reactions of this type are particularly important in biochemistry where it is possible for ten or so reactions to be linked in this way (see page 223).

Table 7.3 summarizes the relationships we have established between equilibrium expressions for reactions that are related to each other in the different situations we have explored here.

■ **Table 7.3**
The equilibrium constant for the same reaction at the same temperature can be expressed in a number of ways

Change in reaction equation	Equilibrium constant expression	Equilibrium constant
Reverse the reaction	Inverse of expression	K_c^{-1}
Halve the stoichiometric coefficients	Square root of the expression	$\sqrt{K_c}$
Double the stoichiometric coefficients	Square of the expression	K_c^2
Sequence of reactions	Multiply the values for the individual steps	$K_c = K_{c1} \times K_{c2} \times K_{c3} \ldots$

Worked example

Write the equilibrium expression for the following reversible reaction. It is an example of a homogeneous equilibrium.

$$2SO_2(g) + O_2(g) \rightleftharpoons 2SO_3(g)$$

Remember to keep in mind the written equation. The concentration of sulfur trioxide will be on top in the equilibrium expression. Remember also to include the balancing coefficients from the equation as powers in the expression for K_c.

$$K_c = \frac{[SO_3(g)]^2}{[SO_2(g)]^2[O_2(g)]}$$

You will see the state symbols for each substance included in the equilibrium expression, emphasizing the fact that this is a homogeneous equilibrium. Unless you are specifically asked to include them they can be omitted. It means that the expression looks less cumbersome. Thus, an answer to this question would read:

$$2SO_2(g) + O_2(g) \rightleftharpoons 2SO_3(g) \qquad K_c = \frac{[SO_3]^2}{[SO_2]^2[O_2]}$$

3 a Write the equilibrium expressions for the following reversible reactions. They are all examples of homogeneous equilibria.
  i $Fe^{3+}(aq) + SCN^-(aq) \rightleftharpoons [Fe(SCN)]^{2+}(aq)$
  ii $4NH_3(g) + 5O_2(g) \rightleftharpoons 4NO(g) + 6H_2O(g)$
  b i The following reaction is an esterification reaction producing ethyl ethanoate:
  $$CH_3CO_2H(l) + C_2H_5OH(l) \rightleftharpoons CH_3CO_2C_2H_5(l) + H_2O(l)$$
  ii The value of K_c for the above reaction at 25 °C is 4.0. This equilibrium can be approached experimentally from the opposite direction. What is the value for K_c for this reaction, the hydrolysis of ethyl ethanoate, at 25 °C?
  $$CH_3CO_2C_2H_5(l) + H_2O(l) \rightleftharpoons CH_3CO_2H(l) + C_2H_5OH(l)$$

The units of the equilibrium constant (K_c)

In order to calculate a standard value of the equilibrium constant, K_c, for a reaction the values of the concentrations entered in the equilibrium expression *must* numerically be in $mol\,dm^{-3}$. Strictly speaking the values entered should be 'activity' values rather than concentrations. For gases and relatively dilute solutions the concentration values are sufficiently close to the 'activity' values that their use does not introduce any significant errors into the calculation. Since the 'activity' values for substances are simply a number – they do not have any units – it follows that *any K_c value will also simply be a number without units no matter which reaction you are studying*. Certainly in the IB examination you will not be asked for any units relating to K_c values.

■ How far will a reaction go?

The magnitude of K_c gives us a useful indication of how far a reaction has gone towards completion under the given conditions (Figure 7.12). The higher the value of K_c, the further to the right the equilibrium position will lie at that temperature. This relationship arises from the structure of the equilibrium expression.

■ **Figure 7.12**
An illustration of how the value of K_c indicates the position of an equilibrium

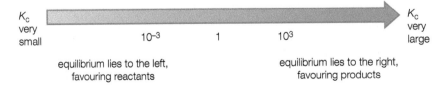

If the value of K_c is high, then this shows that at equilibrium there is a high proportion of products compared to reactants. In this case we say that the equilibrium lies well over to the right, as the equation is written. If the K_c value is low, then this indicates that only a small fraction of the reactants have been converted into products, and the equilibrium lies over to the left.

Two seemingly very similar reactions are those of chlorine and iodine with hydrogen to form the respective hydrogen halides:

$$H_2(g) + I_2(g) \rightleftharpoons 2HI(g) \qquad K_c = 2 \text{ at } 277\,°C$$

$$H_2(g) + Cl_2(g) \rightleftharpoons 2HCl(g) \qquad K_c = 1018 \text{ at } 277\,°C$$

The large difference in magnitude for the values of K_c illustrates how stable hydrogen chloride is at this temperature compared to hydrogen iodide. The reaction between hydrogen and chlorine has gone almost to completion to produce hydrogen chloride (HCl) molecules that do not readily decompose with heat. The bonding in hydrogen iodide is weaker and therefore the reverse reaction is more evident, with an equilibrium being established.

As a general rule, if $K_c \gg 1$ then the reaction is said to have gone almost to completion. There has been an almost complete conversion of reactants to products. If $K_c \ll 1$ the reaction has hardly taken place at all; very little of the reactants have been converted to products. Thus the equilibrium constant indicates the extent of a reaction at a particular temperature (see Table 7.4). Do note, though, that it gives no information at all about how *fast* the equilibrium state is achieved.

■ **Table 7.4** The relationship between the value of K_c and the extent of a reaction

Reaction hardly goes	'Reactants' predominate at equilibrium	Equal amounts of reactants and products	'Products' predominate at equilibrium	Reaction goes virtually to completion
$K_c < 10^{-10}$	$K_c = 0.01$	$K_c = 1$	$K_c = 100$	$K_c > 10^{10}$

It is also important to realize that the value of K_c is not altered by the addition of more reactants, the removal of some product from the system, or any other adjustment of the components of the mixture. Consider the general equation we met before:

$$aA + bB \rightleftharpoons cC + dD$$

for which:

$$K_c = \frac{[C]^c\,[D]^d}{[A]^a\,[B]^b}$$

If we added more A, while keeping the temperature constant, the value of the bottom part of the equation would increase and the overall value of the expression would no longer equal K_c. However, the reaction re-adjusts itself. Some of the extra A reacts with B to form more C and D. The concentrations adjust to establish a new equilibrium mixture so that the overall value for the expression again equals K_c.

The K_c for a given reversible reaction at equilibrium only changes if the temperature changes.

Referring to the reaction below, it is the species on the 'right' of the equation that goes on the top of the equilibrium expression.

$$2CrO_4^{2-}(aq) + H^+(aq) \rightleftharpoons Cr_2O_7^{2-}(aq) + OH^-(aq)$$
$$\text{yellow} \qquad\qquad\qquad \text{orange}$$

$$K_c = \frac{[Cr_2O_7^{2-}][OH^-]}{[Cr_2O_4^{2-}]^2[H^+]}$$

■ **Figure 7.13**
The equilibrium between chromate(VI) and dichromate(VI) ions in solution can be manipulated by the addition of acid or alkali

The shifts in equilibrium of this reaction can be easily seen because of the different colours of the ions involved (Figure 7.13). The reaction can be used to illustrate the language of direction and 'shifts' that we frequently use in this context.

When potassium chromate(VI) is dissolved in water a yellow solution is produced. Adding a few drops of acid (H^+ ions) sets up the equilibrium, though well to the left. Further additions of acid disturb the equilibrium. The equilibrium shifts to the right to remove the additional hydrogen ions, H^+, and the colour of the solution turns orange. The presence of orange dichromate(VI) ions is favoured by low pH.

If hydroxide ions (OH^-) ions are added to this orange solution the equilibrium shifts to the left to remove these ions. The solution turns yellow again; the formation of chromate(VI) ions is favoured.

■ The relationship between the equilibrium constant (K_c) and the reaction quotient (Q_c)

In the discussion above we have emphasized that the concentrations entered in the equilibrium expression when calculating K_c must be those occurring once equilibrium has been established. However, the same general expression, this time with non-equilibrium concentration values fed into it, can be of use in predicting how a given mixture will react. In these cases the value calculated is known as the reaction quotient, Q_c.

The following reaction illustrates the meaning of this.

$$N_2O_4(g) \rightleftharpoons 2NO_2(g) \qquad K_c \text{ at } 500 \text{ K} = 41$$

Suppose a mixture of dinitrogen tetroxide (2 mol dm^{-3}) and nitrogen(IV) oxide (6 mol dm^{-3}) is contained in a sealed tube at 500 K, will the reaction move the composition of the mixture to the left or the right? Or, indeed, will the composition of the mixture change at all? Entering these concentrations into the expression for the reaction quotient, Q_c, we get the following value:

$$Q_c = \frac{[NO_2]^2}{[N_2O_4]} = 18$$

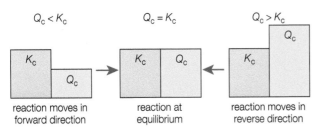

reaction moves in forward direction   reaction at equilibrium   reaction moves in reverse direction

■ **Figure 7.14** The relative sizes of the reaction quotient and equilibrium constant indicate the direction in which a reaction mixture tends to change

So, in this case, Q_c is less than K_c and therefore the reaction will move towards the right, to produce more nitrogen(IV) oxide and eventually achieve equilibrium.

This example illustrates the fact that by comparing the value of Q_c with the equilibrium constant, K_c, the direction of reaction can be predicted (see Figure 7.14):

■ If $Q_c < K_c$ the reaction will move to the right, generating more product to reach equilibrium.

■ If $Q_c = K_c$ the reaction is at equilibrium.

■ If $Q_c > K_c$ the reaction will move to the left, generating more reactants to reach equilibrium.

The value of Q_c in relation to K_c thus indicates the direction in which any net reaction must proceed as the system moves towards its equilibrium state. It is worth noting, however, that this prediction makes no comment on the *rate* at which the equilibrium may be achieved. Certainly some reactions only reach equilibrium very slowly. For instance, the esterification reaction mentioned in question 8 on page 241 can take several weeks to achieve equilibrium in the absence of a catalyst. The stalactites that hang from the roofs of caves in limestone regions take geological periods of time to form. So it is worth remembering that in some cases the prediction based on Q_c may not be realized as the reaction may be so slow in both directions that equilibrium is never reached.

■ Le Châtelier's principle

When the conditions under which a chemical equilibrium has been established are changed there is an effect on 'the position of the equilibrium'. Is it possible to predict the effect of such changes? Indeed we can, on the basis of a principle first proposed by a French chemist Henri Le Châtelier. (Do note that for IB you do not need to learn a statement of the principle, as some published versions use quite complex language. However, it can be very useful to have a familiar version in mind when tackling questions.) This principle is a descriptive statement of what happens when a dynamic equilibrium is disturbed by a change in conditions; it is not an explanation as to why the change happens. Put simply, the system responds to negate the change by responding in the opposite way (Figure 7.15). For instance, if we add more of a reactant, the system will react to remove it; if we remove a product, the system will react to replace it.

Figure 7.15 Henri Le Châtelier, 1850–1936, and the central idea of Le Châtelier's Principle

COUNTERACT – OPPOSE!
- Make it hotter – equilibrium moves to cool it.
- Make it cooler – equilibrium moves to heat it.
- Raise the pressure – equilibrium moves to lower it.
- Lower the pressure – equilibrium moves to raise it.

The possible changes in conditions that we need to consider are:
- changes in the concentration of either reactants or products
- changes in pressure for gas phase reactions
- changes in temperature
- the presence of a catalyst.

This general principle is of importance industrially as it allows chemists to alter the reaction conditions to produce an increased amount of the product and, therefore, increase the profitability of a chemical process.

Note that in all cases, once the equilibrium has been re-established after the change, the value of K_c will be unaltered except when there is a change in temperature (Table 7.5).

Table 7.5 A broad summary of the effects of changing conditions on the position of an equilibrium

Change made	Effect on 'position of equilibrium'	Value of K_c
Concentration of one of the components of the mixture	Changes	Remains unchanged
Pressure	Changes if the reaction involves a change in the total number of gas molecules	Remains unchanged
Temperature	Changes	Changes
Use of a catalyst	No change	Remains unchanged

Changes in concentration

Consider the esterification reaction we looked at earlier:

$$CH_3CO_2H(l) + C_2H_5OH(l) \rightleftharpoons CH_3CO_2C_2H_5(l) + H_2O(l)$$
ethanoic acid   ethanol   ethyl ethanoate   water

If we remove some of the water from the equilibrium mixture then we would predict that more carboxylic acid and alcohol would react to replace it, producing more ester. This can in fact be done by adding a few drops of concentrated sulfuric acid to the mixture. The sulfuric acid provides hydrogen ions, H⁺, which act as a catalyst for the reaction, but also acts as a dehydrating agent, removing water from the mixture. The addition of the acid favours the production of the ester since, by removing water, it shifts the position of equilibrium to the right.

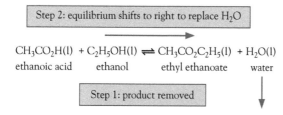

Step 2: equilibrium shifts to right to replace H_2O

$$CH_3CO_2H(l) + C_2H_5OH(l) \rightleftharpoons CH_3CO_2C_2H_5(l) + H_2O(l)$$
ethanoic acid   ethanol   ethyl ethanoate   water

Step 1: product removed

One massively important industrial process that depends on a reversible reaction is the production of ammonia (NH_3). The reaction involved is:

$$N_2(g) + 3H_2(g) \rightleftharpoons 2NH_3(g)$$

Because of its economic significance this reaction has been extensively studied. What, for instance, would be the effect on the equilibrium of increasing the concentration of the nitrogen gas in the reaction mixture?

Before more nitrogen gas is added into the system, the equilibrium concentrations of the reactants would be constant (Figure 7.16a). Then for a short time immediately after the addition of the extra nitrogen the system is no longer at equilibrium. To return the system to equilibrium some of the added nitrogen gas has to be used up and converted to more ammonia. A new equilibrium is established with different concentrations of each of the reactants and products. Most importantly, the equilibrium concentration of the ammonia has increased (Figure 7.16b).

■ **Figure 7.16**
a An equilibrium is established between N_2, H_2 and NH_3
b After the equilibrium has been disturbed, a new equilibrium position is established containing more ammonia

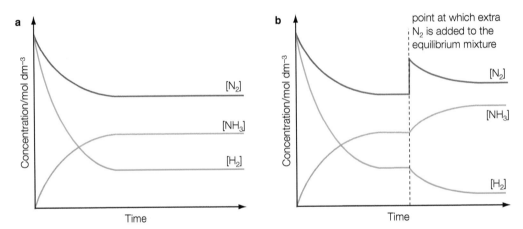

The addition of more nitrogen gas to the system has had the effect predicted by Le Châtelier's principle. The system has counteracted the change by using up some of the added nitrogen to produce more ammonia gas.

Generally:

■ increasing the concentration of a reactant will move the position of equilibrium to the right, favouring the forward reaction and increasing the equilibrium concentrations of the products.

Conversely, the opposite of this is also true:

■ the addition of more product to an equilibrium mixture would shift the position of the equilibrium to the left; the reverse reaction would be favoured.

Note that when the new equilibrium concentrations are substituted into the equilibrium expression the value of K_c remains unchanged.

The link between Le Châtelier's principle and the reaction quotient, Q_c

As we have stressed earlier, Le Châtelier's principle provides a very useful descriptive tool that helps us predict the outcome of a change in conditions on a chemical equilibrium. However, it does not provide an explanation for these effects. Use of the reaction quotient, Q_c, can give an insight into why changing the concentration of a component of an equilibrium mixture gives rise to the effect it does. Take the following reaction as an example:

$$N_2(g) + 3H_2(g) \rightleftharpoons 2NH_3(g)$$

At equilibrium:

$$Q_c = K_c = \frac{[NH_3]^2}{[N_2][H_2]^3}$$

If more hydrogen is added to the equilibrium mixture this will increase the value of the denominator in Q_c. Its value will no longer be equal to K_c – it will have a lower value – and therefore the reaction will adjust to increase Q_c by producing more ammonia (see top of page).

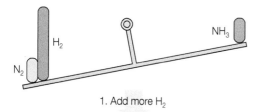

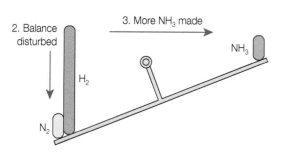

System responds to restore position of see-saw beam – the amounts of N_2, H_2 and NH_3 are different, but the position is the same

■ **Figure 7.17** Diagrammatic representation of the effect of adding more hydrogen to the equilibrium mixture involved in ammonia synthesis

The argument outlined here can be illustrated using the analogy of the 'see-saw' as shown in Figure 7.17. Here the angle of the beam represents the composition of the equilibrium mixture (the pictorial equivalent of K_c). At a particular temperature the value of K_c is constant. So the system must respond to any change in the composition of the mixture in a way that restores the angle of the beam.

Changing the pressure for a gas phase reaction

Changing the pressure under which a chemical reaction is carried out only affects reactions that involve gases. The solid and liquid phases are essentially non-compressible in this context, and so reactions involving these phases are unaffected by changes in pressure. Indeed, gas phase reactions will only be affected by a change of pressure if the reaction involves a change in the number of molecules on the two sides of the equation.

There is a direct relationship between the number of molecules of a gas in a container and the pressure the gas exerts. So if a reaction at equilibrium is subjected to an increase in pressure, then the system will respond by favouring the side of the equation with the smaller number of molecules. In doing this, the pressure of the mixture will be reduced. A useful reaction to study in this context is the decomposition of dinitrogen tetroxide (N_2O_4) because the change can be followed by the colour change observed. Dinitrogen tetroxide is a colourless gas that decomposes to brown nitrogen dioxide gas.

$$N_2O_4(g) \rightleftharpoons 2NO_2(g)$$
colourless   brown

An equilibrium mixture of these two gases can be set up in a gas syringe at a particular temperature (Figure 7.18). You can change the pressure in the reaction mixture by pushing the syringe piston in, or by sharply pulling it out, and compare the resulting colour of the gas mixture with the original. The interpretation of the changes observed is complicated by the simple effects on colour intensity caused by any volume change.

When the pressure is increased by pushing in the piston, there is an initial darkening of the colour of the gas mixture. This is due to the increase in concentration of the mixture. However, this is quickly followed by a lightening of the colour as the equilibrium mixture adjusts to its new composition in which there is a higher concentration of colourless N_2O_4. This produces a mixture involving fewer molecules and therefore reduces the pressure in the syringe, thus counteracting the increase in externally applied pressure.

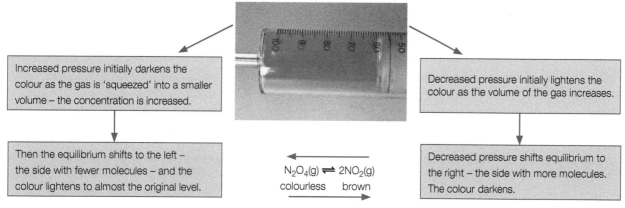

Increased pressure initially darkens the colour as the gas is 'squeezed' into a smaller volume – the concentration is increased.

Decreased pressure initially lightens the colour as the volume of the gas increases.

Then the equilibrium shifts to the left – the side with fewer molecules – and the colour lightens to almost the original level.

$$N_2O_4(g) \rightleftharpoons 2NO_2(g)$$
colourless   brown

Decreased pressure shifts equilibrium to the right – the side with more molecules. The colour darkens.

■ **Figure 7.18** The effect of changing pressure on the gaseous equilibrium involving nitrogen dioxide can be followed by observing the changes in colour intensity

Alternatively, if the pressure in the syringe is lowered by pulling out the piston, the effect of reduced pressure can be seen. After an initial lightening of the colour, as the new equilibrium is established the gas mixture finishes up darker than it was originally. Decreased pressure favours the side of the equation that involves more molecules. This new mixture involves a total of more gas molecules, counteracting the decrease in applied pressure.

For gas phase reactions where there are different numbers of molecules on the two sides of the equation:

■ increased pressure shifts the equilibrium position to the side of the equation with fewer molecules

■ decreased pressure shifts the equilibrium position to the side with more molecules.

None of these changes results in a change in the value of K_c.

If there is no change in the number of molecules during the course of a reaction then changes in pressure will have no effect on the equilibrium position of the reaction at a given temperature. This is illustrated by the reaction of hydrogen and iodine to form hydrogen iodide:

$$H_2(g) + I_2(g) \rightleftharpoons 2HI(g)$$

At a given temperature the position of this equilibrium, and others like it, cannot be manipulated by changing the external pressure applied to the mixture. If the pressure is altered by changing the volume then the concentrations of all the species change by the same factor, leaving K_c unchanged.

ToK Link

From microscopic to macroscopic – a language shift

In discussing the effects of changing pressure, we have considered the number of molecules on each side of the equation and related this to the pressure of the gas in the container. It is possible also to link the number of molecules to the volume that the gas would occupy. This can be done because one mole of any gas has the same volume if the conditions of temperature and pressure are the same (Chapter 1). The Avogadro constant can be viewed as a scaling-up factor that allows us to move from the microscopic, unseen world of molecules to the macroscopic, everyday world that we can see and handle; from number of molecules to volume of gas in this case.

In applying Le Châtelier's principle, therefore, it is possible to use the language of 'volume', and expansion or contraction, in discussing the changes predicted. Thus for the reaction involving the decomposition of dinitrogen tetroxide:

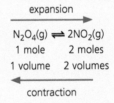

expansion

$N_2O_4(g) \rightleftharpoons 2NO_2(g)$
1 mole   2 moles
1 volume   2 volumes

contraction

An increase in external pressure will favour the side of the reaction that occupies less volume. In this case the equilibrium will shift to the left, the direction of the contraction in volume.

A decrease in pressure will favour the decomposition to nitrogen dioxide, NO_2, as this side of the reaction occupies a greater volume. The equilibrium will shift to the right, the direction of the expansion in volume.

Changing the temperature

Le Châtelier's principle can be used to predict the effect of a temperature change on the position of an equilibrium. The key factor to be considered here is whether the forward reaction is exothermic (a negative ΔH value) or endothermic (a positive ΔH value)(see Chapter 5). Remember that, in a reversible reaction, the reverse reaction has an enthalpy change that is equal and opposite to that of the forward reaction.

When the temperature is increased, the equilibrium position will shift in the direction that will tend to lower the temperature, that is, the endothermic direction that absorbs heat (Figure 7.19). If the temperature is lowered, the equilibrium will shift in the exothermic direction so as to generate heat and raise the temperature. These effects are summarized in Table 7.6.

■ **Figure 7.19**
The effect of increasing temperature on the proportions of reactants and products in the equilibrium mixture for exothermic and endothermic reactions

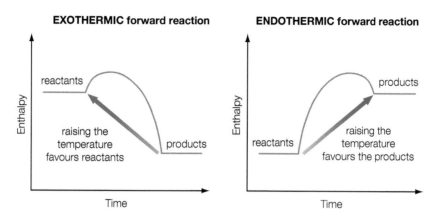

■ **Table 7.6**
The effects of temperature changes on chemical equilibria

Nature of forward reaction (sign of ΔH)	Change in temperature	Shift in the position of equilibrium	Effect on value of K_c
Endothermic (positive ΔH)	Increase	To the right	K_c increases
Endothermic (positive ΔH)	Decrease	To the left	K_c decreases
Exothermic (negative ΔH)	Increase	To the left	K_c decreases
Exothermic (negative ΔH)	Decrease	To the right	K_c increases

Consider the reaction:

$$N_2O_4(g) \rightleftharpoons 2NO_2(g) \qquad \Delta H^{\ominus} = +57\,kJ\,mol^{-1}$$
colourless   brown

When an enthalpy value is quoted alongside an equilibrium equation like this, it refers to the forward reaction. So in this case the decomposition of N_2O_4 is endothermic. If an equilibrium mixture is set up in a sealed container at room temperature it will have a certain intensity of colour.

If the mixture is then placed in an ice bath (Figure 7.20a) its colour will lighten as a new equilibrium mixture containing more N_2O_4 is established. A decrease in temperature causes the equilibrium position to shift to the left. The value of K_c decreases as a result of these changes.

Alternatively, if the original mixture is placed in a hot water bath (Figure 7.20b), then the colour will darken as the new equilibrium mixture will contain more NO_2. An increase in temperature causes the equilibrium position to shift to the right. The value of K_c increases as a result of these changes (Table 7.7a).

a

b

■ **Figure 7.20** An equilibrium mixture of N_2O_4 and NO_2 in a sealed gas syringe is placed first in
a an ice bath and then
b in a hot water bath

	Temperature/K	K_c	
increased temperature	298	4.0×10^{-2}	increased K_c
	400	1.4	
	500	41	

■ **Table 7.7a** Data on the change in the equilibrium constant K_c for the **endothermic** reaction $N_2O_4(g) \rightleftharpoons 2NO_2(g)$ at different temperatures

	Temperature/K	K_c	
increased temperature	298	4.2×10^8	decreased K_c
	400	4.5×10^4	
	500	62	

■ **Table 7.7b** Data on the change in the equilibrium constant K_c for the **exothermic** reaction $N_2(g) + 3H_2(g) \rightleftharpoons 2NH_3(g)$ at different temperatures

It is important to note that, unlike changing the concentration or pressure, a change in temperature will also change the value of K_c. For endothermic reactions, an increase in temperature results in an increase in the concentration of products in the equilibrium mixture and therefore an increased K_c. The opposite will be true for exothermic reactions (see Table 7.7b).

In summary, for a chemical equilibrium:

- an increase in temperature always favours the endothermic process
- a decrease in temperature always favours the exothermic process.

Worked example

Draw up a table showing how the position of equilibrium in reactions A, B and C would be affected by the following changes:

a increased temperature

b increased pressure.

Reaction A: the interconversion of oxygen and ozone.

$$3O_2(g) \rightleftharpoons 2O_3(g) \qquad\qquad \Delta H^{\ominus} = +285 \,kJ\,mol^{-1}$$

Reaction B: the reaction between sulfur dioxide and oxygen in the presence of a platinum/rhodium catalyst.

$$2SO_2(g) + O_2(g) \rightleftharpoons 2SO_3(g) \qquad\qquad \Delta H^{\ominus} = -197 \,kJ\,mol^{-1}$$

Reaction C: the reaction between hydrogen and carbon dioxide.

$$H_2(g) + CO_2(g) \rightleftharpoons H_2O(g) + CO(g) \qquad \Delta H^{\ominus} = +41 \,kJ\,mol^{-1}$$

Using the applications of Le Châtelier's principle to create a table:

Reaction	Effect of increased temperature on equilibrium position	Effect of increased pressure on equilibrium position
Reaction A	Shift to the right – more ozone K_c increased	Fewer molecules on the right; therefore, shift to right – more O_3
Reaction B	Shift to the left – less SO_3 K_c decreased	Fewer molecules on the right; therefore, shift to right – more SO_3
Reaction C	Shift to the right – more CO K_c increased	No change as there are the same number of molecules on both sides

---

4 Using this reaction:

$$CH_3COOH(l) + C_2H_5OH(l) \rightleftharpoons CH_3COOC_2H_5(l) + H_2O(l)$$

explain what happens to the position of equilibrium when:
a more $CH_3COOC_2H_5(l)$ is added
b some $C_2H_5OH(l)$ is removed.

5 Using this reaction:

$$Ce^{4+}(aq) + Fe^{2+}(aq) \rightleftharpoons Ce^{3+}(aq) + Fe^{3+}(aq)$$

explain what happens to the position of equilibrium when:
a the concentration of $Fe^{2+}(aq)$ ions is increased
b water is added to the equilibrium mixture.

6 a Predict the effect on the position of equilibrium of increasing the pressure on the following gas phase reactions:
   i $N_2O_4(g) \rightleftharpoons 2NO_2(g)$
   ii $H_2(g) + I_2(g) \rightleftharpoons 2HI(g)$
   iii $CH_4(g) + H_2O(g) \rightleftharpoons CO(g) + 3H_2(g)$
   b Predict the effect on the position of equilibrium of decreasing the pressure on the reaction:

   $$2NO_2(g) \rightleftharpoons 2NO(g) + O_2(g)$$

7 Predict the effect on the position of equilibrium of increasing the temperature on these reactions:
a $CO_2(g) + 2H_2(g) \rightleftharpoons CH_3OH(g) \qquad \Delta H^{\ominus} = -90\,kJ\,mol^{-1}$
b $H_2(g) + CO_2(g) \rightleftharpoons H_2O(g) + CO(g) \qquad \Delta H^{\ominus} = +41.2\,kJ\,mol^{-1}$

■ The role of catalysts

A **catalyst** is a substance that increases the rate of a chemical reaction by providing an alternative reaction pathway of lower activation energy (E_a)(see Chapter 6). This means that more particles in a reaction mixture have sufficient kinetic energy on collision to react with each other. Industrially

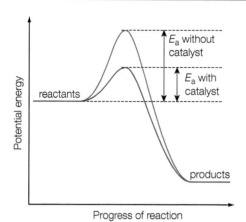

■ **Figure 7.21** Effect of a catalyst in lowering the activation energy for both forward and reverse reactions

catalysts are of significance, as they allow reactions to occur at reasonable rates under milder, and therefore more economic, conditions.

The presence of a catalyst has no effect on the position of a chemical equilibrium. Figure 7.21 shows how a catalyst lowers the activation energy of a reaction. However, the effect is applicable to the E_a values of both the forward and reverse reactions: both values are reduced by the same amount. Consequently the presence of a catalyst increases the rate of the forward and reverse reactions equally. There is no change in the position of the equilibrium or the value of K_c.

However, the advantage of using a catalyst is that its presence reduces the time required for the equilibrium to be established. This effect is demonstrated by the esterification reaction we discussed earlier.

$$CH_3CO_2H(l) + C_2H_5OH(l) \rightleftharpoons CH_3CO_2C_2H_5(l) + H_2O(l)$$
ethanoic acid   ethanol   ethyl ethanoate   water

The uncatalysed reaction takes many weeks to reach equilibrium. However, addition of hydrogen ions, H^+, as a catalyst reduces that time to a few hours.

---

8 The equilibrium constant for the acid hydrolysis of ethyl ethanoate can be found by experiment.

$$CH_3COOC_2H_5(l) + H_2O(l) \rightleftharpoons CH_3COOH(l) + C_2H_5OH(l)$$

A reaction mixture is set up in a sealed flasks and left for 48 hours at 25°C to reach equilibrium. Samples can then be taken from the flask and titrated with alkali to find the concentration of ethanoic acid present at equilibrium (Figure 7.22).

44.0 g of ethyl ethanoate was mixed with 36.0 g of water (acidified with a small amount of hydrochloric acid to act as a catalyst) and allowed to reach equilibrium. The equilibrium mixture was then made up to 250 cm³ with distilled water.

mixtures allowed to equilibrate in a water bath (25 °C)   a 25 cm³ sample is run into a flask containing ice and water   ethanoic acid in the reaction mixture is titrated with alkali

■ **Figure 7.22** Experimental procedure to find equilibrium constant

A 25 cm³ sample of the diluted mixture was titrated with 1.0 mol dm⁻³ sodium hydroxide solution. After allowing for the acid catalyst present, the ethanoic acid in the equilibrium mixture required 29.5 cm³ of alkali to neutralize it.

Find K_c for the reaction by working through the following stages of calculation.
a Calculate the number of moles of ethyl ethanoate and water mixed at the start of the reaction.
b Use the titration value to calculate the number of moles of ethanoic acid present at equilibrium.
c Complete the following table containing data on the changes taking place as the reaction reaches equilibrium.

	Ethyl ethanoate	Water	Ethanoic acid	Ethanol
At start /moles				
At equilibrium /moles				
At equilibrium* /mol dm⁻³				

*Assume that the volume of the reaction mixture is V dm³

d Write an expression for the equilibrium constant, K_c, and calculate its value using the data from the table.
e Why is it still necessary to account for the acid catalyst added at the start of the reaction when analysing the equilibrium mixture?
f Suggest a method by which you could take account of the acid catalyst added.
g Suggest a suitable indicator for the titration of the ethanoic acid produced with sodium hydroxide solution.

■ Equilibrium in industrial processes

The phenomena of reversible reactions and dynamic equilibria are widespread and relevant to many areas of chemistry. Consider, for instance, the whole field of acid–base chemistry (Chapters 8 and 18), where these ideas are crucial to our understanding of what an acid is, as well as to the use of indicators and buffers. In a similar way our conceptual grasp of electrochemistry is very much dependent on the interplay of reversible reactions (Chapter 19). We have commented earlier on how certain important industrial processes are dependent on some key reversible reactions. The ability to predict the effects of changes in physical conditions provided by Le Châtelier's principle is very useful indeed in establishing the best conditions to use for these processes. Such considerations help us to adapt conditions so as to maximize the yield of product. However, these are not the only considerations to be kept in mind. The rate at which a given yield is produced is also important economically, so the time taken to achieve a particular equilibrium is also of significance. Quite often these different considerations work in opposite directions and a compromise set of conditions is employed which gives an acceptable yield in an economically viable time.

The Haber process for ammonia manufacture

Important though nitrogen is for plant growth, most plants cannot 'fix' nitrogen directly from the air. Only certain plants, such as peas for example, can convert nitrogen directly into a usable chemical form because of *Rhizobium* bacteria present in their root nodules. To promote the growth of other crop plants, a nitrogen-containing compound has to be spread as a fertilizer. The important fertilizers include urea, $CO(NH_2)_2$, ammonium sulfate, $(NH_4)_2SO_4$, and ammonium dihydrogen phosphate(v), $NH_4H_2PO_4$. All of these involve the use of ammonia in their manufacture. Ammonia is also used to make nitric acid, some polymers (polyamides such as nylon) and explosives.

The chemical process that produces the ammonia gas can be represented by the following equation:

$$N_2(g) + 3H_2(g) \rightleftharpoons 2NH_3(g) \qquad \Delta H^{\ominus} = -92\,\text{kJ}\,\text{mol}^{-1}$$

Nitrogen gas, from the air, is mixed with hydrogen gas, obtained from the reaction of methane with steam (steam re-forming). The nitrogen and hydrogen are fed into the main reaction vessel in the ratio of $1:3$ by volume.

The production of cheap nitrogen and hydrogen gases in the correct ratio is an essential part of the whole process. Most ammonia plants use methane (as natural gas), air and water as starting materials (Figure 7.23). Following processing of the raw materials the final reaction mixture consists of nitrogen and hydrogen in a ratio of $1:3$. This mixture is then compressed and fed into the reaction vessel.

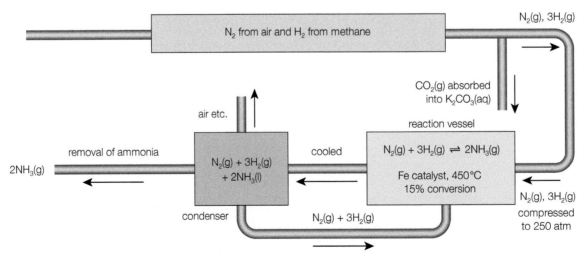

■ **Figure 7.23** Flow diagram showing the stages of the Haber process

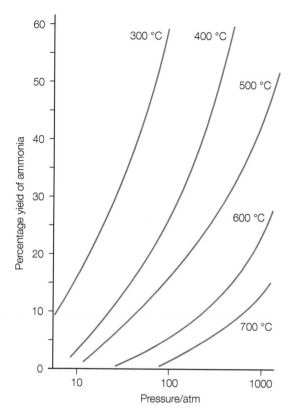

Figure 7.24 Equilibrium percentage yield of ammonia at different temperatures and pressures

The conditions used industrially in the main reaction vessel are arrived at by consideration of both Le Châtelier's principle and kinetic factors (Chapter 6). The aim is to achieve a satisfactory yield of ammonia at a reasonable and economic rate.

The application of Le Châtelier's principle to the reaction

$$N_2(g) + 3H_2(g) \rightleftharpoons 2NH_3(g) \qquad \Delta H^{\ominus} = -92\,kJ\,mol^{-1}$$

concludes that the highest yield of ammonia is obtained by using low temperatures and high pressures. This is shown in Figure 7.24.

In reality, for economic reasons, it is the rate at which equilibrium is achieved that proves the determining factor, rather than simply the percentage of ammonia present at equilibrium. Equilibrium is reached most quickly at relatively high temperatures, high pressures and in the presence of a catalyst. The reasons for these conditions are explained in turn below.

The choice of pressure

The Haber process is markedly affected by changes in pressure. If the pressure is increased then, in accordance with Le Châtelier's principle, the position of the equilibrium will shift to the right as there are fewer molecules on that side of the equation.

$$N_2(g) + 3H_2(g) \rightleftharpoons 2NH_3(g)$$

On the left-hand side of the equation there are four moles of gas, on the right-hand side there are two moles of gas. This means that higher pressures will move the position of the equilibrium to the right, producing more ammonia gas. This can be seen in Figure 7.24, which shows the percentage of ammonia in the equilibrium mixture at different pressures.

The use of higher pressures is also favoured for kinetic reasons, and most industrial plants operate at 200 or 250 atmospheres. Some plants do operate at pressures up to 1000 atmospheres but these very high pressures demand a large expenditure of energy for compression. More importantly, the very thick walls needed for the reaction vessels (special chromium steel is used) so that such pressures can be safely contained are very costly. The decision is one of balancing the high initial set-up costs against the eventual higher profits resulting from increased yield.

The choice of temperature

In the Haber process the forward reaction is exothermic ($\Delta H^{\ominus} = -92\,kJ\,mol^{-1}$). This means that the production of ammonia will be favoured by lower temperatures. Increased temperature will result in less ammonia in the equilibrium mixture (see Figure 7.24). By this consideration it would follow that the Haber process should be carried out at low temperatures.

Industrially, however, a temperature of 450 °C is actually used. Three reasons justify the use of this relatively high temperature:

■ Firstly, at low temperatures the reaction is very slow and would take a long time to reach equilibrium. Even the most efficient catalyst, working at high pressures, does not work fast enough to obtain a reasonable conversion at room temperature. A compromise temperature is used – one that gives a reasonable percentage conversion while achieving equilibrium at a fast enough rate.

■ The second reason is that the catalyst used for the reaction has an optimum operating temperature range (Figure 7.25a) and the process is generally carried out at the upper end of this range. The temperature sensitivity of the catalytic action relates to the mechanism by which the heterogeneous catalyst works. The catalysed reaction mechanism depends on the

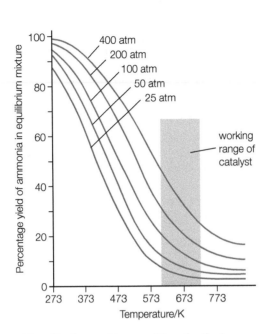

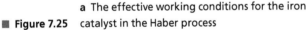

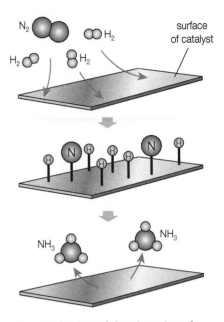

b The mechanism of chemisorption of nitrogen and hydrogen molecules, their dissociation into atoms and subsequent reaction on the iron surface of the catalyst in the Haber process

a The effective working conditions for the iron catalyst in the Haber process

■ **Figure 7.25**

nitrogen and hydrogen molecules adsorbing to the irregular metal surface. The attachment to the surface is by a process known as chemisorption, in which electron density is donated from nitrogen and hydrogen atoms into vacant d orbitals in the iron atoms (Figure 7.25b). This adsorption results in a weakening of the bonds in the nitrogen and hydrogen molecules; particularly significant in the case of the triple-bonded nitrogen molecules (N≡N). The weakening of the bonds in the reacting molecules means they can react more readily, and ammonia molecules are then formed on the metal surface. The final step of the catalytic sequence is desorption of the ammonia from the metal. The catalytic activity is critically dependent on the strength of the interactions involved in the adsorption of the gas molecules to the surface. These interactions must be strong enough for the molecules to attach to the metal, but weak enough to allow the subsequent release of the product molecules.

■ Thirdly, because ammonia is easily condensed out of the equilibrium mixture, the hydrogen and nitrogen are readily recycled. This means that a low yield is less of a concern as the unused reactants are not wasted.

Catalysts

The Haber process uses a catalyst of freshly produced, finely divided iron. This is obtained by reducing iron oxide (magnetite, iron(II,III) oxide, Fe_3O_4) with hydrogen. A catalyst is used in this process as it reduces the time needed to reach equilibrium.

The action of the iron catalyst is modified by the presence, in trace quantities, of a promoter. A promoter is a substance that improves the performance of the catalyst. In some Haber process plants traces of molybdenum are used as the promoter, while in others potassium or aluminium oxides or potassium hydroxide are used.

A typical industrial plant for the Haber process operates at 250 atmospheres pressure and 450 °C and produces an actual conversion to ammonia of about 15%. The ammonia can be removed by liquefaction, and then the unchanged gases are recycled through the converter. This recycling ensures the almost complete use of the nitrogen and hydrogen fed into the plant.

ToK Link

Fritz Haber – a controversial life in science

Fritz Haber (1868–1934), one of Germany's most famous chemists, is also one of the most complex figures to evaluate in the history of science (Figure 7.26). His life and career were inextricably linked with the political upheaval in Europe that led to two world wars. The moral and ethical issues that coloured that period of turmoil impacted on his life and the choices he personally made leave us with a highly equivocal view of his achievements. His was a life of personal striving, immense scientific achievement and personal tragedy.

He studied at several universities, receiving a PhD in Chemistry in 1891. After a few apparently aimless years working for his father and trying to progress in academic life, he gained a position as a lab assistant at the University of Karlsruhe in 1894. He then rose through the ranks to become a professor. He was passionately patriotic and this, together with career interests, led him to renounce Judaism and convert to Christianity.

■ **Figure 7.26** Fritz Haber (1868–1934)

Haber's scientific legacy is unquestionable. He devised a method for the direct synthesis of ammonia from nitrogen and hydrogen. His process used high pressure and temperature, together with an osmium catalyst. This method was then adapted for use with an iron catalyst by Carl Bosch (1874–1949), and the process was scaled up for industrial production. The achievement of industrial nitrogen fixation was crucial for the development of inexpensive fertilizers and revolutionized food production worldwide. Haber received the Nobel Prize in Chemistry in 1918 for his work on ammonia synthesis.

Even this seemingly beneficial contribution to scientific progress had a double edge. Continuing his research, Haber developed a process for converting ammonia into nitric acid. Nitric acid was then used as the basis for synthesizing a variety of insecticides and producing nitrate high explosives. The novel production of explosives significantly helped the German effort in the First World War (1914–18), enabling Germany to negate the effect of the Allied blockades of nitrates from Chile. Haber became increasingly involved in that national war effort; specifically in the military use of gases such as chlorine to subdue enemy troops in the trenches by the toxic effect of the gas (Figure 7.27). His idea seems to have been to use chlorine gas to temporarily incapacitate enemy soldiers and take them out of the war, not to maim or kill them. However, the effects of chlorine have been vividly portrayed in Wilfred Owens's poem 'Dulce et Decorum Est' written just prior to Owen's death on the battlefield in 1914.

GAS! GAS! Quick boys! – An ecstasy of fumbling,
Fitting the clumsy helmets just in time,
But someone still was yelling out and stumbling
And floundering like a man in fire or lime –
Dim through the misty panes and thick green light,
As under a green sea, I saw him drowning.
In all my dreams before my helpless sight
He plunges at me, guttering, choking, drowning.

Chlorine was soon supplanted by phosgene ($COCl_2$) and then by a far worse agent, mustard gas (bis[2-chloroethyl]sulfide). But Haber's involvement in chemical warfare was to have tragic personal consequences. His first wife, Clara, a research chemist in her own right, committed suicide at the height of Haber's connection with the war effort. She appears to have been pushed over the edge by Haber's decision to continue in the gas warfare programme.

■ **Figure 7.27** Trench warfare was fought in horrific conditions of endless shelling and physical deprivation

Haber lived for science, both for its own sake and also for its influence in shaping human life, culture and civilization. His talents were wide-ranging, and he possessed an astonishing knowledge of politics, history, economics, science and industry, meaning he might have succeeded equally well in other fields. He continued to work on a number of areas of chemistry after World War I, and developed friendships with other key scientific figures of the era; Einstein and Max Planck, for instance.

However, despite Haber's clear loyalty to his country, his Jewish ancestry was at odds with the rising tide of anti-semitism in Nazi Germany, making his presence in the country undesirable to the authorities. In 1933, he was forced to leave Germany, and he died of heart problems in Switzerland in 1934. Ironically and as a final tragic twist in this complex story, Zyklon B, a development from the hydrogen cyanide (HCN) insecticide

Haber had originally introduced, was used to kill prisoners in the Nazi concentration camps. Reportedly, among the victims were some of Haber's relatives.

Little has been written about Haber's life until recently; immediate and later generations had preferred to ignore his contradictory memory. When the papers relating to his life were made publicly available in the early 1990s, they served to show the triumphs, failings and tragedy of a man whose life bore out the contradictions of the time in which he lived. Haber was one of the greatest scientists of his generation and yet he has also been described as one of science's greatest scoundrels. His life, its impact and contradictions are recounted in the biography 'Between Genius and Genocide' by Daniel Charles (2005).

It is worth remembering that Haber was not alone in making scientific advances of military significance during his time. Gustav Hertz, James Franck and Otto Hahn, all important figures in the development of atomic and quantum theory, were members of Haber's research team working on chemical weapons. Many modern-day scientists are employed in companies involved in weapons and military equipment development. Science is not divorced from the economic and political pressures of the times.

Consideration of Haber's life raises difficult issues as to the nature of a scientist's responsibilities and the impact of science itself on human development. He was caught up in times of great social and political upheaval and driven by personal needs and ambitions. His work revolutionized agriculture and the ability to feed the expanding world population and yet it fuelled the destruction of life too.

The Contact process for the manufacture of sulfuric acid

Sulfuric acid (H_2SO_4) is the single most produced chemical worldwide and is now almost entirely produced by the Contact process. Some 150 million tonnes are manufactured globally each year, with the main uses being in the manufacture of the following:

- fertilizers
- paints and pigments
- detergents and soaps
- dyestuffs.

The Contact process consists of three stages (see Figure 7.28).

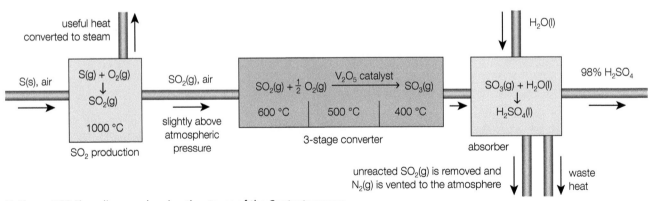

■ **Figure 7.28** Flow diagram showing the stages of the Contact process

Stage 1: In the first stage, sulfur is burnt in air at 1000 °C.

$$S(s) + O_2(g) \rightarrow SO_2(g)$$

Stage 2: The sulfur dioxide produced is then mixed with more air and passed over a vanadium(v) oxide (V_2O_5) catalyst at about 450 °C.

$$2SO_2(g) + O_2(g) \rightleftharpoons 2SO_3(g) \qquad \Delta H^{\ominus} = -197 \, \text{kJ mol}^{-1}$$

It is this key second stage (known as the Contact step) that is reversible and requires the consideration of kinetic and equilibrium ideas. To improve the yield of sulfur trioxide the equilibrium is displaced to the right by mixing the sulfur dioxide with an excess of air – about three times more than is necessary from the equation.

Le Châtelier's principle would suggest that the highest yield of sulfur trioxide would be obtained using high pressures and low temperatures. However, in practice a very low temperature cannot be used as the rate of achieving equilibrium would be so slow as to be uneconomic. Another factor here is that the vanadium(v) oxide catalyst only becomes effective at temperatures above 400 °C. To improve the percentage conversion, the reacting gases are passed through a sequence of four separate catalyst beds. The starting temperature of each bed is 450 °C, but the exothermic reaction raises the temperature by several hundred degrees each time. Therefore the gases are cooled back to 450 °C before passage to the next bed. This repetitive technique produces a 99.5% conversion of sulfur dioxide to sulfur trioxide.

Given this high rate of conversion it is unnecessary, in practice, to use a high pressure to increase the yield of sulfur trioxide, SO_3. The cost of using high pressures is uneconomic and a pressure of 1–2 atmospheres is used to ensure the gases circulate freely through the catalyst beds.

Stage 3: In the third stage the sulfur trioxide produced is dissolved in 98% sulfuric acid and then water is added. Carrying out the production of the acid solution in this way avoids the potentially violent and highly exothermic reaction that would occur if the gas were passed directly into water.

$$SO_3(g) + H_2SO_4(l) \rightarrow H_2S_2O_7(l)$$
$$\text{oleum}$$

$$H_2S_2O_7(l) + H_2O(l) \rightarrow 2H_2SO_4(aq)$$

■ *Examination questions – a selection*

Paper 1 IB questions and IB style questions

Q1 Which statements are correct for a reaction at equilibrium?
  I The forward and reverse reactions both continue.
  II The rates of the forward and reverse reactions are equal.
  III The concentrations of reactants and products are equal.
  A I and II only   **C** II and III only
  B I and III only   **D** I, II and III
  Standard Level Paper 1, May 2005, Q 21

Q2 Consider the following reaction:

  $2A \rightleftharpoons C$ $K_c = 1.1$

  Which statement is correct when the reaction is at equilibrium?
  A [A] >> [C]   **C** [A] = [C]
  B [A] > [C]   **D** [A] < [C]

Q3 Iron(III) ions, Fe^{3+}, react with thiocyanate ions, SCN^-, in a reversible reaction to form a red solution.

  Which changes to the equilibrium will make the solution go red?

  $Fe^{3+}(aq) + SCN^-(aq) \rightleftharpoons [FeSCN](aq)$ $\Delta H^\circ = +ve$
  Yellow   Red

  I Increasing the temperature
  II Adding $FeCl_3$
  III Adding a catalyst
  A I and II only   **C** II and III only
  B I and III only   **D** I, II and III
  Standard Level Paper 1, November 2012, Q 22

Q4 Hydrogen and iodine react in a closed vessel to form hydrogen iodide.

  $H_2(g) + I_2(g) \rightleftharpoons 2HI(g)$

  At 350°C $K_c = 60$ At 445°C $K_c = 47$

  Which statement describes and explains the conditions that favour the formation of hydrogen iodide?

  A Increased temperature as the forward reaction is exothermic, and increased pressure as there are two gaseous reactants and only one gaseous product.

  B Increased temperature as the forward reaction is endothermic, and pressure has no effect as there are equal amounts, in mol, of gaseous reactants and products.

  C Decreased temperature as the forward reaction is exothermic, and decreased pressure as there are two moles of gaseous product but only one mole of gaseous reactant.

  D Decreased temperature as the forward reaction is exothermic, and pressure has no effect as there are equal amounts, in mol, of gaseous reactants and product.
  Standard Level Paper 1, May 2013, Q 21

Q5 Which of the following is a correct statement for the effect of a catalyst on a reversible chemical reaction?
  A It increases the amount of product.
  B It increases the activation energy of the reaction.
  C It allows the chemical reaction to reach equilibrium more quickly.
  D It only increases the rate of the forward reaction.

Q6 What changes occur when the temperature is increased in the following reaction at equilibrium?

$$Br_2(g) + Cl_2(g) \rightleftharpoons 2BrCl(g) \quad \Delta H^\oplus = +14 \, kJ \, mol^{-1}$$

	Position of equilibrium	Value of equilibrium constant
A	Shifts towards the products	Decreases
B	Shifts towards the reactants	Decreases
C	Shifts towards the reactants	Increases
D	Shifts towards the products	Increases

Q7 For a gaseous reaction, the equilibrium constant expression is:

$$K_c = \frac{[O_2]^5[NH_3]^4}{[NO]^4[H_2O]^6}$$

Which equation corresponds to this equilibrium expression?
  A $4NH_3 + 5O_2 \rightleftharpoons 4NO + 6H_2O$
  B $4NO + 6H_2O \rightleftharpoons 4NH_3 + 5O_2$
  C $8NH_3 + 10O_2 \rightleftharpoons 8NO + 12H_2O$
  D $2NO + 3H_2O \rightleftharpoons 2NH_3 + O_2$

Standard Level Paper 1, May 2002, Q21

Q8 Which of the following changes will shift the position of equilibrium of this reaction in the forward direction?

$$N_2(g) + O_2(g) \rightleftharpoons 2NO(g) \quad \Delta H^\oplus = +181 \, kJ \, mol^{-1}$$

  I increasing the pressure
  II adding a catalyst
  III increasing the temperature
  A I only   **C** III only
  B II only   **D** I and III

Standard Level Paper 1, Nov 2001, Q21

Q9 $2H_2(g) + CO(g) \rightleftharpoons CH_3OH(g)$

Methanol is made in industry by means of the reaction above. The equilibrium expression for this reaction is:

  A $K_c = \dfrac{[CH_3OH]}{2[H_2][CO]}$ **C** $K_c = \dfrac{2[H_2][CO]}{[CH_3OH]}$

  B $K_c = \dfrac{[CH_3OH]}{[H_2]^2[CO]}$ **D** $K_c = \dfrac{[H_2]^2[CO]}{[CH_3OH]}$

Q10 $N_2(g) + 3H_2(g) \rightleftharpoons 2NH_3(g) \quad \Delta H^\oplus = -91.8 \, kJ \, mol^{-1}$

The industrial synthesis of ammonia is based on the reaction above. Which factor(s) will increase the equilibrium concentration of ammonia?
  I increase in pressure
  II increase in temperature
  A I only   **C** neither I nor II
  B both I and II   **D** II only

Q11 N_2O_4 and NO_2 produce an equilibrium mixture according to the equation below:

$$N_2O_4(g) \rightleftharpoons 2NO_2(g) \quad \Delta H^\oplus = +57 \, kJ \, mol^{-1}$$

An increase in the equilibrium concentration of NO_2 can be produced by increasing which of the factors below?
  I pressure
  II temperature
  A neither I nor II   **C** I only
  B both I and II   **D** II only

Q12 The hydration of ethene to ethanol occurs according to the following equation:

$$C_2H_4(g) + H_2O(g) \rightleftharpoons C_2H_5OH(g)$$

If this reaction is exothermic, which of the following sets of conditions would give the best equilibrium yield of ethanol?

	Temperature/°C	Pressure/atm
A	1000	3
B	750	2
C	250	10
D	500	4

Q13 The smaller an equilibrium constant, K_c:
  A the slower the reaction rate
  B the lower the concentration of products at equilibrium
  C the more endothermic the reaction
  D the faster the reactants are converted to products

Paper 2 IB questions and IB style questions

Q1 Chemical equilibrium and kinetics are important concepts in chemistry.
  a A glass container is half-filled with liquid bromine and then sealed. The system eventually reaches a dynamic equilibrium. State one characteristic of a system in equilibrium. [1]
  b The oxidation of sulfur dioxide is an important reaction in the Contact process used to manufacture sulfuric acid.

$$2SO_2(g) + O_2(g) \rightleftharpoons 2SO_3(g) \quad \Delta H = -198.2 \, kJ$$

i Deduce the equilibrium constant expression, K_c [1]

ii Predict how each of the following changes affects the position of equilibrium and the value of K_c. [3]

	Position of equilibrium	Value of K_c
Decrease in temperature		
Increase in temperature		
Addition of catalyst		

c Vanadium(v) oxide, V_2O_5, is a catalyst that can be used in the Contact process. It provides an alternative pathway for the reaction, lowering the activation energy, E_a.

i Define the term *activation energy, E_a*.

ii Sketch the two Maxwell–Boltzmann energy distribution curves for a fixed amount of gas at two different temperatures T_1 and T_2 ($T_2 > T_1$). Label both axes. [3]

Standard Level Paper 2, November 2012, Q3

Q2 For the reversible reaction:

$$H_2(g) + I_2(g) \rightleftharpoons 2HI(g) \qquad \Delta H^{\ominus} > 0$$

the equilibrium constant $K_c = 60$ at a particular temperature.

a Give the equilibrium expression. [1]

b For this reaction, what information does the value of K_c provide about the **relative** concentrations of the product and reactants at equilibrium? [1]

c What effect, if any, will an increase in pressure have on the **equilibrium position**? [1]

d Explain why an increase in temperature increases the value of the **equilibrium constant** for the above reaction. [1]

Q3 a The following equilibrium is established at 1700 °C.

$$CO_2(g) + H_2(g) \rightleftharpoons H_2O(g) + CO(g)$$

If only carbon dioxide gas and hydrogen gas are present initially, sketch on a graph a line representing rate against time for **i** the forward reaction *and* **ii** the reverse reaction until shortly after equilibrium is established. Explain the shape of each line. [7]

b K_c for the equilibrium reaction is determined at two different temperatures. At 850 °C, $K_c = 1.1$ whereas at 1700 °C, $K_c = 4.9$. On the basis of these K_c values explain whether the reaction is exothermic or endothermic. [3]

Q4 The table below gives information about the percentage yield of ammonia obtained in the Haber process under different conditions.

Pressure/atm	Temperature/°C			
	200	**300**	**400**	**500**
10	50.7	14.7	3.9	1.2
100	81.7	52.5	25.2	10.6
200	89.1	66.7	38.8	18.3
300	89.9	71.1	47.1	24.4
400	94.6	79.7	55.4	31.9
600	95.4	84.2	65.2	42.3

a From the table, identify which combination of temperature and pressure gives the highest yield of ammonia. [2]

b The equation for the main reaction in the Haber process is:

$$N_2(g) + 3H_2(g) \rightleftharpoons 2NH_3(g) \quad \Delta H^{\ominus} \text{ is negative}$$

Use this information to state and explain the effect on the yield of ammonia of increasing

i pressure [2]

ii temperature. [2]

c In practice, typical conditions used in the Haber process are a temperature of 500 °C and a pressure of 200 atmospheres. Explain why these conditions are used rather than those that give the highest yield. [2]

d Write the equilibrium constant expression, K_c, for the production of ammonia. [1]

e i Suggest why this reaction is important for humanity. [1]

ii A chemist claims to have developed a new catalyst for the Haber process, which increases the yield of ammonia. State the catalyst normally used for the Haber process, and comment on the claim made by this chemist. [2]

8 Acids and bases

ESSENTIAL IDEAS

- Many reactions involve the transfer of a proton from an acid to a base.
- The characterization of an acid depends on empirical evidence such as the production of gases in reactions with metals, the colour changes of indicators or the release of heat in reactions with metal oxides and hydroxides.
- The pH scale is an artificial scale used to distinguish between acid, neutral and basic/alkaline solutions.
- The pH depends on the concentration of the solution. The strength of acids or bases depends on the extent to which they dissociate in aqueous solution.
- Increased industrialization has led to greater production of nitrogen and sulfur oxides leading to acid rain, which is damaging our environment. These problems can be reduced through collaboration with national and intergovernmental organizations.

8.1 Theories of acids and bases – *many reactions involve the transfer of a proton from an acid to a base*

■ Brønsted–Lowry theory

The Brønsted–Lowry theory of acids and bases involves the transfer of protons or hydrogen ions within an aqueous solution. An acid is defined as a molecule or ion that acts as a proton donor and a base is defined as a molecule or ion that acts as a proton acceptor. For example, when hydrogen chloride gas is dissolved in water it reacts to form hydrochloric acid. The following equilibrium is established:

$$HCl(g) + H_2O(l) \rightleftharpoons H_3O^+(aq) + Cl^-(aq)$$

In the forward reaction (left to right) the hydrogen chloride molecule is acting as an acid because it donates a proton or hydrogen ion, H^+, to the water molecule, which is acting as a base since it forms an oxonium or hydronium ion, $H_3O^+(aq)$.

In the reverse or backward reaction (right to left) the hydronium or oxonium ion acts as an acid by donating a hydrogen ion to the chloride ion to form hydrogen chloride. The chloride ion is acting as a base. The equation above can be split into two 'half–equations' which more clearly show the proton transfer:

$$\underset{\text{acid}}{HCl(aq)} \rightleftharpoons \underset{\text{conjugate base}}{Cl^-(aq)} + H^+(aq)$$

This reaction shows that when a species loses a proton, the product has to be a base since the process is reversible (to a varying degree depending on the acid). The chloride ion is described as the conjugate base of the hydrogen chloride molecule.

$$\underset{\text{base}}{H_2O(l)} + H^+(aq) \rightleftharpoons \underset{\text{conjugate acid}}{H_3O^+(aq)}$$

This reaction shows that when a species gains a proton, the product has to be an acid since the process is reversible. The hydronium or oxonium ion is described as the conjugate acid of the water molecule. An acid–base reaction always involves (at least) two conjugate pairs that differ by H^+.

Brønsted–Lowry theory can also be applied to the behaviour of bases in aqueous solution. For example, when ammonia gas is dissolved in water the following chemical equilibrium is established:

$$\underset{\text{base}}{NH_3(g)} + \underset{\text{acid}}{H_2O(l)} \rightleftharpoons \underset{\text{conjugate acid}}{NH_4^+(aq)} + \underset{\text{conjugate base}}{OH^-(aq)}$$

The ammonia is acting as a base by accepting a proton from the water. Water is acting as an acid here, in contrast to its behaviour with acids, when it acts as a base. Species that are able to act as both acids and bases (proton donors and proton acceptors), depending on the species they are reacting with, are termed amphiprotic.

Deducing the Brønsted–Lowry acid and base in a chemical reaction

Chloric(vii) acid, $HClO_4$, acts a monoprotic acid in water. Write an equation showing its dissociation or ionization in water. Identify the Brønsted–Lowry acid and base. Explain your answer.

$$HClO_4(aq) + H_2O(l) \rightleftharpoons H_3O^+(aq) + ClO_4^-(aq)$$

$HClO_4$ is the acid (proton donor) because in the forward reaction it has lost its proton (H^+) and formed the chlorate(vii) ion, ClO_4^-. H_2O is the base (proton acceptor) because in the forward reaction it has gained a proton (H^+) and formed the oxonium ion, H_3O^+.

Phenylamine, C_6H_5–NH_2, is monoacidic. It reacts with only one molecule of a monobasic (monoprotic acid). Write an equation showing its dissociation or ionization in water. Identify the Brønsted–Lowry acid and base. Explain your answer.

$$C_6H_5NH_2(aq) + H_2O(l) \rightleftharpoons OH^-(aq) + C_6H_5NH_3^+(aq)$$

The phenylamine molecule is the base (proton acceptor) because in the forward reaction it has accepted a proton (H^+) and formed $C_6H_5NH_3^+$. H_2O is the acid (proton donor) because in the forward reaction it has lost a proton (H^+) and formed the hydroxide ion, OH^-.

---

1   Identify the Brønsted–Lowry acids and bases in the following reactions:
   a $NaH + H_2O \rightleftharpoons NaOH + H_2$
   b $H_2O + HCO_3^- \rightleftharpoons CO_3^{2-} + H_3O^+$
   c $H_2NCONH_2 + H_2O \rightleftharpoons H_3N^+CONH_2 + OH^-$
   d $HSO_4^- + H_3O^+ \rightleftharpoons H_2SO_4 + H_2O$
   e $NH_4^+ + OH^- \rightleftharpoons NH_3 + H_2O$

■ Amphiprotic species

The term amphiprotic means the substance can both donate and accept a proton (H^+), while amphoteric is a more general term meaning the substance can act as both an acid and a base.

Water molecules (H_2O) can be considered to be both amphoteric and amphiprotic:

$$H_2O(l) + H^+(aq) \rightleftharpoons H_3O^+(aq) \quad \text{water acting as a Brønsted–Lowry base}$$
$$H_2O(l) \rightleftharpoons H^+(aq) + OH^-(aq) \quad \text{water acting as Brønsted–Lowry acid}$$

In these equations we see that water can gain a proton while acting as a base, and lose a proton while acting as an acid. Therefore all amphiprotic substances are amphoteric, because when they donate a proton they are acting as an acid, and when they accept a proton they are acting as a base.

Amino acids are good examples of amphiprotic species. For example, the simplest amino acid glycine, H_2N–CH_2–$COOH$ has two functional groups. The amine group, –NH_2, is basic due to the presence of a lone pair of electrons on the nitrogen atom and the carboxylic acid group is acidic due to the presence of an acidic or ionizable hydrogen atom. In solution and in the solid state there is an internal acid–base transfer of a proton from the carboxylic acid group to the amine group. A dipolar ion or zwitterion is formed: H_3N^+–CH_2–COO^-.

However, not all amphoteric substances are amphiprotic, because only Brønsted–Lowry acids and bases accept and donate protons. If we also consider Lewis acids and bases, these either accept or donate electron lone pairs, which means that a substance that has more than one mechanism of action could show both types of acidity or basicity. For example, a metal oxide such as $Mg(OH)_2$, when placed in water can dissociate to release hydroxide ions:

$$Mg(OH)_2(aq) \rightleftharpoons Mg^{2+}(aq) + 2OH^-(aq)$$

This partial dissociation or ionization makes it a Brønsted–Lowry base, but the magnesium ion, Mg^{2+}, can also have water molecules coordinate to it with a lone pair, via dative bond formation which makes it a Lewis acid (electron pair acceptor):

$$Mg^{2+}(s) + {}_xH_2O(l) \rightarrow [Mg(H_2O)]^{2+}(aq)$$

The distinction between amphoteric and amphiprotic will be clearer after reading Chapter 18. Lewis theory is a more general acid–base theory that includes all Brønsted–Lowry acids and bases.

Nature of Science

Obtaining evidence for theories – observable properties of acids and bases have led to the modification of acid–base theories

It has been known for many hundreds of years that aqueous solutions of acids have a sour taste and react with a wide variety of substances, such as metal oxides and the more reactive metals such as iron. Similarly, bases were known to react with acids and solutions of alkalis to have a soapy feel and bitter taste. The first explanation to account for the common properties of acids was Lavoisier's idea that acids contained oxygen. Many common acids are oxoacids but this idea was falsified by the identification of acids such as hydrochloric acid and hydrocyanic acid, HCN. In 1830 the German chemist Justus von Liebig suggested that acids are hydrogen-containing compounds in which the hydrogen may be replaced by metals. Later studies of acids found that their solutions were excellent electrical conductors, which suggested that acidic solutions contained ions. This is a common property shared with salts. Acids, bases and salts are grouped together into a category called electrolytes, meaning that an aqueous solution of the given substance will conduct an electric current. However, there is considerable spectroscopic evidence to show that the active ion present in an acidic solution is not a proton (H^+) but the oxonium ion, H_3O^+ (a protonated water molecule). In fact the H_3O^+ ion can form hydrogen bonds with three water molecules to form $H_9O_4^+$.

Nature of Science

Falsification of theories and theories being superseded

The first theory of acidity came from the Ancient Greeks who defined sour-tasting substances as acids. Acid substances were eventually found not only to taste sour, but also to change the colour of litmus paper and corrode metals. In contrast, bases were typically defined and studied by their ability to counteract acids – and thus followed behind the acids in their chemical characterization.

Antoine Lavoisier (Chapter 1), the father of modern chemistry, suggested that acids were substances containing oxygen. Claude Berthollet (1748–1822) proved in 1787 that 'prussic acid' (hydrocyanic acid, HCN) contained only hydrogen, carbon and nitrogen. Sir Humphry Davy (1778–1829) was an English chemist who discovered several group 1 and 2 metals. He suggested that all acids contained hydrogen as the essential element. In 1838 the German chemist Justus von Liebig (1803–1873) (Figure 8.1) proposed that acids were substances that can react with metals to produce hydrogen.

The Arrhenius theory was the first scientific theory of acidity: acids provided hydrogen ions, $H^+(aq)$, in an aqueous solution (as the only cations) and bases provided hydroxide ions, $OH^-(aq)$ in aqueous solution (as the only anions). One of the problems with the Arrhenius theory is that it is rather restrictive since many reactions are carried out in solvents other than water or in the gas phase in the absence of solvent. These non-aqueous solvents include liquid ammonia and liquid sulfur dioxide.

The Brønsted–Lowry definition of acids and bases broadened the definition of acids and bases. Acids are proton donors and bases are proton acceptors. This is in agreement with Arrhenius theory but includes reactions such as that between ammonia and hydrogen chloride gases:

$$NH_3(g) + HCl(g) \rightleftharpoons NH_4Cl(s)$$

where water is not involved. It also includes the reaction between hydrogen chloride and ammonia molecules in liquid ammonia:

$$HCl(solv) + NH_3(solv) \rightleftharpoons NH_4Cl(solv)$$

where (solv) refers to salvation by ammonia molecules.

■ **Figure 8.1**
Justus von Liebig

Johannes Brønsted (Figure 8.2) (1879–1947) was a Danish physical chemist. Following a degree in chemical engineering he was appointed as professor of inorganic and physical chemistry at Copenhagen University. In 1923 he introduced his proton-based theory of acid-base reactions (Figure 8.3). The English chemist Thomas Lowry (see Figure 8.2) (1874–1936) published an identical theory in the same year, both realizing that water had an active role in acidity.

■ **Figure 8.2** Johannes Brønsted (left) and Thomas Lowry (right)

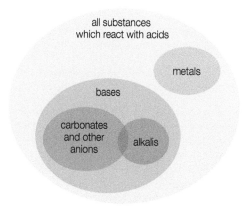

■ **Figure 8.3** Venn diagram showing the Brønsted–Lowry classification of chemicals which react with acids

The American chemist Gilbert Lewis was a very influential chemist who developed our ideas about covalent bonding and introduced dot-and-cross diagrams (Lewis diagrams or structures) (Chapter 4). He decided that an even more general theory of acids and bases was useful. In 1923 he proposed that acids are electron pair acceptors and bases are electron pair donors. Lewis theory can be applied to a wide range of organic and inorganic reactions that are not classified as Brønsted–Lowry or Arrhenius acid–base reactions. These types of reactions involve the donation and sharing of an electron pair from the Lewis base and its interaction with an empty orbital on the Lewis acid (Chapter 18).

■ Conjugate acid–base pairs

A conjugate acid is the molecule or ion formed when a proton is added to a base. A conjugate base is the species formed when a proton is removed from an acid. A pair of species differing by a single proton is called a conjugate acid–base pair. The word conjugate means 'joined together as a pair'.

For example, in the dissociation or ionization of nitric acid, the nitrate(v) ion, NO_3^- (aq), is the conjugate base of nitric acid, while the oxonium ion, H_3O^+, is the conjugate acid of water which acts as the base. Nitric(v) acid and nitrate(v) ions are a conjugate acid–base pair and water and oxonium ions form another conjugate acid–base pair (Figure 8.4).

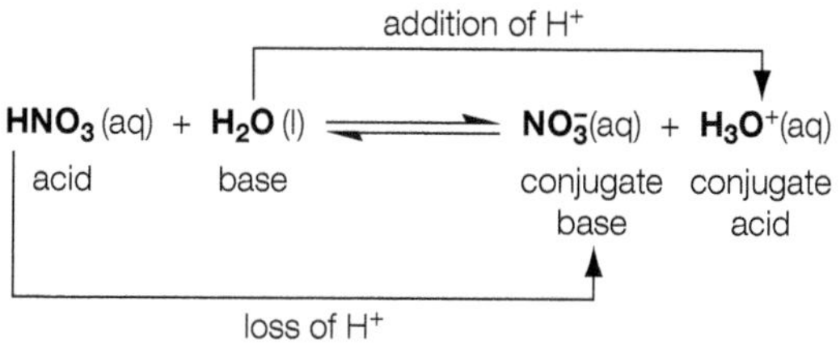

$$\text{addition of H}^+$$
$$\mathbf{HNO_3}\,(aq) + \mathbf{H_2O}\,(l) \rightleftharpoons \mathbf{NO_3^-}(aq) + \mathbf{H_3O^+}(aq)$$
acid · · · · · · base · · · · · · · · · · · · · · conjugate · · · conjugate
· base · · · · · · · acid
$$\text{loss of H}^+$$

■ **Figure 8.4** Equilibrium reaction between nitric acid and water

Similarly, in the dissociation or ionization of phenylamine $C_6H_5NH_2$, the phenylammonium ion $(C_6H_5NH_3)^+$(aq), is the conjugate acid of phenylamine, while the hydroxide ion, OH^-, is the conjugate base of water that acts as the acid. Phenylamine and phenylammonium ions are a conjugate acid–base pair and water and hydroxide ions form another conjugate acid–base pair (Figure 8.5).

■ **Figure 8.5** Equilibrium reaction between phenylamine and water

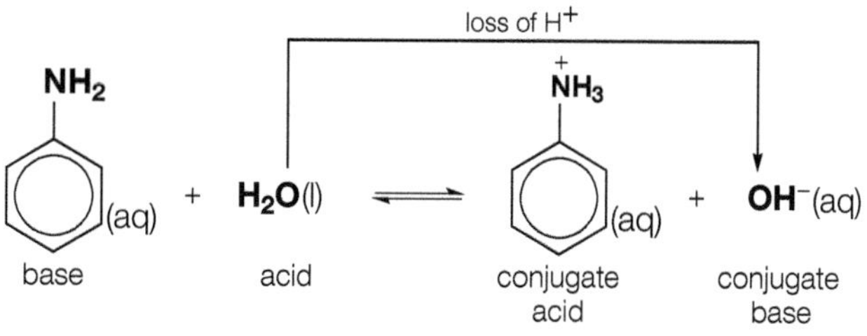

$$\text{loss of H}^+$$

NH₂ + **H₂O**(l) ⇌ **⁺NH₃** + **OH⁻**(aq)
(aq)

base · · · · · · acid · · · · · · · · conjugate · · · · conjugate
· acid · · · · · · · · · base

Deducing the conjugate base or conjugate acid in a chemical reaction

In pure ethanol, C_2H_5OH, the following equilibrium can exist with ammonium ions:

$$NH_4^+(solv) + C_2H_5OH(l) \rightleftharpoons NH_3(solv) + C_2H_5OH_2^+(solv)$$

where (solv) indicates the ions are surrounded by ethanol molecules. Identify the conjugate acid and base in this reaction. Explain your answer.

A conjugate acid is located on the right-hand side of the equilibrium and acts as an acid (proton donor). $C_2H_5OH_2^+(solv)$ is a conjugate acid because in the backward reaction it loses a proton (H^+) and forms $C_2H_5OH(l)$. $NH_3(solv)$ is a conjugate base because in the backward reaction it gains a proton to form $NH_4^+(solv)$.

---

2 Identify the conjugate acid and base in the following reactions:
  a $CO_3^{2-}(aq) + H_2O(l) \rightleftharpoons HCO_3^-(aq) + OH^-(aq)$
  b $2H_2SO_4(aq) + 2H_2O(l) \rightleftharpoons 2H_3O^+(aq) + SO_4^{2-}(aq)$

Nature of Science

Public understanding of science

The term litmus test is understood to mean a test in which a single factor (as an attitude, event, or fact) is decisive. For example, a political party may be using attitudes about gun control as a *litmus test* for political candidates. Those candidates who support gun control will be selected; those who do not support gun control will not be selected by the party. When litmus is placed into an acidic solution it will turn red and when placed into an alkaline solution it will turn blue. There are only two possibilities.

The term acid test is defined as a rigorous and conclusive test to establish worth or value. This is derived from the testing of gold with nitric acid. Testing for gold with acid focuses around the fact that gold is noble or unreactive, that is resistant to change by corrosion, oxidation or dilute acid. The acid test for gold is to rub the gold-coloured item on black stone, which will leave an easily visible mark. The mark is tested by applying *aqua fortis* (concentrated nitric acid), which dissolves the mark of any item that is not gold. If the mark remains, it is tested by applying *aqua regia* (a mixture of concentrated nitric acid and hydrochloric acid). If the mark is removed, then this test dissolved the gold, proving the item to be genuine gold.

■ The vocabulary of acid–base theory

In ancient times, the Egyptians and Greeks defined certain substances based upon their taste. Both the Greeks and the Egyptians had discovered that one particular substance was very sour. This became to be known as vinegar (a solution of ethanoic acid), which was produced from the fermentation of fruits to produce wine. Therefore, a new categorization of substances was developed that included all things that were sour. The word Greek word *acidus* means sour in Latin. *Oxygene* means acid–forming in Greek, reflecting the mistaken belief that the element was responsible for a compound's acidic properties. A large number of acids, for example, sulfuric, nitric and organic acids, do contain oxygen but it is not responsible for the characteristic properties of acids in aqueous solutions.

The Greeks were also familiar with a different category of substances. They found three slippery substances left behind as residue after burning certain materials. These three substances were potash, soda and lime. Potash (potassium carbonate), which must have been the first to be discovered, was produced from wood ashes. When water from some locations was allowed to evaporate, the film left behind was soda (sodium carbonate). Lime (calcium oxide) was produced from burning seashells (calcium carbonate). Ultimately, the Greeks discovered a new category to define substances (later known as alkalis) based upon the property of feeling slippery.

In 1386, to build on the Greeks' definition of sour or slippery, a new terminology was developed to speak about things that felt slippery. From the Arabic word *al-qaliy*, which means 'the ashes' the term alkali was developed. This word was then used to speak about substances that felt slippery. Acid–base theory has been developed by scientists from around the world, and its vocabulary has been influenced by their languages.

ToK Link

Acid and base behaviour can be explained using different theories. How are the explanations in chemistry different from explanations in other subjects such as history?

Scientific explanations are empirical, meaning they must be based on empirical observations and data (based on the senses) or experiments (or at the very least, be directly inferred when direct observation cannot be achieved).

Scientific explanations (theories, hypotheses, models and even scientific laws) are tentative. This means that all scientific knowledge can be potentially falsified. Scientific explanations are testable by experiment and there will be a possible outcome that does not support the proposed theory. In other words, a scientific theory must be potentially falsifiable. There is always a chance that the scientific theory is wrong, no matter how much supporting data there is for the theory.

Scientific explanations are parsimonious, meaning that if there are two or more competing theories that explain the data, the simplest one is usually correct (Occam's razor). Scientific explanations assume causality (i.e. for every cause there is an effect, and cause comes before the effect).

Historical explanations aim at understanding the unfolding of past events through the use of historiography (primary and secondary sources). There are some similarities between scientific and historical explanations. For example, empirical data are used in both explanations of events.

A historical explanation is the explanation of certain events which have taken place. A historical explanation, in general terms, is the explanation of a circumstance in the context of history. Historical explanations give causes of outcomes in particular cases. They are empirical, but can be altered. These explanations are limited to the past. History, like science, can be falsified based on evidence.

There are no general laws in history and historians are often wary about making predictions of future historical events. Yet few would dispute that an understanding of the past gives a better understanding of the present state of the world.

Science and history both assume that objectivity is a necessary component of any scientific or historical data (primary and secondary sources), which should be published and made public. However, it is often institutions and not individual historians that 'control' history. History is written and passed down by the winners of conflicts and by the elites of societies.

However, science is claimed to have universality: the laws of physics apply equally to all cultural groups. However, a person's understanding of history is going to be influenced, if not controlled, by their cultural background. All history is a version, and that is inevitable and unavoidable. However, science itself is acknowledged to be a historical and culturally conditioned process.

E.H. Carr (author of 'What is History?') wrote, *'But the concept of absolute truth is also not appropriate to the world of history, or, I suspect, to the world of science. It is the only the simplest kind of historical statement that can be adjudged true or absolutely false'.*

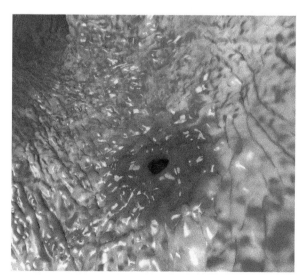

■ **Figure 8.6** Stomach ulcer

Utilization: Weak bases

The stomach secretes hydrochloric acid to help digest protein and kill harmful bacteria. The hydrochloric acid concentration is approximately $0.1 \, \text{mol} \, \text{dm}^{-3}$ HCl or $0.1 \, \text{mol} \, \text{dm}^{-3}$ H^+. The stomach is protected from the corrosive action of hydrochloric acid by a mucosal lining protected by a layer of mucus. Holes can develop in this lining allowing the hydrochloric acid to attack the underlying delicate tissue, causing painful damage. These holes, known as stomach ulcers (Figure 8.6), can be caused by the secretion of excess hydrochloric acid, or by a weakness in the digestive lining.

Recent studies have shown that many ulcers are caused by a specific species of bacteria (*Helicobacter pylori*). The problem of excess acid can be solved in two ways: removing the excess acid or deceasing production of acid. Substances that remove excess acid via neutralization are known as antacids. They are solids containing hydroxide, carbonate or hydrogencarbonate ions. Medicinal drugs that decrease acid production are known as acid-inhibitors, for example, Tagamet and Zantac.

8.2 Properties of acids and bases – the characterization of an acid depends on empirical evidence such as the production of gases in reactions with metals, the colour changes of the indicators or the release of heat in reactions with metal oxides and hydroxides

■ Properties of acids and bases

Acids

Common acids found in the laboratory include ethanoic acid, $CH_3COOH(aq)$, sulfuric acid, $H_2SO_4(aq)$, hydrochloric acid, $HCl(aq)$, and nitric acid, $HNO_3(aq)$. Acids are a group of compounds that exhibit the following properties when dissolved in water to form a dilute solution.

pH

Acids have a pH value less than 7 and turn the indicator blue litmus paper red. The pH value is a measure of the acidity of the solution, and indicators (Figure 8.7) are dyes that change colour according to the pH of the solution.

■ **Figure 8.7**
Blue and red litmus paper

Conductivity

Acids are electrolytes (Chapter 9), meaning they undergo chemical decomposition when an electric current is passed through their aqueous solutions.

Reaction with metals

Most dilute acids react to give hydrogen gas (Figure 8.8) and a solution of a salt when a reactive metal (Chapter 9) such as magnesium, iron or zinc is added.

■ **Figure 8.8**
Apparatus for collecting the hydrogen produced by the reaction of zinc and hydrochloric acid

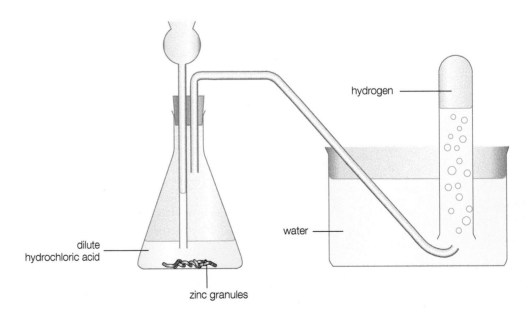

hydrogen

water

dilute hydrochloric acid

zinc granules

For example:
$$Mg(s) + 2HCl(aq) \rightarrow MgCl_2(aq) + H_2(g)$$
$$Mg(s) + 2HNO_3(aq) \rightarrow Mg(NO_3)_2(aq) + H_2(g)$$
$$Mg(s) + H_2SO_4(aq) \rightarrow MgSO_4(aq) + H_2(g)$$
$$Mg(s) + 2CH_3COOH(aq) \rightarrow (CH_3COO)_2Mg(aq) + H_2(g)$$

or, ionically, $\quad Mg(s) + 2H^+(aq) \rightarrow Mg^{2+}(aq) + H_2(g)$

In general,

reactive metal + dilute acid → salt + hydrogen

The more unreactive metals, for example copper and lead, do *not* react with dilute acids (Chapter 9).

Reaction with metal carbonates

Dilute acids react to give carbon dioxide gas when a metal carbonate or metal hydrogencarbonate is added (Figure 8.9). For example:

$$CaCO_3(s) + 2HCl(aq) \rightarrow CaCl_2(aq) + H_2O(l) + CO_2(g)$$
$$NaHCO_3(s) + HCl(aq) \rightarrow NaCl(aq) + H_2O(l) + CO_2(g)$$

■ **Figure 8.9**
The reaction between calcium carbonate and dilute hydrochloric acid

or ionically,

$$CO_3{}^{2-}(aq) + 2H^+(aq) \rightarrow H_2O(l) + CO_2(g)$$
$$HCO_3{}^-(aq) + H^+(aq) \rightarrow H_2O(l) + CO_2(g)$$

In general,

metal carbonate or metal hydrogencarbonate + dilute acid → salt + water + carbon dioxide

The reaction between calcium carbonate and dilute sulfuric acid is *slow* because an almost insoluble layer of calcium sulfate, $CaSO_4$, protects the calcium carbonate from further attack by the acid.

The presence of carbon dioxide can be confirmed by bubbling the gas through limewater (a solution of calcium hydroxide). The solution initially turns cloudy, but then clears if excess carbon dioxide is passed through the limewater:

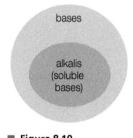

bases

alkalis (soluble bases)

■ **Figure 8.10**
The relationship between alkalis and bases

$$CO_2(g) + Ca(OH)_2(aq) \rightarrow CaCO_3(s) + H_2O(l)$$
$$CaCO_3(s) + H_2O(l) + CO_2(g) \rightarrow Ca(HCO_3)_2(aq)$$

Reaction with bases

Bases include metal oxides, metal hydroxides and aqueous ammonia. A base is a substance that reacts with an acid to form a salt and water *only*. This reaction is known as a neutralization.

Alkalis are bases which are soluble in water (Figure 8.10). They include the group 1 hydroxides, barium hydroxide and aqueous ammonia, $NH_3(aq)$, sometimes called 'ammonium hydroxide', $NH_4OH(aq)$. Alkalis have a soapy feel (they react with oils and fats in the skin) and have a bitter taste.

Reaction with metal oxides

Dilute acids react to give a salt and water when a metal oxide is added (Figure 8.11). For example:

■ **Figure 8.11**
The reaction between excess copper(ıı) oxide and hydrochloric acid to form green copper(ıı) chloride solution

$$CuO(s) + H_2SO_4(aq) \rightarrow CuSO_4(aq) + H_2O(l)$$
$$CuO(s) + 2HNO_3(aq) \rightarrow Cu(NO_3)_2(aq) + H_2O(l)$$
$$CuO(s) + 2HCl(aq) \rightarrow CuCl_2(aq) + H_2O(l)$$
$$CuO(s) + 2CH_3COOH(aq) \rightarrow Cu(CH_3COO)_2(aq) + H_2O(l)$$

or ionically,

$$O^{2-}(s) + 2H^+(aq) \rightarrow H_2O(l)$$

In general,

metal oxide + dilute acid → salt + water

Reaction with metal hydroxides

Dilute acids react to give a salt and water when a metal hydroxide or aqueous ammonia is added. For example:

$$NaOH(aq) + HNO_3(aq) \rightarrow NaNO_3(aq) + H_2O(l)$$
$$NH_3(aq) + HNO_3(aq) \rightarrow NH_4NO_3(aq)$$

or ionically,

$$OH^-(aq) + H^+(aq) \rightarrow H_2O(l)$$
$$NH_3(aq) + H^+(aq) \rightarrow NH_4^+(aq)$$

In general,

metal hydroxide + dilute acid → salt + water

A summary of the reactions of acids in dilute aqueous solution is given in Figure 8.12.

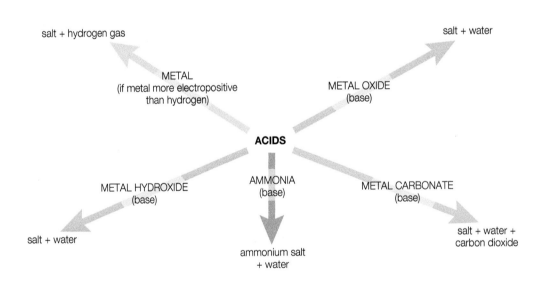

■ **Figure 8.12** Summary of the reactions of acids

Utilization: Everyday acids and bases

A number of acids and bases are used in the home as cleaning agents (Figure 8.13). Rust removers often contain phosphoric(v) acid which forms a protective layer of iron(III) phosphate to help prevent further rusting. Rust stains on clothing can be removed using ethanedioic (oxalic) acid. The reaction involves complexing of iron ions (Chapter 13). Hard water contains a high concentration of calcium ions and forms deposits in kettles and hot water pipes. The carbonate deposits can be removed with acid, for example vinegar (ethanoic acid).

Oven cleaners usually contain sodium hydroxide (Figure 8.14), which converts oils and fats into water-soluble products (propane–1,2,3–triol and carboxylate ions). Ammonia and sodium carbonate are also present in many liquid cleaners. They are both weaker bases and hence less corrosive to the skin and eyes. Sodium carbonate is present in dishwasher crystals. Carbonate ions undergo hydrolysis with water molecules to release excess hydroxide ions.

■ **Figure 8.13** Denture cleaning tablets. Active ingredients include the salts sodium hydrogencarbonate, sodium perborate and citric acid

■ **Figure 8.14** Oven cleaner pads

When a bee stings it injects an acidic solution containing methanoic acid (HCOOH) into the skin. The sting can be neutralized by rubbing on calamine lotion, which contains zinc carbonate ($ZnCO_3$), or baking soda which is sodium hydrogencarbonate ($NaHCO_3$). Wasp stings are alkaline and can be neutralized with vinegar. Ant stings and nettle stings contain methanoic acid.

Generally toothpaste has a pH of 8 or 9, which makes it mildly alkaline. In fact it can range from 7 to 10 depending on its additives. The alkaline pH of toothpaste helps neutralize the plaque acids that cause tooth decay. Toothpastes that contain baking soda will have the highest pH values.

Additional Perspectives

Salts

A salt is an ionic compound formed when the replaceable hydrogen of an acid is completely or partly replaced by a metal (ion). Salts are formed by exothermic neutralization reactions. For example,

$$\begin{array}{ccc} \text{HCl(aq)} & \rightarrow & \text{NaCl(aq)} \\ \text{hydrochloric acid (an acid)} & & \text{sodium chloride (a salt)} \end{array}$$

The number of replaceable hydrogen atoms in an acid is termed the basicity or proticity of the acid. Table 8.1 gives the basicity or proticity of some common acids.

■ **Table 8.1** Basicity or proticity of some common acids

Name of acid	Formula	Basicity or proticity
Hydrochloric acid	HCl	1
Nitric(v) acid	HNO_3	1
Ethanoic acid	CH_3COOH	1
Sulfuric acid	H_2SO_4	2
Carbonic acid	H_2CO_3	2
Phosphoric(v) acid	H_3PO_4	3

In the case of a diprotic or dibasic acid, containing more than one replaceable hydrogen atom, salts can be formed when all or some of the hydrogen is replaced. Salts formed by replacing all of the hydrogen are termed normal salts; those formed by replacing only part of the hydrogen are termed acid salts. Table 8.2 gives examples of the sodium salts formed by common acids.

■ **Table 8.2** Examples of sodium salts formed by common acids

Acid	Salt	Example
Hydrochloric acid, HCl	Chlorides	Sodium chloride, NaCl
Nitric acid, HNO$_3$	Nitrates	Sodium nitrate, NaNO$_3$
Ethanoic acid, CH$_3$COOH	Ethanoates	Sodium ethanoate, CH$_3$COONa
Sulfuric acid, H$_2$SO$_4$	Sulfates (normal salts) and hydrogensulfates (acid salts)	Sodium sulfate, Na$_2$SO$_4$, and sodium hydrogensulfate, NaHSO$_4$
Carbonic acid, H$_2$CO$_3$	Carbonates (normal salts) and hydrogencarbonates (acid salts)	Sodium carbonate, Na$_2$CO$_3$, and sodium hydrogencarbonate, NaHCO$_3$

Aqueous solutions of salts may be neutral, acidic or alkaline (Chapter 18). Salts that form acidic or alkaline solutions have undergone hydrolysis with water. Salts may be prepared in a variety of ways, depending on their solubility (Figure 8.15).

■ **Figure 8.15** Summary of the preparation of salts

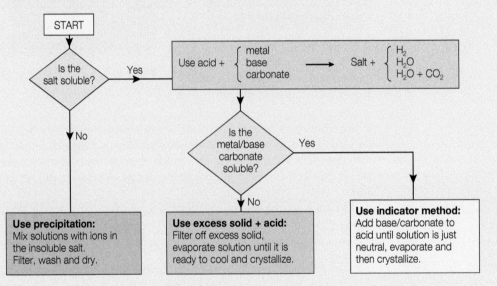

Balancing chemical equations for the reactions of acids

The general equations for the reactions of acids together with a knowledge of balancing equations from Chapter 1 will allow the construction of a wide range of equations describing the reactions of acids.

3 Write equations, including state symbols, for the following reactions:
   a sulfuric acid and copper(II) carbonate
   b hydrobromic acid and calcium hydrogencarbonate
   c phosphoric(v) acid and sodium carbonate
   d ethanoic acid and calcium
   e ammonium phosphate solution and aqueous barium hydroxide

Identifying the acid and base to make different salts

Knowledge of the anions from the various acids and the cations from various bases will allow identification of the acid and base to prepare a specific salt.

4 Identify the acids and bases used to prepare the following salts:
   a silver(I) sulfate
   b magnesium nitrate
   c potassium chloride
   d barium ethanoate

Acid–base titrations and indicators

Chemists can find out if a solution is acidic or alkaline by adding an indicator to the solution. An indicator is a substance that usually has one colour in very acidic solutions and another colour in very alkaline solutions. Table 22 on page 21 of the *IB Chemistry data booklet* lists a number of common indicators, with their two colours and the pH range over which they change colour.

Any indicator can be used for the titration of a strong base with a strong acid. However, if a strong acid is titrated with a weak acid then a suitable indicator is methyl orange (pK_a 3.7), or any other indicator whose pK_a value is below 7. If a weak acid is titrated with a strong base then a suitable indicator is phenolphthalein (pK_a value 9.6) or any other indicator whose pK_a value is above 7. A weak acid and a weak base cannot be titrated in the presence of an indicator. The theory of indicators, pK_a values (as a measure of acid strength) and the choice of indicators for acid–base titrations is discussed in Chapter 18.

■ The importance of water

Pure or anhydrous acids do *not* behave as acids and do not exhibit the characteristic properties of acids described previously. These properties are only shown after the acids have been reacted and dissolved in water to form dilute aqueous solutions.

The importance of water in acid solutions can be demonstrated by dissolving hydrogen chloride gas, HCl, in both water and an organic liquid such as methylbenzene, $C_6H_5CH_3$. Solutions are formed in both cases, *but* only the aqueous solution exhibits typical acidic properties (Table 8.3).

■ **Table 8.3** Reactions of hydrogen chloride with water and methylbenzene

Test	Solution of hydrogen chloride in water	Solution of dry hydrogen chloride in dry methylbenzene
Dry universal indicator paper	Turns red, acidic solution formed	Remains green, neutral solution formed
Addition of calcium carbonate	Carbon dioxide gas produced	No reaction
Electrical conductivity	Good conductor	Non–conductor
Temperature change on formation of solution	Rise in temperature	Little change in temperature

The results are explained by suggesting that when hydrogen chloride dissolves in water, a chemical reaction occurs and ions are formed, resulting in the formation of a hydrochloric acid:

$$HCl(g) + (aq) \rightarrow H^+(aq) + Cl^-(aq)$$

It is the hydrogen ions that are responsible for all the acidic properties of acids previously described, and these are only formed in the presence of water. When hydrogen chloride is dissolved in methylbenzene, no hydrogen ions are formed, and undissociated or un-ionized hydrogen chloride molecules, HCl(solv), are present.

8.3 The pH scale – *the pH scale is an artificial scale used to distinguish between acid, neutral and basic/alkaline solutions*

■ The pH scale

The pH scale is a number scale (Figure 8.16) that is used to describe the acidity, alkalinity or neutrality of an aqueous solution. The scale runs from 0 to 14:

- ■ an aqueous solution with a pH below 7 is acidic
- ■ an aqueous solution with a pH of above 7 is alkaline
- ■ an aqueous solution with a pH of exactly 7 is neutral.

■ **Figure 8.16**
The pH scale

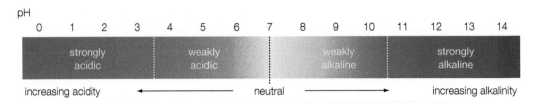

As the pH numbers below 7 become progressively *smaller*, the solution becomes *increasingly acidic*. Conversely, as the pH numbers above 7 become progressively larger, the solution becomes increasingly alkaline.

The pH scale is *logarithmic* to the base 10, which means that every change of one unit on the pH scale means a change in the hydrogen ion concentration by an order of 10. For example, an aqueous solution with a pH of 4 is 10 times more acidic than an aqueous solution with a pH of 5 and 100 times (10 × 10) more acidic than an aqueous solution with a pH of 6. Additionally, an aqueous solution with a pH of 8 is 100 times (10 × 10) less alkaline than an aqueous solution with a pH of 10. pH is directly related to the concentration of hydrogen ions present in the solution (Table 8.4).

This table clearly shows that if the pH of a solution is given the value x, then the corresponding hydrogen ion concentration is 10^{-x} mol dm^{-3}. For now, we shall use only integral values of x, but expressions involving non-integers can be evaluated using a calculator. However, note again that the pH scale is logarithmic, which means that although a pH of 5.5, as a number, is half-way between pH 5 and 6, $10^{-5.5}$ is not half-way between 10^{-5} and 10^{-6}.

Table 8.4 indicates that distilled water (pH 7) and alkalis, for example 1 mol dm^{-3} aqueous sodium hydroxide (pH 14), despite being neutral and alkaline, respectively, contain hydrogen ions, albeit at low concentrations. Hydrogen ions are present in neutral and alkaline aqueous solutions because water itself is very slightly dissociated into hydrogen and hydroxide ions (Chapter 18):

$$H_2O(l) \rightleftharpoons H^+(aq) + OH^-(aq)$$

However, in distilled water (pH 7) the concentrations of hydroxide and hydrogen ions are equal, that is, $[H^+(aq)] = [OH^-(aq)]$. In an acidic solution, the concentration of hydrogen ions will be larger than the concentration of hydroxide ions, that is, $[H^+(aq)] > [OH^-(aq)]$, and in alkaline solution, the concentration of hydroxide ions will be larger than the concentration of hydrogen ions, that is, $[OH^-(aq)] > [H^+(aq)]$ (Table 8.5).

pH	Concentration of hydrogen ions, H^+(aq)/mol dm^{-3}
0	1×10^{0} = 1.0
1	1×10^{-1} = 0.1
2	1×10^{-2} = 0.01
3	1×10^{-3} = 0.001
4	1×10^{-4} = 0.0001
5	1×10^{-5} = 0.000 01
6	1×10^{-6} = 0.000 001
7	1×10^{-7} = 0.000 0001
8	1×10^{-8} = 0.000 0000 1
9	1×10^{-9} = 0.000 000 001
10	1×10^{-10} = 0.000 000 000 1
11	1×10^{-11} = 0.000 000 000 01
12	1×10^{-12} = 0.000 000 000 001
13	1×10^{-13} = 0.000 000 000 000 1
14	1×10^{-14} = 0.000 000 000 000 01

■ **Table 8.4** The relationship between pH and H^+(aq) concentration

Solution	[H^+(aq)]/mol dm^{-3}	[OH^-(aq)]/mol dm^{-3}
Acidic	$>10^{-7}$	$<10^{-7}$
Neutral	10^{-7}	10^{-7}
Basic	$<10^{-7}$	$>10^{-7}$

■ **Table 8.5** Ion concentrations (at 25 °C)

Nature of Science

Occam's razor – the pH scale is an attempt to scale the relative acidity over a wide range of H^+ concentrations into a very simple number

Occam's razor is the philosophical principle that the simplest scientific explanation which fits all known facts is the best one. The pH scale is just a convenient way of expressing a very wide range of numbers in a simpler-to-write form by expressing them on a logarithmic scale – it is a convenience and does not explain anything.

Scientists use a logarithmic scale when there is a wide range of values, and when the significance of a change in that value depends not on the absolute size of the change but on the size of the change in proportion to the value itself. If adding 1 to a value is just as large a change whether the original value is 1 or 1000, a linear scale makes sense. If doubling a value is just as large a change whether it is from 1 to 2 or from 1000 to 2000, a logarithmic scale is appropriate.

pH is the negative of the logarithm (to the base 10) of the concentration of hydrogen (or oxonium) ions. If we just used the concentration as our measure of acidity, then an acid with pH 3 would be said to have a concentration of 0.001 (10^{-3}), and a weaker acid with pH 4 would be 0.0001 mol dm^{-3}. Neutral water would be 0.0000001 mol dm^{-3}, and a strong base with pH 11 would be 0.00000000001 mol dm^{-3}.

Try graphing the values of H$^+$ and pH and you will find that it is impossible to show all these values on the same graph. If you can see acids at all, neutral and basic values will be indistinguishable. You might be able to put 0.001 and 0.0001 on your axis, but 0.0000001 will look like zero, and 0.01 (a really strong acid) will be off your paper. If the difference between 0.000001 and 0.00001 were no more significant than between 0.001 and 0.001001, then this would be appropriate. The very small values would not be worth displaying. But because it is more important to distinguish the former two (weak and weaker acids) than the latter two (practically the same strong acid), we need a way to show all these values on our graph. A logarithmic scale allows us to do this.

■ The ionic product constant of water

When water is purified by repeated distillation its electrical conductivity falls to a very low, constant value. This is evidence that pure water dissociates to a very small extent to form ions:

$$H_2O(l) \rightleftharpoons H^+(aq) + OH^-(aq)$$

or

$$2H_2O(l) \rightleftharpoons H_3O^+(aq) + OH^-(aq)$$

If the equilibrium law (Chapter 7) is applied to the first equation:

$$K_w = [H^+(aq)] \times [OH^-(aq)]$$

where K_w represents a constant known as the ionic product constant of water. (Recall from Chapter 7 that pure liquids do not appear in equilibrium expressions.) At 298 K (25 °C) the measured concentrations of H$^+$(aq) and OH$^-$(aq) in pure water are 1.00×10^{-7} mol dm^{-3}, therefore:

$$K_w = [H^+(aq)] \times [OH^-(aq)] = 1.00 \times 10^{-7} \times 1.00 \times 10^{-7} = 1.00 \times 10^{-14} \text{ mol}^2 \text{ dm}^{-6}$$

This is a key equation in acid–base chemistry. Note that the product of [H$^+$(aq)] and [OH$^-$(aq)] is a *constant* at a given temperature. Thus, as the hydrogen ion concentration of a solution increases, the hydroxide ion concentration decreases (and *vice versa*).

The solution is described as neutral when the concentration of hydrogen ions equals the concentration of hydroxide ions, so that at 298 K (25 °C) the value of K_w is 1.00×10^{-14} mol^2 dm^{-6}.

Worked example

Calculate the hydroxide ion concentration of an aqueous solution whose hydrogen ion concentration at 25 °C is 5.4×10^{-4} mol dm^{-3}.

$$K_w = [H^+(aq)] \times [OH^-(aq)]$$

$$1.00 \times 10^{-14} \text{ mol}^2 \text{ dm}^{-6} = 5.4 \times 10^{-4} \text{ mol dm}^{-3} \times [OH^-(aq)]$$

$$[OH^-(aq)] = 1.9 \times 10^{-11} \text{ mol dm}^{-3}$$

Solving problems involving pH, [H$^+$] and [OH$^-$]

A wide variety of acid–base equilibria problems can be solved using the relationships between pH, hydrogen ion concentration and hydroxide ion concentration in conjunction with the ionic product constant of water.

5 Calculate the pH of a 0.100 mol dm^{-3} HCl(aq) solution.

6 Calculate the pH of a 3.00 × 10^{-7} mol dm^{-3} H$^+$(aq) solution.

7 Calculate the pH of a 0.0100 mol dm^{-3} H$_2$SO$_4$(aq) solution.

8 Calculate the pH of a 2.50 × 10^{-3} mol dm^{-3} OH$^-$(aq) solution.

9 Calculate the pH of a 0.0100 mol dm^{-3} Ba(OH)$_2$(aq) solution.

10 An aqueous solution of hydrochloric acid contains 3.646 g of hydrogen chloride (HCl) in every 250 cm^3 of solution. Calculate the concentration of hydrogen ions, H$^+$(aq).

11 Calculate the pH of a mixture of 25.00 cm^3 of 0.1000 mol dm^{-3} HCl and 15.0 cm^3 of 0.1000 mol dm^{-3} NaOH.

12 Calculate the H$^+$ concentration and pH of a 0.01 mol dm^{-3} solution of KOH(aq).

Measuring pH with a pH meter and with universal indicator

The pH of aqueous solutions can be measured by using universal indicator, either in the form of a solution or as paper. This is a mixture of indicators that has different colours in solutions of different pH. The exact colours usually correspond to a 'rainbow' sequence as the pH increases (Figure 8.17).

■ **Figure 8.17**
pH scale and the colours of universal indicator

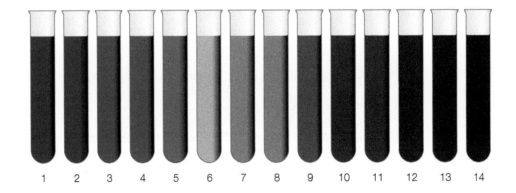

■ **Figure 8.18**
The pH of common substances

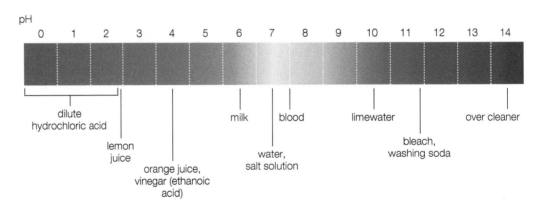

Figure 8.18 shows the pH of some common laboratory chemicals and household substances. A more accurate method of measuring pH involves using a pH probe and meter (Figure 8.19).

■ **Figure 8.19**
pH probe

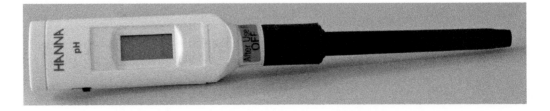

■ **Figure 8.20**
pH meter electrode
assembly

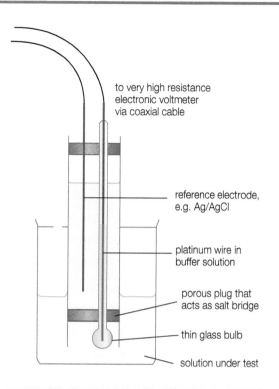

to very high resistance
electronic voltmeter
via coaxial cable

reference electrode,
e.g. Ag/AgCl

platinum wire in
buffer solution

porous plug that
acts as salt bridge

thin glass bulb

solution under test

The pH probe contains a very thin glass bulb filled with acid of known concentration and therefore pH. When the probe is placed in an aqueous solution, a voltage difference is established between the acid inside the bulb and the solution outside the bulb (Figure 8.20). This voltage is then converted to a pH reading by the pH meter. Titrations can also be followed using a pH probe and meter. They can be used to plot titration curves (Chapter 18) where acid is usually gradually added to alkali. These curves can be used to find the values related to the strength of the weak acid or weak base.

ToK Link

Chemistry makes use of the universal language of mathematics as a means of communication. Why is it important to have just one 'scientific' language?

Mathematics is the only language shared by all human beings regardless of culture, nationality, religion, or gender. The Avogadro constant is approximately 6.02×10^{23} regardless of what country you are in. Carrying out a stoichiometry calculation involves the same mathematical process, and using this universal language we will all obtain the same result. Very few people, if any, are literate in all the world's different languages but virtually all of us possess the ability to be 'literate' in the shared and universal language of mathematics. This mathematical literacy is called numeracy, and it is this shared language of numbers that connects us with scientists across continents and through time. It is with this language that all scientific phenomena can be universally described.

8.4 Strong and weak acids and bases – *the pH depends on the concentration of the solution; the strength of acids and bases depends on the extent to which they dissociate in aqueous solution*

■ Strong and weak acids

Acids are often classified into strong and weak acids.

When a strong acid dissolves, virtually all the acid molecules react with the water to produce hydrogen or oxonium ions. In general for a strong acid, HA:

$$HA \rightarrow H^+(aq) + A^-(aq) \quad \text{or} \quad HA + H_2O(l) \rightarrow H_3O^+(aq) + A^-(aq)$$
$$0\% \quad 100\% \qquad\qquad\qquad 0\% \qquad\qquad 100\%$$

This process can be illustrated graphically by means of a bar chart (Figure 8.21).
The four common strong acids are hydrochloric, nitric(v), sulfuric(vi) and chloric(vii) (perchloric):

$$HCl(g) + H_2O(l) \rightarrow H_3O^+(aq) + Cl^-(aq)$$
$$HNO_3(l) + H_2O(l) \rightarrow H_3O^+(aq) + NO_3^-(aq)$$
$$H_2SO_4(l) + H_2O(l) \rightarrow H_3O^+(aq) + HSO_4^-(aq)$$
$$HClO_4(l) + H_2O(l) \rightarrow H_3O^+(aq) + ClO_4^-(aq)$$

■ **Figure 8.21**
Graphical
representation of the
behaviour of a strong
acid in aqueous
solution

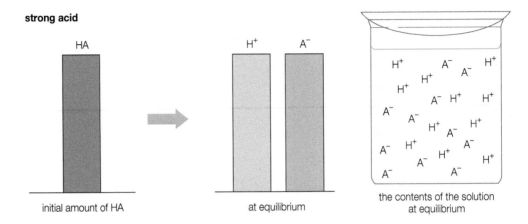

■ **Figure 8.21**
Graphical
representation of the
behaviour of a strong
acid in aqueous
solution

Monoprotic organic acids are usually weak. When a weak acid dissolves in water, only a small percentage of its molecules (typically 1%) react with water molecules to release hydrogen or oxonium ions. An equilibrium is established, with the majority of the acid molecules not undergoing ionization or dissociation. In other words, the equilibrium lies on the left-hand side of the equation.

In general for a weak acid, HA:

$$HA \rightleftharpoons H^+(aq) + A^-(aq) \qquad or \qquad HA + H_2O(l) \rightleftharpoons H_3O^+(aq) + A^-(aq)$$
99% 1%   99%   1%

This process can be illustrated graphically by means of a bar chart (Figure 8.22).

■ **Figure 8.22**
Graphical
representation of
the behaviour of a
weak acid in aqueous
solution

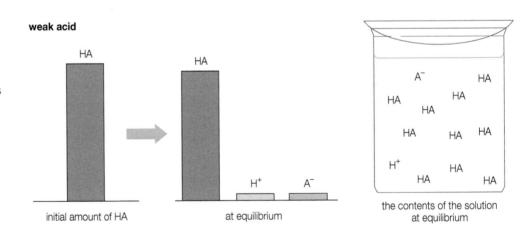

Examples of common weak acids are ethanoic acid and aqueous carbon dioxide or 'carbonic acid':

$$CH_3COOH(l) + H_2O(l) \rightleftharpoons CH_3COO^-(aq) + H_3O^+(aq)$$

and

$$CO_2(g) + 2H_2O(l) \rightleftharpoons HCO_3^-(aq) + H_3O^+(aq)$$

The term carbonic acid is in quotation marks, since the compound carbonic acid, H_2CO_3, does not actually exist and cannot be isolated. Attempts to isolate it result in the formation of carbon dioxide and water.

Looking for trends and discrepancies – patterns and anomalies in relative strengths of acids and bases can be explained at the molecular level

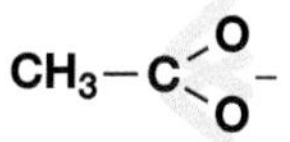

■ **Figure 8.23**
The delocalization
of charge in the
ethanoate ion

■ Factors required for acidity

There are four main requirements that a chemical needs if it is to behave as a strong acid. The first factor is that the ion formed during ionization or dissociation must be energetically stable. For this to happen it should be possible for the charge on the ion to be 'spread out' and its energy reduced rather than concentrated in one place. This is known as resonance or delocalization (Chapter 4).

This explains why organic compounds such as ethanoic acid are acidic in water. The negative charge on the ethanoate ion CH_3COO^-, is spread over three atoms, as shown in Figure 8.23.

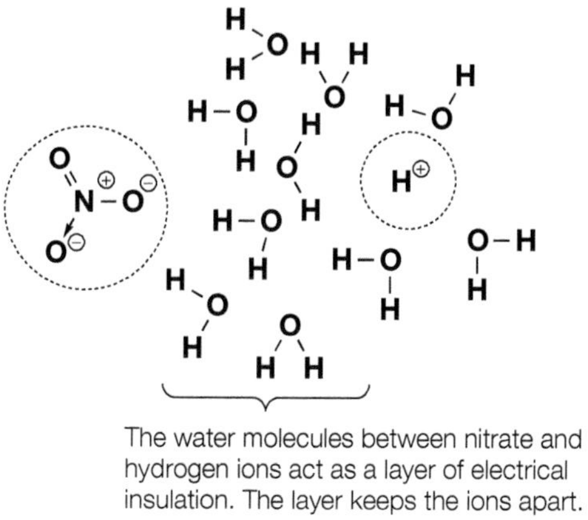

The second factor is that, once the ion is formed, it should not easily change back into the molecule from which it was formed by ionization or dissociation. The best way of ensuring this is to have the ions surrounded by a layer of 'insulating' molecules to prevent ions from interacting. The effectiveness of the insulating power of a liquid is its relative permittivity (also called the dielectric constant): the higher the relative permittivity, the greater insulating ability. It so happens that water has a very high value of relative permittivity (Figure 8.24). It is this value that is partly responsible for the strengths of strong mineral acids, such as nitric and sulfuric acids in aqueous solution.

The third factor is that the chemical nature of the parent molecule, or ion, should encourage the loss of a proton (H^+). For example, the complex ion, hexaaquaferrate(III), $[Fe(H_2O)_6]^{3+}(aq)$, is produced when many iron(III) compounds are dissolved in water. It is the presence of this ion that makes solutions of iron(III) salts slightly acidic (Figure 8.25).

The charge on the central iron(III) ion is so large and spread over such a small volume of space that it polarizes the water molecules that are attached to it. This weakens the polar covalent bonds between the hydrogen and oxygen atoms, and one of the protons can be donated to a neighbouring (solvent) water molecule.

The final factor is that the bond holding the acidic hydrogen atom should not be too strong. It should have a relatively low dissociation energy.

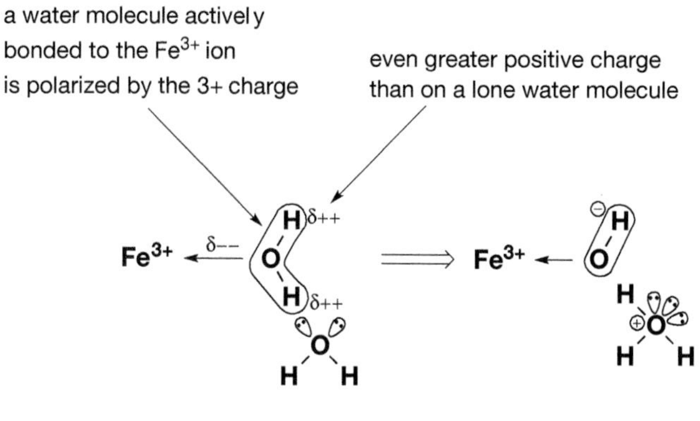

The water molecules between nitrate and hydrogen ions act as a layer of electrical insulation. The layer keeps the ions apart.

■ **Figure 8.24** Water is a solvent with a high relative permittivity

a water molecule actively
bonded to the Fe^{3+} ion
is polarized by the 3+ charge

even greater positive charge
than on a lone water molecule

overall: $Fe(H_2O)_6^{3+} + H_2O \longrightarrow Fe(H_2O)_5(OH)^{2+} + H_3O^+$

■ **Figure 8.25** Explaining the acidity of iron(III) salt solution

■ Factors controlling the strength of inorganic acids

Electronegativity

When all other factors are kept constant, acids become stronger as the X–H bond becomes more polar. The second period non-metal hydrides, for example, become more acidic as the difference between the electronegativity of the X and H atoms increases. Hydrogen fluoride is the strongest of these four acids, and methane is one of the weakest Brønsted–Lowry acids known (Table 8.6).

When these compounds act as acids in aqueous solution, an H–X bond is broken to form $H^+(aq)$ and $X^-(aq)$ ions. The more polar this bond, the easier it is to form these ions. Hence, the greater the polarity of the bond, the stronger the acid (at a constant temperature).

■ **Table 8.6** Effect of electronegativity on the acidity of non-metal hydrides from period 2

	Increasing acidity	Increasing electronegativity difference
HF	↑	↑
H_2O		
NH_3		
CH_4		

The size of the X atom

It might be expected that HF, HCl, HBr and HI would become weaker acids as group 17 is descended because the H–X bond becomes less polar (Chapter 4). Experimentally, the *opposite* trend is found: the acids actually become stronger as the group is descended.

This occurs because the size of the atom X influences the acidity of the H–X bond. Acids become stronger as the H–X bond becomes weaker, and bonds generally become weaker as the atoms become larger.

The K_a data for HF, HCl, HBr and HI reflect the fact that the H–X bond energy becomes smaller as the X atom becomes larger (Table 8.7).

■ **Table 8.7** Effect of the size of the halogen atom on the acidity of hydrides from group 17

Increasing acidity	Decreasing bond energy
HF	
HCl	
HBr	
HI	

The charge on the acid or base

The charge on a molecule or ion can influence its ability to act as an acid or a base. This is clearly shown when the pH of 0.1 mol dm^{-3} solutions of H_3PO_4 and of the $H_2PO_4^{-}$, HPO_4^{2-} and PO_4^{3-} ions are compared:

H_3PO_4	pH = 1.5
$H_2PO_4^{-}$	pH = 4.4
HPO_4^{2-}	pH = 9.3
PO_4^{3-}	pH = 12.0

Compounds become less acidic and more basic as the negative charge increases:

Acidity: $H_3PO_4 > H_2PO_4^{-} > HPO_4^{2-}$
Basicity: $H_2PO_4^{-} < HPO_4^{2-} < PO_4^{3-}$

The oxidation state of the central atom

There is no difference in the polarity, size or charge when we compare oxoacids of the same element, such as H_2SO_4 and H_2SO_3 or HNO_3 and HNO_2, yet there is a significant difference in the strengths of these acids. Consider the following K_a data, for example:

H_2SO_4 $K_a = 1.0 \times 10^3$ HNO$_3$ $K_a = 28$
H_2SO_3 $K_a = 1.7 \times 10^{-2}$ HNO$_2$ $K_a = 5.1 \times 10^{-4}$

The acidity of these oxoacids increases significantly as the oxidation state (Chapter 9) of the central atom becomes larger. H_2SO_4 is a much stronger acid than H_2SO_3, and HNO_3 is a much stronger acid than HNO_2. This trend is easiest to see in the four oxoacids of chlorine (Table 8.8).

■ **Table 8.8** Effect of the oxidation state of the central atom on the acidity of oxoacids

Oxoacid	K_a	Oxidation number of chlorine
HOCl	2.9×10^{-8}	+1
HOClO	1.1×10^{-2}	+3
HOClO$_2$	5.0×10^2	+5
HOClO$_3$	1.0×10^3	+7

This factor of 10^{11} difference in the values of K_a for chloric(I) acid (HOCl) and chloric(VII) acid (HOClO$_3$) can be traced to the fact that there is only one value for the electronegativity of an element, but the tendency of an atom to draw electrons towards itself increases as the oxidation number of the atom increases.

As the oxidation number of the chlorine atom increases, the atom becomes more electronegative. This tends to draw electrons away from the oxygen atoms that surround the chlorine, thereby making the oxygen atoms more electronegative as well. As a result, the O–H bond becomes more polar, and the compound becomes more acidic.

Strong and weak bases

In addition to strong and weak acids there are strong and weak bases. A strong base undergoes almost 100% ionization or dissociation when in dilute aqueous solution. Strong bases include the metal hydroxides of group 1, and barium hydroxide. Strong bases have high pH values and high conductivities (Table 8.9).

Table 8.9
Comparison of a weak and strong base of the same concentration

	0.1 mol dm⁻³ NaOH(aq)	0.1 mol dm⁻³ NH₃(aq)
[OH⁻(aq)]	0.1 mol dm⁻³	≈ 0.0013 mol dm⁻³
pH	13	11–12
Electrical conductivity	high	low

In general for a strong ionic base, BOH:

$$BOH + (aq) \rightarrow OH^-(aq) + B^+(aq)$$
$$0\% \qquad\qquad 100\%$$

The three common strong bases are sodium hydroxide, potassium hydroxide and barium hydroxide:

$$NaOH(s) + (aq) \rightarrow Na^+(aq) + OH^-(aq)$$
$$KOH(s) + (aq) \rightarrow K^+(aq) + OH^-(aq)$$
$$Ba(OH)_2(s) + (aq) \rightarrow Ba^{2+}(aq) + 2OH^-(aq)$$

All bases are weak except the hydroxides of groups 1 and 2. Weak bases are composed of molecules that react with water molecules to release hydroxide ions. In general for a weak molecular base, BOH:

$$BOH + (aq) \rightleftharpoons OH^-(aq) + B^+(aq)$$

An equilibrium is established, with the majority of the base molecules not undergoing ionization or dissociation. In other words, the equilibrium lies on the left-hand side of the equation. Weak bases have low pH values and low conductivities (Table 8.9).

Examples of weak bases include caffeine, the bases of nucleic acids, aqueous ammonia and ethylamine:

$$NH_3(g) + (aq) \rightleftharpoons NH_4^+(aq) + OH^-(aq)$$
$$C_2H_5NH_2(g) + (aq) \rightleftharpoons C_2H_5NH_3^+(aq) + OH^-(aq)$$

Despite the equilibria lying on the left there is a sufficiently high concentration of hydroxide ions in dilute aqueous ammonia (and ethylamine) to precipitate many transition metal hydroxides from aqueous solutions of the metal salt.

Calcium hydroxide is a strong base, but it is very dilute because it is only slightly soluble in water.

$$Ca(OH)_2(s) + (aq) \rightarrow Ca^{2+}(aq) + 2OH^-(aq)$$

Properties of strong and weak acids

Strong and weak acids (see Table 8.10) of the *same concentration*, such as hydrochloric and ethanoic acids, can be easily distinguished:

- A weak acid has a lower concentration of hydrogen ions and hence a higher pH than a strong acid of the same concentration. This can be established using narrow range universal indicator paper or, preferably, a pH probe and meter.

- A weak acid, because of its lower concentration of hydrogen ions, will be a much poorer electrical conductor than a strong acid of the same concentration.
- Weak acids react more slowly with reactive metals, metal oxides, metal carbonates and metal hydrogencarbonates than strong acids of the same concentration. This is again due to a lower concentration of hydrogen ions in the weak acid, since it is the hydrogen ions that are responsible for the typical chemical properties of acids.
- Strong and weak acids can also be distinguished by measuring and comparing their enthalpies of neutralization (Chapter 5).

■ Table 8.10 Comparison of a weak and strong acid of the same concentration

	0.1 mol dm^{-3} HCl(aq)	0.1 mol dm^{-3} CH$_3$COOH(aq)
[H$^+$(aq)]	0.1 mol dm^{-3}	≈ 0.0013 mol dm^{-3}
pH	1.00	2.87
Electrical conductivity	high	low
Relative rate of reaction with magnesium	fast	slow
Relative rate of reaction with calcium carbonate	fast	slow

It is important not to confuse the terms strong and weak with dilute and concentrated (Chapter 1). The term concentrated, as applied to acids, means that a relatively large amount of the pure acid (weak or strong) has been dissolved in a relatively small volume of water. Therefore, a 0.1 mol dm^{-3} solution of hydrochloric acid can be described as a dilute solution of a strong acid and a 0.1 mol dm^{-3} solution of ethanoic acid can be described as a dilute solution of a weak acid. A concentrated solution of a weak acid such as ethanoic acid might contain a greater concentration of hydrogen ions than a very dilute solution of a strong acid, such as hydrochloric acid. Acid strength does not change as the acid is diluted (at constant temperature).

The terms strong and weak acids are not entirely satisfactory since they are qualitative descriptions. Strong and weak are not absolute terms and some acids, such as phosphoric(v) acid, H$_3$PO$_4$(aq), are described as moderately strong. In Chapter 18, a quantitative measure of acid strength that does not vary with dilution, known as the acid dissociation constant, will be introduced.

Nature of Science

Improved instrumentation – the relative strengths of acids and bases can now be measured

As theories of acidity were developing, so was the practical measurement of acidity. This has a long history and is at the foundation of analytical chemistry. The concept of pH is perhaps the most important. It is not a measure of acid strength but the measurement of the pH values of acid solutions at the same concentration allows the relative strengths of acids to be compared.

In 1889 the German chemist Nernst gave the theoretical foundation for the use of electrode potential to measure the concentration of an ion in solution. This led Sørensen in 1900 to develop the pH scale and an early pH meter based on a hydrogen electrode in combination with a calomel reference electrode. At that time pH was measured using known concentrations of coloured indicator dyes which lost or changed colour by drop-wise addition of solutions. This allowed standardized measurements be made. Litmus paper and other indicator strips were also used, with colour comparisons against colour charts to determine pH.

However, the measurement of pH was revolutionized by the development of the pH meter in 1934 by Arnold Beckman. It was originally developed for citrus fruit growers in California who wanted a way of monitoring fruit acidity during the production of pectin and citric acid. The use of sulfur dioxide made standard methods of testing unsuitable.

It must be remembered that no absolute comparison of the strengths of acids can be made. The relative strengths of acids in aqueous solution will vary with dilution and temperature. For example, at 0.1 mol dm^{-3} concentration and room temperature, hydrochloric acid is almost completely ionized or dissociated, while ethanoic acid is about 1.4% ionized. However, at

0.001 mol dm^{-3}, hydrochloric acid is still almost completely ionized, but ethanoic acid is about 14% ionized – hence it has become stronger but more dilute.

Another method to compare strengths of weak acids is observation of standard enthalpy of neutralization (Chapter 5). Let two acids, of which the strengths are to be compared, be A and B. The enthalpy of neutralization of 1 mole of hydrogen ions (H$^+$) from acid A at a given dilution by 1 mole of hydroxide ions from sodium hydroxide in suitable dilution is measured. Let this be x (J) and that from acid B be y (J). Then the heat given out by mixing A and B in the same solution, so that they each provide 1 mole of hydrogen ions (H$^+$), with sufficient sodium hydroxide solution to provide 1 mole of hydroxide ions, is measured. Let this be z (J). In this experiment the acids may be considered as competing for the base. If acid A neutralizes n moles of hydroxide ions and acid B neutralizes $(1 - n)$ moles, the following relationship must hold:

$$nx + (1 - n)y = z$$

From this n can be calculated, and then:

$$\frac{\text{strength of A}}{\text{strength of B}} = \frac{n}{(1 - n)}$$

■ Acids and their conjugates

It is important to note that in the equations below for ethanoic acid and hydrochloric acid the *competition* is between the base and its conjugate for a proton, H$^+$.

$$\underset{\text{acid}}{HCl(g)} + \underset{\text{base}}{H_2O(l)} \rightleftharpoons \underset{\text{conjugate acid}}{H_3O^+(aq)} + \underset{\text{conjugate base}}{Cl^-(aq)}$$

$$\underset{\text{acid}}{CH_3COOH(l)} + \underset{\text{base}}{H_2O(l)} \rightleftharpoons \underset{\text{conjugate acid}}{H_3O^+(aq)} + \underset{\text{conjugate base}}{CH_3COO^-(aq)}$$

if equilibrium lies to the *right* then strong acid but weak conjugate base

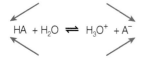

weak acid, stronger conjugate base if the equilibrium lies to the *left*

■ **Figure 8.26** The relationship between an acid and its conjugate base

In the case of hydrochloric acid the water molecule is a much stronger base than the chloride ion. In other words, the water molecule has a much greater tendency to accept a proton, H$^+$(aq), than does the chloride ion. Consequently, the position of the equilibrium will lie on the right and virtually all of the hydrogen chloride molecules will be ionized or dissociated. In general, *strong acids* produce relatively *weak conjugate bases* in aqueous solutions (Chapter 18).

In the case of ethanoic acid the ethanoate ion is a much stronger base than the water molecule. In other words, the ethanoate ion has a much greater tendency to accept a proton, H$^+$(aq), than does the water molecule. In general, *weak acids* produce relatively *strong conjugate bases* in aqueous solutions (Figure 8.26).

Similarly, *strong bases* produce *weak conjugate acids* in aqueous solutions and *weak bases* produce *strong conjugate acids* in aqueous solutions (Table 8.11). The strengths of acids, bases and their respective conjugates can be measured and expressed in terms of K_a or pK_a (Chapter 18).

■ **Table 8.11**
Some common acids and conjugate bases in order of their strengths

Acid	Strength	Base	Strength
H_2SO_4	very strong	HSO_4^-	very weak
HCl		Cl^-	
HNO_3		NO_3^-	
H_3O^+	fairly strong	H_2O	weak
HSO_4^-		SO_4^{2-}	
CH_3COOH		CH_3COO^-	
H_2CO_3	weak	HCO_3^-	less weak
NH_4^+		NH_3	
HCO_3^-	very weak	CO_3^{2-}	fairly strong
H_2O		OH^-	

Acids (Figure 8.27) that have a single proton to donate are said to be monoprotic. Common examples include hydrochloric, HCl(aq), nitric(v), HNO$_3$(aq), nitrous, HNO$_2$(aq) and ethanoic acids, CH$_3$COOH(aq). Acids that have two protons to donate are said to be diprotic. Common examples include 'carbonic acid', $H_2CO_3(aq)$, sulfuric acid, $H_2SO_4(aq)$, and sulfurous acid, $H_2SO_3(aq)$. The only common triprotic acid is phosphoric(v) acid, $H_3PO_4(aq)$.

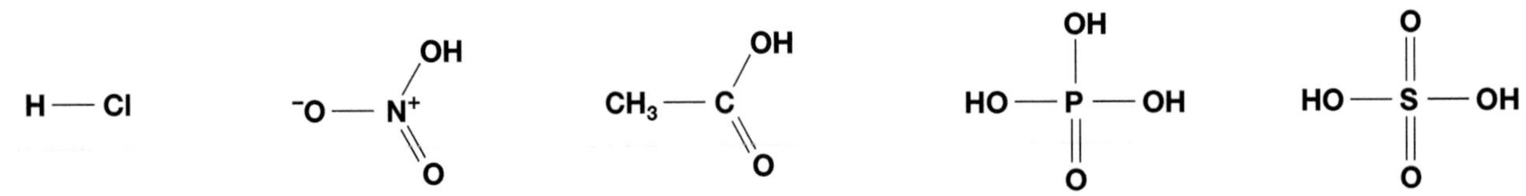

■ **Figure 8.27** Structural formulas for the molecules that form hydrochloric, nitric(v), ethanoic, phosphoric(v) and sulfuric acids in aqueous solution

For a substance to be an acid the hydrogen usually has to be attached to oxygen or a halogen. This accounts for the monoproticity of ethanoic acid: only the hydrogen atom attached to the oxygen atom is acidic and replaceable by a metal ion. The other three hydrogen atoms of ethanoic acid are attached to a carbon atom and are therefore *not* acidic.

Care must be taken when using the term 'conjugate' when referring to diprotic or triprotic acids. For example, consider the ionization or dissociation of the weak acid, sulfurous acid (sulfuric(iv) acid), $H_2SO_3(aq)$:

$$H_2SO_3(aq) \; + \; H_2O(l) \; \rightleftharpoons \; H_3O^+(aq) \; + \; HSO_3^-(aq)$$
$$\text{acid} \qquad\qquad \text{base} \qquad\quad \text{conjugate acid} \quad \text{conjugate base}$$

$$HSO_3^-(aq) \; + \; H_2O(l) \; \rightleftharpoons \; H_3O^+(aq) \; + \; SO_3^{2-}(aq)$$
$$\text{acid} \qquad\qquad \text{base} \qquad\quad \text{conjugate acid} \quad \text{conjugate base}$$

According to the first equation the hydrogensulfite ion, $HSO_3^-(aq)$, is the *conjugate base* of sulfurous acid, *but* according to the second equation it is the *conjugate acid* of the sulfite ion, $SO_3^{2-}(aq)$. The two equations illustrate the fact that 'conjugate' is a relative term and only links a specific pair of acids and bases. The hydrogensulfite ion, like the water molecule, is another example of an amphiprotic species.

The terms 'acid' and 'base' are also *relative* terms. If two concentrated acids are reacted together, then the weaker acid of the two will be 'forced' to act as a base. For example, when concentrated nitric and sulfuric acids are reacted together in a 1: 2 molar ratio, a so-called nitrating mixture is formed which contains a cation known as the nitronium ion, NO_2^+. This cation is involved in the nitration of organic compounds.

The first equilibrium to be established in the nitrating mixture is shown below:

$$HNO_3(aq) \; + \; H_2SO_4(aq) \; \rightleftharpoons \; H_2NO_3^+(aq) \; + \; HSO_4^-(aq)$$
$$\text{base} \qquad\qquad \text{acid} \qquad\quad \text{conjugate acid} \quad \text{conjugate base}$$

Nature of Science **Evidence for weak acids as equilibrium systems**

It is often useful to calculate the amount of weak acid (or weak base) that has dissociated once equilibrium has been reached in an aqueous solution.

$$\text{percentage dissociation} = \frac{\text{concentration of weak acid or base dissociated (mol dm}^{-3})}{\text{initial concentration of weak acid of base (mol dm}^{-3})} \times 100$$

Worked example

A 1.00 mol dm^{-3} aqueous solution of hydrofluoric acid, HF(aq), has a concentration of hydrogen ions of 2.7×10^{-2} mol dm^{-3}. Calculate the percentage dissociation.

$$\text{Percentage dissociation} = \frac{2.7 \times 10^{-2} \text{ mol dm}^{-3})}{1.00 \text{ mol dm}^{-3}} \times 100 = 2.7\%$$

The percentage dissociation of a weak acid or weak base increases upon dilution. This behaviour can be accounted for in terms of Le Châtelier's principle (Chapter 7).

For example, consider the dissociation of ethanoic acid in water:

$$CH_3COOH(aq) + H_2O(l) \rightleftharpoons CH_3COO^-(aq) + H_3O^+(aq)$$

A simple (but *incorrect*) argument is to say that the addition of water increases its 'concentration' and that the equilibrium is restored by a shift to the right. However, this argument, although correctly predicting the response of the system, is invalid because the 'concentration' of water in a dilute solution of ethanoic acid remains effectively constant.

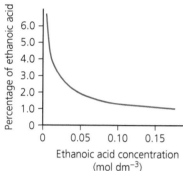

■ **Figure 8.28** The effect of concentration on percentage ionization in an ethanoic acid solution

The correct argument is as follows. The addition of water decreases the concentrations of ethanoic acid molecules, ethanoate ions and hydrogen ions. Two of these species are on the right side of the equation and only one on the left: a shift to the right is more effective at restoring the original concentrations of molecules and ions than a shift to the left. The decrease in concentration reduces the rate of the backward reaction to a greater extent than the forward reaction.

Because ethanoic acid is a weak acid in equilibrium with its ions, the concentration of $H^+(aq)$ is not directly proportional to the concentration of the weak acid. For example, doubling the concentration of a weak acid does not double the concentration of $H^+(aq)$. Figure 8.28 shows the effect on percentage ionization in ethanoic acid solution.

This is consistent with Le Châtelier's principle. The equilibrium is $CH_3COOH(aq) \rightleftharpoons CH_3COO^-(aq) + H^+(aq)$. If the percentage ionization remained constant as the ethanoic acid concentration increased, the concentrations of all three species would increase at the same rate. However, because there are two products and only one reactant, the total concentration of products would increase faster than the concentration of reactants. To offset this effect, the percentage ionization decreases as the acid concentration increases.

■ Bases and their conjugates

It is important to note that in the equations below for the weak bases ammonia and carbonate ions the *competition* is between the base and its conjugate for a proton, H^+:

$$\underset{\text{base}}{NH_3(g)} + \underset{\text{acid}}{H_2O(l)} \rightleftharpoons \underset{\text{conjugate acid}}{NH_4^+(aq)} + \underset{\text{conjugate base}}{OH^-(aq)}$$

$$\underset{\text{base}}{CO_3^{2-}(aq)} + \underset{\text{acid}}{H_2O(l)} \rightleftharpoons \underset{\text{conjugate acid}}{HCO_3^-(aq)} + \underset{\text{conjugate base}}{OH^-(aq)}$$

In the case of ammonia solution, the hydroxide ion is a much stronger base than the ammonia molecule. In other words, the hydroxide ion has a much greater tendency to accept a proton, $H^+(aq)$, than does the ammonia. Consequently, the position of the equilibrium will lie on the left and few of the ammonia molecules will be ionized or dissociated. In general, *weak bases* produce relatively *strong conjugate bases* in aqueous solutions (Chapter 18).

In the case of the second equilibrium, the ethanoate ion is a stronger base than the ammonia molecule (although both are classified as weak). In other words, the carbonate ion has a much greater tendency to accept a proton, $H^+(aq)$, than does the ammonia molecule. In general, *strong bases* produce relatively *weak conjugate bases* in aqueous solutions.

ToK Link

The strength of an acid can be determined by the use of pH and conductivity probes. In what ways do technologies, which extend our senses, change or reinforce our view of the world?

Sense refers to information gained by our five senses (sight, sound, smell, touch and taste). Although our senses have many limitations, they are a 'window to the world', because we gain so much empirical knowledge through them. The technologies humans have invented expand them to play an important role in gaining empirical knowledge beyond the ranges of our five senses. However, sense perception is highly unreliable – as knowers, we sense the world as being hard and solid but science tells us it is largely all vacuum since atoms are mainly empty space. Common sense gives us knowledge about the world but quantum mechanics gives us knowledge that is totally different and initially incompatible. We can find out about acids and bases by their sour taste – risky! – or by indicators, but pH and conductivity probes are much more precise.

8.5 Acid deposition *– increased industrialization has led to greater production of nitrogen and sulfur oxides leading to acid rain, which is damaging our environment; these problems can be reduced through collaboration with national and intergovernmental organizations*

■ Acid deposition

Pollution refers to changes in the equilibrium (or balance) of biological and non-biological systems, as a result of human activity. Note that many so-called pollutants are substances that occur naturally, such as ozone and oxides of sulfur and nitrogen. However, human activity has led to an increase in the concentrations of such substances, which upsets the delicate balance of natural cycles.

Primary pollutants are emitted directly from the sources and remain unchanged once they enter the environment. Examples include particulate matter and inorganic gases, such as sulfur dioxide. Secondary pollutants, for example sulfurous acid, are formed in the atmosphere by chemical reactions involving primary pollutants and gases normally present in the air.

Sulfur dioxide (SO_2) is an important primary pollutant. It is pungent smelling, toxic gas, which damages the respiratory system and may lead to asthma attacks. It is highly soluble in water, and contributes to the formation of acid rain.

Natural rain water is acidic, with a pH of around 5.6. This acidity arises from the reaction of carbon dioxide and water in the atmosphere. Carbon dioxide dissolved in water is sometimes referred to as carbonic acid, but only a very small percentage of molecular carbonic acid, H_2CO_3, exists in solution:

$$H_2O + CO_2 \rightarrow H_2CO_3$$

The carbonic acid molecules immediately dissociate in water to form hydrogencarbonate ions, HCO_3^-, and oxonium ions, H_3O^+:

$$H_2CO_3 + H_2O \rightarrow HCO_3^- + H_3O^+$$

Small amounts of natural sulfur dioxide and oxides of nitrogen, formed by volcanic activity or lightning, may also contribute to the acidity of natural rainwater. Rainwater at pH values of 5.6 or higher does not have environmentally damaging effects.

Rain water in polluted areas may have a pH between 5 and 2. The main acid present in acid rain is sulfurous acid (sulfuric(IV) acid) (H_2SO_3) and the major sources are cars and coal-fired power stations. Coal is commonly used in power stations for electricity generation. Crude oil also contains sulfur, but the refining process leads to the sulfur being concentrated in the heaviest fractions, which are mostly used in oil-fired power stations (Figure 8.29).

Acid rain does not account for all of the acidity that falls back to Earth from pollutants. About half of the acidity in the atmosphere is deposited as particles and gases. This process is called dry deposition. The combination of acid rain (wet deposition) plus dry deposition is called acid deposition.

■ **Figure 8.29**
An oil–fired power station

ToK Link

All rain is acidic but not all rain is 'acid rain'. Scientific terms have a precise definition. Does scientific vocabulary simply communicate our knowledge in a neutral way or can it have value-laden terminology?

Pure unpolluted rain is acidic due to the presence of dissolved carbon dioxide which is in equilibrium with hydrogen and hydrogencarbonate ions. 'Acid rain' is more acidic (lower pH) than carbonic acid due to the presence of sulfurous and sulfuric acids, which are stronger acids than carbonic acid.

Language is an essential 'tool' for scientists and for many years language was regarded as a 'faithful servant' which could not deceive us, but language has a number of pitfalls. Scientific language is intended to be meaningful: it expresses the thoughts of scientists, it connects scientists with the physical world and helps determine empirical facts. But it also evokes emotional responses.

There are two broad areas of meaning of a word. The denotation is the 'dictionary' meaning of the word. The connotation is the emotional overtone that amplifies the denotation. Scientific words are defined to remove connotations from scientific terms in an attempt to make them neutral and emotion free.

When there is no ambiguity between the sign and reference, linguists would say that one denotes the other. When there is ambiguity, when the sign suggests other associations, then linguists would say the sign connotes these associations.

Scientific language is institutionalized within a community and is governed by the rules of those who use the words. However, people outside the scientific community may take scientific words and redefine their denotation or change their connotation. The term 'acid rain' when used in a newspaper article may conjure up the image of rain that corrodes buildings to a pile of dust and dissolves plants.

It should also be noted that language is in a constant process of change and the meanings of many words have changed with time. For example, in Shakespeare's time 'villain' originally meant serf.

Some philosophers have argued that language and thought developed together and are complementary. Language, including scientific language, will be geared to the prevailing mode of thought in a particular scientific community, but it also limits the development of new and different scientific modes of thought which could conflict with old paradigms. Many philosophers believe that there is no way to avoid the constraints of language upon our thought because we cannot think without language

In George Orwell's 1984 Newspeak, the meanings of some words were actually changed or even reversed. Is this possible or is there some 'essential link' between word and meanings? Many philosophers would agree there is not, but in practice it is very hard to break the link between a word and the meaning which a society or scientific community has come to expect of that word. It also plays havoc with the scientific communication process.

Ambiguity and puzzlement within science, or in the relations between science and the non-scientific world of the public, result from errors in the choice of terms, or from semantic change or decay.

'What's in a name? That which we call a rose by any other name would smell as sweet'. Shakespeare, Romeo and Juliet.

■ Formation of acid rain

Sulfur (in coal or fuel oil) is oxidized during the combustion process in the power station:

$$S + O_2 \rightarrow SO_2$$

Sulfur dioxide dissolves and reacts with water to produce sulfurous acid (sulfuric(IV) acid), H_2SO_3:

$$SO_2 + H_2O \rightarrow H_2SO_3$$

Sulfur dioxide also undergoes photochemical oxidation in the atmosphere. This process occurs inside water droplets in which the sulfur dioxide is dissolved, and is catalysed by particulates, such as soot and fine metallic particles:

$$2SO_2 + O_2 \rightarrow 2SO_3$$

Sulfur trioxide dissolves and reacts with water to produce sulfuric acid:

$$SO_3 + H_2O \rightarrow H_2SO_4$$

At high temperatures, nitrogen and oxygen can react together to form oxides of nitrogen. This can occur during a lightning storm and in car engines.

The primary pollutant produced in vehicle engines is nitrogen monoxide:

$$N_2(g) + O_2(g) \rightarrow 2NO{\bullet}(g)$$

Nitrogen monoxide oxidizes further in the atmosphere. This reaction can be summarized as:

$$2NO{\bullet} + O_2 \rightarrow 2NO_2$$

The direct reaction only occurs at very high concentrations of nitrogen monoxide.

Nitrogen dioxide dissolves in and reacts in water to give a mixture of nitrous (nitric(III)) and nitric(v) acids:

$$2NO_2(g) + H_2O(l) \rightarrow HNO_2(aq) + HNO_3(aq)$$

Nitrogen dioxide may also catalyse the oxidation of sulfur dioxide to sulfur dioxide in the atmosphere, and hence speed up the production of acid rain:

$$NO_2(g) + SO_2(g) \rightarrow SO_3(g) + NO(g)$$
$$2NO(g) + O_2(g) \rightarrow 2NO_2(g)$$

■ Environmental effects of acid deposition

Acid deposition impacts the environment in five ways:

1   It affects the pH of lakes and rivers, which impacts the organisms living in them.
2   It affects the availability of metal ions in soil, which goes on to affect nearby plant life or surface water.
3   It directly affects plants.
4   It affects buildings and other materials.
5   It directly affects human health.

Impact on lakes and rivers

A low pH has a direct impact on aquatic organisms. Below pH 5.5 some species of fish, such as salmon, are killed, and algae and zooplankton, which are food for larger organisms, are depleted. In addition, low pH prevents hatching of fish eggs.

Fish are also killed when aluminium, leached from the soil by acid rain, enters lakes and rivers. The function of fish gills is affected by aluminium, leaving the fish unable to extract oxygen from the water.

Impact on soils

The pH of soils is a key factor determining whether certain species of plants will grow. Aluminium ions are present in soil in a number of forms. At high pH aluminium forms an insoluble hydroxide, $Al(OH)_3$. As the pH falls due to acid deposition, the aluminium ions are released into solution. For example, if the acid deposition, contains sulfuric acid, aluminium is released into nearby lakes and streams as soluble aluminium sulfate:

$$2Al(OH)_3 + 3H_2SO_4 \rightarrow Al_2(SO_4)_3 + 3H_2O$$

Other ions such as magnesium and calcium, which are essential for plant growth, are washed out of the soil in a similar way. They are therefore unavailable for absorption by the roots of plants. Low pH also favours the release of excessive concentrations of metal ions such as iron and manganese, which may be toxic to plants.

Direct effects on plants

As well as damaging the soil, and lowering the availability of nutrients, acid deposition can damage plants directly. For example, it can damage leaf chlorophyll, turning leaves brown and reducing the photosynthetic ability of the plant.

Effects on buildings

Limestone and marble are forms of calcium carbonate. Many historical buildings are made from these materials, so they can be eroded by acid rain:

$$CaCO_3 + H_2SO_4 \rightarrow CaSO_4 + H_2O + CO_2$$

Metallic structures, especially those made of iron (or steel) or aluminium, are readily attacked by acid deposition. Sulfur dioxide gas may directly attack iron as follows (an example of damage by dry deposition):

$$Fe + SO_2 + O_2 \rightarrow FeSO_4$$

or sulfuric acid may attack the iron (an example of wet deposition):

$$Fe + H_2SO_4 \rightarrow FeSO_4 + H_2$$
$$Fe + 2H^+ \rightarrow Fe^{2+} + H_2$$

◼ Measures to counteract acid deposition

Most measures to counteract acid deposition involve lowering the amount of acidic substances released into the atmosphere. Nitrogen oxides are removed from vehicle emissions using catalytic converters, and sulfur dioxide emissions from coal–fired power stations can be decreased in several ways.

Soil and lakes whose pH has been significantly decreased by acid deposition can be treated with limestone (calcium carbonate, $CaCO_3$) or calcium hydroxide ($Ca(OH)_2$) to raise the pH.

Balancing the equations that describe the formation of H_2SO_3, H_2SO_4, HNO_2 and HNO_3

Sulfur when combusted in air forms sulfur dioxide:

$$S(s) + O_2(g) \rightarrow SO_2(g)$$

This is an oxidation reaction.

Some sulfur dioxide may be oxidized to form sulfur trioxide. The unbalanced equation is balanced by writing coefficients of 2 in front of the oxides of sulfur. However, this oxidation reaction is slow in the absence of a catalyst:

$$2SO_2(s) + O_2(g) \rightarrow 2SO_3(g)$$

The oxides of sulfur react with water in a hydrolysis reaction to form the oxoacids:

$$SO_2(g) + H_2O(l) \rightarrow H_2SO_3(aq)$$
$$SO_3(g) + H_2O(l) \rightarrow H_2SO_4(aq)$$

Note there is no change in the oxidation number of sulfur during these reactions. Sulfur(IV) oxide forms sulfuric(IV) acid and sulfur(VI) oxide forms sulfuric(VI) acid.

Nitrogen reacts directly with oxygen at high temperature to produce nitrogen monoxide (a free radical):

$$N_2(g) + O_2(g) \rightarrow 2NO\bullet(g)$$

The equation is balanced by writing a coefficient of 2 in front of the nitrogen monoxide since nitrogen and oxygen are diatomic.

Nitrogen monoxide can be oxidized to nitrogen dioxide and the equation is balanced by coefficients of 2 in front of the two oxides of nitrogen:

$$2NO\bullet(g) + O_2(g) \rightarrow 2NO_2(g)$$

Nitrogen dioxide undergoes hydrolysis with water to form a mixture of nitric(III) and nitric(V) acids:

$$NO_2(g) + H_2O(l) \rightarrow HNO_2(aq) + HNO_3(aq)$$

This is balanced by adding a coefficient of 2 in front of the nitrogen dioxide (nitrogen(IV) oxide):

$$2NO_2(g) + H_2(l) \rightarrow HNO_2(aq) + HNO_3(aq)$$

This is a hydrolysis reaction and a disproportionation, since the nitrogen in the nitrogen dioxide is oxidized to nitric(V) acid, but reduced to nitric(III) (nitrous) acid.

Oxides of non-metals are usually neutral or acidic (Chapter 3). Acidic oxides are neutralized by bases and some acidic oxides react with water to form acidic solutions.

These four acids (sulfuric, sulfurous, nitric and nitrous acids) are much stronger than carbonic acid, H_2CO_3. They dissociate to a much greater extent (almost 100% in the case of nitric and sulfuric acids) and may lead to a rainwater pH as low as 2. This represents a concentration of $H_3O^+(aq)$ over 1000 times greater than in normal rainwater.

Methods of reducing sulfur oxides emissions

There are three methods by which sulfur dioxide emissions from power stations can be limited:

1 The coal or oil can be refined to remove the sulfur before combustion.
2 Fluidized bed combustion (FBC) is a method by which the amount of sulfur oxides resulting from combustion is lowered.
3 Flue gas desulfurization (FGD) (Figure 8.30) removes sulfur dioxide from the exhaust gases before they leave the power station flue (chimney).

The first method is a pre-combustion method and the second and third methods are post-combustion methods for reducing sulfur oxides emissions.

■ **Figure 8.30**
A coal–fired power station FGD plant

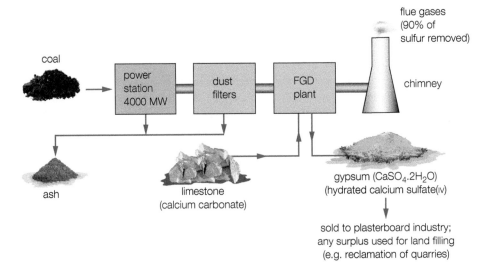

Fluidized bed combustion

A fluidized bed suspends the solid coal on an upward flowing jet of air during combustion. Coal dust is mixed with limestone powder (calcium carbonate, $CaCO_3$) and blasted into the furnace with a jet of air. The jet of air suspends the solid particles so they flow like a fluid.

At the high temperatures of the furnace, calcium carbonate decomposes to form calcium oxide:

$$CaCO_3 \rightarrow CaO + CO_2$$

The calcium oxide neutralizes the sulfur dioxide as it is formed. Further oxidation with oxygen produces particles of calcium sulfate:

$$2CaO + 2SO_2 + O_2 \rightarrow 2CaSO_4$$

The calcium sulfate must be removed by electrostatic precipitation.

Flue gas desulfurization

Sulfur dioxide emissions can be removed from the flue gases by passing the gases through a suspension of calcium carbonate and calcium oxide in water. The product is calcium sulfite (sulfate(IV)):

$$CaCO_3 + SO_2 \rightarrow CaSO_3 + CO_2$$
$$CaO + SO_2 \rightarrow CaSO_3$$

The calcium sulfite (calcium sulfate(IV)) is then further oxidized, producing calcium sulfate:

$$2CaSO_3 + O_2 \rightarrow 2CaSO_4$$

Acid rain – an international problem

The smoke and gas from coal-fired power stations is usually released into the air from very tall chimneys. For the people who live close to the power station this is beneficial; but the acidic oxides can travel many hundreds of kilometres in the winds higher in the atmosphere. The oxides then give rise to acid rain in regions far from the power station. The death of lakes and forests in Germany and parts of Scandinavia (e.g. Sweden) were blamed on coal-fired power stations in the United Kingdom, which, at that time, had inefficient purification systems. Reducing this problem in the 1980s required international political cooperation.

---

13 Find out about acid rain in your own country, including the impact of both acid rain and dry deposition in the lakes, forests, or other natural resources in your country. Find about practical steps that you as an individual can take to reduce oxide production, such as the use of public transport, cycling and car pooling.

Deducing equations for acid deposition with reactive metals and carbonates

Knowledge of chemical formulas, salt solubility and the construction of equations, including ionic equations, is necessary for constructing equations showing the reaction between an acid and reactive metals or metal carbonates.

---

14 Write equations for the following reactions:
   a sulfuric acid and magnesium carbonate
   b sulfurous acid with iron
   c nitric acid with calcium carbonate
   d nitrous acid with iron

15 Design an experiment examining the effect of acid rain on snail shells. Imagine that you have access to a large supply of snail shells and common acids and laboratory apparatus. Include a research question, methodology including the control of variables, and a prediction and explanation for your expected results.

Risks and problems – acid rain

The oxides of metals and non-metals can be characterized by their acid–base properties. Oxygen forms compounds with all the elements except the noble gases. It reacts directly with all elements except the halogens, a few noble metals, such as silver and gold, and the noble gases.

Metal oxides are ionic solids, non-metal oxides are simple molecular covalent gases and liquids. The variation of acid–base properties of the oxides in aqueous solution is strongly correlated with the position of the metal–non-metal line in the periodic table.

One of the most important aspects of the properties of oxides is their acid–base properties. Many oxides are basic or acidic anhydrides; that is, they are compounds that are formed by the removal of water from a corresponding acid or base. For example, sulfur(VI) oxide is the acid anhydride of sulfuric acid:

$$H_2SO_4 \rightarrow SO_3 + H_2O$$

and sodium oxide is the basic anhydride of sodium hydroxide:

$$2NaOH \rightarrow Na_2O + H_2O$$

Ionic oxides are usually basic anhydrides, whereas covalent oxides are usually acidic anhydrides.

Acid deposition is a topic that can be discussed from different perspectives. These include: sources (man-made and natural), geography and geology (for example, volcanoes), potential solutions (for example, neutralization by bases), environmental impact (on humans, on buildings and on living organisms), economics, politics and human health (for example, respiratory diseases).

Knowledge of the chemical reactions and reaction mechanisms involved in acid rain formation allows chemists to understand and to reduce the environmental impact of human activities from burning fossil fuels, especially coal.

■ Examination questions – a selection

Paper 1 IB questions and IB style questions

Q1 Which one of the following descriptions defines a strong acid?
- **A** It is concentrated.
- **B** It does dissociate in water.
- **C** It absorbs water from the air.
- **D** It almost completely dissociates in water.

Q2 Which of the following represents the reaction between zinc powder and a dilute aqueous solution of sulfuric acid?
- **A** $Zn + 2H_2SO_4 \rightarrow 2ZnS + 2H_2O + 3O_2$
- **B** $4Zn + H_2SO_4 \rightarrow 4ZnO + H_2S$
- **C** $Zn + H_2SO_4 \rightarrow ZnSO_4 + H_2$
- **D** $Zn + H_2SO_4 \rightarrow ZnH_2 + SO_2 + O_2$

Q3 When the following $1.0\,mol\,dm^{-3}$ solutions are listed in increasing order of pH (lowest first), what is the correct order?
- **A** $HNO_3 < H_2CO_3 < NH_3 < Ba(OH)_2$
- **B** $NH_3 < Ba(OH)_2 < H_2CO_3 < HNO_3$
- **C** $Ba(OH)_2 < H_2CO_3 < NH_3 < HNO_3$
- **D** $HNO_3 < H_2CO_3 < Ba(OH)_2 < NH_3$

Standard Level Paper 1, Nov 2005, Q24

Q4 What is the pH of pure distilled water?
- **A** 0   **B** 4   **C** 7   **D** 6

Q5 Which one of the following represents the reaction between calcium hydroxide and dilute hydrochloric acid?
- **A** $Ca(OH)_2 + HCl \rightarrow CaOCl + H_2O$
- **B** $CaOH + HCl \rightarrow CaCl_2 + H_2O$
- **C** $CaOH + 2HCl \rightarrow Cl_2 + CaOH_2$
- **D** $Ca(OH)_2 + 2HCl \rightarrow CaCl_2 + 2H_2O$

Q6 The amino acid alanine has the structure:
$$H_2N–CH(CH_3)–COOH$$
Which of the following species represents its conjugate acid?
- **A** $^+NH_3CH(CH_3)COOH$ **C** $^+NH_3CH(CH_3)COO^-$
- **B** $^+NH_3CH(CH_3)COOH_2^+$ **D** $NH_2CH(CH_3)COO^-$

Q7 Four flasks labelled A, B, C and D contain equal volumes of hydrochloric acid at different concentrations. When equal volumes of $1\,mol\,dm^{-3}$ sodium hydroxide are added to each flask the pH values below are produced.

Flask	A	B	C	D
pH	2	6	8	12

Which flask has the most concentrated acid?
- **A** flask A   **B** flask B   **C** flask C   **D** flask D

Q8 In the equilibrium below, which species represents a conjugate acid–base pair?
$$CH_2ClCOOH(aq) + H_2O(l) \rightleftharpoons CH_2ClCOO^-(aq) + H_3O^+(aq)$$
- **A** $CH_2ClCOOH / H_2O^-$
- **B** CH_2ClCOO^- / H_3O^+
- **C** H_2O / CH_2ClCOO^-
- **D** H_2O / H_3O^+

Q9 Hydrogen chloride dissolved in water reacts with magnesium. Hydrogen chloride dissolved in ethanol does not react with magnesium. Which statement accounts for this observation?
- **A** Ethanol accepts hydrogen ions (protons) and water does not.
- **B** Water is a hydrogen ion/proton acceptor.
- **C** Magnesium is very soluble in ethanol but insoluble in water.
- **D** Hydrogen chloride does not form ions in water.

Q10 Which of the following 1.00 mol dm^{-3} aqueous solutions would have the highest pH value?
A ammonia **C** sulfuric acid
B ethanoic acid **D** sodium hydroxide

Q11 A dilute aqueous solution of benzenecarboxylic acid (an organic acid) is a poor conductor of electricity. Which of the following statements accounts for this observation?
A Benzenecarboxylic acid solution has a high concentration of ions.
B Benzenecarboxylic acid is only slightly dissociated in water.
C Benzenecarboxylic acid is completely dissociated in water.
D It is a strong acid.

Q12 Which is the correct description for an aqueous solution with a pH of 9.5?
A alkaline **B** acidic **C** neutral **D** amphoteric

Q13 Methanoic acid, HCOOH, is a stronger acid than propanoic acid, CH$_3$CH$_2$COOH. Which one of the statements about these acids is correct?
A Propanoic acid is more dissociated in water than methanoic acid.
B Magnesium will react with methanoic acid but not with propanoic acid.
C A 1.0 mol dm^{-3} solution of methanoic acid will turn blue litmus red, but a 1.0 mol dm^{-3} solution of propanoic acid will turn red litmus blue.
D The pH of a solution of 1 mol dm^{-3} propanoic acid is higher than that of 1 mol dm^{-3} methanoic acid.

Q14 A decrease in the pH of an aqueous solution corresponds to:
A a decrease in the H$^+$ concentration and an increase in the OH$^-$ concentration
B an increase in the H$^+$ concentration and a decrease in the OH$^-$ concentration
C a decrease in the H$^+$ concentration with no change in the OH$^-$ concentration
D an increase in the OH$^-$ concentration and an increase in the H$^+$ concentration

Q15 Calcium oxide is added to a lake to neutralize the effects of acid rain. The pH value of the lake water rises from 4 to 6. What is the change in concentration of H$^+$(aq) in the lake water?
A an increase by a factor of 2
B an increase by a factor of 100
C a decrease by a factor of 2
D a decrease by a factor of 100

Q16 Which chemical can behave as a Brønsted–Lowry base and as a Brønsted–Lowry acid?
A CO$_3$$^{2-}$ **C** NO$_3$$^-$
B HSO$_4$$^-$ **D** Such a species does not exist.

Q17 The pH of solution X is 1 and that of Y is 2. Which statement is correct about the hydrogen ion concentrations in the two solutions?
A [H$^+$] in X is half that in Y.
B [H$^+$] in X is twice that in Y.
C [H$^+$] in X is one tenth of that in Y.
D [H$^+$] in X is ten times that in Y.

Standard Level Paper 1, May 2005, Q23

Q18 In which one of the following reactions does the nitric acid molecule act as a base?
A HNO$_3$ + H$_2$O → H$_3$O$^+$ + NO$_3$$^-$
B HNO$_3$ → H$^+$ + NO$_3$$^-$
C HNO$_3$ + CH$_3$COOH → CH$_3$COOH$_2$$^+$ + NO$_3$$^-$
D HNO$_3$ + 2H$_2$SO$_4$ → NO$_2$$^+$ + 2HSO$_4$$^-$ + H$_3$O$^+$

Q19 Which of the following would exactly neutralize 100 cm^3 of 1 mol dm^{-3} sulfuric acid?
A 0.1 mol of Ba(OH)$_2$ **C** 0.2 mol of Na$_2$CO$_3$
B 0.1 mol of KOH **D** 0.1 mol of NH$_3$

Q20 Which of the following compounds containing hydrogen acts as an acid in aqueous solution?
A hydrogen chloride **C** methane
B ammonia **D** ethene

Q21 Which is not a strong acid?
A nitric acid **C** carbonic acid
B sulfuric acid **D** hydrochloric acid

Standard Level Paper 1, Nov 06, Q23

Q22 Which equation correctly describes phosphoric(v) acid behaving as a monoprotic acid in aqueous solution?
A H$_3$PO$_4$(aq) → H$^+$(aq) + H$_2$PO$_4$$^-$(aq)
B H$_2$PO$_4$$^-$(aq) → H$^+$(aq) + HPO$_4$$^{2-}$(aq)
C H$_3$PO$_4$(aq) → 3H$^+$(aq) + PO$_4$$^{3-}$(aq)
D H$_3$PO$_4$(aq) → 2H$^+$(aq) + HPO$_4$$^{2-}$(aq)

Q23 Which list contains only strong bases?
A ammonia, sodium hydroxide, ethylamine
B potassium hydroxide, ammonia, sodium hydroxide
C lithium hydroxide, potassium hydroxide, barium hydroxide
D ammonia, ethylamine, barium hydroxide

Higher Level Paper 1, Nov 2013, Q27

Q24 Which of the following species is **not amphiprotic** in aqueous solution?
A HC$_2$O$_4$$^-$ **B** CH$_3$COO$^-$ **C** HPO$_4$$^{2-}$ **D** HCO$_3$$^-$

Q25 Which of the following is/are formed when a metal oxide reacts with a dilute acid?

   I   a metal salt
   II water
   III hydrogen gas

A I only   **C** II and III only
B I and II only   **D** I, II and III only

Standard Level Paper 1, Nov 2003, Q7

Paper 2 IB questions and IB style questions

Q1 **a** The pH values of solutions of three organic acids of the same concentration were measured.

   acid X   pH = 5
   acid Y   pH = 2
   acid Z   pH = 3

   i   Identify which solution is the least acidic. [1]
   ii Deduce how the $[H^+]$ values compare in solutions of acids Y and Z. [1]
   iii Arrange the solutions of the three acids in decreasing order of electrical conductivity, starting with the greatest conductivity, giving a reason for your choice. [2]

Q2 Carbonic acid (H_2CO_3) is described as a weak acid and hydrochloric acid (HCl) is described as a strong acid.

   a Explain, with the help of equations, what is meant by strong and weak acid using the above acids as examples. [4]
   b Outline **two** ways, other than using pH, in which you could distinguish between carbonic acid and hydrochloric acid of the same concentration. [2]
   c A solution of hydrochloric acid, HCl(aq), has a pH of 1 and a solution of carbonic acid, H_2CO_3(aq), has a pH of 5. Determine the ratio of the hydrogen ion concentrations in these solutions. [2]
   d The relative strengths of the two acids can be illustrated by the following equation:

   $$HCO_3^-(aq) + HCl(aq) \rightleftharpoons H_2CO_3(aq) + Cl^-(aq)$$

   i Identify the acid and its conjugate base and the base and its conjugate acid in the above equation. [2]
   ii Name the theory that is illustrated in **d i**. [1]

Standard Level Paper 2, Nov 2002, Q5

Q3 In aqueous solution, potassium hydroxide, KOH, is a strong base and ethylamine, $C_2H_5NH_2$, is a weak base.

   a Use Brønsted–Lowry theory to state why both substances are classified as bases. [1]
   b The pH value of $0.1\,mol\,dm^{-3}$ aqueous ethylamine solution is approximately 11. State and explain how the pH and hydroxide ion concentration of the $0.1\,mol\,dm^{-3}$ potassium hydroxide solution would compare. [3]
   c Write an equation to show the reaction of ethylamine with water and classify each product as a Brønsted–Lowry acid or base. [2]
   d Write an equation to show the neutralization reaction between ethylamine and hydrochloric acid. [1]
   e Explain why hydrochloric acid is not used to treat wasp stings. [1]

Standard Level Paper 2, Nov 2002, Q5

Q4 **a** Sulfuric (IV) acid, H_2SO_3, can be described as a Brønsted–Lowry acid. State what you understand by this description. [1]
   b The hydrogen sulfate (IV) ion, HSO_3^-, is amphiprotic. In the reaction of HSO_3^- with the oxonium cation, H_3O^+, identify the two species acting as bases.

   $$HSO_3^-(aq) + H_3O^+(aq) \rightleftharpoons H_2SO_3(aq) + H_2O(aq) \quad [1]$$

   c State one other acid present in acid rain that originates from car exhaust emissions. [1]
   d Describe two harmful effects of acid deposition on the natural environment. [2]
   e Starting with sulfur, S(s), write a series of molecular equations to illustrate how sulfuric (IV) acid, H_2SO_3(aq), is formed in the atmosphere. [3]

9 Redox processes

9.1 Oxidation and reduction – *redox (reduction–oxidation) reactions play a key role in many chemical and biochemical processes*

■ Introduction to oxidation and reduction

Oxidation

Many chemical reactions involve oxidation. This was originally defined as:

- the addition of oxygen to a substance

or

- the loss or removal of hydrogen from a substance.

An example of the first type of oxidation involves the burning or combustion of magnesium (Figure 9.1) in air or oxygen:

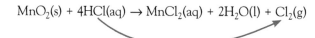

$$2Mg(s) + O_2(g) \rightarrow 2MgO(s)$$

■ **Figure 9.1**
The combustion of magnesium to form magnesium oxide

The magnesium has gained oxygen and we say that the magnesium has been oxidized.

An example of the second type of oxidation involves the reaction between manganese(IV) oxide ('manganese dioxide') and concentrated aqueous hydrochloric acid:

$$MnO_2(s) + 4HCl(aq) \rightarrow MnCl_2(aq) + 2H_2O(l) + Cl_2(g)$$

The hydrochloric acid loses hydrogen and is therefore oxidized. Later, we will see why these two apparently very different reactions are both regarded as oxidation reactions.

Strictly speaking, both these reactions are correctly described as redox reactions since they involve both oxidation and reduction. The formation of rust (hydrated iron(III) oxide) (Figure 9.2) is a familiar redox reaction. It involves the reaction between iron, oxygen and liquid water.

■ **Figure 9.2**
A rusting railway trolley (showing pitting)

Reduction

Many chemical reactions involve reduction. Reduction is the reverse of oxidation and was originally defined as:

- the loss or removal of oxygen from a substance

or

- the addition of hydrogen to a substance.

An example of the first type of reduction involves the reaction between hydrogen gas and heated copper(II) oxide:

$$CuO(s) + H_2(g) \rightarrow Cu(s) + H_2O(l)$$

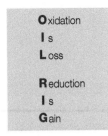

Oxidation
Is
Loss

Reduction
Is
Gain

■ **Figure 9.3**
Mnemonic for redox
reactions and electron
transfer

The copper(II) oxide loses oxygen and we therefore say that the copper(II) oxide has been reduced. An example of the second type of reduction involves the reaction between ethene and hydrogen to form ethane in the presence of a hot metal catalyst (Chapter 10):

$$C_2H_4(g) + H_2(g) \rightarrow C_2H_6(g)$$

The ethene gains hydrogen and we therefore say that the ethene has been reduced. This reaction is also an example of hydrogenation (Chapter 10), where hydrogen is added to an organic or carbon-containing compound.

Strictly speaking, both of these reactions are correctly described as redox reactions. The term reduction should be restricted to what happens to the copper(II) oxide and ethane, respectively.

Later, when electrolysis was discovered and modern theories of atomic structure (Chapter 2) and chemical bonding (Chapter 4) were developed, the terms oxidation and reduction were redefined in terms of electrons. Specifically, oxidation was defined as the loss of electrons from a substance and reduction was defined as the gaining of electrons by a substance (Figure 9.3).

Note that these modern definitions include many of the oxidation and reduction reactions previously defined in terms of loss and gain of oxygen and hydrogen. For example:

$$2Mg(s) + O_2(g) \rightarrow 2MgO(s)$$

can be rewritten to emphasize the loss and gain of electrons that occur during this reaction.

Magnesium oxide, MgO, is an ionic compound [Mg^{2+} O^{2-}], so the magnesium atom has lost two electrons to form a magnesium ion, Mg^{2+}. Oxygen is a molecular substance, so each oxygen atom has gained two electrons to become an oxide ion, O^{2-}.

These two processes can be described by the following equations:

Oxidation: $Mg \rightarrow Mg^{2+} + 2e^-$
Reduction: $O_2 + 4e^- \rightarrow 2O^{2-}$

Since during reduction one substance gains electrons, there must be a second process involving oxidation where a substance is losing electrons. Reduction and oxidation processes must therefore occur together simultaneously. Such processes are called redox (reduction–oxidation) reactions. They are the basis for voltaic cells.

The two equations are known as half-equations since they only describe one of the two reactions that must occur together. The ionic equation to describe the redox reaction is obtained by adding the two half-equations together and cancelling the electrons that appear on both sides of the equation:

Half-equations: $Mg \rightarrow Mg^{2+} + 2e^-$ and $O_2 + 4e^- \rightarrow 2O^{2-}$

The first half-equation has to be multiplied through by 2 so the number of electrons is the same as that in the second half-equation:

$$2Mg \rightarrow 2Mg^{2+} + 4e^-$$

Sum of the two half-equations:

$$2Mg + O_2 + 4e^- \rightarrow 2Mg^{2+} + 4e^- + 2O^{2-}$$

Cancelling of electrons:

$$2Mg + O_2 \rightarrow 2[Mg^{2+} O^{2-}]$$

The new definitions of oxidation and reduction, as electron loss and electron gain respectively, also include many examples of redox reactions which do *not* involve oxygen or hydrogen, for example, the burning of sodium metal in chlorine gas (Chapter 3) to form sodium chloride:

$$2Na(s) + Cl_2(g) \rightarrow 2NaCl(s)$$

The sodium atoms lose electrons to form sodium ions:

$$2Na \rightarrow 2Na^+ + 2e^-$$

and are therefore oxidized. The chlorine molecules gain electrons to form chloride ions:

$$Cl_2 + 2e^- \rightarrow 2Cl^-$$

and are therefore reduced.

Two half-equations can only be added together if the numbers of electrons in both are the same. If they are not, then one or both of the equations needs to be multiplied through by an appropriate coefficient. For example,

Half-equations: $Na \rightarrow Na^+ + e^-$ and $O_2 + 4e^- \rightarrow 2O^{2-}$

Multiplying the first half-equation through by 4:

$$4Na \rightarrow 4Na^+ + 4e^-$$

Summing the two half-equations:

$$4Na + O_2 + 4e^- \rightarrow 4Na^+ + 2O^{2-} + 4e^-$$

Cancelling of electrons and conversion of the ionic formula to a 'molecular formula':

$$4Na + O_2 \rightarrow 2Na_2O$$

Utilization: Photochromic lenses

It is very uncomfortable on the eyes to move rapidly in and out of intense sunlight and shadow, even if we are wearing sunglasses. Our eyes cannot adjust quickly enough to sudden changes of light intensity, unless we are wearing sunglasses made from photochromic lenses (Figure 9.4), which use chemical changes to compensate for changes in brightness.

■ **Figure 9.4**
Photochromic lenses

Lens glass is made photochromic by adding tiny amounts of silver chloride and copper(I) chloride to the molten glass as it cools, which traps the crystals within the structure of the glass. When bright sunlight strikes the glass, the silver chloride decomposes to form silver atoms, which darken the glass. This greatly reduces the intensity of the light that is absorbed by the retina. The half equation for this reduction is:

$$Ag^+ + e^- \rightarrow Ag$$

At the same time, chlorine atoms are formed and they react with copper(I) ions to form copper(II) ions and chloride ions. The half equations for these reactions are:

$$Cl^- \rightarrow Cl + e^- \quad \text{and} \quad Cl + Cu^+ \rightarrow Cu^{2+} + Cl^-$$

As soon as the exposure to intense sunlight ends, the copper(II) ions are reduced by silver atoms to re-form silver chloride and copper(I) chloride. This lightens the glass and allows all available light to reach the eyes. The ionic equation for these reactions is:

$$Cu^{2+} + Ag \rightarrow Ag^+ + Cu^+$$

■ Oxidation numbers

The electron transfer approach to oxidation (electron loss) and reduction (electron gain) is useful, *but* it does have some drawbacks and limitations. For example, consider the combustion of sulfur in air or oxygen to form sulfur dioxide:

$$S(s) + O_2(g) \rightarrow SO_2(g)$$

According to the historical definition of oxidation, as the addition of oxygen, the sulfur has been oxidized. However, neither the two reactants, nor the product, are ionic, and there is no obvious transfer of electrons. There are a large number of reactions that fit the historical definitions of oxidation and reduction, such as the hydrogenation of ethene, but *not* the modern definitions in terms of electron loss and gain.

One way to overcome this problem is to develop new definitions of oxidation and reduction that cover both the historical definitions in terms of oxygen and hydrogen and the modern definitions in terms of electrons. The concept of an oxidation number, which consists of a number and a sign, allows chemists to avoid the problems associated with using two separate and sometimes conflicting definitions for oxidation and reduction.

The concept applies equally well to reactions involving ionic compounds, where there is obvious electron transfer, and reactions involving covalent compounds, where there is no obvious transfer of electrons. Oxidation is now defined as an increase in oxidation number and reduction is defined as a decrease in oxidation number.

There are some simple rules (based on the electronegativities of the elements and their bonding) that we can apply to find oxidation numbers:

- The oxidation number of any uncombined element is zero.
  Example: in $O_2(g)$ the oxidation number of oxygen is 0.

- For a simple ion, the oxidation number of the ion is equal to the charge on the ion.
  Examples: in Cl^- and Fe^{2+}, the oxidation numbers are −1 and +2, respectively. Note the different order for the sign and number in the oxidation number compared with the ion.

- For a compound, the sum of the oxidation numbers of the elements is zero.
  Example: in NaCl $[Na^+ Cl^-]$ the sum of the oxidation numbers (+1 and −1) is 0.

- For a polyatomic ion, the sum of the oxidation numbers of the elements is equal to the charge on the ion.
  Example: in the sulfate ion, SO_4^{2-}, the sum of the oxidation numbers is −2, that is, $[+6 + (-2 \times 4)]$.

- The oxidation number of hydrogen is +1 (except where it is combined with a reactive metal, for example in sodium hydride, NaH $[Na^+ H^-]$, where it is −1).

- The oxidation number of oxygen is −2 (except in a few compounds such as hydrogen peroxide, H_2O_2, where it is −1 and oxygen difluoride, OF_2, where it is +2).

Worked examples

Deduce the oxidation number of sulfur in sulfur dioxide, SO_2.

(O.N. of S) + (2 × O.N. of O) = 0

(O.N. of s) + (2 × −2) = −4

O.N. of S = +4

Deduce the oxidation number of nitrogen in the nitrate ion, NO_3^-.

(O.N. of N) + (3 × O.N. of O) = −1

(O.N. of N) + (3 × −2) = −1

O.N. of N = +5

In a covalent bond in a molecule, the more electronegative element is given a negative oxidation number and the less electronegative element, a positive oxidation number. For example, in chlorine fluoride, ClF, the chlorine atom is less electronegative than the fluorine atom (the most electronegative element). Therefore chlorine is assigned an oxidation number of +1 and fluorine that of −1. By convention, the less electronegative element appears first in the formula of a binary compound, so chlorine fluoride has the formula ClF and not FCl. (In some compounds whose formulas were established before the concept of oxidation number was developed, the convention is not observed. For example, the formula of ammonia is NH_3, although nitrogen is more electronegative than hydrogen.)

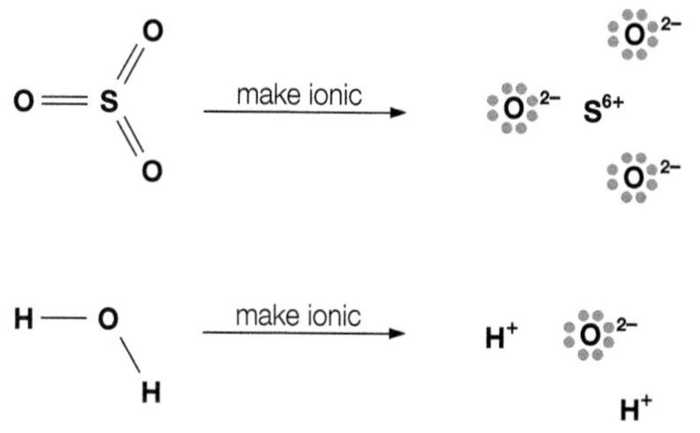

■ **Figure 9.5** The ionic formulations of the sulfur trioxide and water molecules

In sulfur trioxide, SO_3, the oxygen is the more electronegative element (it is above sulfur in the periodic table) and is therefore assigned the negative oxidation number. The three oxygen atoms, each of oxidation number −2, are balanced by the one sulfur atom with an oxidation number of +6. The sum of the oxidation numbers $[(−2 \times 3) + 6]$ equals zero.

The idea of an oxidation number is an artificial concept since it considers all compounds, even covalent ones, to be ionic. An alternative, but equivalent, expression is that it is assumed that the atom with the greater electronegativity 'owns' or 'controls' all the bonding or shared electrons of a particular covalent bond.

For example, the sulfur trioxide molecule, SO_3, is assumed to be $[S^{6+} \, 3O^{2-}]$ and the water molecule, H_2O, is assumed to be $[2H^+ \, O^{2-}]$, as shown in Figure 9.5. The oxidation numbers for the central sulfur and oxygen in these two species are +6 and −2, respectively.

A negative sign for an oxidation number means the atom has gained 'control' of the electrons (compared to the element) and a positive sign for an oxidation number means that the atom has lost 'control' of the electrons (compared to the element). The numerical value of an oxidation number indicates the number of electrons over which electron 'control' has changed compared to the situation in the element.

So in the example above, SO_3, sulfur has lost 'control' of six electrons and each oxygen has gained 'control' of the two electrons, compared to their elements.

The oxidation number is written as a Roman numeral if included in the name of a compound. This is common practice for transition metal compounds: for example, the correct name for the permanganate ion, MnO_4^-, is manganate(VII), pronounced 'manganate seven'.

How evidence is used

Changes in the definition of oxidation and reduction from one involving specific elements (oxygen and hydrogen), to one involving electron transfer, to one invoking oxidation numbers, is a good example of the way that scientists broaden similarities to general principles.

The word oxidation was first used to describe a substance in which oxygen reacted with a substance. In the same way, reduction, the opposite process, originally referred to a reaction in which oxygen was removed from a substance. However, in due course this narrow definition of oxidation and reduction gave way to more comprehensive and general ones involving a much wider range of reactions. The first type to be included was those involving the transfer of hydrogen. Due to its ability to react with oxygen to form water, hydrogen was regarded as the chemical opposite of oxygen. As a result, oxidation was extended and generalized to mean not only the addition of oxygen, but also the removal of hydrogen. As more reactions were studied, it was seen that many of them were fundamentally of the same type as the redox reactions involving oxygen transfer. These reactions involved the combination of a substance with an electronegative element, such fluorine, oxygen, sulfur and other non-metallic elements. In a similar way, the definition of reduction was extended to include the removal of electronegative elements as well as the addition of electropositive elements, that is, elements which, like hydrogen, have a tendency to lose electrons and form cations. A further important extension of the concept of oxidation was to an even broader and more general view that includes any process which involves the loss of electrons. Thus a substance loses electrons when it is oxidized and gains electrons when it is reduced, while a redox reaction is a transfer of electrons from the reducing agent (electron donor) to the oxidizing agent (electron acceptor). Later the concept of oxidation number and a set of arbitrary rules were introduced to keep track of the electrons. Figure 9.6 summaries the concept of redox in terms of electrons.

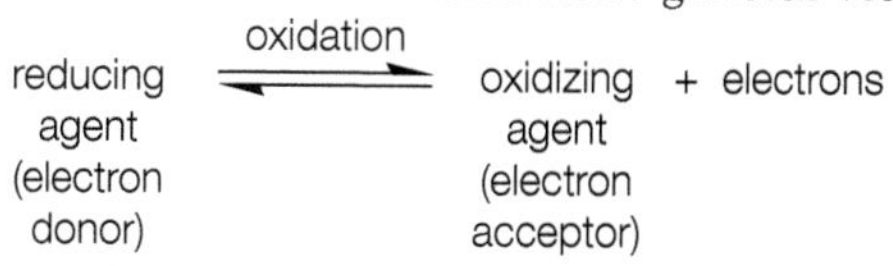

■ **Figure 9.6** A summary of the concept of redox in terms of electrons

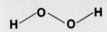

■ **Figure 9.7**
Structural formula of the hydrogen peroxide molecule

■ **Figure 9.9**
Structural formula of the thiosulfate ion

Difficulties with oxidation numbers

Bonds between elements

Another rule for determining oxidation numbers is that bonds between atoms of the same element do not count towards the oxidation number. So, for example, in hydrogen peroxide (Figure 9.7), the oxidation numbers of hydrogen and oxygen are +1 and −1, respectively. Since hydrogen peroxide is a molecule, the sum of the oxidation numbers [(+1 × 2) + (−1 × 2)] will be zero.

Sodium thiosulfate (Figure 9.8) contains the thiosulfate ion $S_2O_3^{2-}$, (Figure 9.9) which has the systematic name thiosulfate(VI) to indicate its relationship to the sulfate(VI) ion, SO_4^{2-}. However, this is incorrect if the rule for calculating oxidation numbers in the case of element–element bonds is applied (cf. H_2O_2). Applying this rule we find that that the sulfur atom bonded only to the other sulfur has an oxidation number of zero and the central sulfur atom has an oxidation number of +4.

■ **Figure 9.8** Sodium thiosulfate crystals

Organic chemistry

Because of the large number of element–element bonds present in organic (carbon-containing) compounds, the concept of oxidation numbers is not very helpful and adds very little to the understanding of organic chemistry. However, the 'old-fashioned' definitions of oxidation and reduction in terms of hydrogen and oxygen are frequently applied to oxygen-containing compounds such as aldehydes, ketones, carboxylic acids and alcohols (Chapter 10). For example:

$$CH_3CH_2OH \quad \xrightarrow{[2H]} \quad CH_3CHO \quad \xrightarrow{[O]} \quad CH_3COOH$$

$$\text{ethanol} \qquad\qquad \text{ethanal} \qquad\qquad \text{ethanoic acid}$$
$$\text{(an alcohol)} \qquad \text{(an aldehyde)} \qquad \text{(a carboxylic acid)}$$

The first conversion involves the loss of hydrogen and is hence classified as oxidation. The second conversion involves the addition of oxygen and is again classified as an oxidation. The [O] and [H] are a shorthand for oxidation and reduction; they do *not* imply that oxygen and hydrogen atoms are intermediates in the oxidation process.

The oxidation of ethanol to ethanoic acid can be brought about by heating ethanol with an acidified aqueous solution of potassium dichromate(VI), $K_2Cr_2O_7$. Half-equations can also be written for the two oxidations shown above:

$$CH_3CH_2OH \rightarrow CH_3CHO + 2H^+ + 2e^-$$
$$CH_3CHO + H_2O \rightarrow CH_3COOH + 2H^+ + 2e^-$$

The electrons will be accepted by the dichromate(VI) ion.

Another common oxidizing agent used in organic chemistry is acidified or alkaline potassium manganate(VII). A reducing reagent used in organic chemistry is hydrogen gas and a heated metal catalyst (Chapter 10).

1 Deduce the oxidation states of vanadium in the following ions and compounds:
   a VO_2^+ b V^{2+} c $[V(H_2O)_6]^{3+}$ d V_2O_5 e NH_4VO_3 f VO^{2+}

■ Naming inorganic compounds

The concept of oxidation number is used in the modern chemical naming of ionic inorganic substances. This system of nomenclature, or naming, is called the Stock notation. In this system the oxidation number is inserted immediately after the name of an ion. Roman numerals are inserted after the name or symbol of the element. For example:

$FeCl_2$ $[Fe^{2+} \ 2Cl^-]$ iron(II) chloride

$FeCl_3$ $[Fe^{3+} \ 3Cl^-]$ iron(III) chloride

This notation is only used for the transition metals, and tin and lead from group 14 (IV) of the periodic table where variable or multiple oxidation states are exhibited. For the metals from groups 1 (I), 2 (II) and 13 (III) it is not usually necessary to indicate the oxidation state of the metal, for example calcium chloride rather than calcium(II) chloride. Some compounds contain two cations, for example the 'mixed oxide' of lead:

Pb_3O_4 $[2Pb^{2+} \ Pb^{4+} \ 4O^{2-}]$ dilead(II) lead(IV) oxide

The Stock system is also used to name complex ions (Chapter 13). For example, $[Fe(CN)_6]^{3-}$, which consists of an iron(III) ion surrounded by six cyanide ions, that is, $[Fe^{3+} \ 6CN^-]$, is named as the hexacyanoferrate(III) ion. Stock names are used for the following oxoanions:

■ Figure 9.10
Photograph of crystals of sodium chlorate(v), a powerful oxidizing agent

Chromate(VI)	CrO_4^{2-}	Dichromate(VI)	$Cr_2O_7^{2-}$
Manganate(VII)	MnO_4^-	Manganate(VI)	MnO_4^{2-}
Chlorate(I)	ClO^-	Chlorate(III)	ClO_2^-
Chlorate(V)	ClO_3^-	Chlorate(VII)	ClO_4^-

This is because, for example, the names 'chlorate' (Figure 9.10) and 'manganate' are not precise enough and potentially refer to more than one species. For compounds between non-metals the Stock notation is generally not used and the actual numbers of the atoms in the molecular formula are shown in the name. For example, dinitrogen oxide, N_2O, rather than nitrogen(I) oxide and sulfur hexafluoride, SF_6, rather than sulfur(VI) fluoride.

---

2 Deduce Stock names for the following transition compounds:
   a $Na_2Cr_2O_7$ c V_2O_5 e $CuSO_4.H_2O$ g $Zn(NO_3)_2$
   b K_2CrO_4 d NH_4VO_3 f Cu_2SO_4 h $ScCl_3$

ToK Link

Oxidation states are useful when explaining redox reactions. Are artificial conversions a useful or valid way of clarifying knowledge?

Manganese in the manganate(VII) ion, MnO_4^-, has an oxidation number of +7. This implies the presence of Mn^{7+}. It must be remembered that the oxidation state of an atom does not represent the 'real' charge on that atom. This is particularly true of high oxidation states, where the ionization energy required to produce a highly charged positive ion is far greater than the energies available in chemical reactions. The manganese–oxygen bonds in the manganate(VII) ion are polar covalent bonds. The assignment of electrons between atoms in calculating an oxidation state is purely a set of useful but artificial beliefs for the understanding of many chemical reactions. Oxidation numbers are not 'real' – they are simply useful mathematical constructs used to keep track of electrons during redox reactions.

ToK Link

Chemistry has developed a systematic language that has resulted in older names becoming obsolete. What has been lost and gained in this process?

The alchemists gave names to many inorganic compounds which were often related to their method of preparation or appearance. Examples include 'spirit of salt' (hydrochloric acid) because it was made from salt, 'the green lion' (iron(II) sulfate), 'spirit of hartshorn' (aqueous ammonia) which was distilled from harts' horns, and *aqua regia* (King's water), a mixture of hydrochloric and nitric acids, which could dissolve gold.

Many inorganic compounds are now named according to the Stock system that specifies the oxidation number of the cation. The advantage of this system is that it removes the possibility of confusion about the actual compound and its formula. However, the Stock system makes no connection between the name and the appearance or preparation of the compound. The Stock name is purely a 'label' that is centred on the charges (real or imagined) within the formula unit.

There are enormous numbers of organic compounds, partly because there are many possibilities for isomers. Since isomers are different compounds, they need to have different names. Furthermore, the name assigned to a given compound must be unambiguous, so that chemists all over the world draw the same structure when they see the name. Organic names are based on finding the longest unbranched chain and then identifying alkyl side chains and functional groups (see Chapter 10). However, some complex organic molecules are given trivial names (Figures 9.11 and 9.12) that may provide additional information about the molecules.

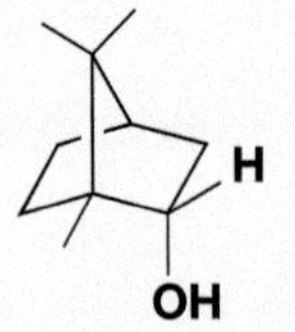

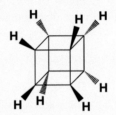

■ **Figure 9.11** Borneol, which is obtained by reduction from the camphor tree found in Borneo and Sumatra

■ **Figure 9.12** Cubane (a hydrocarbon whose eight carbon atoms occupy the vertices of a cube)

▩ Identifying redox reactions

Redox reactions or redox equations are easily recognized by:

■ deducing all of the oxidation numbers of the atoms in the chemical species present in the molecular, ionic or half-equation. Note that the equation does not have to be balanced in order to do this.

■ examining the numbers to see if the oxidation number of any atom has changed. If it has, the reaction is a redox reaction. An increase in oxidation number is oxidation and a decrease in oxidation number is reduction.

If there are *no* changes in oxidation numbers during the chemical reaction, then the reaction is *not* a redox reaction. Examples of non-redox reactions include most acid–base reactions (Chapter 8), precipitation reactions (Chapter 1) and complex ion formation (Chapter 13).
Consider the following reactions.

$$2FeCl_2(s) + Cl_2(g) \rightarrow 2FeCl_3(s)$$

The oxidation numbers of iron are +2 and +3, respectively and the oxidation numbers for chlorine are 0 and −1, respectively. The iron has undergone oxidation and the chlorine has undergone reduction.

$$Mn(NO_3)_2(s) \rightarrow MnO_2(s) + 2NO_2(g)$$

The oxidation numbers of manganese are +2 and +4, respectively, and the oxidation numbers for nitrogen are +5 and +4, respectively. The manganese has undergone oxidation and the nitrogen has undergone reduction.

$$(NH_4)_2Cr_2O_7(s) \rightarrow Cr_2O_3(s) + 4H_2O(g) + N_2(g)$$

The oxidation numbers of chromium are respectively +6 and +3, and the oxidation numbers for nitrogen are −3 and 0, respectively. The chromium has undergone reduction and the nitrogen has undergone oxidation.

$$MgO(s) + 2HCl(aq) \rightarrow MgCl_2(aq) + H_2O(l)$$

The oxidation numbers of magnesium, chlorine, hydrogen and oxygen remain unchanged at +2, −1, +1 and −2. Acid–base reactions are therefore *not* redox reactions.

$$[Cu(H_2O)_6]^{2+}(aq) + 4NH_3(aq) \rightarrow [Cu(NH_3)_4(H_2O)_2]^{2+}(aq) + 4H_2O(l)$$

The oxidation number of copper is +2 in both of the complex ions. There is no change in oxidation number and this reaction, an example of ligand replacement (Chapter 13), is therefore *not* a redox reaction.

Disproportionation

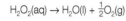

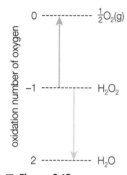

Disproportionation occurs when a single species is both oxidized and reduced simultaneously (Figure 9.13). An example of disproportionation is the catalytic decomposition of hydrogen peroxide (Chapter 6).

One of the oxygen atoms in the hydrogen peroxide molecule becomes part of an oxygen molecule and during this change the oxidation number increases from −1 to zero. Hence, this is oxidation. The other oxygen atom in the hydrogen peroxide molecule becomes part of a water molecule and during this change the oxidation number decreases from −1 to −2. Hence, this is reduction.

Another example of disproportionation is the reaction between chlorine and water (Chapter 3) to form a mixture of hydrochloric and chloric(I) ('hypochlorous') acids:

$$\underset{0}{Cl_2}(g) + H_2O(l) \rightarrow HO\underset{+1}{Cl}(aq) + H\underset{-1}{Cl}(aq)$$

■ Figure 9.13
The disproportionation of hydrogen peroxide

One of the chlorine atoms in the chlorine molecule becomes a chloride ion, and during this change the oxidation number decreases from 0 to −1. Hence, this is reduction. The other chlorine atom in the chlorine molecule becomes part of the chlorate(I) ion, and during this change the oxidation number increases from 0 to +1. Hence, this is oxidation.

Other examples of disproportionation include:

- the reaction between chlorine and cold dilute aqueous sodium hydroxide
- the reaction between soluble copper(I) compounds, such as copper(I) sulfate, and water (Chapter 13)

- the overall cell reaction that occurs in a lead–acid car battery during discharge (Chapter 24 on the accompanying website).

Redox equations

Constructing half-equations

Many of the oxidizing and reducing agents previously described only bring about oxidation and reduction in an acidified aqueous solution. Their half-equations frequently involve water molecules and hydrogen ions. The following procedure describes how such half-equations can be constructed.

1 Write down the formulas of the reactant and products, for example:

$$Cr_2O_7^{2-} \rightarrow Cr^{3+}$$

2 Balance with respect to the chromium:

$$Cr_2O_7^{2-} \rightarrow 2Cr^{3+}$$

3 Balance the oxygen atoms of the dichromate(VI) ion with water molecules:

$$Cr_2O_7^{2-} \rightarrow 2Cr^{3+} + 7H_2O$$

4　Balance the hydrogen atoms present in the water with hydrogen ions:

$$14H^+ + Cr_2O_7^{2-} \rightarrow 2Cr^{3+} + 7H_2O$$

5　Determine the total charges on both sides of the almost completed half-equation:

LHS: $+14 + -2 = +12$　　RHS: $(2 \times +3) = +6$

6　Balance the two charges by adding electrons to the side of the equation with the more positive value:

$$6e^- + 14H^+(aq) + Cr_2O_7^{2-}(aq) \rightarrow 2Cr^{3+}(aq) + 7H_2O(l)$$
LHS: $+14 + -2 + -6 = +6$　　RHS: $(2 \times +3) = +6$

An identical process is used to construct half-equations for reducing agents that operate in an aqueous acidic solvent. The one difference is that the electrons will appear on the right-hand side of the half-equation.

1　Write down the formulas of the reactant and products, for example:

$$HNO_2 \rightarrow NO_3^-$$ (the equation is already balanced with respect to the nitrogen)

2　Balance the oxygen of the nitrous acid (nitric(III) acid) with a water molecule:

$$H_2O + HNO_2 \rightarrow NO_3^-$$

3　Balance the hydrogen present in the water and nitrous acid with hydrogen ions:

$$H_2O + HNO_2 \rightarrow NO_3^- + 3H^+$$

4　Determine the total charges on both sides of the almost completed half-equation:

LHS: $= 0$　　RHS: $-1 + (3 \times +1) = +2$

5　Balance the two charges by adding electrons to the side of the equation with the more positive value:

$$H_2O(l) + HNO_2(aq) \rightarrow NO_3^-(aq) + 3H^+(aq) + 2e^-$$
LHS: 0　　RHS: $-1 + (3 \times +1) + -2 = 0$

Forming redox equations

Ion–electron method

Redox equations are written by combining two half-equations: one describing the action of an oxidizing agent and the other describing the action of a reducing agent. Often one or both of the two half-equations must be multiplied by suitable coefficients so that the number of electrons gained by the oxidizing agent equals the number of electrons lost by the reducing agent. The electrons can then be cancelled from both sides of the equations and, if necessary, the numbers of water molecules and hydrogen ions (if present) simplified.

Worked example

Write a redox equation for the reduction of acidified manganate(VII) ions and the oxidation of methanol using the balanced half-equations below:

$$2H_2O(l) + CH_3OH(l) \rightarrow CO_2(g) + H_2O(l) + 6H^+(aq) + 6e^-$$
$$MnO_4^-(aq) + 8H^+(aq) + 5e^- \rightarrow Mn^{2+}(aq) + 4H_2O(l)$$

Multiplying through the top half-equation by 5 and the bottom half-equation by 6:

$$10H_2O(l) + 5CH_3OH(l) \rightarrow 5CO_2(g) + 5H_2O(l) + 30H^+(aq) + 30e^-$$
$$6MnO_4^-(aq) + 48H^+(aq) + 30e^- \rightarrow 6Mn^{2+}(aq) + 24H_2O(l)$$

Adding the two half-equations together:

$$10H_2O(l) + 5CH_3OH(l) + 6MnO_4^-(aq) + 48H^+(aq) + 30e^-$$
$$\rightarrow 5CO_2(g) + 5H_2O(l) + 30H^+(aq) + 30e^- + 6Mn^{2+}(aq) + 24H_2O(l)$$

Cancelling electrons:

$$10H_2O(l) + 5CH_3OH(l) + 6MnO_4^-(aq) + 48H^+(aq)$$
$$\rightarrow 5CO_2(g) + 5H_2O(l) + 30H^+(aq) + 6Mn^{2+}(aq) + 24H_2O(l)$$

Simplifying the number of water molecules on the right-hand side of the equation:

$$10H_2O(l) + 5CH_3OH(l) + 6MnO_4^-(aq) + 48H^+(aq)$$
$$\rightarrow 5CO_2(g) + 30H^+(aq) + 6Mn^{2+}(aq) + 29H_2O(l)$$

The consumption of 10 water molecules and the production of 29 water molecules is equivalent to the production of 19 molecules:

$$5CH_3OH(l) + 6MnO_4^-(aq) + 48H^+(aq) \rightarrow 5CO_2(g) + 30H^+(aq) + 6Mn^{2+}(aq) + 19H_2O(l)$$

The consumption of 48 hydrogen ions and the production of 30 hydrogen ions is equivalent to the consumption of 18 hydrogen ions:

$$5CH_3OH(l) + 6MnO_4^-(aq) + 18H^+(aq) \rightarrow 5CO_2(g) + 6Mn^{2+}(aq) + 19H_2O(l)$$

Oxidation number method

This method allows the reacting ratio of the species to be determined more quickly than the ion–electron half-equation method. The procedure involves the following steps:

1 Identify the elements that have undergone a change in oxidation number.
2 Balance the atoms that have to undergo a change in oxidation number.
3 Find the change in oxidation number and the number of electrons transferred for each redox species.
4 Balance the charge by adding the correct number of protons, $H^+(aq)$, for acidic aqueous solution.
5 Balance the oxygen by adding water molecules, H_2O, and the rest of the atoms not involved in redox.

In a redox reaction, the sum of the *increases* in the oxidation number of oxidized species *equals* the sum of the *decreases* in the oxidation number of the reduced species. This concept can be used to balance redox equations.
For example:

$$2Fe^{3+} + 2Br^- \rightarrow 2Fe^{2+} + Br_2$$

$+6 \qquad\qquad \rightarrow +4 \qquad\qquad$ (decrease in oxidation number by 2, reduction)

$\qquad\qquad -2 \rightarrow \qquad\quad 0 \quad$ (increase in oxidation number by 2, oxidation)

Worked example

Balance the redox reaction between acidified potassium manganate(vii) and iron(ii) sulfate using the oxidation number method.

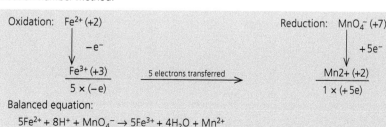

Balanced equation:

$$5Fe^{2+} + 8H^+ + MnO_4^- \rightarrow 5Fe^{3+} + 4H_2O + Mn^{2+}$$

■ Redox titrations

Redox titrations are similar to acid–base titrations (Chapter 1). Acid–base titrations involve the transfer of one or more hydrogen ions from the acid to the base. A redox titration involves the transfer of one or more electrons from a reducing agent to an oxidizing agent.

As demonstrated above, a redox reaction can be described by two half-equations: in one half-equation the reducing agent loses electrons and in the other half-equation the oxidizing agent gains electrons. The overall or stoichiometric equation for a redox titration can be obtained by combining the two half-equations, so that the number of electrons lost by the reducing agent equals the number of electrons gained by the oxidizing agent. For example:

$$MnO_4^-(aq) + 8H^+(aq) + 5e^- \rightarrow Mn^{2+}(aq) + 4H_2O(l)$$

and

$$H_2O_2(aq) \rightarrow O_2(g) + 2H^+(aq) + 2e^-$$

The bottom half-equation is multiplied through by 5 and the top half-equation by 2 so that they both contain the same number of electrons. The two equations are then added together and simplified:

$$2MnO_4^-(aq) + 16H^+(aq) + 10e^- \rightarrow 2Mn^{2+}(aq) + 8H_2O(l)$$

and

$$5H_2O_2(aq) \rightarrow 5O_2(g) + 10H^+(aq) + 10e^-$$

Adding together:

$$2MnO_4^-(aq) + 16H^+(aq) + 5H_2O_2(aq) \rightarrow 2Mn^{2+}(aq) + 8H_2O(l) + 5O_2(g) + 10H^+(aq)$$

Simplifying the numbers of hydrogen ions:

$$2MnO_4^-(aq) + 6H^+(aq) + 5H_2O_2(aq) \rightarrow 2Mn^{2+}(aq) + 8H_2O(l) + 5O_2(g)$$

Common oxidizing and reducing agents used in redox titrations, together with their appropriate half-equations, are shown below.

Oxidizing agents for redox titrations

Acidified manganate(VII) ions

$$MnO_4^-(aq) + 8H^+(aq) + 5e^- \rightarrow Mn^{2+}(aq) + 4H_2O(l)$$

Manganate(VII) ions are purple in colour but the reduced form, manganese(II) ions, is almost colourless. Solutions of potassium manganate(VII) are *not* primary standards (Chapter 1) because potassium manganate(VII) is difficult to prepare pure and it reacts slowly with water to form manganese(IV) oxide, especially in the presence of light.

Acidified dichromate(VI) ions

$$14H^+(aq) + Cr_2O_7^{2-}(aq) + 6e^- \rightarrow 2Cr^{3+}(aq) + 7H_2O(l)$$

Dichromate(VI) ions are orange in colour but the reduced form, chromium(III), is green. Solutions of potassium dichromate(VI) can be used as primary standards.

Iron(III) ions or salts

$$e^- + Fe^{3+}(aq) \rightarrow Fe^{2+}(aq)$$

Iodine

$$I_2(aq) + 2e^- \rightarrow 2I^-(aq)$$

Iodine (in potassium iodide solution) is red brown in colour, but colourless when in the reduced form as the iodide ion.

Indicators are not needed for titrations that involve manganate(VII) ions, dichromate(VI) ions or iodine since there is a significant colour change. At the end-points of these titrations, adding a slight excess of the reducing agent will produce a permanent colour change in the solution.

However, the sensitivity of the iodine colour change is often improved by adding starch solution as an indicator. This gives a deep blue-black coloured complex in the presence of iodine. The complex disappears at the end-point when all the iodine is converted to iodide.

Acidified hydrogen peroxide

$$H_2O_2(aq) + 2H^+(aq) + 2e^- \rightarrow 2H_2O(l)$$

Hydrogen peroxide is a moderately powerful oxidizing agent; however, when in the presence of a more powerful oxidizing agent it is 'forced' to act as a reducing agent.

Reducing agents for redox titrations

Iron(II) salts or iron(II) ions

$$Fe^{2+}(aq) \rightarrow Fe^{3+}(aq) + e^-$$

Ethanedioic (oxalic) acid and ethanedioate (oxalate) ions

$$(COOH)_2(aq) \rightarrow 2CO_2(g) + 2H^+(aq) + 2e^-$$

$$(COO^-)_2(aq) \rightarrow 2CO_2(g) + 2e^-$$

This autocatalytic reaction (Chapter 16) is carried out at 80 °C since the reaction is relatively slow at room temperature.

Ethanedioic acid (Figure 9.14) and its salts are primary standards and are frequently used to standardize solutions of potassium manganate(VII), that is, determine their concentration to a high degree of accuracy.

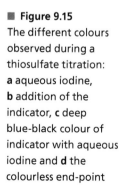

■ **Figure 9.14**
Ethanedioic acid crystals

Hydrogen peroxide

$$H_2O_2(aq) \rightarrow 2H^+(aq) + O_2(g) + 2e^-$$

This reaction occurs when hydrogen peroxide is in the presence of a more powerful oxidizing agent, such as dichromate(VI) or manganate(VII) ions.

Iodide ions

$$2I^-(aq) \rightarrow I_2(aq) + 2e^-$$

Sodium thiosulfate(VI) or thiosulfate(VI) ions

$$2S_2O_3^{2-}(aq) \rightarrow S_4O_6^{2-}(aq) + 2e^-$$

A common redox reaction is the reaction of an oxidizing agent with excess potassium iodide solution to form iodine. The iodine is then titrated with sodium thiosulfate solution, using starch as an indicator (Figure 9.15).

■ **Figure 9.15**
The different colours observed during a thiosulfate titration:
a aqueous iodine,
b addition of the indicator, **c** deep blue-black colour of indicator with aqueous iodine and **d** the colourless end-point

The overall equation for the reaction is:

$$2S_2O_3^{2-}(aq) + I_2(aq) \rightarrow S_4O_6^{2-}(aq) + 2I^-(aq)$$

■ Oxidizing agents

An oxidizing agent is defined as a substance that brings about the oxidation of substances by accepting electrons from the substance they oxidize. Oxidizing agents undergo a process of reduction.

Some common oxidizing agents, some examples of their reactions and their appropriate half-equations are described below. The strengths of oxidizing agents are described by their standard electrode potentials (Chapter 19).

Oxygen

During the reaction in the gas phase, oxygen molecules gain electrons to form oxide ions:

$$\frac{1}{2}O_2(g) + 2e^- \rightarrow O^{2-}(g)$$

Ozone (trioxygen)

Ozone is an extremely powerful oxidizing agent in acidic solution:

$$O_3(aq) + 2H^+(aq) + 2e^- \rightarrow O_2(g) + H_2O(l)$$

It produces iodine from neutral or alkaline potassium iodide solution:

$$2KI(aq) + O_3(aq) + H_2O(l) \rightarrow 2KOH(aq) + O_2(g) + I_2(aq)$$

Chlorine

During the reaction chlorine molecules gain electrons to form chloride ions:

$$Cl_2(aq) + 2e^- \rightarrow 2Cl^-(aq)$$

This reaction occurs both in the gas phase and in acidic solution.

Similar reactions occur with the other halogens, but with a decreasing tendency as you go down the group.

Acidified potassium manganate(VII)

During the reaction purple manganate(VII) ions are converted, under strongly acidic conditions, to pale pink manganese(II) ions:

$$MnO_4^-(aq) + 8H^+(aq) + 5e^- \rightarrow Mn^{2+}(aq) + 4H_2O(l)$$

Acidified aqueous potassium dichromate(VI)

During the reaction the orange solution containing dichromate(VI) ions is converted to a solution containing green chromium(III) ions:

$$Cr_2O_7^{2-}(aq) + 14H^+(aq) + 6e^- \rightarrow 2Cr^{3+}(aq) + 7H_2O(l)$$

This reaction and its associated colour change was the basis for the 'breathalyser' formerly used by many police forces around the world to detect and measure alcohol levels in the breath of drivers (Chapter 23 on the accompanying website). Large numbers of people are killed every day by car accident, many of which occur because of excessive consumption of alcohol.

A breathalyser (Figure 9.16) uses sodium dichromate(VI) to oxidize alcohol in breath to ethanoic acid. The sodium dichromate(VI) changes color from orange to green when consumed by the reaction. The extent of this colour change is monitored and used to determine the blood alcohol level of the person undergoing the test.

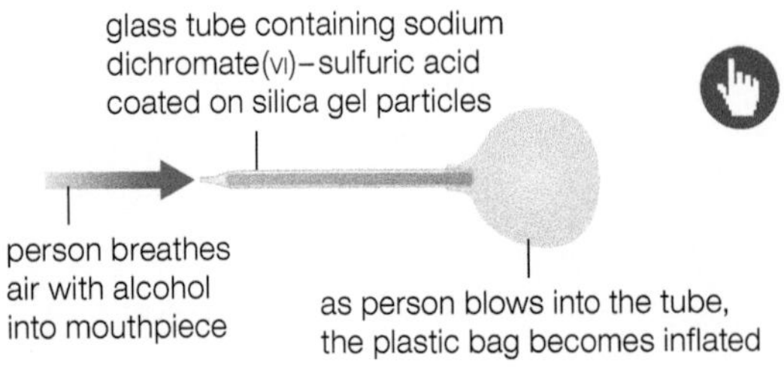

glass tube containing sodium dichromate(VI)–sulfuric acid coated on silica gel particles

person breathes air with alcohol into mouthpiece

as person blows into the tube, the plastic bag becomes inflated

■ **Figure 9.16** A simple breathalyser

Acidified hydrogen peroxide

$$H_2O_2(aq) + 2H^+(aq) + 2e^- \rightarrow 2H_2O(l)$$

Metal ions

Metal ions or cations of unreactive metals can behave as weak oxidizing agents, for example:

$$Ag^+(aq) + e^- \rightarrow Ag(s)$$

Hydrogen ions ('protons')

Hydrogen ions from dilute aqueous solutions of acids, for example the reaction between hydrochloric acid and magnesium:

$$Mg(s) + 2HCl(aq) \rightarrow MgCl_2(aq) + H_2(g)$$

The half-equation for the reduction of the hydrogen ion is:

$$2H^+(aq) + 2e^- \rightarrow H_2(g)$$

This reaction can be regarded as a replacement reaction where the hydrogen ions are replaced from the acid by the magnesium atoms.

Manganese(IV) oxide

Manganese dioxide or manganese(IV) oxide in acidic solution:

$$MnO_2(s) + 4H^+(aq) + 2e^- \rightarrow Mn^{2+}(aq) + 2H_2O(l)$$

---

3 A solution of potassium manganate(VII) can be standardized by titration under suitable conditions with a solution of arsenic(III) oxide, As_2O_3. 5 moles of arsenic(III) oxide are oxidized by 4 moles of manganate(VII) ions. Calculate the oxidation state to which the manganate (VII) is reduced.

4 A piece of steel (an alloy of iron and carbon) of mass 0.200 g reacts with dilute sulfuric acid. The resulting solution requires 34.00 cm³ of 0.0200 mol dm⁻³ potassium manganate(VII) in acidic solution in a titration. Determine the percentage by mass of iron in the steel.

5 Determine the volume of acidified potassium manganate(VII) of concentration 0.0200 mol dm⁻³ decolourized by 100.00 cm³ of hydrogen peroxide of concentration 0.100 mol dm⁻³.
   The unbalanced ionic equation is:

   $$MnO_4^-(aq) + H_2O_2(aq) + H^+(aq) \rightarrow Mn^{2+}(aq) + H_2O(l)$$

   Determine the volume (in cm³) of oxygen gas produced at STP. Assume ideal behaviour.

 ■ Drinking water

In 2010, following many years of discussion, debate and negotiation, 122 countries formally acknowledged the 'right to water' in a United Nations General Assembly resolution. It recognizes the human right to water as part of an adequate standard of living. While now recognized in international law, the human right to water is not enforceable at a national level until incorporated into national legislation.

The human right to water places certain responsibilities upon governments to ensure that people can enjoy 'sufficient, safe, accessible and affordable water, without discrimination'. Governments are expected to take reasonable steps to avoid a *contaminated water* supply and to ensure there are no water access distinctions between citizens. However, it is estimated that one billion people out of a global population of seven billion lack this provision.

Disinfection of water supplies commonly uses oxidizing agents such as chlorine or ozone to kill microbial pathogens (bacteria and viruses). Chlorine gas forms chloric(I), HOCl, acid in water. The chlorate(I) ions, ClO⁻, formed in water are responsible for its germicidal properties. Use of chlorine as a disinfectant is of concern due to its ability to oxidize other species, forming harmful by-products (for example, trichloromethane, $CHCl_3$).

Ozone (trioxygen, O_3) is much more reactive than O_2. It is a very powerful oxidizing agent, second among elements only to fluorine. It can oxidize many organic compounds and is used commercially as a bleach and as a deodorizing agent to remove bad odours (smells). Because it is a powerful germicide and kills pathogenic (disease-causing) bacteria it is also used to sterilize air and drinking water. Ozone is usually manufactured by passing an electrical discharge through O_2 gas or through dry air.

◼ Reducing agents

A reducing agent is defined as a substance that brings about the reduction of a substance by donating electrons to the substance it reduces. Reducing agents undergo a process of oxidation (Figure 9.17).

Some common reducing agents and examples of their reactions are described below. The strengths of reducing agents, like oxidizing agents, are described by their standard electrode potentials (Chapter 19).

Hydrogen

For example, with lead(II) oxide:

$$PbO(s) + H_2(g) \rightarrow H_2O(l) + Pb(s)$$

The half-equation is:

$$O^{2-}(s) + H_2(g) \rightarrow H_2O(l) + 2e^-$$

Carbon

For example, with lead(II) oxide:

$$PbO(s) + C(s) \rightarrow Pb(s) + CO(g)$$

The half-equation is:

$$O^{2-}(s) + C(s) \rightarrow CO(g) + 2e^-$$

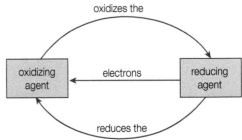

◼ **Figure 9.17** The relationship between oxidizing and reducing agents

Carbon monoxide

When carbon monoxide acts as a reducing agent, carbon dioxide is produced, for example with iron(III) oxide (at high temperature):

$$Fe_2O_3(s) + 3CO(g) \rightarrow 2Fe(l) + 3CO_2(g)$$

The half-equation is:

$$O^{2-}(g) + CO(g) \rightarrow CO_2(g) + 2e^-$$

This is the basis of the extraction of iron on an industrial scale in a blast furnace. Carbon monoxide is a more powerful reducing agent at low temperatures than carbon, but at high temperatures carbon is the more powerful reducing agent.

Metals

The more reactive metals are strong reducing agents. For example, zinc acts as a reducing agent with aqueous copper(II) sulfate solution:

$$CuSO_4(aq) + Zn(s) \rightarrow ZnSO_4(aq) + Cu(s)$$

Ionically, this can be written as:

$$Cu^{2+}(aq) + Zn(s) \rightarrow Zn^{2+}(aq) + Cu(s)$$

after removing the 'spectator' sulfate ions.

This and similar reactions involving metals and metal ions are known as replacement reactions and occur when a more reactive metal reacts with the ions of a less reactive metal.

Additional Perspectives

Substances that can act as both oxidizing and reducing agents

The terms oxidizing agent and reducing agent, like the terms acid and base, are *relative terms*. A weak reducing agent may be 'forced' to act as an oxidizing agent in the presence of a more powerful reducing agent. Conversely, a weak oxidizing agent may be 'forced' to act as a reducing agent in the presence of a more powerful oxidizing agent.

For example, with acidified aqueous potassium iodide, hydrogen peroxide acts as an oxidizing agent and converts iodide ions to iodine:

$$H_2O_2(aq) + 2H^+(aq) + 2I^-(aq) \rightarrow 2H_2O(l) + I_2(aq)$$

The hydrogen peroxide is reduced to water during the reaction:

$$H_2O_2(aq) + 2H^+(aq) + 2e^- \rightarrow 2H_2O(l)$$

However, in the presence of acidified potassium manganate(VII), a stronger oxidizing agent than hydrogen peroxide, hydrogen peroxide is 'forced' to act as a reducing agent:

$$5H_2O_2(aq) + 2MnO_4^-(aq) + 6H^+(aq) \rightarrow 5O_2(g) + 2Mn^{2+}(aq) + 8H_2O(l)$$

The hydrogen peroxide is oxidized to water and oxygen:

$$H_2O_2(aq) \rightarrow O_2(g) + 2H^+(aq) + 2e^-$$

Substances like hydrogen peroxide that are able to act as both oxidizing and reducing agents can be converted to stable compounds that have higher and lower oxidation states.

Additional Perspectives

Redox reactions in biology

Oxidation occurs when hydrogen is removed from a molecule:

$$AH_2 + B \rightarrow A + BH_2$$

Substance A has been oxidized by transferring hydrogen to a second substance, called B, which acts as a hydrogen carrier. Oxidation steps like this are important to respiration because they allow hydrogen atoms to be removed from the glucose molecule, at the same time releasing energy in a useful form. The most important hydrogen carrier in cells is nicotinamide adenine dinucleotide (NAD). NAD is usually present in solution in the form of NAD^+, and the reduced form NADH is formed according to the following equation:

$$NAD^+ + 2[H] \rightarrow NADH + H^+$$

NAD passes on hydrogen atoms to a system of carrier molecules located in the mitochondria. At the end of the chain, hydrogen atoms react with oxygen molecules to form water.

Utilization: Natural and synthetic antioxidants

Natural antioxidants

An antioxidant is a natural or synthetic substance that delays the onset or slows the rate of oxidation. They are used to extend the shelf life of food.

Naturally occurring antioxidants include vitamins C and E, which are found in many plants, including citrus fruits, vegetables, nuts and seeds. Specific sources of vitamin C (ascorbic acid) include citrus fruits (oranges, lemons and limes), green peppers, broccoli, green leafy vegetables, strawberries, raw cabbage and potatoes.

Vitamin C is a water-soluble vitamin and is oxidized by exposure to air. The rate of oxidation increases with temperature and with the presence of alkali. The oxidation of vitamin C is catalysed by the presence of various oxidases which are released when the fruits and vegetables are chopped or crushed.

Vitamin C or ascorbic acid (Figure 9.18), although referred to as an acid, does not contain a free carboxylic acid functional group. The –COOH group reacts with an –OH group in the molecule to eliminate a molecule of water and form a cyclic or ring compound.

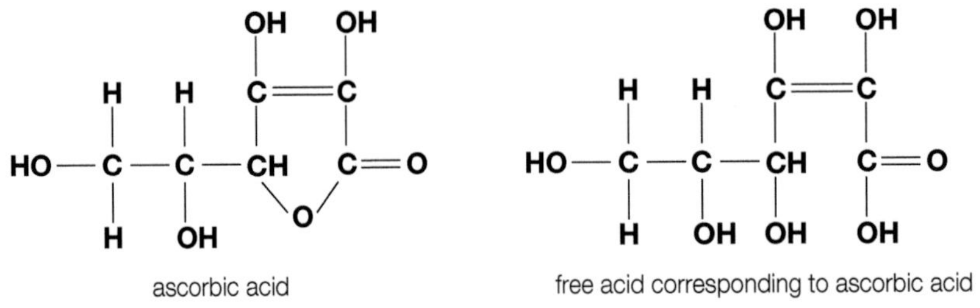

■ **Figure 9.18**
Structures of ascorbic acid

ascorbic acid

free acid corresponding to ascorbic acid

Specific sources of vitamin E (*alpha*-tocopherol) include carrots, squash, broccoli, sweet potatoes, tomatoes, kale, cantaloupe melon, peaches and apricots. Vitamin E (Figure 9.19) is the main lipid-soluble antioxidant. It occurs in cell membranes together with polyunsaturated fatty acids in phospholipids, and vegetable oils (especially those rich in polyunsaturated fatty acids) are a major dietary source. It is a phenolic antioxidant, as are most natural antioxidants.

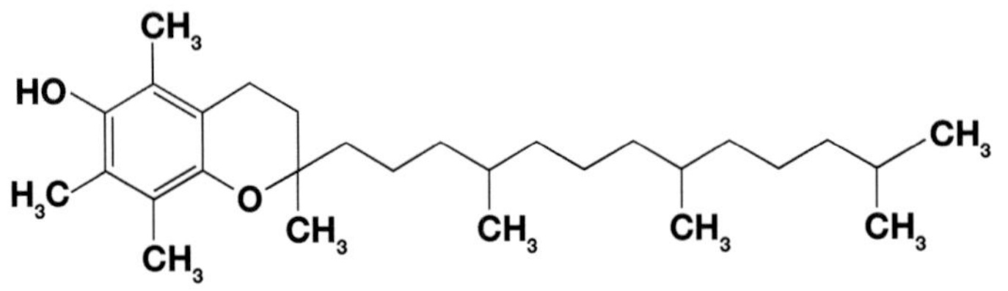

■ **Figure 9.19** Skeletal structure of vitamin E (*alpha*-tocopherol)

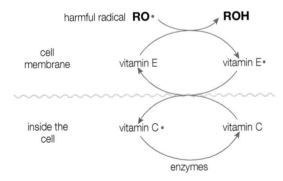

■ **Figure 9.20** The combined action of vitamins E and C

It has been suggested that *alpha*-tocopherol and vitamin C work together, with vitamin C reducing it back to its active form after reaction with a radical (Figure 9.20).

Artificial antioxidants

Butylated hydroxyanisole (BHA) (Figure 9.21) is a mixture of two isomeric organic compounds, 2-*tert*-butyl-4-hydroxyanisole and 3-*tert*-butyl-4-hydroxyanisole. The conjugated aromatic ring of BHA is able to act as a free radical scavenger, and thus further free radical reactions are prevented.

Butylated hydroxytoluene (BHT) (Figure 9.22) is a related antioxidant food additive. It is also used as an antioxidant in cosmetics, pharmaceuticals, jet fuels, rubber and petroleum products, and embalming fluid.

These two synthetic antioxidants are hindered phenols whose phenoxy radicals are stabilized by steric hindrance. The large bulky alkyl groups prevent propagation of the free radical chain reaction. Figure 9.23 shows a phenoxy radical derived from a hindered phenol. It has two very large bulky alkyl groups surrounding the radical centre on the oxygen atom so that recombination reactions are physically prevented. In the presence of free radicals vitamin E loses a hydrogen atom from its single –OH group to form a phenoxy radical (Figure 9.24).

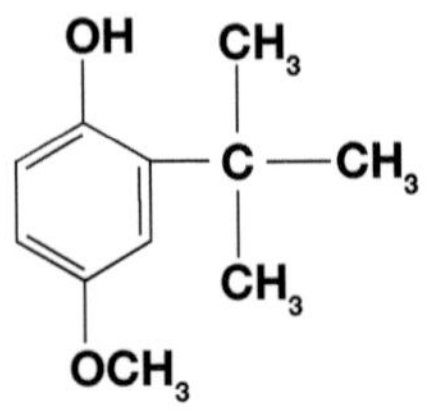

■ **Figure 9.21** Structure of 2-*tert*-butyl-4-hydroxyanisole (BHA)

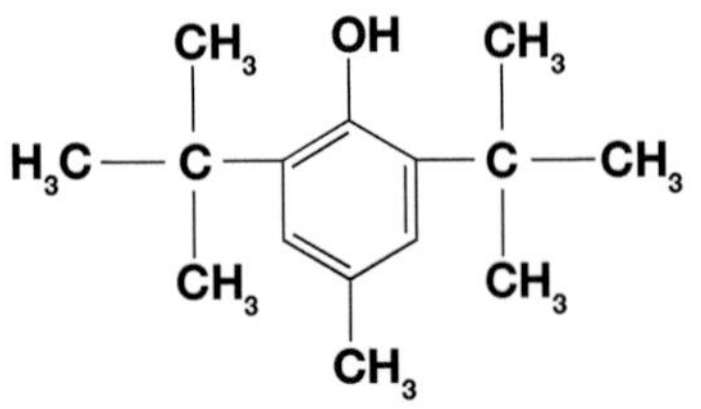

■ **Figure 9.22** Structure of butylated hydroxytoluene (BHT)

Recombination of these phenoxy radicals is hindered by the presence of two methyl groups on either side of the phenoxy group. Vitamin E hence behaves as a 'hindered phenol'.

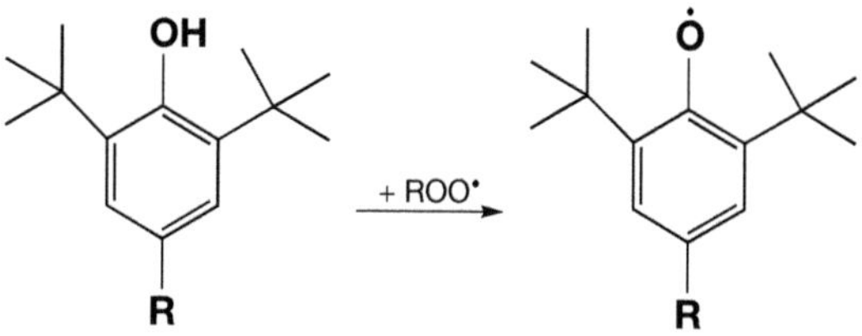

■ **Figure 9.23** A long-lived phenoxy radical derived from a hindered phenol

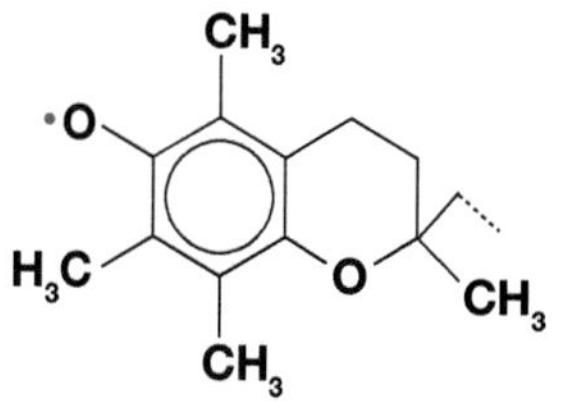

■ **Figure 9.24** Phenoxy radical derived from vitamin E

6 Balance the following redox equations under acidic conditions:

a $H_2O_2 + I_2 \rightarrow I^- + O_2$ b $Cr_2O_7^{2-} + Fe^{2+} \rightarrow Cr^{3+} + Fe^{3+}$ c $S_2O_3^{2-} + Cl_2 \rightarrow SO_4^{2-} + Cl^-$

Additional Perspectives

Trends in the redox properties of the elements in period 3

The trends in the redox properties of the elements in period 3 are summarized in Table 9.1. Chlorine is a strong oxidizing agent and will oxidize all the other elements in period 3. A trend is observed from strong reducing agent to strong oxidizing agent. This correlates with an increase in electronegativity (Chapter 4), which is a measure of the ability of an atom to attract a pair of electrons in a covalent bond. Note that oxidation numbers for non-metals generally differ by 2, as a consequence 'of there being more (or fewer) electron pairs being involved in bonding'.

Element	Sodium, Na	Magnesium, Mg	Aluminium, Al	Silicon, Si	Phosphorus, P	Sulfur, S	Chlorine, Cl
Oxidation numbers	+1 only	+2 only	+3 only	+4 (−4 rarely)	+5, +3, −3	+6, +4, +2, −2 [and more]	+7, +5, +3, +1, −1
Examples of compounds in these oxidation states	NaBr	MgSO$_4$	Al$_2$O$_3$	SiO$_2$, SiH$_4$	PCl$_5$ PCl$_3$ PH$_3$	SO$_3$ SO$_2$ SCl$_2$ H$_2$S	HClO$_4$ NaClO$_3$ NaClO$_2$ NaClO HCl
Redox properties (all reactions of elements are redox)	Strong reducing agent; chemistry is summarized by Na → Na$^+$ + e$^-$	Strong reducing agent; chemistry is summarized by Mg → Mg^{2+} + 2e$^-$	Strong reducing agent; chemistry is summarized by Al → Al^{3+} + 3e$^-$	Usually a reducing agent	Usually a reducing agent	A reducing agent, but can be an oxidizing agent with hydrogen and reactive metals	An oxidizing agent, especially in solution. Can be a reducing agent with fluorine and water
Standard electrode potential, E^θ/V	−2.71	−2.36	−1.66	—	—	—	1.36
Electronegativity of element	0.9	1.3	1.6	1.9	2.2	2.6	3.2
Type of element	Metal	Metal	Metal	Metalloid	Non-metal	Non-metal	Non-metal

■ **Table 9.1** Summary of redox properties of the elements in period 3

The standard electrode potential is a measurement of the reducing power of an element in aqueous solution under standard conditions (Chapter 19). The more negative the value, the greater the reducing power of the element concerned.

Identifying the species oxidized and reduced, and the oxidizing and reducing agents, in redox reactions

The equations below describe typical redox reactions exhibited by some of the elements in period 3. Deduce the oxidation numbers to indicate the nature of the redox reaction. Identify the species oxidized and the species reduced, and identify the reducing and oxidizing agents.

Sodium

$$2Na(s) + 2H_2O(l) \rightarrow 2NaOH(aq) + H_2(g)$$
$$0 +1 +1 0$$

Sodium is oxidized; hydrogen in water is reduced. Sodium is the reducing agent and water is the oxidizing agent.

Magnesium

$$2Mg(s) + CO_2(g) \rightarrow 2MgO(s) + C(s)$$
$$0 +4 +2 0$$

Magnesium is oxidized; carbon in carbon dioxide is reduced. Magnesium is the reducing agent and carbon dioxide is the oxidizing agent.

Phosphorus

$$4P(s) + 8H_2SO_4(aq) \rightarrow 4H_3PO_4(aq) + S(s) + 7SO_2(g) + 2H_2O(l)$$
$$0 +6 +5 0 +4$$

Phosphorus is oxidized; sulfur in the sulfuric(VI) acid is reduced. Phosphorus is the reducing agent and sulfuric(VI) acid is the oxidizing agent.

$$P(s) + 3Na(s) \rightarrow Na_3P(s)$$
$$0 0 -1\,-3$$

Phosphorus is reduced; sodium is oxidized. Phosphorus is the oxidizing agent and sodium is the reducing agent.

Chlorine

$$8NH_3(aq) + 3Cl_2(g) \rightarrow N_2(g) + 6NH_4Cl(aq)$$
$$-3 0 0 -1$$

Chlorine is reduced and some of the ammonia is oxidized. Chlorine is the oxidizing agent and ammonia is the reducing agent.

$$Cl_2(g) + F_2(g) \rightarrow 2ClF(g)$$
$$0 0 +1\,-1$$

Chlorine is oxidized; the fluorine is reduced. Chlorine is the reducing agent and fluorine is the oxidizing agent.

| **Additional Perspectives** | ## Oxidation numbers and the periodic table |

Oxidation numbers of elements in compounds generally increase regularly as you move across periods 2 and 3 in the periodic table (Table 9.2). For example, the maximum oxidation number of the elements in oxides increases from +1 in sodium to +7 for chlorine. Elements not in the transition block are known as main group elements.

■ **Table 9.2** Formulas of the highest oxides and their oxidation numbers in the elements of period 3

Na	Mg	Al	Si	P	S	Cl
Na_2O	MgO	Al_2O_3	SiO_2	P_4O_{10}	SO_3	Cl_2O_7
+1	+2	+3	+4	+5	+6	+7

The maximum oxidation number corresponds to the number of electrons in the outer shell, all of which are involved in bonding in the highest oxide. The maximum oxidation number also corresponds to the group number in the periodic table (Table 9.3) for groups 1 and 2 and then (group number minus 10) for groups 13 to 17.

■ **Table 9.3** Electron arrangements and group numbers of the elements in period 3

Na	Mg	Al	Si	P	S	Cl
2,8,1	2,8,2	2,8,3	2,8,4	2,8,5	2,8,6	2,8,7
1	2	3	4	5	6	7

The term 'highest oxide' is used since phosphorus, sulfur and chlorine can all exhibit lower oxidation states: sulfur dioxide, SO_2 (oxidation number of sulfur +4), tetraphosphorus hexaoxide, P_4O_6 (oxidation number of phosphorus +3) and chlorine monoxide (chlorine(I) oxide), Cl_2O (oxidation number of chlorine +1). Sulfur hexafluoride (sulfur(VI) fluoride), SF_6, is a stable compound with sulfur in an oxidation number of +6.

Transition metals

The fact that the transition metals form a variety of relatively stable oxidation states is due, in part, to the availability of 3d and 4s electrons for ion and covalent bond formation (Chapter 13). The common oxidation states of the first row transition metals are shown in Table 9.4.

■ **Table 9.4** Examples of compounds showing common oxidation states of the first row transition metals

d-block metal	Ti	V	Cr	Mn	Fe	Co	Ni	Cu
Common oxidation states	+3 +4	+2 +3 +4 +5	+2 +3 +4 +6	+2 +4 +6 +7	+2 +3	+2 +3	+2	+1 +2
Examples of ions in these oxidation states	Ti^{3+} Ti^{4+}	V^{2+} V^{3+} VO^{2+} VO_2^{+}	Cr^{2+} Cr^{3+} CrO_4^{2-} $Cr_2O_7^{2-}$	Mn^{2+} Mn^{4+} MnO_4^{2-} MnO_4^{-}	Fe^{2+} Fe^{3+}	Co^{2+} Co^{3+}	Ni^{2+}	Cu^{+} Cu^{2+}

Scandium at the beginning of the first row of the d-block and zinc at the end only exhibit one stable oxidation state in their compounds, +3 (Sc^{3+}) and +2 (Zn^{2+}), respectively. Notice that the lower oxidation states correspond to simple or atomic ions, for example, Mn^{2+} (+2), while the higher oxidation states correspond to covalently bonded oxoanions, for example, MnO_4^{-} (+7).

■ Utilization of redox reactions

Aerobic respiration

The aerobic respiration of glucose can be represented by the following overall equation:

$$C_6H_{12}O_6(s) + 6O_2(g) \rightarrow 6CO_2(g) + 6H_2O(l)$$

It occurs inside the mitochondria of animal and plant cells and is a complex series of redox reactions involving electron transfer.

Cells apply the principles of electrochemical cells to generate energy. Respiration is a complex multi-step reaction under the control of enzymes. The energy contained in the bonds of the glucose and oxygen is used to generate a proton (H^+) difference across the inner membrane of mitochondria. The potential energy is then used to form ATP, a short-term store of energy.

The redox species involved in the electron transfer steps are part of the electron transport chain (Figure 9.25) located in the inner mitochondria membrane. They are proteins that pass electrons from one protein to another, and each time some of the energy is used to move protons through the cell membrane. The reaction that ultimately drives the electron transport chain is the oxidation of hydrogen molecules to form water molecules:

$$2H^+ + 2e^- + \tfrac{1}{2}O_2 \rightarrow H_2O$$

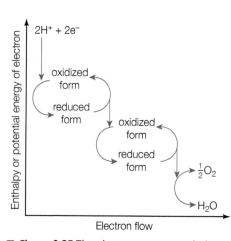

■ **Figure 9.25** The electron transport chain

■ **Figure 9.26** Electric vehicles in Cambodia

■ **Figure 9.27** Solar cells on top of government-built flats in Singapore

Batteries

A simple battery is a voltaic cell that is used as an energy source. Some types of battery, for example a car battery, have several voltaic cells in series, thereby combining the individual cell potentials to give a large potential difference (voltage) at the output terminals. Batteries are of two types: primary cells, which cannot be recharged, and secondary cells (Figure 9.26), which can be recharged. The dry cell battery is an example of a primary cell and a lead–acid battery, a lithium-ion battery and Ni-Cads (nickel–cadmium batteries) are all examples of secondary cells (Chapter 24 on the accompanying website). A fuel cell is an electrochemical cell designed so that reactants, often gases, are replenished all the time. This enables the fuel cell to supply electric current continuously and hence it does not need recharging.

Solar cells

Most of the world's electricity requirements are met by burning fossil fuels, using the heat generated by nuclear reactors or hydroelectric power, all of which have environmental consequences. Fossil fuels produce carbon dioxide, which contributes to the greenhouse effect and climate change. Many fossil fuels, especially coal, contain sulfur which results in sulfur dioxide emission and acid rain (Chapter 8).

The Earth receives more energy in solar energy in two days than is stored in all the known energy resources. Solar cells (Figure 9.27) are used to convert solar or radiant energy into electrical energy. One form of solar cells consists of two joined layers of silicon. One layer is doped with a small amount of arsenic or phosphorus and is known as n-type silicon. The atoms of these group 15 elements each release an extra electron into the silicon lattice, making it conducting. The other layer is doped with boron atoms and is called p-type silicon. This layer has a shortage of electrons (a surplus of electron 'holes'). The cell is connected to an external circuit (wires) and electrons (current) flow from the n-type to the p-type. An equilibrium is established with a potential difference (voltage) between the two layers. When sunlight interacts with the cells' surface the equilibrium is disturbed and electrons move from the p-type to the n-type. The electrons return to the p-type layer via the external circuit and generate an electric current (see Chapter 24 on the accompanying website).

Bleaching of hair

Hair is primarily composed of a fibrous protein known as keratin. However, the natural colour of hair depends on the presence of two other proteins, eumelanin and phaeomelanin. Varying ratios and quantities of these proteins in people's hair give the wide range of colours ranging from red, grey, blond to pure black. An absence of either of these melanin proteins, results in the grey or white hair associated with old age.

Bleaching is an irreversible chemical reaction that lightens the colour of the hair by chemically removing the colour from each hair strand. It is done using a strong oxidizing agent, usually an alkaline solution of hydrogen peroxide. This results in the melanin proteins being decolorized, although they are still present in the hair. Bleached hair is characteristically a yellow colour due to the natural colour of the primary protein in keratin, which is no longer hidden by the melanin. The bleaching of hair by hydrogen peroxide is a complex process. It is accelerated by the presence of ultraviolet radiation and copper(II) ions, suggesting that a Fenton-like process (see Chapter 22 on the accompanying website) is operating.

Permanently changing the colour of hair involves a more complex chemical pathway, where initially ammonia is used to chemically open the outer layer of the hair (the cuticle). Hydrogen peroxide is then used to oxidize the melanin and, as with bleaching, remove the natural hair colour.

Household bleach

Chlorine gas is moderately soluble in water and reacts with it to form a mixture of chloric(I) acid and hydrochloric acid:

$$Cl_2(g) + 2H_2O(l) \rightleftharpoons HOCl(aq) + H^+(aq) + Cl^-(aq)$$

This is known as chlorine water and is a mild bleach. When chlorine is dissolved in alkaline solution, chloric(I) acid molecules are deprotonated and the equilibrium is shifted to the right-hand side. This allows compounds containing chlorate(I) ions to be isolated:

$$Cl_2(g) + 2OH^-(aq) \rightarrow OCl^-(aq) + H_2O(l) + Cl^-(aq)$$

Household or domestic bleach consists of an alkaline solution of sodium chlorate(I). It is a strong oxidizing and bleaching agent. It acts as a bleaching agent by reacting with certain chemical groups known as chromophores in coloured compounds. Their bonds are broken, which changes the molecule into a different substance that either does not contain a chromophore, or contains a chromophore that does not absorb visible light.

Browning of food

■ **Figure 9.28** Enzyme-controlled browning in apples

When fruits or vegetables are peeled or cut, enzymes contained in the plant tissue are released. In the presence of oxygen from the air, the enzyme polyphenol oxidase (phenolase) catalyses one step in the conversion of plant phenolic compounds to brown melanins. This reaction, known as enzymatic browning (Figure 9.28), occurs readily at room temperature when the pH is between 5 and 7. The presence of iron and copper increases the rate of the reaction. Bruising or injury to the plant tissue disrupts the cellular structure and allows the contents to come into contact with oxygen. This will lead to the browning of uncooked fruit tissue but also contributes to the colour and flavour of coffee, tea, raisins and cocoa. Enzyme controlled browning can be slowed down by the presence of sulfite ions (sulfate(IV) ions), ascorbic acid (vitamin C) and ethanoic acid (vinegar).

■ Reactions of metals with metal ions in solution

■ **Figure 9.29** The reaction between zinc and copper(II) ions to form zinc ions and copper atoms

It has previously been stated that metals often act as reducing agents and that the greater the chemical reactivity of the metal, the greater its ability to bring about reduction. A group of metals can be readily sorted into order of reactivity, and hence reducing power, by performing a number of simple experiments involving the metals and aqueous solutions of their ions (Figure 9.29).

This approach to establishing an activity series is tabulated below for copper, lead, iron, magnesium, zinc and tin. Test tubes are filled with a small volume of the following aqueous solutions (each of which have the same concentration): copper(II) nitrate; lead(II) nitrate, iron(II) sulfate, magnesium nitrate, zinc nitrate and tin(II) chloride. (The nitrate, sulfate and chloride ions are 'spectator' ions and do not participate in any reactions that occur. These solutions can therefore be regarded as aqueous solutions of the metal ions.)

Into each of these solutions is placed a small piece of freshly cleaned magnesium ribbon. The surface of the magnesium is observed for several minutes for any colour changes indicative of a chemical reaction.

The process is then repeated, in turn, with fresh solutions and pieces of the other metals in the place of magnesium. The results are tabulated, where a tick indicates a reaction has occurred and a cross indicates no observable reaction has taken place (Table 9.5).

■ **Table 9.5** Summary of results for a series of reactions between selected metals and their ions

Ion in solution/ Metal	Cu^{2+}(aq)	Pb^{2+}(aq)	Fe^{2+}(aq)	Mg^{2+}(aq)	Zn^{2+}(aq)	Sn^{2+}(aq)
Copper	✗	✗	✗	✗	✗	✗
Lead	✓	✗	✗	✗	✗	✗
Iron	✓	✓	✗	✗	✗	✓
Magnesium	✓	✓	✓	✗	✓	✓
Zinc	✓	✓	✓	✗	✗	✓
Tin	✓	✓	✗	✗	✗	✗

Metal	Number of replacement reactions
Mg	5
Zn	4
Fe	3
Sn	2
Pb	1
Cu	0

■ **Table 9.6** An activity series for selected metals based on replacement reactions

Each tick represents a chemical reaction and by summing the number of reactions that each metal has produced, as shown in Table 9.6, an activity series can be constructed.

Up the **reactivity** or **activity series** the metals become increasingly chemically reactive and their reducing power, or ability to donate electrons, increases.

The reactions that occur, as indicated by the ticks in Table 9.5, are known as **replacement reactions** since they involve a more reactive metal replacing, or 'pushing out', a less reactive metal from its salt. Formulas, ionic reactions and half-equations can be written for all the replacement reactions, for example:

Formula equation:	$Mg(s) + CuSO_4(aq) \rightarrow MgSO_4(aq) + Cu(s)$
Rewriting in terms of ions:	$Mg(s) + Cu^{2+}(aq) + SO_4^{2-}(aq) \rightarrow Mg^{2+}(aq) + SO_4^{2-}(aq) + Cu(s)$
Cancelling spectator ions:	$Mg(s) + Cu^{2+}(aq) \rightarrow Mg^{2+}(aq) + Cu(s)$
Rewriting in terms of half-equations:	$Mg(s) \rightarrow Mg^{2+}(aq) + 2e^-$ $Cu^{2+}(aq) + 2e^- \rightarrow Cu(s)$

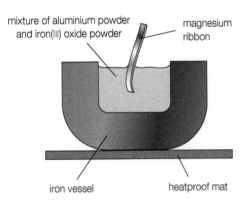

mixture of aluminium powder and iron(III) oxide powder

magnesium ribbon

iron vessel

heatproof mat

■ **Figure 9.30** Thermite reaction mixture apparatus

Replacement reactions can also be carried out in the solid state using powdered samples of metals and metal compounds. For example, if iron(III) oxide and aluminium are heated together, a very exothermic reaction known as the thermite reaction occurs, resulting in the formation of aluminium oxide and molten iron (Figure 9.30).

$$Fe_2O_3(s) + 2Al(s) \rightarrow 2Fe(l) + Al_2O_3(s)$$

The thermite reaction (Figure 9.31) occurs because aluminium is a more powerful reducing agent than iron and has a stronger tendency to lose its electrons.

Some metals react with water and these can be regarded as replacement reactions with hydrogen being replaced from water. For example, the reaction between sodium and water:

$$2Na(s) + 2H_2O(l) \rightarrow 2NaOH(aq) + H_2(g)$$

The relevant half-equations are:

$$2Na(s) \rightarrow 2Na^+(aq) + 2e^- \quad \text{and} \quad 2H_2O(l) + 2e^- \rightarrow 2OH^-(aq) + H_2(g)$$

Corrosion and galvanization

Rusting

The process of rusting requires the presence of liquid water and oxygen. An approximate equation describing rusting is:

$$4Fe(s) + 3O_2(g) + 2xH_2O(l) \rightarrow 2Fe_2O_3.xH_2O(s)$$

where the number of water molecules present in the rust is uncertain or variable.

A steel nail which has a drop of ferroxyl indicator (Figure 9.32) added shows the two important electrochemical aspects of this redox reaction. A blue mass forms showing that iron(II) ions are present. This anodic process is the oxidation of iron atom to iron(II) ions:

$$Fe(s) \rightarrow Fe^{2+}(aq) + 2e^-$$

The pink colour indicates that hydroxide ions are present. The cathodic process is the reduction of oxygen molecules:

$$O_2(g) + 2H_2O(l) + 4e^- \rightarrow 2Fe^{2+}(aq) + 4OH^-(aq)$$

■ **Figure 9.31** The thermite experiment

■ **Figure 9.32** A rusting nail in the presence of ferroxyl indicator (an aqueous mixture of potassium hexacyanoferrate(III) and phenolphthalein)

Combining these two half-equations and multiplying the first by 2 gives the following ionic equation:

$$2Fe(s) + O_2(g) + 2H_2O(l) \rightarrow 2Fe^{2+}(aq) + 4OH^-(aq)$$

The iron(II) hydroxide formed by precipitation then is rapidly oxidized under basic conditions to form red-brown hydrated iron(III) oxide. This is rust and can be represented by the formula $Fe_2O_3.xH_2O$. The rust flakes off the surface of iron, partly because rust has a lower density than iron and partly because it weakly adheres to the underlying iron. This exposes more iron surface and the rusting process continues.

Any layer that is waterproof protects iron from rusting. However, the protection from paints and other widely used materials is of limited duration, because of such factors as physical damage, chemical deterioration and weathering. So, alternative methods of rust protection use electrochemical principles instead.

Iron pipes, ships and tanks in the ground are often protected by a block of magnesium or zinc (Figure 9.33). The block of magnesium (or zinc) is electrically attached to the iron object and since magnesium (or zinc) is higher up the activity series (higher positive electrode oxidation potential) than iron, it oxidizes in preference (sacrificially) to the iron. The iron objects acts as the cathode in this method. The use of zinc blocks on the hull of a ship is an example of a sacrificial method. Zinc, being more reactive than iron, is oxidized to form zinc ions:

$$Zn(s) \rightarrow Zn^{2+}(aq) + 2e^-$$

■ **Figure 9.33** Sacrificial protection of an iron ship

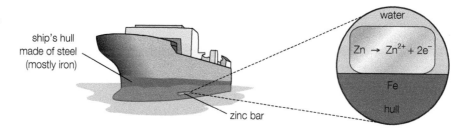

ship's hull made of steel (mostly iron)

zinc bar

water

$Zn \rightarrow Zn^{2+} + 2e^-$

Fe

hull

The electrons released reduce dissolved oxygen molecules to form hydroxide ions, $OH^-(aq)$:

$$O_2(g) + 2H_2O(l) + 4e^- \rightarrow 4OH^-(aq)$$

Tin-plated cans used in the food industry provide another example of electrochemical protection. Tin is likely to react with moist oxygen and so protects the surface of the iron. There is one drawback with tin plating. It is easily scratched to reveal the iron, in which case the can rusts very rapidly. What happens is that once iron is in contact with moist air, it gives sacrificial protection to the less reactive tin. Tin is used to protect cans made of iron because zinc would poison the food.

■ **Figure 9.34** If tin plating is damaged it increases the rate at which the iron rusts

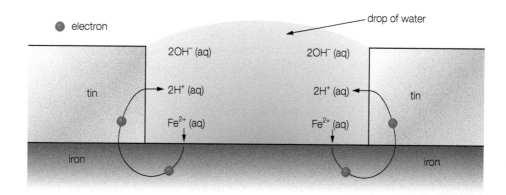

● electron

drop of water

$2OH^-$ (aq) $2OH^-$ (aq)

tin

$2H^+$ (aq) $2H^+$ (aq)   tin

Fe^{2+} (aq) Fe^{2+} (aq)

iron   iron

Galvanization

A coating of zinc protects iron from rusting and is known as galvanized iron. Galvanized iron is protected mainly because, in the electrochemical cell formed by galvanization (Figure 9.35), the zinc is preferentially oxidized. Zinc is higher up the activity series than iron. However, were it not for another reaction taking place at the same time, all the zinc would eventually be oxidized and rusting could start. The zinc hydroxide produced reacts with carbon dioxide in the air to form a layer of a zinc carbonate – a compound that adheres firmly to the iron to give further protection.

■ **Figure 9.35**
How zinc plating prevents further corrosion of iron

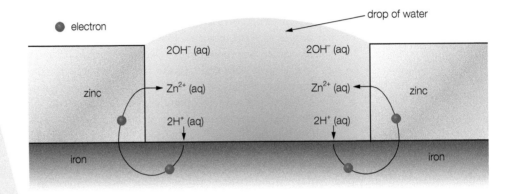

Lithium
Caesium
Rubidium
Potassium
Barium
Strontium
Calcium
Sodium
Magnesium
Beryllium
Aluminium
(Carbon)
Zinc
Chromium
Iron
Cadmium
Cobalt
Nickel
Tin
Lead
(Hydrogen)
Antimony
Arsenic
Bismuth
Copper
Silver
Palladium
Mercury
Platinum
Gold

■ Activity series for metals

■ Using the activity series

When metals are placed in an activity series (shown on the left), their order is very similar to an arrangement based on standard electrode potentials (Chapter 19).

The position of aluminium may be somewhat surprising since everyday experience suggests that aluminium is a relatively unreactive metal that does not undergo corrosion. The apparent low reactivity of aluminium is accounted for by the presence of an extremely thin protective layer of aluminium oxide present on the metal surface that prevents the metal underneath from oxidizing further.

The inclusion of the non-metals carbon and hydrogen extends the usefulness of the activity series. In these reactions hydrogen is behaving like a metal, since aqueous solutions of acids contain positively charged hydrogen ions (cf. positive ions of metals in salts). Metals above hydrogen, for example zinc, will replace hydrogen from dilute acids, but metals below it, for example copper, will not replace hydrogen from dilute acids.

Formula equation: $Zn(s) + 2HCl(aq) \rightarrow ZnCl_2(aq) + H_2(g)$

Ionic equation: $Zn(s) + 2H^+(aq) \rightarrow Zn^{2+}(aq) + H_2(g)$

Half-equations: $Zn(s) \rightarrow Zn^{2+}(aq) + 2e^-$
$2H^+(aq) + 2e^- \rightarrow H_2(g)$

Metals above carbon in the activity series, such as sodium and aluminium, cannot be produced by reduction of metal oxides with carbon; instead electrolysis has to be used. Metals below carbon, such as iron and zinc, can be produced by reduction of metal oxides with carbon.

$ZnO(s) + C(s) \rightarrow Zn(g) + CO(g)$

The reactions of selected metals with their ions, water (Figure 9.36), dilute acid, carbon and hydrogen are summarized in Table 9.7.

■ **Table 9.7** Activity series of selected metals

Reactivity series	Reaction with dilute acid	Reaction with air/ oxygen	Reaction with water	Ease of extraction
Potassium (K)	Producing H_2 with decreasing vigour	Burn very brightly and vigorously	Produce H_2 with decreasing vigour with cold water	Difficult to extract
Sodium (Na)				
Calcium (Ca)		Burn to form an oxide with decreasing vigour	React with steam with decreasing vigour	Easier to extract
Magnesium (Mg)				
Aluminium (Al)				
Zinc (Zn)				
Iron (Fe)				
Lead (Pb)		React slowly to form the oxide		
Copper (Cu)	Do not react with dilute acids		Do not react with cold water or steam	
Silver (Ag)				
Gold (Au)				
Platinum (Pt)		Do not react		Found as the element (native)

■ **Figure 9.36** The apparatus used to test the action of steam on a metal

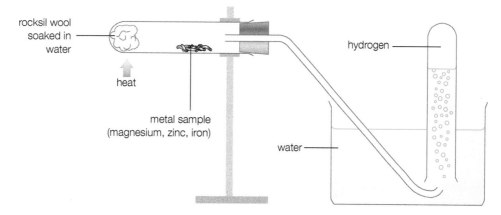

rocksil wool soaked in water

heat

metal sample (magnesium, zinc, iron)

hydrogen

water

■ **Figure 9.37** Replacement reactions of halogens

Replacement reactions (Figure 9.37) also occur with non-metals, in particular the halogens, where a more reactive halogen will replace a less reactive halogen from one of its compounds (Chapter 3). An activity series can be written for the halogens, which corresponds to the positions of the elements of the periodic table:

Fluorine
Chlorine
Bromine
Iodine

As you move up the activity series the halogens become increasingly chemically reactive and their oxidizing power, or ability to receive electrons and form halide ions, increases.

For example, when chlorine gas or chlorine water is added to an aqueous solution of potassium bromide, the chlorine (being higher up the activity series) replaces the less reactive bromine. The colourless solution of potassium bromide turns orange as the bromine is produced. The bromine is more easily identified if a small volume of non-polar organic solvent, such as tetrachloromethane (carbon tetrachloride), is added to the reaction mixture. The bromine, being non-polar, will enter the organic layer and due to its higher concentration will be more visible. Formula equations, ionic equations and half-equations can be written for this replacement reaction, for example:

Formula equation: $2KBr(aq) + Cl_2(g) \rightarrow 2KCl(aq) + Br_2(aq)$

Rewriting in terms of ions (and ignoring any reactions between the halogens and water):

$$2K^+(aq) + 2Br^-(aq) + Cl_2(g) \rightarrow 2K^+(aq) + 2Cl^-(aq) + Br_2(aq)$$

Cancelling spectator ions: $\qquad 2Br^-(aq) + Cl_2(g) \rightarrow 2Cl^-(aq) + Br_2(aq)$

Rewriting in terms of half-equations: $\qquad 2Br^-(aq) \rightarrow 2e^- + Br_2(aq)$

$$2e^- + Cl_2(g) \rightarrow 2Cl^-(aq)$$

You can see that the bromide ions have undergone oxidation and the chlorine has undergone reduction. Chlorine has behaved as an oxidizing agent and bromide ions have behaved as a reducing agent. No reaction of course occurs if iodine solution is added to potassium bromide solution because iodine is lower down the activity series than bromine and is therefore a less powerful oxidizing agent.

The reactivity and hence oxidizing power of the halogens is correlated with the size of their atoms (Chapter 3). As the halogen atoms get larger, the nucleus has decreasingly less electrostatic attraction for the electrons in the outer shell and becomes progressively less able to attract an extra electron to complete its outer shell: hence the oxidizing power of the halogens decreases from fluorine to iodine.

Conversely, the larger halide ions, such as iodide, have weaker electrostatic attraction for the electrons in their outer shell, compared to smaller halide ions such as fluoride. Consequently, iodide ions give up their extra electrons very readily; they are easily oxidized. The smaller fluoride ions have stronger electrostatic attraction for their outer electrons and are much less readily oxidized.

Worked example

In order to determine the position of three metals in an activity series, the metals were placed in different aqueous solutions of metal ions. The table below summarizes whether or not a reaction occurred.

	$Ag^+(aq)$	$Cu^{2+}(aq)$	$Fe^{2+}(aq)$
Ag(s)	—	No reaction	No reaction
Cu(s)	Reaction	—	No reaction
Fe(s)	Reaction	Reaction	—

State the equations for the three reactions that take place. Use this information to place the metals silver, copper and iron in a reactivity series, with the strongest reducing agent first, and explain your reasoning.

$$Fe(s) + Cu^{2+}(aq) \rightarrow Fe^{2+}(aq) + Cu(s)$$

$$Fe(s) + 2Ag^+(aq) \rightarrow Fe^{2+}(aq) + 2Ag(s)$$

$$Cu(s) + 2Ag^+(aq) \rightarrow Cu^{2+}(aq) + 2Ag(s)$$

Iron is a stronger reducing agent than copper and/or silver; iron is the most reactive as it can reduce/replace both copper(II) ions, Cu^{2+}, and silver(I) ions, Ag^+;

Copper is a stronger reducing agent than silver but not iron. Copper is in the middle (of the three), metals, as it can reduce/replace silver(I) ions, Ag^+, but not iron(II) ions, Fe^{2+}.

The Winkler method

Fish can only survive in fresh water because of the oxygen dissolved in it. Hence it is important to monitor the dissolved oxygen concentration. If this is less than $5\,mg\,dm^{-3}$ then most species of fish cannot survive.

One of the most accurate methods for measuring dissolved oxygen concentrations in water is the Winkler method. Under alkaline conditions manganese(II) ions are rapidly oxidized to manganese(III) by dissolved oxygen, producing a pale brown precipitate of manganese(III) hydroxide, $Mn(OH)_3$:

$$4Mn(OH)_2(aq) + O_2(g) + 2H_2O(l) \rightarrow 4Mn(OH)_3(s)$$

A sample of river or stream water is shaken with excess alkaline manganese(II) ions, and the resulting pale brown precipitate is then reacted with an excess of potassium iodide, which it oxidizes to iodine:

$$2KI(aq) + 2Mn(OH)_3(s) \rightarrow I_2(aq) + 2Mn(OH)_2(aq) + 2KOH(aq)$$

The amount of iodine is then determined by titration with sodium thiosulfate of known concentration. Starch is used to show the end-point.

$$2S_2O_3^{2-}(aq) + I_2(aq) \rightarrow S_4O_6^{2-}(aq) + 2I^-(aq)$$

Applying the Winkler method to calculate biological oxygen demand

$25.0\,cm^3$ of a sample of river water treated in this way required $25.0\,cm^3$ of $0.00100\,mol\,dm^{-3}$ sodium thiosulfate solution. Calculate the concentration of dissolved oxygen in milligrams per cubic decimetre ($mg\,dm^{-3}$).

$$\text{Amount of } S_2O_3^{2-} = \frac{25.0\ cm^3}{1000} \times 0.00100\,mol\,dm^{-3} = 2.50 \times 10^{-5}\,mol$$

This reacts with $1.25 \times 10^{-5}\,mol$ of iodine, which is formed from $2.50 \times 10^{-5}\,mol\ Mn(OH)_3$.

$2.5 \times 10^{-5}\,mol\ Mn(OH)_3$ is formed from $6.25 \times 10^{-6}\,mol$ of O_2.

Mass of $O_2 = 6.25 \times 10^{-6} \times 32 = 0.200\,mg$ in $25.0\,cm^3$ of water.
Hence, concentration of $O_2 = 8.00\,mg\,dm^{-3}$.

9.2 Electrochemical cells *– voltaic cells convert chemical energy to electrical energy and electrolytic cells convert electrical energy to chemical energy*

■ Physics background

There are close links between chemistry and electricity. It is the attraction of opposite electric charges that holds electrons in atoms (Chapter 2). This attraction is also the basis for chemical bonding and intermolecular forces (Chapter 4). Electrolysis and voltaic cells (simple 'batteries') (Chapter 19) are part of a branch of chemistry termed electrochemistry.

Electric charge

There are two types of electric charge: positive and negative. Like charges repel, so a negative ion is repelled by a positively charged surface. Opposite charges attract, so a negative ion is attracted to a positively charged surface. Electric charge is measured in coulombs, symbol C. An electron has a charge of 1.6×10^{-19} coulombs. In an electric circuit, electric charge flows through wires. The charge is carried by electrons, which therefore flow from the negative terminal to the positive terminal.

Electric current

The rate at which electric charge flows through a circuit is called the current and is measured in amperes (usually abbreviated to amps), symbol A. A large current could be produced by a large amount of charge moving slowly or a small amount of charge moving quickly. A current of one amp is a flow of charge of one coulomb per second.

Potential difference

Electric current flows through a circuit *if* there is a difference in electric potential between two points in the circuit. This is analogous to a ball rolling down a ramp: at the top of the ramp it has high potential energy, at the bottom it has less potential energy. This potential difference gives electrical energy to the charge. Potential difference is measured in volts, symbol V, and is often loosely termed voltage.

One volt gives a charge of one coulomb one joule of energy. The charge then transfers the energy into other forms, for example heat, light or chemical energy (in a chargeable battery). The charge is not used, it simply travels round the circuit carrying energy. An analogy is a postman (charge) who picks up letters (energy) at the post office (power supply or battery). He delivers the letters (transfers their energy) as he follows his route and then returns to the post office to pick up more letters (Figure 9.38).

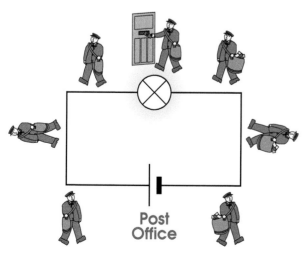

■ **Figure 9.38** Model of an electrical circuit showing the flow of electrons

ToK Link

Is energy just an abstract concept used to justify why certain types of changes are always associated with each other? Are concepts such as energy real?

'It is important to realize that in physics today, we have no knowledge of what energy is. We do not have a picture that energy comes in little blobs of a definite amount. It is not that way. However, there are formulas for calculating some numerical quantity and when we add it together it gives "28" – always the same number. It is an abstract thing in that it does not tell us the mechanisms or the reasons for the various formulas'. A quote from the physicist Richard Feynman.

Feynman means that physicists can define quantities in classical mechanics like kinetic energy for a particle and potential energy for a pair of particles. That is, specific energy types can be defined and for an isolated system, their sum is a constant. This does not tell us just what energy is, but does tell us that for defined types of energy there is a conservation law (Chapter 5). (A similar statement holds in quantum mechanics, within the bounds of the uncertainty principle, see Chapters 2 and 12).

Energy is not that mysterious at the macroscopic level. Energy is a defined quantity and is the ability to do work. Work is the product of force and displacement (distance in a specified direction). It is a useful concept because it is a quantity that is conserved in energy changes.

However, energy is a subtle concept since it has a passive mode when energy is at rest (as in an electrostatically charged body) or as inertial energy (for example, in the kinetic energy of a steadily moving body) when it cannot be described in this way, because in this mode there is no work being done. Then it seems to be an inferred property and not an observed property, something known indirectly although true.

But energy is not an entirely abstract quantity either (such as entropy, Chapter 15). It is tangible, and in its active mode can be perceived by sense perception as a Way of Knowing. The amount of damage a bullet does, for example, is proportional to its kinetic energy (mass of the bullet and square of its velocity). The amount of heat we feel (mass × temperature change) is proportional to the amount of energy involved in creating that increase in heat.

Perhaps for Feynman the real mystery is why energy behaves it does at the quantum level, where it comes in 'packets' known as quanta (Chapter 2).

Nature of Science

Ethical implications of research – the desire to produce energy can be driven by social needs or profit

A fundamental feature of science, as believed by most scientists, is that it deals with facts, not values. Further, science is objective, while values are not. The common characterization of science as value-free or value-neutral can be misleading. Scientists strongly disapprove of fraud, error and 'pseudoscience', for example. At the same time, scientists value reliability, testability, accuracy, precision, generality and theoretical simplicity. The pursuit of science as an activity is an endorsement of the value of developing knowledge of the physical world. However, where science is publicly funded and has an impact on society, the value of scientific knowledge will often be subjected to ethical or social considerations. The researcher can be viewed as an ethical agent responsible for the consequences of his or her actions, good or bad.

Ethical debates and decisions rely upon considering the following questions: Who are the stakeholders? What are their interests? Are they involved in the decision-making? What are the foreseeable consequences (possibly remote or hidden)? What are the alternatives? Is the worst case scenario acceptable? What intentions or motives guide the choice? What are the benefits? What are the costs? Who benefits? Who risks or pays the costs?

■ Voltaic cells

A simple voltaic cell, known as the Daniell cell (Figure 9.39), can be constructed by placing a zinc electrode in a solution of zinc sulfate and a copper electrode in a solution of copper(II) sulfate. The two electrodes are connected via wires and a high-resistance voltmeter. This is known as the external circuit and allows electrons to flow. This is a spontaneous process and no external energy source is required. The circuit is completed by a salt bridge which allows ions to flow in order to maintain electrical neutrality (Chapter 19). A simple salt bridge consists of a filter paper soaked in saturated potassium nitrate. Potassium and nitrate ions are chosen because they will not react with the other ions in solution or with the electrodes.

■ **Figure 9.39**
A Daniell cell

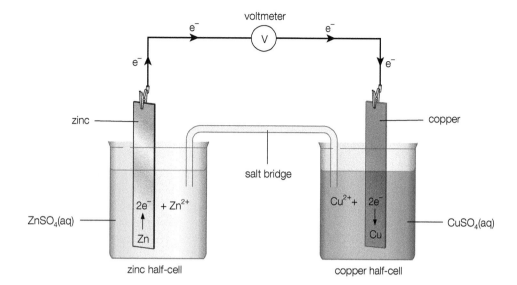

Since zinc is higher than copper in the activity series it will undergo oxidation and release electrons onto the surface of the zinc electrode (making it negative). The zinc ions produced dissolve into the water (Figure 9.40). The electrons flow from the surface of the zinc electrode through the external circuit to the surface of the copper electrode. Copper(II) ions on the surface of the copper electrode accept the electrons and undergo reduction (Figure 9.41).

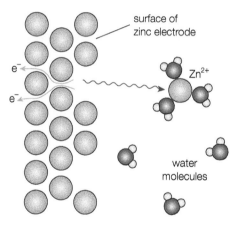
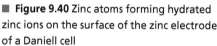

■ **Figure 9.40** Zinc atoms forming hydrated zinc ions on the surface of the zinc electrode of a Daniell cell

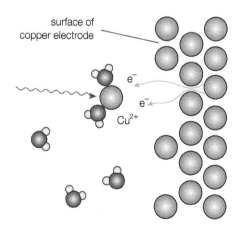

■ **Figure 9.41** Hydrated copper(II) ions forming copper atoms on the surface of the copper electrode of a Daniell cell

The process continues until either all the zinc electrode or all the copper(II) ions are consumed. The zinc is acting as a reducing agent and copper(II) ions are acting as an oxidizing agent. By definition, the anode in a voltaic cell is the electrode at which oxidation occurs and the cathode is the electrode at which reduction occurs.
The relevant half-equations are:

Anode:	$Zn(s) \rightarrow Zn^{2+}(aq) + 2e^-$
Cathode:	$Cu^{2+}(aq) + 2e^- \rightarrow Cu(s)$
Overall ionic equation:	$Zn(s) + Cu^{2+}(aq) \rightarrow Cu(s) + Zn^{2+}(aq)$

The overall chemical change is the same as that which occurs when zinc is placed in copper(II) sulfate solution. Heat energy is released in that situation, but the arrangement in the voltaic cell, where the two reactions are physically separated, enables the release of electrical energy.

There is a flow of electrons (electric current) from the anode to the cathode because there is a difference in electric potential energy between the electrodes. Experimentally the difference in electric potential between the anode and the cathode is measured by a voltmeter and the reading (in volts) is called the cell potential.

The voltage of a cell depends not only on the nature of the electrodes and the ions, but also on the concentrations of the ions and the temperature at which the cell is operated. Voltaic cell voltages are normally measured under standard conditions (Chapter 19). The cell potential of the Daniell cell under standard conditions is 1.1 volts.

The Daniell cell is one example of a simple voltaic cell. Similar voltaic cells can be made from two different metals in contact with an aqueous solution of their ions and connected by a salt bridge and external circuit. In each case the more reactive metal forms the anode which supplies electrons to the cathode.

Table 9.8 summarizes some experimental results from a number of voltaic cells operating under standard conditions. These cell potentials can also be calculated from standard electrode potentials (Chapter 19).

Of these metals, copper and magnesium are *furthest apart* in the activity series. This combination of electrodes gives the *highest* cell potential. Lead and iron are the *closest* in the activity series and give the *lowest* voltage. Hence, the further apart the two metals are in the activity series, the higher the cell potential.

Metal electrodes	Cell potential/V
Copper and magnesium	2.70
Copper and iron	0.78
Lead and zinc	0.64
Lead and iron	0.32

■ **Table 9.8** Selected voltaic cells and cell potentials

Utilization: Heart pacemakers

The heart has its own natural pacemaker that sends nerve impulses (electrochemical in nature) throughout the heart approximately 72 times per minute. These impulses cause the heart muscle to contract (beat), which pumps blood through the heart. The fibres that carry the nerve impulses can be damaged by disease, drugs, heart attacks and surgery. When these heart fibres are damaged, the heart may beat too slowly, stop temporarily, or stop altogether. To correct this condition, an artificial heart pacemaker is surgically inserted in the human body (Figure 9.42). A pacemaker is a battery-driven device that sends an electric current (pulse) to the heart about 72 times per minutes. Yearly operations used to be necessary to replace the pacemaker's batteries but pacemakers now use improved batteries that last much longer, but even these must be replaced eventually. Mercury batteries were initially used but were replaced by lithium anode batteries.

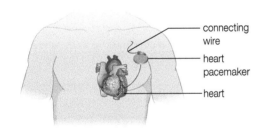

connecting wire

heart pacemaker

heart

■ **Figure 9.42** A heart pacemaker

Utilization: Fuel cells

A fuel cell (Figure 9.43) uses the reaction between molecular hydrogen (some use hydrocarbons, such as methane) and molecular oxygen to produce water. The energy is released as electrical energy, not heat (thermal energy). As the reactants are consumed more are added, so a fuel cell can give a continuous supply of electricity. The electrolyte is a strong base, usually aqueous sodium hydroxide. It is contained within the fuel cell using porous electrodes, which allow the movement of gases and water molecules.

Oxidation: loss of electrons (negative electrode)

$$H_2(g) + 2OH^-(aq) \rightarrow 2H_2O(l) + 2e^-$$

Reduction: gain of electrons (positive electrode)

$$O_2(g) + 2H_2O(l) + 4e^- \rightarrow 4OH^-(aq)$$

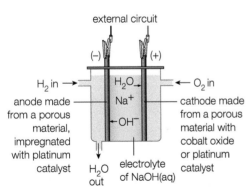

■ **Figure 9.43** Hydrogen oxygen fuel cell (in cross section)

The advantages of fuel cells are that they do not need recharging or directly cause pollution, as water is the only product. However, they are relatively expensive to produce. One major disadvantage of hydrogen as a fuel is how to store it. Liquefying it means cooling it to −253 °C, which costs four times more than making an equivalent amount of petrol (gasoline). Then it has to be kept cold in a well-insulated container.

Magnesium hydride, MgH_2, is 7.7 per cent hydrogen by mass and the hydrogen is released by the following reaction:

$$MgH_2(s) + H_2O(l) \rightarrow Mg(OH)_2(aq) + H_2(g)$$

In magnesium hydride, magnesium is ionically bonded to hydrogen in a small whole number ratio. But another type of metal hydride – an interstitial transition metal hydride – can soak up hydrogen rather like a sponge. The metal is bathed in hydrogen. At the metal surface, the hydrogen molecule splits into its atoms and the atoms occupy holes in the metal lattice. Very large quantities of hydrogen can be absorbed and released on heating.

In the 1960s, fuel cells specific for ethanol were built. In its simplest form, the alcohol fuel cell consists of a porous, chemically inert layer coated on both sides with finely divided platinum oxide, called platinum black (used in the standard hydrogen electrode). The manufacturer fills the porous layer with an acidic electrolyte solution, and applies platinum wire electrical connections to the platinum black surfaces. The manufacturer mounts the entire assembly in a case, which also includes a gas inlet that allows ethanol gas to be introduced.

The following reactions occur in an ethanol fuel cell:

Anode: $\qquad\qquad\qquad C_2H_5OH(l) + 3H_2O(l) \rightarrow 12H^+(aq) + 12e^- + 2CO_2(g)$

Cathode: $\qquad\qquad\quad 3O_2(g) + 12H^+(aq) + 12e^- \rightarrow 6H_2O(l)$

Overall ionic equation: $\;\; C_2H_5OH(l) + 3O_2(g) \rightarrow 3H_2O(l) + 2CO_2(g)$

> 7 Find out about the use of fuel cells in vehicles and the current barriers to the development and use of fuel cells.

Research in space exploration

In cooperation with the Russian cosmonauts, American astronauts began work on a permanent space station in 1998. It is the largest space project so far undertaken and is the biggest structure ever to orbit the Earth. It is a research facility 400 km above the Earth, and has been in operation since 1 November 2000. It can be seen in the sky with the naked eye.

It is known as the International Space Station (ISS) because 15 nations take part in its programmes. It has permanent accommodation for six people and short-term accommodation for up to 15 people when a space shuttle visits.

From the ISS, components of which were built in 15 countries, scientists conduct research and experiments that are impossible to conduct on Earth.

The purpose of the ISS is to make it possible for long-term exploration of space and to allow research into how humans cope with living and working outside Earth's atmosphere. This research is needed for future human exploration of space. New materials and technology, including nanotechnology, will be tested, often centred on energy factors.

The electrical system of the ISS uses solar cells to convert solar radiation into electrical energy (photovoltaics). This process of collecting sunlight, converting it to electricity, and managing and distributing this electricity builds up excess heat that can damage spacecraft equipment. This heat must be eliminated for reliable operation of the ISS. The ISS power system uses radiators to dissipate the heat away from the spacecraft. The radiators are shaded from sunlight and aligned towards deep space.

Since the station is often not in direct sunlight, it uses rechargeable nickel–hydrogen batteries to provide continuous power during the 'eclipse' part of the orbit (35 minutes of every 90 minute orbit). The batteries ensure that the station is never without power to sustain life-support systems and experiments. During the sunlit part of the orbit, the batteries are recharged. Fuel cells are not used on the ISS because it is not economical to continually supply oxygen and hydrogen by spacecraft from Earth.

■ Electrolytic cells

Conductors and insulators

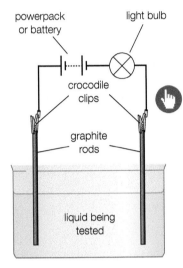

■ **Figure 9.44** A circuit for testing the conductivity of liquids and solutions

A substance that allows electricity to pass through itself is called a conductor. A substance that does not allow electricity to pass through itself is called an insulator. Common insulators include non-metallic elements (with the exception of graphite), dry samples of covalent compounds and solid samples of ionic substances.

Some substances, for example silicon and germanium, conduct electricity very slightly and are known as semi-conductors (Chapter 24 on the accompanying website). Conductors include metals and graphite (Chapter 4), aqueous solutions (Figure 9.44) of acids and alkalis (Chapter 8), and ionic compounds when they are dissolved in water or molten.

In order for a substance to conduct electricity it must contain electrically charged particles that are free to move when the substance is subjected to a potential difference or voltage. In metals, in both the solid and liquid states, the charged particles are the valence electrons (Chapter 4). It is a flow of these valence electrons through the metal that constitutes an electric current (Figure 9.45). All the other substances mentioned in the list of conductors above contain negatively and positively charged ions that are free to move through the substance. These ions, in effect, constitute an electric current since electrons are transported from one electrode to another.

Ionic solids do *not* conduct electricity, because the ions are firmly held in the lattice by powerful electrostatic forces and cannot move. Only when the ionic substance is molten or dissolved in water are the ions released from the lattice and free to move.

■ **Figure 9.45** Electrons flowing along a metal wire form an electric current

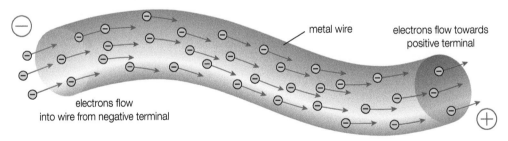

The electrolysis of a molten salt

■ **Figure 9.46** Lead(ii) bromide, which acts as an electrolyte when molten

An important and fundamental difference between conduction in a metal (or graphite) and in an aqueous solution of an ionic compound or a molten sample is that when an electric current passes through a metal, the metal itself is chemically unaffected. However, when an electric current passes through an ionic substance, either molten or in solution, the compound undergoes chemical decomposition. A substance that conducts electricity and is decomposed by the passage of an electric current is known as an electrolyte (Figure 9.46). The process of decomposing an electrolyte with an electric current is called electrolysis. This is a non-spontaneous process and needs a constant input of electrical energy. It is an important technique used on the industrial scale to prepare aluminium, chlorine, sodium hydroxide and hydrogen.

When electricity is passed through an electrolyte, the electricity enters and leaves via electrical conductors known as electrodes, which are usually made of graphite or metal. The electrode connected to the positive terminal of the battery or direct current (dc) power supply

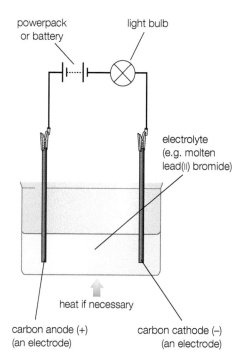

powerpack or battery

light bulb

electrolyte (e.g. molten lead(II) bromide)

heat if necessary

carbon anode (+) (an electrode)

carbon cathode (–) (an electrode)

■ **Figure 9.47** Experimental apparatus for electrolysis

■ **Figure 9.48** Electrolysis of molten lead(II) bromide

is known as the anode and the negative electrode is known as the cathode. Negative ions, or anions, are attracted towards the anode and positive ions, or cations, are attracted towards the cathode. When the ions reach the surface of the electrodes they undergo redox reactions.

The simplest form of electrolysis is the electrolysis of a molten binary salt, such as lead(II) bromide, $PbBr_2$ [Pb^{2+} $2Br^-$]. Inert or chemically unreactive graphite or metal electrodes are used (Figure 9.47) and the decomposition products are molten lead and bromine vapour. The overall reaction is:

$$PbBr_2(l) \rightarrow Pb(l) + Br_2(g)$$

The lead is formed at the cathode and the bromine vapour is formed at the anode (Figure 9.48).

At the anode: Negatively charged bromide ions are electrostatically attracted towards the positively charged anode. At the anode they lose electrons and form bromine molecules. The relevant half-equations describing the oxidation of bromide ions are shown below.

$$2Br^-(l) \rightarrow Br_2(g) + 2e^-$$

or

$$Br^-(l) \rightarrow Br(g) + e^- ; \quad 2Br(g) \rightarrow Br_2(g)$$

At the cathode: Positively charged lead(II) ions are attracted towards the negatively charged cathode. At the cathode they gain electrons and form lead atoms. The relevant half-equation describing the reduction of lead(II) ions is shown below.

$$Pb^{2+}(l) + 2e^- \rightarrow Pb(l)$$

During electrolysis, each lead(II) ion accepts two electrons from the cathode and at the same time two bromide ions each release an electron to the anode. The overall effect of these two processes is equivalent to two electrons flowing through the liquid lead(II) bromide from the cathode to the anode.

Electrolysis of other compounds

All ionic compounds undergo electrolysis in the molten state and obey two simple rules:

■ Metals always form positively charged ions, or cations, which migrate to the cathode and are discharged as atoms.

■ Non-metals always form negatively charged ions, or anions, which migrate to the anode and are discharged as molecules.

Examples of the products of the electrolysis of molten or fused electrolytes are shown in Table 9.9.

■ **Table 9.9** Examples of electrolysis of molten electrolytes

Electrolyte	Overall decomposition	Cathode half-equation	Anode half-equation
Sodium chloride, NaCl	$2NaCl(l) \rightarrow 2Na(l) + Cl_2(g)$	$Na^+ + e^- \rightarrow Na$	$2Cl^- \rightarrow Cl_2 + 2e^-$
Potassium iodide, KI	$2KI(l) \rightarrow 2K(l) + I_2(g)$	$K^+ + e^- \rightarrow K$	$2I^- \rightarrow I_2 + 2e^-$
Copper(II) chloride, $CuCl_2$	$CuCl_2(l) \rightarrow Cu(l) + Cl_2(g)$	$Cu^{2+} + 2e^- \rightarrow Cu$	$2Cl^- \rightarrow Cl_2 + 2e^-$
Aluminium oxide, Al_2O_3	$2Al_2O_3(l) \rightarrow 4Al(l) + 3O_2(g)$	$Al^{3+} + 3e^- \rightarrow Al$	$2O^{2-} \rightarrow O_2 + 4e^-$

Table 9.10 compares a voltaic cell (with two half-cells with metal electrodes connected by a salt bridge) with an electrolytic cell (of a molten binary ionic compound).

■ **Table 9.10**
Comparing a voltaic cell with an electrolytic cell

A voltaic cell	An electrolytic cell
Oxidation occurs at the anode (negative)	Oxidation occurs at the anode (positive)
Reduction occurs at the cathode (positive)	Reduction occurs at the cathode (negative)
It uses a redox reaction to produce a voltage	It uses electricity to carry out a redox reaction
It involves a spontaneous redox reaction (exothermic)	It involves a non-spontaneous redox reaction (endothermic)
It converts chemical energy to electrical energy	It converts electrical energy to chemical energy
The cathode is the positive electrode and the anode is the negative electrode (during discharge)	The cathode is the negative electrode and the anode is the positive electrode
There are two separate aqueous solutions connected by a salt bridge and an external circuit	There is one molten liquid

Deducing the products of the electrolysis of a molten salt

The cations (metal ions) are attracted to the cathode and the anions (non-metal ions) are attracted to the anode.

---

8 Deduce the products of electrolysing the following molten salts:
   a lithium bromide, LiBr   b   caesium nitride, Cs_3N c   iron(II) bromide, $FeBr_2$

Distinction between electron and ion flow in both types of electrochemical cells

Ions flow in the electrolytes of both electrolytic and voltaic cells. Electrons only flow in the external circuit of all types of electrochemical cells.

Electrolytic cell

In an electrolytic cell, ions migrate (move) to the electrode with the opposite charge. Cations (positive ions) migrate to the cathode (negatively charged) and anions (negative ions) migrate to the anode (positively charged). At the cathode the cations accept electrons and undergo reduction. At the anode the anions lose electrons and undergo oxidation. There is electron flow from the anode to the cathode via the external circuit (wires etc.).

Voltaic cell

In an electrochemical cell, the more reactive metal acts as the anode and the metal atoms undergo oxidation and lose electrons. The electrons on the surface of the electrode make it negative. The electrons flow to the cathode via the external circuit. The electrons on the surface react with the cations present in the half-cell forming the cathode (positive). The cations undergo reduction to form atoms. There is a flow of ions due to the operation of the salt bridge (Chapter 18) to maintain electrical neutrality.

The important differences between the conduction of electricity through metals and through electrolytes are summarized in Table 9.11.

■ **Table 9.11**
The differences between metallic and electrolytic conduction

Metallic conduction	Electrolytic conduction
Conduction through metals is carried out by the movement of delocalized valence electrons	Conduction through electrolytes is carried out by the movement of cations and anions
No change is observed in the chemical properties of the conductors	It involves a chemical change resulting in the decomposition of electrolytes
It does not involve any transfer of matter	It involves the transfer of matter as ions
It shows an increase in resistance with an increase in temperature	It shows a decrease in resistance with an increase in temperature
The conductivity of metals is generally high	The conductivity of electrolytic solutions is generally low
Measured using an ohmmeter	Measured using a conductivity meter

A solution will conduct electricity if it contains mobile ions. This idea can be used to explain the results of electrolysis. When a direct current is passed through an ionic solution electrolysis occurs and ions are removed from the solution. Electrolysis can be avoided by using an alternating voltage.

A conductivity meter (Chapter 19) consists of two platinum electrodes bonded into the glass walls of the cells. The cell is placed into a solution and the electrodes are connected to a conductivity meter which connects an alternating voltage to the cell and measures the resistance of the solution between the electrodes.

Constructing and annotating both types of electrochemical cells

Voltaic cells should be drawn with two half-cells connected by a salt bridge and an external circuit: wire and voltmeter (Figure 9.49). The electrodes and electrolytes should be clearly identified and labelled. The anode (−) and cathode (+) should be identified. Electron flow (from the anode to the cathode) through the external circuit should be identified.

An electrolytic cell should be drawn with a power pack or battery connected to two electrodes (Figure 9.50). The cathode (−) and anode (+) should be labelled and identified. The molten electrolyte should be identified and labelled. Electron flow (from the anode to the cathode) through the external circuit should be identified.

It is time consuming to keep drawing the electrodes used in voltaic cells. Therefore a system of notation has been devised so that a whole voltaic cell can be described on a single line. The anode is written on the left and the cathode on the right. A single vertical line distinguishes components that are in different physical states (phases), for example, a solid electrode and the aqueous metal ions with which it is in contact. The salt bridge is shown by two dashed vertical bars. This 'shorthand notation' is known as a cell diagram.

Consider a Daniell cell consisting of zinc and copper half-cells:

$$Zn(s) + Cu^{2+}(aq) \rightarrow Zn^{2+}(aq) + Cu(s)$$

We can describe the resulting galvanic cell completely by

$$Zn(s) \mid Zn^{2+}(aq) \mathbin{\vdots\vdots} Cu^{2+}(aq) \mid Cu(s)$$

As we read from left to right, we see that the first half-cell has a half-reaction where solid zinc loses electrons to give zinc ions (an oxidation half-reaction). The second half-cell has the half-reaction where copper ions gain electrons to become solid copper (the reduction half-reaction).

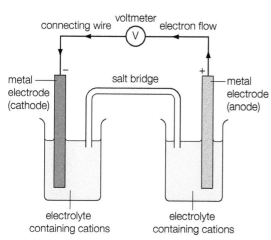

■ **Figure 9.49** Generalized annotated voltaic cell

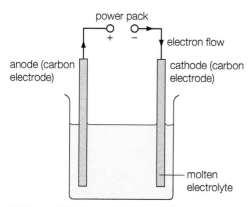

■ **Figure 9.50** Generalized electrolytic cell

Worked examples

Write the shorthand notation for a galvanic cell that uses the reaction Fe(s) + Sn^{2+}(aq) → Fe^{2+}(aq) + Sn(s)

Since the solid iron is oxidized it should be our anode on the left. Since the solid tin results from the reduction of tin(II) ions, it is our cathode on the right.

Fe(s) | Fe^{2+}(aq) ⫶ Sn^{2+}(aq) | Sn(s)

Write a balanced equation for the overall cell reaction and give a brief description of the galvanic cell represented by Pb(s) | Pb^{2+}(aq) ⫶ Br$_2$(l) | Br$^-$(aq) | Pt(s)

Pb(s) + Br$_2$(aq) → Pb^{2+}(aq) + 2Br$^-$(aq)

The lead atoms are oxidized to lead(II) ions and form the anode. Bromine is reduced to bromide ions and forms the cathode.

Examination questions – a selection

Paper 1 IB questions and IB style questions

Q1 In the reaction

$$MnO_2(s) + 4HCl(aq) \rightarrow Cl_2(g) + MnCl_2(aq) + 2H_2O(l)$$

A HCl is the oxidizing agent.
B Cl_2 is the oxidation product.
C MnO_2 is the reducing agent.
D H_2O is the reduction product.

Q2 The following reaction occurs in acid solution:

$$\_H^+(aq) + \_NO_3^-(aq) + I^-(aq) \rightarrow$$
$$IO_3^-(aq) + \_NO_2(g) + \_H_2O(l)$$

The equation is not balanced. What is the coefficient of NO_3^- in the balanced equation?
A 4   **B** 2   **C** 5   **D** 6

Q3 Which one of the following equations represents the half-equation (or half-reaction) that occurs at the anode during the electrolysis of molten potassium iodide?
A $K^+ + e^- \rightarrow K$
B $2H_2O \rightarrow O_2 + 4H^+ + 4e^-$
C $2H_2O + 2e^- \rightarrow H_2 + 2OH^-$
D $2I^- \rightarrow I_2 + 2e^-$

Q4 The following information is given about reactions involving the metals X, Y and Z and solutions of their sulfates.

$$X(s) + YSO_4(aq) \rightarrow \text{no reaction}$$

$$Z(s) + YSO_4(aq) \rightarrow Y(s) + ZSO_4(aq)$$

When the metals are listed in decreasing order of reactivity (most reactive first), what is the correct order?
A Z > Y > X   **C** Y > X > Z
B X > Y > Z   **D** Y > Z > X

Standard Level Paper 1, Nov 2005, Q27

Q5 Which one of the following represents an oxidation–reduction reaction?
A $I_2(s) + 2OH^-(aq) \rightarrow I^-(aq) + OI^-(aq) + H_2O(l)$
B $PO_4^{3-}(aq) + H_2O(l) \rightarrow HPO_4^{2-}(aq) + OH^-(aq)$
C $SO_3(g) + 2H_2O(l) \rightarrow HSO_4^-(aq) + H_3O^+(aq)$
D $Cu^{2+}(aq) + H_2S(aq) \rightarrow CuS(s) + 2H^+(aq)$

Q6 All of the following would be expected to function as both oxidizing and reducing agents except:
A NO_2 **B** Cl^- **C** ClO^- **D** S

Q7 Magnesium is a more reactive metal than copper. Which is the strongest oxidizing agent?
A Mg   **B** Mg^{2+} **C** Cu   **D** Cu^{2+}

Standard Level Paper 1, Nov 2003, Q26

Q8 When a direct current of electricity is conducted by an aqueous solution of an electrolyte, which one of the following statements is false?
A The movement of ions accounts for the current flow through the solution.
B During electrolysis, the solution remains electrically neutral.
C Electrons flow from the current source towards the solution at one electrode, and an equal number of electrons flow away from the solution at the other electrode.
D The number of positive ions moving towards one electrode is always equal to the number of negative ions moving towards the other electrode.

Q9 In acid solution, manganate(VII) ions, MnO_4^-(aq), undergo reduction to manganese(II) ions, Mn^{2+}(aq). What amount of MnO_4^-(aq) is required to convert 5.36×10^{-3} moles of the ion Y^{2+}(aq) to YO_3^-(aq)?
A 1.07×10^{-3} mol   **C** 5.36×10^{-3} mol
B 3.22×10^{-3} mol   **D** 8.93×10^{-3} mol

Q10 Which statement is correct for the electrolysis of molten sodium chloride?
A Sodium ions move towards the positive electrode.
B A gas is produced at the negative electrode.
C Only electrons move in the electrolyte.
D Both sodium and chloride ions move towards electrodes.

Q11 In which of the following does the metal undergo a change in oxidation state?
   I $2MnO_4^{2-} + F_2 \rightarrow 2MnO_4^- + 2F^-$
   II $2CrO_4^{2-} + 2H^+ \rightarrow Cr_2O_7^{2-} + H_2O$
   III $[Fe(H_2O)_6]^{2+} + 6CN^- \rightarrow [Fe(CN)_6]^{3-} + 6H_2O$
A I only   **C** I and II only
B II only   **D** I and III only

Q12 In which one of the following species does chlorine exhibit the highest oxidation number?
A Cl_2O **C** $HClO_4$
B Cl_2 **D** PCl_5

Q13 Which of the following chemicals is **not** involved in the Winkler method for determining the concentration of dissolved oxygen in water?
A sodium thiosulfate   **C** manganese(II) salt
B potassium dichromate(VI)   **D** alkali

Q14 What are the products when molten magnesium fluoride is electrolysed with inert electrodes?

	Cathode	**Anode**
A	Hydrogen	Fluorine
B	Magnesium	Fluoride
C	Magnesium	Fluorine
D	Fluorine	Magnesium

Q15 Which is the oxidizing agent in the following reaction?

$$5SO_2(g) + 2IO_3^-(aq) + 4H_2O(l) \rightarrow 5SO_4^{2-}(aq) + I_2(aq) + 8H^+(aq)$$

A SO_2 **B** IO_3^- **C** H_2O **D** SO_4^{2-}

Higher Level Paper 1, May 2013, Q30

Q16 The overall reaction in the voltaic cell below is:

$$Ni(s) + Pb^{2+} \rightarrow Ni^{2+}(aq) + Pb$$

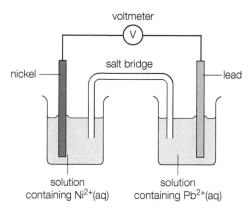

Which statement is correct for the nickel half-cell?
A Nickel is the positive electrode (cathode) and is reduced.
B Nickel is the negative electrode (anode) and is reduced.
C Nickel is the positive electrode (cathode) and is oxidized.
D Nickel is the negative electrode (anode) and is oxidized.

Higher Level Paper 1, May 2013, Q31

Q17 Which statement is correct for electroplating an object with gold?
A The object must be the negative electrode (cathode).
B The negative electrode (cathode) must be gold.
C The object must be the positive electrode (anode).
D The gold electrode must be pure.

Higher Level Paper 1, May 2013, Q32

Paper 2 IB questions and IB style questions

Q1 **a** Use these equations, which refer to aqueous solutions, to answer the questions that follow:

$$Fe(s) + Cu^{2+}(aq) \rightarrow Fe^{2+}(aq) + Cu(s)$$
$$Cu(s) + 2Au^+(aq) \rightarrow Cu^{2+}(aq) + 2Au(s)$$
$$Mg(s) + Fe^{2+}(aq) \rightarrow Mg^{2+}(aq) + Fe(s)$$

(Au represents gold, which is below silver in the reactivity series.)
  i List the metals above in order of **decreasing** reactivity. [1]
  ii Define oxidation, in electronic terms, using **one** example from above. [2]
  iii Define reduction, in terms of oxidation number, using **one** example from above. [2]

  iv State and explain which is the **strongest reducing agent** in the examples above. [2]
  v State and explain which is the **strongest oxidizing agent** in the examples above. [2]
  vi Deduce whether a gold coin will react with aqueous magnesium nitrate. [2]
b Sketch a diagram of a cell used to electrolyse a molten salt. Label the essential components. [4]
c Describe how electrode reactions occur in an electrolytic cell and state the products at each electrode when molten copper(II) iodide is electrolysed. [4]

Q2 **a** Electrolysis can be used to obtain fluorine from molten potassium fluoride. Write an equation for the reaction occurring at each electrode and describe the two different ways in which electricity is conducted when the cell is in operation. [4]
b In one experiment involving the electrolysis of molten potassium fluoride, 0.1 mol of fluorine was formed. Deduce, giving a reason, the amount of potassium formed at the same time. [2]
c Sodium will replace aluminium from its chloride on heating:

$$3Na + AlCl_3 \rightarrow Al + 3NaCl$$

  i Explain, by reference to electrons, why the reaction is referred to as a redox reaction. [2]
  ii Deduce the oxidation numbers of sodium and aluminium in the reactants and products. [2]

Q3 The percentage of iron(II) ions, Fe^{2+}, in a vitamin tablet can be estimated by dissolving the tablet in dilute sulfuric acid and titrating with standard potassium manganate(VII) solution, $KMnO_4(aq)$. During the process iron(II) is oxidized to iron(III) and the manganate(VII) ion is reduced to the manganese(II) ion, $Mn^{2+}(aq)$. It was found that one tablet with a mass of 1.43 g required 11.6 cm^3 of 2.00×10^{-2} mol dm^{-3} $KMnO_4(aq)$ to reach the end-point.
a **i** State the half-equation for the oxidation of the iron (II) ions. [1]
  ii State the half-equation for the reduction of the MnO_4^- ions in acidic solution. [1]
  iii Deduce the overall redox equation for the reaction. [1]
b **i** Calculate the amount, in moles, of MnO_4^- ions present in 11.6 cm^3 of 2.00×10^{-2} mol dm^{-3} $KMnO_4(aq)$. [1]
  ii Calculate the amount, in moles, of Fe^{2+} ions present in the vitamin tablet. [1]
  iii Determine the percentage by mass of Fe^{2+} ions present in the vitamin tablet. [2]

Higher Level Paper 2, May 2009

10 Organic chemistry

ESSENTIAL IDEAS

- Organic chemistry focuses on the chemistry of compounds containing carbon.
- Structure, bonding and chemical reactions involving functional group interconversions are key strands in organic chemistry.

10.1 Fundamentals of organic chemistry – *organic chemistry focuses on the chemistry of compounds containing carbon*

■ Modern organic chemistry

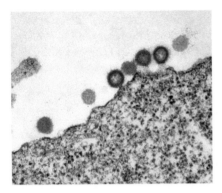

■ **Figure 10.1** HIV viruses budding from a cell

Viruses straddle the junction between the inanimate world and life (Figure 10.1). They are not themselves living, but can reproduce themselves amazingly quickly when they infect a host. They manipulate the genetic 'machinery' of the host cells to use it for their own ends.

Viruses can be crystallized and their structures analysed. These structures are made up of carbon-containing molecules such as DNA or RNA and proteins. Molecules such as these are the basis of life and illustrate the versatility of carbon to form a range of complex molecules. All living things on Earth, from micro-organisms such as bacteria to the largest plants and animals, reproduce and grow using systems based on nucleic acids and proteins. These are macromolecules – molecules on a very large scale. Proteins are made by assembling amino acids into long chains. These chains then fold and organize themselves into complex structures. For example, a molecule of hemoglobin contains four protein chains. Each of these chains is made up of more than 100 amino acids. The molecules of life are based on the distinctive properties of one element – carbon. Carbon is unique in the variety of molecules it can form. The chemistry of these molecules forms a separate branch of chemistry known as organic chemistry.

Modern organic chemistry deals with both naturally occurring and synthetic compounds, including plastics, pharmaceuticals, petrochemicals, fuels and foods. As it provides a link between the properties of atoms and the functioning of living organisms, it is through organic chemistry that we come to biochemistry and hence to the chemical foundations of life itself.

Nature of Science

'Vitalism' and the birth of organic chemistry

■ **Figure 10.2**
a Friedrich Wöhler (1800–1882) and **b** the structure of urea

The nature of life and the features essential to its chemistry have long been the subject of speculation. Historically, organic molecules were believed to be a distinctive type of chemical substance unique to living things (part of a set of ideas known as 'vitalism'). It was thought that organic molecules could not be made outside a living organism. However, in 1828, the German chemist Friedrich Wöhler (Figure 10.2) synthesized urea from inorganic substances without the presence of any biological tissue. He wrote to his mentor, Berzelius, saying: 'I must tell you that I can make urea without the use of kidneys, either man or dog. Ammonium cyanate is urea.' The synthesis of urea had not been the intention of his experiment, but in attempting to prepare ammonium cyanate from silver cyanide and ammonium chloride he had completed a revolutionary experiment. Upon analysis, the white powder produced proved to have the composition and properties of urea, a compound that had previously been isolated from urine.

Wöhler pursued these experiments further and discovered that urea and ammonium cyanate had the same chemical formula, but very different chemical properties. This was an early discovery of isomerism, since urea has the formula $CO(NH_2)_2$ and ammonium cyanate has the formula NH_4CNO. Wöhler's results conclusively destroyed the belief that there was a distinction between the chemistry of life and general inorganic chemistry. It opened up the door to a whole branch of organic chemistry centred on the properties and reactions of carbon-containing compounds.

The distinctive features of carbon

Around *six million* compounds of carbon are already known! This versatility is made possible by certain unique properties of carbon. Carbon is a non-metal in group 14 of the periodic table and forms predominantly covalent compounds. There are three special features of covalent bonding involving carbon:

- Carbon atoms can join to each other to form long chains. Atoms of other elements can then attach to the chain.

- The carbon atoms in a chain can be linked by single, double or triple covalent bonds.

- Carbon atoms can also arrange themselves in rings involving both single and multiple bonds.

Bond	Average bond enthalpy/ $kJ\,mol^{-1}$
C–C	346
Si–Si	226
Ge–Ge	188
Sn–Sn	151

■ **Table 10.1** The bond strengths of X–X bonds for the group 14 elements

Atoms of other elements can copy some of this versatility to a limited extent (e.g. silicon atoms can form short chains, while sulfur atoms can arrange themselves in rings). But only carbon can achieve all these different bonding arrangements, and do so to an amazing extent. The ability of carbon to form chains and rings is known as catenation.

There are other features of carbon that help to reinforce its unique position as the most versatile of the elements as regards compound formation. Carbon not only forms multiple bonds with itself, but it can also form double and triple bonds with other elements such as oxygen (the carbonyl group, >C=O, is an important feature of aldehydes, ketones and carboxylic acids), and with nitrogen (in nitriles, which contain the >C≡N group).

The C–C bond is particularly strong compared with the strength of similar bonds between other group 14 elements (Table 10.1). This contributes to the thermal stability of organic compounds.

Allied to the thermal stability of the C–C bond is the fact that the C–H bond is also significantly more stable than other comparable bonds, such as the Si–H bond (bond enthalpies: $C–H = 412\ kJ\ mol^{-1}$; $Si–H = 318\ kJ\ mol^{-1}$).

When a carbon atom is bonded to four other atoms it is kinetically stable as the outer shell of the carbon atom (electron shell $n = 2$) has a full octet of electrons which cannot be expanded. Thus tetrachloromethane (CCl_4) cannot be hydrolysed by water whereas silicon tetrachloride ($SiCl_4$) can be. Water molecules are thought to attack the $SiCl_4$ molecules through lone pairs on their oxygen atoms expanding the octet of electrons around the central silicon atom in each molecule.

These properties suggest a versatility and stability of carbon-containing compounds that cannot be matched by any other element. One highly speculative consequence of this is that, in considering the possibility of life on distant planets, it is difficult to imagine complex life forms based on any element other than carbon.

With so many possible molecules to describe and categorize, it is important to find ways of relating the different types of structure to the chemical properties of the compounds. The formation of chains or rings of carbon atoms provides the basis of a means of classifying organic compounds. When looking at the basic structure of any organic compound, therefore, it is important to see whether the structure is based on a chain or a ring. This forms the 'backbone' of the molecule.

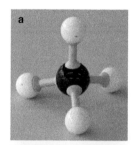

■ **Figure 10.3** Models of the structure of methane, CH_4. These models show the tetrahedral structure of the molecule. **a** A ball-and-stick model, showing the four single C–H bonds; **b** a space-filling model

■ The nature of a homologous series

The most obvious basic structure is that of a chain of carbon atoms with only hydrogen attached. It is easy then to think of a series of compounds that result from simply extending the chain progressively by one carbon atom at a time. Figure 10.3 shows models of the simplest compound of this series – one carbon atom with four hydrogen atoms covalently bonded to it. This is a model of the simplest hydrocarbon: methane, CH_4.

Thus a series of compounds exists in which the molecules get progressively extended by a carbon atom, or, more precisely, by a $–CH_2–$ group (see Table 10.2). Such a series of compounds is known as a homologous series; and this particular one is known as the alkanes.

■ **Table 10.2**
Some details of the early members of a homologous series – the alkanes

Alkane	Molecular formula C_nH_{2n+2}	Number of carbon atoms	Melting point/K	Boiling point/K		Physical state at room temperature and pressure
Methane*	CH_4	1	91	109		gas
Ethane	C_2H_6	2	90	186	b.p. increasing	gas
Propane	C_3H_8	3	83	231		gas
Butane	C_4H_{10}	4	135	273		gas
Pentane	C_5H_{12}	5	144	309		liquid
Hexane	C_6H_{14}	6	178	342		liquid

*The naming of these compounds will be discussed shortly (page 334).

ToK Link

Computer modelling carbon structures

One key to understanding the microscopic world of atoms and molecules is to build models that help us 'visualize' the unseeable. We can do this with words and with mathematical models but in chemistry there has been the very practical development of various types of model structures such as those shown in Figure 10.3. The most famous and significant model-building exercise in history must surely have been Watson and Crick's elucidation of the structure of DNA.

Model-building kits have their virtues and limitations: the bond lengths in ball-and-stick models give a false impression of the space between the atoms, for instance. Recent developments in computer modelling make it easy to switch between various means of depicting structures and display the distances and angles in the structures with great accuracy. Figure 10.4 shows two computer-generated models of methane. The second is a space-filling model aimed at showing the inter-penetration of atoms as they bond to make a simple molecule.

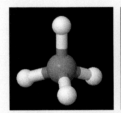

■ **Figure 10.4** Computer-generated models of methane. These are generated using the computer program *Rasmol*. A similar program, *Chime*, allows the molecule to be rotated on-screen

Such models are useful in giving us an understanding of the crucial ideas of shape and the three-dimensional arrangement of molecules. Figure 10.5 shows different types of model of ethanol. All of these have their uses, and you will encounter them in your reading.

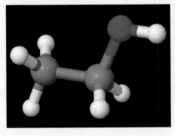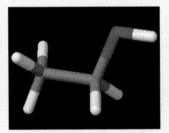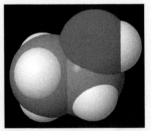

■ **Figure 10.5** Three different styles of model for the structure of ethanol.

The merits of the computer modelling of molecules come into their own when depicting more complex molecules. Pharmaceutical companies invest a great deal in sophisticated programs for molecular design. Figure 10.6 shows the ring structure of glucose as an example of a slightly more complex molecule.

Both in solid models and in computer graphics, the following colour code is used to indicate which element is being represented:

black or grey = carbon
white = hydrogen
red = oxygen
yellow = sulfur
blue = nitrogen
green = chlorine

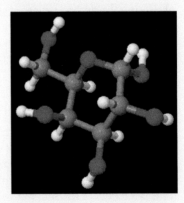

■ **Figure 10.6** The ring form of D-glucose. Note the six-membered ring involving five carbon atoms and one oxygen atom

This homologous series of compounds illustrates certain key features of all such series:

■ The names of the compounds all contain a consistent feature that denotes the series; in this case the names all have the same ending, *-ane*.

■ The formulas show the increase in chain length, in this case of a $-CH_2-$ group between one member and the next.

- The molecules all have the same general formula, for alkanes it is C_nH_{2n+2}, where n is the number of carbon atoms in the chain.
- There is a progressive and gradual change in basic physical properties as the chain length increases – illustrated here by the increasing boiling point of the compounds in the series. Figure 10.7 shows how the structures of these first six alkanes develop with the lengthening of the chain.

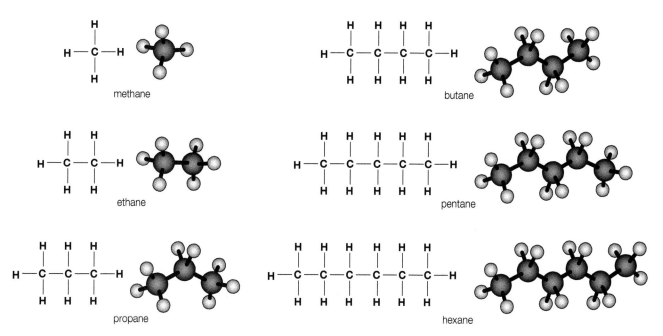

- **Figure 10.7** The structures of the first six alkanes

1 The homologous series of alkanes has the general formula C_nH_{2n+2}. The first four alkanes are gases at room temperature but the fifth member is a liquid, as are the next 11 members of the series.
   a What is the molecular formula of octane given that its molecules each contain eight carbon atoms?
   b The members of the series continue to be liquids up to carbon-16. What are the molecular formulas of this liquid alkane and the first of the alkanes that is a waxy solid at room temperature?
   c Table 10.2 gives details of the melting and boiling points of the first six alkanes. Suggest a possible melting and boiling point for i heptane, which has seven carbon atoms and ii octane, which has eight carbon atoms.

2 The densities of the early members of the alkane series are given in Table 10.3. Plot a graph of the densities against the number of carbon atoms in each compound, and see if there is a similar regular trend in these values.

- **Table 10.3**
The densities of members of the alkane series

Alkane	Molecular formula	Density at 273 K/g cm^{-3}
Methane	CH_4	0.466*
Ethane	C_2H_6	0.572*
Propane	C_3H_8	0.585*
Butane	C_4H_{10}	0.601*
Pentane	C_5H_{12}	0.626
Hexane	C_6H_{14}	0.659
Heptane	C_7H_{16}	0.684
Octane	C_8H_{18}	0.703
Nonane	C_9H_{20}	0.718
Decane	$C_{10}H_{22}$	0.730

*These four alkanes are gases at 273 K; the densities quoted here are values at a temperature just below the boiling point of each compound.

Table 10.2 shows the trend in boiling points for the first six alkanes. They show a gradual, though not linear increase in value. Do other physical properties of the alkanes show a similar gradual progression?

From the table we can see that the values do increase with chain length. Plotting the graph shows that, for the alkanes that are liquid at 273 K, there is a regular smooth increase in the density values. Indeed, the values for propane and butane are not too far from fitting the pattern (Figure 10.8).

■ **Figure 10.8** Graph of the densities of the early members of the alkane series. This graph is drawn, and the line fitted, by feeding data into the computer program *Graphical Analysis* (Vernier).

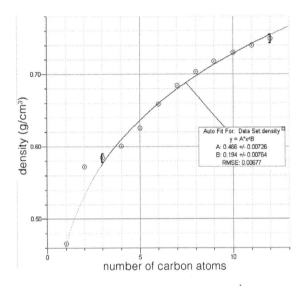

The alkanes are the simplest homologous series because the molecules contain only two elements, carbon and hydrogen, and all the carbon–carbon bonds are single bonds. There are two further homologous series that are straight-chain hydrocarbons, whose molecules contain carbon and hydrogen only. These are:

■ the alkenes, which contain a carbon–carbon double bond and have the general formula C_nH_{2n} and

■ the alkynes, having a carbon–carbon triple bond and the general formula C_nH_{2n-2}.

The properties of these two series are distinct from those of the alkanes and determined by the multiple bonds in the molecules. For this reason the multiple carbon–carbon bond is known as the functional group of each series (see Table 10.5).

The three series we have looked at so far have contained just the two elements, carbon and hydrogen. However, it is easy to imagine a different series of molecules where one of the hydrogen atoms in the chain is replaced by, say, a halogen atom or a hydroxyl (–OH) group. This latter series of compounds is known as the alcohols. Table 10.4 gives some details of the early compounds of the alcohol homologous series.

■ **Table 10.4** Some data on the early members of the alcohol homologous series

Alcohol	Molecular formula $C_nH_{2n+2}O$ ($C_nH_{2n+1}OH$)	Boiling point/K (at atmospheric pressure)	
Methanol	CH_4O (CH_3OH)	338	b.p. increasing
Ethanol	C_2H_6O (C_2H_5OH)	351	
Propan-1-ol	C_3H_8O (C_3H_7OH)	370	
Butan-1-ol	$C_4H_{10}O$ (C_4H_9OH)	390	
Pentan-1-ol	$C_5H_{12}O$ ($C_5H_{11}OH$)	410	
Hexan-1-ol	$C_6H_{14}O$ ($C_6H_{13}OH$)	431	

The properties of this series of compounds are dictated by the presence of the $-OH$ group that gives the alcohols their distinctive properties. For this reason the hydroxyl ($-OH$) group is known as the functional group of the alcohols.

The presence of different functional groups in these series adds the final distinctive feature to our definition of a homologous series. In summary, a homologous series is a group of organic compounds that:

- contain the same functional group
- have the same general formula, with successive members of the series having an additional $-CH_2-$ group
- have similar chemical properties
- show a steady gradation in certain basic physical properties.

Table 10.5 shows some of the different functional groups present in several homologous series. These groups are attached to, or part of, the hydrocarbon 'backbone' or 'skeleton' of the molecules in the series. They give the molecules the distinctive properties of the particular chemical 'family' or homologous series.

■ **Table 10.5** Some functional groups

Homologous series	Functional group and condensed structural formula	Suffix in name of compound	General formula	Structure of the functional group
Alkanes	$-CH_2-CH_2-$	-ane	C_nH_{2n+2}	*
Alkenes	$-CH=CH-$ alkenyl	-ene	C_nH_{2n}	$\diagdown C = C \diagup$
Alkynes	$-C\equiv C-$ alkynyl	-yne	C_nH_{2n-2}	$-C\equiv C-$
Halogenoalkanes	$-X$ (where X = F, Cl, Br, I)	name uses a prefix (chloro-, bromo-, etc)	$C_nH_{2n+1}X$	$-X$ (where X = F, Cl, Br, I)
Alcohols	$-OH$ hydroxyl	-ol	$C_nH_{2n+1}OH$ or ROH	$-O-H$
Aldehydes	$-CHO$ aldehyde (carbonyl)	-al	$C_nH_{2n+1}CHO$ or RCHO	$-C\diagup{}^O_H$
Ketones**	$-CO-$ carbonyl	-one	$C_nH_{2n+1}COC_mH_{2m+1}$ or RCOR'	$R \diagdown_{R'} C = O$
Carboxylic acids	$-COOH$ or $-CO_2H$ carboxyl	-oic acid	$C_nH_{2n+1}COOH$ or RCOOH	$-C\diagup{}^O_{O-H}$

*The alkane structure is the basic backbone into which the functional groups are introduced.

**R and R' represent hydrocarbon chains (alkyl groups) attached to the group. These chains can be identical or different (as represented here).

Trends in physical properties in a series

You will see from Tables 10.2 and 10.4 that the boiling points of a series of compounds in a homologous series increase steadily with the lengthening of the carbon chain. The alkanes show a smooth variation in boiling point, becoming less volatile with increasing molecular mass.

The alkanes are a useful starting point in considering the effect of increasing molecular size on such essential physical properties because, by their non-polar nature, the interactive forces between the molecules are solely London (dispersion) forces (Chapter 4). These forces are based on interactions between temporary dipoles created by momentary shifts in electron distribution. The strength of the forces is related to the number of electrons involved in the structure and

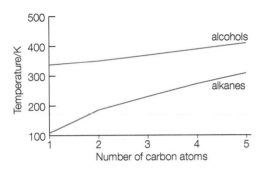

■ **Figure 10.9** Graph of the increasing boiling points of the early alkanes and alcohols with increasing chain length

■ **Figure 10.10** An oil refinery at night

the surface area of the molecules over which the interactions can be spread. Increasing the chain length of the molecules increases both these features and so the strength of the London forces increases with increasing molecular size. Physical properties dependent on these interactions, such as melting point, boiling point and enthalpy of vaporization (ΔH_{vap}), will also show an increase with chain length (Figure 10.9).

If the plot is extended to larger molecules, the effect of the addition of each $-CH_2-$ becomes less significant as the chain gets longer; the change is not linear, but it is regular and smooth. The gradient of the curves for melting point and boiling point for the alkanes decreases with increasing chain length.

The trend in boiling point values for the early alcohols also shows an almost linear increase with increasing molecular size (Figure 10.9). The values are all significantly higher than for the corresponding alkane, suggesting that there are stronger intermolecular forces acting in this case. This idea will be looked at in more detail later in the chapter (see page 349).

The regular increase in boiling point of the alkanes with increasing chain length is of immense commercial importance. It is the basis of the initial refinery process of fractional distillation whereby crude oil is separated into useful 'fractions' (Figures 10.10 and 10.11). Crude oil (or petroleum) is the major commercial source of hydrocarbons for a variety of uses as fuels and chemical feedstock. Figure 10.11 shows the components present in the major fractions obtained by distillation at an oil refinery.

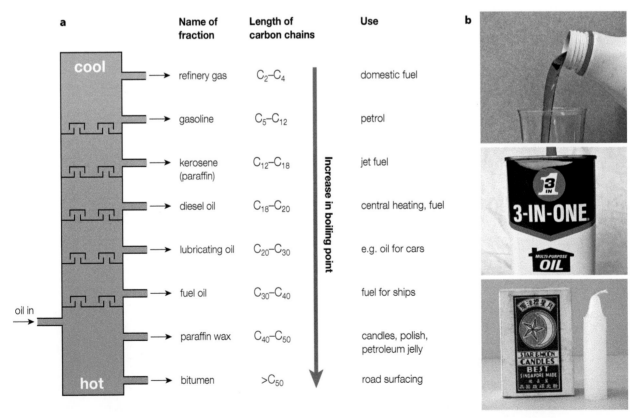

■ **Figure 10.11 a** The fractions obtained industrially from crude oil using a fractionating tower; **b** some examples of useful components

■ Formulas of organic compounds

Types of formulas

In the discussion so far we have referred to two different ways of writing the formulas of the organic molecules that have been used as examples. Tables 10.2 and 10.4 show the molecular formulas of the alkanes and alcohols, while Figure 10.7 gives the full structural formulas of the first six straight-chain alkanes. These different types of formulas provide different levels of information and are each useful in their own distinctive way. Three different types of formulas are used for organic compounds: empirical, molecular and structural formulas.

The empirical formula of a compound is the simplest whole number ratio of the atoms it contains (Chapter 1). For some alkanes, methane and propane for instance, the empirical formula is the same as the actual molecular formula. However, for others this is not true. The empirical formula of ethane, whose molecular formula is C_2H_6, is CH_3. In practical terms the empirical formula is the formula that can be derived from the percentage composition data obtained from combustion analysis. In order to use this to establish the actual formula, data on the relative molecular mass (M_r) of the compound is required.

Nature of Science	**Improved instrumentation – the practical determination of formulas**

Historically, our knowledge of the chemical composition of compounds and their formulas came from practical work on elemental analysis. This analysis was remarkable as it was carried out at a time when nothing was known about the structure of the atom or chemical bonding. The work has been termed gravimetric analysis and the progression to modern techniques illustrates how technical development builds on and expands scientific horizons. Subsequently, more sophisticated methods have been added to the armoury of techniques by which we can determine not just the composition of compounds, but also their structures.

■ The empirical formula of an organic compound can be obtained from its percentage composition by mass. For compounds that contain only carbon, hydrogen and oxygen this can be found in a quantitative combustion experiment in an excess of oxygen. The number of carbon atoms in an organic molecule can be calculated if the volume of carbon dioxide produced by complete combustion of a known volume of pure gaseous compound is measured (Chapter 1).

■ The presence of functional groups can be established using chemical tests, for example bromine water for alkenes, and by infrared spectroscopy (Chapter 21).

■ The molecular formula can be obtained from the empirical formula if the relative molecular mass is known (Chapter 1). The relative molecular mass can be accurately measured by mass spectrometry (Chapter 2).

■ The structural formulas of organic compounds can be determined by nuclear magnetic resonance (NMR) and mass spectrometry (Chapter 21).

The molecular formula of a compound is the actual number of atoms of each type present in a molecule. For example, the molecular formula of ethane is C_2H_6, of ethanol is C_2H_6O and of ethanoic acid is $C_2H_4O_2$. For many organic compounds the molecular formula and empirical formula are not the same. However, the molecular formula must be a whole number multiple of the empirical formula and therefore can be deduced if you know both the empirical formula and the relative molecular mass (M_r) of the compound.

Worked example

A halogenoalkane has a relative molecular mass of 99. Calculations based on elemental analysis of the compound show that it has an empirical formula of CH_2Cl. What is the molecular formula of this halogenoalkane?

The relative molecular mass of the empirical formula, CH_2Cl, is $12 + (2 \times 1) + 35.5 = 49.5$

The actual relative molecular mass is 99

Therefore the actual molecular formula is $2 \times (CH_2Cl)$, i.e. $C_2H_4Cl_2$

Molecular formulas such as those for ethanol (C_2H_6O) are of limited value in that they give no indication of the functional group(s) involved in a compound, and hence no clue as to the properties of the compound. Often the formula of ethanol is written as C_2H_5OH, which has the advantage of showing the presence of the alcohol group. Similarly the formula for ethanoic acid is written as CH_3COOH to indicate the presence of a carboxylic acid group in the structure.

■ **Figure 10.12**
The structural formulas and models of ethanol and ethanoic acid

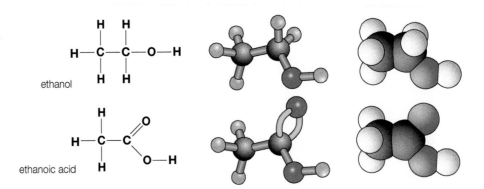

These representations of the molecules begin to show exactly how the atoms are bonded to each other – the structure of the molecule. The full structural formula (also known as the graphic formula or displayed formula) shows *every* bond and atom (see Figure 10.7 for the full structural formulas of the first six alkanes). Note that all the carbon atoms and, importantly, all the hydrogens should be shown. Sometimes it is sufficient to use a condensed structural formula that omits bonds where they can be assumed and groups atoms together. So, for example, propane can be written as $CH_3CH_2CH_3$, and butane can be written either as $CH_3CH_2CH_2CH_3$ or as $CH_3(CH_2)_2CH_3$. Figure 10.12 shows the full structural formulas, with models, for ethanol and ethanoic acid, both of which are important organic compounds.

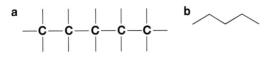

■ **Figure 10.13** The skeletal formula of pentane. In **a** the hydrogen atoms are simply missed off. In **b** there are no symbols for atoms at all; the carbon atoms (with the appropriate number of hydrogen atoms) are located at the joints

It is important that any structural formula is unambiguous and there is only one possible structure that could be described by the formula as it is written.

It is possible to miss the hydrogen atoms from a structural formula. With the hydrogen atoms omitted we have what is known as a skeletal structure or skeletal formula (Figure 10.13). In certain cases of complex molecules this can be quite useful.

The skeletal formula of the type in Figure 10.13a is very rarely used, and certainly should not be used in an examination answer. Skeletal formulas of the type in Figure 10.13b can be very useful for quickly writing out alternative structures and for depicting molecules of substantial complexity (Figure 10.14). We will use this type of skeletal structure later when working out the possible structural isomers for a given molecular formula.

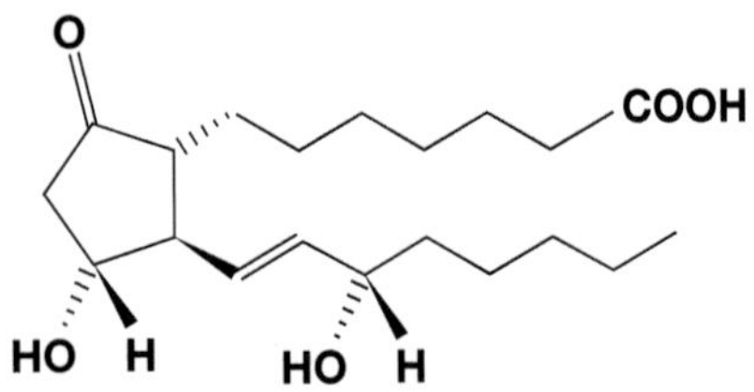

There are other ways in which an abbreviation to a formula can be made:

■ Sometimes we do not need to show the exact details of the hydrocarbon, or alkyl, part of the molecule, so we can abbreviate this to R.

■ For molecules which contain a benzene ring – aromatic compounds – we use ⬡ to show the ring.

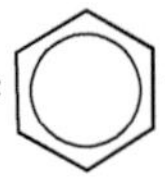

■ **Figure 10.14** A representation of the structure of a prostaglandin in skeletal form. This structure involves some double bonds and also uses the spatial notation to give some idea of the three-dimensional arrangement

■ Chains and rings

In discussing the alkane series of hydrocarbons we have described the molecules as chains that are extended by a $-CH_2-$ unit as we progress up the series. These molecules are often referred to as straight-chain hydrocarbons as there are no branches from the main chain. However, because each carbon atom is involved in a tetrahedral arrangement of bonds, the actual progression is zigzagged (Figure 10.15).

■ **Figure 10.15**

A model of the alkane, $C_{14}H_{30}$ showing the zigzag chain of the carbon atoms

There are hydrocarbon molecules that are genuinely branched-chain molecules, and these are an important group of compounds. One of the most significant is 2,2,4-trimethylpentane, whose ignition properties are the basis of the octane rating of gasoline (petrol) for cars. The system for numbering the positions where the branches attach to the main hydrocarbon chain is outlined on page 335.

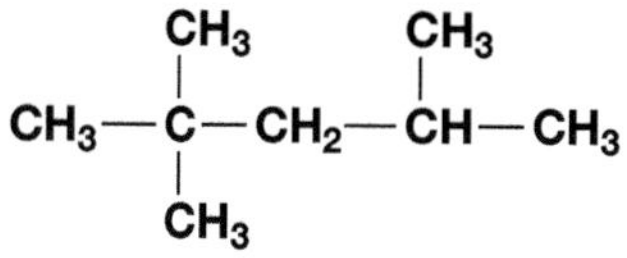

2,2,4-trimethylpentane

In discussing the properties of hydrocarbons in general there are two other terms that it is important to understand clearly. These are the terms saturated and unsaturated. The alkanes are saturated hydrocarbons as all the C to C bonds in the chain are single bonds. The molecules have as much hydrogen as possible attached to the carbon chain. If there is a C=C bond in the chain then additional hydrogen atoms could be attached to the chain, and the molecule is said to be unsaturated. Thus the alkenes are a series of unsaturated hydrocarbons. The same is true for the alkynes. They are also unsaturated hydrocarbons.

Molecules such as butane, $CH_3CH_2CH_2CH_3$, have their carbon atoms connected in a chain. Carbon atoms can also be joined together in rings, in which case a cyclic molecule is formed. The structures of these cyclic hydrocarbon molecules are often represented by the appropriate polygon – the corners of the polygon represent a carbon atom together with the hydrogen atoms joined to it (this is similar to the skeletal structures for chain alkanes). The cycloalkanes have a general formula of C_nH_{2n}. Some examples of these cycloalkanes are shown in Figure 10.16.

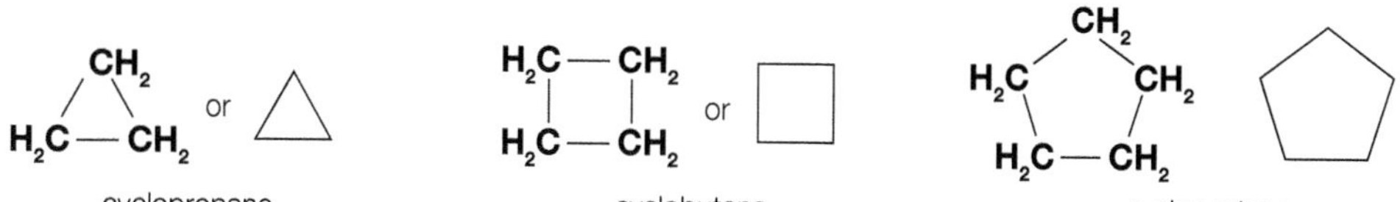

■ **Figure 10.16**

The structure of the first three members of the cycloalkane homologous series

cyclopropane   cyclobutane   cyclopentane

Despite their general formula, the cycloalkanes are saturated molecules and should not be confused with the alkenes. There is a series of unsaturated cycloalkenes that includes such compounds as cyclopentene and cyclohexene.

ToK Link

Representing formulas in 3-D

Chemistry is immersed in symbolism of all kinds. Amongst the most important of these are the symbols we use to represent and convey our ideas of the 'unseen' at a molecular and atomic level. Organic molecules are so complex that different ways of depicting the formulas of these compounds have been developed, depending on how much information is required.

Systems of symbols have their limitations, however. When representing organic molecules on the two-dimensional page we usually use structural formulas involving 90° and 180° angles when showing the bonds because this is the clearest way of showing them in this context. However, this does not show the true geometry of the molecule. When carbon forms four single bonds, as in methane or ethane, the arrangement is tetrahedral with the bonds at 109.5° to each other (Figure 10.17a and b). When it forms a double bond, as in ethene, the arrangement is trigonal planar, with bonds at 120° (Figure 10.17b). (Ethene is the first member of the homologous series called the alkenes, in which the molecules contain a C=C double bond – see Table 10.5.)

These bond angles are consistent with the hybridization of the atomic orbitals of the carbon atom involved in the bonds: sp³ hybridization in methane, sp² hybridization in ethene (see Chapter 14). For some molecules it is particularly useful to show the relative three-dimensional positions of atoms or groups around a selected carbon atom – the stereochemistry of the molecule. To show this, the convention is that a bond sticking forwards from the page is shown as a solid, enlarging wedge, whereas a bond directed behind the page is shown as a broken line (Figure 10.17b). Figure 10.18 shows models illustrating the bonding in some simple hydrocarbon molecules.

a methane, CH_4 ethane, C_2H_6

carbon sp³ hybridized

carbons sp³ hybridized

109.5°

109.5°

b methane, CH_4 ethene, C_2H_4

109.5°

120°

■ **Figure 10.17 a** The hybridization of each carbon atom in any alkane is sp³ hybridization. **b** Diagrams showing the bond angles in methane and ethene

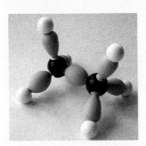

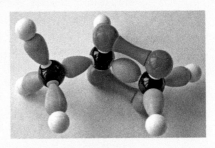

ethane   ethene   propene

■ **Figure 10.18** These models illustrate the shape of the molecule around each carbon atom and the sigma (σ) and pi (π) bonds in these molecules. The model of propene shows clearly the different orientations of the carbon atoms within the same molecule

Ethyne is a linear molecule with the nuclei of all four atoms in the molecule being in a straight line. The bond angles are both 180° and the atomic orbitals of the carbon atoms both showing sp hybridization (see Chapter 14).

■ Structural isomerism

The complexity and diversity of organic chemistry is increased by the fact that molecular formulas involving a reasonable number of carbon atoms can represent several different structures, i.e. different compounds. For the alkane series (general formula C_nH_{2n+2}) the first three formulas, CH_4, C_2H_6 and C_3H_8, are unambiguous; there is no other way in which the atoms can be arranged other than as shown in Figure 10.7.

However, looking at the condensed structural formula of butane, $CH_3CH_2CH_2CH_3$, there is an alternative way of arranging the atoms, which involves a branched chain. This alternative form is $CH_3CH(CH_3)CH_3$, where there is a $-CH_3$ group branching off the middle carbon atom. Figure 10.19 shows the full structural formulas of these two forms.

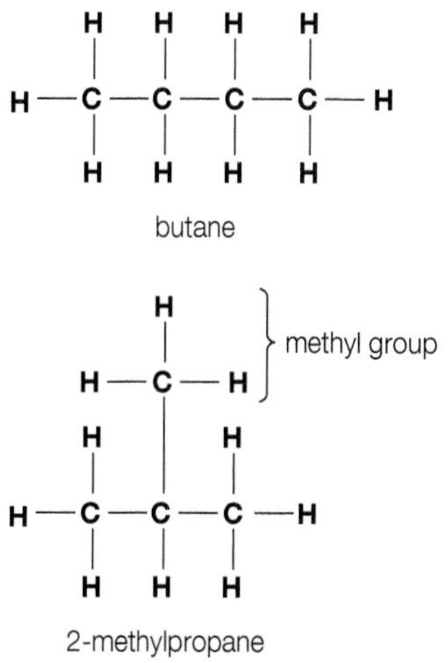

These two possible ways in which the carbon and hydrogen atoms can be bonded are both valid, as each carbon atom has four bonds and each hydrogen atom has one bond. The two structures represent different compounds: one is butane and the other 2-methylpropane (formerly known as *iso*-butane). Their chemical properties are quite similar, but their physical properties show differences. For instance, the two compounds have different melting and boiling points. When two or more compounds have the same molecular formula but different structural formulas they are known as structural isomers.

In the alcohol series the first possible examples of isomerism occur with propanol and butanol. Here the isomerism depends on the fact that the alcohol group (–OH) can be attached on the terminal carbon atom, or to one in the middle of the chain (Figure 10.20).

Note that it is important when working out possible isomers to remember the limitations of the two-dimensional representation of structures on paper. Thus the structures represented in Figures 10.21a and 10.21b are not isomers at all. In Figure 10.21a the chain appears to 'turn a corner' on paper, but remember that, in reality, the structure around each carbon atom is tetrahedral and that there is free rotation around each bond. In Figure 10.21b, one structure is just the other turned over on the paper. It is crucial to remember that *isomers are compounds with the same molecular formula but with different arrangements of atoms in the molecules.*

■ **Figure 10.19** Two isomers of formula C_4H_{10}

■ **Figure 10.20** The two structural isomers of butanol

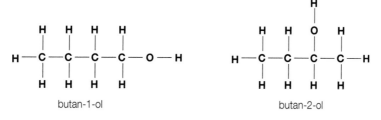

■ **Figure 10.21** Structural formulas that could be mistaken as isomers

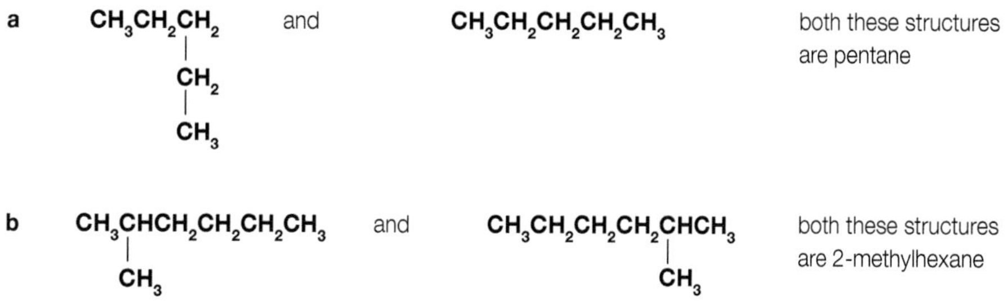

a $CH_3CH_2CH_2$ and $CH_3CH_2CH_2CH_2CH_3$ both these structures are pentane
          |
        CH_2
          |
        CH_3

b $CH_3CHCH_2CH_2CH_2CH_3$ and $CH_3CH_2CH_2CH_2CHCH_3$ both these structures are 2-methylhexane
        | |
      CH_3 CH_3

■ Deducing structural formulas of alkanes

After butane, the longer the carbon chain the more structural isomers are possible for a given molecular formula. For example, there are 75 isomers with the formula $C_{10}H_{22}$, and over 350 000 with the formula $C_{20}H_{42}$! When trying to work out the different straight-chain and branched isomers that fit a particular molecular formula it is important to remember the points mentioned above regarding the free rotation about a single C–C bond, and not to be fooled by the limitations of the two-dimensional representation of the molecular structures. Often just the simplicity of the skeletal formula can help clarify possibilities. Figure 10.22 shows the skeletal forms of two possible branched isomers of C_5H_{12}.

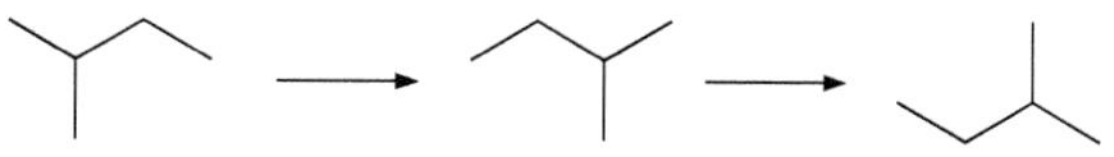

These three structure may look different, but they are just the same structure rotated in different ways in the page

■ **Figure 10.22** Using skeletal formulas to establish whether structures are isomers or not – these are not!

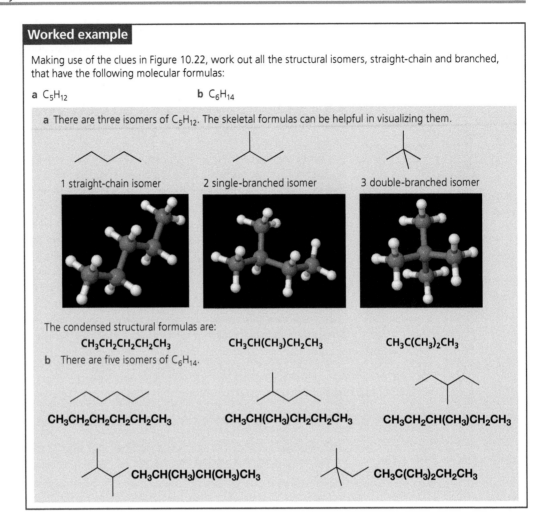

Worked example

Making use of the clues in Figure 10.22, work out all the structural isomers, straight-chain and branched, that have the following molecular formulas:

a C_5H_{12} **b** C_6H_{14}

a There are three isomers of C_5H_{12}. The skeletal formulas can be helpful in visualizing them.

1 straight-chain isomer   2 single-branched isomer   3 double-branched isomer

The condensed structural formulas are:

$CH_3CH_2CH_2CH_2CH_3$ $CH_3CH(CH_3)CH_2CH_3$ $CH_3C(CH_3)_2CH_3$

b There are five isomers of C_6H_{14}.

$CH_3CH_2CH_2CH_2CH_2CH_3$ $CH_3CH(CH_3)CH_2CH_2CH_3$ $CH_3CH_2CH(CH_3)CH_2CH_3$

$CH_3CH(CH_3)CH(CH_3)CH_3$ $CH_3C(CH_3)_2CH_2CH_3$

◼ Naming alkanes

You have now seen how complicated the naming of even just one homologous series of organic compounds can become. In this context a systematic method of naming compounds becomes very important. The system must be unambiguous and universal. Such a system has been devised by the IUPAC (International Union of Pure and Applied Chemistry).

Methane, ethane, propane and butane appear to have little logic in their names except that they all end in *-ane*, which signifies that they are all *alkanes* (see Figure 10.7). By looking at the next member of the series, you can begin to learn how the IUPAC system of naming works. For the next members of the alkane series, from *n* = 5 onwards, the prefix in the name follows the Greek prefixes for these numbers. Simply remember the names of the geometrical figures – *pent*agon, *hex*agon and *hept*agon, etc. – to help you remember these. Table 10.6 shows the names of the straight-chain alkanes.

◼ **Table 10.6**
Naming alkanes

Prefix of name	Number of carbon atoms in chain	Name of alkane	Condensed structure
Meth-	1	Methane	CH_4
Eth-	2	Ethane	CH_3CH_3
Prop-	3	Propane	$CH_3CH_2CH_3$
But-	4	Butane	$CH_3CH_2CH_2CH_3$
Pent-	5	Pentane	$CH_3CH_2CH_2CH_2CH_3$
Hex-	6	Hexane	$CH_3CH_2CH_2CH_2CH_2CH_3$

For the branched isomers of the alkanes the system needs to give names that apply to the side-chain groups of atoms. Table 10.7 gives the names used for the hydrocarbon side-chains of differing lengths. You can see that the same prefixes are used to designate the number of carbon atoms, followed by the ending *-yl*. These groups are known generally as alkyl groups.

Name of side-chain (R group)	Condensed structure
Methyl	$-CH_3$
Ethyl	$-CH_2CH_3$
Propyl	$-CH_2CH_2CH_3$
Butyl	$-CH_2CH_2CH_2CH_3$

■ **Table 10.7** Names of some alkyl groups

Knowing the component parts of the names for alkanes, you can follow some simple steps to generate the name for both straight-chain and branched-chain molecules. The example here shows how to apply the steps to one of the isomers of C_6H_{14} identified earlier, namely the one with this condensed structure:

$$^1CH_3{}^2CH(CH_3){}^3CH(CH_3){}^4CH_3$$

Step 1 First, identify the longest continuous chain of carbon atoms; this gives the stem of the name using the prefixes in Table 10.6. When identifying the longest straight chain, do not be confused by the way the molecule is drawn on paper, as sometimes the same molecule can be represented differently owing to the free rotation around the C–C single bonds.

So, in the example above, the longest chain is four carbon atoms long (identified in blue on the structure above). This molecule is a form of butane.

Step 2 Then identify and name the side-chains or substituent groups as the first part or prefix of the name (see Table 10.7). In this case there are two different methyl groups.

Step 3 Where there is more than one side-chain of the same type, as in this case, use the prefixes *di-*, *tri-*, *tetra-* and so on, to indicate this. If there are several side-chains within a molecule, put them in alphabetical order. Here there are two methyl groups – hence the prefix *dimethyl* in this case.

Step 4 The position of these side-chains is then identified. This is done using a number which refers to the number of the carbon atom in the stem. The carbon chain is numbered starting at the end which will give the substituent groups the smallest numbers.

In this case one methyl group is attached to carbon atom number 2, the other to carbon number 3. These numbers precede the name. This means that the name of this compound is 2,3-dimethylbutane.

Worked example

Name the following hydrocarbons:

a $C(CH_3)_4$ **b** $CH_3CH(C_2H_5)CH_3$ **c** $CH_3CH_2CH(C_2H_5)CH_2CH_3$

a Look at this structure carefully. The longest chain is three carbons long. The central carbon atom of the three has two methyl groups attached. The name of this compound is 2,2-dimethylpropane.

b Again this structure needs to be drawn out carefully. The longest chain is four carbons long, with a methyl group attached to the second carbon. The name of this compound is 2-methylbutane.

c The longest chain in this molecule is five carbon atoms long. There is an ethyl group attached to the third carbon in the chain. The name of this structure is 3-ethylpentane.

■ Deducing structural formulas of alkenes

The second homologous series of hydrocarbons is the alkenes (see Table 10.5). These compounds are distinguished by the fact that they contain a C=C double bond at some point in the hydrocarbon chain. They have the general formula C_nH_{2n}. The simplest alkene is ethene, C_2H_4, and the series develops by adding a $-CH_2-$ group to the chain. In the alkene molecules containing more than three carbon atoms, the double bond can exist in different positions along

3 How many chain isomers are there with the molecular formula C_5H_{10}? Remember that the double bond can be moved, and the chain can be branched as well as straight. There are five structural isomers of C_5H_{10} to be found.

the chain. The chain can also be branched. Thus there are two straight-chain isomers, and one branched-chain isomer, having the formula C_4H_8:

$CH_3CH_2CH=CH_2$ $CH_3CH=CHCH_3$ $CH_2=C(CH_3)_2$

Naming isomers of non-cyclic alkenes and alkynes

The IUPAC system for naming organic compounds extends to the naming of alkenes by stipulating how to indicate the position of the double bond in the chain. The basic names of the alkenes are assembled as for the alkanes, except that the names end in *-ene* rather than *-ane*. A fifth step needs to be added to those we identified before so that we can indicate the position in the chain of the C=C double bond:

Step 5   The position of the double bond is noted by inserting the number of the carbon atom at which the C=C bond 'starts'. Thus the two straight-chain isomers of C_4H_8 are known as but-1-ene and but-2-ene, while the branched-chain isomer is 2-methylprop-1-ene (named according to the rules described earlier).

$CH_3CH_2{}^2CH={}^1CH_2$ ${}^1CH_3{}^2CH={}^3CHCH_3$ ${}^1CH_2={}^2C(CH_3)_2$
but-1-ene   but-2-ene   2-methylprop-1-ene

A similar fifth step is involved in the naming of alkynes as the position of the carbon–carbon triple bond needs to be indicated. The simplest alkyne is ethyne, C_2H_2, and again the series develops by the addition of a $-CH_2-$ group to the chain. The first alkyne molecule that can show isomerism due to a difference in position of the triple bond is butyne in which the triple bond can either be central to the molecule or at the end of the chain. The first alkyne molecule that can show a branched chain isomer must contain five carbon atoms.

4   a   What are the names of the following alkenes?
       i $CH_3CH=CHCH_2CH_2CH_3$
      ii $CH_3CH_2CH(CH_3)CH=CH_2$
     iii $CH_2=C(CH_3)CH_2CH=CH_2$
    b   Which of these molecules are isomers of each other?
    c   Give the names and structural formulas of the alkynes with the molecular formula C_5H_8.

Introducing the diversity of organic compounds

The different functional groups listed in Table 10.5 give rise to a range of differing homologous series that begin to illustrate the diversity of organic compounds. There are four oxygen-containing functional groups with characteristic suffixes that appear at the end of the name for the organic compound. Halide groups have characteristic prefixes.

Alcohols – general formula R–OH or $C_nH_{2n+1}OH$

These compounds are characterized by the presence of the hydroxyl (–OH) group. The names of alcohols end in *-ol*. The position of the group is designated by the number of the carbon atom in the chain. Thus $CH_3CH_2CH_2OH$ and $CH_3CH(OH)CH_3$ are known as propan-1-ol and propan-2-ol, respectively (Figure 10.23).

■ **Figure 10.23**
The structures of propan-1-ol and propan-2-ol

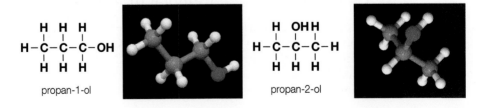

propan-1-ol   propan-2-ol

The alcohol group can be attached to any carbon atom in a straight chain or branched structure. The compound $CH_3C(CH_3)(OH)CH_3$ has the structure shown on the right.

The longest chain here is three carbons long, with a methyl group and the hydroxyl group both attached to carbon-2 in the chain. The name of this compound then is 2-methylpropan-2-ol.

Additional Perspectives

More complex alcohol (alkanol) structures

The condensed structural formula of 2-methylpropan-2-ol is given above as $CH_3C(CH_3)(OH)CH_3$. It is possible to condense this even further to $C(CH_3)_3OH$, but arguably this makes the formula more difficult to interpret. Over-simplification can lead to a confusing loss of definition.

There are a series of important organic molecules that contain more than one hydroxyl group. Compounds exist that contain two and three hydroxyl (−OH) groups attached to a hydrocarbon stem. Anti-freeze for car engines is ethane-1,2-diol, $CH_2(OH)CH_2(OH)$. Glycerol, an important compound in biochemistry as the central component of triglyceride fats, has the structure $CH_2(OH)CH(OH)CH_2(OH)$. The IUPAC systematic name for glycerol is propane-1,2,3-triol (Figure 10.24). Do note the use of the prefixes *di-* and *tri-* in this context.

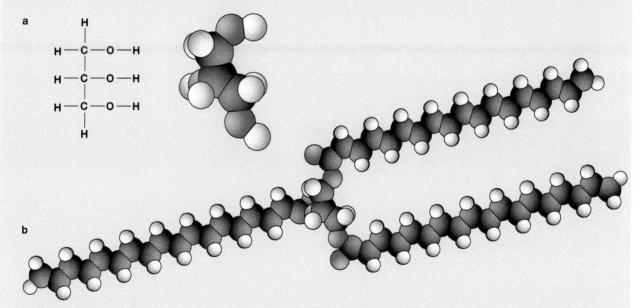

■ **Figure 10.24** Glycerol (propane-1,2,3-triol) **(a)** and three stearic acid molecules combine together to form an ester **(b)** found in animal fat

When dealing with more complex structures that may contain more than one functional group, it is important to realize that there is a hierarchy to the functional groups when naming compounds. Most obviously, the carboxylic acid and the aldehyde group always take priority. Thus the compound lactic acid, that you may have heard of in connection with muscle cramps, has the condensed formula $CH_3CH(OH)COOH$. The systematic name for lactic acid is 2-hydroxypropanoic acid; here the acid group takes precedence in the naming, forcing the −OH group to be referred to as the hydroxyl group.

Aldehydes – general formula R–CHO or $C_nH_{2n+1}CHO$

The –CHO group always occurs at the end of a carbon chain – it is always terminal. Hence the carbon atom in the aldehyde group is always number 1 if any counting of atoms in the chain is required. Because of this, it is not usually necessary to number the position of the aldehyde group in the name of the compound (see the final example in Figure 10.25). The name of an aldehyde usually ends in *-al*.

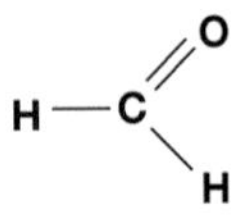

HCHO
methanal

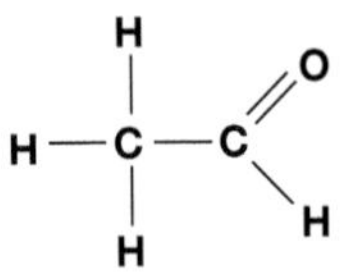

CH₃CHO
ethanal

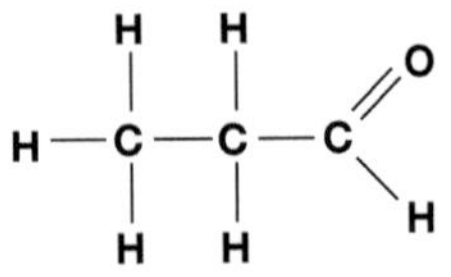

C₂H₅CHO
propanal

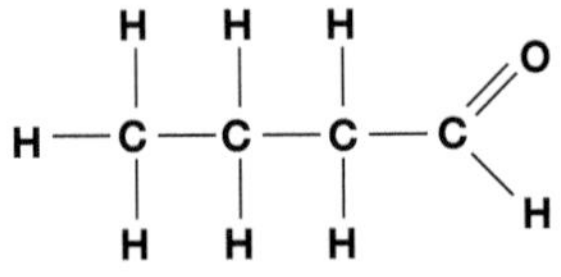

C₃H₇CHO
butanal

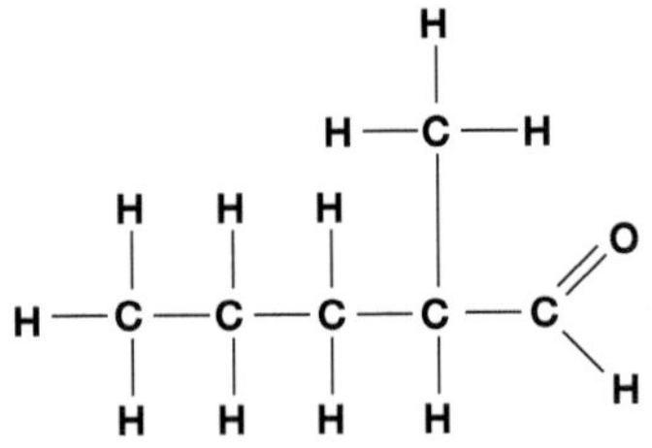

CH₃CH₂CH₂CH(CH₃)CHO
2-methylpentanal

■ **Figure 10.25** The structural formulas of some aldehydes

Ketones – general formula R–CO–R′, where R′ represents either the same alkyl group as R or a different alkyl group

The name of a ketone always ends with the suffix *-one*. The group can be inserted anywhere in a hydrocarbon chain except at the end. Because of this, the carbon atom of the ketone group is counted when establishing the chain length and its position must be shown in the name, except for the first two members of the series (where there is no alternative position and a number is therefore unnecessary).

■ **Figure 10.26** The formulas and structures of some ketones

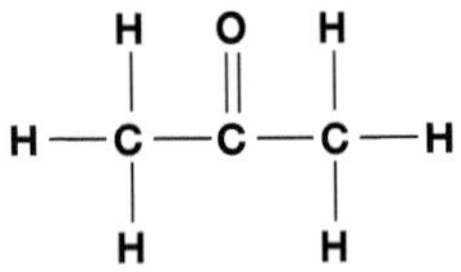

CH₃COCH₃
propanone

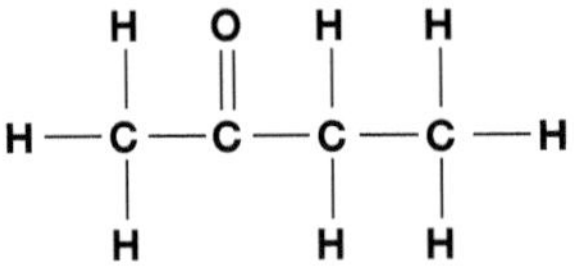

CH₃COCH₂CH₃
butanone

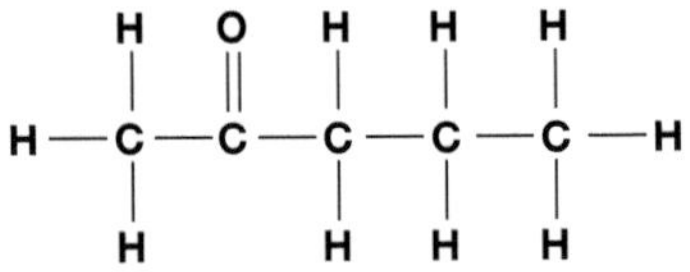

CH₃COCH₂CH₂CH₃
pentan-2-one

Carboxylic acids – general formula R–COOH or R–CO₂H

Carboxylic acids all have names that end in *-oic acid*. The acid group is always terminal and the carbon atom at the centre of the group is always counted as the first in the chain, no matter how complex the molecule.

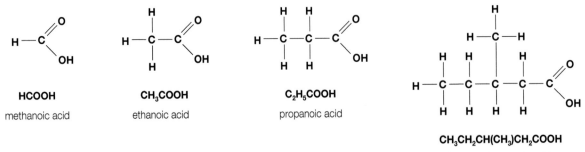

HCOOH
methanoic acid

CH₃COOH
ethanoic acid

C₂H₅COOH
propanoic acid

CH₃CH₂CH(CH₃)CH₂COOH
3-methylpentanoic acid

■ **Figure 10.27** The structural formulas of some carboxylic acids

Halogenoalkanes – general formula R–X, where X = F, Cl, Br, I

The halogenoalkanes are an important and useful group of compounds. Their structure is straightforward in that the halogen atom simply replaces a hydrogen atom in the given hydrocarbon structure, whether that structure is a straight or branched chain.

Halogenoalkanes are named in a different way from the other homologous series examined so far. In the aldehydes, ketones and carboxylic acids, the part of the compound's name that indicates the functional group is placed as a suffix, at the end of the name. In halogenoalkanes the halogen is designated by a prefix: *fluoro-*, *chloro-*, *bromo-* or *iodo-*. The numbering of the carbon atom to which the halogen is attached follows the guidelines already established.

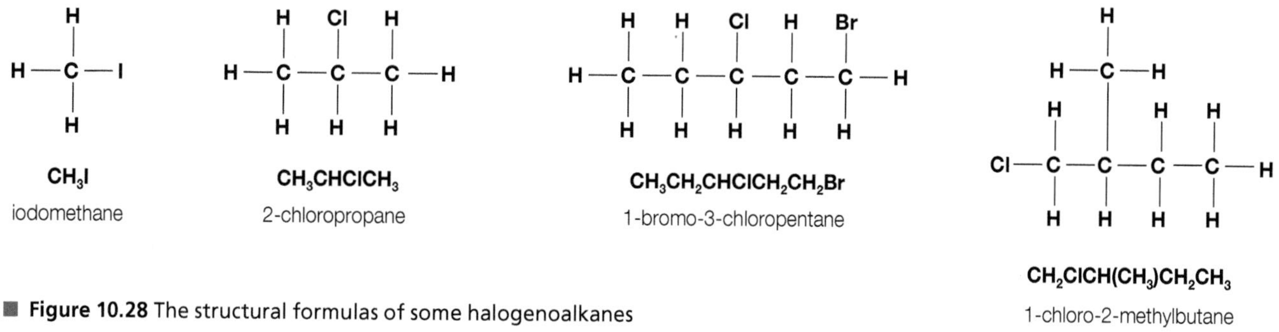

CH₃I
iodomethane

CH₃CHClCH₃
2-chloropropane

CH₃CH₂CHClCH₂CH₂Br
1-bromo-3-chloropentane

CH₂ClCH(CH₃)CH₂CH₃
1-chloro-2-methylbutane

■ **Figure 10.28** The structural formulas of some halogenoalkanes

■ Summarizing structural isomerism

In exploring the different ways in which organic molecules can have the same molecular formula but different structures, or connectivity, we have identified two different forms of structural isomerism: these are chain isomerism, which involves branching of the hydrocarbon backbone of the molecule, and position isomerism, where the functional group occupies a different point of attachment to the chain. The different forms of structural isomerism are summarized in Figure 10.29. The summary indicates a third form of structure isomerism, in which the isomers belong to an entirely different homologous series. In this case the isomers show very different properties as the functional groups present in the isomers are entirely different. For this reason this type of isomerism is known as functional group isomerism.

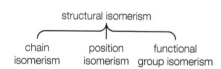

structural isomerism

chain isomerism | position isomerism | functional group isomerism

■ **Figure 10.29** The different forms of structural isomerism

Two such isomers are ethanol, C₂H₅OH, and methoxymethane, CH₃OCH₃ (Figure 10.30). Both these molecules have the molecular formula C₂H₆O, but one is an alcohol and the other is the simplest example of an ether. Ethers are molecules in which the hydrocarbon chain is broken by the insertion of an oxygen atom and we will introduce them in the next section.

■ **Figure 10.30** Models of the functional group isomers of formula C₂H₆O: **a** ethanol and **b** methoxymethane

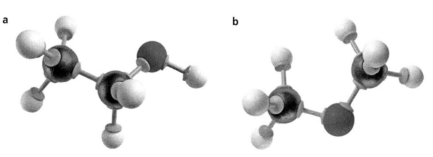

a   b

■ Further functional groups

There are several other main functional groups. One of these groups is fundamental to a whole separate area of organic chemistry based on aromatic hydrocarbons (**arenes**). Two other groups extend the rage of oxygen-containing compounds, while the remaining compounds are important nitrogen-containing series of compounds.

These additional homologous series are outlined in Table 10.8, and in the notes that follow.

■ Table 10.8 Further functional groups

Homologous series	Functional group and condensed structural formula	Suffix in name of compound	General formula	Structure of the functional group
ethers	R–O–R' ether	alkoxy- (prefix)	$C_nH_{2n+1}OC_mH_{2m+1}$	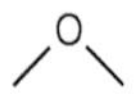
esters	R–COO–R' ester	-oate	$C_nH_{2n+1}COOC_mH_{2m+1}$	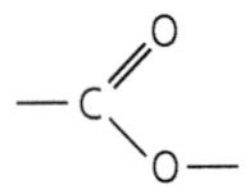
amines	R–NH$_2$ amino	-amine (or prefix amino-)	$C_nH_{2n+1}NH_2$	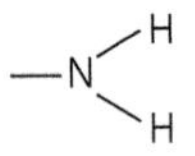
amides	R–CONH$_2$ carboxamide	-amide	$C_nH_{2n+1}CONH_2$	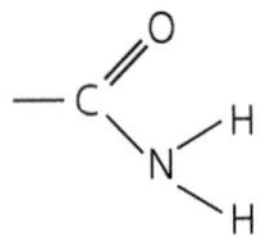
nitriles	R–CN nitrile	-nitrile	$C_nH_{2n+1}CN$	
arenes	phenyl-	-benzene (or prefix phenyl-)	C_6H_5-	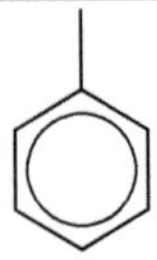

Ethers – general formula R–O–R', where R' is an alkyl group

Ethers are molecules with an oxygen atom inserted in the hydrocarbon chain. They are volatile solvents and are named for the two alkyl groups they contain (see Figure 10.31). Unlike the homologous series considered so far, all of which are based on a single carbon chain, ethers contain two carbon chains (alkyl or R groups) separated by an oxygen atom. They are isomers of alcohols but more volatile because, although they contain oxygen, there is no capability of forming hydrogen bonds between molecules. They do not mix with water as they cannot form hydrogen bonds with water molecules. Ethoxyethane (diethyl ether) is the ether most commonly referred to in everyday terms. It was used as an early anaesthetic.

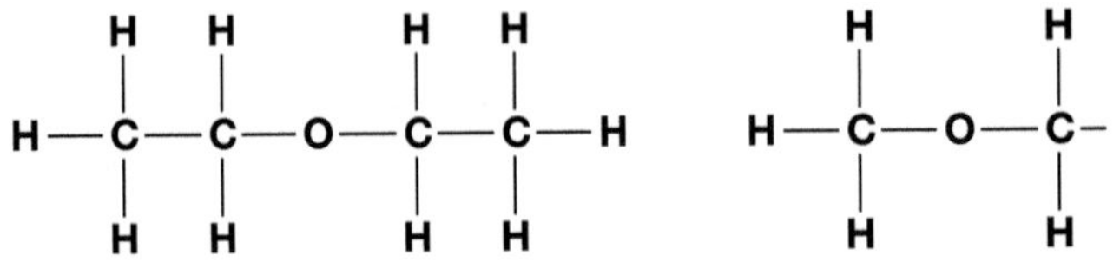

■ Figure 10.31 The structures of ethoxyethane and methoxypropane; both are isomers of butanol

Esters – general formula R–COO–R', where R' is an alkyl group

Esters are derived from carboxylic acids by reaction with an alcohol. The first part of the name of an ester is taken from the alkyl group of the alcohol from which it was synthesized. The second part of its name denotes the acid from which the compound is derived. This is the part of the structure that contains the carbonyl group >C=O. Thus an 'ethanoate' is the product made from ethanoic acid, and so on.

Some examples are shown in Figure 10.32: ethyl methanoate, propyl ethanoate, ethyl propanoate and phenyl ethanoate.

■ **Figure 10.32**
The naming of esters

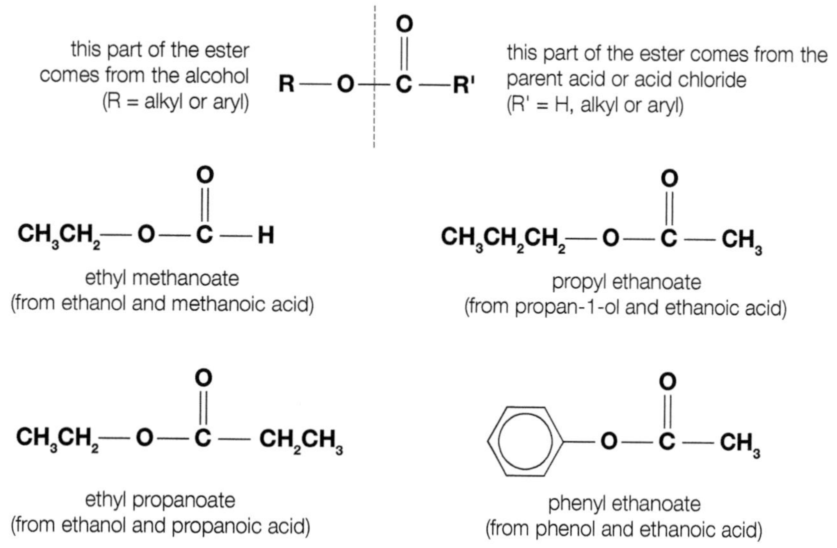

this part of the ester comes from the alcohol (R = alkyl or aryl)

this part of the ester comes from the parent acid or acid chloride (R' = H, alkyl or aryl)

ethyl methanoate
(from ethanol and methanoic acid)

propyl ethanoate
(from propan-1-ol and ethanoic acid)

ethyl propanoate
(from ethanol and propanoic acid)

phenyl ethanoate
(from phenol and ethanoic acid)

From Figure 10.32 we can see how the structure of an ester is built up. However, it is more conventional to draw the condensed or full structural formulas of esters the other way round. Thus, ethyl ethanoate is usually written $CH_3COOC_2H_5$ in chemical equations, for instance. Figure 10.33 shows the structures of some esters (propyl methanoate, methyl ethanoate and ethyl propanoate) written or drawn in this more usual format.

■ **Figure 10.33**
The structure of esters – showing the conventional way of writing the structural formulas, with the acid grouping first

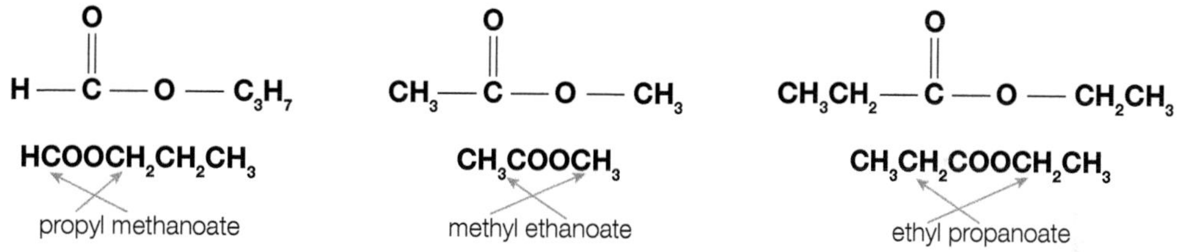

$HCOOCH_2CH_2CH_3$
propyl methanoate

CH_3COOCH_3
methyl ethanoate

$CH_3CH_2COOCH_2CH_3$
ethyl propanoate

Amides – general formula $R-CONH_2$

Amides are compounds derived from carboxylic acids by replacement of the –OH group in the acid grouping by an –NH_2 group. As such they retain the >C=O group as part of the amide functional group –$CONH_2$. It is worth noting, though, that the amide group behaves as a distinctive entity in its own right – not as a ketone and an amine – because the resonance interaction between the oxygen, carbon and nitrogen atoms makes the group function as a unit.

As when we name carboxylic acids, the carbon atom of the amide group is counted when assessing the longest unbranched chain present, and as such is counted as the first in the chain. Thus amides are named after the longest carbon chain, followed by the suffix *-amide*. Figure 10.34 shows the structures of ethanamide (see also Figure 10.35 overleaf) and 2-methylpropanamide.

■ **Figure 10.34**
The names and structures of two primary amides

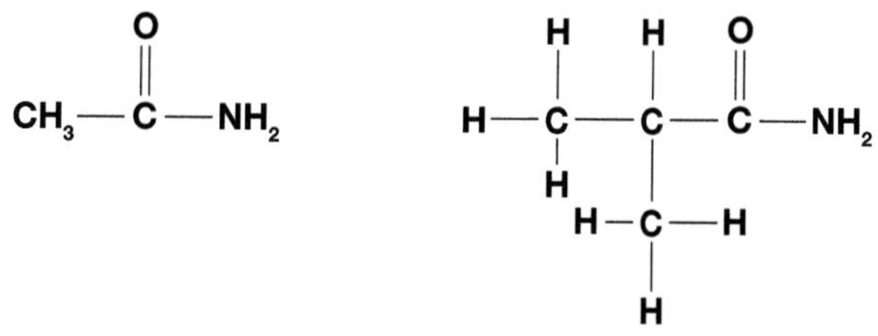

CH_3CONH_2
ethanamide

$CH_3CH(CH_3)CONH_2$
2-methylpropanamide

Nitriles (R–CN)

Nitriles are another homologous series derived from carboxylic acids. They are important intermediate compounds in the synthesis of new organic compounds. The early members of the series are pleasant smelling liquids at room temperature. They used to be called cyanides as they contain the $-C\equiv N$ group which resembles the inorganic cyanide ion, $C\equiv N^-$. So C_2H_5CN used to be known as ethyl cyanide. However, the IUPAC way of naming nitriles is to consider the carboxylic acid from which they are derived, as the $-COOH$ group has been replaced by a $-CN$ group. This means that the carbon atom of the nitrile group counts as the first atom of the hydrocarbon chain of the molecule. The suffix *-nitrile* is added to the name of the hydrocarbon chain. For example, C_2H_5CN now becomes propanenitrile (note there are three carbon atoms in the chain), and ethanenitrile has the formula CH_3CN (Figure 10.36).

CH_3CN
ethanenitrile

CH_3CH_2CN
propanenitrile

$CH_3CH_2CH_2CN$
butanenitrile

■ **Figure 10.36** The structure and naming of simple nitriles

In certain circumstances the nitrile group must give precedence in the naming of a compound to, say, a carboxylic acid group. In this situation it is referred to in the name by the prefix *cyano-*. So, for example, the compound $CH_2(CN)COOH$ is called cyanoethanoic acid.

Worked examples

Give the condensed structural formulas of the following organic compounds:

a ethyl butanoate
c 2-hydroxypropanenitrile

b phenyl propanoate
d 2-cyanopropanoic acid

a $CH_3CH_2CH_2COOCH_2CH_3$
c $CH_3CH(OH)CN$

b $CH_3CH_2COOC_6H_5$
d $CH_3CON(CH_3)_2$

Name the following compounds:

a $CH_3CH_2CH_2COOCH_3$ b $CH_3CH_2CH_2CH(CH_3)CN$ c $CH_3CH_2CH(NH_2)CH(NH_2)CH_3$

a methyl butanoate b 2-methylpentanenitrile c 2,3-diaminopentane

Amines – general formula R–NH₂

The amine group has the formula $-NH_2$ and can be found attached to a hydrocarbon backbone in a similar way to a halogen or an alcohol group. The presence of the group can be denoted by either the prefix *amino-* or the suffix *-amine* (Figure 10.37).

CH_3NH_2
methylamine

$C_3H_7NH_2$
propylamine

$CH_3CH(NH_2)CH_2CH_3$
2-aminobutane

From these discussions we can begin to see how the prolific nature of carbon's compound formation is generated. Each of these different homologous series is made up of compounds with a set of properties distinct to that series and determined by the functional group present.

Before we move to consider the aromatic hydrocarbons, there is one further aspect of organic classification we need to introduce.

■ Classifying molecules: primary, secondary and tertiary compounds

A functional group defines the chemistry of a particular homologous series, but its reactivity can be influenced by its position in the carbon chain. We have seen that position isomers can exist within a series. It is important to realise that the characteristic properties of the group can be moderated by those shifts in position. Consequently it is useful to be able to describe different positions in a structure exactly. This is done by applying the terms primary, secondary and tertiary to identify the location of the carbon atom to which the functional group (e.g. $-OH$, $-X$ or $-NH_2$) is attached in a molecule.

Alcohols and halogenoalkanes

When applied to alcohols and halogenoalkanes, the terms primary, secondary and tertiary refer to the degree of chain branching at the carbon atom to which the functional group ($-OH$ or $-X$) is attached. This is most easily seen by counting the hydrogen atoms attached to this particular carbon atom in the chain (Figure 10.38).

■ **Figure 10.38** The structures of primary, secondary and tertiary alcohols. R, R', and R'' are alkyl groups (they may all be the same group, or different)

primary alcohol   secondary alcohol   tertiary alcohol

Note from the examples in Figure 10.38 that the following rules apply:

■ A primary carbon atom is attached to the functional group ($-OH$ above) and also to *at least two hydrogen atoms*. Molecules with this arrangement are known as primary molecules. For example, ethanol is a primary alcohol, CH_3CH_2OH, while 1-chloropropane is a primary halogenoalkane, $CH_3CH_2CH_2Cl$.

■ A secondary carbon atom is attached to the functional group and to *just one hydrogen atom* and two alkyl groups. These molecules are known as secondary molecules. For example, propan-2-ol is a secondary alcohol, $CH_3CH(OH)CH_3$, while 2-bromobutane is a secondary halogenoalkane, $CH_3CHBrCH_2CH_3$.

■ A tertiary carbon atom is attached to the functional group and is also bonded to three alkyl groups. *There are no hydrogen atoms attached to a tertiary carbon atom.* These molecules are known as tertiary molecules. For example, 2-methylpropan-2-ol, $C(CH_3)_3OH$ is a tertiary alcohol, and 2-chloro-2-methylpropane, $CH_3C(CH_3)ClCH_3$, is a tertiary halogenoalkane.

5 Are the following molecules primary, secondary or tertiary?
a 3-methylpentan-3-ol
b pentan-2-ol
c 1-chlorobutane

Amines

Amines are compounds derived from ammonia and, as such, have similar properties to ammonia. This relationship to ammonia provides an alternative way of looking at, and classifying, their structures. Rather than regarding the molecules as substituted hydrocarbons, as we did above, it is possible to view them as compounds based on ammonia in which the hydrogen atoms are progressively replaced by alkyl (R) groups. Amines can therefore also be classified as one of the three types of organic compound – primary, secondary or tertiary – these terms have a different meaning in this context than when they were applied to alcohols and halogenoalkanes.

When applying these terms to amines (and indeed to amides) it is the level of branching at the nitrogen that is the key. Again the clue to the type of compound being considered is the number of hydrogen atoms attached, in this case to the nitrogen atom (Figure 10.39).

■ **Figure 10.39**
A comparison of the use of the terms primary, secondary and tertiary as applied to alcohols and amines

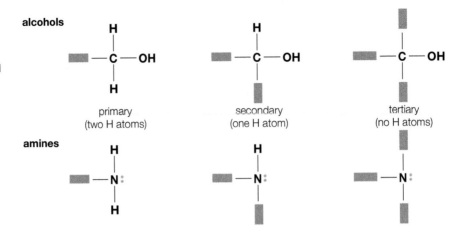

The IUPAC system of naming organic compounds allows for two different ways of naming amines. In the first of these the suffix *-amine* is used to indicate the presence of the $-NH_2$ group. Amines are then named by calling them after the longest unbranched hydrocarbon chain present, with the suffix *-amine*: for example, butan-1-amine, $CH_3CH_2CH_2CH_2NH_2$, and pentan-2-amine, $CH_3CH(NH_2)CH_2CH_2CH_3$. The following system is then applied to naming primary, secondary or tertiary amines:

■ If only one hydrogen atom in ammonia has been replaced then a **primary amine** is formed. For example, methanamine or methylamine (Figure 10.40a) – note that it is acceptable to use either prefix, *methan* or *methyl*.

■ **Figure 10.40** The structures of a primary, secondary and tertiary amine

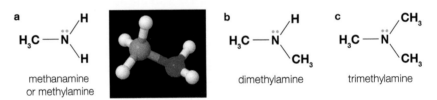

■ A **secondary amine** is formed when two of the hydrogen atoms from ammonia are replaced. For example, dimethylamine (Figure 10.40b). The alkyl groups are not necessarily of the same type.

■ If alkyl groups replace all three hydrogen atoms then a **tertiary amine** is formed. For example, trimethylamine (Figure 10.40c).

However, the IUPAC system also makes it possible to use the prefix *amino-*, with the location of the $-NH_2$ group being indicated by numbering the carbon atoms in the chain. This method is most often used when the number of carbon atoms in the chain is four or more. Examples (Figure 10.41) of the application of this system are 2-aminopentane, 1,2-diaminoethane (an example of a bidentate ligand, see Chapter 13) and 1,6-diaminohexane (often used in the laboratory preparation of nylon-6,6).

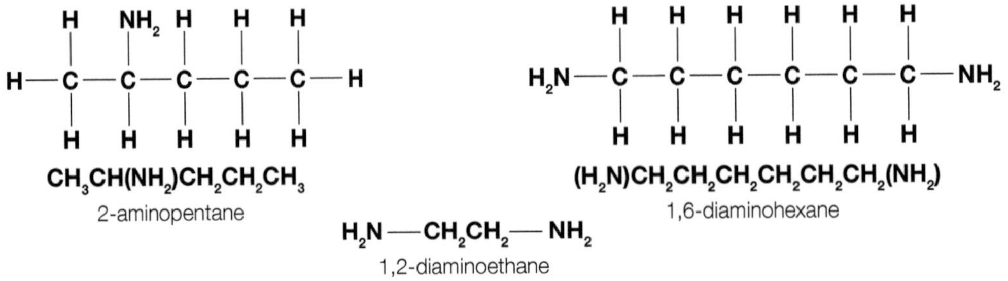

■ **Figure 10.41**
The names and structures of some more complex amines

The secondary and tertiary amines shown in Figure 10.40 were simple to name, as the alkyl groups replacing the hydrogen atoms were identical; hence dimethylamine and trimethylamine. In general, when naming a secondary amine the main name of the amine is taken from the longest unbranched carbon chain attached to the nitrogen atom. The other chain is prefixed as an alkyl group, with the location prefix given as an italic *N*. Examples include *N*-methylethylamine and *N*-ethylpropylamine. For tertiary amines there are two prefixes, each with an italic *N*: for example, $CH_3CH_2N(CH_3)_2$ is *N,N*-dimethylethylamine (Figure 10.42).

■ **Figure 10.42**
Secondary and tertiary amines

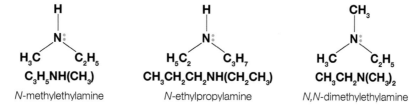

Using this systematic way of naming amines, dimethylamine should be named *N*-methylmethylamine and trimethylamine should be named *N,N*-dimethylmethylamine.

Aromatic amines are compounds in which an –NH_2 group is bonded directly to the benzene ring. The most common is phenylamine, $C_6H_5NH_2$ (also known as aminobenzene):

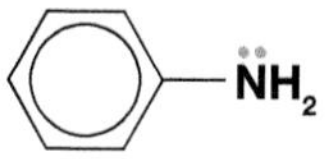

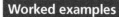

Worked examples

1   Name the following amines:
   a $CH_3CH_2CH_2CH_2NH_2$ **b** $(CH_3CH_2CH_2)_2NH$ **c** $(C_6H_5)_2NH$

2   Give the structural formulas of the following amines:
   a hexane-1,6-diamine   **b** *N*-ethylpropanamine   **c** *N,N*-dimethylpropanamine

> 1   **a** 1-butylamine, or 1-aminobutane, or 1-butanamine
>   **b** *N*-propylpropanamine, or *N*-propylpropylamine, or dipropylamine
>   **c** diphenylamine or *N*-phenylphenylamine
>
> 2   **a** $H_2NCH_2CH_2CH_2CH_2CH_2CH_2NH_2$
>   **b** $CH_3CH_2CH_2NH(CH_2CH_3)$
>   **c** $CH_3CH_2CH_2N(CH_3)_2$

The classification into primary, secondary and tertiary compounds can also be applied to amides. Secondary and tertiary amides are named rather like amines, in that the other alkyl group attached to the nitrogen atom is prefixed by an *N*: for example, *N*-methylethanamide (Figure 10.43) is a secondary amide, whereas *N,N*-dimethylpropanamide, $CH_3CH_2CON(CH_3)_2$, would be a tertiary amide.

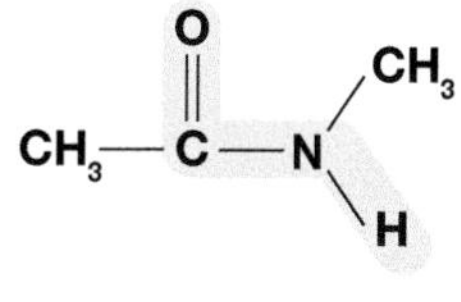

■ **Figure 10.43**
The structure of the secondary amide *N*-methylethanamide contains the peptide link group present in proteins

$CH_3CONH(CH_3)$
N-methylethanamide

You will note from the structure of *N*-methylethanamide that secondary amides contain the highlighted group that is known as the amide link or peptide bond. It is highly significant biologically as it is the group linking the amino acid residues together in all proteins. It is also present in some important artificial condensation polymers, the polyamides: most notably, nylon and Kevlar.

ToK Link

Chemistry, language and literature

To facilitate the international communication and understanding of chemistry there is a need for a standardized language with which to refer to compounds. The IUPAC system of naming organic molecules is very useful in connecting the naming of a compound unambiguously with its structure. However, it is helpful to remember that this system is a relatively recent development and that there is a whole set of trivial names for these compounds in the wider world of chemistry.

Thus ethanamide can also be found referred to as acetamide, ethanenitrile as acetonitrile, and phenylamine as aniline, for instance. It is worth being aware of this when you see reagent bottles in a laboratory; but do not be too disturbed, the IB syllabus and examination papers will use the IUPAC names exclusively and consistently.

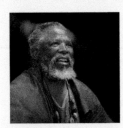

Figure 10.44 Caliban, Prospero's servant in *The Tempest*

At a broader cultural level it can be intriguing to see how the different disciplines of intellectual understanding give an insight into one another. Shakespeare's Caliban is a 'wild' uncivilized character in *The Tempest*, the only human inhabitant of the island on which the play is set (Figure 10.44). In Act 2 Scene 2, Trinculo, the court jester, raises questions as to Caliban's nature:

What have we here? A man or a fish? Dead or alive?
A fish: he smells like a fish; a very ancient and fish-like smell;
a kind of not-of-the-newest poor-John.
A strange fish!'

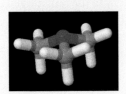

Figure 10.45 The structure of trimethylamine – a tertiary amine

It has been suggested that this is an early written description of a human metabolic disorder known as *trimethylaminuria*. This is a rare, genetically inherited condition in which the sufferer gives off a fishy smell due to the fact they cannot oxidize the trimethylamine (Figure 10.45) produced from the digestion of foods such as eggs, liver and various vegetables and grains. Normally the trimethylamine is oxidized in the liver to odourless trimethylamine oxide, which is then excreted from the body in the urine. However, if the ability to oxidize the amine is impaired, large amounts of the unchanged trimethylamine are excreted, producing a highly unpleasant, fishy body odour. It is estimated that one person in 10 000 suffers from this syndrome.

Aromatic compounds (arenes)

Hydrocarbons with linear chains of carbon atoms as the backbone of the compound are described as **aliphatic hydrocarbons**. The other class of hydrocarbons are called aromatic hydrocarbons, or **arenes** (Table 10.8). The term 'aromatic' was originally applied to these compounds because of their smells. However, this was somewhat misleading as many have unpleasant and indeed dangerous vapours. More recently the alternative and systematic name of arenes has been applied to them. Arenes are compounds that contain the benzene ring – with the simplest being benzene itself.

Arenes represent a distinctive range of organic compounds where the features and properties of the benzene ring, or similar structures, produce a very different chemistry from that of the 'families' of compounds based on the straight and branched hydrocarbon chains examined so far.

Benzene has the formula C_6H_6. The carbon atoms are arranged in a ring structure and can be represented in several different ways (Figure 10.46).

Figure 10.46 Representations of the structure of the benzene molecule (C_6H_6). The three ring structures are all valid structural formulas. In the centre is a computer-generated electrostatic potential map

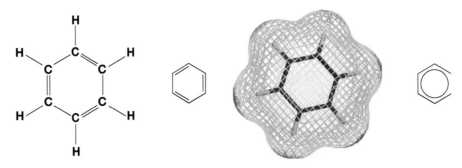

Instead of R representing an alkyl group, it can also mean an aryl group. Aryl groups are based on a benzene ring, with the simplest being the $-C_6H_5$ or phenyl group. This group can be attached to a wide range of other functional groups to produce a vast range of compounds (Figure 10.47). These structures show what is now the usual convention for depicting the benzene ring: a hexagon with a ring inside it to denote the delocalized electrons.

■ **Figure 10.47**
The structures of some aromatic compounds

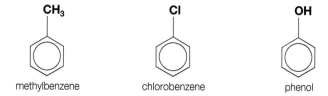

methylbenzene   chlorobenzene   phenol

Establishing the structure of benzene

Benzene is a colourless liquid that is immiscible with water. It was widely used as a solvent but this is now more limited because benzene has been found to be carcinogenic – methylbenzene is used as a safer alternative. However, the importance of benzene in defining a type of organic structure and reactivity still stands.

Friedrich Kekulé (1829–1896) was Professor of Chemistry at the Universities of Ghent (in Belgium) and Bonn (in Germany). He was a structural chemist and proposed the concept of carbon chain formation (catenation) as the basic structure of many organic compounds. In the 1860s he focused on the question of the structure of aromatic compounds, and benzene in particular. Benzene had been identified in whale oil by Michael Faraday in 1825 and it was known that its formula was C_6H_6. Its structure remained problematic. In 1865, Kekulé suggested a cyclic structure involving alternating carbon–carbon double and single bonds (Figure 10.48).

The Kekulé structure for benzene was accepted for many years as the best explanation available. However it steadily became evident through the early 20th century that there were a range of problems in reconciling mounting experimental evidence with this structure. Some of these problems were:

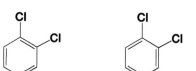

■ **Figure 10.48**
The Kekulé structure of benzene

■ The carbon–carbon bond lengths in the benzene molecule are all the same – they have a value of 0.139 nm, which lies between the values for C–C (0.154 nm) and C≡C (0.134 nm).

■ Only one isomer exists for 1,2-disubstituted benzene compounds – if there were alternate double and single carbon–carbon bonds in the benzene molecule then two isomers of compounds such as 1,2-dichlorobenzene would exist (Figure 10.49).

■ **Figure 10.49** The hypothetical (Kekulé) isomers of 1,2-dichlorobenzene – in fact the compound has a single, unique structure

■ If benzene does simply contain three double bonds, cyclohexa-1,3,5-triene, then it should undergo electrophilic addition reactions readily. In fact, it undergoes addition reactions only with difficulty – benzene undergoes electrophilic substitution reactions more usually.

■ The enthalpy change (ΔH) of hydrogenation of benzene ($-208\,\text{kJ mol}^{-1}$) is not equal to three times the enthalpy change of hydrogenation of cyclohexene ($-120\,\text{kJ mol}^{-1} \times 3 = -360\,\text{kJ mol}^{-1}$) (as discussed in Chapter 14). The difference of $152\,\text{kJ mol}^{-1}$ means that the actual structure is more stable than the Kekulé structure (Figure 10.50).

■ **Figure 10.50**
Comparison of the enthalpy of hydrogenation of the Kekulé structure and the actual structure of benzene

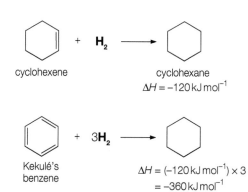

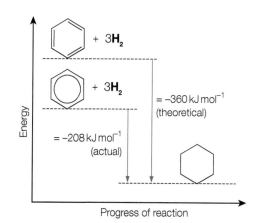

To overcome these problems, in 1931 Linus Pauling proposed that the actual structure for the benzene molecule was midway between the two Kekulé structures – a resonance hybrid. A resonance hybrid is a structure that is a blend of the characteristics of both resonance forms, as shown in Figure 10.51a; it is important to realize that the structure does not oscillate between the two forms. The modern representation of benzene is abbreviated to the structure shown in Figure 10.51b.

■ **Figure 10.51 a** The two resonance forms of benzene; **b** the usual representation of benzene

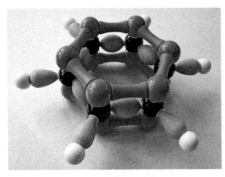

The resonance approach to molecular structure is one way of explaining the bonding in benzene. An alternative, but equivalent, approach considers the atomic orbitals involved in the bonding. The benzene ring has a planar structure, and all the bonds between the carbon atoms in the ring have the same length and same bond enthalpy (strength). All six carbon atoms in the benzene ring are sp^2-hybridized. The molecular orbital theory of bonding for benzene shows that each carbon atom is joined to two other carbon atoms and a hydrogen atom by three σ bonds to form a planar molecule (Figure 10.52).

So the six carbon atoms and the attached hydrogen atoms are held together by a 'skeleton' of σ bonds. Each carbon atom has one electron remaining in a 2p orbital, the lobes of which lie above and below the plane of the molecule. These six unhybridized 2p orbitals combine by side-on overlap to form a delocalized π bond containing six electrons (Chapter 14). It is the presence of these delocalized π electrons that makes the benzene molecule more energetically stable than predicted for the Kekulé structure, and it accounts for the fact that the molecule undergoes electrophilic attack.

■ **Figure 10.52** The delocalized structure of benzene

Nature of Science   Improved instrumentation – ways of 'seeing'

The structure of benzene was something of a challenge to the various theories of bonding that have developed over the past century. The elucidation of the structure demonstrated how science draws on several different strands of evidence to assemble an overall model that best explains both structural and chemical evidence. The final problem is that we have not had a means of 'seeing' the actual structure itself.

In recent years the use of scanning tunnelling and atomic force microscopy has given us some iconic images of the atomic world, from the IBM logo picked out in individual atoms to the 'corralling' of a copper atom amongst the circling 'enemy'.

By 2009 the IBM research team had progressed even further and given us the first images of molecules in which the bonds between the atoms can be discerned. The pictures are of a molecule of pentacene – a linear construct of five benzene rings – and it is possible to make out even the bonds between the outer carbon atoms and the hydrogens attached to them (Figure 10.53). Such images provide impressive support for the model of the benzene ring structure that had been drawn from so many different threads of evidence.

■ **Figure 10.53** An atomic force microscope image of the pentacene molecule: note the bonds protruding from the edges of the rings to the adjoining hydrogen atoms

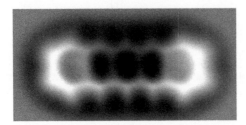

■ Further trends in physical properties within homologous series

Volatility

Members of each homologous series have the same functional group and therefore we expect them to have similar chemical properties. We also expect there to be a regular trend in their physical properties with increasing chain length – as shown for the alkanes and alcohols by the data presented on pages 324–326.

Volatility is a measure of how easily a substance evaporates – a highly volatile substance evaporates easily and has a low boiling point. How easily a substance evaporates depends on the molecules having sufficient kinetic energy to overcome the forces between the molecules. So substances with stronger intermolecular forces will evaporate less easily, and have higher boiling points. There are three factors which contribute to the observed pattern for the different homologous series.

■ First, volatility decreases and boiling point increases with increasing molecular size (chain length). As we go up a series the chain length increases by the addition of a $-CH_2-$ unit. This results in a longer molecule, stronger London forces between the molecules and, therefore, an increase in the boiling point (see Figure 10.9). Thus, at room temperature, the early members of a series are generally gases or liquids, while the later members are more likely to be solids.

■ Second, a branched isomer of a compound is likely to have a lower boiling point than its straight-chain isomer. The branching of a chain results in a more spherical overall shape to the molecule. This means there is less surface contact between molecules other than for straight-chain isomers, so these branched isomers will have weaker intermolecular forces and hence lower boiling points (Figure 10.54).

a

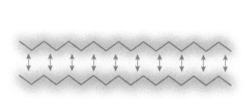

Elongated molecules have greater surface area for attraction

b

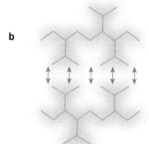

More oval or spherical molecules have less surface area for attraction

■ **Figure 10.54 a** Elongated straight-chain molecules will have greater surface contact with each other and therefore stronger London forces between molecules
b Branched molecules tend to be more spherical in shape, and therefore have a smaller contact area and weaker intermolecular forces

■ Finally, the nature of the functional group present in the molecules will influence volatility, depending on its effect on the intermolecular forces. Polar groups will lead to stronger dipole–dipole interactions between the molecules and hence higher boiling points. Groups that are capable of forming hydrogen bonds will result in even stronger forces between the molecules, giving rise to even higher boiling points (see Figure 10.9 for a comparison between the early alkanes and alcohols). We also commented earlier on the difference in volatility of ethers compared to their isomeric alcohols (see page 340). The absence of the possibility of hydrogen bonding between molecules makes ethers more volatile than alcohols of the same molecular size.

The factors that influence the physical properties of compounds containing the different functional groups are summarized in Figure 10.55.

One crucial thing to remember when making comparisons of boiling points of compounds in different homologous series, or indeed other properties dependent on intermolecular forces, is to compare molecules that have similar M_r values. This may mean comparing molecules with different numbers of carbon atoms. For example, ethanol, C_2H_5OH ($M_r = 46$), has a boiling point of 78 °C (351 K) and can be usefully compared with propane, C_3H_8 ($M_r = 44$), whose boiling point is −42 °C (83 K). By comparing molecules of similar size, it becomes clear that the higher boiling point in ethanol is due to the presence of the alcohol (–OH) group which causes hydrogen bonding between the molecules, rather than being an effect of molecular size. In this context, some would argue that we should, in fact, count the total number of electrons in the molecules involved, as it is the distortions and shifting patterns of these that create the temporary dipoles that are the basis of the underlying London forces.

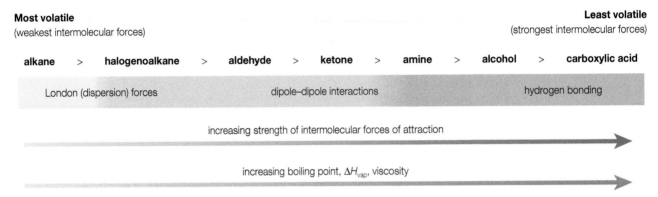

■ **Figure 10.55** The influence of the functional group on intermolecular forces and certain physical properties

Solubility in water

The solubility (which can be referred to as miscibility if dealing with a liquid) of an organic compound in water is largely determined by two factors that tend to have opposing effects. These factors relate to the two essential parts of the molecule – the functional group and the hydrocarbon 'backbone'.

■ If the functional group in the compound is able to interact with water, for example by forming hydrogen bonds, then this will favour the compound being soluble.

■ The hydrocarbon chain of the molecule is non-polar, and so does not help the solubility of the molecule in water. Indeed, a long hydrocarbon chain can counteract any solubility-favouring effect of the functional group. In general, the solubility of organic molecules decreases with increasing chain length.

Applying these two factors to the types of homologous series met so far explains why the earlier members of the alcohols, aldehydes, ketones and carboxylic acids are quite soluble in water, but the solubility decreases as we progress up the series. Halogenoalkanes and ethers are not soluble in water as, despite their polarity, they are unable to form hydrogen bonds with water.

10.2 Functional group chemistry *– structure, bonding and chemical reactions involving functional group interconversions are key strands in organic chemistry*

■ Alkanes

The alkanes are perhaps the simplest of the homologous series of organic compounds. The following are key points to remember:

■ The alkanes are hydrocarbons, and therefore contain carbon and hydrogen *only*.

■ The alkanes have the general formula C_nH_{2n+2}.

■ Alkanes are saturated hydrocarbons (the term saturated means that all the carbon–carbon bonds are single bonds).

■ Although they are relatively unreactive compounds, some of their reactions are highly significant and important.

In Section 10.1 we looked at the physical properties and structures of the alkanes. In this section we look at their chemical properties.

■ **Figure 10.56** The burning of methane, a highly exothermic reaction, can provide a spectacular laboratory demonstration (note that the demonstrator should be wearing a lab coat)

Explaining the low reactivity of the alkanes

The alkanes are chemically very unreactive. Indeed their old name was the *paraffins*, which came from the Latin and literally means 'little activity' (from the Latin *parum affinis*). This inertness may seem initially surprising given that the alkanes burn extremely well (Figure 10.56), resulting in their principal use as fuels. The relatively strong covalent bonding in the molecules means that they are kinetically stable until sufficient activation energy is provided.

Because of their chemical simplicity, alkanes contain only carbon–carbon single bonds and carbon–hydrogen bonds. Both these bonds are strong (C–C, 348 kJ mol⁻¹ and C–H, 412 kJ mol⁻¹). Consequently alkane molecules will only react when a strong source of energy is being used, providing enough energy to break these bonds. Alkanes are generally stable under most conditions and can be stored, transported and even compressed safely. These latter points are particularly important in view of the uses these compounds are put to.

The C–C and C–H bonds are also characteristically non-polar, as carbon and hydrogen have very similar electronegativities (the electronegativity difference is 0.4, $^{\delta-}$C–H$^{\delta+}$). This means that alkane molecules are not susceptible to attack by the most common attacking agents in organic chemistry: nucleophiles or electrophiles (electron pair donors or acceptors).

These two factors, together with those mentioned earlier in the chapter, are responsible for the very low reactivity of the alkanes. There are, however, two very significant reactions of alkanes to be considered here.

The combustion of alkanes

■ **Figure 10.57** Butane is used as a fuel in camping stoves. The butane is stored under pressure as a liquid in the canisters

Because they release significant amounts of energy when they burn (Figure 10.56), the alkanes are widely used as fuels, for example in the internal combustion engines of cars and in aircraft engines and household heating systems (Figure 10.57). The combustion reactions of these molecules are highly exothermic. This is mainly a result of the high relative strength of the carbon–oxygen double bonds (C=O) in carbon dioxide and the oxygen–hydrogen (O–H) bonds in water molecules. These are the products formed in these combustion reactions and the large amount of heat energy released in making these bonds means that the reactions are strongly exothermic. Remember that bond formation is an exothermic, energy-releasing process (Chapter 5).

Alkanes burn in the presence of excess oxygen to produce carbon dioxide and water, for example:

$$CH_4(g) + 2O_2(g) \rightarrow CO_2(g) + 2H_2O(l) \quad \Delta H_c^{\ominus} = 890 \text{ kJ mol}^{-1}$$

$$C_3H_8(g) + 5O_2(g) \rightarrow 3CO_2(g) + 4H_2O(l) \quad \Delta H_c^{\ominus} = -2220 \text{ kJ mol}^{-1}$$

However, when the oxygen supply is limited, carbon monoxide and water can be produced, for example:

$$2CH_4(g) + 3O_2(g) \rightarrow 2CO(g) + 4H_2O(g)$$

$$2C_3H_8(g) + 7O_2(g) \rightarrow 6CO(g) + 8H_2O(g)$$

In conditions when oxygen is extremely limited, carbon itself can also be produced, for example:

$$C_3H_8(g) + 2O_2(g) \rightarrow 3C(s) + 4H_2O(g)$$

We can see that the incomplete combustion of an alkane can result in a mixture of carbon-containing products, including the element itself. The following equation is a possible reaction that may take place in a candle flame where the solid wax burns to give the characteristic flame we are familiar with (Figure 10.58a):

$$C_{20}H_{42}(s) + 15O_2(g) \rightarrow 11C(s) + 9CO(g) + 21H_2O(g)$$

It is the incandescent glow of the hot solid carbon particles (soot) that gives the flame its yellow colour. The same is true for the yellow (safety) flame of the Bunsen burner (Figure 10.58b).

■ **Figure 10.58 a** The yellow candle flame; **b** the safety flame of a Bunsen burner. Both these flames are characterized by the yellow glow of incandescent carbon particles

Methane as a 'greenhouse gas' and the burning of fossil fuels

Earlier in the chapter we looked at the range of products available from the distillation of crude oil (Figure 10.11). A significant number of these products are fuels for various forms of transport and heating systems (Figure 10.59). Methane is also the major component of natural gas.

■ **Figure 10.59**
A representation of some of the useful products from the fractional distillation of crude oil. Emphasis here is on those uses involving combustion

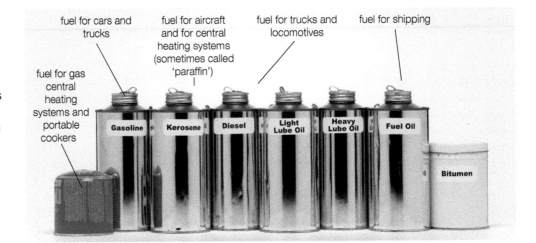

fuel for cars and trucks

fuel for aircraft and for central heating systems (sometimes called 'paraffin')

fuel for trucks and locomotives

fuel for shipping

fuel for gas central heating systems and portable cookers

Gasoline   Kerosene   Diesel   Light Lube Oil   Heavy Lube Oil   Fuel Oil   Bitumen

The combustion reactions outlined earlier are thus amongst the most significant chemical reactions on the planet. They become even more important now that we have realized that products of all these reactions have a serious impact on the environment. This is why the burning of these and other 'fossil fuels' on a very large scale is now widely recognized as a global problem. Carbon dioxide and water are both 'greenhouse gases'. Such gases in the atmosphere absorb infrared radiation and so help retain heat from the Sun in the atmosphere, contributing to global warming. Rising levels of carbon dioxide caused by human activities – mainly the burning of fossil fuels – are being implicated in the significant increase in average world temperatures. The Intergovernmental Panel on Climate Change (IPCC) that met in Paris in January 2007 acknowledged that 11 of the preceding 12 years had been the warmest since 1850. Climate change has risen to the top of the political agenda in recent years. Growing awareness of this problem has raised the profile of the issues involved in fuel availability and consumption.

Methane itself is a 'greenhouse gas' released in large quantities from cattle, termite mounds, rice paddy fields and swamps. The methane produced is the product of bacteria living under anaerobic conditions. In recent years focus has been directed towards a potential source of methane that represents both an opportunity and a threat. Methane has been found stored in the sediments of the continental shelf beneath the deep ocean, underneath the permafrost of the Arctic and in deep Antarctic ice cores (Figure 10.60). In these circumstances the methane is stored in the form of *methane clathrates*. Clathrates are structures formed by the inclusion of atoms or molecules of one kind, in this case methane, in cavities of the crystal lattice of another, in this case ice. The open, hydrogen-bonded structure of ice (see Chapter 4) lends itself to the formation of such caged structures.

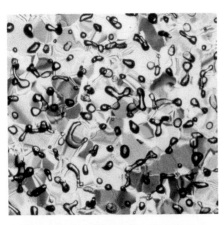

■ **Figure 10.60** Bubbles of methane gas frozen in the polar ice. This is a polarized light micrograph of an ice sample extracted in Antarctica. The sample was from an ice core drilled to a depth of 234m

Many countries are investing in research into the extraction of methane from these clathrates. An exploration well drilled on land by Imperial Oil in 1971–1972 discovered methane clathrates under the Canadian Arctic permafrost at the edge of the Mackenzie Delta and the Beaufort Sea. This site is known as the Mallik gas hydrate field. It has become a major centre of research into methane clathrates with groups from Canada, the USA, Japan and India working under the umbrella organization known as the International Continental Scientific Drilling Program (ICDP).

However, there is potential for great concern regarding these methane deposits. Global warming is already causing the permafrost in the Arctic to melt, which in turn leads to release of methane gas from these terrestrial buried methane clathrates. Methane has a global warming potential greater than carbon dioxide. The potential contribution to global warming and climate change would be considerable. Thus increased methane emissions are of major environmental concern.

Methane is produced from organic waste (biomass) when it decays in the absence of air. This can be exploited as a source of energy. In the rural areas of countries such as India and China, biomass digesters are important sources of fuel for the villages (Figure 10.61). The methane is useful for heating and cooking, and the solid residue is used as a fertilizer.

Industrialized areas produce large amounts of waste, much of which is deposited in landfill sites. Biogas forms as the rubbish decays (Figure 10.62). This gas can be used as a fuel for local industry. In Merseyside in the UK, biogas is used to heat the ovens in a Cadbury's biscuit factory.

■ **Figure 10. 61** A small-scale biogas generator uses animal waste to produce methane for a village's needs.

■ **Figure 10.62** Deep in the waste of landfill sites, methane gas accumulates and must be burnt off or it becomes dangerous – a landfill flare-off

Additional Perspectives

The role of the fuel in a petrol engine

The current use of hydrocarbon fuels represents a massive investment of research and development, while the issues surrounding the continued use of these fuels are a major focus of international discussion. It is worth considering how these fuels have developed to gain some insight into the demands placed on the fuel.

The gasoline (petrol) engine

The car engine still in use in the majority of motor transport is based on the four-stroke cycle developed by Nikolaus Otto in the 19th century. This cycle places key requirements on the fuel at the various stages (Figure 10.63).

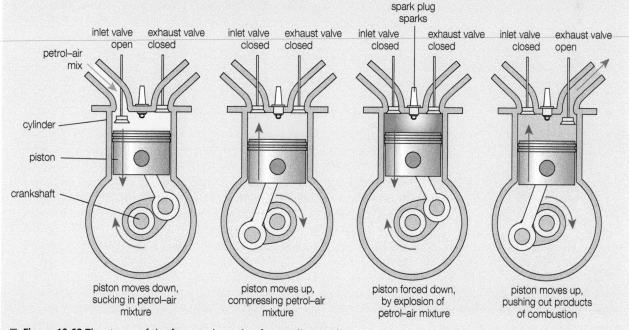

■ **Figure 10.63** The stages of the four-stroke cycle of a gasoline engine

The first downstroke of the piston

The fuel must be drawn into the cylinder from the carburettor through the inlet valve. For this to happen the fuel must be volatile enough to have formed a homogeneous fuel–air mixture in the carburettor. In a fuel-injection car, the first downstroke sucks in only air; the fuel is injected near the top of the first upstroke.

First upstroke

At this stage, the fuel–air mixture is compressed, being reduced to about one-tenth of its volume. This compression results in the temperature of the mixture being raised by several hundred degrees. This temperature rise is due to more London (dispersion) forces between the gas molecules as they are pushed closer together. The fuel should not have an ignition temperature such that this self-heating causes pre-ignition of the fuel, before the piston has reached the top of the cylinder. This phenomenon is called 'knocking'.

Second downstroke

Following the sparking of the spark plug, the fuel–air mixture ignites and expands. The piston is pushed down the cylinder. The burning of the fuel must be smooth and completed in the fraction of a second that it takes the piston to travel down the cylinder.

Second upstroke

In the ideal situation, the fuel will have completely burnt to form gaseous carbon dioxide and water. However, if insufficient oxygen (air) has been drawn in with the fuel, or there has been poor mixing, or insufficient time for complete burning, then other substances will be produced.

Carbon particulates (soot) can be a problem, shorting the spark plug, and causing a smoky exhaust. Unburnt hydrocarbons and carbon monoxide can be components of the exhaust gases. These gaseous pollutants, along with nitrogen oxides produced at the high engine temperatures, can be removed at a later stage by using a catalytic converter fitted into the exhaust system.

The quality of petrol

Long-chain hydrocarbons tend to burn unevenly in car engines, tending to ignite too soon and cause a rattling noise ('knocking'). Branched-chain alkanes burn in a more controlled manner and so are added to the gasoline fraction when petrol is blended. Branched-chain alkanes are produced from straight-chain alkanes by catalytic cracking of fractions from fractional distillation (Figure 10.64).

The octane number of petrol is a measure of its quality, and is based on the ignition properties of an isomer of octane, C_8H_{18}. The branched alkane, 2,2,4-trimethylpentane, has good anti-knock properties (Figure 10.65).

2,2,4-trimethylpentane is given an octane number value of 100. Heptane, a straight-chain alkane, has poor ignition properties and is given an octane number of 0. For a particular petrol, if the octane number is 100, then the fuel is equivalent to pure 2,2,4-trimethylpentane. Many petrol blends have an octane number of 70; they burn in a similar way to a mixture of 70% 2,2,4-trimethylpentane and 30% heptane. The octane number is not a measure of the energy content of the fuel but rather an indicator of the control and 'smoothness' of its combustion without causing excessive knocking. Multinational and national oil companies have widespread and indeed global markets so it is somewhat surprising to see that there is such diversity in the expressions of the octane rating system in different countries. This makes comparisons between the fuels used in different parts of the world difficult. The 'research octane number' (RON) is the most common method of determining a value, but the alternative 'motor

■ **Figure 10.64** A steam cracker at an oil refinery

octane number' (MON) system is also used. As a consequence the methods of stating octane numbers at the pump vary from country to country and this leads to an inconsistency in communication to consumers.

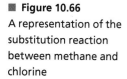

$$CH_3-C(CH_3)_2-CH_2-CH(CH_3)-CH_3$$

■ **Figure 10.65** Structure of 2,2,4-trimethylpentane

Historically, tetraethyllead(IV) ($Pb(C_2H_5)_4$) has been used as a gasoline additive to improve the anti-knock properties of gasoline (known as leaded fuel). Leaded gasoline is now being phased out for antipollution reasons and also because it 'poisons' the platinum/rhodium catalyst in a catalytic converter. Catalytic converters change pollutants, such as carbon monoxide, unburnt hydrocarbons and nitrogen oxides, into more environmentally friendly compounds. Leaded petrol should therefore not be used in a car that contains a catalytic converter.

Reactions of alkanes with halogens

The alkanes are saturated molecules and as such the main type of reaction they can undergo is a substitution reaction in which a hydrogen atom is replaced by an atom of another element. Under appropriate conditions, a mixture of methane and chlorine gases reacts to form chloromethane and hydrogen chloride (Figure 10.66):

$$CH_4(g) + Cl_2(g) \rightarrow CH_3Cl(l) + HCl(g) \qquad \text{conditions: sunlight or ultraviolet radiation}$$

■ **Figure 10.66**
A representation of the substitution reaction between methane and chlorine

Further substitution can take place with excess chlorine to produce dichloromethane (CH_2Cl_2), trichloromethane ($CHCl_3$) and tetrachloromethane (CCl_4). For example:

$$CH_4(g) + 2Cl_2(g) \rightarrow CH_2Cl_2(l) + 2HCl(g) \qquad \text{conditions: sunlight or ultraviolet radiation}$$

The degree of substitution achieved in these reactions cannot be easily controlled. The initial proportions of reacting gases can be varied but the result of the reaction is always likely to be a mixture of products.

Ethane and other alkanes will undergo similar substitution reactions with chlorine or bromine. For example:

6 Consider the reaction between ethane and bromine where the conditions are such as to produce dibromoethanes as products. Name and give the structures of the different products formed, and estimate the proportions of the products.

$$C_2H_6(g) + Br_2(g) \rightarrow C_2H_5Br(l) + HBr(g) \qquad \text{conditions: sunlight or ultraviolet radiation}$$
bromoethane

$$C_2H_6(g) + 2Br_2(g) \rightarrow C_2H_4Br_2(l) + 2HBr(g)$$
mixture of
dibromoethanes

The product of this second reaction will be a mixture of dibromoethanes (1,1-dibromoethane and 1,2-dibromoethane) as there is no control over which hydrogen atom is substituted.

The halogen molecules are able to act in this way because they are split into energized separate atoms which have an unpaired electron under these conditions. Such energized particles with an unpaired electron are known as free radicals. Once formed, these radicals initiate a chain reaction in which halogenoalkanes are produced. Studies on these reactions have shown that the reaction can be divided into a sequence of steps, known as the reaction mechanism for the substitution.

The halogenoalkane products of these substitution reactions have uses as solvents (dry cleaning for example), anaesthetics and fire retardants. Dichloromethane, for instance, can be used as a solvent glue for polystyrene in model making (Figure 10.67).

■ **Figure 10.67**
Dichloromethane can
be used to dissolve
polystyrene in model
making

Nature of Science

Bond breaking and formal charge

Chemical reactions involve the breaking of existing bonds so that new bonds can form. In aiming to understand the processes taking place we have developed a 'language' and system of indicating electron transfer that helps us understand reaction mechanisms. The mechanisms put forward for a particular reaction are our best understanding of what may take place given the experimental data.

A covalent bond between two atoms consists of a shared pair of electrons, for instance, the Cl–Cl bond in molecular chlorine. When this bond breaks there are two possible ways in which the electrons in the bond can distribute themselves.

In homolytic fission, the bond breaks so that one electron remains with each fragment:

$$Cl–Cl \rightarrow Cl\bullet + Cl\bullet$$

Here two chlorine free radicals are produced by the effect of ultraviolet radiation. When a chlorine free radical encounters a methane molecule, they can then react together:

$$H–CH_3 + Cl\bullet \rightarrow \bullet CH_3 + HCl$$

The carbon–hydrogen bond is broken homolytically by the chlorine free radical (Cl•) to produce a methyl free radical (•CH$_3$). The chlorine free radical removes a hydrogen atom to form hydrogen chloride.

In heterolytic fission, the bond breaks so that one atom retains both electrons and ions are produced:

$$X–Y \rightarrow X^+ + Y^- \qquad \text{here atom Y retained the electrons from the bond}$$
$$\text{or} \qquad X–Y \rightarrow X^- + Y^+ \qquad \text{here atom X retained the electrons}$$

Both these types of bond fission play their part in reaction mechanisms. In the case of the substitution of halogens into alkanes, it is homolytic fission that is involved in the reaction mechanism.

The prefix *homo*, meaning 'the same,' is from the Greek and refers to the fact that the two products have an equal assignment of electrons from the bond. The prefix *hetero* means 'different' and refers to the fact that the electrons are unequally shared between the fragments, producing oppositely charged ions. The concept of formal charge can be demonstrated with reference to the species of particle produced in these two types of fission. Table 10.9 illustrates this with reference to both methyl free radicals and carbocations.

■ **Table 10.9**
The formal charge
calculations for
certain carbon-
containing species

Name of species	Carbon atom	Methane molecule	Methyl free radical	Methyl carbocation
Structure	•C̈•	H H ⦂C⦂ H H	H H ⦂C• H	H H ⦂C₊ H
Carbon valence shell electrons	4	$8 \div 2 = 4$	$(6 \div 2) + 1 = 4$	$6 \div 2 = 3$
Charge	neutral	neutral	neutral	+1

The free-radical reaction mechanism

The formation of halogenoalkanes by substitution requires the presence of ultraviolet light. The reaction cannot take place in the dark. The reaction is a photochemical reaction.

The energy of a photon of ultraviolet radiation is of the order of $400 \, kJ \, mol^{-1}$. This is enough energy to break a chlorine molecule into energized chlorine atoms, chlorine free radicals:

$$Cl–Cl \rightarrow Cl\bullet + Cl\bullet \qquad \Delta H = +242 \, kJ \, mol^{-1}$$

This homolytic fission of the bond between the chlorine atoms is thought to be the initial step in this reaction.

The next stage is thought to involve a chlorine free radical reacting with a methane molecule. In this way a hydrogen chloride molecule is produced, along with a methyl free radical:

$$CH_4 + Cl\bullet \rightarrow \bullet CH_3 + HCl$$

The methyl free radical reacts further:

$$\bullet CH_3 + Cl_2 \rightarrow CH_3Cl + Cl\bullet$$

Do note that these two reactions produce one of the products of the overall reaction and, importantly, a further free radical. These free radicals can go on to produce further reactions. In this way the reaction propagates itself: it is a chain reaction.

As the reaction proceeds there is a build up of free radicals and this leads to the final stage of the sequence of reactions – the termination step. This step involves the recombination of two free radicals with each other. The three possible termination steps are shown below:

$$Cl\bullet + Cl\bullet \rightarrow Cl_2$$

$$\bullet CH_3 + Cl\bullet \rightarrow CH_3Cl$$

$$\bullet CH_3 + \bullet CH_3 \rightarrow C_2H_6$$

Note that in these reactions free radicals are being removed from the reaction mixture. The presence of small amounts of ethane in the final products of the reaction is an indication that this is indeed a plausible mechanism for the reaction. The experimental finding that for each original ultraviolet photon absorbed there are, on average, 10 000 molecules of chloromethane produced confirms the idea of this being a chain reaction.

Thus there are three main steps to this reaction mechanism: initiation, propagation and termination (Figure 10.68).

Free-radical mechanisms are also thought to be important in other significant organic reactions such as the cracking of hydrocarbon chains and the formation of polymers such as poly(ethene).

■ **Figure 10.68**
The reaction mechanism for the free-radical substitution between methane and chlorine in ultraviolet light

initiation	**Cl — Cl**(g)	$\xrightarrow{\text{ultraviolet}}$ 2**Cl**•(g)
propagation	**Cl**•(g) + **CH₄**(g)	⟶ •**CH₃**(g) + **HCl**(g)
	•**CH₃**(g) + **Cl₂**(g)	⟶ **CH₃Cl**(g) + **Cl**•(g)
possible termination steps	**Cl**•(g) + **Cl**•(g)	⟶ **Cl₂**(g)
	Cl•(g) + •**CH₃**(g)	⟶ **CH₃Cl**(g)
	•**CH₃**(g) + •**CH₃**(g)	⟶ **C₂H₆**(g)
overall reaction	**Cl₂**(g) + **CH₄**(g)	$\xrightarrow{\text{ultraviolet}}$ **CH₃Cl**(g) + **HCl**(g)

ToK Link

Pathways and mechanisms

Organic reaction mechanisms are theories, and cannot be proved beyond doubt. Chemists are led to accept a mechanism for a particular reaction because it provides the most satisfactory way of understanding all the data about that reaction. Close analysis may well supply evidence that the thinking behind a mechanism is along the right lines – the finding of a small quantity of ethane in the reaction mixture from the chlorination of methane is unexpected and a good indicator that methyl free radicals are involved in the progress of the reaction. Any proposed mechanism is open to falsification. New facts may later be discovered which are not consistent with the current accepted theory and it must then be rejected or, more often, modified. So the field of organic chemistry is a continually developing one.

Chemical reactions involving the interconversion of functional groups are the basis for the synthesis of new organic compounds and the understanding of mechanism is key to our understanding of what is feasible and can be exploitable. The accumulation of a great deal of data on the chemistry of the different functional groups has enabled chemists to utilize various reaction pathways to further advances in health care, food production and a whole range of developmental areas. Even the production of seemingly destructive materials can also produce substances that have a beneficial use too. Nitroglycerine is a case in point.

Nitroglycerine (propan-1,2,3-triol trinitrate) is an explosive liquid. It is synthesized by heating glycerol (propane-1,2,3-triol) with a mixture of concentrated sulfuric and nitric acids. In its pure form it is extremely sensitive to shock and will explode violently. Alfred Nobel found that the chemical could be safely absorbed into kieselguhr, a soft chalk-like rock. The combination of nitroglycerine and kieselguhr is known as dynamite. This is safer and will not explode with shock – a detonation is required. Dynamite is widely used in mining and demolishing old buildings. The overall equation for its decomposition is:

$$4C_3H_5N_3O_9(l) \rightarrow 6N_2(g) + O_2(g) + 12CO_2(g) + 10H_2O(l)$$

Nitroglycerine is also used to treat angina (contraction of cardiac muscle) and heart disease. It acts as a vasodilator and widens the blood vessels.

■ Alkenes

The alkenes are also hydrocarbons, and therefore contain carbon and hydrogen only. They have the general formula C_nH_{2n}. The alkenes are unsaturated hydrocarbons containing a carbon–carbon double bond; this double bond is made up of a sigma (σ) bond and a pi (π) bond. The carbon atoms which form the double bond have an arrangement of groups around them which is trigonal planar with angles of 120°, as shown for ethene on the right. It is important to note that a carbon–carbon double bond is shorter than a carbon–carbon single bond.

Alkenes are relatively more reactive compounds than alkanes because of the carbon–carbon double bond. They undergo a range of addition reactions.

The reactions of alkenes with hydrogen and halogens

The carbon–carbon double bond is the functional group of the alkenes and is the site of chemical reactivity in the structure. The pi (π) bond is weaker than the sigma (σ) bond and is relatively easily broken without the molecule falling apart. Thus addition reactions can take place in which various molecules add to the carbon atoms originally participating in the double bond. The products of such reactions are all saturated molecules.

Hydrogenation

The simplest of these addition reactions is the addition of hydrogen across the carbon–carbon double bond to produce the alkane (Figure 10.69).

■ **Figure 10.69**
A representation of the hydrogenation of ethene to produce ethane

Hydrogen reacts with alkenes to form alkanes in the presence of a nickel catalyst at about 180 °C:

■ **Figure 10.70** Margarine is solid but spreadable at room temperature

Note that any isomerism due to the position of the double bond is lost once the hydrogen is added.

This process, known as hydrogenation, is used in the margarine industry to convert oils containing unsaturated hydrocarbon chains into more saturated compounds which have higher melting points. This is done so that margarine will be a solid at room temperature (Figure 10.70). However, there are now widespread concerns about the health effects of some of the fats produced in this way, known as *trans* fats.

Halogenation

Halogens react with alkenes to produce disubstituted compounds. These reactions take place readily at room temperature and are accompanied by the loss of colour of the reacting halogen. Note that the halogen atoms become bonded across the carbon–carbon double bond so the structure of the product will have the halogen atoms on *adjacent* carbon atoms. The halogen is usually dissolved in a non-polar solvent such as hexane.

Further addition reactions

Hydrogen halides (HCl, HBr, etc.) react with alkenes to produce halogenoalkanes. These reactions take place rapidly in solution at room temperature. For example, ethene reacts with hydrogen chloride to form chloroethane, and but-2-ene reacts with hydrogen bromide to form 2-bromobutane:

The hydrogen halides all react similarly, but the reactivity is in the order HI > HBr > HCl because of the decreasing strength of the hydrogen halide bond going down group 17. Thus hydrogen iodide, HI, having the weakest and longest H–X bond, reacts the most readily.

Hydration

The reaction with water is known as hydration and the alkene is converted into an alcohol. Water does not itself react directly with alkenes. However, in the laboratory, this reaction can be accomplished using concentrated sulfuric acid to form an addition product. The reaction involves an intermediate in which both H^+ and HSO_4^- ions are added across the double bond. Cold water is then added and hydrolysis takes place with replacement of the HSO_4^- by OH^- and re-formation of the sulfuric acid (H_2SO_4):

There is an industrial process for synthesizing ethanol by hydration of ethene. This involves passing ethene and steam at high pressure (60 atmospheres) over a catalyst of immobilized phosphoric(v) acid at 300 °C. The phosphoric(v) acid is adsorbed on silicon dioxide pellets. An equilibrium is set up which achieves a conversion to ethanol of 5%. However, the unconverted ethene is recycled until it is all reacted (see Chapter 7). This method is of industrial significance because ethanol is a very important solvent and the product has a high degree of purity.

Testing for unsaturation

The fact that alkenes readily undergo addition reactions, whereas alkanes do not (they only undergo substitution reactions in the presence of ultraviolet light), can be used as the basis of chemical tests to distinguish between the two homologous series. If separate samples of an alkane (cyclohexane) and an alkene (cyclohexene) are shaken with bromine water at room temperature, the orange-yellow colour of the bromine water is immediately decolorized by the alkene (Figure 10.71). The alkane produces no reaction and so the colour remains unchanged.

It is worth noting that the test uses bromine water as the test reagent. In this case the product is not the dibromo- addition product because a hydroxyl (–OH) group replaces one of the bromine atoms.

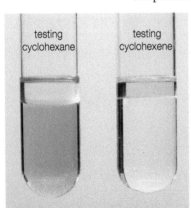

Figure 10.71 The bromine water test for unsaturated hydrocarbons. The unsaturated hydrocarbon decolorizes the bromine water; the saturated compound does not

Alkenes also differ from alkanes when they are burnt. Because they have a higher ratio of carbon to hydrogen, alkenes contain much more unburnt carbon than alkanes when they burn under similar conditions. This gives them a much dirtier, smokier flame. Aromatic compounds – which contain a benzene ring – have a higher carbon : hydrogen ratio still, and so burn with an even smokier flame.

Addition polymerization of alkenes

Alkenes and substituted alkenes readily undergo addition reactions by breaking one of their double bonds (it is the pi (π) bond that breaks). Because of this they can be joined together to produce long chains known as polymers. The alkene used in this type of reaction is known as the monomer

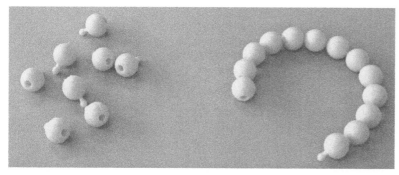

and its chemical nature will determine the properties of the polymer. Polymers, typically containing thousands of molecules of the monomer, are among the major products of the organic chemical industry. Indeed, many of our most common and useful plastics are polymers of alkenes. Figure 10.72 shows an analogy for the polymerization process – the individual beads are the monomers, and they are able to join together in a long chain, which represents the polymer molecule.

■ **Figure 10.72**
The assembly of beads into a chain represents a model of the polymerization process

For example, ethene polymerizes to form poly(ethene), commonly known as polythene (Figure 10.73). This molecule was first synthesized in 1935 at the Imperial Chemical Industries (ICI) in the United Kingdom. The process was discovered largely by accidental contamination of the reactants with oxygen, and the product was originally called 'Alkathene'. It had excellent electrical insulating properties and was used in the development of radar during the Second World War. It is commonly used in household containers, carrier bags, water tanks and piping.

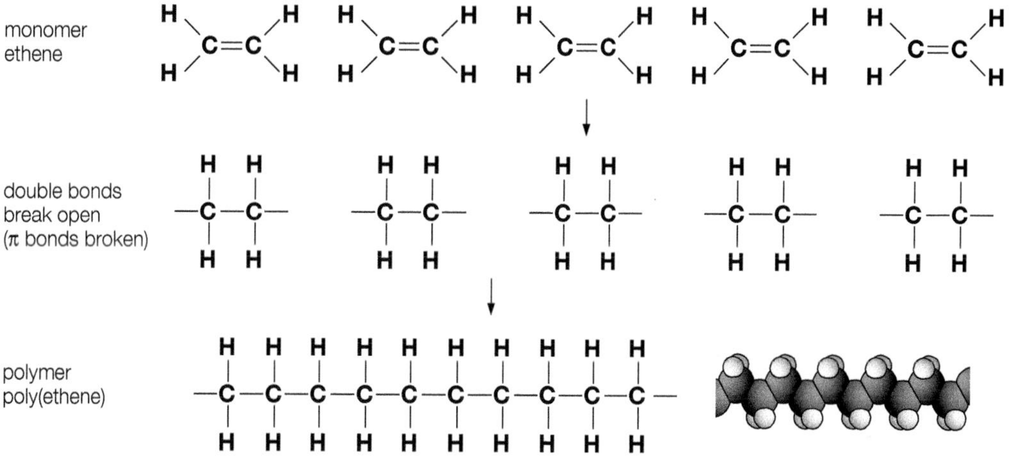

■ **Figure 10.73**
A diagrammatic representation of the polymerization of ethene to form poly(ethene)

The process outlined in Figure 10.73 is summarized in an equation that is often written as shown below. Here *n* represents the number of repeating units and is a large number.

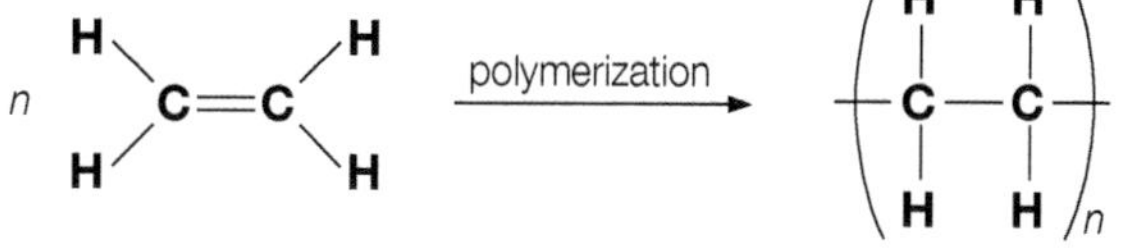

Although the chains formed by the addition polymerization process are saturated, the names of the polymers formed still contain the suffix *-ene*. This is because the standard way of naming the polymer is to use the prefix *poly-* followed by the name of the monomer in brackets, for example poly(propene). Do also note the standard way of representing a polymer in an equation – with the repeating unit in brackets followed by the letter *n* symbolizing a large number.

Following the discovery of poly(ethene) and its usefulness, considerable research was carried out to produce other addition polymers with modified properties to suit many diverse practical uses. Propene polymerizes to form poly(propene), often called polypropylene. This polymer is used in the manufacture of clothing, especially thermal wear for outdoor activities.

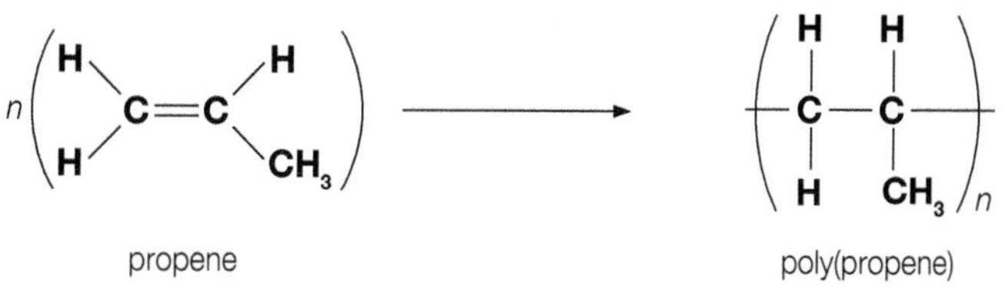

propene   poly(propene)

**Additional
Perspectives**

Other addition polymers

Poly(chloroethene), also known as PVC (polyvinyl chloride), is very widely used in all forms of construction materials, packaging, electrical cable sheathing and so on. It is one of the world's most important plastics. Its widespread use is, however, somewhat controversial as its synthesis is associated with some toxic by-products known as dioxins which must be very carefully contained. Dioxins (Chapter 22) are linked to reproductive disorders and a variety of cancers.

chloroethene
(vinyl chloride)

poly(chloroethene)
(PVC)

Another interesting polymer is known as PTFE – poly(tetrafluoroethene). It has distinctive non-adhesive surface properties, and is widely used in non-stick pans under registered trademark names such as Teflon®. It also comprises one of the layers in the manufacture of waterproof and breathable fabrics such as Gore-tex®.

tetrafluoroethene

poly(tetrafluoroethene)
(PTFE)

Figure 10.74 shows model structures of these three highly useful polymers. The uses of these manufactured polymers are varied and diverse and are summarized in Table 10.10.

■ **Figure 10.74**
Representations of
the chain structures
of **a** poly(propene),
b poly(chloroethene) and
c poly(tetrafluoroethene).
Do note that the –Cl or
–CH$_3$ side-chains in **a** and
b are attached to every
alternate carbon atom in
the chain

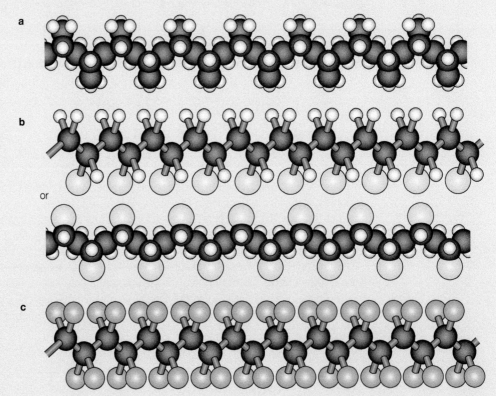

■ **Table 10.10**
Some uses of
addition polymers

Polymer (and trade-name(s))	Monomer	Properties	Examples of use
Poly(ethene) (polyethylene, polythene, PE)	Ethene $CH_2=CH_2$	Tough, durable	Plastic bags, bowls, bottles, packaging
Poly(propene) (polypropylene, PP)	Propene $CH_3CH=CH_2$	Tough, durable	Crates and boxes, plastic rope
Poly(chloroethene) (polyvinyl chloride, PVC)	Chloroethene $CH_2=CHCl$	Strong, hard (not as flexible as polythene)	Insulation, pipes and guttering
Poly(tetrafluoroethene) (polytetrafluoroethylene, Teflon, PTFE)	Tetrafluoroethene $CF_2=CF_2$	Non-stick surface, withstands high temperatures	Non-stick frying pans, non-stick taps and joints
Poly(phenylethene) (polystyrene, PS)	Phenylethene (styrene) $C_6H_5CH=CH_2$	Light, poor conductor of heat	Insulation, packaging (foam)

The economic importance of the reactions of alkenes

Alkenes readily undergo addition reactions and they are used as starting materials in the manufacture of many industrially important chemicals. Figure 10.75 shows some of the different major industrial addition reactions that involve ethene, which is obtained from the catalytic cracking of the hydrocarbon fractions in the distillation of crude oil.

■ **Figure 10.75**
Some of the industrial products derived from ethene

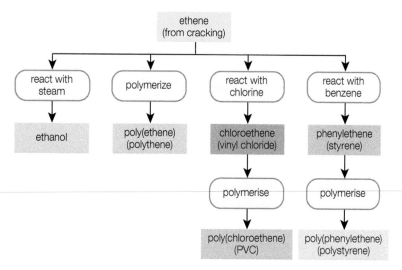

Serendipity in science

Historically there have been some famous examples of 'accidental' discoveries. Such examples serve to show that not all scientific advances are as planned. As mentioned above, the discovery of the first form of poly(ethene), known as 'Alkathene' was somewhat fortuitous, though the researchers were looking at polymerizations. Roy Plunkett (1910–1994) was an American industrial chemist who worked for DuPont. In 1938 he accidentally invented Teflon. He was working on tetrafluoroethene when he found that a sample had polymerized into a waxy solid with amazing properties such as low surface friction, high heat resistance and resistance to corrosion. A further piece of polymeric serendipity was the discovery of cyanoacrylate 'superglues'. The original cyanoacrylates were discovered in 1942 in a search for materials to make clear plastic gun sights during World War II, when a team of scientists headed by Harry Coover Jr. stumbled upon a formulation that stuck to everything that it came in contact with; consequently it was rejected for that particular application. However, in 1951 cyanoacrylates were rediscovered and recognized for their true commercial potential. The first cyanoacrylate adhesive – the compounds contain the ester and nitrile functional groups mentioned in this chapter – was sold in 1958. Today they have a wide use not just in the home but in construction and medicine, for instance.

You may possibly be able to think of other examples of scientific serendipity in other fields of research. Not all scientists and engineers had similar good fortune. Thomas Midgley was an American research scientist who patented tetraethyl lead as an additive to counteract premature ignition ('knocking') in car engines. It was very successful at this but eventually awareness and concern grew over the levels of lead in the atmosphere. Lead is a neurotoxin and particularly dangerous for young children. From 1986 onwards the use of leaded petrol has been progressively phased out, particularly as it also 'poisons' the catalyst in car exhaust catalysers, and there are now very few countries left where it is still used. Intriguingly, Midgley was also involved in the discovery and marketing of chlorofluorocarbons (CFCs) – another remarkably effective product that eventually turned out to have detrimental environmental effects.

■ Alcohols

Alcohols contain the hydroxyl (–OH) functional group, and have the general formula $C_nH_{2n+1}OH$. As the hydroxyl group is a polar group containing a hydrogen atom, it increases the solubility in water of the molecules relative to the corresponding alkanes. The most common alcohol, ethanol C_2H_5OH, is readily soluble in water. The alcohol molecules can form hydrogen bonds with water through the hydroxyl group.

The complete combustion of alcohols

Alcohols burn in air or oxygen to form carbon dioxide and water. The reactions are strongly exothermic. Indeed, alcohols are important fuels and are used in alcohol burners and similar heaters. The amount of energy released per mole of alcohol increases as we go up the homologous series. This is mainly due to the fact that the amount of carbon dioxide produced per mole of the alcohol increases going up the series. We have seen before that it is the strength of the bonding in carbon dioxide that contributes greatly to the exothermic nature of these combustion reactions.

The equations for the burning of a number of different alcohols are given below:

CO_2 : *alcohol ratio*

$$2CH_3OH(l) + 3O_2(g) \rightarrow 2CO_2(g) + 4H_2O(l) \qquad \Delta H_c^\circ = -726\,kJ\,mol^{-1} \qquad 1:1$$

$$C_2H_5OH(l) + 3\tfrac{1}{2}O_2(g) \rightarrow 2CO_2(g) + 3H_2O(l) \qquad \Delta H_c^\circ = -1371\,kJ\,mol^{-1} \qquad 2:1$$

$$2C_5H_{11}OH(l) + 15O_2(g) \rightarrow 10CO_2(g) + 12H_2O(l) \qquad \Delta H_c^\circ = -3330\,kJ\,mol^{-1} \qquad 5:1$$

Even though they contain oxygen, the alcohols will still behave as hydrocarbons do and produce carbon monoxide instead of carbon dioxide when burnt in a limited supply of oxygen.

For several years some countries, such as Brazil, have combined ethanol with gasoline to produce a fuel for cars known as gasohol. This makes a country less dependent on the supply of gasoline but, weight for weight, gasohol is not as efficient in terms of energy production.

7 Working from the figures given for the burning of ethanol, and those for octane given in the equation below, show that one gram of octane produces over 60% more energy than the same mass of ethanol.

$$2C_8H_{18}(l) + 25O_2(g) \rightarrow 16CO_2(g) + 18H_2O(l) \quad \Delta H_c^\circ = -5512\,kJ\,mol^{-1}$$

Even though the alcohols are less energy efficient than hydrocarbon fuels, they still have the advantage that they can be produced from renewable sources. Ethanol can be produced by fermentation, which initially suggested that ethanol was a 'carbon-neutral' fuel.

Additional Perspectives

Biofuels

Following the early example of Brazil, which has used bioethanol as a transport fuel for many years (Figure 10.76), other countries have increased their production of fuels from carbohydrate-rich crops such as corn or sugar cane. These fuels were initially seen as 'carbon neutral' because re-growing the crops would absorb the same amount of carbon dioxide as was released when burning the fuel. In 2003 the European Union set a target of replacing 5.75% of all transport fossil fuels (petrol and diesel) with biofuels by 2010. The key advantage of these 'first-generation' biofuels was that they were easy to make with established technology. The methods used were not fundamentally different from those used to make vodka or cooking oil.

■ **Figure 10.76**
Both ethanol and methanol find their use as biofuels

However, this increased production of such biofuels has quickly shown up some unforeseen economic shortcomings. Fuel crop production competes with food crops for land use and this situation is making food less affordable in developing countries. The green credentials of these early biofuels have come under question, too, as the intensive farming methods required for efficient mass production use significant amounts of energy. By the end of 2007, it had become clear that the potential solution had become part of the problem.

These considerations have led to other sources of ethanol being explored, including, for instance, using sawdust from sawmills as a starting point for production. Vegetable oils from crops such as rape and sunflowers are also being developed as fuels. Recycled cooking oil is being used as a component of biodiesel. Biodiesel contains esters, which are made from vegetable oils such as rapeseed or animal fats. The continual growth of new oil-producing plants, which absorb carbon dioxide from the air through photosynthesis, means that biodiesel contributes less to global warming than fossil fuels do. Motor manufacturers have all developed cars with engines adapted to run on these new fuels.

The oxidation reactions of alcohols

The alcohol functional group is capable of being oxidized to other important organic molecules. Such reactions alter the functional group. The remaining part of the carbon skeleton is left unaffected. The products possible from oxidation depend on whether the alcohol concerned is primary, secondary or tertiary.

Various oxidizing agents can be used for these reactions. The most commonly used laboratory oxidizing agent is acidified potassium dichromate(VI). This is a bright orange solution. When the reaction mixture is heated a colour change takes place as the Cr(VI) is reduced to Cr(III), which is green, while the alcohol is oxidized (Figure 10.77).

■ **Figure 10.77** The oxidation of alcohols with acidified potassium dichromate(VI) solution. The different alcohols react differently; tertiary alcohols do not react

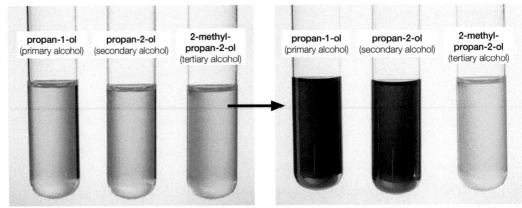

In writing equations for these reactions it is often easier to show the oxidizing agent simply as [O]. The oxidation reactions of the different alcohols are described below.

Primary alcohols

Primary alcohols, such as ethanol, are oxidized in a two-stage process: firstly to an aldehyde, and then to a carboxylic acid. Thus ethanol is first oxidized to ethanal. This can be viewed as oxidation by removal of hydrogen.

$$CH_3CH_2OH + [O] \longrightarrow CH_3CHO + H_2O$$

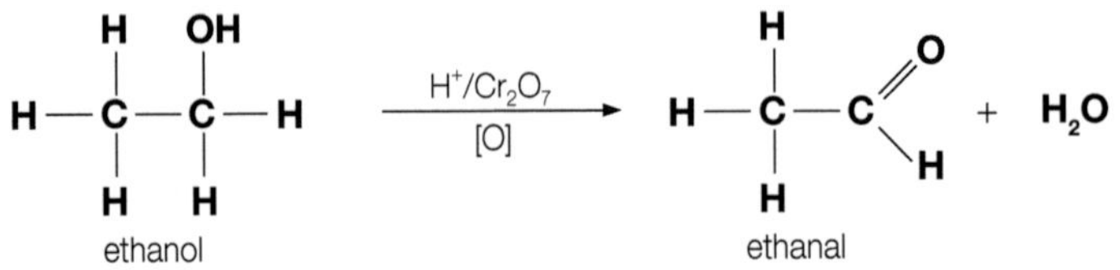

The second stage is the conversion of ethanal to ethanoic acid. The oxidation of ethanol to ethanoic acid is one of the oldest chemical oxidations practised by humans. It is the reaction used when wine is left exposed to air and bacterial action to produce vinegar.

$$CH_3CHO + [O] \longrightarrow CH_3COOH$$

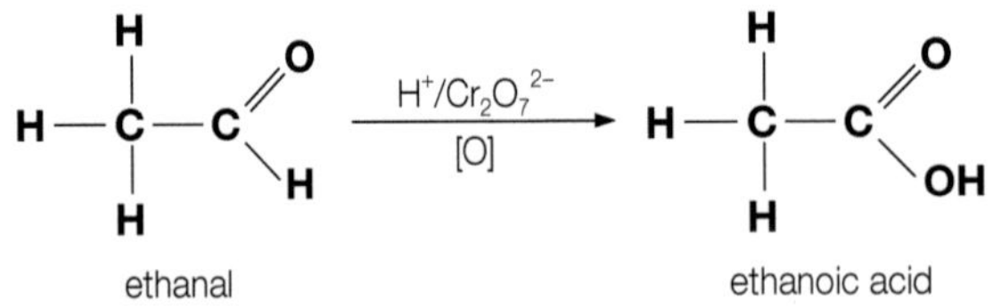

In summary, any primary alcohol will undergo the following sequence of oxidation reactions:

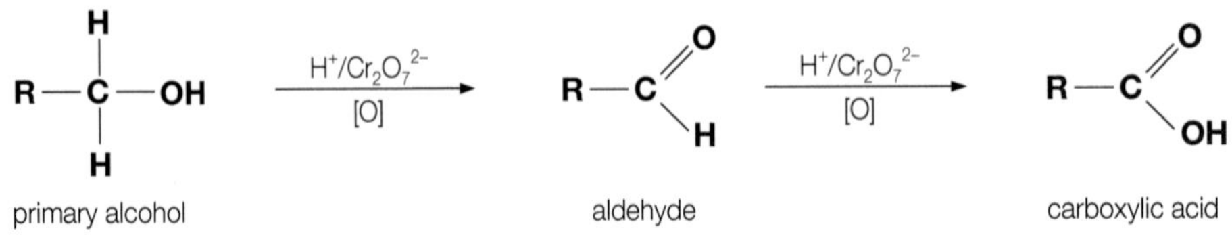

Experimental conditions can be adjusted when carrying out these oxidations in order to prepare the different products. If the aldehyde is the desired product, then it is possible to remove it from the reaction mixture by distilling it off as it forms (Figure 10.78a). This is achievable because aldehydes have lower boiling points than either alcohols or carboxylic acids. Unlike the alcohols or the carboxylic acids, they do not have the capacity for hydrogen bonding between their molecules. An excess of the alcohol over the oxidizing agent can also favour the production of the aldehyde.

However, if we want to obtain the carboxylic acid as the product, we must leave the aldehyde in contact with the oxidizing agent for a prolonged period of time. In this case the apparatus is set up for reflux (Figure 10.78b), and an excess of the oxidizing agent is used to favour complete oxidation to the carboxylic acid.

■ **Figure 10.78**
a The distillation apparatus used to obtain the aldehyde product from the oxidation of ethanol
b The reflux apparatus used in the complete oxidation of ethanol to ethanoic acid

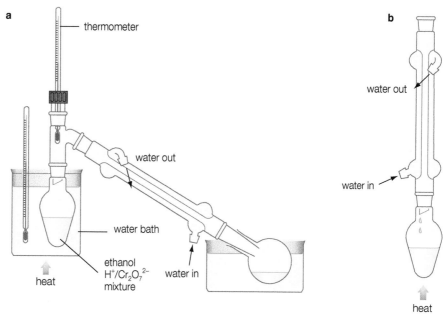

Secondary alcohols

Secondary alcohols have just a single hydrogen attached to the carbon atom that carries the functional group. This means that when secondary alcohols are oxidized there is just one product possible – a ketone. The oxidation of propan-2-ol produces propanone as the organic product.

$$CH_3CH(OH)CH_3 \ + \ [O] \longrightarrow CH_3COCH_3 \ + \ H_2O$$

propan-2-ol
(secondary alcohol)   propanone
(ketone)

Tertiary alcohols

Tertiary alcohols are not readily oxidized under comparable mild conditions, as there is no hydrogen atom attached to the carbon atom to which the hydroxyl group is attached. Any oxidation of tertiary alcohols requires more drastic conditions as it is necessary to break the carbon skeleton of the molecule. Therefore we do not see a colour change in the acidified potassium dichromate(VI) oxidizing agent when it is heated with a tertiary alcohol (Figure 10.77).

no oxidation possible as
no hydrogen atom on carbon
atom bonded to the alcohol group

Additional Perspectives

Redox half-equations for the oxidation of alcohols

The oxidation of alcohols by acidified potassium dichromate(VI) can be represented by equations in which the oxidizing agent is written as [O] and the reactions are considered in terms of the removal of hydrogen or the gain of oxygen.

However, equations involving the loss of electrons can also be written and the overall reaction represented as the combination of two half-equations, one for the oxidation and the other for the associated reduction. See Chapter 9 for examples involving ethanol and ethanal.

Taking another example, the oxidation of propan-2-ol to propanone can be represented by the following half-equation:

$$CH_3CH(OH)CH_3(aq) \rightarrow CH_3COCH_3(aq) + 2H^+(aq) + 2e^-$$

Oxidation products of primary and secondary alcohols

The initial products of the oxidation of alcohols, whether from primary or secondary alcohols, all contain the >C=O group. This group is present in both aldehydes and ketones.

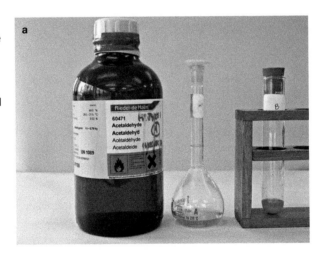 

■ **Figure 10.79 a** The 2,4-dinitrophenylhydrazine test for aldehydes and ketones. An orange precipitate is formed in either case. **b** A commercial melting-point apparatus

The standard test for an aldehyde or ketone is that they both form orange crystalline precipitates with 2,4-dinitrophenylhydrazine solution (Figure 10.79a). The precipitate can be recrystallized and its melting point determined (Figure 10.79b). Knowing the melting point of the crystals enables us to identify the particular aldehyde or ketone tested.

The 2,4-dinitrophenylhydrazine test does not distinguish between aldehydes and ketones. However, there are two simple tests which can do so, based on the fact that aldehydes can be oxidized whereas ketones cannot. Fehling's solution and Tollens' reagent are both mild oxidizing reagents that react with aldehydes to produce carboxylic acids (Figure 10.80).

■ **Figure 10.80 a** Fehling's solution produces an orange-brown precipitate with aldehydes; **b** Tollens' reagent produces a 'silver mirror' on the inside of the test tube. The middle tube in each case contained ethanal, while the right-hand tube contained propanone. The first tube in each case is the unreacted starting reagent

Fehling's solution contains alkaline copper(II) sulfate and the precipitate is copper(I) oxide. Tollens' reagent is a solution of silver nitrate in ammonia, and the precipitate of metallic silver coats the inside of the test tube producing a 'mirror'.

Esterification reactions

Esters are derived from carboxylic acids by reaction with alcohols. They have a wide variety of applications ranging from flavouring agents to solvents and explosives. One of the most used painkillers in medication, aspirin, is an ester, while a major class of polymers are the poly(esters). Fats and vegetable oils are naturally occurring esters and the alkaline hydrolysis of such esters (saponification) is used to produce soaps.

Esterification is a reversible reaction that occurs between an alcohol and a carboxylic acid when they are heated under reflux in the presence of a catalyst, usually concentrated sulfuric acid:

alcohol + carboxylic acid ⇌ ester + water

The reaction can be regarded as a condensation reaction because as the addition of the two molecules takes place there is the elimination of water (Figure 10.81).

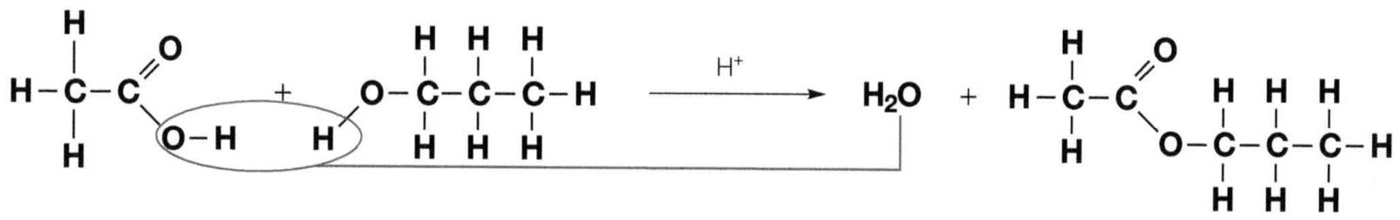

ethanoic acid   propanol   water   propyl ethanoate

■ **Figure 10.81** The esterification reaction involves the elimination of water

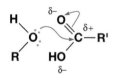

■ **Figure 10.82** The nucleophilic attack of an alcohol molecule on a carboxylic acid

The initial stage of the reaction can be viewed as the nucleophilic attack of the alcohol molecule on the electron deficient carbon atom at the centre of the carboxylic acid group. The alcohol molecule is a nucleophile because of the lone pairs of electrons on the oxygen atom (Figure 10.82). We will look further at the nature of nucleophiles in the next section when discussing halogenoalkanes.

The ester has the lowest boiling point of the components of the reaction mixture and so can be separated by distillation. The stages in the purification of a sample of an ester, in this case ethyl ethonoate, are shown in Figure 10.83 overleaf. Esters have distinct smells that can often be detected if the reaction mixture is poured into a beaker of water. The ester will spread out on the surface of the water as it is insoluble in water, having no free –OH groups in the molecule and so being unable to interact with water by hydrogen bonding.

■ Halogenoalkanes

Halogenoalkanes contain an atom of fluorine, chlorine, bromine or iodine bonded to the carbon skeleton of the molecule. They have the general formula $C_nH_{2n+1}X$, where X = a halogen. They are generally oily liquids (Figure 10.84) that do not mix with water.

The substitution reactions of halogenoalkanes with sodium hydroxide

Halogenoalkanes are saturated molecules but the halogen atom can be replaced by other atoms or groups in substitution reactions. This means that halogenoalkanes are very useful in reaction pathways that enable us to synthesize a range of important organic products.

Halogenoalkanes are also used directly in many products. In particular, the group of compounds known as CFCs (chlorofluorocarbons) were used in refrigerants and aerosol propellants in many parts of the world from the 1930s. The growing awareness of their role in breaking down the stratospheric ozone layer, which protects the Earth from harmful ultraviolet radiation, has led to regulations for their distribution and use being introduced following the Montreal Protocol. Sadly, the stability of these molecules is such that even though they are no longer being released in large quantities they are likely to remain active and hence destructive in the atmosphere for generations.

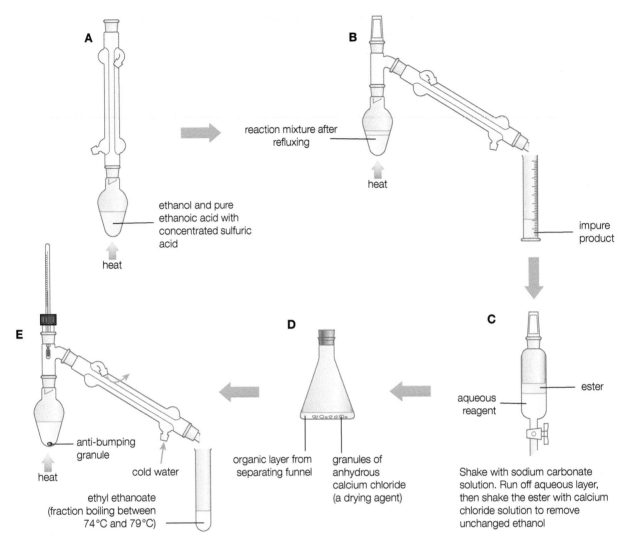

■ **Figure 10.83** The various stages in the practical method of purifying the ethyl ethanoate produced by an esterification reaction

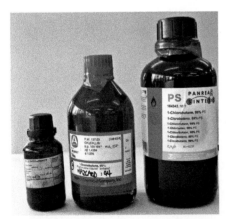

■ **Figure 10.84** Halogenoalkanes are usually oily liquids

The greater electronegativity of the halogen atom means that the carbon–halogen bond is polarized, resulting in a charge distribution as follows:

$$-\overset{|}{\underset{|}{C}} \overset{\delta+}{\longrightarrow} X^{\delta-}$$

The carbon atom attached to the halogen therefore has a partial positive charge and can be described as being electron deficient. This makes it susceptible to attack by a group of chemicals called nucleophiles – species which are themselves electron rich and hence are attracted to a region of electron deficiency. Nucleophiles have a lone pair of electrons and may be negatively charged.

The halogenoalkanes are saturated molecules (like alkanes), and as such they undergo substitution reactions. A good example of this is the substitution reaction involving the hydroxide ion (OH⁻) from alkalis such as sodium hydroxide solution (NaOH(aq)). In this reaction, the OH⁻ ion is the nucleophile and will replace (substitute for) the halogen. In the process the halogenoalkane is converted into an alcohol. These reactions are commonly described as nucleophilic substitution reactions (S_N reactions).

The exact mechanism of these reactions depends on whether the halogenoalkane is primary, secondary or tertiary, as this influences the environment of the carbon–halogen bond. In organic reaction mechanisms, it is customary to use curly arrows to represent the movement of electron pairs during the transformations that take place during chemical reactions.

Nature of Science

Curly arrows and reaction mechanisms

In describing the detail of the transformations that take place in reaction mechanisms that involve the breaking of existing bonds and the making of new bonds, we need a system that illustrates the movement of the electrons involved. Each covalent bond is made up of two electrons and so we are effectively having to denote the movement of *electron pairs*.

The generally accepted system is based on depicting the movement of pairs of electrons using 'curly arrows'. The blunt end of the arrow indicates the initial position of the electron pair – illustrated below by the arrow starting at the lone pair on the OH^- ion on the left. The arrow head is positioned to show where the electrons end up – thus the pair of electrons indicated will form a bond between the oxygen atom and the carbon atom.

It is worth noting the slightly different second 'curly arrow' on the diagram. This shows that the electrons involved in the C–X bond move from between those two atoms to a position on the more electronegative X atom. This shows the departure of the X atom as an X^- ion. You will be expected to use 'curly arrows' accurately in your IB examination papers. This system of indicating the movement of electrons is useful in depicting mechanisms such as S_N1 and S_N2 (see Chapter 20).

There is a second aspect to the system of illustrating the movement of electrons which applies in the other reaction mechanism we have discussed in this chapter – namely the free-radical mechanism for substitution of halogens into alkanes (see page 357). Here we indicate the movement of single electrons by the use of 'half arrows'. The following diagrams show the movement of the electrons in the two propagation steps involved in the chlorination of methane using these 'half arrows':

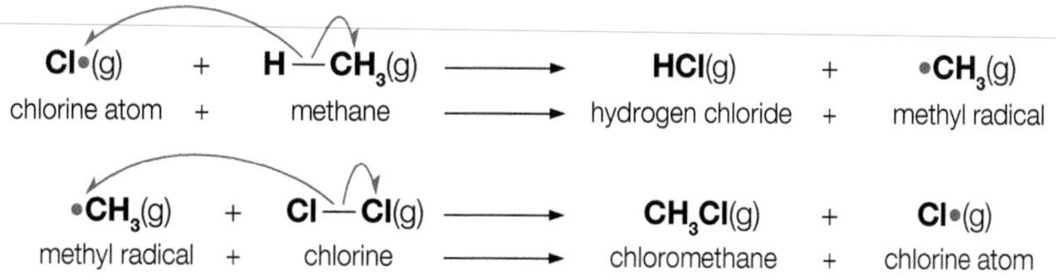

■ Electrophilic substitution reactions of benzene

We have discussed earlier the fact that benzene does not readily undergo addition reactions. Benzene has an electron-rich structure and therefore is more likely to take part in reactions that involve electrophiles. Electrophiles are reacting species that are themselves electron deficient; they are positively charged or have a partial positive charge. These species are therefore attracted to the electron-rich benzene structure with the delocalized pi cloud above and below the ring. The overall result of these reactions with benzene is substitution, and such reactions are referred to as electrophilic substitution reactions.

Two such substitution reactions (which will be discussed in more detail in Chapter 20) are the chlorination and nitration of benzene. Chorination is carried out in an anhydrous environment (in dry ethoxyethane) and uses a halogen-carrier to catalyse the reaction. This halogen-carrier is a Lewis base, often aluminium chloride ($AlCl_3$). One chlorine replaces a hydrogen atom on the ring to form chlorobenzene, the other product being hydrogen chloride:

$$C_6H_6 + Cl_2 \xrightarrow{\text{AlCl}_3,\ \text{dry ethoxyethane}} C_6H_5Cl + HCl$$

Nitrobenzene is formed when benzene is refluxed with a nitrating mixture of concentrated nitric(v) and sulfuric acids. The species that attacks the benzene ring is the electrophile, NO_2^+ (the nitronium ion).

$$C_6H_6 + HNO_3 \xrightarrow{\text{conc. HNO}_3/\text{H}_2\text{SO}_4} C_6H_5NO_2 + H_2O$$

■ *Examination questions – a selection*

Paper 1 IB questions and IB style questions

Q1 Which statement about a homologous series is correct?
A Members of the series differ by CH_3.
B Members of the series have the same physical properties.
C Members of the series have the same empirical formula.
D Members of the series have similar chemical properties.
Standard Level Paper 1, November 2012, Q26

Q2 Which compound is **not** an isomer of hexane?
A $CH_3CH(CH_3)CH_2CH_2CH_3$
B $CH_3CHCHCH_2CH_2CH_3$
C $(CH_3)_3CCH_2CH_3$
D $CH_3CH_2CH(CH_3)CH_2CH_3$
Standard Level Paper 1, November 2012, Q27

Q3 Which of the following groups of compounds are consecutive members of the same homologous series?
A HCOOH, HCHO, CH_3OH
B HCOOH, CH_3COOH, C_2H_5COOH
C CH_4, CH_3Cl, CH_2Cl_2
D C_2H_2, C_2H_4, C_2H_6

Q4 Which of the following molecules is capable of forming an addition polymer?
A $H_2NCH_2CHCHCH_2NH_2$ C $H_2N(CH_2)_6CO_2H$
B $H_2N(CH_2)_6NH_2$ D $HO(CH_2)_2CO_2H$

Q5 How many structural isomers are possible with the molecular formula C_6H_{14}?
A 4   B 6   C 5   D 7

Q6 Which compound is a member of the aldehyde homologous series?
A $CH_3CH_2COCH_3$ C $CH_3CH_2CH_2OH$
B CH_3CH_2CHO D CH_3CH_2COOH

Q7 Which compound is a member of the same homologous series as 1-chloropropane?
A 1-chloropropene
B 1,2-dichloropropane
C 1-bromopropane
D 1-chlorobutane

Q8 The following is a three-dimensional representation of an organic molecule.

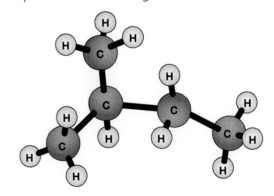

Which statement is correct?

A The correct IUPAC name of the molecule is 2-methylpentane.

B All the bond angles will be approximately 90°.

C One isomer of this molecule is pentane.

D The boiling point of this compound would be higher than that of pentane.

Standard Level Paper 1, Specimen 2009, Q26

Q9 Which one of the following is the best method of distinguishing between an alkane and an alkene?

A test with universal indicator paper

B burn the gases in excess oxygen

C test their solubility in water

D add bromine water

Q10 How do the bond angles and bond lengths in ethane and ethene compare?

	H–C–H bond angle in ethane	C–C bond length in ethane
A	larger	longer
B	smaller	longer
C	smaller	shorter
D	larger	shorter

Q11 The oxidation of propan-2-ol, $CH_3CH(OH)CH_3$, by sodium dichromate(VI) leads to the formation of:

A propanone (CH_3COCH_3)

B propan-1-ol ($CH_3CH_2CH_2OH$)

C propanal (CH_3CH_2CHO)

D propanoic acid ($CH_3CH_2CO_2H$)

Q12 Which of the following descriptions can be correctly applied to the homologous series of alkanes?

I Members of the series have the general formula C_nH_{2n+2}.

II Members of the series have similar chemical properties.

III Members of the series are isomers of each other.

A I only   **C** I and II only

B II only   **D** I and III only

Paper 2 IB questions and IB style questions

Q1 An alkane has the percentage composition 84.5% carbon and 15.5% hydrogen by mass.

a Calculate the empirical formula of the alkane. [2]

b The molecular mass of the alkane was found to be 142 using a mass spectrometer. What is the molecular formula? [2]

c i The hydrocarbon can be used as a fuel. Write the balanced equation for the complete combustion of this alkane in oxygen. [2]

ii Write a balanced equation for the incomplete combustion of this alkane in a limited supply of oxygen. [2]

d When a hydrocarbon is cracked, it is broken into smaller molecules. Complete the following cracking reactions:

i $C_8H_{18} \rightarrow C_4H_8 +$ _____ [1]

ii $C_{13}H_{28} \rightarrow C_4H_{10} + C_4H_8 +$ _____ [1]

Q2 a An organic compound, **A**, containing only the elements carbon, hydrogen and oxygen was analysed.

i **A** was found to contain 54.5% C and 9.1% H by mass, the remainder being oxygen. Determine the empirical formula of the compound. [3]

ii The molecular mass of **A** is 88. What is the molecular formula of **A**? [2]

b An organic compound **X** contains 40.00% carbon, 6.72% hydrogen and 53.28% oxygen by mass.

i Determine the empirical formula of compound **X**. [2]

ii Compound **X** has a relative molecular mass of 60.0. Deduce its molecular formula. [2]

Q3 a Give the structural formulas for the isomers of molecular formula C_4H_{10} and name each isomer. [4]

b Several compounds have the molecular formula $C_3H_6O_2$. Three of them, **A**, **B** and **C**, have the following properties:

A is soluble in water and is acidic.

B and **C** are neutral and do not react with bromine or organic acids.

Give a structural formula for each of these compounds and name them. [6]

c i Explain the solubility and acidity of **A** in water. [2]

ii Write an equation for the reaction of **A** with sodium hydroxide solution. [1]

iii Explain why **B** and **C** do not react with bromine. [1]

d State and explain which one of **A**, **B** or **C** has the highest boiling point. [2]

e i Name the class of compounds to which **B** and **C** belong and state a use of this class of compounds. [2]

ii Name the **two** classes of compounds used to form **B** or **C**, and state the other product formed in this reaction. [3]

f Suggest the structural formula of an isomer of $C_3H_6O_2$ which does react rapidly with bromine. Name this type of reaction, and describe an observation that can be made during the reaction. [3]

Q4 **a** **i** List **three** characteristics of a homologous series. [3]

ii Draw the **four** different structural isomers with the formula C_4H_9OH that are alcohols. [4]

b **i** Ethanoic acid reacts with ethanol in the presence of concentrated sulfuric acid and heat. Identify the type of reaction that takes place. Write an equation for the reaction, name the organic product formed and draw its structure. [4]

ii State and explain the role of sulfuric acid in this reaction. [2]

iii State **one** major commercial use of the organic product from this type of reaction. [1]

c Two compounds are shown below.

I $HCOOCH_2CH_3$ and **II** $HCOOCHCH_2$

i State and explain which of these two compounds can react readily with bromine. [2]

ii Compound **II** can form polymers. State the type of polymerization compound **II** can take part in, and draw the structure of the repeating unit of the polymer. [2]

Q5 **a** Name the following alcohols:

i $CH_3CH(OH)CH_3$

ii $CH_3CH_2CH_2OH$

iii $CH_3CH_2C(OH)(CH_3)CH_3$

iv $CH_2(OH)CH_2(OH)$ [4]

b For the four alcohols listed in **a**, state whether they are primary, secondary or tertiary alcohols. [4]

c If the alcohols in **a** are oxidized using acidified sodium dichromate(VI) under reflux, give the name and condensed structural formula of the organic product. [7]

Q6 One of the major chemistry-based industries in the world today, requiring high levels of investment in research and development but generating huge returns for successful products, is the global pharmaceutical industry. The products of this industry are of use in both human and vetinary medicine.

a Bute is a painkiller used on horses, but there has been concern recently that it may have entered the human food chain through horse meat labelled as beef. Analytical tests showed that the levels were minute and non-threatening to health (the drug is suspected of causing cancer).

i Elemental analysis of a sample of bute carried out in a food safety laboratory gave the following percentage composition by mass:

carbon, 73.99%; hydrogen, 6.55% nitrogen, 9.09%; oxygen, the remainder

Calculate the empirical formula of bute, showing your working. [3]

ii The molar mass, *M*, of bute is $308.37 \, g \, mol^{-1}$. Calculate the molecular formula. [1]

iii Deduce the index of hydrogen deficiency (IHD) or degree of unsaturation of bute. [1]

b Atorvastatin is a drug which has recently gained attention from the global media. It is used to lower the level of cholesterol in the bloodstream and has the structure shown below.

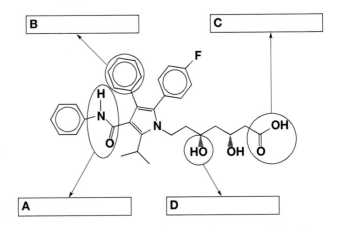

Identify the **four** functional groups, A, B, C and D formed in Atorvastatin. [2]

Measurement and data processing

11.1 Uncertainties and errors in measurements and results – *all measurement has a limit of precision and accuracy, and this must be taken into account when evaluating experimental results*

Qualitative data: observations

Qualitative data includes descriptions of observations before, during and after a chemical reaction. These may include differences in colour, solubility, physical nature or quantity of chemical substances. Other common observations may involve production of a gas, formation of a precipitate and release or absorption of heat. Observations may be recorded with a digital camera or video recorder (Figure 11.1).

Observations of qualitative variables such as colour should be recorded in simple language such as 'green' or 'orange'. Where fine discrimination is required, terms such as 'pale' or 'dark' should be used, and comparisons made such as 'darker orange than at 3 minutes' or 'paler green than at $0.20\,mol\,dm^{-3}$, but darker than at $0.40\,mol\,dm^{-3}$'. These types of data give information about changes in concentrations of coloured species.

Qualitative data is defined as data observed with more or less unaided senses (colour, change of state, etc.) or rather crude estimates (hotter, colder, pink, finely powdered black solid, etc.), whereas quantitative data implies numerical observations (i.e. actual measurements). Both types of data are important and required when describing and interpreting chemical reactions.

It should be noted that solutions may be described as colourless – there are no white or black solutions. A solution may appear white or black due to the presence of a precipitate or suspension. In some situations there may be a two layers: an aqueous solution and an immiscible organic layer. These should be described and the order recorded, for example 'colourless organic layer floats on water'.

Qualitative analysis involves identifying or classifying substances based on their chemical or physical properties. Examples include flame tests (Chapter 2) to identify metal ions and precipitation reactions to identify cations or anions, such as the halides (Chapter 3). The melting and boiling points of substances are commonly used to identify organic substances and detect the presence of impurities.

■ **Figure 11.1**
A photograph of the oscillating BZ reaction (a suitable Extended Essay topic)

Quantitative chemistry: uncertainty and error in measurement

Quantitative chemistry involves the measurement of physical properties, for example mass, volume, temperature, voltage, pH, density and absorbance. A measurement involves comparing the property of a substance with a known standard.

Practical chemistry during your IB chemistry programme will involve recording many types of measurements. Remember that when a measurement is recorded, there is *always* an experimental error or random uncertainty associated with the value. No experimental measurement can be exact.

SI units

SI stands for the International System of Units, which is abbreviated to SI from French (*le Système international d'unités*).

The SI base units relevant to the majority of IB chemical measurements and calculations are shown in Table 11.1.

Measurement	Unit	Symbol
Length	metre	m
Mass	kilogram	kg
Time	second	s
Amount	mole	mol
Electric current	ampere	A
Temperature	kelvin	K

Note the following points about the use of symbols:

■ Never add s to indicate a plural form, for example, 5 kg, not 5 kgs.

■ A full stop is not written after symbols, except at the end of a sentence.

■ Units named after a person have a capital letter for the first letter in their symbol, for example, Pa for Pascal.

■ When the name of the unit is written in full it has a small letter, for example, 5 newtons.

Derived units

A number of important SI derived units used in IB chemistry are shown in Table 11.2.

Measurement	Unit	Symbol
Frequency	hertz (reciprocal of seconds)	$Hz\ (s^{-1})$
Pressure	pascal (newton per square metre)	$Pa\ (N\,m^{-2})$
Energy or enthalpy	joule	J
Electrical charge	coulomb	C
Potential difference	volt	V
Specific heat capacity	joule per kilogram per kelvin	$J\,kg^{-1}\,K^{-1}$
Heat capacity	joule per kelvin	$J\,K^{-1}$
Entropy	joule per kelvin	$J\,K^{-1}$
Enthalpy change or Gibbs free energy change	joule per mole	$J\,mol^{-1}$
Density	kilogram per cubic metre	$kg\,m^{-3}$

Multiples of units

The sizes of the units are not always the most suitable for certain measurements and decimal multiples are often used (Table 11.3).

Coherence

The SI base and derived units make a coherent system of units, that is, all the units for the derived physical quantities are obtained from the base units by multiplication or division without the introduction of numerical factors. This simplifies many calculations.

Multiple	Prefix
10^{-12}	pico (p)
10^{-9}	nano (n)
10^{-6}	micro (μ)
10^{-3}	milli (m)
10^{-1}	deci (d)
10^{3}	kilo (k)
10^{6}	mega (M)

■ **Table 11.3** Prefixes for common multiples of units

1 Express the following in SI base units:
a $l = 25\,nm$
b $t = 4\,min\,5\,s$
c $m = 8\,mg$
d $T = 2\,°C$
e $V = 6\,cm^3$
f $p = 4\,MPa$
g $v = 14\,MHz$
h $\lambda = 295\,\mu m$

For example, the following calculation involving the ideal gas equation illustrates how numerical values for the volume, amount, gas constant and absolute temperature in coherent SI units give a value for pressure in coherent SI units, namely pascals.

If $R = 8.31\,J\,K^{-1}\,mol^{-1}$, $T = 300\,K$, $V = 6.34 \times 10^{-3}\,m^3$ and $n = 0.250$, then

$$p = \frac{nRT}{V} = \frac{0.250\,mol \times 8.31\,J\,K^{-1}\,mol^{-1} \times 300\,K}{6.34 \times 10^{-3}\,m^3} = 9.83 \times 10^4\,Pa$$

■ Random uncertainties and systematic errors

Errors or uncertainties can be caused by:

- imperfections in the apparatus used to record the measurement
- imperfections in the experimental method or procedure
- judgements made by the person operating the measuring apparatus.

There are two types of errors: random uncertainties and systematic errors.

Random uncertainties

A random uncertainty can make the measured value either smaller or larger than the true value. Chance alone determines if it is smaller or larger, and both are equally probable. Reading the scale of any instrument – balance, measuring cylinder, thermometer, pipette – produces random errors. Digital instruments, such as electronic balances and pH meters, also have random uncertainties. In other words, you can weigh a weighing bottle on a balance and get a slightly different answer each time simply due to random errors.

Random uncertainties *cannot* be avoided; they are part of the measuring process. Uncertainties are measures of random errors. These are errors incurred as a result of making measurements on imperfect apparatus which can only have a certain degree of accuracy. They are predictable, and the degree of error can be calculated. They can be reduced by repeating and *averaging* the measurement.

General examples where random uncertainties occur include:

- reading a scale (Figure 11.2)
- recording a digital readout
- taking a reading which changes with time.

■ Figure 11.2
Dual scale voltmeter showing two analogue scales

Random uncertainties are also known as random errors. However, the term 'error' has the everyday meaning of mistake. Random uncertainties are *not* due to mistakes and cannot be avoided.

Distinction between random errors and systematic errors

Random errors

In a series of repeated measurements, the sizes of the uncertainties are never the same. Some measurements may be higher than the true value, and others lower. These uncertainties associated with the measurements are random in nature as it is not possible to predict what the magnitude of the uncertainty is and whether it will be higher or lower than the true value in each measurement. Hence they are known as random uncertainties.

What is known is that the measurement will lie within a range of values from the true value, and this is termed the uncertainty range. The following are some examples of how some measurements are recorded with the uncertainty ranges:

- mass of magnesium = $(2.457 \pm 0.002)\,g$
- volume of $KMnO_4$ titrant = $(22.40 \pm 0.10)\,cm^3$
- temperature of $K_2CO_3(aq)$ = $(25.10 \pm 0.02)\,°C$

The random uncertainties are recorded with a '±' (plus-or-minus) after the measurements. The values that follow indicate the range that the measurements will lie within.

As each pair of measurement and uncertainty has the same unit, brackets (parentheses) are used, with the unit stated after the brackets.

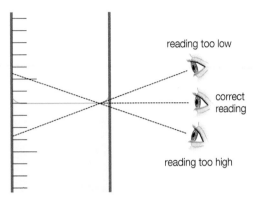

■ **Figure 11.3** Parallax error with a measuring cylinder

Systematic errors

Systematic errors arise from a problem within the experimental set-up or measuring device and they are usually very difficult to detect. They can arise from inaccurate calibration of an instrument or from a fault, either in the equipment or the procedure. Sometimes, a systematic error can also arise from an erroneous operation or from human reaction time.

Any glassware (e.g. burettes and pipettes) used for quantitative measurements is a potential source of systematic error. For example, a burette may have a mislabelled graduation or contain a small fragment of un-melted glass which produced an internal bump inside the burette. During the calibration process this defect will cause a systematic error in the delivered volume. It will be less than the stated volume. Similarly, consistently reading a measuring cylinder, for example, from too high or too low introduces another systematic error (parallax error) (Figure 11.3).

Where more sophisticated equipment is used, namely electronic measuring apparatus, systematic errors can come about as the result of low batteries, poor electrical contact within the device, sensitivity to temperature and humidity and even mechanical defects in the case of meter movements.

2 Deduce whether each of these operations results in a random or a systematic error.
   a Using a pipette calibrated at 20 °C to measure volumes of hot solutions at 85 °C.
   b Using a 50 cm³ measuring cylinder to measure 50.00 cm³ of solution.
   c Using 25 drops of phenolphthalein indicator in the titration between ammonia solution and sulfuric acid.
   d The melting point of ice is determined by the same data-logger temperature probe in three separate measurements to be 270.50 K, 270.20 K and 270.10 K.
   e An electronic balance reads 0.05 g too high for all three measurements of a weighing bottle with chemical.
   f A tape measure used to measure the circumference of a large copper calorimeter has been stretched out after years of use.

Ways to reduce uncertainties in an experiment

Random errors are 'two-sided' errors, because, in the absence of other types of errors, repeated measurements yield results that fluctuate above and below the true or accepted value. Measurements subject to random errors differ from each other due to random, unpredictable variations in the measurement process. The precision of measurements subject to random errors can be improved by repeating those measurements and averaging consistent results. Random errors are easily analysed by statistical analysis. Random errors can be easily detected, but can be reduced by repeating the measurement or by improving the measurement method or technique. Common sources of random errors are problems in estimating a quantity that lies between the graduations (the lines) on an instrument and the inability to read an instrument because the reading fluctuates during the measurement.

3 The following burette readings were obtained from an acid–base titration.

	1	2	3	4	5
Final burette reading/cm³	24.25	46.85	25.25	28.30	24.35
Initial burette reading/cm³	0.00	22.25	0.55	25.00	0.10
Volume of sodium carbonate solution used/cm³	24.25	24.60	24.70	23.30	24.25

With reference to the set of data shown in the table above, explain how random error can be reduced in the titration. Find out how a *Q* test can be used to statistically identify outliers (note that this is not a syllabus requirement).

Design and analysis of drug trials

There are many sources of error, both random and systematic, in collecting clinical data from patients involved in drug trials.

The wide variation in the human population leads to relatively large random variation in clinical trials. This is reduced by having a large sample of patients and applying a range of statistical tests on the data.

There are many potential sources of bias or systematic error in drug trials. For example, selection bias refers to selecting a sample that is not representative of the population because of the method used to select the sample. Selection bias in the study group can reduce the validity of the results.

Suppose a researcher decides to use only hospital employees in a study to evaluate a drug intended to treat asthma. This sample is not likely to be representative of the general population. The hospital employees may be more health conscious and conscientious in taking medications than others. They may also be more effective at managing their surroundings to prevent attacks.

One approach is to also test the asthma drug on a control group who have been sampled randomly. Randomized controls increase the validity of a study.

There are three main types of clinical trial: blind, double-blind (the most common) and open-label. In blind and double-blind trials one group of volunteers, called the test group, receives the new drug. Another, the control group, receives the existing drug for that illness. If there is no existing treatment, the control group is given a fake drug that has no effect on the body. This is called a placebo. The researchers look for differences between the experimental group and the control group.

Blind trials

In a blind trial, the volunteers do not know which group they are in but the researchers or doctors do. The problem is that the researchers may give away clues to the volunteers without being aware. This is called observer bias; it can make the results unreliable.

Double-blind trials

In a double-blind trial (Figure 11.4), the volunteers or patients do not know which group they are in, and neither do the researchers or doctors, until the end of the trial. This removes the chance of bias and makes the results more reliable.

■ **Figure 11.4**
Double-blind trial

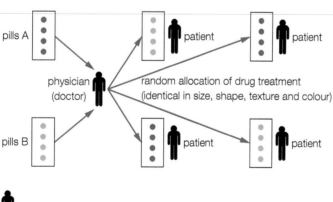

study manager for drug

Open-label trials

In an open-label trial the patient and doctor both know the treatment. This type of trial happens when there is no other treatment and the patients are so ill that doctors believe they will not recover from their illnesses. This type of trial is usually carried out with HIV or cancer patients.

Evaluating the quality of measurements

Evaluating the quality of measurements is an essential step in drawing scientific conclusions. Scientists use a special vocabulary that helps them think clearly about their data. Key terms that describe the quality of measurements are accuracy and precision. Accuracy describes how closely a measurement comes to the true value of a physical quantity. Precision gives the closeness of agreement between replicate measurements on the same or similar objects under specified conditions. The difference between accuracy and precision is shown in Figure 11.5.

■ **Figure 11.5**
Accuracy versus precision

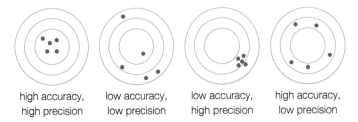

| high accuracy, high precision | low accuracy, low precision | low accuracy, high precision | high accuracy, low precision |

Reporting random uncertainty as an uncertainty range

Random uncertainties of measured quantities are reported as an uncertainty range. For example, a length may be reported as (5.2 ± 0.5) cm, which means that actual length is located between 4.7 and 5.7 cm. The last digit in the measurement is effectively an estimate. Generally, random uncertainties are expressed to one significant figure only. However, the random error or uncertainty should not have more decimal places than the absolute value and *vice versa*.

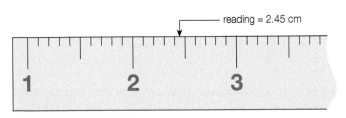

reading = 2.45 cm

■ **Figure 11.6** A single reading obtained from a metre ruler

A reading is the single determination of a value at one point on a measuring scale. *Generally*, a reading can be estimated to one-half of the smallest division (least count) on a measuring scale. In the case of the ruler in Figure 11.6, half of the smallest division (least count) would be 0.5 mm or 0.05 cm. Hence the value of the reading is 2.45 cm. The maximum range within which the reading will lie is between 24.0 mm and 25.0 mm or 2.40 cm to 2.50 cm.

The *least count* is the smallest division that is marked on the scale of the apparatus. For example, a 50 cm³ burette will have a least count of 0.1 cm³, and an electronic chemical balance giving up to three decimal places of a gram (e.g. 1 g reads as 1.000 g) will have a least count of 0.001 g, that is, 1 mg. For a digital reading, such as on an electronic balance, the random uncertainty is the least count. Hence, the random uncertainties in this burette and this balance may be reported as ± 0.05 cm³ and ± 0.001 g.

It is usually not justified to specify the random error or uncertainty to more than two significant digits; often one is enough. The random error or uncertainty cannot have more decimal places than the absolute value and *vice versa*. It is a mistake to write $x = (56.7 \pm 0.914606)$ cm, or $x = (56.74057 \pm 0.9)$ cm. Instead, write $x = (56.7 \pm 0.9)$ cm. You cannot increase either the accuracy or precision by extending the number of digits in your mean value beyond the decimal place occupied by the error.

Absolute random errors can be used to decide whether or not your experimental errors are in agreement to within experimental error or uncertainty. For example, the two measurements 9.5 ± 0.2 cm and 10.3 ± 0.2 cm do not have overlapping ranges. Hence taking into account experimental uncertainty the two measurements do not agree. However, the two measurements 9.7 ± 0.3 cm and 10.3 ± 0.3 cm do agree when the experimental error or uncertainty is taken into account, since the uncertainty or error ranges now overlap.

4 State the implied absolute random uncertainty in the following measurements:
   a 50.04 g (on an electronic balance)
   b 5.000 s (on a computer controlled timer without human reaction time)
   c A speedometer that is reading 60 miles per hour (with an uncertainty of ± 5%)
   d 30.1 mm (with a measurement to the nearest tenth of a millimetre)
   e An absorbance value (no units) that reads on a scale to two decimal places

Accuracy of glassware

Uncertainty is often taken to be half a division on either side of the smallest unit on the scale. However, the accuracy of measurements also depends on the quality of the glassware used, for example, Class A and Class B glassware. Class B volumetric glassware usually has ± ml errors or random uncertainties greater (often twice) than those of Class A glassware. For example, for Class A and Class B 100 cm^3 volumetric flasks the uncertainties are Class A ± 0.08 ml and Class B ± 0.20 ml (Figure 11.7).

▮ Uncertainties in calculated results

Absolute and percentage uncertainties

For IB chemistry investigations, estimated uncertainties should be indicated for all measurements. These uncertainties may be estimated in different ways:

▪ from the smallest division on a scale

▪ from the last significant figure in a digital measurement

▪ from data provided by the manufacturer.

The amount of uncertainty attached to a reading is usually expressed in the same units as the reading. This is the absolute uncertainty, for example, 25.4 ± 0.1 s. (The mathematical symbol for absolute uncertainty is δx, where x represents the measurement; in the example, $x = 25.4$ and $\delta x = 0.1$.)

The absolute uncertainty is often converted to a percentage uncertainty. For the example, this would be 25.4 s ± 0.4% $\left(\text{since } \dfrac{0.1\,\text{s}}{25.4\,\text{s}} \times 100 = 0.4\%\right)$.

(The mathematical symbol for fractional uncertainty is $\delta x / x$.)

Note that uncertainties are themselves approximate and are generally not reported to more than one significant figure, so the percentage uncertainty is reported as 0.4%, not 0.39370%.

The last significant figure in a measurement should be in the same place as the uncertainty. For example, 1261.29 mA ± 200 mA is incorrect, but 1300 mA ± 200 mA is correct. Since the uncertainly is stated to the hundreds place, we also state the answer to the hundreds place. Note that the uncertainty determines the number of significant figures in the answer.

Calculations involving uncertainties

▪ When adding or subtracting uncertain values, add the absolute uncertainties:

   initial temperature = (34.50 ± 0.05) °C

   final temperature = (45.21 ± 0.05) °C

   change in temperature, ΔT = 45.21 − 34.50 = 10.71 °C (± 0.05 + 0.05 = ± 0.1 °C)

Hence, the change in temperature, ΔT, should be reported as (10.7 ± 0.1) °C.

▪ When multiplying or dividing, add the percentage uncertainties:

   mass = (9.240 ± 0.005) g and volume = (14.10 ± 0.05) cm^3

Perform the calculation:

$$\text{density} = \frac{9.240\,\text{g}}{14.10\,\text{cm}^3} = 0.655\,\text{g cm}^{-3}$$

▪ Figure 11.7
Class B 500 cm^3
volumetric flask

Convert the absolute uncertainties to percentage uncertainties:

$$mass = \frac{0.005}{9.24} \times 100 = 0.054\% \text{ and volume} = \frac{0.05}{14.10} \times 100 = 0.35\%$$

Add the percentage uncertainties:

$$0.054\% + 0.35\% = 0.40\%; \text{ density} = 0.655\,g\,cm^{-3}\,(\pm\,0.40\%)$$

Convert the total uncertainty back to an absolute uncertainty:

$$0.655 \times \frac{0.40}{100} = 0.00262; \text{ density} = (0.655 \pm 0.003)\,g\,cm^{-3}$$

- When multiplying or dividing by a pure (whole) number, multiply or divide the uncertainty by that number:

$$(4.95 \pm 0.05) \times 10 = 49.5 \pm 0.5$$

- When raising to the *n*th power, multiply the percentage uncertainty by *n*. When extracting the *n*th root, divide the percentage uncertainty by *n*.

$$(4.3 \pm 0.5\,cm)^3 = 4.3^3 \pm \left(\frac{0.5}{4.3}\right) \times 3$$

$$= 79.5\,cm^3\,(\pm\,0.349\%)$$

$$= (79.5 \pm 0.3)\,cm^3$$

- Averaging: repeated measurements can lead to an average value for a calculated quantity. The final answer could be given to the propagated error of the component values in the average. For example:

$$\text{average } \Delta H_c^{\ominus} = [+100\,kJ\,mol^{-1}\,(\pm\,10\%) + 110\,kJ\,mol^{-1}\,(\pm\,10\%) + 108\,kJ\,mol^{-1}\,(\pm\,10\%)] \div 3$$

$$= 106\,kJ\,mol^{-1}\,(\pm\,10\%)$$

This is more appropriate than adding the percentage errors to generate 30%, since that would grossly exaggerate the error and be contrary to the purpose of repeating and averaging measurements.

---

5   Add or subtract the following expressions:
   a $(25.02 \pm 0.02) + (4.70 \pm 0.02)$
   b $(15.37 \pm 0.01) - (5.31 \pm 0.01)$
   c $(0.056 \pm 0.002) + (1.143 \pm 0.005)$
   d $(3.8 \pm 0.5) - (1.3 \pm 0.2)$

6   Determine the percentage errors in the following:
   a 2.57 ± 0.20
   b 17.49 ± 0.04
   c 0.00426 ± 0.00005
   d 943 ± 2

7   Determine the error resulting from the following calculations:
   a $(2.0\,m \pm 1.0\%)^3$
   b $\sqrt{(2.0m \pm 1.05)}$
   c $1.5 \times (2.0 \pm 0.2)\,m$
   d $1.5 \times (2.0 \pm 1.0\%)\,m$

Propagation of uncertainties in processed data, and percentage uncertainties

> ### Worked examples
>
> The following weighings were made during an experiment.
>
> Mass of empty weighing bottle and hydrated copper(II) sulfate crystals = $(6.721 \pm 0.001)\,g$
>
> Mass of empty weighing bottle = $(5.221 \pm 0.001)\,g$
>
> Calculate the mass of hydrated copper(II) sulfate and determine the percentage uncertainty in its mass.
>
> Mass of hydrated copper(II) sulfate crystals weighed = $(1.500 \pm 0.002)\,g$
>
> Percentage uncertainty for the mass = $\frac{0.002}{1.500} \times 100\% = 0.1333\% = 0.14\%$ (rounded upwards)

(200.00 ± 0.05) g of glucose is dissolved in (500.00 ± 0.10) cm³ of distilled water. Find its concentration in grams per cubic decimetre, g cm⁻³.

Absolute value calculation	Percentage uncertainty determination
Mass of glucose = (200.00 ± 0.05) g [2 decimal points (dp) and 5 significant figures (sf)]	Percentage uncertainty in mass reading of glucose = $\dfrac{0.05}{200.00} \times 100\% = 0.025\%$
Volume of solution = (500.00 ± 0.10) cm³ [2 dp and 5 sf]	Percentage uncertainty in volume reading $= \dfrac{0.10}{500.00} \times 100\% = 0.020\%$
Concentration of glucose solution = $\dfrac{200.00}{500.00}$ = 0.40000 g cm⁻³ (5 sf)	Percentage uncertainty of glucose concentration = 0.025% + 0.020% = 0.045%

Absolute uncertainty of glucose concentration = 0.4000 × 0.45%
= 0.00018 g cm⁻³

So, concentration of glucose = (0.40000 ± 0.00018) g cm⁻³

The volume, *V*, of an ideal gas is given by the following equation:

$$V = \frac{nRT}{p}$$

where *n* is the amount of moles of the gas, *T* is the absolute temperature in kelvins (K), and *p* is the pressure of the gas in pascals (Pa). (1 Pa = 1 J m⁻³).

Calculate the volume of the ideal gas to the appropriate number of significant figures and decimal places for *n* = 2.505 moles, *T* = 298.05 K and *p* = 101 325 Pa using the following values for *R*, the gas constant.

a $R = 8.3\,J\,mol^{-1}\,K^{-1}$ **b** $R = 8.314\,J\,mol^{-1}\,K^{-1}$

a $V = \dfrac{2.505\,mol \times 8.3\,J\,mol^{-1}\,K^{-1} \times 298.05\,K}{101\,325\,Pa} = 0.061158712 = 0.061\,m^3$ (2 sf)

b $V = \dfrac{2.505\,mol \times 8.314\,J\,mol^{-1}\,K^{-1} \times 298.05\,K}{101\,325\,Pa} = 0.0116\,m^3$ (4 sf)

Guide to the Expression of Uncertainty in Measurement

Over the years, many different approaches to evaluating and expressing the uncertainty of measurement results have been used. Because of this lack of international agreement on the expression of uncertainty in measurement, in 1977 the International Committee for Weights and Measures (CIPM, *Comité International des Poids et Mesures*), the world's highest authority in the field of measurement science (i.e. metrology), asked the International Bureau of Weights and Measures (BIPM, *Bureau International des Poids et Mesures*), to address the problem in collaboration with the various national metrology institutes and to propose a specific recommendation for its solution. The end result of the work of ISO/TAG 4/WG 3 is the 100-page *Guide to the Expression of Uncertainty in Measurement* (or GUM as it is now often called). It was published in 1993 (corrected and reprinted in 1995) by the ISO in the name of the seven international organizations that supported its development in ISO/TAG 4, including the IUPAC.

ToK Link

Science has been described as a self-correcting and communal public endeavour. To what extent do these characteristics also apply to the other areas of knowledge?

One of the most valuable aspects of science is the self-correcting nature of its methodology. Science is concerned with finding knowledge about the physical world. However, this knowledge is always provisional and is always open to revision or even falsification based upon new data, and this is – contrary to what some might think – one of its greatest strengths. What science can do is approach, although slowly and asymptotically, an increasingly accurate view of the physical world around us as a result.

This ability of science to always be open to new data and theories, to be capable of being revised or even having a paradigm shift, is perhaps in opposition to the kind of rigid thought which may be present in some other areas of knowledge, for example politics and religion.

Science is a human endeavour and prone to making mistakes. In fact, the history of science is full of errors, failed experiments, and even outright fraud and fabrication of raw data; but the self-correcting nature of modern science via publications and conferences ensures that these are discarded.

It was scientists who exposed the false findings behind the cold fusion case in 1989, when a pair of researchers (Martin Fleischmann and Stanley Pons) publicly claimed (mistakenly) that they had produced fusion and heat production during the electrolysis of heavy water; it was careful and persistent application of scientific methodology that identified the errors in the claim from CERN that neutrinos were superluminal and could travel faster than light.

There are a number of methods for determining the value of the Avogadro constant. Several methods were outlined in Chapter 1 and all should give the same value. The value of the Avogadro constant has changed over the years with different methods and with the refining of each approach, as shown in Table 11.4. Avogadro's constant is connected to a number of physical values including the Faraday constant.

The changes in the value of Avogadro's constant obviously provide a good example of how science is a self-correcting and public endeavour by scientists.

Year	Source	Method	Value
1901	Planck	R/k, where R is the gas constant and k is the Boltzmann constant	6.175×10^{23}
1924	PL du Nouy	Thin oil film	6.004×10^{23}
1908	Einstein	Diffusion in fluids	6.56×10^{23}
1909	Rutherford	Alpha particle theory	6.16×10^{23}
1917	RA Millikan	Oil drop method	6.064×10^{23}
1932	JA Bearden	Crystal (X-ray crystallography)	6.019×10^{23}
2011	BIPM	Crystal (X-ray crystallography)	$6.02214078 \times 10^{23}$

■ **Table 11.4** The measurement of the Avogadro constant

8   The alpha particles emitted in the radioactive decay of radium-226 can be counted by means of a Geiger counter. Each alpha particle (helium nucleus) gains electrons to form helium gas. It is found that 1.82×10^{17} alpha particles give 6.75×10^{-3} cm^{-3} of helium, measured at standard temperature and pressure (STP). Using any data required from the *IB Chemistry data booklet* calculate a value for the Avogadro constant, L.

$$^{226}_{88}Ra \longrightarrow\ ^{222}_{86}Rn + ^{4}_{2}He$$

Combining errors in independent measurements in quadrature

The approach to error propagation described previously involves the combination of individual errors or uncertainties in sums or differences to give an overall error that is too pessimistic (too high). It is unlikely that the individual errors or uncertainties will both be in the same direction, though not of course, impossible. An alternative method of propagating errors is known as 'summing in quadrature'.

If $X = A + B$ or $X = A - B$, then $\Delta x = \sqrt{(\Delta A)^2 + (\Delta B)^2}$

The expression is the same whether the quantities are added or subtracted. If more than two quantities are involved, the expression is simply extended in a similar way:

If $X = A + B + C$ or $X = A - B - C$, then $\Delta x = \sqrt{(\Delta A)^2 + (\Delta B)^2 + (\Delta C)^2}$

The resulting overall error or uncertainty is always larger than any of the individual errors, but not as large as their sum. If two very similar values are subtracted, the resulting error or uncertainty can be large.

Worked examples

The initial temperature of a solution was $(18.2 \pm 0.2)\,°C$ and the final temperature was $(25.4 \pm 0.2)\,°C$. Calculate the temperature rise and its error or uncertainty.

$\Delta T = (T_2 - T_1) \pm \Delta T;\ \Delta T = (25.4 - 18.2) = 7.2 \pm \Delta T\,°C$

The overall error or uncertainty is given by the following expression:

$\Delta T = \sqrt{(\Delta T_1)^2 + (\Delta T_2)^2} = \sqrt{(0.2\,°C)^2 + (0.2\,°C)^2} = 0.28\,°C$

Hence, $\Delta T = (7.2 \pm 0.3)\,°C$

In an experiment to measure a quantity, ΔQ, two values $Q_1 = (90 \pm 2)$ and $Q_2 = (82 \pm 2)$, were obtained. Determine the value and associated uncertainty of $Q_1 - Q_2$.

$Q_1 - Q_2 = (90 - 82) \pm \Delta Q$

$\Delta Q = \sqrt{(\Delta Q_1)^2 + (\Delta Q_2)^2} = \sqrt{2^2 + 2^2} = 2.8$

Hence $Q_1 - Q_2 = 8 \pm 3$

If errors or uncertainties need to be propagated in ratios or products:

$$\text{If } X = AB \text{ or } X = \frac{A}{B}, \text{ then } \frac{\Delta X}{X} = \sqrt{\left(\frac{\Delta A}{A}\right)^2 + \left(\frac{\Delta B}{B}\right)^2}$$

As previously noted, the percentage or fractional errors need to be used when dealing with products or ratios.

Worked example

Tin reacts on heating with iodine (in an organic solvent) to give tin iodide of formula SnI_x. In an experiment to determine x, $(6.00 \pm 0.01)\,g$ of iodine was found to have reacted with $(1.40 \pm 0.01)\,g$ of tin. Determine the value of x.

Amount of iodine atoms $= \dfrac{(6.00 \pm 0.01)\,g}{126.90\,g\,mol^{-1}}$

Amount of tin atoms $= \dfrac{(1.40 \pm 0.01)\,g}{118.71\,g\,mol^{-1}}$

Therefore $x = \dfrac{[(6.00 \pm 0.01)\,g / 126.90\,g\,mol^{-1}]}{[(1.40 \pm 0.01)\,g / 118.71\,g\,mol^{-1}]}$

$x = 4.01 \pm \Delta x$

The molar masses can be regarded as constants (though they are experimentally determined), so it is only necessary to calculate the errors in the mass of the tin and iodine.

$\dfrac{\Delta x}{x} = \sqrt{\left(\dfrac{0.01\,g}{3.00\,g}\right)^2 + \left(\dfrac{0.01\,g}{0.70\,g}\right)^2} = 0.015$

Therefore $\Delta x = 0.015x = 0.06$, so $x = 4.01 \pm 0.06$

■ Systematic errors

A systematic error makes the measured value always smaller or larger than the true value, but not both. In other words, a systematic error causes a bias in an experimental measurement in one direction, but always in the same direction. For example, all volumetric glassware is usually calibrated at $20\,°C$. Thus, when this equipment is used at any other temperature, a small systematic error is introduced. An experiment may involve more than one systematic error and these errors may cancel one another, but each alters the true value in one way only.

Accuracy (or validity) is a measure of the systematic error. If an experiment is accurate or valid then the systematic error is very small. Accuracy is a measure of how well an experiment measures what it was trying to measure. This is difficult to evaluate unless you have an idea of the expected value (e.g. a textbook value or a calculated value from a data book). Compare your experimental value to the literature value. If it is within the margin of error for the random errors, then it is most likely that the systematic errors are smaller than the random errors. If it is larger, then you need to determine where the systematic errors have occurred.

General examples of systematic errors include:

■ non-zero reading on a meter (a zero error) (Figures 11.8 and 11.9)
■ incorrectly calibrated scale
■ reaction time of experimenter.

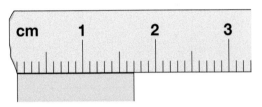

■ **Figure 11.8** Zero error with a metre rule

■ **Figure 11.9** An ammeter reading with a zero error of about –2 A

Zero errors can be avoided by checking for a 'zero reading' before starting the investigation or by recording the measurement with two separate pieces of apparatus and checking that the readings agree (within experimental error). To correct for a zero error the value should be subtracted from every reading. For example, a balance with a zero error of –0.2 g reports a mass of 100.0 g. The true mass (ignoring the random uncertainty) is 100.2 g.

Specific examples of systematic chemical errors include:

■ leaking gas syringes
■ calibration errors in pH meters and balances
■ use of equipment outside its appropriate operating range
■ changes in external influences, such as temperature and atmospheric pressure, which affect the measurement of gas volumes
■ volatile liquids evaporating
■ slow chemical reactions that make it difficult to judge end-points accurately
■ interfering reactions where a chemical species reacts with the titrant
■ retention or loss of chemicals
■ poor or no insulation during experiments involving calorimeters
■ loss of enzyme activity.

■ Specific examples of chemical systematic and random errors

Consider a simple titration where a solution of sodium hydroxide is prepared from its solid. A sample of the solution is then titrated against hydrochloric acid in the presence of a suitable acid–base indicator (Chapter 1).

Systematic errors

■ Sodium hydroxide is not a primary standard and absorbs water vapour and carbon dioxide from the atmosphere.
■ Sodium hydroxide is left behind in the weighing bottle.

Random errors (some of these can be systematic too)

■ Judgements about whether the indicator has changed colour.
■ Judgements about whether the bottom of the meniscus is touching the calibration line on a pipette.

- Temperature variations in the glassware and solutions.
- Random uncertainties in the measurement of the mass of sodium hydroxide.
- Random uncertainties in the measurement of the volumes of sodium hydroxide and hydrochloric acid.

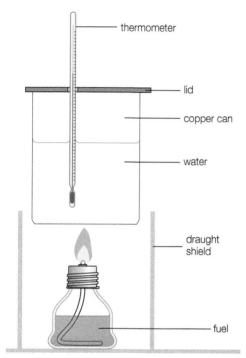

thermometer

lid

copper can

water

draught shield

fuel

■ **Figure 11.10** An approximate method for determining the enthalpy of combustion of a liquid hydrocarbon or alcohol

Consider a simple investigation where small known masses of alcohols are burnt in a spirit burner placed underneath a copper can acting as a calorimeter (Figure 11.10). The masses of the alcohols and the water in the calorimeter are both determined using an electronic balance. The temperature of the water is measured before and after the combustion.

Systematic errors

- A large proportion of the heat released by the burning alcohol will be lost to the surrounding air.
- Some heat will be lost from the water; some will be used to heat up the thermometer.
- Some alcohol and water may evaporate.

Random errors (some of these can be systematic too)

- Random uncertainties in the measurement of the masses of the alcohols and water.
- Random uncertainties in the measurement of the temperatures of the water before and after combustion of the alcohol.

Systematic and random uncertainty errors can often be recognized from a graph of the results (Figure 11.11).

Systematic errors may be constant errors or proportional errors. For example, consider a gravimetric determination of sulfate, where a precipitate of barium sulfate is formed in a $400\,cm^3$ solution. It is expected that in the transfer process that the same reasons for loss of sample are present at all stages. It is expected that approximately the same amount of barium sulfate might be lost regardless of the mass of the sample. A constant error is an error that does not change with the size of the sample. Hence a large sample mass would be preferred over a small sample mass, because such a constant error will produce a smaller relative error when using a larger sample.

■ **Figure 11.11** Perfect results (no errors), random uncertainties and systematic errors (positive bias) of two proportional quantities

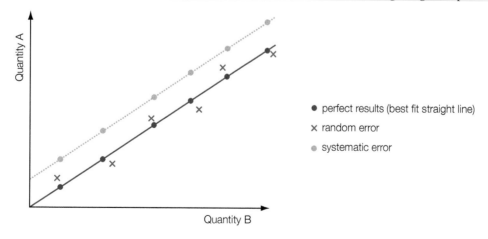

Quantity A

Quantity B

- perfect results (best fit straight line)
- × random error
- systematic error

A proportional error is any error that is proportional to the quantity of the sample. Contaminating chemicals that interfere with the reaction to be used in analysis will cause proportional errors because the absolute size of the error increases with the size of the sample. For example, the presence of iron in a sample of brass can interfere with the reduction of copper during the analysis of brass with potassium iodide.

Calculating percentage error when the experimental result can be compared with a theoretical or accepted result

Systematic errors are difficult to evaluate unless you have an idea of the expected or true value (for example a textbook value or a calculated value from a data book). Compare your experimental value to the literature value. If it is within the range of error for the random uncertainties then it is most likely that the systematic errors are smaller than the random uncertainties. If it is larger, then you will need to determine where the systematic errors have occurred.

For example, consider a student who has determined via a back titration using sodium hydroxide (Chapter 1) the molar mass of an organic acid (molar mass $126\,g\,mol^{-1}$). The total experimental uncertainty is calculated to be 1.5%. The student's experimentally determined value for the organic acid is $(130 \pm 2)\,g\,mol^{-1}$. This means that the student's result lies between 132 and $128\,g\,mol^{-1}$.

$$\text{The percentage error} = \frac{130 - 126}{126} \times 100 = 3.2\%$$

The percentage error is greater than the sum of the all random uncertainties present in the measurements recorded during the titration. Hence, there are systematic errors present in the investigation, for example the sodium hydroxide solution may have absorbed carbon dioxide from the air, thus reducing the concentration of hydroxide ions.

Discussing systematic errors in experimental work, their impact on the results and how they can be reduced

Consider the analysis of copper in brass (a mixture of copper and zinc) by dissolving brass in concentrated nitric acid followed by the addition of excess iodide ions. Iodine is produced in an amount equivalent to that of the oxidizing agent (Cu^{2+}) present in the sample. The liberated iodine is then titrated with sodium thiosulfate.

$$Cu(s) + 4HNO_3(l) \rightarrow Cu^{2+}(aq) + 2NO_2(g) + 2H_2O(l) + 2NO_3^-(aq)$$

Nitrogen dioxide is an oxidizing agent and can oxidize iodide ions (I^-) to iodine (I_2), a potential positive systematic error for the copper(II) determination. Thus, the nitrogen oxides must be removed from solution prior to the titration by warming the solution. Residual nitrogen oxides are removed by the addition of urea:

$$2NO_2(g) + H_2O(l) \rightarrow HNO_2(aq) + HNO_3(aq);$$

$$2HNO_3(aq) + (NH_2)_2CO(aq) \rightarrow 2N_2(g) + CO_2(g) + 3H_2O(l)$$

Iron (Fe(III)) is present in most brasses and can also oxidize iodide ions. This interference can be eliminated by addition of sodium fluoride, which forms a stable complex with iron(III) ions but not with copper(I) ions, preventing iron from reaction with iodide but not affecting the reaction between copper(II) ions and iodide ions.

Excess potassium iodide is then added to the solution. Copper(II) ions react with an equivalent amount of iodide to produce iodine and copper(I) iodide:

$$2Cu^{2+}(aq) + 4I^-(aq) \rightarrow Cu_2I_2(s) + I_2(aq)$$

In the presence of excess I^-, I_2 is partially present in the form of triiodide (I_3^-). This complex formation is helpful in that it stabilizes the iodine in solution and minimizes its loss through volatilization. Other means of reducing losses of the volatile iodine include keeping the temperature low and titrating quickly.

---

9 Consider an experiment to determine the empirical formula of a compound of magnesium and oxygen by weighing a known mass of magnesium in a crucible and combusting in air to form magnesium oxide which is weighed (Chapter 1). List all the possible systematic and random errors in this experiment.

Precision and accuracy

If the measurement is repeated several times and values are obtained which are close together, then the results are said to be precise. If the same student obtained these results, then the method or procedure is said to be repeatable. If the same method or procedure was carried out by a number of different students, then the method or procedure can be said to be reproducible. If the results are close to the true value, then the results are described as accurate. The differences between accuracy and precision are summarized in Figures 11.12 and 11.13.

■ **Figure 11.12**
a Precise and accurate readings; **b** imprecise but accurate readings (where *T* represents the true value)

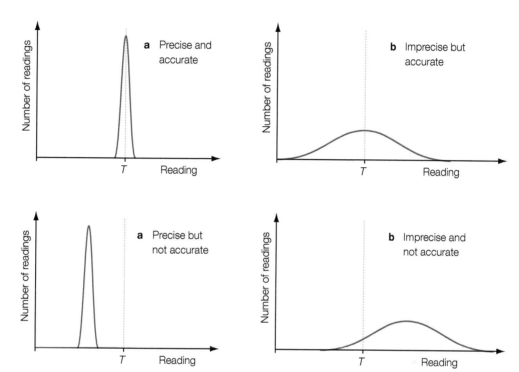

■ **Figure 11.13**
a Precise but not accurate readings; **b** imprecise and not accurate readings (where *T* represents the true value)

A mercury thermometer could measure the normal boiling point of pure water as (99.5 ± 0.5) °C whereas a data-logging probe recorded it as (98.25 ± 0.05) °C. In this example the mercury thermometer is more accurate whereas the data-logging probe has a greater resolution. Resolution characterizes the ability of the instrument's output or display to show changes in the measured quantity. It is formally defined as the smallest change in the measured quantity that the instrument can detect. For digital instruments, resolution is associated with the number of digits displayed on the output. Instrument precision is often associated with instrument resolution but an instrument can have great resolution but poor precision.

Resolution is also related to how closely you can read the divisions on the scale of an instrument or measuring device. For example, a metre rule is sometimes divided into centimetre measurements, but a 30 cm ruler is commonly divided into millimetre measurements (Figure 11.14). This means that the 30 cm ruler if used correctly (for repeated measurements) should be more precise (× 10) than the metre rule – it has smaller divisions.

When measuring liquids that have a curve at the surface, you must measure from the bottom or top of the meniscus (Figure 11.15), depending on the liquid. The meniscus is the curve formed at the surface of a liquid due to attraction of the liquid for the sides of the container. The curve will be convex for water and aqueous solutions; it is concave for mercury.

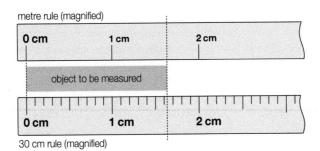

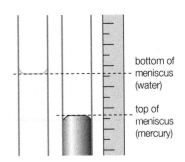

■ **Figure 11.14** Rulers for measurement

■ **Figure 11.15** The correct approach to accurately reading the meniscuses of water (left) and mercury (right)

Incorrect technique can lead to the recording of measurements which are precise but inaccurate. For example, suppose a student consistently reads the top of the meniscus in a pipette, burette or measuring cylinder when recording volumes used. These measurements may be precise but are inaccurate. However, if measurements are taken of the initial volume and the volume after adding or removing liquid and their *difference* is recorded, then the two systematic errors will cancel.

The measurement of an object on an electronic balance will fluctuate. If this occurs, start with the numbers that are not fluctuating and then make your best guess as to what the next digit would be. For example, consider the following electronic balance readings:

$$13.345\,g \quad 13.320\,g \quad 13.349\,g \quad 13.357\,g \quad 13.327\,g$$

This measurement could then be reported as 13.34 g.

Precise measurements have small random errors (uncertainties) and are reproducible in repeated trials of experiments; accurate measurements have small systematic errors and give a result close to the true or accepted value. If a large number of measurements are made of the same quantity, the readings will all lie on a normal or Gaussian distribution curve as shown in Figure 11.16.

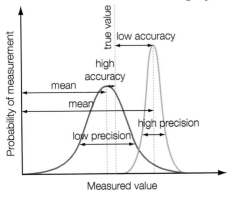

■ **Figure 11.16** Accuracy and precision

---

10 Four stopwatches are used to measure a time span. Their displays record:
  a 46 s   b 43 s   c 44.189 s   d 45.624 s.
  The exact, true, or actual time span is 45.623451 s. What be deduced about the accuracy, precision, and resolution of each stopwatch?

■ ## Reducing the effect of random uncertainty

Small random errors occur during all practical investigations and are beyond the control of the person recording the measurements. However, the effect of random errors can be reduced by carrying out repeated measurements. The average value from a set of repeated measurements should give a better estimate of the true value of the measurement. Systematic errors cannot be reduced by averaging and can be corrected for only when a true value (such as the value assigned to a calibration or reference specimen) is known.

Averages of non-linear measurements

If the measurement scale is *not* linear, simple averages may give a false value. For example, if three solutions have pH values of 7, 8 and 9, the mean pH is *not* 8 because the pH scale is logarithmic: $pH = -\log_{10} [H^+(aq)]$ (Chapter 18). To obtain the true mean, the pH values should be converted to hydrogen ion concentrations ($[H^+(aq)] = 10^{-pH}$), the mean calculated and then converted back to a pH value.

In this case, average $[H^+(aq)] = \dfrac{(10^{-7} + 10^{-8} + 10^{-9})}{3} = 3.7 \times 10^{-8}$; average pH = 7.4

Estimating whether a particular source of error is likely to have a major or minor effect on the final result

The object of a good experiment is to minimize both the errors of precision and the errors of accuracy. Usually, a given experiment has one or the other type of error dominant, and the experimenter devotes the most effort towards reducing that one. For example, in titrating a sample of hydrochloric acid with sodium hydroxide base using a phenolphthalein indicator, the major error in the determination of the original concentration of the acid is likely to be one of the following: (1) the accuracy of the markings on the side of the burette; (2) the transition range of the phenolphthalein indicator; or (3) the skill of the experimenter in dividing the last drop of base. Thus, the accuracy of the determination is likely to be much worse than the precision; this is often the case for experiments in chemistry.

■ Significant figures

Experimental measurements always have some uncertainty associated with them. One method of expressing the uncertainty in a measurement is to express it in terms of significant figures. In this method, it is assumed that all the digits are known with certainty except the last digit, which is uncertain. Hence, a measurement is expressed in terms of a number which includes all digits which are certain and a last digit which is uncertain. The total number of digits in the number is called the number of significant figures.

The concept of significant figures is illustrated in Figure 11.17, which shows a magnified part of a thermometer scale. The temperature is obviously between 18.5 °C and 19.0 °C but three significant figures are justified. Reporting the temperature to three significant figures as 18.7 °C indicates that there is uncertainty in the final figure.

■ **Figure 11.17**
A magnified thermometer scale

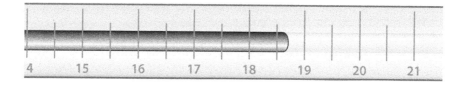

■ **Table 11.5** Masses with associated random uncertainties and significant figures

Measured value	Precision of measurement	Random uncertainty in the measurement	Significant figures of measured value
3 g	1 g	±0.5 g	1
3.1 g	0.1 g	±0.05 g	2
2.53 g	0.01 g	±0.005 g	3
2.531 g	0.001 g	±0.0005 g	4

Table 11.5 shows how the precision of a measurement increases with the number of significant figures. Random uncertainties are also shown: these decrease as the precision of the measurement increases.

The number of significant figures in a measurement is the number of figures that are known with certainty plus one that is uncertain, beginning with the first non-zero digit. In order to determine the number of significant figures in a measurement the following rules should be applied:

■ All non-zero digits are significant.

For example, 549 g has three significant figures and 1.892 g has four significant figures.

■ Zeros to the left of the first non-zero digit are not significant.

For example, 0.000 034 g has only two significant figures (this is more easily seen if it is written in scientific notation as 3.4×10^{-5} g). The value 0.001 111 g has four significant figures.

■ Zeros between non-zero digits are significant.

For example, 4023 g has four significant figures and 50 014 g has five significant figures.

■ Zeros to the right of the decimal point are significant.

For example, 2.50 g has three significant figures and 5.500 g has four significant figures.

- Exact numbers, for example 2, and irrational numbers, for example π and $\frac{4}{3}$, have an infinite number of significant figures.
- If a number ends in zeros that are not to the right of a decimal point, the zeros may or may not be significant.
  For example, 1500 g may have two, three or four significant figures.

Numbers like this with trailing zeros are best written in scientific notation, where the number is written in the standard exponential form as $N \times 10^n$, where N represents a number with a single non-zero digit to the left of the decimal point and n represents some integer.

The mass above can be expressed in scientific notation in the following forms depending upon the number of significant figures:

1.5×10^3 g   (2 significant figures)

1.50×10^3 g   (3 significant figures)

1.500×10^3 g   (4 significant figures)

In these expressions all the zeros to the right of the decimal point are significant. Scientific notation is an excellent way of expressing the significant figures in very large or very small measurements or physical constants, such as Avogadro's constant (6.02×10^{23} mol^{-1}) and Planck's constant (6.63×10^{-34} J s).

The measured value of any quantity can be characterized by two important terms:

- the maximum uncertainty
- the number of significant figures.

The maximum uncertainty is an indication of the scale sensitivity or the accuracy of the instrument used. Table 11.6 shows the sensitivity of some commonly used measuring instruments.

Instrument or apparatus	Tolerance	Example
Metre rule	0.001 m	0.544 m
Digital stopwatch	0.01 s	10.85 s*
Thermometer	0.5 °C	68.5 °C
Electronic balance	0.1 g	4.3 g
Electronic balance	0.01 g	6.03 g
Electronic balance	0.001 g	1.689 g
Voltmeter	0.05 V	1.35 V

■ **Table 11.6** Typical sensitivities of commonly used apparatus and measuring instruments

■ **Figure 11.18** Digital stopwatch

*Since the average human reaction time is about 0.2 seconds, the times obtained from a manually operated stopwatch (Figure 11.18) must be rounded to 1 decimal place. Hence the time in Table 11.6 should be reported as 10.9 s. The human reaction time is an example of a systematic error.

■ **Table 11.7** Tolerance values of apparatus in the laboratory

Apparatus	Manufacturer's tolerance
Pipette (Class B) (25.0 cm³)	± 0.06 cm³
Burette (Class B) (25.0 cm³)	± 0.1 cm³
Volumetric flask (100 cm³)	± 0.1 cm³
Volumetric flask (250 cm³)	± 0.3 cm³
Measuring cylinder (100 cm³)	± 0.1 cm³

For volumetric glassware, the manufacturers often print the random uncertainty (or tolerance) on the glass. Some typical tolerance values of apparatus in a school chemistry laboratory are shown in Table 11.7.

As general rules the uncertainty ranges due to readability from analogue scales and digital displays are summarized in Table 11.8.

■ **Table 11.8** Estimating uncertainties from analogue scales and digital displays

Instrument or apparatus	Example	Random uncertainty
Analogue scale	Rulers, voltmeters, colorimeters, volumetric glassware	± (half the smallest scale division (least count))*
Digital display	Top pan balances, spectrophotometers, stopwatches, pH meters	± (1 in the least significant digit)

*If the least count is relatively wide, then it can be mentally divided into fifths or tenths. A magnifying glass may help interpolate the scale in this way.

The random uncertainty of the digital thermometer in Figure 11.19 is ± 0.1 °C, hence the temperature shown should be reported as 22.1 °C ± 0.1 °C.

■ **Figure 11.19**
Digital thermometer

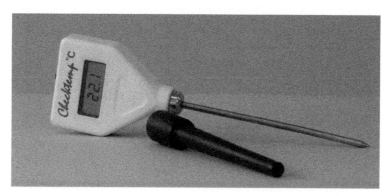

■ Calculations with significant figures

When performing calculations with measured quantities the rule is that the accuracy of the final result is limited to the accuracy of the least accurate measurement. In other words, the final result cannot be more accurate than the least accurate number involved in that calculation.

Rounding off

The final result of a calculation often contains figures that are not significant. When this occurs the final result is rounded off. The following rules are used to round off a number to the required number of significant figures:

■ If the digit following the last digit to be kept is less than 5, the last digit is left unchanged.

For example, 46.32 rounded to two significant figures is 46.

■ If the digit following the last digit to be kept is 5 or more, the last digit to be kept is increased by 1.

For example, 52.87 rounded to three significant figures is 52.9.

Calculations involving addition and subtraction

In addition and subtraction, the final result should be reported to the same number of decimal places as the number with the least number of decimal places. For example:

35.52 + 10.3 = 45.82   which is rounded to 45.8

In this sum, the number 10.3 has the least number of decimal places – one decimal place. The final result is therefore rounded to only one decimal place. The digit 2 is dropped and the sum is expressed as 45.8.

Here is an example involving subtraction:

3.56 – 0.021 = 3.539   which is rounded to 3.54

In this subtraction, the number 3.56 has the least number of decimal places – two decimal places. The final result is therefore limited to two decimal places. The result will be rounded to 3.54.

Calculations involving multiplication and division

In multiplication and division, the final result should be reported as having the same number of significant figures as the number with the least number of significant figures. This rule is illustrated in the following example:

$$6.26 \times 5.8 = 36.308 \quad \text{which is rounded to } 36$$

The number with the least number of significant figures is 5.8 – two significant figures. The final result is therefore limited to two significant figures.

Here is an example involving division:

$$\frac{5.27}{12} = 0.439 \quad \text{which is rounded to } 0.44$$

In this division, the number 12 has the least number of significant figures – two significant figures. The final result of the calculation is therefore rounded off to two significant figures.

A calculator can give a misleading impression of precision. For example:

$$3.02 \times 11.11 = 33.5522$$

This appears to be a very precise value, but the answer must be given as 33.5, as 3.02 has only three significant figures.

---

11 Give the answer to each of the following calculations to the appropriate number of significant figures or decimal places.
 a $45.50 \, cm^3 - 32.0 \, cm^3$
 b $45 \, g \times 4.21 \, J \, mol^{-1} \, K^{-1} \times 10 \, ^\circ C$
 c $10.4539 \, g \div 10.4 \, cm^3$
 d $1.04 \, kJ \, mol^{-1} + 945.1 \, J \, mol^{-1}$
 e $37.76 \, cm + 3.907 \, cm + 226.4 \, cm$
 f $(5.5 \, cm)^3$
 g $0.556 \times (40 - 32.5)$
 h Average of the following absorbance values: 0.1707, 0.1713, 0.1720, 0.1704 and 0.1715

Logarithms and antilogarithms

When calculating the logarithm of a number, retain in the mantissa (the number to the right of the decimal point in the logarithm) the same number of significant figures as there are in the number whose logarithm is being found.

For example:

$$\log_{10}(3.000 \times 10^4) = 4.477\,121 \qquad \text{which should be rounded to } 4.4771$$
$$\log_{10}(3.0 \times 10^4) = 4.477\,121 \qquad \text{which should be rounded to } 4.47$$

When calculating the antilogarithm of a number, the resulting value should have the same number of significant figures as the mantissa in the logarithm. For example:

$$\text{antilog}(0.301) = 1.9998 \qquad \text{which should be rounded to } 2.00$$
$$\text{antilog}(0.30) = 1.9953 \qquad \text{which should be rounded to } 2.0$$

Multiple mathematical operations

If a calculation involves a combination of mathematical operations, then perform the calculation using more figures than will be significant to arrive at a final value. Then, go back and look at the individual steps of the calculation and determine how many significant figures would carry through to the final result based on the above rules.

For example:

$$\frac{(5.254 + 0.0016)}{34.6} - 2.231 \times 10^{-3}$$

Calculate the value of the expression using more figures than will be significant. In this example, 0.149 664 953 8 (depending on the calculator used).

Then, examine each part of the equation to determine the number of significant figures.

5.254 + 0.0016 = 5.256   (since the sum is limited to the thousandths place by 5.254)

$$\frac{5.256}{34.6} = 0.152$$ (since the quotient is limited to three significant figures by 34.6)

0.152 − 0.002231 = 0.150   (since the difference is limited to the thousandths place by 0.152)

The value 0.149 664 953 8 initially obtained should be rounded to have three significant figures.

Therefore, the final answer is 0.150 or 1.50×10^{-1}.

■ Utilization: The importance of measurements

Mars Climate Orbiter Spacecraft

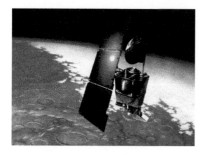

■ **Figure 11.20** Mars Climate Orbiter spacecraft

NASA lost a $125 million Mars orbiter because one engineering team used metric units while another used English units for a key spacecraft operation. For that reason, information failed to transfer between the Mars Climate Orbiter spacecraft team at Lockheed Martin in Colorado and the mission navigation team in California. Lockheed Martin built the spacecraft. The navigation mishap pushed the spacecraft too close to the planet's atmosphere, where it presumably burned and broke into pieces, ending the mission on a day when engineers had expected to celebrate the craft's entry into Mars's orbit.

Speed of neutrinos

In 2011, the OPERA experiment at CERN mistakenly observed neutrinos appearing to travel faster than light. Even before the mistake was discovered, the result was considered anomalous because speeds higher than that of light in a vacuum violate Einstein's theory of special relativity. Later, the team reported two flaws in their equipment set-up that had caused errors far outside of their original confidence interval (a statistical measure of reliability): a fibre optic cable not attached properly, which caused the apparently faster-than-light measurements, and a clock oscillator ticking too fast.

11.2 Graphical techniques – *graphs are a visual representation of trends in data*

■ Graphing

Graphs are often used in chemistry because on a simple level they provide an instant visual representation of data. 'Visual learners' make up the majority of the population and they absorb and recall information most effectively by seeing. 'Visual learners' relate best to written information, notes, diagrams, maps and graphs. However, graphs are not just visual representations of the physical world – they are powerful tools that can be used to establish numerical relationships, determine physical quantities and make predictions.

Graphing is an excellent way to average a range of values. When a range of experimental values (Table 11.9) is plotted, each point could have error bars drawn on it as in Figure 11.21 (but this is not a requirement of the current IB Chemistry programme). The size of the bar is calculated from the uncertainty due to random errors. Any line that is drawn should be within the error bars of every point. If it is not possible to draw a line of best fit within the error bars, then the systematic errors are greater than the random errors. The values of the variable which is manipulated are plotted on the *x*-axis and the values of the variable which is measured as the results are plotted on the *y*-axis.

Absolute temperature/K ± 5 K	Volume of air/cm³ ± 0.3 cm³
274	10.2
301	11.2
316	11.8
342	12.7
369	13.7

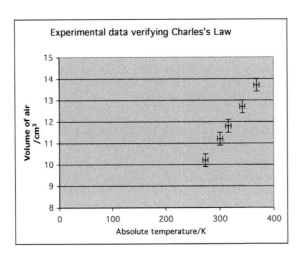

Constructing graphs

Remember the following points when plotting graphs from experimental data:

■ Plot the independent variable on the *x*-axis and the dependent variable on the *y*-axis.

■ Choose a scale which makes full use of the graph paper. A useful rule is that if you can double the scale (in either the *x*- or the *y*-direction) and still fit all the points on the paper, you should do so.

■ Choose a convenient scale, such as 1 cm = 1 unit, or 2 units, or 5 units or 10 units.

■ Label each axis and include (where appropriate) the units (usually SI units).

■ Plot the points as accurately as possible with small crosses. A minimum of five readings is required.

■ For most graphs you will need to draw a straight line (the line of best fit) or a curve of best fit.

■ The graph needs a title and, if there are two or more lines or curves, then it needs to have a key.

■ A best trend line is added. This line or curve *never* 'joins the dots' – it is added to show the overall trend (see page 400).

■ Any anomalous data points that do not agree with the line or curve of best fit must be identified.

(It is acceptable to use software, such as Excel, to plot a graph. Similar considerations to those above apply.)

Table 11.10 and Figure 11.22 summarize some idealized experimental data from burning known masses of magnesium and weighing the mass of magnesium oxide (the product). (For simplicity, random uncertainties have not been included; graphs do not need to include error bars.)

Mass of magnesium/g	Mass of magnesium oxide/g
0.10	0.16
0.20	0.32
0.30	0.48
0.40	0.64
0.50	0.80

■ **Table 11.10** Experimental data for the combustion of known masses of magnesium

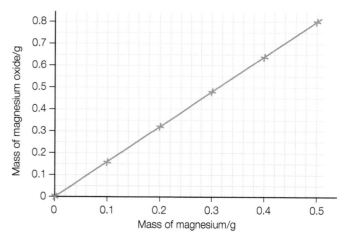

■ **Figure 11.22** A graph of the mass of magnesium oxide against the mass of magnesium

Table 11.11 and Figure 11.23 summarize some idealized experimental data from the reaction between excess powdered calcium carbonate and hydrochloric acid.

Time/s	Volume of carbon dioxide released/cm³
10	25
20	45
30	60
40	70
50	75
60	78
70	80
80	80

■ **Table 11.11** Total volume of carbon dioxide gas released against time

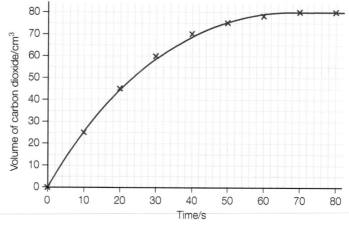

■ **Figure 11.23** A graph showing the volume of carbon dioxide collected against time for the reaction between excess powdered calcium carbonate and hydrochloric acid

Drawing graphs of experimental results, including the correct choice of axes and scale

Table 11.12 shows the densities and molar volumes for several common gases. Since the volume and, therefore, the density of a gas changes significantly with changes in temperature and pressure, all these values were measured for gases at 25 °C and 100 kPa atmosphere pressure.

■ **Table 11.12** Densities and molar volumes for selected common gases

Gas	Formula	Molar mass/g mol⁻¹	Density/g dm⁻³	Molar gas volume/dm³ mol⁻¹
Hydrogen	H_2	2	0.08	24.3
Helium	He	4	0.16	24.4
Ammonia	NH_3	17	0.70	24.4
Oxygen	O_2	32	1.32	24.3
Carbon dioxide	CO_2	44	1.79	24.6
Chlorine	Cl_2	71	3.10	22.9

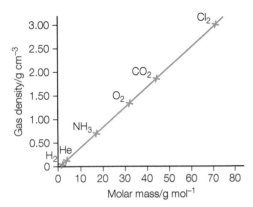

■ Figure 11.24 A graph of gas density (g cm⁻³) against molar mass (g mol⁻¹) for selected common gases

The data shows that as the molar mass of a gas increases, so does the density. A graph of density against molar mass shows a linear relationship (Figure 11.24). This is not an experiment but the molar mass of a gas can be regarded as an independent variable since it determines the gas density.

Look at the data table to establish the limits of the graph (maximum and minimum values) for both variables and select the axis. The lower left corner of the graph does not have to represent zero on either axis unless you have data in this region. Select divisions on the axes which are easy to read. Common graph paper is divided into groups of ten small squares. Hence one square may represent 1, 2, 5, 10, or 10 (as in this example), 20, 50, 100, but never 2.75 or some other 'odd' number. For greatest accuracy, select scales so that the graph nearly fills the page. Label each axis with both quantity and units.

Remember that the precision of any information obtained from the graph should match the precision of the data that went into the graph. It is not desirable to lose significant figures when reading the graph, nor is it possible to generate more. Therefore, if the data used to generate the graph had N significant figures, numbers read from the graph should also have N significant figures. This rule also holds true for values of the slope and the y-intercept obtained by linear regression analysis (see later). It will generally be necessary to round the values obtained from your calculator or computer program to the correct number of significant figures.

Interpretating graphs, in terms of the relationships of dependent and independent variables

There are a number of common relationships shown by dependent and independent variables in chemistry.

In a linear relationship there is a directly proportional relationship between the two variables. The relationship is described by the formula $y = mx + c$, where c is the intercept on the y-axis and m is the slope or gradient of the line (Figure 11.25). This is characteristic of Charles' law: the relationship between the volume and temperature of an ideal gas (at constant pressure) (Chapter 1).

In an inverse relationship (Figure 11.26) there is an inversely proportional relationship between the two variables. As one increases the other decreases, and *vice versa*. The graph is 'linearized' by plotting the dependent variable on the y-axis against the inverse of the independent variable on the x-axis. The resulting formula will be $y = A/x$ or $xy = A$. This is typical of Boyle's law: PV = constant (Chapter 1).

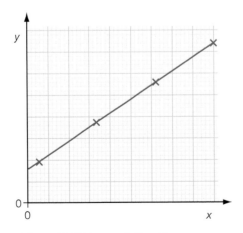

■ Figure 11.25 Linear relationship

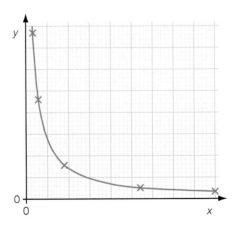

■ Figure 11.26 Inverse relationship

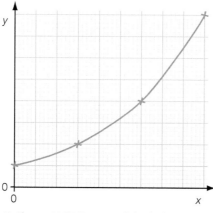

■ **Figure 11.27** Exponential relationship

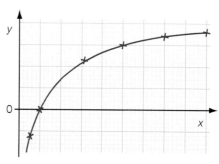

■ **Figure 11.28** Natural logarithm relationship

An exponential relationship takes the form $y = e^x$ or $y = e^{-x}$. It is characteristic of exponential growth or decay. The graph in Figure 11.27 shows exponential growth.

A natural logarithmic relationship is shown in Figure 11.28. This relationship is shown, for example by enzymes when substrate concentration becomes saturated or by adsorption of gases onto a surface.

■ 'Big Data' and the impact of graphics

The use of graphics to depict data can clarify and drive home the message and significance of experimental results. The image conveys the message and interpretation in a manner that to some extent transcends linguistic and cultural differences.

One of the graphs that has had the most universal impact in recent years is the Keeling curve (Figure 11.29). Named after Charles Keeling who worked at the Scripps Institution of Oceanography in San Diego, this graph plots the on-going change in the concentration of carbon dioxide in the Earth's atmosphere since 1958. The data is based on the continuous measurements taken at the Mauna Loa Observatory in Hawaii.

The curve's significance lies in the fact that this evidence fuelled the development of the debate concerned with global warming and the part played by man-made increases in greenhouse gases in this phenomenon.

The Keeling curve is a relatively simple depiction that provoked the collection of measurements at other global sites. The influence of such depictions of data is increasingly being recognized and an exhibition of such ground-breaking graphical representations that have influenced policy was held in 2014 in the UK. Included in that exhibition was Florence Nightingale's 'rose diagram'. Sent to Queen Victoria in 1858, the 'Diagram of the causes of mortality' in the Crimean War was a pie chart that has had an immense impact on the development of modern nursing, and not just in war situations.

Modern computing and communication have made for increased collaborative collection and processing of data, and spawned a new subject area of development and concern referred to as 'Big Data'. Governments and industrial conglomerates are interested in progress in this field, as are scientists involved in international projects that come under the umbrella of 'big science'. Climate modelling, the Large Hadron Collider and the Human Genome Project are all examples of areas where science is benefiting from the accumulation, processing and interpretation of massive amounts of data. There are positive benefits to this integration of huge data resources, and many argue that it opens new frontiers in scientific research.

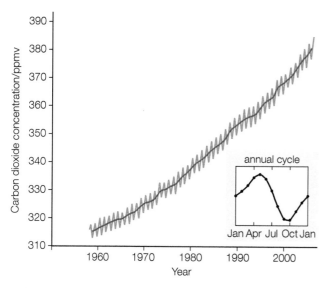

■ **Figure 11.29** The Keeling curve: the concentration of atmospheric carbon dioxide (measured at Mauna Loa, Hawaii)

However, some argue that there are concerns about how too much dependence on the sheer size of the data set will lead to a neglect of the principles of representative sampling. Care needs to be exercised as to how the accumulated information is integrated to avoid unforeseen bias in the results.

Empirical equations

Some chemical relationships take the form of an empirical equation of the form

$$y = ax^n$$

where a represents a constant and n represents an unknown exponent.

An empirical relationship is one that is derived from experimental data, rather than from theory.

One method of determining the value of n is to take logarithms of the equation and to plot the logarithm of y against the logarithm of x. Logarithms to the base 10 or natural logarithms may be used.

For example, taking logarithms to base 10 gives the following equation:

$$\log_{10} y = \log_{10} a + n \log_{10} x$$

This equation is of the form $y = mx + c$, if you identify $\log_{10} y$ with y and $\log_{10} x$ with x. The straight line obtained by plotting $\log_{10} y$ against $\log_{10} x$ would have a gradient equal to n, which allows n to be determined.

This method can be used to determine the order of a chemical reaction (Chapter 16).

■ Fitting a line to a graph

When a graph is plotted from experimental data, it is often found that the data points do not fall on a smooth line or curve, but instead display a degree of random scatter. The scatter occurs from random uncertainties present in the data being plotted.

It is assumed that the variable being measured would vary in a regular way without scatter if the measurements were totally accurate. Hence, it is *incorrect* to join adjacent points together with straight lines ('dot-to-dot').

The data points marked on the graph shown in Figure 11.30 are assumed to indicate that there exists a linear relationship between the variable y and the variable x. The straight line assumes a linear relationship between the two variables and is known as the line of best fit.

It can be drawn by hand (there should be roughly the same number of points above the line as below the line) or using a mathematical approach known as the method of least squares. Spreadsheets, such as Excel, can be programmed to fit a line of best fit through the data with an assumed linear relationship.

The data point circled in Figure 11.30 is anomalous data since it is clear that it does not fit in with the trend shown by the other data points and hence suggests a mistake was made during the recording. Anomalous data is not included in the analysis of the data.

One of the advantages of graphing raw data from an investigation is that it allows anomalous data to be easily recognized. If the graph is plotted (either manually or via a data-logger) when measurements are being taken, an anomalous point indicates that the measurement may be wrong and may need to be repeated.

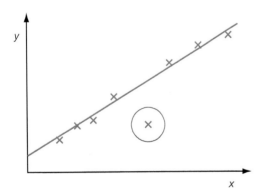

■ **Figure 11.30** A graph of experimental data showing linear behaviour and anomalous data

■ Measuring the intercept, gradient and area under a graph

Graphs can be used to analyse data. This is relatively easy and accurate for straight-line graphs, but the principles can also be applied to curved graphs. Determining the gradient and the intercept is often helpful. For a small number of graphs in chemistry, the area under the graph may be a useful quantity.

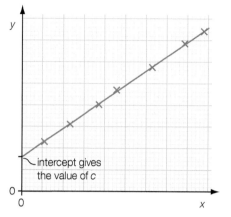

■ **Figure 11.31** A straight-line graph with an intercept, *c*, on the *y*-axis

Intercept

A straight-line graph will intercept (cut) the axis once and often it is the *y*-intercept that has a physical significance (Figure 11.31). For example, the intercept in an Arrhenius plot (Chapter 16) gives the value of the Arrhenius constant, A.

If a graph has an intercept of zero it passes through the origin. Two quantities are said to be proportional if the graph is a straight line that passes through the origin.

Gradient

The gradient of a straight-line graph is the increase in the *y*-axis value divided by the increase in the *x*-axis value. Note the following points:

- A straight-line graph has a constant gradient.

- The triangle used to calculate the gradient should be as large as possible to maximize accuracy.

- The gradient has units. Theses are the units on the *y*-axis divided by units on the *x*-axis.

- If the *x*-axis is a measurement of time then the gradient represents the rate at which the quantity on the *y*-axis changes.

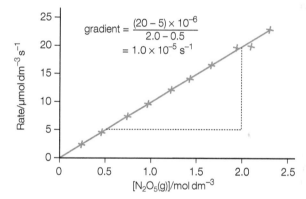

■ **Figure 11.32** A graph of initial rate against concentration for a first-order reaction (decomposition of dinitrogen pentoxide): $2N_2O_5(g) \rightarrow 4NO_2(g) + O_2(g)$

A graph of initial rate against concentration for a first-order reaction (Chapter 16) gives a straight-line graph that passes through the origin (Figure 11.32). The gradient of the graph gives you the value of the rate constant, *k*. This is characteristic for the reaction under standard conditions.

Since the reaction is first order the rate equation is:

rate = k [$N_2O_5(g)$]

so k = rate/[$N_2O_5(g)$]

= gradient of graph

= $1.0 \times 10^{-5}\,s^{-1}$

A rate versus concentration graph (Chapter 6) is obtained by drawing tangents to the curves of concentration versus time graphs (Figure 11.33) for a reactant or a product.

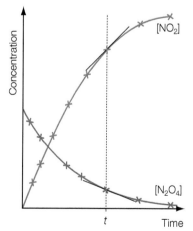

■ **Figure 11.33** Concentration–time graphs for the decomposition of dinitrogen tetroxide, N_2O_4: $N_2O_4 \rightarrow 2NO_2$

Interpolation

Interpolation is a technique where a graph is used to determine data points between those at which you have taken measurements. Figure 11.34 is a graph of concentration of hydrogen peroxide against time. It is an exponential graph and the dotted construction lines are interpolation lines to 'prove' that it is a first-order reaction (Chapter 16). The half-life of the reaction is approximately 25 seconds.

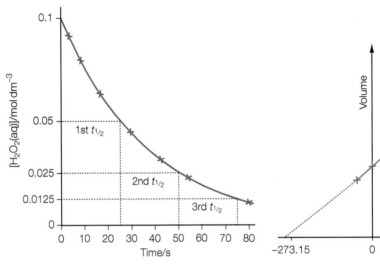

■ **Figure 11.34** A graph showing the concentration of decomposing hydrogen peroxide against time

■ **Figure 11.35** A graph of the volume of an ideal gas against temperature (in degrees Celsius) showing the theoretical derivation of absolute zero

Extrapolation

Extrapolation is a technique used to find values outside the range for which measurements are made. The straight line or smooth curve is simply extended.

When the volume of an ideal gas is plotted against its temperature using the Celsius temperature scale, a straight line with a positive gradient is obtained. This relationship (at constant pressure) is known as Charles' law (Chapter 1). If the line is extrapolated back to the intercept on the x-axis, it gives the value of the temperature at which the volume of gas would be zero (Figure 11.35). Accurate measurements give the value of −273.15 °C. The same temperature is obtained regardless of the volume of gas used, the pressure at which the investigation is carried out or the nature of the gas. Absolute zero is the basis of the thermodynamic temperature scale which uses units of kelvins.

Area under a graph

The area (Figure 11.36) under a straight-line graph can be easily calculated using simple arithmetic. If the graph is a curve the area can be estimated by dividing the shape into a number of squares (of known dimensions) and counting the squares. If the equation of the line is known, the area under the graph can be calculated using integration.

■ **Figure 11.36**
Areas under a straight-line graph and a curve graph

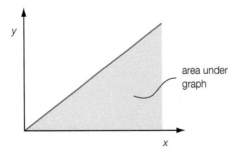
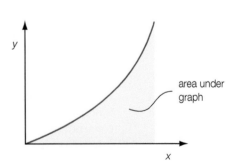

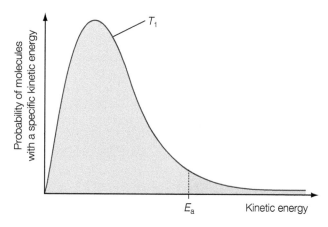

Figure 11.37
The Maxwell–Boltzmann distribution curve at temperature T_1

For the majority of the graphs in chemistry the area under the graph does not represent a useful physical quantity. However, the area under the curve is relevant to the Maxwell–Boltzmann distribution curve (Chapter 6), which is useful in accounting for the rate of reaction at different temperatures. It is a frequency distribution curve which shows the distribution of kinetic energies among reacting gas particles at a particular absolute temperature, T (in kelvins) (Figure 11.37).

The area under the graph in Figure 11.37 is proportional to the number of gas particles. The graph shows that a certain number of particles with kinetic energies equal to or greater than the activation energy E_a, are able to undergo reaction. At a higher temperature (T_2), a greater proportion or percentage of the gas particles have energies equal to or greater than the activation energy and hence more reactions occur, which increases the rate of reaction (Figure 11.38).

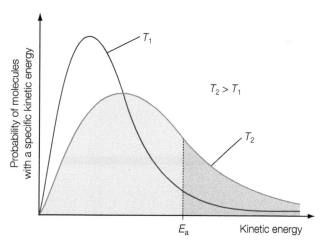

■ **Figure 11.38**
The Maxwell–Boltzmann distribution curves for temperatures T_1 and T_2

■ **Displaying discontinuous data**

Dot-to-dot graphs such as that shown in Figure 11.39 are useful for showing patterns. Strictly speaking, this is not a graph and is an incorrect approach to presenting this type of data. This is because 'type of hydrogen' halide is not an example of continuous data. A histogram would be a more appropriate approach to presenting this type of data.

■ **Figure 11.39**
Boiling points of hydrogen halides

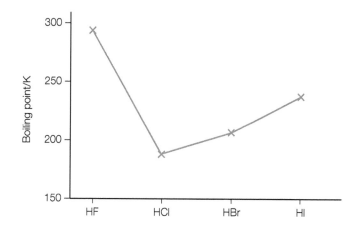

◼ Sketching graphs

When drawing graphs from data the *y*-axis is often used to show values of a dependent variable and the *x*-axis shows the values of the independent variable. The dependent variable is the variable that is measured after the independent variable is changed.

For example, in showing how concentration changes with time, concentration is regarded as the dependent variable because its value depends upon time (the independent variable).

If an investigation involved changing the volume of a gas and recording the resulting changes in pressure, then pressure would be regarded as the dependent variable and be plotted along the *y*-axis.

A graph of pressure against volume for a fixed mass of ideal gas at constant temperature takes the form of a hyperbolic curve (Figure 11.40). The graph clearly illustrates the inverse dependence between the pressure and volume.

A linear graph can be obtained for this dependence by plotting a graph of pressure against the reciprocal of volume (Figure 11.41). This implies that the product of the pressure and volume will be a constant: $PV = k$. This is known as Boyle's law (Chapter 1). The equation for a straight line, $y = mx + c$, yields the expression $P = m/V$ which is equivalent to $PV =$ constant.

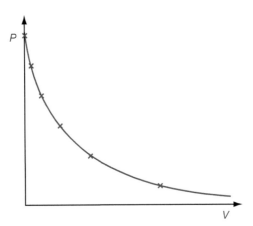

◼ **Figure 11.40** Sketch of gas pressure against gas volume (for a fixed mass of ideal gas at constant temperature)

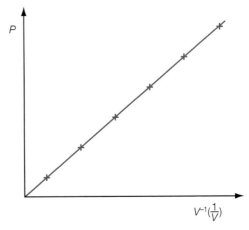

◼ **Figure 11.41** Sketch of gas pressure against reciprocal of gas volume (for a fixed mass of ideal gas at constant temperature)

Exponential relationships

Exponential relationships are often found in physical chemistry. The function $y = e^x$ or $y = \exp(x)$ is referred to as the exponential function. The form e^x is referred to as 'e to the power of *x*' and $\exp(x)$ is referred to as 'exponential *x*'. General forms of the exponential function that appear in chemistry are $y = Ae^x$ and $y = Ae^{-x}$. These functions depend upon *x* as shown in Figure 11.42.

Exponential relationships encountered during the IB Chemistry programme include the relationship between temperature and rate, and concentration versus time for a first-order reaction (Chapter 16).

Plotting of drawn graphs with labelled and scaled axes is an essential part of the presentation and analysis of quantitative scientific data. They can be used to establish the relationship between the two variables. These relationships can be directly proportional, inversely proportional, hyperbolic, exponential or more complex, such as a titration curve (Figure 11.43), which consists of two logarithmic curves reflected around a central point (equivalence point).

■ Figure 11.42
Sketches of **a** positive and **b** negative exponential functions

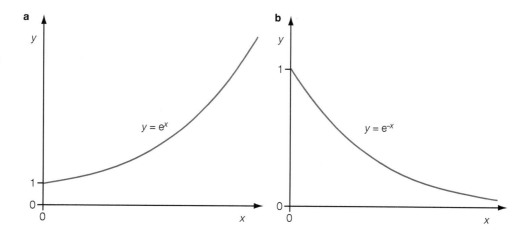

■ Figure 11.43
An Excel-generated acid–base titration curve

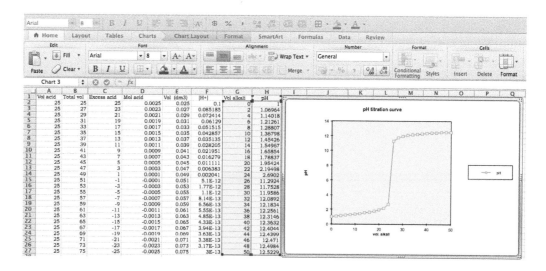

Graphs can also be used in a variety of measurements, for example, finding tangents to a curve, finding the intercept of a line or curve or determining the gradient of a line. Drawn graphs can also be used for interpolation and extrapolation.

Calculating quantities from graphs by measuring slope (gradient) and intercept, including appropriate units

The voltage of a galvanic cell varies with the concentration of one or both half-cells (see Chapter 24 on the accompanying website). A half-cell consisting of lead dipping into lead(II) ions is connected to a half-cell consisting of a nickel electrode dipping into nickel(II) ions. The two half-cells are connected via a salt bridge and high-resistance voltmeter. The nickel(II) concentration is kept constant, but the concentration of lead(II) ions is progressively changed (at a constant temperature of 25 °C), being diluted by a factor of 10 five times.

The voltage of the cell was measured at each concentration:

$[Pb^{2+}(aq)]/mol\,dm^{-3}$	1.000×10^{-1}	1.000×10^{-2}	1.000×10^{-3}	1.000×10^{-4}	1.000×10^{-5}	1.000×10^{-6}
Potential difference of lead–nickel cell/V	0.0901	0.0602	0.0310	0.0020	−0.00270	−0.0561

■ **Figure 11.44**
A plot of cell voltage against $\log_{10}$ (lead(II) ion concentration) for a lead–nickel galvanic cell in which the nickel ion concentration is $1\,mol\,dm^{-3}$

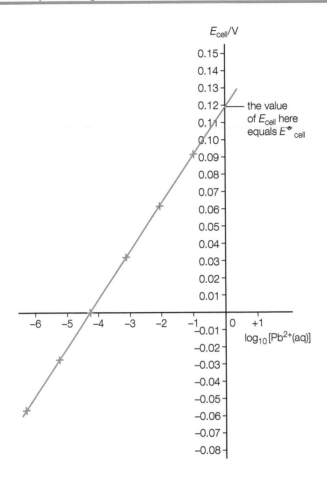

To obtain a linear relationship, logarithms to the base 10 should be calculated for the lead(II) ion concentrations. A graph (with a line of best fit) should then be plotted with $\log_{10}$ of the lead(II) ion concentration along the x-axis since it is the independent variable (Figure 11.44). Note the extension of the scales to include negative numbers. Extrapolation of the line to intercept the y-axis gives the value of the cell voltage under standard conditions, when all ion concentrations are $1\,mol\,dm^{-3}$.

Producing and interpreting best-fit lines or curves through data points, and assessing whether it can be considered as a linear function

A student performed an experiment to investigate the decomposition of sodium thiosulfate, $Na_2S_2O_3$, in dilute acidic solution. In each trial the student mixed a different concentration of sodium thiosulfate with hydrochloric acid at constant temperature and determined the rate of disappearance of $S_2O_3^{2-}(aq)$.

Trial	Initial concentration of $Na_2S_2O_3(aq)$/ $mol\,dm^{-3}$	Initial rate of disappearance of $Na_2S_2O_3^{2-}(aq)$/$mol\,dm^{-3}\,s^{-1}$
1	0.051	0.020
2	0.076	0.030
3	0.089	0.034
4	0.113	0.045
5	0.126	0.051

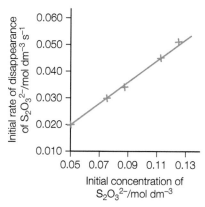

Figure 11.45 Graph of initial rate of disappearance against initial concentration of thiosulfate ions

The independent variable is the initial concentration of sodium thiosulfate solution since this is what changed during the experiment. Hence it is plotted along the horizontal or *x*-axis. The rate of disappearance of sodium thiosulfate is measured and changes because the independent variable is changed. It is the dependent variable and hence is plotted up the vertical or *y*-axis.

Figure 11.45 shows a linear graph. A line of best fit has been added; this is the best-fit straight line through linear data that shows some 'scatter' due to experimental errors. A linear function is appropriate here because kinetic theory predicts a linear relationship.

12 A number of important relationships in chemistry are exponential in nature, for example, the relationship between vapour pressure and temperature. Vapour pressure is the gas pressure produced when a liquid comes into equilibrium when placed in a sealed container (closed system). Plot the following data using Excel and add a trend line for an exponential function.

Saturated vapour pressure/mm Hg	Temperature/°C
4.6	0
5.3	2
6.1	4
7.0	6
8.0	8
9.2	10
10.5	12
11.9	14
13.5	16
15.0	18
17.0	20
19.0	22
22.5	24

13 Enzymes (see Chapter 23 on the accompanying website) show saturation kinetics. At high substrate concentrations the enzyme is said to be saturated with respect to substrate. At low concentrations of substrate the enzyme activity is first order with respect to substrate but becomes almost zero order with respect to substrate concentration at higher concentrations. Plot the following enzyme kinetic data and use a logarithmic function to plot a hyperbolic curve of substrate concentration on the *x*-axis and enzyme rate or activity on the *y*-axis. Extrapolate the curve to estimate the maximum rate of enzyme activity.

Substrate concentration/ μmol dm⁻³	Amount of product formed/ nanomoles per minute
25	8.20
50	12.86
75	15.51
100	17.95
150	20.02
200	22.64

The idea of correlation can be tested in experiments whose results can be displayed graphically

A line of best fit can easily be generated using Excel using the 'add trend line' function (Figure 11.46). This feature provides a quick test of the linearity of your calibration data. It also allows you to view the equation of the best-fit line, as well as the correlation coefficient; both of these are determined using the mathematical technique of linear regression analysis.

■ **Figure 11.46**
Adding a trend line with Excel

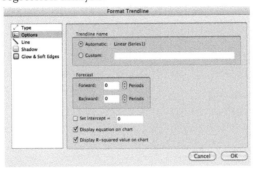

The correlation coefficient, R, is a measure of how close the data points are to the line. If the correlation coefficient is ± 1, it is a perfect fit and the line accurately describes the data. An R value of 0 indicates no linear correlation, and the straight line does not describe the data at all. An R value close to ± 1 is desirable. The sign of R indicates the slope of the regression line. The square of the correlation coefficient (R^2) is also a common measure.

14 Enter the following spectroscopic calibration data into Excel and plot the data (insert XY scatter plot) and then add a line of best fit (chart then add trend line). Display the equation of the line and the R^2 value.

Intensity of emission/arbitrary units	Concentration/picograms per cubic centimetre
2.2	0.0
5.1	2.0
9.1	4.0
12.7	6.0
17.4	8.0
21.1	10.0
24.8	12.0

There are many non-linear relationships in chemistry and they include the following curves: exponential curves (for example, rate and rate constant against temperature), hyperbolic or logarithmic curves (reaction kinetics and titration curves) and parabolic curves (for example, a plot of pressure versus volume at constant temperature).

15 Search on the internet for annual data on global temperatures and global atmospheric levels of carbon dioxide. The following sites may be helpful:
Scripps Oceanic Institute at Mauna Loa: http://scrippsco2.ucsd.edu/data/in_situ_co2/monthly_mlo.csv
NASA: http://data.giss.nasa.gov/gistemp/graphs_v3/

16 Plot a dual graph of global temperature and global atmospheric levels of carbon dioxide on the vertical axis against year.
Comment on the graph and discuss whether there is any visual correlation between the two variables. Consider natural processes and human activities when discussing whether there is a likely causal relationship between the two variables.

11.3 Spectroscopic identification of organic compounds — *analytical techniques can be used to determine the structure of a compound, analyse the composition of a substance or determine the purity of a compound; spectroscopic techniques are used in the structural identification of organic and inorganic compounds*

■ Index of hydrogen deficiency

Before a nuclear magnetic resonance (NMR) or infrared (IR) spectrum is analysed, chemists can learn about the structure of a compound from its molecular formula. One method of doing so is using the index of hydrogen deficiency (IHD). This method allows chemists to determine the degree of unsaturation – the number of carbon–carbon double bonds (pi bonds) and/or rings a molecule contains.

Using the general formulas of the alkanes (C_nH_{2n+2}) and alkenes/cycloalkanes (C_nH_{2n}) the hydrogen difference between the two is 2 given the same number of carbon atoms (n). Dividing the hydrogen difference by 2 will give the index of hydrogen deficiency or unsaturation index of 1. This index provides the information that the molecule contains either one double bond or one ring.

To determine the index of hydrogen deficiency for a compound, the following steps can be employed. This is shown using the compound $C_5H_3ClN_4$ as an example.

1 Determine the formula for the saturated, acyclic hydrocarbon containing the same number of carbon atoms as the compound being considered:

C_5H_{12}

2 Adjust the formula from step 1 for the non-hydrocarbon element(s) present in the compound being considered. For each group 15 atom, add one H atom, and for each group 17 atom take away one H atom. No change is needed for any group 16 atoms.
Add 4 N atoms. This means adding 4 H atoms: $C_5H_{16}N_4$
Add 1 Cl atom. This means taking away one H atom: $C_5H_{15}ClN_4$

3 Determine the difference in hydrogen atoms between the actual formula of the compound and that in step 2:

$15 - 3 = 12$

4 Divide the difference in hydrogen atoms by 2:

$12 \div 2 = 6$

The index of hydrogen deficiency is 6.

Determining the IHD from a molecular formula

The steps described above can be used to determine the IHD, or the following general formula can be applied:

$$\text{IHD} = 0.5 \times [2c + 2 - h - x + n]$$

which applies to the generic molecular formula $C_cH_hN_nO_oX_x$.

Worked example

Determine the IHD from the following molecular formulas:

a C_6H_{10} **b** C_6H_6 **c** C_4H_8O **d** C_4H_9N **e** C_2Cl_2 **f** C_7H_7NO

a IHD = 2 since $\frac{1}{2}[(2 \times 6) + 2 - 10] = 2$

b IHD = 4 since $\frac{1}{2}[(2 \times 6) + 2 - 6] = 4$

c IHD = 1 since $\frac{1}{2}[(2 \times 4) + 2 - 8] = 1$

d IHD = 1 since $\frac{1}{2}[(2 \times 4) + 2 - 9 + 1] = 1$

e IHD = 2 since $\frac{1}{2}[(2 \times 2) + 2 - 2] = 2$

f IHD = 5 since $7 + 1 - 3.5 + 0.5 = 5$

---

17 Deduce the number of double bond equivalents in the following molecules:
   a $CH_3(CH_2)_4CH_2OH$ b $CH_3(CH_2)_4CHO$ c $CH_3(CH_2)_4CH_2Br$

Analytical techniques

Analytical chemistry involves the use of a range of techniques and instruments to obtain information about chemical substances. Qualitative analysis is the identification of elements or compounds present in a sample. Quantitative analysis is the determination of the amounts of elements or compounds present in a sample. It is also often used to ensure that levels of contaminants are below specified levels. Structural analysis involves determining the structure of molecules and materials and the identification of functional groups.

Analytical techniques used in qualitative analysis include flame tests (Chapter 2) and precipitation reactions (Chapters 3 and 13). Analytical techniques used in quantitative analysis include titrations (Chapter 1), inductively coupled plasma (ICP) spectroscopy (Chapter 22 on the accompanying website), ultraviolet–visible spectroscopy (Chapter 23 on the accompanying website), infrared spectroscopy and various chromatographic techniques (Chapter 23). Analytical techniques used in structural analysis include NMR, IR spectroscopy, mass spectrometry and visible–ultraviolet spectroscopy. Important areas that employ analytical techniques include:

- **Monitoring and control of pollutants** The presence of heavy metals (for example lead, cadmium and mercury), organic chemicals (for example polychlorinated biphenyls (PCBs)) and vehicle exhaust gas emissions (polyaromatic hydrocarbons (PAHs)) are all health hazards that need to be monitored by accurate methods of analysis. Atmospheric pollutants also need to be monitored.

- **Clinical and biological studies** The levels of important nutrients and minerals, such as sodium and potassium ions, naturally produced molecules (for example cholesterol) and drugs in the body fluids of patients need to be measured and monitored.

- **Geological studies** The commercial value of ores and minerals (Chapter 22 on the accompanying website) is determined by the levels of particular metals or metal compounds.

- **Drug discovery** The structures of newly synthesized drugs (Chapter 25 on the accompanying website) will be confirmed using a variety of spectroscopic and other techniques.

- **Food purity** Samples of foods are regularly tested for the presence of pollutants, harmful pathogens or toxins. Food samples may also be analysed to ensure that legal levels of food additives are not exceeded and that they are free of pesticides.

For complex molecules it is often necessary to use several analytical techniques, either alone or in combination. For organic molecules, infrared spectroscopy can only identify the presence (or probable absence) of functional groups; nuclear magnetic resonance and mass spectrometry (Figure 11.47) are needed to establish the structure.

The electromagnetic spectrum

Electromagnetic waves are transverse waves, consisting of electric and magnetic fields that oscillate at right angles to each other and to the direction in which the wave is travelling (Figure 11.48). Electromagnetic waves show all the properties common to waves: they can undergo reflection, refraction and diffraction. Because they are transverse waves, they can be polarized (Chapter 20). In a vacuum all electromagnetic waves travel at the same speed (c), namely $3.00 \times 10^8 \, \text{m s}^{-1}$.

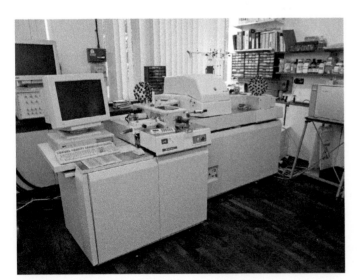

■ **Figure 11.47** Mass spectrometer

■ **Figure 11.48**
An electromagnetic wave

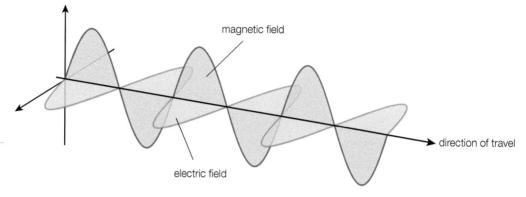

18 Calculate the frequency (in hertz) of a radio wave with a wavelength of 1515 metres. The velocity of light (in a vacuum) is $3.00 \times 10^8\,\text{m s}^{-1}$. (The hertz is a unit of frequency equal to one cycle (complete wave) per second.)

The wavelength (λ) and frequency (v) are *inversely* related by the following relationship:

$$\lambda v = c$$

Note that the *shorter* the wavelength, the *higher* the frequency of the radiation. The electromagnetic spectrum is divided into different regions according to the frequency and wavelength of the radiation (Figure 11.49), but note that there are no clear boundaries between the regions.

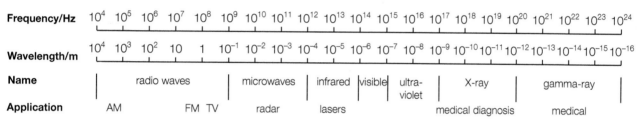

■ **Figure 11.49** The electromagnetic spectrum

According to quantum theory, a beam of electromagnetic radiation of frequency v consists of a stream of photons, each of which has energy E:

$$E = hv$$

where h represents Planck's constant ($6.63 \times 10^{-34}\,\text{J s}$).

Hence, a photon of high frequency electromagnetic radiation has more energy than one of low frequency.

19 Calculate the energy of one photon of electromagnetic radiation with a frequency of $4.60 \times 10^9\,\text{Hz}$. Calculate the energy of a mole of these photons. (Planck's constant is $6.63 \times 10^{-34}\,\text{J s}$ and the Avogadro constant is $6.02 \times 10^{23}\,\text{mol}^{-1}$.)

■ The interaction of radiation with matter

When electromagnetic radiation interacts with simple covalent substances, energy is transferred to the molecules. The molecules absorb energy, and the absorbed energy can cause a variety of changes to occur. The changes that occur depend on the chemical substance and the amount of electromagnetic energy involved. A molecule has energy associated with several different aspects of its behaviour, including:

■ energy associated with translation (the molecule moving from one position to another)

■ energy associated with rotation (of the molecule as a whole or specific bonds within the molecule)

■ energy associated with vibration of the covalent bonds (Chapter 4)

■ potential energy associated with electrons in energy levels (Chapter 2).

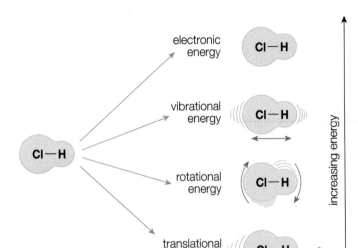

■ **Figure 11.50** The different types of energy associated with a hydrogen chloride molecule

These different types of energy and energy changes involve different amounts of energy. For example, making the bonds in a molecule vibrate generally involves more energy than making the molecule as a whole rotate. The energy needed increases in the general order shown in Figure 11.50.

The potential energy possessed by electrons in atoms and molecules, the vibrational and rotational energy of molecules and the kinetic energy of moving molecules are all quantized. This means the energies can only be of certain definite values. There are separate energy levels for all these types of energy, with fixed energy gaps or differences between these energy levels (Figure 11.51).

If an atom or molecule is in its ground state (lowest energy state) and gains energy *equivalent* to the difference between two energy levels (electronic, vibrational or rotational) then it is promoted to a higher energy level. The atom or molecule is then said to be in an excited state. Spectroscopy is the branch of chemistry that studies the absorption and emission of energy by atoms and molecules. The changes in energy can reveal valuable information about the electronic and atomic structure of molecules.

■ **Figure 11.51**
The electronic, vibrational and rotational energy levels in a molecule

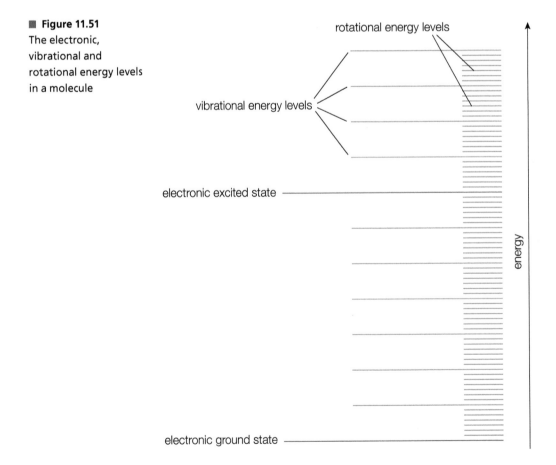

■ Types of spectroscopy

The various regions of the electromagnetic spectrum are the basis of the different types of spectroscopy, the study of the way matter interacts with electromagnetic radiation and the various techniques that are used to identify the structures of ionic and molecular substances.

X-rays

Atomic X-rays are emitted during electronic transitions to the inner shells of atoms. These X-rays have characteristic energies related to the atomic number, and each element therefore has a characteristic X-ray spectrum. Crystalline solids will diffract X-rays and the diffraction patterns can be used to derive bond distances and bond angles in a molecular structure. X-ray diffraction can also be used to study ionic substances and forms the basis of X-ray crystallography.

Visible–ultraviolet radiation

Radiation in the ultraviolet and visible regions gives rise to electronic transitions in molecules, often involving pi electrons, and hence this type of spectroscopy gives information about the energies of the molecular orbitals in a molecule or atomic orbitals in an atom or ion.

Infrared radiation

Infrared radiation causes certain bonds, especially non-polar bonds, to vibrate and undergo stretching and bending. This provides information about which functional groups are present and is the basis of infrared spectroscopy. It can also give information about bond strength.

Microwaves

Microwaves cause rotations in polar molecules and can give information on bond lengths, geometrical structures and dipole moments.

Radio waves

Radio waves can cause nuclear transitions in a strong magnetic field because radio waves of certain frequencies can be absorbed by certain nuclei, which causes their nuclear spin state to change. NMR is based on this principle and information on the relative proportions of the different chemical environments of atoms can be deduced, which leads to structural information about molecules.

■ Emission and absorption spectroscopy

In emission spectroscopy, a molecule or atom undergoes a transition from a state of high energy (E_2) to a state of lower energy (E_1) and emits the energy difference as a photon. In absorption spectroscopy, a molecule or atom undergoes a transition from a state of low energy (E_1) to a state of higher energy (E_2) by absorption of a photon (Figure 11.52). The absorption of electromagnetic radiation (of a single frequency) is monitored over a range of frequencies.

■ **Figure 11.52**
The relationship between **a** emission and **b** absorption for the same transitions

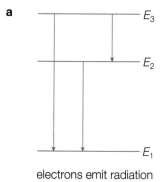

a
electrons emit radiation as they drop to lower energy levels

b
electrons absorb radiation at the same wavelengths as they are promoted to higher energy levels

The energy, $h\nu$, of the photon emitted or absorbed, and therefore the frequency, ν, of the electromagnetic radiation emitted or absorbed, is given by the following relationship:

$$h\nu = E_2 - E_1$$

Absorption spectroscopy is more widely used than emission spectroscopy. NMR, IR and ultraviolet–visible (UV–VIS) spectroscopy are all forms of absorption spectroscopy.

ToK Link

Electromagnetic waves can transmit information beyond that of our sense perceptions. What are the limitations of sense perception as a way of knowing?

Human senses have a particular range and can only detect electromagnetic radiation in the visible region of the electromagnetic spectrum. This is only a very small proportion of the electromagnetic spectrum. There are senses that humans do not possess (e.g. the echo-location used by bats and dolphins), and other senses may be limited compared to other animals (e.g. we cannot see as well as hawks or smell as well as dogs).

One philosophical view of sense perception is that we directly perceive the physical world as it is. We see colours, for example, because the world is coloured. This is termed naïve realism and is not in agreement with biological and philosophical thinking.

Though objects may appear to be coloured to us, our experience of colour is merely representative of the surface properties of objects; the physical property of reflecting certain wavelengths or frequencies of light and the colour blue as we experience it are two quite different issues.

This has led to the idea of representative realism, which suggests that perception is not a passive process and that we do not simply receive information about the physical world through our senses. Rather, our brain is actively involved in sense perception, supplying much of the content of our experiences. Our senses give us limited and fragmented information, which the brain fills in. Involuntary interpretation is therefore present even in our recognition of what we sense. Our observations are influenced by the categories and classification of scientific language, just as our languages are influenced by our observations of the world. Our powers of sense perception are selective, depending on a range of psychological factors and can be tricked or deceived, as shown by mirages and optical illusions.

Sense perception gives us a very incomplete, limited and imperfect contact with the physical world, but it is the basis of all knowledge of the physical world.

■ Infrared spectroscopy

Infrared radiation is not energetic enough to cause the promotion of electrons, but can bring about an increase in the vibrational energy of the bonds in molecules. The bonds connecting the atoms behave like tiny springs and may be considered to vibrate at characteristic frequencies (Figure 11.53). The frequency of vibrations is determined by the strength of the bond and the masses of the atoms. Infrared spectroscopy is used to identify functional groups present in a molecule, and to identify substances. This information is usually combined with that obtained from other techniques to identify the complete structure of the molecule. If the infrared spectrum of the molecule is already on record, it can be used to directly identify the molecule.

■ **Figure 11.53**
Vibrational and rotational motions in a triatomic molecule

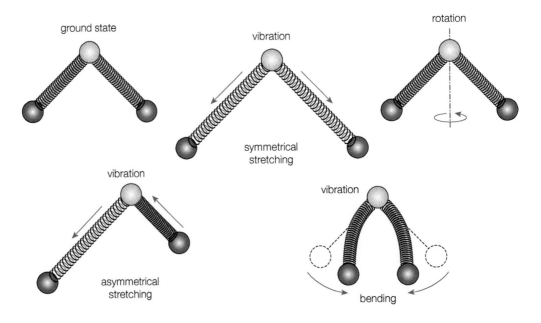

The infrared spectrometer

An infrared spectrometer measures the extent to which infrared radiation is absorbed by a sample over a particular frequency range of infrared radiation. A schematic diagram of an infrared spectrometer is shown in Figure 11.54.

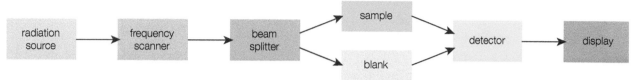

■ **Figure 11.54** Principle of a double-beam infrared spectrometer

The source produces infrared radiation over a particular frequency range. The beam of infrared radiation is then split and passed through a sample and a blank. The blank is identical to the sample *except* that the sample to be analysed is not present. The relative intensities of bands of the beam leaving the sample tube are then compared in the detector with those leaving the blank tube. The differences are caused by the sample absorbing infrared radiation. The results in the form of an infrared spectrum are then displayed on a screen, a chart recorder or a computer screen.

Interpreting infrared spectra

Certain bonds show characteristic absorption frequencies. The actual frequency does vary slightly between molecules, so the vibration bands are in a region of the infrared spectrum, rather than at a specific frequency. Some characteristic frequencies are given in Table 11.13.

■ **Table 11.13** Characteristic ranges for infrared absorption due to stretching vibrations in organic molecules

Bond	Organic molecules	Wavenumber (cm⁻¹)	Intensity
C–I	iodoalkanes	490–620	strong
C–Br	bromoalkanes	500–600	strong
C–Cl	chloroalkanes	600–800	strong
C–F	fluoroalkanes	1000–1400	strong
C–O	alcohols, esters, ethers	1050–1410	strong
C=C	alkenes	1620–1680	medium-weak; multiple bands strong
C=O	aldehydes, ketones, carboxylic acids and esters	1700–1750	strong
C≡C	alkynes	2100–2260	variable
O–H	hydrogen bonding in carboxylic acids	2500–3000	strong, very broad
C–H	alkanes, alkenes, arenes	2850–3090	strong
O–H	hydrogen bonding in alcohols and phenols	3200–3600	strong, broad
N–H	primary amines	3300–3500	medium, two bands

The same table may be found (Table 26) on page 25 of the IB *Chemistry data booklet*.

There are two main uses for infrared spectra:

■ to identify the functional groups present in an organic molecule
■ to identify the molecule (since every molecule has a unique infrared spectrum).

Comparison of an infrared spectrum with those in databases enables chemists to identify a substance or to assess its purity.

The infrared spectrum of ethanol is shown in Figure 11.55. The vertical axis represents the percentage of infrared radiation that passes through the sample. Absorptions are recorded as dips, not peaks, in infrared spectra. 100% transmittance corresponds to no absorption and 0% transmittance corresponds to total absorption. Transmittance is defined as the ratio of the intensities of the emerging beam and the incident beam expressed as a percentage. The horizontal scale represents the wavenumber (Figure 11.56) of the infrared radiation. The wavenumber is equal to the number of wavelengths per centimetre and the unit is referred to as the reciprocal centimetre, cm^{-1}. Wavenumbers are used because infrared frequencies are very large and hence inconvenient to use.

■ **Figure 11.55**
The infrared spectrum of ethanol

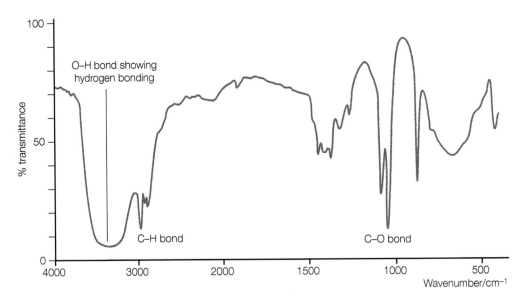

■ **Figure 11.56**
The relationship between wavenumber, wavelength and frequency

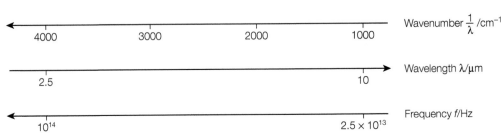

20 A photon of infrared radiation has a frequency of 5.000×10^{13} Hz. Calculate its wavelength in wavenumbers. (Velocity of light in a vacuum = 3.00×10^8 m s^{-1}.)

21 Calculate the frequency and wavelength of electromagnetic radiation having a wavenumber of 1750 cm^{-1}.

The infrared spectrum of ethanol shows the stretching vibrations of the O–H and C–O bonds. The O–H bond absorption is broad (wide) because of hydrogen bonding. The C–O bond vibration occurs at 1050 cm^{-1} and the O–H bond vibration occurs at 3350 cm^{-1}.

Figures 11.57 to 11.67 show the infrared spectra of a range of organic compounds. All of them have a strong absorption at around 3000 cm^{-1} due to the carbon–hydrogen bond, C–H. Water and the alcohols have a broad absorption band between 3000 and 3500 cm^{-1} due to the presence of an oxygen–hydrogen bond, O–H. The strong absorptions at around 1700 cm^{-1} in carbon dioxide, propanone and ethyl ethanoate are due to the presence of a carbonyl functional group, >C=O.

■ **Figure 11.57**
IR spectrum of hexane

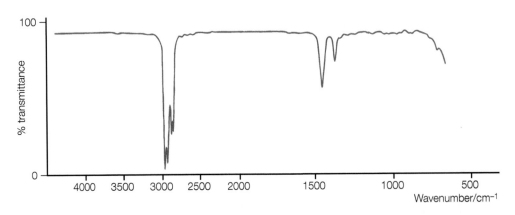

■ **Figure 11.58**
IR spectrum of
cyclohexane

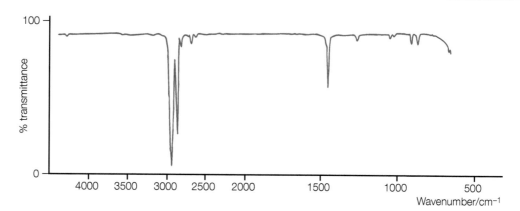

■ **Figure 11.59**
IR spectrum of
cyclohexene

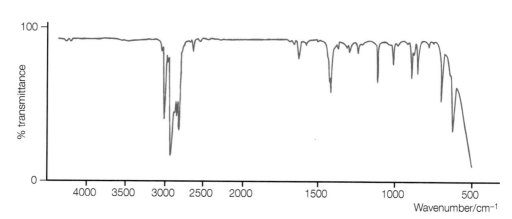

■ **Figure 11.60**
IR spectrum of
methylbenzene

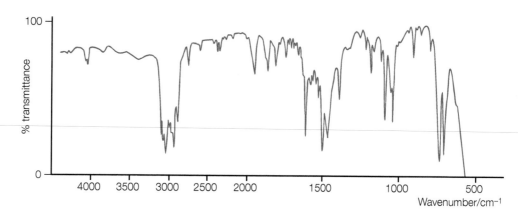

■ **Figure 11.61**
IR spectrum of
methanol

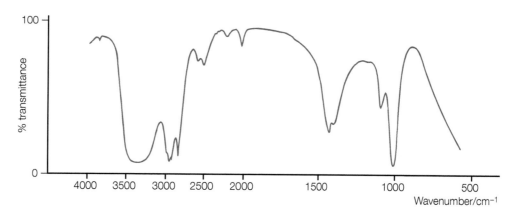

■ **Figure 11.62**
IR spectrum of
propanone

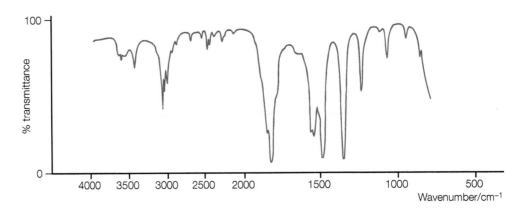

■ **Figure 11.63**
IR spectrum of
ethoxyethane

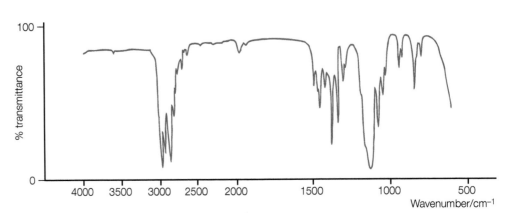

■ **Figure 11.64**
IR spectrum of ethyl
ethanoate

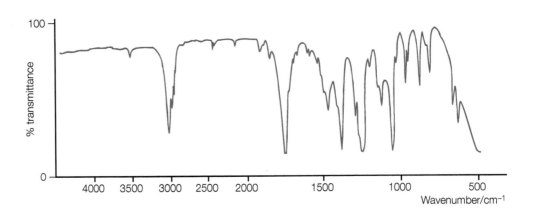

■ **Figure 11.65**
IR spectrum of carbon
dioxide

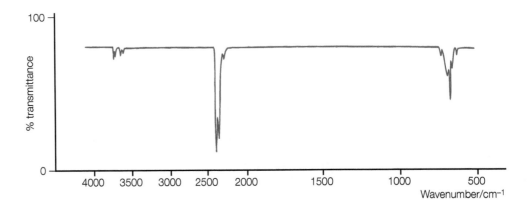

■ **Figure 11.66**
IR spectrum of water

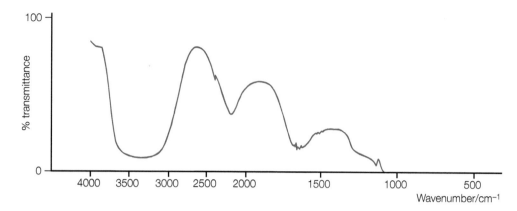

■ **Figure 11.67**
IR spectrum of methane

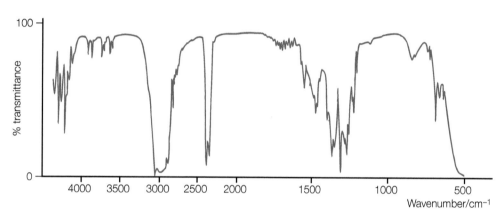

General approach to analysing infrared spectra

■ Examine the spectrum from left to right, starting at $4000\,cm^{-1}$.

■ Note which are the strongest absorptions and attempt to match them to the data in Table 11.13.

■ Note any absence of peaks in important areas.

■ Do not attempt to match all the peaks, especially in the fingerprint region.

Fingerprint region

Although there are characteristic bond absorption bands below $1500\,cm^{-1}$, these are less reliable indicators of specific bonds as this region also contains absorption bands that involve vibrations of the entire molecule or part of the molecule. This can be observed in the infrared spectra of hexane and cyclohexane, which are very similar above $1500\,cm^{-1}$ but have significant differences at lower wavenumbers. The part of the spectrum below $1500\,cm^{-1}$ is determined by the structure of the molecule, rather than by its bonds, and is referred to as the fingerprint region since it acts as a unique identifier.

How IR radiation interacts with molecules

There are two types of infrared excitation that can occur when a molecule absorbs infrared radiation: bond stretching and bond bending (Figure 11.68). Bond stretching requires more energy than bond bending and therefore bond-stretching absorptions will require shorter-wave radiation (higher frequency) than bond-bending absorptions.

■ **Figure 11.68**
Bond stretching and bond bending (also known as wagging or rocking)

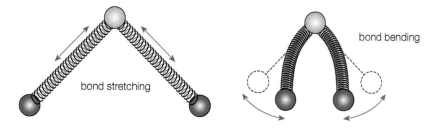

■ **Figure 11.69**
Bond stretching
in the non-polar
chlorine molecule

■ **Figure 11.70**
Bond stretching
in the hydrogen
chloride molecule

However, not every molecular vibration gives rise to an infrared absorption. In order to be infrared active, the molecule must undergo a change in dipole moment (Chapter 4), that is, the distribution of electric charge must alter. Diatomic molecules of elements, such as hydrogen, oxygen and the halogens (Figure 11.69), do not experience a change in dipole moment during a vibration and therefore will not absorb in the infrared region of the electromagnetic spectrum. Molecules such as the hydrogen halides (Figure 11.70) that are composed of two *different* atoms will have a permanent dipole because of a difference in electronegativity. The vibrations will alter the positions of the centres of positive and negative charge.

Triatomic molecules have various modes of vibration, some of which are infrared active and give rise to infrared absorption, while others may be infrared inactive. Only modes of vibration that result in a change in the overall dipole moment of the molecules will be infrared active.

Carbon dioxide is a linear molecule and has three possible vibration modes (Figure 11.71). In symmetric stretching, both carbon–oxygen bonds lengthen at the same time. The dipole moments of each bond increase, but they act in opposite directions and so cancel out (vectorially). This can also be confirmed from the fact that the mid-point of the negative charge always coincides with the centre of positive charge on the carbon. There is no change in the overall dipole moment of the carbon dioxide molecule and so symmetric stretching is infrared inactive. The ability of carbon dioxide molecules to absorb and re-emit infrared radiation is what makes carbon dioxide an effective heat-trapping greenhouse gas (Chapter 24 on the accompanying website).

■ **Figure 11.71**
Stretching and bending
(rocking) vibrations
in the carbon dioxide
molecule

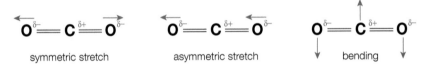

A water molecule (Figure 11.72) has modes of vibration similar to those shown for the carbon dioxide molecule. However, it is a V-shaped molecule rather than a linear molecule. All the vibration modes shown for the water molecule are infrared active. In a 'bent' molecule the changes in bond dipole for symmetric stretching are not in opposite directions. They do not, therefore, cancel out vectorially and, since there is a change in the overall dipole moment of the molecule, infrared absorption occurs.

■ **Figure 11.72**
Stretching and bending
(rocking) vibrations in
the water molecule

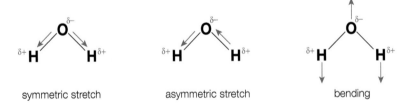

Figure 11.73 shows the vibrations in the sulfur dioxide molecule. Sulfur dioxide and carbon dioxide molecules have different shapes, and hence the vibrations causing changes in the dipole moment differ. The vibrational modes of sulfur dioxide are similar to those of water.

■ **Figure 11.73**
Stretching and bending
(rocking) vibrations
in the sulfur dioxide
molecule

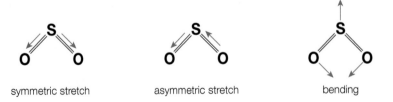

Stretching and bending (rocking) are the main modes of vibration, but bending (rocking) can be subdivided into scissoring, wagging and twisting, as exemplified by the methylene group, $-CH_2-$ (Figure 11.74). Symmetric stretching and asymmetric stretching are the only infrared active modes; all the others are infrared inactive.

■ **Figure 11.74**
Stretching and bending (rocking) vibrations in the methylene group, $-CH_2-$

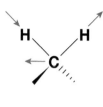

asymmetric stretching

symmetric stretching

bending or scissoring

22 Illustrate and explain why primary amine groups ($-NH_2$) show two absorption bands in the N–H stretch region.

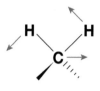

rocking or in-plane bending

twisting or out-of-plane bending

wagging or out-of-plane bending

↓ and ↥ show a movement out of and into the plane of the paper respectively

Nature of Science

Modelling of covalent bonds

Models are developed to explain certain phenomena that may not be observable, for example the interpretation of spectra is based on the bond vibration model.

Molecules are held together by electrons in bonding molecular orbitals (Chapter 14). The representation of covalent bonds by straight lines gives the impression that bonds behave like rigid rods. However, they are more accurately represented, for spectroscopic purposes, by springs connecting the atoms. The vibration in a diatomic molecule can be treated as behaving like the stretching and compressing of a spring. Stretching or compressing a spring produces potential energy. When a spring is released, this energy becomes a restoring force which results in vibration about the equilibrium length of the spring. Similarly, when a bond is stretched or compressed, and then released, vibrational motion occurs.

Vibrational frequencies can be calculated by using this simple 'ball and spring' model and applying Hooke's law to correlate bond strength and atomic masses. The calculated frequencies often agree closely with experimental values.

The fundamental frequency of the vibration of the bond, v, based on a system obeying Hooke's law can be related to the mass, m, by the expression

$$v = \frac{1}{2\pi}\sqrt{\frac{k}{m}},$$ where k is the spring constant.

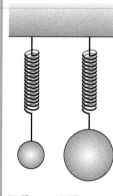

■ **Figure 11.75**
Suspended light and heavy balls

This principle can be demonstrated in a qualitative manner with balls of different mass and a pair of identical springs. A ball suspended on a stretched spring will vibrate up and down with a characteristic frequency. A heavier ball suspended from the same spring will vibrate more slowly (Figure 11.75). In a similar way the stretching frequency of the bond between two atoms in a molecule also depends upon their mass.

This simple 'ball and spring' model of covalent bonds is supported by data for the carbon–halogen bonds (Table 11.14). The stretching frequency of the carbon–halogen bond decreases down group 17.

■ **Table 11.14**

Stretching frequencies for carbon–halogen bonds (1 THz = 10^{12} Hz)

Bond	C–Cl	C–Br	C–I
Typical stretching frequency/THz	21	17	15

This simple model also suggests that the stretching frequency will be affected by the strength of the bond. The stronger the bond, the faster the vibrations. This is supported by the stretching frequencies of carbon–carbon bonds (Table 11.15).

■ **Table 11.15**
Stretching frequencies for carbon–carbon bonds

Bond	C–C	C=C	C≡C
Typical stretching frequency/THz	27	50	65

Utilization: Remote sensing

Remote sensing can be defined as the collection of data about an object from a distance. Humans and many other types of animals accomplish this task with the aid of eyes or by the sense of smell or hearing. Scientists use the technique of remote sensing to monitor or measure phenomena found on the Earth or its atmosphere. Remote sensing of the environment is usually done with the help of mechanical devices known as remote sensors. These devices have a greatly improved ability to receive and record information about an object without any physical contact. Often, these sensors are positioned away from the object being studied by using helicopters, planes and satellites. Most sensing devices record information about an object by measuring its transmission of electromagnetic energy from reflecting and radiating surfaces. Spectroscopic sensing is one of the most powerful techniques for determining the surface composition of inaccessible targets, for example stars and planets.

Environmental xenobiotics

Environmental xenobiotics are xenobiotic (foreign) substances with a biological activity that are found as pollutants in the natural environment.

A xenobiotic is a chemical substance found within an organism that is not normally naturally produced by or expected to be present within that organism. The term also include chemical substances which are present in much higher concentrations than usual.

Many environmental xenobiotics are pharmaceuticals, such as antibiotics, analgesics, X-ray contrast media and chemotherapy drugs. These can be discharged into the environment by the discharge of waste water from hospitals and pharmaceutical companies.

One common indirect source of xenobiotics into the environment is the passing of antibiotics, anaesthetics and growth hormones by farm animals in urine and manure. This is often stored in large pits before being pumped and applied to fields as fertilizers, where many of the chemicals can be washed away by rainfall into lakes and rivers. This pollution is then widely spread, and dealing with it may require the cooperation of scientists in different countries that share a common water system. Other common environmental xenobiotics include pesticides and fungicides (from farming), and a variety of other chemicals mainly from the chemical industry.

Once xenobiotics enter the environment they suffer one of three fates: they undergo biodegradation into carbon dioxide and water; they undergo chemical degradation and form metabolites; or they persist in the environment unchanged. Xenobiotics accumulate in living organisms and become more concentrated higher up in the food chains.

Exposure to xenobiotics raises the risk of male infertility, breast cancer in females, feminization of male animals and the evolution of antibiotic resistant strains of bacteria. Of particular concern are endocrine disruptors such as polychlorinated biphenyls (PCBs), which are chemicals that at certain doses can interfere with the endocrine (or hormone) system in mammals. These disruptions can cause cancerous tumours, birth defects and other developmental disorders.

Mass spectrometry

Analysing molecular ions

Chapter 2 described how the mass spectrometer (Figure 11.76) can be used to analyse elements and determine relative atomic mass. If molecules are vaporized and subjected to the ionizing conditions inside a mass spectrometer, the mass-to-charge (m/e) ratio for the molecular ion can be measured, and hence the relative molecular mass can be determined.

Electrons with a high kinetic energy can ionize molecules. An outer electron is removed from the molecule, leaving an unpaired electron and thereby forming a radical cation: a positive ion with an unpaired electron (Figure 11.77).

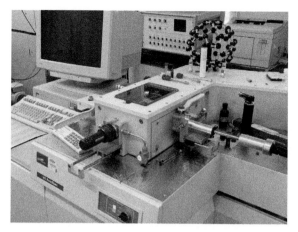

■ **Figure 11.76** Close-up of a mass spectrometer

■ **Figure 11.77**
The formation of a radical cation

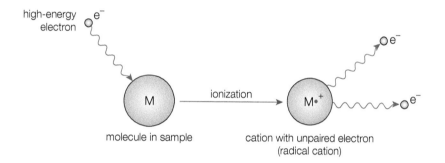

For example, an electron in one of the lone pairs of electrons on the oxygen atom of the propanone molecule can be removed by electron bombardment (Figure 11.78), to give a unipositive ion. The m/e ratio is $((3 \times 12) + (6 \times 1) + 16) : 1$, which gives a relative molecular mass of 58.

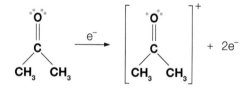

■ **Figure 11.78** Ionization of a propanone molecule

Analysing molecular fragments

If the ionizing electron beam in a mass spectrometer has sufficient kinetic energy, the molecular ions can undergo bond cleavage (Figure 11.79) and molecular fragments are formed. Some of these fragments will carry a positive charge and therefore appear as further peaks in the mass spectrum (Figure 11.80). The mass spectrum of propanone will therefore contain peaks at $m/e = 15$ and 43 (Figure 11.81), as well as the molecular ion peak at 58.

■ **Figure 11.79**
The fragmentation process in a mass spectrometer

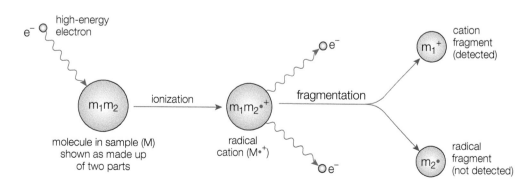

■ **Figure 11.80**
Mass spectrum of propanone

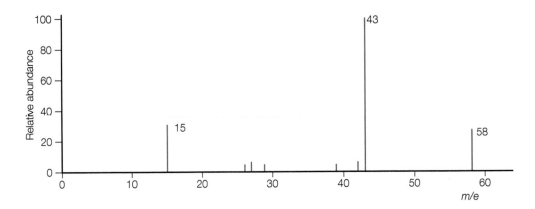

■ **Figure 11.81**
Ionic fragments formed by the fragmentation of the propanone molecule

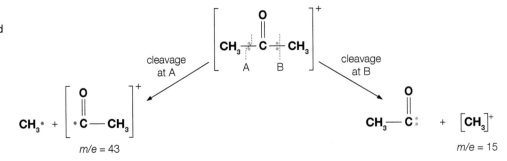

The more stable an ion, the more likely it is to form and the higher its peak height (relative abundance) will be. The order of stability of carbocations is primary < secondary < tertiary. This means that cleavage that produces a secondary carbocation will be favoured over a cleavage that produces a primary carbocation. Tertiary carbocation formation will be favoured because the inductive effect is maximized. Ions with the positive charge on the carbon of a carbonyl group, >C=O, are also relatively stable due to resonance (Chapters 4 and 14) in the resulting acylium ion (Figure 11.82). Small highly charged ions, for example H^+, are not favoured.

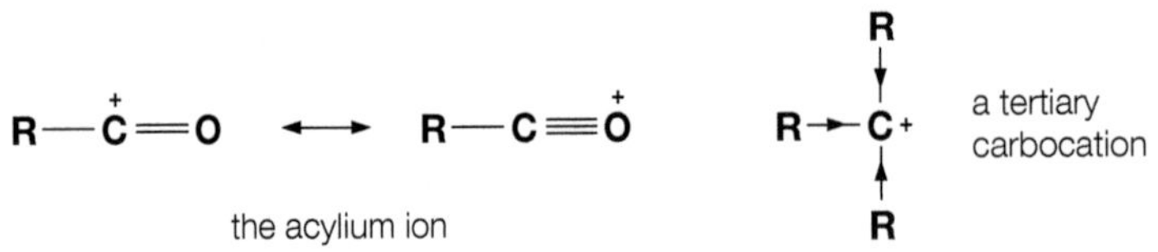

■ **Figure 11.82**
The acylium ion and a tertiary carbocation. Note the positive inductive effect of the alkyl groups, R, in the tertiary carbocation.

$$R - \overset{+}{C} = O \quad \longleftrightarrow \quad R - C \equiv \overset{+}{O}$$

the acylium ion

$$R \rightarrow \overset{R}{\underset{R}{\overset{\downarrow}{\underset{\uparrow}{C}}}} {}^+$$

a tertiary carbocation

Table 11.16 lists peaks that are commonly seen in the fragmentation patterns of mass spectra – they usually provide very useful clues for determining the structure of a molecule.

■ **Table 11.16**
Common peaks in mass spectra

Mass lost	Fragment lost	Mass lost	Fragment lost
15	CH_3^+	29	$CH_3CH_2^+$, CHO^+
17	OH^+	31	CH_3O^+
18	H_2O	45	$COOH^+$
28	$CH_2=CH_2$, $C=O^+$		

Worked example

Figure 11.83 shows the spectra of two compounds with the molecular formula $C_2H_4O_2$. One compound is methyl methanoate and the other is ethanoic acid. Decide from the major fragments which mass spectrum corresponds to which substance.

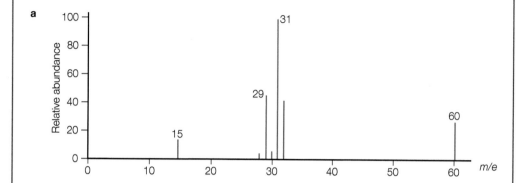

a

b

■ **Figure 11.83** Mass spectra for two compounds with molecular formula $C_2H_4O_2$

The major peaks in mass spectrum **a** are due to CH_3^+ (m/e = 15), $C_2H_5^+$ or CHO^+ (m/e = 29), and CH_3O^+ (m/e = 31). These fragments can be readily generated from methyl methanoate (Figure 11.84).

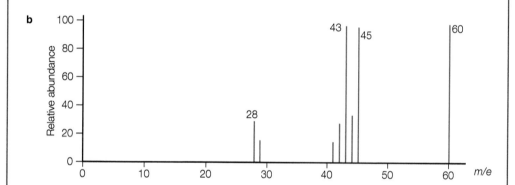

■ **Figure 11.84** Ionic fragments formed from methyl methanoate

The peak at m/e = 31 can only be generated from methyl methanoate, and not from ethanoic acid.

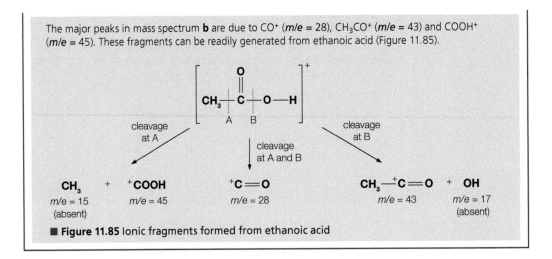

The major peaks in mass spectrum **b** are due to CO⁺ (*m/e* = 28), CH₃CO⁺ (*m/e* = 43) and COOH⁺ (*m/e* = 45). These fragments can be readily generated from ethanoic acid (Figure 11.85).

■ Figure 11.85 Ionic fragments formed from ethanoic acid

Most elements have more than one naturally occurring, stable isotope (Chapter 2). For example, the element chlorine has two isotopes, ^{35}Cl and ^{37}Cl. These are present in the ratio $^{35}C : ^{37}Cl = 3 : 1$. Therefore, any molecule or fragment that contains chlorine atoms will give rise to two peaks, separated by two mass units and in a ratio of $3 : 1$ in height. For example, Figure 11.86 shows the mass spectrum of chloroethane, C_2H_5Cl. There are two molecular ion peaks, at masses of 64 and 66. These are due to the formation of the ions $CH_3CH_2{}^{35}Cl^+$ and $CH_3CH_2{}^{37}Cl^+$, respectively. There are also peaks at masses of 49 and 51. These also are in the ratio of $3 : 1$. These peaks represent the loss of 15 units of mass, or a CH_3 group, from the molecule, leaving $CH_2{}^{35}Cl^+$ and $CH_2{}^{37}Cl^+$ ions.

■ Figure 11.86
The mass spectrum of chloroethane

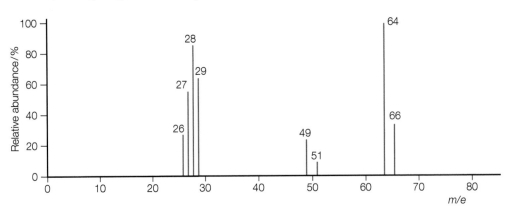

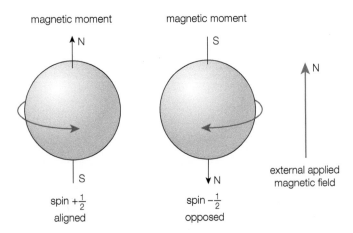

■ Figure 11.87 Spinning protons aligned with and opposed to an external magnetic field (the $\pm\frac{1}{2}$ represents the spin quantum number)

■ Nuclear magnetic resonance spectroscopy

Nuclear magnetic resonance (NMR) is a very powerful and widely used spectroscopic technique. It is also the basis for MRI (magnetic resonance imaging), widely used in hospitals. The technique relies upon the fact that certain atomic nuclei, most notably hydrogen (^1H), have the property of spin (Figure 11.87).

The proton can spin clockwise or anticlockwise and generates a magnetic field, represented in the diagram by an arrow. In the absence of an applied magnetic field, the spins of the proton are of the same energy and a collection of hydrogen-1 atoms (at equilibrium) will have equal numbers of both spin states.

The property of nuclear spin makes the nuclei of hydrogen-1 atoms behave like tiny bar magnets. When they are placed in a strong magnetic field they interact with it and will line up with the magnetic field (in an almost parallel manner) or against it (anti-parallel). The two different orientations or spin states give rise to two energy levels with a very small energy gap (Figure 11.88). The nuclear spins aligned parallel to the external magnetic field are in a lower energy orientation and more probable (in a population of ^1H atoms); the nuclear spins aligned anti-parallel to the external field are in a higher energy orientation and less likely.

■ **Figure 11.88**
The spin states of a proton in the absence and the presence of an applied magnetic field

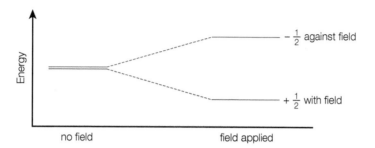

If the hydrogen nuclei or protons are subjected to a frequency of electromagnetic radiation equivalent to the energy gap between the two energy levels, then the hydrogen nuclei that are aligned with the magnetic field will move into the higher energy state. They are said to have 'flipped over' or, more accurately, undergone spin resonance (Figure 11.89). In the case of nuclear magnetic resonance, low-energy radio waves are used to bring about resonance, typically in the frequency range 200 to 600 MHz. (Imaging spectrometers used for MRI (Figure 11.90) operate at lower frequencies.)

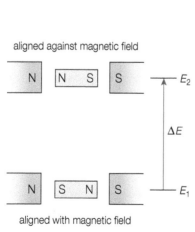

■ **Figure 11.89** The principle of nuclear magnetic resonance

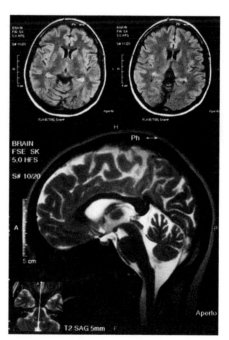

■ **Figure 11.90** MRI scans of the brain

The principle of an NMR spectrometer is shown in Figure 11.91. The sample for analysis is usually dissolved in a solvent. It is much more convenient to analyse if the solvent used does not generate its own NMR spectrum. The sample is placed in a narrow glass tube (NMR tube), which is transparent to radio waves. The tube is lowered into the magnetic field and spun rapidly and smoothly. This is to ensure that all variations in the magnetic field are averaged out, so that each of the hydrogens (or protons) experiences the same magnetic field. The sample is then irradiated with a pulse that can be regarded as containing a range of radio frequencies. When the radio frequency corresponds to the amount of energy equivalent to the energy gap between the nuclear spin states, the molecules in the sample absorb some of the radio waves. The radio wave interacts with the nuclei to cause a rotation of the nuclear magnets. The rotating magnet produces an electrical current in a wire placed around the sample, and this is what is detected.

■ **Figure 11.91**
The basic features of an NMR spectrometer

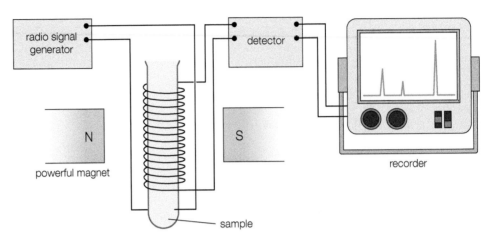

If all the hydrogen atoms in a compound are bonded to a common carbon atom and are chemically equivalent, then only one absorption would be observed in the ^{1}H NMR spectrum of the molecule. For example, the methane molecule, CH_4, has four chemically equivalent hydrogen atoms and has only one peak in its NMR spectrum.

However, hydrogen atoms in different structural arrangements (or **chemical environments**) give rise to peaks at different positions in the NMR spectrum. This occurs because the nuclei of the hydrogen atoms are shielded by other electrons in the molecule to different extents. The hydrogen nuclei are said to be in different chemical environments. For example, the butane molecule, CH_3–CH_2–CH_2–CH_3, gives rise to two peaks in the (low-resolution) NMR spectrum. One peak is due to resonance involving the terminal hydrogens in the methyl groups, –CH_3, at the end of the molecule; the other is due to the hydrogens in the methylene groups, –CH_2–, in the centre of the molecule. (This is a low-resolution NMR spectrum; a more complex spectrum is generated in a high-resolution NMR spectrometer (see Chapter 21)).

Because the nuclei of the hydrogen atoms are shielded by other electrons in the compound to a greater or lesser extent, the protons in different chemical environments will experience slightly different net magnetic fields. This creates different energy gaps, ΔE. Hence, the hydrogen atoms will absorb different radio frequencies and give rise to different NMR absorptions. An NMR spectrum is a plot of the radio frequency energy absorbed against the particular radio frequency. Hence, a proton NMR spectrum reveals hydrogen atoms in different structural environments.

The positions of the NMR absorption peaks are measured relative to the signal of a reference compound, **tetramethylsilane** (TMS), which provides a convenient zero because it has a single peak in its ^{1}H NMR spectrum. The extent to which the other hydrogen atom (proton) signals differ from the TMS signal position is called the **chemical shift** (units ppm) and given the symbol δ (lower case delta).

The chemical shift is defined as:

$$\delta = \frac{(\text{frequency of signal} - \text{frequency of TMS}) \times 10^6}{\text{frequency of TMS}}$$

The signal produced by TMS is given a chemical shift of 0.0 ppm by convention. The chemical shifts of some of the protons in some common molecules are shown in Table 11.17. The same table is found on pages 26–27 of the IB *Chemistry data booklet* (Table 27).

■ Table 11.17 Typical proton chemical shift values (δ) relative to tetramethylsilane (TMS) = 0. R represents an alkyl group, and Hal represents fluorine, chlorine, bromine or iodine (i.e. halogens). These values may vary in different solvents and conditions.

Type of proton	Chemical shift (ppm)
—CH₃	0.9–1.0
—CH₂—R	1.3–1.4
—R₂CH	1.5
RO—C(=O)—CH₂—	2.0–2.5
R—C(=O)—CH₂—	2.2–2.7
⬡—CH₃ (aryl)	2.5–3.5
—C≡C—H	1.8–3.1
—CH₂—Hal	3.5–4.4
R—O—CH₂—	3.3–3.7

Type of proton	Chemical shift (ppm)
R—C(=O)—O—CH₂—	3.7–4.8
R—C(=O)—O—H	9.0–13.0
R—O—H	1.0–6.0
—HC=CH₂	4.5–6.0
⬡—OH (aryl)	4.0–12.0
⬡—H (aryl)	6.9–9.0
R—C(=O)—H	9.4–10.0

Figure 11.92 shows the low-resolution ¹H NMR spectrum of anhydrous ethanol, CH_3CH_2OH. The NMR spectrum has *three* peaks at different chemical shift positions relative to TMS, showing that the hydrogen atoms in this molecule are located in *three* distinct structural environments. By comparing the chemical shift data for the three peaks with the values given in Table 11.17 it is possible to identify the structural units in the molecule.

■ Figure 11.92 The low-resolution ¹H NMR spectrum of anhydrous ethanol, showing peaks and integration trace

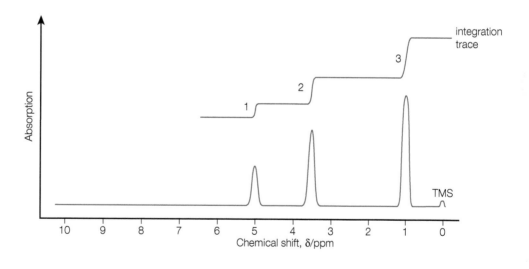

In addition to the NMR spectrum, the NMR spectrometer has drawn what is termed 'an integrated spectrum trace'. The height of each step is a measure of the area under the peak. It is proportional to the number of hydrogen atoms (protons) resonating at this point in the NMR spectrum. In this case there are three steps, which are in the ratio of 1 : 2 : 3 (from left to right).

Table 11.18 summarizes the chemical shifts, integration ratios and structural features of ethanol. Note that the presence of the oxygen atom has a 'deshielding' effect on the hydrogen attached directly to it.

Chemical shift, δ	Integration ratio	Structural feature
5.0	1	H in R–O–H
3.6	2	H in R–CH$_2$–OH
1.0	3	H in R–CH$_3$

■ **Table 11.18** Low-resolution NMR data for ethanol

This is due to the electronegative nature of the oxygen atom, drawing electron density towards itself, and has a marked effect on the chemical shift of these hydrogens. The hydrogen nuclei are shielded by their electrons from the external magnetic field, but the hydrogen attached to the oxygen is said to be deshielded.

The exact resonance frequency is determined by the net magnetic field experienced. The induced field will obviously depend on the electron density around the nucleus. The greater the electron density around the nucleus, the greater the induced field, therefore the greater the shielding and the smaller the separation of the energy levels (i.e. the nuclear spin behaves as if it were in a smaller magnetic field).

23 The low-resolution ^{1}H NMR spectrum of compound A with the molecular formula $C_4H_8O_2$ is shown in Figure 11.93. Suggest the structure of A.

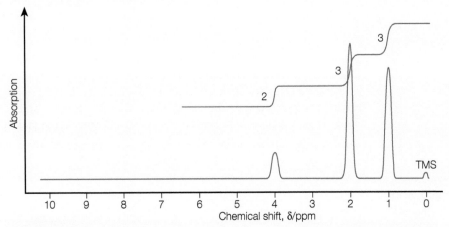

■ **Figure 11.93** The low-resolution ^{1}H NMR spectrum of a compound with the molecular formula $C_4H_8O_2$

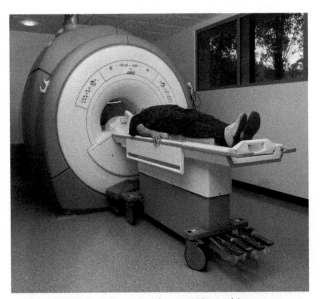

■ **Figure 11.94** A patient entering an MRI machine

Utilization: Magnetic resonance imaging

Magnetic resonance imaging (MRI) uses NMR for medical diagnosis. The patient is placed inside a cylinder (Figure 11.94) that contains a very strong magnetic field (usually generated by a superconducting magnet). Radio waves then cause the hydrogen atoms in the water molecules of the body to resonate. Each type of body tissue emits a different signal, reflecting the different hydrogen density of the tissue. The spatial information from MRI is derived by imposing magnetic field gradients in different directions across the body. Computer software then translates these signals into a three-dimensional picture (Figure 11.95).

MRI does not 'see' bone and can only produce images of soft tissues such as blood vessels, cerebrospinal fluid, bone marrow and muscles. This is because the amount of water in bone is very small compared to the amount in soft tissue. MRI is used to detect brain tumours (Figure 11.96), damage caused by multiple sclerosis (MS) or strokes, joint injuries,

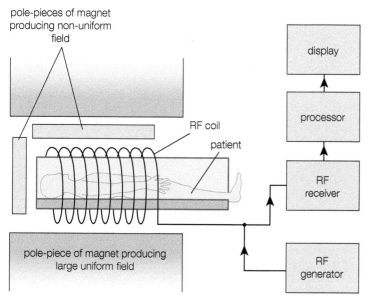

■ **Figure 11.95** Schematic diagram of a magnetic resonance scanner. (The magnetic field is usually generated by a.c. currents in wires rather than using permanent magnets.)

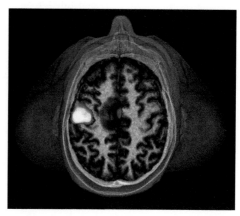

■ **Figure 11.96** MRI of a brain in cross section showing a tumour (in white)

heart disease (caused by the narrowing of arteries) and herniated discs. It is regarded as a harmless procedure *except* to those patients who have metal implants, such as a pacemaker, joint pins, shrapnel or artificial heart valves. Patients may also be given a contrast agent to help produce images with a higher contrast of organs and tissues. The contrast agent may be simply water or a gadolinium compound (a lanthanoid or rare earth compound with unpaired electrons).

Developments and advances in spectroscopy

The introduction of ultraviolet spectroscopy during the 1930s was an important milestone in analytical chemistry as it showed the advantages of non-destructive analysis. Prior to the use of spectroscopic techniques, chemists had relied upon destructive chemical analysis, such as ozonolysis and oxidative cleavage using potassium manganate(VII). The huge saving in time and the ability to work with much smaller samples demonstrated the power of spectroscopic analysis to organic chemists. They wanted to use the technique to determine the structures of molecules without being concerned about the full details of the physical background. This paved the way for the development and acceptance of the other spectroscopic techniques. NMR spectroscopy is the most powerful and versatile of all analytical techniques used by organic chemists. The phenomenon was first observed experimentally in 1938, but within five years was being used to solve chemical problems. It is a useful technique because its spectroscopic features correlate with individual atoms within a molecule, rather than a group of atoms (functional group) as in UV–VIS or IR spectroscopy. In early NMR instruments, the radio frequency was kept constant and the magnetic field altered (each type of proton is brought into resonance at a constant frequency by changing the magnetic field). These were called field-sweep instruments. The legacy of this is the use of the terms low-field and high-field for high frequency/chemical shift and low frequency/chemical shift, respectively, in today's terminology. Modern NMR machines (Figure 11.97) are fixed-field instruments and keep the magnetic field constant and homogeneous, a requirement for high-resolution NMR. This approach is known as pulse NMR.

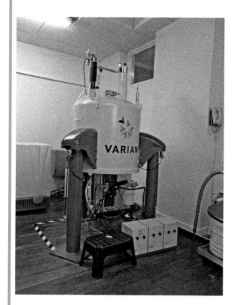

■ **Figure 11.97** A modern pulse NMR machine

■ Spectral databases

There are a number of online databases that contain chemical spectra and spectral data. A small selection is given below:

- NIST Chemistry WebBook (http://webbook.nist.gov/chemistry/)

  Contains IR, mass, electronic/vibrational, and UV–VIS spectra as well as constants of diatomic molecules (spectroscopic data) and ion energetics data, etc., drawn from various evaluated sources.

- SDBS – Spectral database system (http://sdbs.db.aist.go.jp/sdbs/cgi-bin/cre_index.cgi)

  IR, ^{1}H-NMR, ^{13}C-NMR, mass, and ESR spectra of organic compounds, searchable by name, formula, Registry Number, NMR shifts, and IR and MS peaks. (National Institute of Materials and Chemical Research, Japan)

- Reaxys (http://libguides.lib.uci.edu/reaxys)

  The Beilstein and Gmelin files (now contained in the Reaxys system) include spectral data for organic and inorganic compounds respectively, excerpted from the journal literature. Reaxys does not contain graphical spectra diagrams, and may only provide the pertinent literature reference.

■ *Examination questions – a selection*

Paper 1 IB questions and IB style questions

Q1 Perform the indicated operation and give the answer to the appropriate accuracy.

$$48.2\,m + 3.87\,m + 48.4394\,m$$

- **A** 100.5094 m
- **C** 100.51 m
- **B** 100.5 m
- **D** 101 m

Q2 The dimensions of a cube are measured. The measured length of each side is 40 mm ± 0.1 mm. What is the approximate uncertainty in the value of its volume?

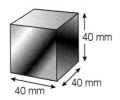

40 mm
40 mm
40 mm

- **A** 1/64%
- **C** 4/10%
- **B** 1/4%
- **D** 0.75%

Q3 What is the percentage random uncertainty in a mass of pure water measured to the nearest microgram (µg) in a kilogram (kg)? (1 000 000 µg = 1 g)

- **A** 10^{-4}
- **C** 10^{-7}
- **B** 10^{-6}
- **D** 10^{-12}

Q4 An object of mass 2.000 kg is placed on four different balances (**A**, **B**, **C** and **D**) and for each balance the reading is recorded five times. The table shows the values obtained with the averages.

Which balance has the smallest systematic error *but* is imprecise?

Balance	1	2	3	4	5	Average/ kg
A	2.000	2.000	2.002	2.001	2.002	2.001
B	2.011	1.999	2.001	1.989	1.995	1.999
C	2.012	2.013	2.012	2.014	2.014	2.013
D	1.993	1.987	2.002	2.000	1.983	1.993

Q5 An IB Chemistry student records a series of precise measurements from which the student calculates the enthalpy of combustion of a hydrocarbon as 327.66 kJ mol^{-1}. The student estimates that the result is accurate to ±3%.

Which of the following gives the student's result expressed to the appropriate number of significant figures?

- **A** 300 kJ mol^{-1}
- **C** 330 kJ mol^{-1}
- **B** 328 kJ mol^{-1}
- **D** 327.7 kJ mol^{-1}

Q6 Which of the following four recorded measurements has the smallest percentage error?

- **A** 9.99 cm ± 0.005 cm
- **C** 1.11 cm ± 0.005 cm
- **B** 4.44 cm ± 0.005 cm
- **D** 5.55 cm ± 0.005 cm

Q7 A titration is carried out by a large number of students in class and the number N of measurements giving a titre volume x is plotted against *x*. The true value of the titre volume is x_0. Which graph best represents precise measurements with poor accuracy?

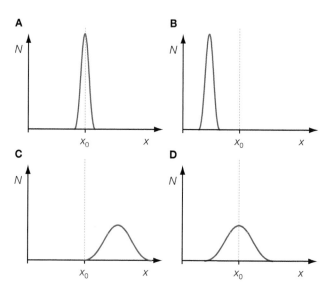

Q8 The first mass reading is a weighing bottle and sodium hydroxide. The second mass reading is the empty weighing bottle.

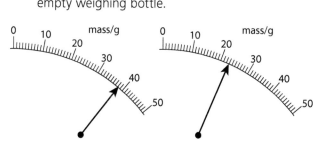

What is the mass of the sodium hydroxide, and what is the random uncertainty in the value?

A 15 g ± 2 g   C 18 g ± 2 g
B 15 g ± 0.5 g   D 18 g ± 0.5 g

Q9 What is the following measurement with the possible random uncertainty shown as a percentage instead of an absolute error?

6.25 cm³ ± 0.005 cm³

A 6.25 cm³ ± 0.4%   C 6.25 cm³ ± 0.04%
B 6.25 cm³ ± 0.8%   D 6.25 cm³ ± 0.08%

Q10 When comparing systematic errors and random uncertainties during an investigation, the following pairs of properties of errors in an experimental measurement may be considered:
I   error can possibly be removed
II error cannot possibly be removed
III error is of constant sign and size
IV error is of varying sign and size
V   error will be reduced by averaging repeated measurements
VI error will not be reduced by averaging repeated measurements

Which properties apply to random uncertainties?
A I, II, III   C II, IV, V
B I, IV, VI   D II, III, V

Q11 In a school laboratory, which of the pieces of apparatus listed below has the greatest random uncertainty in a measurement?
A A 50 cm³ burette when used to measure 25 cm³ of ethanol.
B A 25 cm³ pipette when used to measure 25 cm³ of ethanol.
C A 50 cm³ measuring cylinder when used to measure 25 cm³ of ethanol.
D An analytical balance (4 decimal places) when used to weigh 25 cm³ of ethanol.

Q12 Using an accurate pH meter, the pH of lemonade was found to be 2.30. Some students found the pH of the lemonade by titration with a 0.10 mol dm⁻³ sodium hydroxide solution. Their determined values of pH were 2.4, 2.6, 2.2 and 2.4. What is the best description of the precision and accuracy of these measurements?

	Precision	Accuracy
A	precise	inaccurate
B	not precise	inaccurate
C	precise	accurate
D	not precise	accurate

Higher Level Paper 1, November 2013, Q40

Q13 What is the index of hydrogen deficiency for testosterone, $C_{19}H_{26}O_2$?
A 5   C 7
B 6   D 8

Paper 2 IB questions and IB style questions

Q1 One method a chemist can use to investigate acid–base reactions is a titration. A pH titration is performed by adding small, accurate amounts of sodium hydroxide solution to hydrochloric acid of unknown concentration. The pH is recorded and is plotted versus the volume of base added to the acid solution.

State how the following would affect the calculated concentration of acid:

a i   The burette is dirty and drops of sodium hydroxide cling to the side walls of the burette as it is drained. [2]
  ii The burette is not rinsed with sodium hydroxide prior to filling. [2]
  iii The burette tip is not filled at the start of the titration. [1]
  iv The sodium hydroxide solution is added too rapidly in the region of rapid pH change. [1]

b i It is suspected that the pH meter consistently gives a reading 0.5 units above the actual value. What type of error is this? [1]

ii How would you verify this error? [1]

Q2 The graph below shows how the mass of copper deposited during electrolysis varies with time.

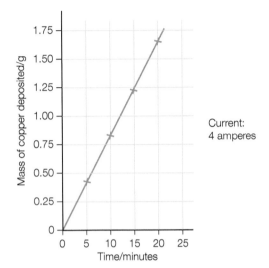

Current: 4 amperes

a Identify the dependent, independent and controlled variables. [3]

b State the relationship between the independent and dependent variables. [1]

c Calculate the rate (in $g\,min^{-1}$) of copper deposition (to two decimal places). [2]

d State **two** useful mathematical operations that could be performed on the graph. [2]

Q3 The length of a piece of paper was measured as 298 mm ± 1 mm. Its width was measured as 210 mm ± 1 mm.

a Calculate the percentage random uncertainty in its length. [1]

b Calculate the percentage random uncertainty in its width. [1]

c Calculate the area of the piece of paper and its random uncertainty. [2]

Q4 a Describe what happens on a molecular level when hydrogen sulfide molecules absorb infrared radiation. [3]

b Explain the following observations:

i The absorptions obtained from ^1H NMR spectroscopy occur at much lower frequencies than those obtained from IR spectroscopy. [4]

ii Hydrogen bromide is infrared active whereas bromine is infrared inactive. [2]

c Wavenumbers are the most common unit used to specify infrared absorptions. State the relationship between wavenumber and wavelength, and show how wavenumber is related to energy. [2]

d Explain why stretching frequencies decrease from C–Cl to C–Br to C–I. [2]

Q5 Figure 11.98 shows the mass spectrum of butane, C_4H_{10}, showing the molecular ion and fragments.

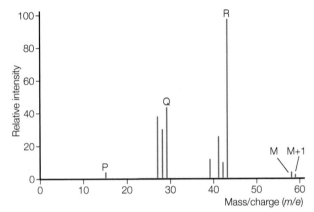

■ **Figure 11.98** Mass spectrum of butane

a Suggest the identity of the fragments labelled P, Q and R in the mass spectrum of butane. [3]

b Identify one analytical technique, different in each case, that can be used to obtain the following information.

Information	Analytical technique
Relative atomic mass of an element	Mass spectrometry
Functional groups and strength of bonds present in an organic molecule	
Potassium ions in a sample of blood serum	
Detailed structure of an organic molecule (without degrading the sample)	

[3]

Q6 a Deduce the number of peaks in the low resolution ^1H NMR spectrum of 1-fluorobutane and 2-fluorobutane. Explain how the integration trace can be used to distinguish between the two compounds. [4]

b Compare the low resolution ^1H NMR spectrum of 1-fluoro-2-methylpropane with the two spectra considered in **a**. Include the number of peaks and the integration trace. [3]

12 Atomic structure

ESSENTIAL IDEA

■ The quantized nature of energy transitions is related to the energy states of electrons in atoms and molecules.

Nature of Science

Experimental evidence to support theories – emission spectra provide evidence for the existence of energy levels

One phenomenon that was of great interest to the physicists of the 19th century was the production of atomic emission spectra. They found that atoms of a sample of gas at low pressure could be stimulated electrically to emit light whose colour could be used to identify the chemical nature of the gas. The light was passed through a diffraction grating or prism to create a spectrum. Light is dispersed in this way using a spectroscope or spectrometer. The existence of a unique spectrum for each different element suggested that there must be some internal structure to the atom.

Johann Balmer was a German mathematics teacher who measured the distances between the lines in the emission spectrum of atomic hydrogen. In 1885 he produced an empirical relationship relating all the emission lines of the atomic hydrogen spectrum. The wavelength of the lines is given by the following relationship:

$$\frac{1}{\lambda} = R_H\left(\frac{1}{2^2} - \frac{1}{m^2}\right) \text{ where } R_H \text{ is the Rydberg constant } (1.097 \times 10^7\,\text{m}^{-1})$$

In this relationship, m is an integer greater than 2, with each value of m representing a different spectral line. Balmer was able to predict the wavelength of some spectral lines that were in the near ultraviolet range. The success of Balmer's equation was strengthened when other spectral series of emission lines were discovered in the ultraviolet (Lyman series) and in the infrared (Paschen series). The lines in their series could be determined by modified Balmer equations:

$$\text{Lyman series: } \frac{1}{\lambda} = R_H\left(\frac{1}{1^2} - \frac{1}{m^2}\right) \text{ where } m = 2, 3, 4, \ldots$$

$$\text{Paschen series: } \frac{1}{\lambda} = R_H\left(\frac{1}{3^2} - \frac{1}{m^2}\right) \text{ where } m = 4, 5, 6, \ldots$$

1 Use a spreadsheet to calculate the wavelengths of the lines in the Balmer, Lyman and Paschen series. Plot them against the value of m.

12.1 Electrons in atoms – *the quantized nature of energy transitions is related to the energy states of electrons in atoms and molecules*

■ The Bohr model

The Bohr model of atomic structure was introduced in Chapter 2. This model has the following postulates about atoms:

■ The electrons are arranged in a series of energy levels or orbits which are located at various precise distances away from the nucleus. Each of the energy levels has electrons with definite and fixed values of energy.

■ These energy levels correspond to the shells and sub-shells. Each energy level contains electrons with the same value of potential energy.

■ The energies of electrons are quantized. This means that an electron moving in an energy level or orbit can only have a certain amount of energy.

■ The electron nearest the nucleus has the lowest energy level ($n = 1$). The further the electron is from the nucleus, the higher its energy.

■ The integer n is known as the principal quantum number; n can have values from 1 to infinity (∞).

■ A ground state atom is one in which the total energy of the electrons cannot be lowered by transferring one or more of them to different orbits. That is, in a ground state atom all the electrons are in the lowest possible energy levels.

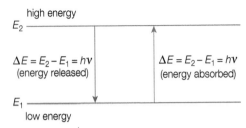

■ **Figure 12.1** Electronic transitions between energy levels

When sufficient energy is supplied to atoms, electrons will be promoted from a lower energy level (state) to a higher one. This process absorbs energy and is known as excitation. The atom and electron are now said to be in an excited state.

As long as the electron remains in a particular energy level (orbit), its energy is constant. A transition from one energy level (state) to another energy level (state) further away from the nucleus is accompanied by absorption of a definite amount of energy, and a transition to another energy level closer to the nucleus results in the emission of electromagnetic radiation of a definite wavelength (or frequency) (Figure 12.1).

The energy difference between two energy levels (ΔE) corresponds to the amount of energy absorbed or emitted during the electron transition. $\Delta E = E_2 - E_1 = h\nu$, where h = Planck's constant (6.63×10^{-34} Js) and ν, the Greek letter 'nu', represents the frequency of the radiation.

■ Determination of ionization energy from an atomic emission spectrum

As the energy increases, the energy levels in the gaseous hydrogen atom (and all other atoms) become more closely spaced, until they converge at a point, which corresponds to the electron leaving the atom. The electron is free to move around and no longer under the electrostatic influence of the nucleus. The hydrogen atom has lost its electron and becomes a hydrogen ion, H^+. This is simply a proton. This is ionization and the energy difference between this energy level ($n = \infty$) and the ground state ($n = 1$) is termed the ionization energy. It can be represented by the equation:

$$H(g) \rightarrow H^+(g) + e^-$$

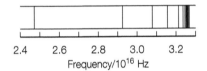

■ **Figure 12.2**
The Lyman series in the emission spectrum of atomic hydrogen

In the case of hydrogen, we can determine the ionization energy from the point in the atomic emission spectrum where the lines of the Lyman series (Figure 12.2) converge together. (A theoretical value can also be calculated from the Rydberg formula, but this is not tested in the syllabus). Ionization energies are useful in deciding which ions a metal will form and hence the formulas and properties of its compounds.

Worked example

For the atomic emission spectrum of hydrogen, the convergence limit occurs at a frequency of 3.27×10^{15} Hz. Calculate the ionization energy for a single hydrogen atom and for a mole of hydrogen atoms.

Planck's relationship is used to convert the frequency to energy:

$E = h\nu$ so $E = 3.27 \times 10^{15}$ Hz $\times 6.63 \times 10^{-34}$ Js $= 2.168 \times 10^{-18}$ J

To convert to ionization energy in kilojoules per mole, multiply by the Avogadro constant:

2.168×10^{-18} J $\times 6.02 \times 10^{23}$ mol^{-1} = 1305142 Jmol^{-1} = 1310 kJmol^{-1} (3 s.f.)

The Rydberg equation can also be used to calculate the first ionization energy (IE) of hydrogen (though this is not a syllabus requirement). It is given by the expression:

$\frac{1}{\lambda} = R_H\left(\frac{1}{n_1^2} - \frac{1}{n_2^2}\right)$, where n_1 is the initial energy level and n_2 is the final energy level.

Since $E = h\nu$, IE $= E_\infty - E_1 = h\nu = hc/\lambda$ (since $c = \nu\lambda$). The value of $\frac{1}{\lambda}$ from the Rydberg equation, can be inserted into this expression for the ionization energy and rearranged to:

IE $= hcR_H\left(\frac{1}{1^2} - \frac{1}{\infty^2}\right) = (6.63 \times 10^{-34}$ Js$) \times (3.00 \times 10^8$ ms$^{-1}) \times (1.097 \times 10^7$ m$^{-1}) \times (1 - 0)$

$= 2.182 \times 10^{-18}$ J

IE $= 2.182 \times 10^{-18}$ J $\times 6.02 \times 10^{23}$ mol^{-1} = 1314 kJmol^{-1}

Calculating the value of the first ionization energy from the wavelength or frequency of the convergence limit

2 For the sodium atom emission spectrum the convergence limit occurs at a wavelength of 242 nm. Calculate the ionization energy in kJ mol⁻¹.

In the helium atom emission spectrum, the convergence limit occurs at a wavelength of 5.04×10^{-7} m. Calculate the ionization energy for a single helium atom and a mole of helium atoms.

$c = v \times \lambda$, so $3.00 \times 10^8 \, \text{m s}^{-1} = v \times 5.04 \times 10^{-7}$ m, and $v = 5.95 \times 10^{14}$ Hz

$E = hv$, so $E = 6.63 \times 10^{-34} \times 5.95 \times 10^{14} \, \text{s}^{-1} = 3.94 \times 10^{-19}$ J

$E = 3.94 \times 10^{-19}$ J $\times 6.02 \times 10^{23} \, \text{mol}^{-1} = 237\,188 \, \text{J mol}^{-1} = 2372 \, \text{kJ mol}^{-1}$

■ Heisenberg's uncertainty principle

The uncertainty principle was introduced in Chapter 2. It can be expressed mathematically by the following expression:

$\Delta x \times \Delta p \geq \dfrac{h}{4\pi}$, where Δp = uncertainty in momentum (mv) measurement, Δq = uncertainty in position measurement and h = Planck's constant.

If we wish to measure the location of a moving electron with accuracy, then Δx will approach zero. To determine what happens to Δp, the equation has to be rearranged:

$$\Delta p \geq \frac{h}{4\pi} \times \frac{1}{\Delta x}$$

As Δx tends to zero then $1/\Delta x$ tends towards infinity, so Δp tends towards infinity.

3 If the position of an electron in an atom is measured to an accuracy of 0.0100 nm, deduce the uncertainty in the electron's velocity.

It is impossible to measure position x and momentum p simultaneously with uncertainties Δx and Δp that multiply to be less than $h/4\pi$. Neither uncertainty can be zero. Neither uncertainty can become small without the other becoming large.

A small wavelength allows accurate position measurement, but it increases the momentum of the probe to the point that it further disturbs the momentum of a system being measured.

For example, if a free electron (acting as a probe) is scattered from an atom and has a wavelength small enough to detect the position of electrons within the atom, its momentum can knock the electrons from their orbits in a manner that loses information about their original motion. It is therefore impossible to follow an electron in its orbit around an atom.

■ de Broglie's equation

In 1923 the French physicist Louis de Broglie suggested that any particle with mass m and velocity v would also have wave properties.

This is known as wave–particle duality and is the idea that all particles have wave properties and all waves show particle properties. The concept of wave–particle duality means that neither the particle nor the wave model can be used consistently to explain every behaviour and property of matter and light. The waves associated with particles are termed matter waves (Figure 12.3) and should not be confused with electromagnetic waves, such as light.

The wavelength, λ, of the matter wave associated with the particle is given by the de Broglie relationship:

$\lambda = h/mv$, where h is Planck's constant (6.63×10^{-34} J s) and mv is the momentum.

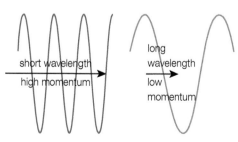

■ **Figure 12.3** An illustration of the relationship between momentum and wavelength; each wave is associated with a particle

This equation applies to all particles from electrons to golf balls. De Broglie's equation was useful in explaining why the energies of electrons in atoms are quantized.

Worked example

Calculate and comment on the de Broglie wavelengths associated with a golf ball (0.0500 kg) travelling at 10.00 m s⁻¹ and an electron (9.110 × 10⁻³¹ kg) travelling at 60% of the speed of light (3.00 × 10⁸ m s⁻¹).

$$\text{Golf ball: } \lambda = \frac{h}{mv} = \frac{6.63 \times 10^{-34}\,\text{J s}}{0.0500\,\text{kg} \times 10.00\,\text{m s}^{-1}} = 1.33 \times 10^{-34}\,\text{m}$$

$$\text{Electron: } \lambda = \frac{h}{mv} = \frac{6.63 \times 10^{-34}\,\text{J s}}{9.110 \times 10^{-31}\,\text{kg} \times 1.800 \times 10^{8}\,\text{m s}^{-1}} = 4.04 \times 10^{-12}\,\text{m}$$

The de Broglie wavelength associated with the golf ball is too small to be experimentally detected, as it is many orders of magnitude smaller than an atomic nucleus. However, the matter wave associated with the electron can be detected experimentally (diffraction from a crystal), as it is the same order of magnitude as the size of an atom. Clearly, the de Broglie wavelength (matter wave) associated with a particle is inversely proportional to the mass of the particle (provided the velocity is constant).

---

4 The mass of an electron is 9.109383 × 10⁻³¹ kg. If its kinetic energy is 3.000 × 10⁻²⁵ J calculate its wavelength in nm.

5 An electron has a velocity of 1.600 × 10⁶ m s⁻¹ in an electron microscope. Calculate the de Broglie wavelength associated with this electron.

ToK Link

The de Broglie equation shows that macroscopic particles have too short a wavelength for their wave properties to be observed. Is it meaningful to talk of properties which can never be observed from sense perception?

Calculations with the de Broglie relationship predict that moving macroscopic objects, such as golf balls, are accompanied by a matter wave with a wavelength that is too short for their wave properties to be experimentally observed by sense perception. These matter waves currently remain a theoretical concept whose existence cannot be physically verified.

Physicists' current knowledge about the sub-atomic composition of the universe is summarized by the standard model of particle physics. However, the standard model does not include the gravitational interaction or force of gravity, although it does propose the existence of the graviton, which couples with all particles. A quantum theory of gravity has not been developed and in the late 1960s physicists developed and explored a radically different group of related theories known collectively as string theory. This controversial theory claims that the fundamental 'building blocks' of matter are not elementary particles behaving as points, quarks and leptons but tiny strings with dimensions less than 10⁻³⁵ m. In the original string theories, the strings could be open (i.e. have two ends) or closed (i.e. form a loop) (Figure 12.4). An open string has length, but no other dimension, like an infinitely thin piece of string. The world sheets in Figure 12.4 show the history of open and closed strings in space–time. The world sheet is the two-dimensional subset of space–time swept out by a moving string. It could be argued that string theory is 'unscientific' unless it can be shown to predict something new that can be confirmed by experimental measurements.

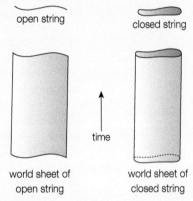

■ **Figure 12.4** Open and closed strings and their corresponding world sheets

■ Quantization

The Bohr model adds quantization to what is a classical mechanics description involving simple electrostatics. The Bohr model is certainly not a full quantum mechanical description of the atom. It assumes that the laws of classical mechanics do not apply during an electron transition between energy levels, but it does not state what laws should replace classical mechanics.

However, the Bohr theory of the hydrogen atom was a great achievement for its time. It was developed into a quantitative theory by Bohr and used to predict the energies and radii of the energy levels in the hydrogen atom. It was the first theory to predict and explain the spectral lines of the hydrogen atom, and it suggested that the quantum ideas of energy could be applied to matter as well. Bohr showed that classical physics alone could not be used to solve the problem of atomic structure and that the quantum approach was needed.

The two diagrams in Figure 12.5 provide a useful analogy for understanding the concept of quantization. A staircase is a quantized system. A person walking down the staircase must place their feet on the stairs. Hence they will possess certain definite values of potential energy corresponding to the energies of the steps. The potential energy of the person is quantized. In contrast, if a person walks down a ramp, then their potential energy changes continuously and they can have any value of potential energy corresponding to any specific point on the ramp. Potential energy in this case is not quantized.

■ **Figure 12.5**
Analogies of quantized
and non-quantized
systems

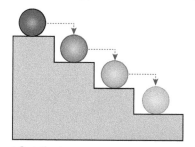

a Quantized energy

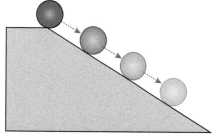

b Continuous change of energy

a

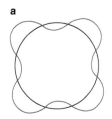

b

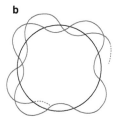

■ **Figure 12.6 a** Constructive interference (electron standing wave) and **b** destructive interference (no standing wave)

De Broglie described the electron in a hydrogen atom as a standing wave. Only electrons whose orbits allowed a whole number of wavelengths would be able to exist (Figure 12.6). This concept provides a very simple and visual explanation of electron quantization. In the first diagram the wavelength fits an exact number of times around the circle. However, in the second diagram the wavelength does not fit exactly and there is destructive interference.

Besides the atomic hydrogen spectrum, the Bohr theory can be applied to any ion with a single electron, for example, He^+, Li^{2+} and so on. In the treatment of these ions, the same procedure is taken, except that the nucleus has a larger positive charge. The spectra of these ions have lines corresponding to photons of higher frequencies. This is because the electron in its ground state is more strongly bound to the nucleus than in the case of the hydrogen atom because of the stronger attractive forces operating on the electron.

Bohr theory cannot predict the line spectrum for any atom or ion with two or more electrons. In addition, the theory cannot explain why the spectral lines have different intensities. Nor can it explain why some lines in emission spectra are very close together. The two yellow lines that dominate the sodium atom emission spectrum at 589.0 nm and 589.6 nm are a good example.

Another problem with the Bohr model of the atom is its inability to explain the splitting of spectral lines when excited atoms are placed in a strong magnetic field. This occurs because of electron spin but cannot be accounted for by the Bohr theory.

ToK Link

'What we observe is not nature itself, but nature exposed to our method of questioning.'—Werner Heisenberg. An electron can behave as a wave or a particle depending on the experimental conditions. Can sense perception give us objective knowledge about the world?

The quantum mechanical concept of wave–particle duality means that neither the particle nor the wave model can be used consistently to explain every behaviour and property of matter and light. A wave function is used to describe the probability of finding an electron in a given volume of space around the nucleus of an atom. A wave function is a function describing the probability of a particle's quantum state as a function of position and time.

According to Bohr, the energies of photons and electrons are always transferred and observed as complete quanta. When an observation is made, the wave function 'collapses' instantaneously everywhere. One of Einstein's most famous sayings is *'God does not play dice'*, which is a reference to Bohr's interpretation of quantum mechanics, with which he disagreed.

Bohr imagined that something strange happens when a photon (or electron) is detected. Before the detection, the wave function represents the probability that the photon might be detected at a particular position. After the detection, it must change to represent the new state of affairs – either the photon is there (probability 1) or not (probability 0). This means that the wave function changes everywhere whenever a measurement or observation is made. This is known as the collapse of the wave function.

Figure 12.7 shows a continuous wave just before a photon interacts with a metal surface. The wave collapses and all the energy is transferred to a single electron at one point in the metal.

If this view of the quantum world is accepted, quantum entities do not exist until they are observed. If the standard commonsense view of the macro world is accepted, things continue to exist regardless of whether they are being observed. One way of seeing the macro world is that existence or reality can be seen as a relationship between the observer, the conditions of observation and the observed. Such a relative view would appear to reflect the facts

6 Find out about the philosophical views of Hume, Plato and Kant about perception. Find out about the 'many worlds' interpretation of quantum physics.

of perception much better than either the idealist view that locates our perceptions exclusively in our minds and the realist view that there is a single objective reality 'out there'. All we can know is the variety of worlds created by the relationship between our sensory apparatus, the circumstances of the observation and that unknown and unknowable entity, the external world, if it exists at all.

John Gribbin in his book *In Search of Schrodinger's Cat* says: 'not only do we not know what an atom is 'really' we cannot ever know what an atom is 'really'. We can only know what an atom is like. By probing it certain ways, we find that under those circumstances, it is 'like' a billiard ball. Probe it another way and we find it is 'like' a solar system. Ask a third set of questions, and the answer we get is it is 'like' a positively charged nucleus surrounded by a fuzzy cloud of electrons' (Gribbin, 1984).

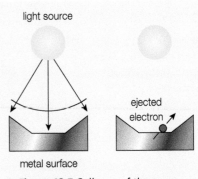

■ **Figure 12.7** Collapse of the wave function during the photoelectric effect

■ Wave nature of electrons

Experimental evidence for the wave nature of matter comes from interference and diffraction experiments involving sub-atomic particles, such as electrons, neutrons and photons (light particles). When a beam of electrons is directed at a thin metal foil with two narrow slits as shown in Figure 12.8, the interference patterns can be recorded on photographic film. Similar interference patterns can be observed with protons, neutrons and with some molecules.

When an accelerated beam of electrons strikes a thin carbon (graphite) film, a diffraction pattern (Figure 12.9), consisting of a series of circular rings, can be observed on a fluorescent screen. This experiment was first performed in 1925 by the physicists Davisson and Germer and is strong experimental evidence for de Broglie's relationship and his concept of wave–particle duality. If the velocity of the electrons is increased, the ring separation decreases, indicating a decrease in the wavelength of electrons as predicted by the de Broglie relationship.

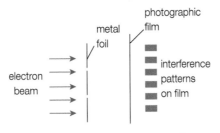

■ **Figure 12.8** Schematic diagram of electron interference experiment

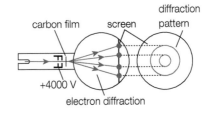

■ **Figure 12.9** Davisson and Germer's apparatus and electron diffraction pattern

Utilization: Scanning tunnelling microscope (STM)

A scanning tunnelling microscope (STM) makes use of a quantum effect known as barrier tunnelling to produce detailed images of surfaces, with resolutions close to the size of a single atom. This is achieved by bringing a very sharp conducting tip (stylus) consisting of a single atom close to the surface of a sample (Figure 12.10). The gap between the stylus and the surface atoms of the sample represents the potential barrier when a voltage (potential difference) is applied at the stylus. Electrons move (tunnel) between the stylus and the sample, producing an electric current. This current is kept constant by raising or lowering the probe as it moves across the surface of the sample. The electrical signal is processed and a computer-generated contour map is obtained.

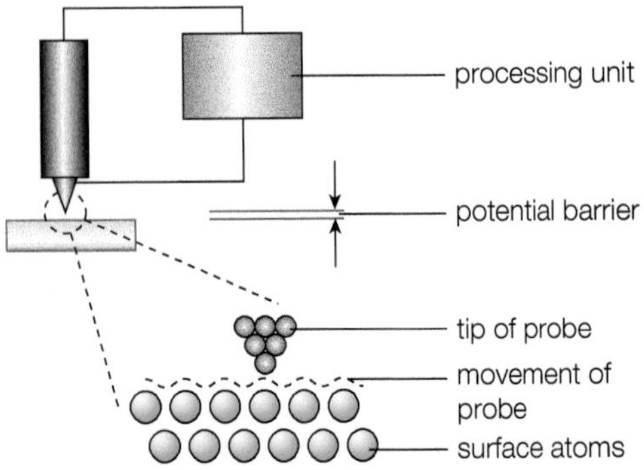

Utilization: Electron microscope

The observation from the Davisson–Germer experiment that electrons have wave properties led to the development of the electron microscope (Figure 12.11) An electron beam is passed through a series

■ **Figure 12.10** Principle of the scanning tunnel microscope

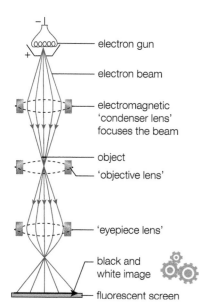

Figure 12.11 The operation of the transmission electron microscope

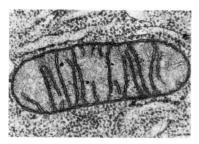

Figure 12.12 Mitochondrion surrounded by endoplasmic reticulum

of electromagnets shaped in a ring that act as 'lenses' and control the direction of the electron beam. The first 'lens' is the condenser to focus the electron beam on the object being studied (target) to increase the 'illumination'. The second magnetic ring acts as the objective lens, and forms a magnified image of the target. The third electromagnetic ring acts like the eyepiece of a microscope. It magnifies the image and forms a digital image on the screen or on photographic film.

In an electron microscope, electrons are accelerated to a high speed before striking the target to be studied. The higher the speed, the shorter the wavelength (de Broglie's relationship). The shorter the wavelength, the better the resolution – the ability to distinguish between two points.

The use of the electron microscope has revolutionized biology, allowing biologists to visualize and study virus particles. It has also allowed biologists to study the ultrastructure of cells and view organelles, such as ribosomes, which are not visible with a light microscope. It has revealed the detailed internal structure of organelles such as the chloroplast and mitochondrion (Figure 12.12).

Solving problems using $E = h\nu$

Planck's quantum theory of radiation has the following postulates:

- Electromagnetic radiation is emitted or absorbed in the form of small 'packets' known as quanta.
- Quanta of light are known as photons.
- Each quantum is associated with a definite amount of energy.
- An atom can emit or absorb a quantum of energy in the form of electromagnetic radiation only at particular frequencies (and hence particular energies, given by $E = h\nu$).

The amount of energy associated with a quantum of radiation is proportional to the frequency: $E = h\nu$, where h is Planck's constant. This is known as Planck's relationship and can be rewritten as $E = h \times c/\lambda$ since $c = \nu \times \lambda$ (the wave equation). A wide variety of problems can be solved using Planck's relationship, the wave equation and the Avogadro constant.

Worked examples

Calculate and compare the energies of two electromagnetic radiations with wavelengths of 400 nm and 800 nm.

$$E = h \times \frac{c}{\lambda}$$

$$E_1 = \frac{(6.63 \times 10^{-34}\,\text{J s} \times 3.00 \times 10^8\,\text{m s}^{-1})}{400 \times 10^{-9}\,\text{m}} = 4.95 \times 10^{-19}\,\text{J}$$

$$E_2 = \frac{(6.63 \times 10^{-34}\,\text{J s} \times 3.00 \times 10^8\,\text{m s}{-1})}{800 \times 10^{-9}\,\text{m}} = 2.48 \times 10^{-19}\,\text{J}$$

$$\frac{E_1}{E_2} = \frac{4.95 \times 10^{-19}\,\text{J}}{2.48 \times 10^{-19}\,\text{J}} = 2, \text{ so } E_1 = 2E_2$$

Electromagnetic radiation with a wavelength of 400 nm has quanta with twice as much energy as electromagnetic radiation of wavelength 800 nm.

Find the energy of photons whose light rays have a frequency of 3.00×10^{15} Hz.

$$E = h\nu = (6.63 \times 10^{-34}\,\text{J s} \times 3.00 \times 10^{15}\,\text{s}^{-1}) = 1.99 \times 10^{-18}\,\text{J}$$

Find the energy of photons whose light rays have a wavelength of 5.00×10^{-9} m.

$$E = \frac{hc}{\lambda} = \frac{(6.63 \times 10^{-34}\,\text{J s} \times 3.00 \times 10^8\,\text{m s}^{-1})}{5.00 \times 10^{-9}\,\text{m}} = 3.98 \times 10^{-15}\,\text{J}$$

The retina of a human eye can detect light when radiant energy incident on it is at least 4.0×10^{-17} J. For light of 600 nm wavelength, how many photons does this correspond to?

7 Calculate the wavelength (in m) of electromagnetic radiation with a frequency of 1368 kHz. Deduce which part of the electromagnetic spectrum it belongs to.

8 Calculate the frequency of yellow light with a wavelength of 5800×10^{-8} cm.

9 The laser used to read information from a compact disc has a wavelength of 780 nm. Calculate the energy associated with one photon of this radiation.

$$E = \frac{hc}{\lambda} = \frac{(6.63 \times 10^{-34} \text{J s} \times 3.00 \times 10^{8} \text{m s}^{-1})}{600 \times 10^{-9} \text{m}} = 3.31 \times 10^{-19} \text{J per photon}$$

$$\frac{4.0 \times 10^{-17} \text{J}}{3.31 \times 10^{-19} \text{J/photon}} = 1.2 \times 10^{2} \text{ photons}$$

Calculate the number of photons with wavelength 4.00 nm that can provide 1 joule of energy.

$$\text{For one photon: } E = \frac{hc}{\lambda} = \frac{(6.63 \times 10^{-34} \text{J s} \times 3.00 \times 10^{8} \text{m s}^{-1})}{4 \times 10^{-9} \text{m}} = 4.9725 \times 10^{-17} \text{J}$$

$$\text{So for one joule: } \frac{1}{4.9725 \times 10^{-17}} = 2.01 \times 10^{16} \text{ photons}$$

■ Electron configuration

Ionization energy

The first ionization energy is the minimum energy per mole required to remove electrons from one mole of isolated gaseous atoms to form one mole of gaseous unipositive ions under standard thermodynamic conditions. For example, the first ionization energy of chlorine is the energy required to bring about the reaction:

$$Cl(g) \rightarrow Cl^+(g) + e^-$$

The electron is removed from the outer sub-shell (energy sub-level) of the chlorine atom (that is, a 3p electron). Table 12.1 gives some examples of ionizations, and in each case the ionization energy, which is the enthalpy change for the equation. Ionization energies are listed Table 8 of the IB *Chemistry data booklet*.

■ **Table 12.1** Selected ionization energies

Element	Ionization equation	First ionization energy/kJ mol^{-1}
Oxygen	$O(g) \rightarrow O^+(g) + e^-$	1314
Sulfur	$S(g) \rightarrow S^+(g) + e^-$	1000
Copper	$Cu(g) \rightarrow Cu^+(g) + e^-$	745

Factors that affect ionization energy

Values of ionization energies depend on the following factors:

■ the size of the atom (or ion)

■ the nuclear charge

■ the shielding effect.

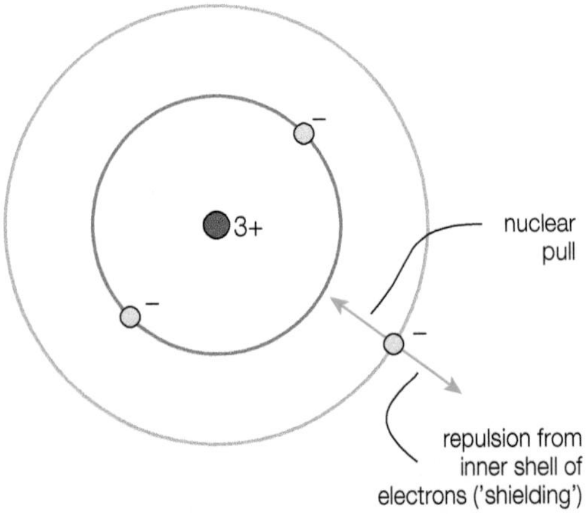

■ **Figure 12.13** Electrostatic forces operating on the outer or valence electron in a lithium atom

Atomic radius

As the distance of the outer electrons from the nucleus increases, the attraction of the positive nucleus for the negatively charged electrons falls. This causes the ionization energy to decrease. Hence, ionization energy decreases as the atomic or ionic radius increases.

Nuclear charge

When the nuclear charge becomes more positive (due to the presence of additional protons), its attraction on all the electrons increases. This causes the ionization energy to increase.

Shielding effect

The outer or valence electrons are repelled by all the other electrons in the atom in addition to being attracted by the positively charged nucleus. The outer electrons are shielded from the attraction of the nucleus by the shielding effect (an effect of electron–electron repulsion) (Figure 12.13).

In general, the shielding effect is most effective if the electrons are close to the nucleus. Consequently, electrons in the first shell (energy level), where there is high electron density, have a stronger shielding effect than electrons in the second shell, which in turn have a stronger shielding effect than electrons in the third shell. Electrons in the same shell exert a relatively small shielding effect on each other.

Figure 12.14 shows the first ionization energies for the chemical elements of periods 1, 2 and 3. The general increase in ionization energy across each period is due to the increase in nuclear charge. This occurs because across the period each chemical element has one additional proton, which increases the nuclear charge by +1.

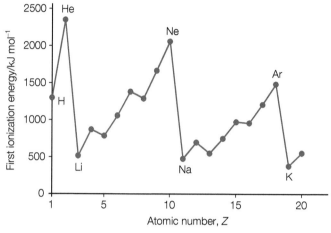

■ **Figure 12.14** First ionization energies for periods 1, 2 and 3

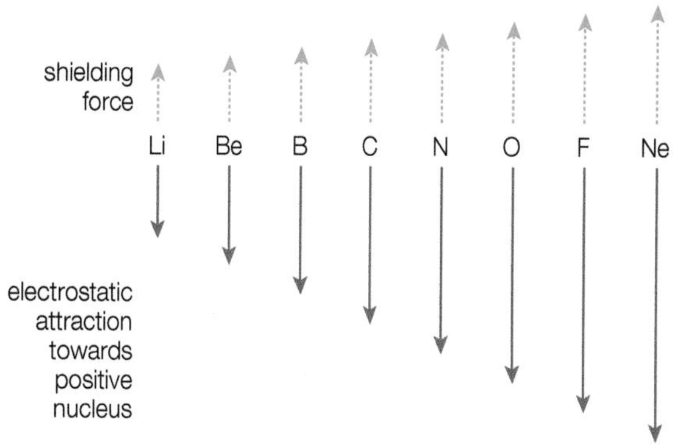

■ **Figure 12.15** A diagram illustrating how the balance between shielding and nuclear charge changes across period 2

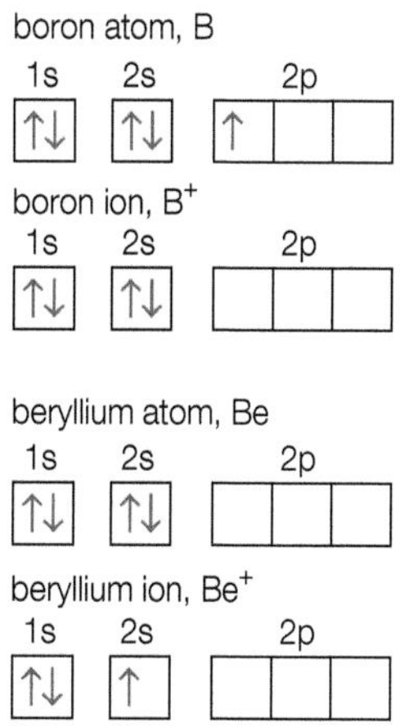

The increase in nuclear charge increases the force of attraction on all the electrons, so they are held closer and hence more strongly. Each additional electron across a period enters the same shell (energy level) and hence the increase in shielding is minimal (Figure 12.15).

Although the general trend is for the ionization energy to increase across the period, there are two distinct dips in ionization energy across periods 2 and 3 (Figure 12.14). These dips can only be explained using an *orbital model of electronic structure*.

The first decrease in each period is the result of a change in the sub-shell (sub-level) from which the electron is lost and a change in electron shielding. These have a greater effect than the increase in nuclear charge and decrease in atomic radius. In period 2, this first decrease occurs between the elements beryllium and boron. When it is ionized, the beryllium atom ($1s^2 2s^2$) loses a 2s electron, whereas a boron atom ($1s^2 2s^2 2p^1$) loses a 2p electron (Figure 12.16). More energy is required to remove an electron from the lower energy 2s orbital in beryllium than from the higher energy 2p orbital in boron. Although the 2s and 2p sub-levels are in the same shell, the energy difference is relatively large. Recall (Chapter 2) that the energy gap between shells and sub-levels becomes smaller with an increase in shell number. In addition, a single electron in the 2p sub-level is more effectively shielded by the inner electrons than the $2s^2$ electrons (Figure 12.17).

■ **Figure 12.16** Orbital notations for boron and beryllium atoms and their unipositive ions

■ **Figure 12.17** Electron density clouds of the 2s and 2p orbitals (only one lobe shown). The dotted line shows the extent of the 1s orbital; the 2s electron can partially penetrate the 1s orbital, increasing its stability

nitrogen atom, N

1s   2s   2p

nitrogen ion, N⁺

1s   2s   2p

oxygen atom, O

1s   2s   2p

oxygen ion, O⁺

1s   2s   2p

■ **Figure 12.18** Orbital notation for nitrogen and oxygen atoms and their unipositive ions

A similar explanation also accounts for the first decrease observed in period 3 for the elements magnesium and aluminium. The decrease in first ionization energy from magnesium ($1s^22s^22p^63s^2$) to aluminium ($1s^22s^22p^63s^23p^1$) arises largely because the electrons in the filled 3s orbital are more effective at shielding the electron in the 3p orbital than they are at shielding each other.

The second decrease in first ionization energy in period 2 occurs between nitrogen ($1s^22s^22p_x{}^12p_y{}^12p_z{}^1$) and oxygen ($1s^22s^22p_x{}^22p_y{}^12p_z{}^1$). The three valence (outer) electrons in the nitrogen atom are in three separate orbitals. This is in accordance with **Hund's rule**, which states that every orbital in a sub-shell is singly occupied with one electron before any one orbital is doubly occupied. However, in the oxygen atom two electrons are in the same 2p orbital. The two electrons in the same orbital experience severe repulsion. This electron–electron repulsion makes it easier to remove one of these $2p_x$ electrons than an unpaired electron from a half-filled $2p_z$ orbital. Hence, the decrease in first ionization energy between nitrogen and oxygen is due to the additional repulsion present in the $2p^4$ configuration of the oxygen atom (Figure 12.18).

A similar explanation accounts for the decrease in first ionization energy observed between phosphorus and sulfur in period 3. The first ionization energy of sulfur ($1s^22s^22p^63s^23p_x{}^23p_y{}^13p_z{}^1$) is less than that of phosphorus ($1s^22s^22p^63s^23p_x{}^13p_y{}^13p_z{}^1$) because less energy is required to remove an electron from the $3p^4$ orbitals of sulfur than from the half-filled 3p orbitals of phosphorus.

The patterns of first ionization energies across periods 2 and 3 are identical except that all the corresponding ionization energies for period 2 are higher. This is because the electrons being removed are in a second shell closer to the nucleus, compared to the third shell for the period 3 elements. The outer electrons in period 2 experience a higher nuclear charge than those in period 3.

Explaining the trends and discontinuities in first ionization energy across a period

Figure 12.19 shows the relationship between first ionization energy and atomic number. The general increase in first ionization energy across a period is because the nuclear charge (proton number) increases across the period; shielding by other electrons only increases slightly and hence there is a greater attraction (higher effective nuclear charge) for the electrons.

■ **Figure 12.19** The relationship between first ionization energy and atomic number

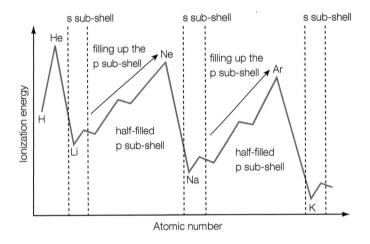

The 'drops' between groups 2 and 13 occur because an electron is removed from a p orbital which is higher in energy than an s orbital and hence is easier to remove. There is also an increase in shielding.

The 'drops' between groups 15 and 16 occurs because there are paired electrons in a p orbital, so less energy is required to remove one. This is due to the increased electron–electron repulsion.

There is a large drop at the end of each period because an electron shell has been completed, which results in a large increase in shielding. Hence there is less attraction for the electrons by the nucleus.

For the s- and p-blocks the increase in nuclear charge across a period has a large effect on the outer shell (valence) electrons because the inner shielding only increases slightly and

10 Explain why the hydrogen atom, H(g) has a smaller value of first ionization energy than the helium ion, He⁺(g).

the electrons in the same outer shell do little to shield each other from the attractive force of the nucleus. However, the d-block elements (Chapter 13), show relatively little change. This is because the increase in nuclear charge has only a small effect on the 4s sub-level because the nucleus is well shielded by electrons in the inner 3d sub-level.

Relating successive ionization energy data to electron configuration

The first ionization energy is the minimum energy required to remove a mole of electrons from a mole of gaseous atoms to form a mole of unipositive ions. The second ionization energy is the minimum energy required to remove a mole of electrons from a mole of gaseous unipositive ions to form a mole of dipositive ions. The third ionization energy is the minimum energy required to remove a mole of electrons from a mole of gaseous dipositive ions to form a mole of tripositive ions (Table 12.2), and so on until all the electrons are removed from the atom.

■ **Table 12.2** Successive ionization energies for oxygen

Ionization energy	Ionization equation	Ionization energy/kJ mol^{-1}
First	$O(g) \rightarrow O^+(g) + e^-$	+1314
Second	$O^+(g) \rightarrow O^{2+}(g) + e^-$	+3388
Third	$O^{2+}(g) \rightarrow O^{3+}(g) + e^-$	+5301

Ionization energies are always endothermic: energy has to be absorbed and work done so that the negatively charged electron can be removed from the influence of the positively charged nucleus.

The second ionization energy is always larger than the first ionization energy because more energy is required to remove an electron from a unipositive ion (compared with a neutral atom for the first ionization energy). Further successive ionization energies increase because the electrons are being removed from increasingly positive ions and so the electrostatic forces are greater. There are also fewer remaining electrons to provide shielding.

Figure 12.20 shows the successive ionization energies for potassium atoms. It is possible in a mass spectrometer to progressively raise the kinetic energy of the bombarding beam of electrons to remove the electrons one at a time from gaseous atoms and to measure the amount of energy required to carry out each individual removal.

■ **Figure 12.20** Successive ionization energies for a potassium atom

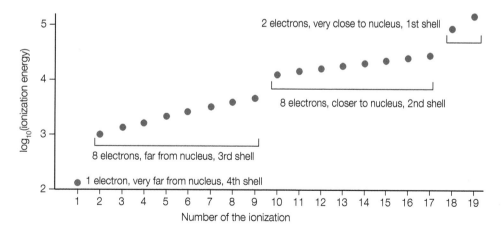

Figure 12.20 provides strong experimental evidence that the electron configuration of a potassium atom is 2.8.8.1 (or 2,8,8,1), as the greatest increases in energy required to remove an electron occur after 1, 9 and 17 electrons are removed (1 + 8 = 9, 1 + 8 + 8 = 17). These large increases in ionization energy correspond to removing electrons from inner shells whose electrons are progressively located nearer to the nucleus. A logarithmic scale is used to reduce the size of these 'jumps'.

Understanding the relationship between successive ionization data and electron configuration allows you to make deductions about the shell structure of elements. You can also use your knowledge to sketch a graph of successive ionization values for a given element. Examples of the sorts of question you may be asked are given below.

> **Worked example**
>
> Sketch a graph of the successive ionization energies of silicon against the number of electrons removed.
>
> Figure 12.21 shows the answer for this question.
>
>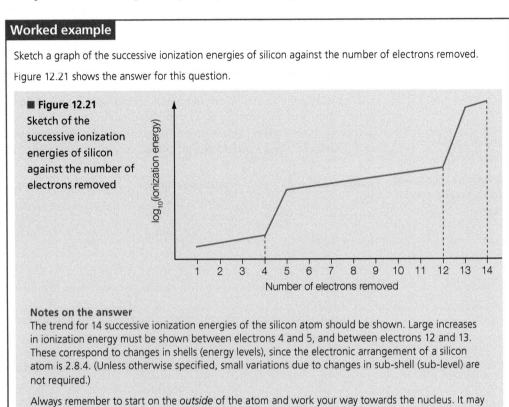
>
> ■ **Figure 12.21** Sketch of the successive ionization energies of silicon against the number of electrons removed
>
> **Notes on the answer**
> The trend for 14 successive ionization energies of the silicon atom should be shown. Large increases in ionization energy must be shown between electrons 4 and 5, and between electrons 12 and 13. These correspond to changes in shells (energy levels), since the electronic arrangement of a silicon atom is 2.8.4. (Unless otherwise specified, small variations due to changes in sub-shell (sub-level) are not required.)
>
> Always remember to start on the *outside* of the atom and work your way towards the nucleus. It may therefore be helpful to write the electron configuration of the atom back to front, for example 4.8.2.

You should also be able to deduce to which group in the periodic table a chemical element belongs from successive ionization data listed as numbers.

 ### Deducing the group of an element from its successive ionization energy data

The first eight experimentally determined ionization energies for a chemical element are as follows (in $kJ\,mol^{-1}$):

| 580 | 1800 | 2750 | 11580 | 14850 | 18400 | 23300 | 27500 |

Deduce the following:

■ the number of electrons in the outer shell of an atom of the element
■ the group in the periodic table to which the element belongs
■ the outer detailed electron configuration of the atom.

There is a relatively large increase in the ionization energy when the fourth electron is removed. The increase is much larger than the increase for the first four electrons. Hence, the first three electrons must be located in the outer or valence shell. The element must be located in group 13 since it has three outer electrons. All group 13 elements have three valence electrons.

The detailed outer electron configuration is: (s) ↑↓ (p) ↑ □ □

Successive ionization energy data can also be used to provide evidence for sub-shells (sub-levels) and electron pairing in atoms. Consider the successive ionization energies of the argon atom (2.8.8) (Figure 12.22). The reason for the relatively large increase in ionization energy between electrons 8 and 9 is that up to electron number 8, the electrons were removed from the third shell, but electron 9 is removed from the second shell. The slight increase in ionization energy between electrons 6

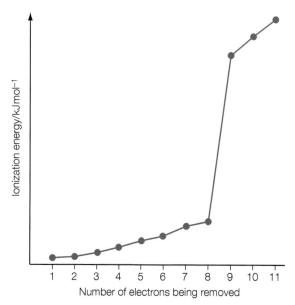

Figure 12.22 Eleven successive ionization energies of an argon atom

and 7 is due to a change in sub-shell from 3p to 3s. The slight increase in ionization energy for electrons 4, 5 and 6 relative to electrons 1, 2 and 3 can be accounted for by enhanced electron–electron repulsion.

11 Use a reliable source on the internet to find twelve successive ionization energies for calcium and vanadium. Plot logarithms (to the base 10) of the values. Relate the oxidation states and detailed electron configuration of each element to the graphs.

■ Electron-in-a-box model

The electron-in-a-box model (Figure 12.23) is a very simple quantum mechanical model that describes an electron in a covalent bond (Chapter 14). This simple model imagines an electron trapped between two infinitely high potential 'walls'. The potential energy of the electron is zero inside the box but is infinite at the walls. The electron is trapped in a potential well and cannot escape.

This model assumes that the electron behaves as a standing wave (wave–particle duality) and is subject to boundary conditions similar to those applied to the tension waves of a violin string fixed at both ends. The standing waves have nodes (regions of no vibration or zero electron density) and antinodes (regions of maximum vibration and maximum electron density).

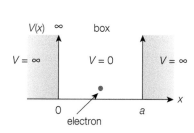

Figure 12.23 The electron-in-a-box model (*V* represents the potential energy of the electron)

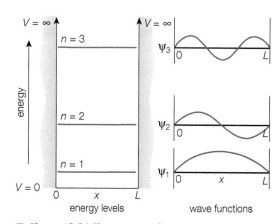

Figure 12.24 Electron standing waves

The walls of the box must always be nodes, so these standing waves must have an integer (whole) number of half wavelengths within the 'box'. This results in quantization (Figure 12.24) of the energy levels available to the electron, just as the boundary conditions for a violin string (see Chapter 24 on the accompanying website) produce first, second and third harmonics etc. The electron-in-a-box model is important because it shows how discrete energy levels arise when an electron is confined to a tiny region of space. The model can be made quantitative and can be used to calculate the energy levels and to show that that as the 'box' is made larger, the wavelengths increase and the energy decreases.

■ Quantum numbers

Each electron in an atom can be uniquely described by a set of four quantum numbers (Table 12.3): the principal quantum number (*n*), the angular momentum quantum number (*l*), the magnetic quantum number (*m*) and the spin quantum number (*s*).

■ **Table 12.3**
The relationship between the values of the principal, angular momentum and magnetic quantum numbers

n	(0 to $n-1$)	Sub-shell notation	m	Number of orbitals in sub-shell	Total number of orbitals in the main shell
1	0	1s	0	1	1
2	0	2s	0	1	4
	1	2p	1, 0, −1	3	
3	0	3s	0	1	9
	1	3p	1, 0, −1	3	
	2	3d	2, 1, 0, −1, −2	5	
4	0	4s	0	1	16
	1	4p	1, 0, −1	3	
	2	4d	2, 1, 0, −1, −2	5	
	3	4f	3, 2, 1, 0, −1, −2, −3	7	

Knowledge of quantum numbers is not formally examined in the IB Chemistry diploma, but you are required to be familiar with energy levels (shells), sub-levels (sub-shells), atomic orbitals and electron spin.

The magnetic quantum number can be any whole number from $+l$ to $-l$ which accounts for the numbers of s, p, d and f orbitals. Pauli's exclusion principle states that no two electrons in the same atom can have the same four quantum numbers. n defines the energy of the orbital, l defines the shape of the orbital, m defines the orientation of the p, d or f orbital and s defines the spin of the electron.

The standard model and the Higgs boson

The standard model (Figure 12.25) of physics is currently the best theory of how the universe works. It identifies 12 fundamental particles from which all matter is made and the four fundamental forces that control interactions between the particles. The 12 fundamental particles divide into two distinct groups: six types of quarks (which form the proton, neutron and some other less stable particles) and six types of leptons, including electrons and neutrinos. The four fundamental forces are all caused through the exchange of particles, referred to as force carriers or exchange particles. They include the photon responsible for the electrostatic force operating between charged particles.

The Higgs boson is a very massive elementary particle also predicted to exist by the standard model. In 2012 two independent teams using the Large Hadron Collider at CERN in Geneva, the world's largest and most powerful linear accelerator, confirmed the existence of the Higgs boson. The Higgs particle is postulated to interact with and give quarks and leptons mass.

The Large Hadron Collider at CERN was designed to prove or disprove the existence of the Higgs boson. A very powerful particle accelerator was needed, because Higgs bosons might not be seen in lower energy experiments, and because huge numbers of collisions would need to be studied.

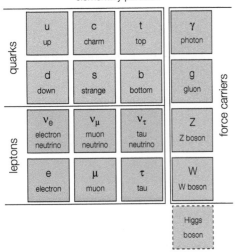

■ **Figure 12.25** The standard model

■ *Examination questions – a selection*

Paper 1 IB questions and IB style questions

Q1 Which of the following statements is/are consistent with the Bohr model of the hydrogen atom?
> **I** The lowest energy levels (orbits) are those closest to the nucleus.
> **II** An electron transition from $n = 2$ energy level (orbit) to an $n = 3$ energy level (orbit) emits a photon of definite energy.
> **III** An electron can remain in a particular energy level (orbit) provided it emits radiation of constant frequency.

> **A** I only
> **B** III only
> **C** II only
> **D** I and II only

Q2 For the species below, which one would require the most energy for the removal of an electron?
> **A** Na^+
> **B** F
> **C** F^-
> **D** Ar

Q3 A beam of electrons can be made to diffract (scatter). What is this evidence for?
> **A** Electrons have a negative charge.
> **B** Electrons have a smaller mass than protons.
> **C** Electrons have wave properties.
> **D** Electrons are spinning particles.

Q4 Which one of the following species would require the least amount of energy for the removal of a mole of electrons (under standard thermodynamic conditions)?
> **A** $Na^+(g)$
> **B** $Mg^+(g)$
> **C** $Al^{2+}(g$
> **D** $F^+(g)$

Q5 Which of the following elements has the smallest first ionization energy?
> **A** $_{19}K$
> **B** $_6C$
> **C** $_{12}Mg$
> **D** $_4He$

Q6 Which is the correct description of the appearance of an atomic emission spectrum for a sample of gaseous atoms?
> **A** a continuous spectrum
> **B** a series of dark lines
> **C** a series of even-spaced bright and coloured lines
> **D** a series of bright and coloured lines that converge at high frequency

Q7 What is the energy difference (in joules) corresponding to an electron transition that emits a photon of light with a wavelength of 600 nm?
> **A** 3.32×10^{-28}
> **B** 3.32×10^{-19}
> **C** 3.32×10^{-26}
> **D** 3.32×10^{-17}

Q8 For which element would neutral isolated atoms in the ground state have two half-filled orbitals?
> **A** $_{15}P$
> **B** $_4Be$
> **C** $_6C$
> **D** $_7N$

Q9 Which one of the following statements is **true** about light and other electromagnetic radiation?
> **A** The product of the wavelength and frequency is a constant.
> **B** As the frequency decreases, the energy increases.
> **C** As the wavelength of the light increases, the frequency increases.
> **D** Red light has a higher frequency than blue light.

Q10 The successive ionization energies of an element are:

760, 1540, 3310, 4400, 8955 and 11 900 kJ mol^{-1}.

Which of the following can be deduced from this data?
> **A** It is a d-block element.
> **B** It is an s-block element.
> **C** It is a p-block element.
> **D** Its atoms have half-filled p orbitals.

Q11 In which of the following series are the atoms arranged in order of increasing first ionization energy?
> **A** Be, Mg, Ca
> **B** O, F, Ne
> **C** Be, B, C
> **D** Ne, O, F

Q12 What increases **in equal steps of one** from left to right in the periodic table for the elements lithium to neon?
> **A** the number of occupied electron energy levels
> **B** the number of neutrons in the most common isotope
> **C** the number of electrons in the atom
> **D** the atomic mass

Higher Level Paper 1, May 2005, Q6

Q13 A transition metal ion has the electronic configuration $X^{3+} = [Ar]3d^4$. What is the atomic number of element X?
> **A** 24
> **B** 22
> **C** 25
> **D** 26

Q14 Which electron transition in a gaseous atom would absorb radiation (photons) with the least energy?

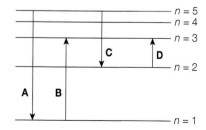

Q15 A gallium atom has the electronic configuration $[Ar]3d^{10}4s^24p^1$ where [Ar] represents the configuration of argon. In which order are the electrons lost in forming the $Ga^{4+}(g)$ ion?

	1st	2nd	3rd	4th
A	4s	4s	4p	3d
B	3d	4s	4s	4p
C	4p	3d	4s	4s
D	4p	4s	4s	3d

Q16 Which one of the following represents the third ionization energy of bismuth (Bi)?

A $Bi^+(g) \rightarrow Bi^{3+}(g) + e^-$
B $Bi^{2+}(g) \rightarrow Bi^{3+}(g) + e^-$
C $Bi(g) \rightarrow Bi^+(g) + e^-$
D $Bi^{2+}(g) + e^- \rightarrow Bi^{3+}(g)$

Paper 2 IB questions and IB style questions

Q1 The graphs in Figures 1 and 2 show the variation in first ionization energy of some chemical elements. Figure 1 refers to the chemical elements and Figure 2 refers to chemical elements in the same group as element C.

Figure 1

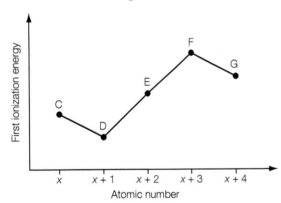

Figure 2

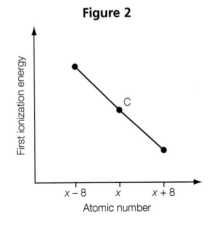

a Define the term *first ionization energy* of an element. [2]
b Element C, with atomic number x, is in group 2 of the periodic table. Justify this using all the information from Figure 1. [4]
c Explain the trend in the first ionization energy as shown in Figure 2. [3]
d State which period element C is in and explain your reasoning. [3]
e Why is the first ionization energy of element G lower than that of element F? [2]

Q2 Values of first ionization energy for the elements are in Table 8 of the IB *Chemistry data booklet*.
a Define the term first ionization energy and write an equation to illustrate it, using magnesium as an example. [3]
b Explain why the first ionization energy of aluminium is lower than that of magnesium. [2]
c Explain why the third ionization energy of magnesium is much higher than its first ionization energy. [1]
d Use the Aufbau principle to deduce the full electron configuration of cobalt. Identify the sub-level from which an electron is removed when the first ionization energy of cobalt is measured. [2]

Higher Level Paper 2, May 2008, Q3

Q3 The successive ionization energies of germanium are shown in the following table:

	1st	2nd	3rd	4th	5th
Ionization energy/ kJ mol⁻¹	76	1540	3300	4390	8950

a Identify the sub-level from which the electron is removed when the first ionization energy of germanium is measured. [1]
b Write an equation, including state symbols, for the process occurring when measuring the second ionization energy of germanium. [1]
c Explain why the difference between the 4th and 5th ionization energies is much greater than the difference between any two other successive values. [2]

Higher Level Paper 2, Nov 2005, Q2

13 The periodic table – the transition metals

ESSENTIAL IDEAS

- The transition elements have characteristic properties; these properties are related to their all having incomplete d sub-levels.
- d-orbitals have the same energy in an isolated atom, but split into two sub-levels in a complex ion. The electric field of ligands may cause the d-orbitals in complex ions to split so that the energy of an electron transition between them corresponds to a photon of visible light.

13.1 First-row d-block elements – *the transition elements have characteristic properties; these properties are related to their all having incomplete d sub-levels*

The d-block metals

The d-block metals are a group of metals that occur in a large block between group 2 (s-block) and group 13 (p-block) of the periodic table (Figure 13.1). These elements have *similar* physical and chemical properties.

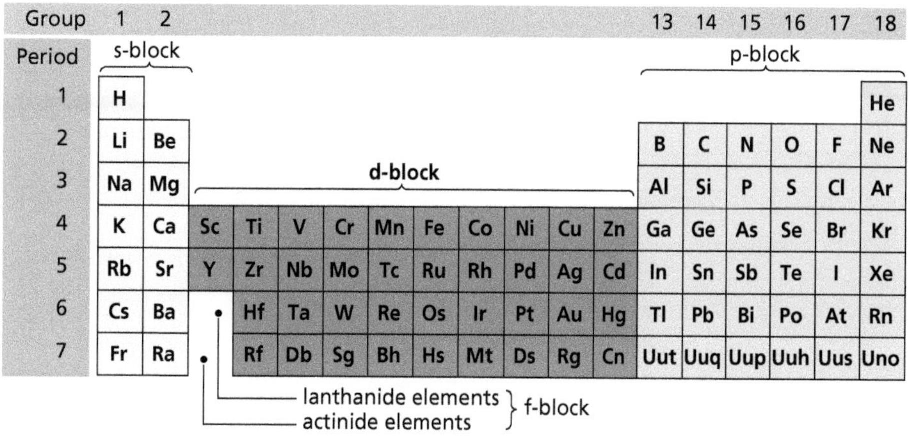

■ **Figure 13.1** Position of the d-block metals in the periodic table

The first row of the d-block contains ten elements, scandium to zinc, in which the 3d sub-level is being filled with electrons. It is these electrons that are responsible for their characteristic properties.

Nine of these elements are classified as transition elements, but the last member of the row, zinc, does not fully share the properties of the other nine and is not classified as a transition element.

The characteristic properties of the transition elements are:

- high densities, melting and boiling points
- the ability to exist in a variety of stable oxidation states; that is, they can form a variety of ions, both simple ions, for example manganese(II), Mn^{2+} (in solid compounds) and oxoanions, for example manganate(VII), MnO_4^-
- the ability to form a variety of complex ions, where the transition metal ion becomes datively bonded to molecules or ions
- the formation of coloured ions (Figure 13.2), both simple and complex
- the ability to act as catalysts (Chapter 6) and increase the rates of chemical reactions
- the ability to show magnetism in their elements and compounds
- the ability to form alloys.

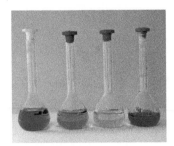

■ **Figure 13.2** Aqueous solutions of copper(ii), dichromate(vi), chromate(vi) and cobalt(ii) ions

Zinc does not share these properties: it has a relatively low melting point, boiling point and density compared to the transition metals. Zinc has only one stable oxidation state: +2. The zinc ion is colourless. Zinc shows some catalytic properties and does form complex ions, although this property is not unique to transition metals. Scandium shows some similarities to zinc but *is* classified as a transition element because it can exist in multiple oxidation states: +3 (common), +2 (rare) and +1 (rare).

There are some 'vertical' chemical similarities between the elements to justify the 'numbering' of the groups within the d-block in the periodic table. For example, in group 3, scandium, yttrium and lutetium all have a common oxidation state of +3. In most cases the three elements in each vertical column have the same outer electron configuration, for example, scandium $3d^14s^2$, yttrium $4d^15s^2$ and lutetium $5s^16s^2$.

■ Group 3: Scandium and yttrium have very similar properties, with a simple M^{3+} ion chemistry.
■ Group 10: Nickel, palladium and platinum are good hydrogenation catalysts. They all tend to form more square planar complexes compared to other transition elements.
■ Group 11: Copper, silver and gold are relatively unreactive metals in terms of corrosion. They form linear complexes and are extremely good conductors of heat and electricity.
■ Group 12: Zinc and cadmium chemistry is mainly about the M^{2+} ion.

Table 13.1 compares the physical and chemical properties of metals in the s-, p- and d-blocks.

■ **Table 13.1** A comparison of metals in the three main blocks of the periodic table

	s-block (groups 1 and 2)	d-block (groups 3 to 12)	p-block (groups 13 to 18)
Physical properties	Soft, low melting points	Harder, with higher melting points than p-block elements	Harder, with higher melting points than s-block elements
Reaction with water	React, often vigorously (rapidly)	React only slowly with cold water, faster with steam (if it all)	React only slowly with cold water, faster with steam
Type of bonding in compounds	Ionic	Ionic, covalent or complex ions	Usually covalent or complex ions
Properties of ions	Simple ions formed with noble gas configuration (octet)	Complex ions formed readily; usually coloured	Simple ions have a completed d sub-level; easily form complex ions
Complex ions	Simple ions can be hydrated (via ion–dipole forces) to form colourless complex ions	Complex ions are formed readily; usually highly coloured	Colourless complex ions are formed, rather than simple ions
Oxidation state	Oxidation state = group number	Oxidation state usually varies by 1 unit; +2 and +3 are common	Highest oxidation state = group number – 10

1 The lanthanoids and actinoids in the f-bock are sometimes described as the 'inner transition metals'. Find out about the similarities and differences between the f-block and d-block elements.

Electron configurations of the d-block elements

The last element before the first member of the d-block is calcium, whose atom has the detailed electron configuration $1s^22s^22p^63s^23p^64s^2$. However, with the next element, scandium, the additional electron is placed in a 3d sub-level which was unoccupied (empty) in the calcium atom.

For calcium the 3d sub-level was too high in energy for electrons to enter, so the extra electron entered the first sub-level of the fourth shell. But for scandium the extra proton has lowered the energy of the d-orbitals so they can now be filled (Figure 13.3).

The 3d sub-level has five orbitals into which successive electrons are placed according to the Aufbau or building up principle (Chapter 2). In particular:

■ Electrons are, if possible, placed in 3d orbitals without being paired up, unless there are no more empty orbitals.
■ If electrons are paired up in the same 3d orbital, then a spin pair results. The electron configurations of the first-row d-block metals are given in Table 13.2.

■ **Figure 13.3** The 3d and 4s energy levels on crossing the first row of the d-block

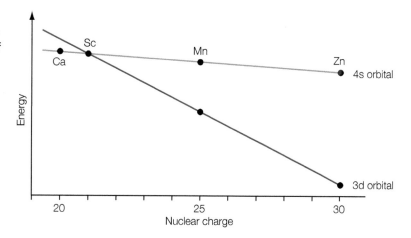

■ **Table 13.2** Outer electron configurations of the first-row d-block metals, where [Ar] represents the electron configuration of the noble gas argon

Element	Atomic number	Electron configuration		3d					4s
Sc	21	[Ar]3d¹4s²	[Ar]	↑					↑↓
Ti	22	[Ar]3d²4s²	[Ar]	↑	↑				↑↓
V	23	[Ar]3d³4s²	[Ar]	↑	↑	↑			↑↓
Cr	24	[Ar]3d⁵4s¹	[Ar]	↑	↑	↑	↑	↑	↑
Mn	25	[Ar]3d⁵4s²	[Ar]	↑	↑	↑	↑	↑	↑↓
Fe	26	[Ar]3d⁶4s²	[Ar]	↑↓	↑	↑	↑	↑	↑↓
Co	27	[Ar]3d⁷4s²	[Ar]	↑↓	↑↓	↑	↑	↑	↑↓
Ni	28	[Ar]3d⁸4s²	[Ar]	↑↓	↑↓	↑↓	↑	↑	↑↓
Cu	29	[Ar]3d¹⁰4s¹	[Ar]	↑↓	↑↓	↑↓	↑↓	↑↓	↑
Zn	30	[Ar]3d¹⁰4s²	[Ar]	↑↓	↑↓	↑↓	↑↓	↑↓	↑↓

There are, however, two unexpected or anomalous electron configurations that break the Aufbau principle, namely, those of chromium and copper. A *simple explanation* to explain the existence of these electronic arrangements is to suggest that half-filled and filled 3d sub-levels are both particularly stable electron configurations.

For all the d-block metals the 3d and 4s sub-levels, despite being from different shells, are relatively close in energy. The low energy difference means that the 3d and 4s electrons can *both* be regarded as valence electrons and involved in bonding.

Ions of the d-block elements

When a d-block metal ionizes to form a simple positive ion, the first electrons to be lost are the 4s electrons, followed by the 3d electrons. In other words, when a d-block metal ionizes, positive ions are formed which possess $4s^0 3d^n$ electron configurations.

For example, if the iron(II) ion is formed, only the two 4s electrons are lost, but if the iron(III) ion is formed an additional electron is lost from the spin pair of the 3d sub-level. Some examples of common d-block simple ions are shown in Table 13.3.

d-block metal	Simple ion	Detailed outer electron configuration
Scandium	Sc^{3+}	$3d^0 4s^0$
Titanium	Ti^{3+}	$3d^1 4s^0$
	Ti^{4+}	$3d^0 4s^0$
Vanadium	V^{2+}	$3d^3 4s^0$
	V^{3+}	$3d^2 4s^0$
Chromium	Cr^{3+}	$3d^3 4s^0$
Manganese	Mn^{2+}	$3d^5 4s^0$
	Mn^{4+}	$3d^3 4s^0$
Iron	Fe^{2+}	$3d^6 4s^0$
	Fe^{3+}	$3d^5 4s^0$
Cobalt	Co^{2+}	$3d^7 4s^0$
Nickel	Ni^{2+}	$3d^8 4s^0$
Copper	Cu^+	$3d^{10} 4s^0$
	Cu^{2+}	$3d^9 4s^0$
Zinc	Zn^{2+}	$3d^{10} 4s^0$

2 Explain why vanadium is a d-block metal and transition element. Give the full detailed electron configuration for the copper(III), cobalt(III) and chromium(II) ions.

A **transition element** is defined as a d-block metal that forms at least one stable cation with an incomplete 3d sub-level. All the elements in Table 13.3 conform to this *except* zinc which is therefore not a transition element. Copper *is* regarded as a transition element since it forms the stable copper(II) ion, which has an incomplete d sub-level. Scandium is also regarded as a transition element since it can form Sc^+ ($[Ar]3d^1 4s^1$) and Sc^{2+} ($[Ar]3d^1 4s^0$) in a limited number of compounds. For example the compound $CsScCl_3$ [$Cs^+ Sc^{2+} 3Cl^-$] has scandium in oxidation state +2.

Ions with a half-filled 3d sub-level ($3d^5$) or a filled 3d sub-level ($3d^{10}$) are usually relatively stable, but a number of factors are involved in determining the stability of transition metal compounds in the solid state (including lattice enthalpies).

Nature of Science

Looking for trends and discrepancies – the anomalous behaviour of zinc, chromium and copper

The elements from scandium to zinc form the first row of the d-block (3d-block). The first row of this block contains ten elements, because the 3d sub-level contains five 3d orbitals, each able to accommodate two electrons (a spin pair). All of the elements from scandium to copper are in the d-block because the 3d sub-level is being progressively filled. Originally the d-block was known as the 'transition metals' because some of their properties show a gradual change between the reactive metal calcium in group 2 to the much less reactive metal gallium in group 13. The term 'transition metal' is now reserved for those metals in the d-block that show properties characteristically different from those in the s- and p-blocks (the representative elements). Table 13.4 compares the properties of a typical transition element with calcium.

■ **Table 13.4** Comparison of a typical transition element with calcium

Property	Transition element	Calcium
Melting point	Very high (>1000 °C)	Lower than transition elements (850 °C)
Density	Very high	Lower than transition elements
Atomic radius	Smaller than calcium	Larger than transition elements
Ionic radius (M^{2+} ion)	Smaller than calcium	Larger than transition elements
First ionization energy	Larger than calcium	Smaller than transition elements
Electrical conductivity	Good, but poorer than calcium	Very good – better than most transition elements

Zinc is a d-block element that is excluded from being classified as a transition element. A transition element is defined as a d-block metal that forms at least one stable cation with an incomplete 3d sub-level. Zinc forms only the colourless Zn^{2+} ion, isoelectronic with the Ga^{3+} ion, with ten electrons in the 3d sub-level.

By contrast, copper, $[Ar]3d^{10}4s^1$, forms two simple ions (cations). In the copper(I) ion (Cu^+) the electronic configuration is $[Ar]3d^{10}$. However, the more common copper(II) ion (Cu^{2+}) has the structure $[Ar]3d^9$. Copper is classified as a transition metal because the Cu^{2+} ion has an

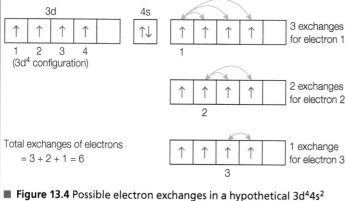

Figure 13.4 Possible electron exchanges in a hypothetical $3d^44s^2$ configuration for chromium

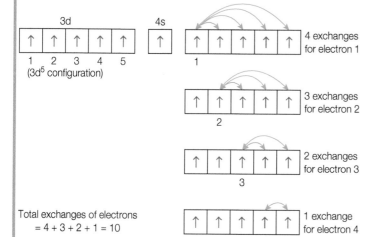

Figure 13.5 Possible electron exchanges in the observed $3d^54s^1$ configuration for chromium

3 Use similar diagrams to illustrate the exchange effect for copper and to explain why the preferred configuration of copper is $[Ar]3d^{10}4s^1$ and not $[Ar]3d^94s^2$.

incomplete d sub-level. The most stable cation of chromium, Cr^{3+}, has the electronic configuration $3d^3$ and hence chromium is classified as a transition element. However, elemental copper and chromium both have anomalous $4s^1$ electron configurations that correspond to a half-filled and a fully filled 3d sub-level. The stability of these $4s^1$ configurations is explained by a quantum mechanical effect known as exchange energy, which increases with the number of unpaired electrons.

In a half-filled and in a fully filled 3d sub-level, electrons can exchange their positions among themselves to the maximum extent. This exchange leads to stabilization, which is expressed in terms of exchange energy. The exchange refers to the imaginary shifting of electrons from one orbital to another within the same sub-level.

Consider the number of exchanges within a hypothetical $3d^44s^2$ configuration and the observed $3d^54s^1$ configuration of chromium (Figure 13.4). In the hypothetical $3d^4$ configuration for chromium there are six possible exchanges, which implies there are six possible arrangements with parallel spin in the $3d^4$ configuration.

However, Figure 13.5 shows that the total number of electron exchanges in the observed $3d^54s^1$ configuration is larger, with ten possible exchanges. This lowers the energy of the configuration, making it more stable (compared to the hypothetical $3d^4$ configuration).

■ Physical and atomic properties

Melting and boiling points

The d-block metals (except mercury and cadmium) typically have relatively high melting and boiling points (Figure 13.6) compared to the non-d-block metals. This is a consequence of strong metallic bonding (Chapter 4) because the first-row d-block metals have valence electrons from the 3d and 4d sub-levels.

Atomic radii

The atoms become smaller in passing along across the first row of the d-block metals from titanium to nickel. The extra electrons are entering an inner 3d sub-level and it is the increase in the nuclear charge that causes the atoms to shrink and their radii to decrease. However, the *inner* 3d sub-level provides a very poor shielding effect between the nucleus and the outer 4s electron. Hence the decrease in radius is small.

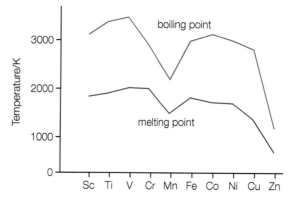

Figure 13.6 Melting and boiling points of the first-row 3d-block metals

Formation of alloys

The atoms of the d-block elements have similar atomic radii and hence these elements can mutually substitute for each other within their crystal lattices. For example, copper atoms can fit into the zinc lattice and zinc atoms can fit into the copper lattice to form the alloy brass. Consequently, many mixtures of metals or alloys (Chapter 4, and Chapter 22 on the accompanying website), can be formed between transition metals and are held together by metallic bonding. The alloys formed are relatively hard and have high melting points. Chromium, vanadium, tungsten, molybdenum and manganese are used for the production of a range of steels and stainless steels. Alloys of transition metals, such as brass and bronze (a mixture of copper and tin) are also very important in industry. A mercury-based alloy with tin, known as dental amalgam, has been used for tooth fillings.

Ionization energies and electrode potentials

In general, ionization energies ($M^{n+}(g) \rightarrow M^{(n+1)+}(g) + e^-$) rise slightly in passing from scandium to nickel, which follows the trend in increasing nuclear charge holding the electrons more strongly and closer to the nucleus (Figure 13.7).

Electrode potentials ($M^{(n+1)+}(aq) + e^- \rightarrow (M^{n+}(aq))$ (Chapter 19) of M^{2+} tend to increase (becoming either more positive or less negative) across the first row of the d-block. This means that M^{2+} ions become weaker reducing agents and less willing to release electrons and be converted to M^{3+}.

The values of *third* ionization energies gradually increase from scandium to zinc, but drop from manganese to iron. The formation of the iron(III) ion, Fe^{3+}, involves the removal of an electron from a doubly occupied 3d orbital; this electron is more easily removed because it is repelled by the other electron in the orbital (Figure 13.8).

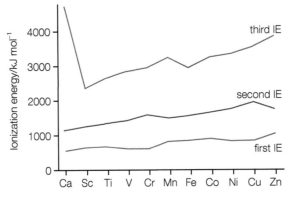

■ **Figure 13.7** Ionization energies of the first-row d-block metals and calcium (s-block)

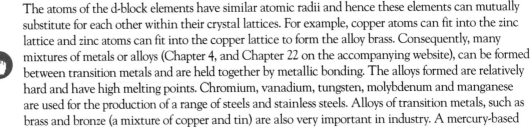

■ **Figure 13.8** The electronic configurations of manganese and iron atoms and their simple ions

Magnetic properties

Substances that contain a species (atom, ion or molecule) with unpaired electrons in its orbitals behave as paramagnetic substances. These substances, such as liquid oxygen (Chapter 14) are weakly attracted by a powerful magnetic field. In contrast, substances whose species do not contain any unpaired electrons are repelled by a magnetic field and termed diamagnetic. All transition metal atoms (except zinc) have unpaired electrons and would be expected to show paramagnetism (though iron, cobalt and nickel show a stronger form of magnetism, known as ferromagnetism).

The transition metal ions generally contain one or more unpaired electrons and hence their compounds, including their complexes, are generally paramagnetic. The occurrence of unpaired electrons in transition metal complexes is often a consequence of the number, geometry and electronic properties of the ligands bonded to the transition metal ion. Paramagnetic character increases with the number of unpaired electrons, and is quantified and expressed in terms of the magnetic moment. The magnetic moment is related to the number of unpaired electrons according to the following relationship (known as the spin-only formula):

$$\text{magnetic moment}, \mu = \sqrt{n(n + 2)}$$

It has units of μB, where n is the number of unpaired electrons and μ_B stands for the Bohr magneton, a unit of magnetic moment:

$$1\,\mu_B = 9.27 \times 10^{-24}\,A\,m^2 \text{ (or } J\,T^{-1})$$

(This is the formula for the spin-only magnetic moment, and ignores orbital angular momentum.) Table 13.5 shows the magnetic moments of some ionic species belonging to the first-row transition series.

■ **Table 13.5** Magnetic moments of some d-block ions

Ion	Outer electron configuration	Number of unpaired electrons	Experimentally measured total magnetic moment/μB	Calculated magnetic moment/μB
Sc^{3+}	$3d^0$	0	0.0	0.00
Ti^{3+}	$3d^1$	1	1.75	1.73
V^{3+}	$3d^2$	2	2.76	2.83
Cr^{3+}	$3d^3$	3	3.80	3.87
Mn^{2+}	$3d^5$	5	5.96	5.92
Fe^{2+}	$3d^6$	4	5.10	4.89

The experimentally measured total magnetic moment depends not only upon the spin magnetic moment, but also the orbital magnetic moment, which is the magnetic field associated with the motion of an electron about a nucleus rather than with its spin. Magnetic interactions may occur between paramagnetic atoms or ions that are close to each other, for example, as in bulk metals or separated by small linking atoms in compounds. If the magnetic dipoles are aligned in the same direction then the paramagnetism is greatly enhanced, resulting in ferromagnetism. This behaviour is observed in iron, cobalt, nickel and some compounds, for example, CrO_2 and Fe_3O_4.

Explaining the magnetic properties in transition metals in terms of unpaired electrons

If the paramagnetism of a complex can be measured then the number of unpaired electrons can be deduced. For example, $[Fe(H_2O)_6]^{2+}$ and $[Fe(CN)_6]^{4-}$ are both octahedral complexes. The first complex has a magnetic moment corresponding to four unpaired electrons and the second is diamagnetic (no unpaired electrons). These results can be explained by invoking structures known as high-spin and low-spin complexes, which are discussed later.

4 Deduce the number of unpaired electrons in the following species: Ti^{4+}, Cu^+, Fe^{3+}, V^{2+}, Co^{2+}, V^{4+} and Zn^{2+}. State which ion shows the strongest paramagnetism (largest magnetic moment). Assume that the ions are in the gaseous state with the ground state configuration.

5 Deduce the number of unpaired electrons in the following chromium species: $Cr^{2+}(g)$, $Cr^{3+}(g)$ and $Cr^{4+}(g)$. Find out about the construction and use of a Gouy balance and an Evans balance and their use in measuring paramagnetism.

ToK Link

The medical symbols for female and male originate from the alchemical symbols for copper and iron.
What role has the pseudoscience of alchemy played in the development of modern science?

■ **Figure 13.9** Alchemical symbol for copper

The alchemists used various pictorial symbols to represent elements and stable compounds. Each of these symbols had a deep philosophical meaning. There are several alchemical symbols for copper, but one is the traditional symbol representing Venus, the Roman goddess of love (Figure 13.9).

In alchemy iron is representative of the planet Mars and symbolizes male energy and strength. The symbol for iron is the same symbol as used to represent male in medicine and genetics (Figure 13.10).

■ **Figure 13.10** Alchemical symbol for iron

Modern chemistry is a science describing the interaction between different substances through chemical reactions and explains their composition, structure and properties. Chemistry is a science that seeks the understanding of various chemical phenomena within the physical world.

Modern chemistry dates back to the 18th century and is therefore not a very old practice, but the principles of how to gain knowledge through experiments and observations on different types of chemical substances go back for more than two thousand years for alchemy (Figure 13.11).

As in modern chemistry, alchemy involved the concept of understanding and acquiring knowledge on different kinds of matter through experiments and observations. Although the alchemists' studies were based on ancient theories and concepts, such as the ancient Greek concept that all matter consists of Earth, Fire, Water and Air, they gave many alchemists and philosophers a foundation for the understanding of nature.

■ **Figure 13.11** 'The Alchemist', by David Teniers the Younger, depicts alchemy in the 17th century

But around the 17th and 18th centuries there were scientists showing that this theory was false, such as Robert Boyle (1627–1691) with his book *The Skeptical Chemist*, proving that nature does not consist only of those four 'elements', and Antoine Lavoisier (1743–1794) explaining the process of combustion in terms of oxidation rather than phlogiston. Those theoretical developments thus paved the way for the start and development of modern chemistry.

■ Metallic properties

The physical properties of the transition metals may be related to the incomplete 3d sub-level. Table 13.6 summarizes the metallic properties of the transition metals.

■ **Table 13.6** Metallic properties of transition elements and their associated uses

Metallic property	Associated uses
Ductile, malleable	Wide range of equipment and machines
Dense, high melting point	Structures, structural materials and tools
Very high boiling point, hard and high tensile strength	Uses requiring good mechanical characteristics
Electrically and thermally conducting	Copper wire and cooking utensils
Lustrous (shiny) and sonorous	Coins, chromium plating and musical instruments

Mining for precious metals

Mining for copper and other rare metals offers a source of wealth for several countries including, for instance, Mongolia. The economic advantage to such countries seems immense at first sight and potentially lifts the development of that country across a wide range of socially beneficial areas. However, in Mongolia, the massive mining developments that offer economic advancement for the region come at an environmental and ecological cost.

Mongolia has recently opened one of the world's biggest copper mines, the Oyu Tolgoi. This project alone will account for 30% of Mongolia's entire gross domestic product (GDP). The project raises a complex set of issues, with the deal seemingly favouring the international mining company as the government receives just 34% of the profits from the mining activity. Located in the South Gobi desert where water is a precious commodity, particularly in the life of the nomadic herdsmen of the region, there are concerns that the mine has closed off open water sources.

Aside from the particular concerns about individual cases, the increasing demand for copper and rare transition metals raises issues around the balance between the benefit and costs of development, and the pressures of consumerism. The development of smartphones and the other electronic devices implicit in the modern technological revolution is heavily dependent on the availability of chemical elements, many of which are from unfamiliar regions of the periodic table. While, to a chemist, it is fascinating and intriguing to see the utilization of elements that have previously been considered rather esoteric, our increasing dependence on these resources poses wide-ranging problems of economy, availability and sustainability linked with associated ecological and environmental issues.

Modern electronic technology depends heavily on copper as an excellent conductor of electricity, placing demands on its sustainable availability. Metals such as cobalt and nickel are also of importance; however, other, rarer metals have also grown to be highly significant. It can be argued that modern technology, and the miniaturization involved, is impossible without access to these elements and their exceptional physical properties. Examples of these metals include neodymium (Nd), tantalum (Ta) and indium (In).

■ Neodymium has exceptional magnetic properties and is therefore used to produce the small, very powerful magnets required for computer hard drives, audio speakers and headphones (the earpieces of mobile phones, for instance).

■ Tantalum has excellent heat and electrical conductivities and as such is significant in the production of very small capacitors for mobile phones and satellite navigation devices.

■ Indium has very high electrical conductivity and is used in LCD screens where the minute pixels are switched on and off to provide the display.

The abundance of these materials, including copper, is under pressure, and new sources are continually being sought to resource the revolution in electronic devices. Can we control our desire for the 'latest' electronic products – can companies such as Apple control the release of new models so as to impose less pressure on the availability of rare 'niche' elements?

The potential environmental impact of a proposal to exploit the mineral deposits of Alaska's Bristol Bay is currently being evaluated. The mining here will involve both open-cast and shaft mining and bring jobs and wealth to a region where the population depends on subsistence living. However, the mining will have impact on one of the last pristine wildernesses of the planet and on some of the major salmon-spawning rivers and streams of the region. The impact assessment must weigh carefully the implications of such a large-scale mining development designed to satisfy the need to support technological development. One important dimension of this is the effect on the lifestyle and rights of the indigenous Inuit peoples.

This development in the Arctic region highlights the considerations involved in the opening up of the northern regions as the area becomes more accessible with the contraction of Arctic ice-cap. Political negotiations are in process regarding national interests in the region and may well be indicative of the controversies that may arise when the treaty currently protecting the Antarctic region comes to its end.

Rusting

Iron and steel react with oxygen and water, both of which are present in most natural environments, to form hydrated iron oxides (rust), similar in chemical composition to the original iron ore.

The effects of corrosion in our daily lives are both direct, in that corrosion reduces the useful service lives of our possessions, and indirect, in that producers and suppliers of goods and services suffer corrosion costs, which they pass on to consumers.

At home, corrosion can be seen on vehicle body panels, barbecue grills, outdoor furniture, and metal tools. The main reason for replacing car radiator coolant every year is to replenish the corrosion inhibitor that limits corrosion of the cooling system. Corrosion protection is built into all major household appliances such as water heaters, furnaces, washers and dryers.

More serious is how corrosion may affect our lives during travel from home to work or school. The corrosion of steel reinforcing bars in concrete can occur unseen and suddenly result in failure of a section of an elevated road, the collapse of electrical towers, and damage to buildings, parking structures and bridges, etc. This will result in significant repair costs and put people at risk of injury and death. Perhaps most dangerous of all is corrosion that occurs in major industrial plants, such as electrical power plants or chemical processing plants. Plant shutdowns can and do occur as a result of corrosion.

In the early hours of 3rd December, 1984 approximately 45 tonnes of methyl isocyanate, CH_3NCO, escaped from a pesticide plant in Bhopal, India. The pesticide plant was owned by the American multinational company Union Carbide and was situated 4.8 kilometres from Bhopal.

The methyl isocyanate had escaped when a valve in the plant's underground storage tank broke under pressure and allowed water to enter and react with the organic compound. This caused a cloud of lethal gas to diffuse from the factory over Bhopal. The release was made worse because the hydrolysis reaction was catalysed by iron from corrosion of the stainless steel tank. It was estimated that 10 000 to 16 000 people were killed and up to 100 000 others were affected,

making this the worst industrial accident of all time. It is believed that 20 000 people have subsequently died from the effects of the leak. The people of Bhopal were treated for many terrible symptoms, including frothing at the mouth, swollen eyes, respiratory (breathing) difficulties, blindness, kidney and liver failure.

Rusting of iron and steel is not inevitable, however. The iron pillar shown in Figure 13.12 is located in Delhi, India. It is a 7 metre column located in the Qutb mosque. It is 1600 years old and famous for the rust-resistant composition of the metals used in its construction. The pillar has been studied by archaeologists and metallurgists and termed 'a testament to the skill of ancient Indian blacksmiths' because of its high resistance to rusting. The corrosion resistance results from an even layer of crystalline iron hydrogen phosphate that has formed on the high-phosphorus iron, which serves to protect it from the effects of the Indian climate.

■ Chemical properties

Oxidation states

The common oxidation states for the first row of the d-block are shown in Figure 13.13. The most common oxidation state is +2 resulting from the loss of two 4s electrons to form an M^{2+} ion. The maximum stable oxidation state frequently corresponds to the maximum number of electrons (3d and 4s) available for bonding. For example, manganese ($3d^5 4s^2$) has a maximum oxidation state of +7.

■ **Figure 13.13** Common oxidation states for the first row of the d-block

Sc	Ti	V	Cr	Mn	Fe	Co	Ni	Cu	Zn
								+1	
	+2	+2	+2	+2	+2	+2	+2	+2	+2
+3	+3	+3	+3	+3	+3	+3			
	+4	+4		+4					
		+5							
			+6	+6					
				+7					

The stability of the higher oxidation states decreases with atomic number from left to right across the series (scandium to zinc).

The stability of the +2 oxidation state relative to the +3 oxidation state increases with atomic number from left to right across the first row of the d-block.

Compounds with elements in the intermediate oxidation states tend to disproportionate, for example, MnO_4^{2-} (+6). At low pH the ions will disproportionate to form manganate(VII) ions and manganese(IV) oxide.

The greater stability of Mn^{2+} (relative to Mn^{3+}) and Fe^{3+} (relative to Fe^{2+}) may be related to the stability of the half-filled 3 sub-level.

Transition metals tend to exist as cations in low oxidation states (e.g. Mn^{2+} (+2)) and as oxoanions in high oxidation states (e.g. MnO_4^- (+7)).

The relative stability of the oxidation states is extremely important and is usually discussed in terms of standard electrode potentials (Chapter 19). Standard electrode potentials can be used to establish whether a redox reaction is feasible or spontaneous (under standard thermodynamic conditions).

The variable oxidation states are due, in part, to the relatively small energy difference between the 3d and 4s sub-levels. This can be illustrated by examining the successive ionization energies of iron and magnesium (Table 13.7).

■ **Table 13.7** Successive ionization energies of iron and magnesium

Element	First ionization energy/kJ mol⁻¹	Second ionization energy/kJ mol⁻¹	Third ionization energy/kJ mol⁻¹	Fourth ionization energy/kJ mol⁻¹
Magnesium	738	1450	7740	10 500
Iron	762	1560	2960	5 400

When iron and magnesium form ions, energy must be supplied to remove electrons from the atoms of the two elements. Ionization is an endothermic process. Iron is able to form stable compounds containing iron (II) or iron (III) ions. Formation of Fe^{2+} requires the sum of the first and second ionization energies. Formation of Fe^{3+} requires the sum of the first, second and third ionization energies. The energy required can be supplied by lattice formation.

When magnesium forms an ionic compound, such as magnesium oxide, MgO [Mg^{2+} O^{2-}], the energy released during lattice formation (Chapter 15) is much greater than the energy required to form the magnesium and oxide ions (the sum of the first and second ionization energies and the first and second electron affinities).

However, the lattice enthalpy is *not* able to supply the energy required to remove the third electron from a magnesium atom. This is because the electron is from an inner shell and close to the nucleus. This electron and others in the inner shells are known as 'core' electrons and never participate in ion formation.

Explaining the ability of transition metals to form variable oxidation states from successive ionization energies

The known oxidation states of each first-row d-block element are shown in Figure 13.13. With the exception of scandium, nickel and zinc, the metals each show several stable and common oxidation states. This is possible because the 3d and 4s electrons have similar energies and are available for bonding. It is seen that the maximum oxidation state rises to a peak on passing from scandium to manganese and then decreases. The maximum oxidation state is never greater than the total number of 3d and 4s electrons, since further electrons would have to come from the core and this would require large amounts of energy.

For example, the electron configuration of titanium is $[Ar]3d^2 4s^2$ and hence titanium has a maximum oxidation state of +4 since the 3d and 4s electrons can be removed relatively easily. Oxidation states of +2 and +3 are also expected. However, an oxidation state of +5 is not expected since the fifth electron would have to come from the inner argon core.

This is confirmed by the successive ionization energies (IEs) for titanium: first IE $659\,kJ\,mol^{-1}$; second IE $1310\,kJ\,mol^{-1}$; third IE $2653\,kJ\,mol^{-1}$; fourth IE $4175\,kJ\,mol^{-1}$; and fifth $9581\,kJ\,mol^{-1}$. Note the sharp increase between the fourth and fifth ionization energies.

The sum of the ionization energies (an endothermic process) would be greater than the energy released by hydration or ionic bonding (exothermic). The higher oxidation states are formed less readily on going across the d-block (left to right) because the ionization energies generally increase. Covalent character also increases as the oxidation state increases.

The size of the ionization energies gives some indication of the energy required to raise the transition metal to a particular oxidation state. From the knowledge of values of ionization energies for metals it is possible to explain the relative stabilities of various oxidation states. A comparison with groups 1, 2 and 13 may also help.

For example, the sum of the first three ionization energies for copper is $6258\,kJ\,mol^{-1}$ and the sum of the first three ionization energies for cobalt is $5640\,kJ\,mol^{-1}$. Therefore cobalt(III) compounds may be more thermodynamically stable than copper(III) compounds. This prediction is confirmed, with stable cobalt(III) compounds being common and copper(III) ions being rare and only found in a small number of copper-containing compounds (see Chapter 22 on the accompanying website) and some proteins.

However, it should be noted that in addition to ionization energy, the other factors that determine the stability of a particular oxidation state in a compound are the enthalpy of atomization of the metal, the lattice enthalpy and the hydration enthalpies. These enthalpy changes need to be considered in the context of a Born–Haber cycle (Chapter 15).

6   The graph in Figure 13.14 was obtained from a first-row transition metal. Explain the important changes on the graph and hence identify the transition metal.

■ **Figure 13.14** Successive ionization energies for an unknown transition metal

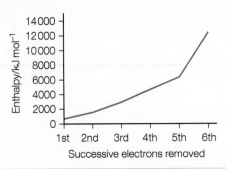

Redox reactions and redox titrations

Many of the reactions involving transition metals are redox reactions (Chapter 9) involving electron transfer. These can be described by half-equations and by ionic equations formed from the combination of two half-equations (with equal numbers of electrons). Disproportionation is a redox reaction involving the simultaneous increase and decrease in oxidation state of the same element.

The ionic equation below describes the reaction between dichromate(VI) and sulfate(IV) (sulfite) ions. It is balanced with respect to charge and the chemical species.

$$Cr_2O_7^{2-}(aq) + 8H^+(aq) + 3SO_3^{2-}(aq) \rightarrow 2Cr^{3+}(aq) + 3SO_4^{2-}(aq) + 4H_2O(l)$$

The dichromate(VI) ions undergo reduction to form chromium(III) ions. The dichromate(VI) ions are acting as the oxidizing agent and have gained electrons (from the reducing agent). The sulfate(IV) (sulfite) ions undergo oxidation to sulfate(VI) (sulfate) ions – the oxidation state increases from +4 to +6. The sulfate(IV) (sulfite) ions act as the reducing agent and have lost electrons.

Transition metals are commonly used in redox titrations. For example, oxoanions of transition metals are powerful oxidizing agents and can be used in redox titrations.

Worked example

Potassium dichromate(VI) is a powerful oxidizing agent and will oxidize tin(II) ions to tin(IV) ions. The half-equations are:

$Cr_2O_7^{2-}(aq) + 14H^+(aq) + 6e^- \rightarrow 2Cr^{3+}(aq) + 7H_2O(l)$

$Sn^{2}(aq) \rightarrow Sn^{4+}(aq) + 2e^-$

20.00 cm^3 of a solution of tin(II) ions required 18.40 cm^3 of a 0.100 mol dm^{-3} potassium dichromate(VI) solution for complete oxidation. Calculate the mass of tin(II) ions contained in 1 dm^3 of the solution.

From the equation 3 moles of tin(II) ions are oxidized by 1 mole of dichromate(VI) ions.

From the equation 3 moles of tin(II) ions are oxidized by 1 mole of dichromate(VI) ions.

Hence the concentration of tin(II) ions is $\dfrac{0.100 \times 18.40}{20.00} \times 3 = 0.276$ g dm^{-3}

Therefore the mass of tin(II) ions is 118.71 g mol^{-1} × 0.276 g dm^{-3} = 32.76 g

---

7   A 2.41 g nail made from an alloy containing iron is dissolved in 100.00 cm^3 of acid. The solution formed contains iron(II) ions, Fe^{2+}(aq). 10.00 cm^3 portions of this solution are titrated with potassium manganate(VII) solution of 0.02 mol dm^{-3}. 9.80 cm^3 of potassium manganate(VII) solution were needed to react with the solution containing the iron. Calculate the percentage of iron by mass in the nail.

■ Complex ions

A d-block metal complex ion consists of a d-block metal ion surrounded by a definite number of ligands. These are molecules or negative ions that have a lone pair of electrons. Common ligands are water molecules, H_2O, ammonia molecules, NH_3, chloride ions, Cl^-, hydroxide ions, OH^-, and cyanide ions, CN^-.

The ligands share their lone pair with empty orbitals in the central d-block metal ion. The bonds formed between the d-block metal ion and the ligands are dative covalent bonds (Chapter 4). They are sometimes called coordinate bonds. The ligands are behaving as Lewis bases (electron pair donors) (Chapter 18).

The number of dative bonds formed by the ligands with the d-block metal ion is known as the coordination number. Common coordination numbers are 4 and 6; 2 is less common. Complexes with a coordination number of 2 will be linear, those with 4 are usually tetrahedral (occasionally square planar) and those with 6 are octahedral (Figure 13.15). (Some octahedral complexes may have distorted shapes.)

The net charge on a complex ion is the sum of the charge on the d-block metal ion and the charges on the ligands (if they are ions). The net charge may be positive, negative or zero.

Ions of d-block metals have a strong tendency to form complex ions because they are relatively small and highly charged. They are highly polarizing due to a high charge density, which favours covalent bond formation. Ions from groups 1 and 2 are less polarizing and form ion–dipole bonds (Chapter 4) with ligands.

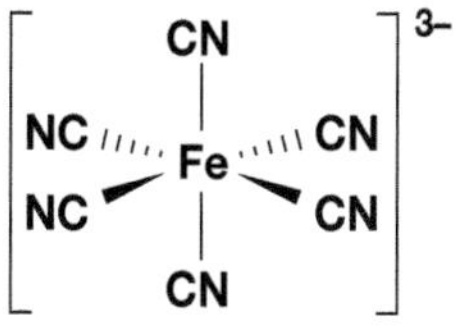

Polydentate ligands

Water, ammonia, chloride and cyanide ions usually behave as monodentate ligands, meaning that they form only one dative bond with the central d-block metal ion. A number of larger ligands are able to form two or more dative bonds with the central metal ion and are said to be polydentate. The resulting complexes can be very stable and are known as chelates or chelating complexes. Polydentate ligands are often known as chelating agents. Ethanedioate ions and 1,2-diaminoethane molecules are bidentate ligands, while the negative ion derived from EDTA (ethanediaminetetraethanoic acid) is hexadentate, forming up to six dative bonds per ion (Figure 13.16).

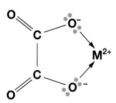

octahedral

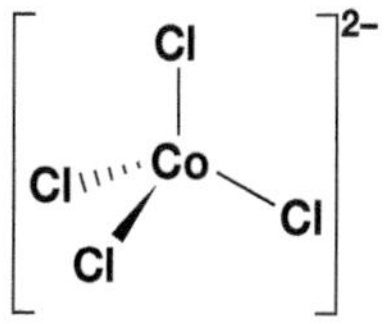

tetrahedral

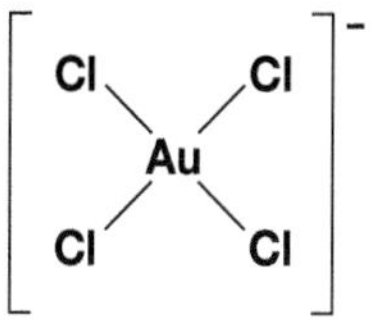

square planar

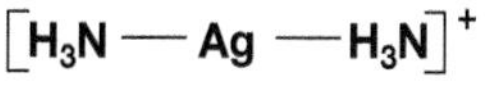

linear

■ **Figure 13.15**
Common shapes of complex ions

■ **Figure 13.16**

a The ethanedioate (oxalate) ion acts as a bidentate ligand via the lone pairs on its charged oxygens

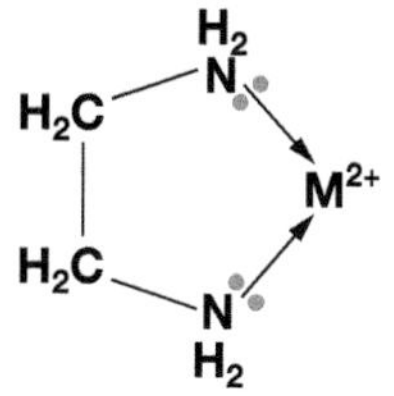

b The 1,2-diamino-ethane molecule acts as a bidentate ligand via the lone pairs on the nitrogen atoms in its amine groups

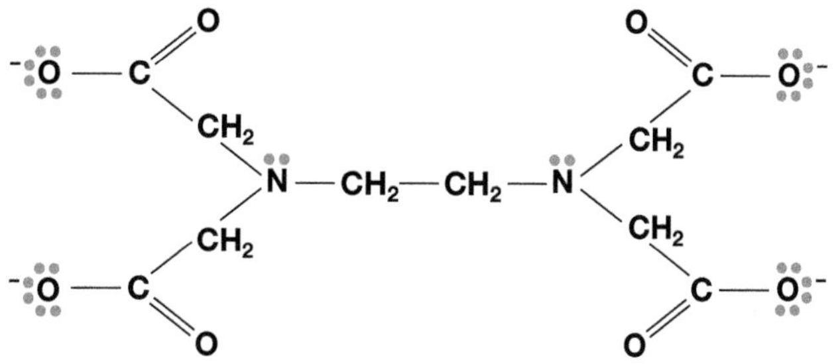

c The EDTA^{4-} ion acts as a hexadentate ligand, using lone pairs on both its nitrogen atoms and its charged oxygens

Ethanediaminetetraethanoic acid (Figure 13.17), usually just called EDTA or H₄EDTA, is a widely used chelating agent (Figure 13.18). It is present in shampoos (Figure 13.19), fertilizers, cosmetics and soft drinks containing ascorbic acid and sodium benzoate to prevent formation of benzene. It is also used as a preservative in foods and cosmetics. EDTA is also used in chelation therapy to remove harmful heavy metals or their ions from the body.

■ **Figure 13.20**
Ligand exchange
reactions. From top
to bottom: copper(ɪɪ)
ions, copper(ɪɪ) ions
after addition of
concentrated aqueous
ammonia, cobalt(ɪɪ)
ions, cobalt(ɪɪ) ions
after the addition
of concentrated
hydrochloric acid

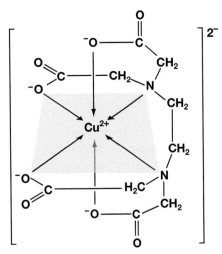

■ **Figure 13.18** The [Cu(EDTA)]²⁻ complex

■ **Figure 13.19** Shampoos often contain the EDTA⁴⁻ ion which helps soften the water by complexing calcium ions present in hard water

■ Ligand replacement reactions

All the stable, simple d-block metal ions exist in water in the hydrated form where the d-block metal ion is surrounded by six octahedrally arranged water molecules. For example, the hydrated copper(ɪɪ) ion, $Cu^{2+}(aq)$, is more accurately represented by $[Cu(H_2O)_6]^{2+}$.

If aqueous ammonia solution is added to a solution of a copper(ɪɪ) salt, a process of ligand replacement (Figure 13.20) occurs; four of the water molecules are replaced by ammonia molecules and the colour changes from light blue to dark blue:

$$[Cu(H_2O)_6]^{2+}(aq) + 4NH_3(aq) \rightarrow [Cu(H_2O)_2(NH_3)_4]^{2+}(aq) + 4H_2O(l)$$

blue   dark blue

If EDTA is added to the dark blue solution of tetraamminediaquacopper(ɪɪ) ions, the ammonia and water molecules are replaced by the hexadentate ligand to give a pale blue solution:

$$EDTA^{4-}(aq) + [Cu(H_2O)_2(NH_3)_4]^{2+}(aq) \rightarrow [Cu(EDTA)^{2-}](aq) + 4NH_3(aq) + 2H_2O(l)$$

dark blue   pale blue

The increase in entropy (Chapter 15) accompanying the replacement of six monodentate ligands by one hexadentate ligand accounts for the high degree of stability of EDTA complexes and for the use of EDTA in the titration of metal ions.

If a solution of a copper(ɪɪ) salt is treated with an excess of concentrated hydrochloric acid, the water molecules are replaced in a similar ligand replacement reaction. The six water molecules are replaced by four chloride ions to form a yellow complex ion:

$$[Cu(H_2O)_6]^{2+}(aq) + 4Cl^-(aq) \rightarrow [CuCl_4]^{2-}(aq) + 6H_2O(l)$$

blue   yellow

A ligand replacement reaction also occurs when concentrated hydrochloric acid is added to a solution of cobalt(II) chloride (Figure 13.20). The colour changes from pink to blue:

$$[Co(H_2O)_6]^{2+}(aq) + 4Cl^-(aq) \rightarrow [CoCl_4]^{2-}(aq) + 6H_2O(l)$$
pink ⟶ blue

Standard electrode potentials

Changing the ligands not only changes the colour of a complex ion, but can also affect the standard electrode potential (Chapter 19) of a complexed d-block metal. This is because different ligands provide different 'environments' for the ion.

For example, consider the following reduction potentials for iron(III) ions complexed with water and with cyanide ions:

$$[Fe(H_2O)_6]^{3+}(aq) + e^- \rightarrow [Fe(H_2O)_6]^{2+}(aq) \quad E^\ominus = +0.77 \text{ V}$$
$$[Fe(CN)_6]^{3-}(aq) + e^- \rightarrow [Fe(CN)_6]^{4-}(aq) \quad E^\ominus = +0.36 \text{ V}$$

The decrease in electrode potential means that the iron(III) ion in the more stable cyano complex has less tendency to accept electrons and hence is a weaker oxidizing agent than in the aqua complex.

Naming complex ions and complexes

Complex ions are named according to the following rules:

- The prefixes *di* (2), *tetra* (4) and *hexa* (6) are used to indicate the number of ligands.
- The type of ligand(s) present is indicated by names: ammonia molecule (*ammine*), chloride ion (*chloro*), water molecule (*aqua*), cyanide ion (*cyano*), carbon monoxide molecule (CO, *carbonyl*), ethanedioate ion ($C_2O_4^{2-}$, *oxalato*), hydroxide ion (*hydroxo*) and the sulfide ion (*thio*).
- If the complex ion has a positive charge then the name of the complex ion ends with the d-block metal ion and its oxidation state as a Roman numeral.
  For example, $[Fe(H_2O)_6]^{3+}$ is the hexaaquairon(III) ion.
- If the complex has a negative charge then the name ends with a shortened name, or the Latin name, of the element followed by *-ate*.
  For example, $[CoCl_4]^{2-}$ is the tetrachlorocobaltate(II) ion and $[Ni(CN)_4]^{2-}$ is the tetracyanonickelate(II) ion.
- Complexes are named with the positive counter ion named first.
  For example $K_2[Co(NH_3)_2Cl_4]$ is named as potassium diamminetetrachlorocobaltate(II). In solution this complex dissociates:
  $$K_2[Co(NH_3)_2Cl_4] \rightarrow 2K^+(aq) + [Co(NH_3)_2Cl_4]^{2-}(aq)$$
- The prefixes *bis* and *tris* are used to indicate the number of polydentate ligands present.
  For example, $[CrCl_2(en)_2]_2SO_4$ is dichlorobis(1,2-diaminohexane)chromium(III) sulfate.

8 Name the following complex ions and complexes.
  a $[Zn(OH)_4]^{2-}$
  b $[Zn(H_2O)_4]^{2+}$
  c $[Fe(Cn)_6]^{3-}$
  d $[Co(NH_3)_4Cl_2]Cl$
  e $[Cu(NH_3)_2(H_2O)_2]^{2+}$
  f $[Fe(H_2O)_6]^{3+}$
  g $[CuCl_4]^{2-}$
  h $[CrCl_2(NH_3)_4]^+$

9 Write formulas for the following complex ions and complexes.
  a hexachloroplatinate(IV) ion
  b bis(1,2-diaminohexane)copper(II) ion
  c tetraamminediaquachromium(II) sulfate
  d tetraaquadihydroxoaluminium(III) chloride
  e dicyanoargentate(I) ion
  f tetraamminenickel(II) chlorate(VII)
  g dichlorobis(1,2-diaminohexane) chloride
  h sodium hexafluoroaluminate(III)

Other complex ions and complexes

The formation of complex ions is *not* unique to d-block metals; for example, tin and lead can form complex ions such as $[PbCl_4]^{2-}$, $[PbCl_6]^{2-}$ and $[Sn(H_2O)_6]^{2+}$. The formation of these complex ions is due to the presence of empty low-energy d-orbitals that can accept lone pairs of electrons.

■ **Figure 13.21**
One resonance
structure for the
thiocyanate ion

Some ligands are known as ambidentate ligands. An ambidentate ligand has two lone pairs of electrons, for example the thiocyanate ion (Figure 13.21). Hence it can form a dative bond via the sulfur or the nitrogen. Other examples of ambidentate ligands include the nitrite ion, NO_2^-, and the cyanide ion, CN^-.

Transition metal atoms may also form complexes via dative bond formation. The extraction of nickel involves the formation and thermal decomposition of a transition metal complex. Nickel is usually extracted from its sulfide ore. This is roasted in air to give nickel(II) oxide, NiO, which is then reduced by carbon to the impure metal. Refinement (purification) can be achieved by reaction with carbon monoxide at about 50 °C and normal pressure, which results in the formation of tetracarbonylnickel(0), $Ni(CO)_4$. This complex is easily thermally decomposed to form extremely pure nickel (Mond process).

Deducing the total charge given the formula of the ion and ligands present

The total or net charge on a complex depends upon the number of ligands, their charge and the oxidation state of the central transition metal ion to which the ligands are bonded. The total or net charge on a complex can be deduced from its composition and the oxidation state of the central cation. The oxidation state of the central ion can be deduced from the formula and charge of the complex.

Worked example

Deduce the charge on the tetraamminedichlorochromium(III) complex ion. What is its formula?

> The formula has two chloride ions, Cl^-, and four ammonia molecules, NH_3, so the ligands contribute two negative charges (–2). The central chromium cation has an oxidation number of +3, so it contributes three positive charges (+3). Hence the total or net charge on the complex ion is +1. The formula is therefore $[CrCl_2(NH_3)_4]^+$.

Deduce the oxidation state of copper in the $[Cu(CN)_4]^{3-}$ complex ion. What is its name?

> The complex ion is an anion with a total or net charge of –3. The formula has four cyanide ions acting as ligands which contribute a total of four negative charges (–4). Hence the central copper ion must contribute one positive charge so its oxidation state is +1. This ion is the tetracyanocuprate(I) ion.

---

10 Deduce the total charge and formulas of the following complex ions: a nickel(II) ion with six ammonia ligands, and a copper(II) ion with four chloride ions.

11 Find about the mechanism of action of cisplatin and outline any changes that occur to the complex ion during its use as an anti-cancer agent.

■ Isomerism in complex ions

Cis–trans isomerism

Where a complex ion contains two different ligands, it can exist as two isomers in which there are different arrangements of the ligands (Figure 13.22). This is termed *cis–trans* isomerism, referring to the relative positions of the two ligands. *Cis* means same side, *trans* means opposite side. This form of isomerism is only possible for complex ions with coordination numbers greater than or equal to 4. The *cis* complex $[PtCl_2(NH_3)_2]$, systematic name *cis*-diamminedichloroplatinum(II), is known as cisplatin (Figure 13.23) and is used in chemotherapy for treating certain types of cancer. The *trans* isomer, known as transplatin, has no anti-cancer properties.

■ **Figure 13.22**
Cis–trans isomerism
in a transition metal
complex ion

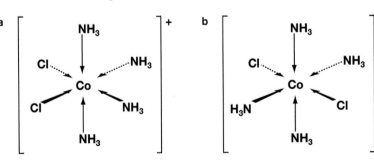

cis-$[Co(NH_3)_4Cl_2]^+$
blue-violet

trans-$[Co(NH_3)_4Cl_2]^+$
green

■ **Figure 13.23**
Structure of cisplatin

Optical isomerism

Octahedral isomers containing a bidentate ligand can form a pair of complexes that are mirror images of each other (Figure 13.24). These molecules are known as enantiomers. This form of isomerism is called optical isomerism (Chapter 20) because the two forms will rotate plane-polarized light in equal but opposite directions.

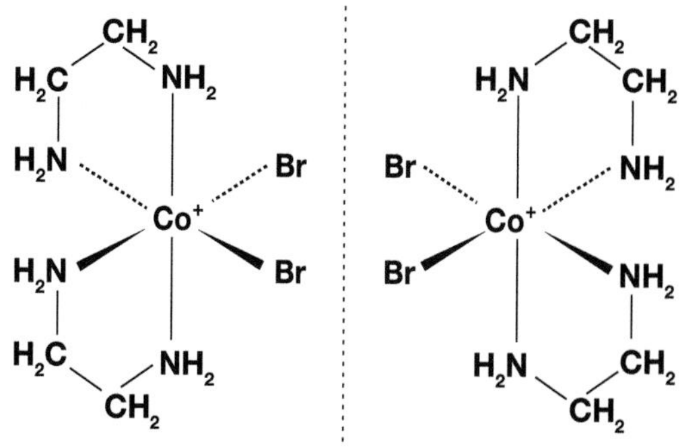

■ Valence bond (VB) theory

Bonding in complex ions

If ammonia is added to a solution containing chromium(III) ions, a purple complex is formed. The chromium(III) ion has a d^3 configuration and so has three unpaired electrons. This leaves two empty d-orbitals as well as one 4s and three 4p orbitals that can receive lone pairs from the ammonia molecules to form the hexaamminechromium(III) complex ion, $[Cr(NH_3)_6]^{3+}$ as shown in Figure 13.25. The diagram is appropriate for all octahedral chromium(III) complexes because the 3d electrons always singly occupy different orbitals.

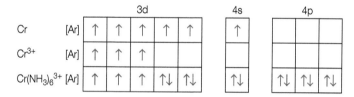

■ **Figure 13.24** The enantiomers of *cis*-[Co(en)$_2$Br$_2$]$^+$, where en represents 1,2-diaminoethane ($H_2NCH_2CH_2NH_2$)

■ **Figure 13.25** The formation of the $[Cr(NH_3)_6]^{3+}$ complex ion

The formation of a chromium(III) complex ion with six monodentate ligands therefore requires no electronic reorganization of the d electrons. However, the situation is more complicated if a transition metal ion has more than three 3d electrons, for example the iron(III) ion, which has a d^5 configuration with half-filled 3d orbitals (Figure 13.26).

■ **Figure 13.26** The formation of the complex ions $[Fe(H_2O)_6]^{3+}$ and $[Fe(CN)_6]^{3-}$

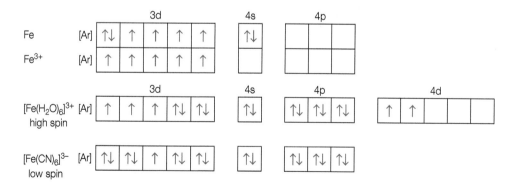

In order to form a complex ion with six monodentate ligands, two of the 3d orbitals must be cleared of electrons by a process of electron promotion. With ligands that are only weakly attracted, for example, water molecules, two of the 3d electrons in the iron(III) ion are promoted to higher energy 4d orbitals. The resulting complex ion still has five half-filled orbitals and is known as a high-spin complex.

With ligands that are strongly attracted, for example, the cyanide ion, two of the 3d electrons in the iron(III) ion pair off with electrons in other 3d orbitals. The resulting complex ion has only one half-filled 3d orbital and is known as a low-spin complex.

A complex ion with the same number of unpaired electrons as the uncomplexed metal ion is a high-spin complex. A complex ion with fewer unpaired electrons than the uncomplexed metal ion is a low-spin complex. The existence of these two types of complexes can be explained by crystal field theory and the spectrochemical series, which are discussed later.

Nickel(II) ions, a d^8 species, forms paramagnetic tetrahedral and octahedral complexes and diamagnetic square planar complexes. Bonding in a tetrahedral complex can be represented as shown in Figure 13.27 and an octahedral nickel(II) complex can be described as shown in Figure 13.28.

■ **Figure 13.27**
Bonding in a nickel(II) tetrahedral complex

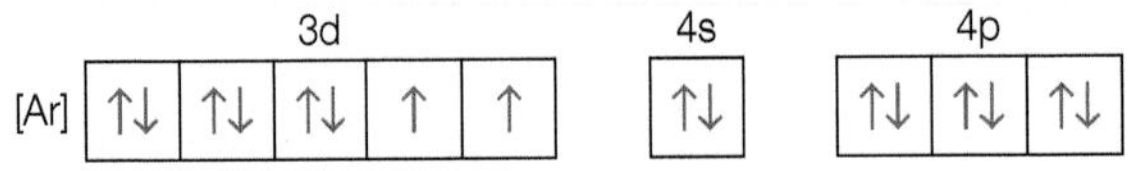

■ **Figure 13.28**
Bonding in an octahedral nickel(II) complex

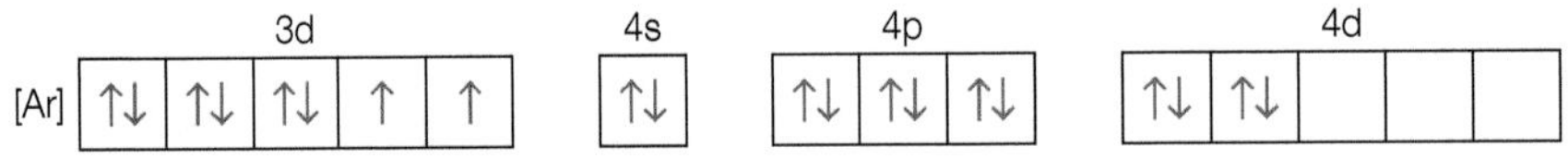

The bonding in diamagnetic square planar nickel(II) complexes can be represented as shown in Figure 13.29.

■ **Figure 13.29**
Bonding in a square planar nickel(II) complex

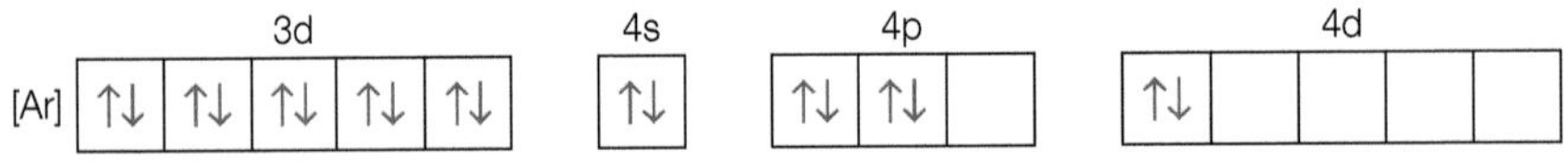

12 Draw an 'electrons in boxes' notation for the tetrachloro-cuprate(II) ion, $CuCl_4^{2-}$. The chloride ion is a weak ligand and forms low-spin complexes.

Valence bond (VB) theory can explain the shape and magnetic properties of transition metal complexes, but only at a simple level. It is an unrealistic model since it invokes the use of 4d orbitals in some complexes, such as $[Fe(H_2O)_6]^{3+}$. The 4d atomic orbitals are at a significantly higher energy than the 3d atomic orbitals.

VB theory is a very old bonding model developed by Linus Pauling in the 1930s and has been superseded by a number of other bonding theories, including crystal field theory and molecular orbital theory. It cannot explain spectroscopic properties and cannot explain why certain ligands are associated with the formation of low-spin or high-spin complexes.

Ligands can be classified into order of strength by the spectrochemical series (see section 13.2). High and low-spin complexes can be distinguished by magnetic measurements. The high-spin complex has a greater magnetic moment and this can be determined experimentally.

The hybridization model used for main group elements, such as carbon (Chapter 14), can also be applied to d-block elements: an empty hybrid orbital on the transition metal centre can accept a pair of electrons from a ligand to form a sigma (σ) bond, for example, in octahedral complexes of chromium(III) as described previously. The atomic orbitals required for an octahedral complex are the $3d_{z^2}$, $3d_{x^2-y^2}$, 4s, $4p_x$, $4p_y$, and $4p_z$. These orbitals must be unoccupied so as to be available to accept six pairs of electrons from the ligands. A process of hybridization occurs between the two empty 3d orbitals and the empty 4s and 4p orbitals to form six identical d^2sp^3 hybrid orbitals (Figure 13.30).

■ **Figure 13.30**
Hybridization of atomic orbitals in the chromium(III) ion

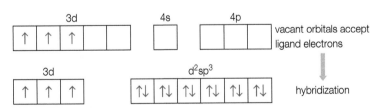

Table 13.8 summarizes the shapes of complex ions and their hybridization.

■ **Table 13.8** Hybrid orbitals for common geometries in complexes

Number of ligands	Geometry	Hybrid orbitals
2	Linear	sp
4	Tetrahedral	sp^3
4	Square planar	dsp^2
6	Octahedral	d^2sp^3

■ **Figure 13.31** Models of d^2sp^3 and dsp^2 hybrid orbitals

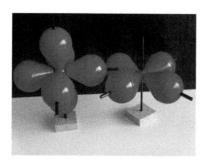

Figure 13.31 shows models showing d^2sp^3 and dsp^2 hybrid orbitals. Note the identical shapes of the hybrid orbitals and their arrangement to match the observed geometries. The bonding in sulfur (VI) fluoride, SF_6 can also be described using d^2sp^3 hybridization.

However, the valence bond theory approach to transition metals has severe limitations. It fails to account for the absorption spectra and magnetic properties of coordination compounds. These and other properties are more satisfactorily explained by crystal field theory or ligand field theory.

---

13 Describe the hybridization scheme and electron configuration of $[FeF_6]^{3-}$, which is a high-spin complex.

Explaining the nature of the coordinate bond within a complex ion

In a complex ion, the ligands (attached ions or molecules) each donate an electron pair to form a covalent bond to the central transition metal ion. The bonding is called dative coordinate bonding, because the lone pair is donated from the bonding species.

This behaviour is characteristic of the transition metals. The first-row transition elements have partially filled d-orbitals in the 3d sub-level, but they also have empty 4p and 4d orbitals that can become involved in bonding. This allows the transition elements to form structures in which there are four, five or six attached ligands (Figure 13.32). The ligands are Lewis bases with one or more lone pairs and the transition metal ion is a Lewis acid with empty orbitals.

■ **Figure 13.32** Generalized explanation for formation of transition metal complex ions: the transition metal ion can accept lone pairs (ligands) into suitably orientated empty hybridized orbitals

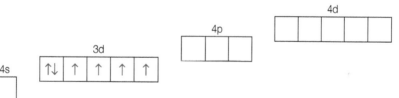

an iron(II) ion, showing all of the orbitals available for bonding

■ Factors affecting the stability of complex ions

The stability of a complex ion depends upon the nature of the central ion and the nature of the ligand. The nature of the central ion refers to its charge density: the greater the charge density (charge/radius ratio), the more stable the complex. For example, the iron(III) complex is more stable because iron(III) has a higher charge density than iron(II):

$$Fe^{3+} + 6CN^- \rightleftharpoons [Fe(CN)_6]^{3-} \qquad K = 1.2 \times 10^{31}$$
$$Fe^{2+} + 6CN^- \rightleftharpoons [Fe(CN)_6]^{4-} \qquad K = 1.8 \times 10^6$$

For cations that carry the same charge, the one with the smaller size will form the more stable complexes. For example, among Cu^{2+}, Ni^{2+} and Fe^{2+} complexes, the copper(II) complexes will be the most stable as copper has the smallest ionic radius.

The more basic a ligand, the more able it is to donate its electron pair and therefore the greater the stability of the complex. For example, complex ions involving fluoride ions, F^-, are more stable than those involving chloride or bromide ions. For charged ligands, the higher the charge and the smaller their size, the more stable the complex ions.

Complexes containing chelating agents are usually much more stable than those formed from monodentate ligands. This is termed the chelate effect, and is due to an increase in entropy. For example:

$$[Ni(H_2O)_6]^{2+}(aq) + 6NH_3(aq) \rightleftharpoons [Ni(NH_3)_6]^{2+}(aq) + 6H_2O(l) \qquad K = 4.0 \times 10^8$$
$$[Ni(H_2O)_6]^{2+}(aq) + 3en(aq) \rightleftharpoons [Ni(en)_3]^{3+}(aq) + 6H_2O(l) \qquad K = 2.0 \times 10^{18}$$

where en represents the bidentate ligand, 1,2-diaminoethane, $H_2N–(CH_2)_2–NH_2$.

■ Finding the formula of a complex ion

A colorimeter can be used to measure the concentrations of chemicals that are themselves coloured or which produce a coloured substance during a chemical reaction (Chapter 6). By following the changes in absorbance that take place in reactions involving the formation of coloured complex ions, a colorimeter can be used to determine the formulas of these complex ions. Figure 13.33 shows the results of measuring the absorbance of a series of mixtures of $0.01\,mol\,dm^{-3}$ copper(II) ions, $Cu^{2+}(aq)$, and $0.01\,mol\,dm^{-3}$ $EDTA^{4-}(aq)$. $EDTA^{4-}$ is a hexadentate ligand and forms very stable complex ions with d-block metal ions.

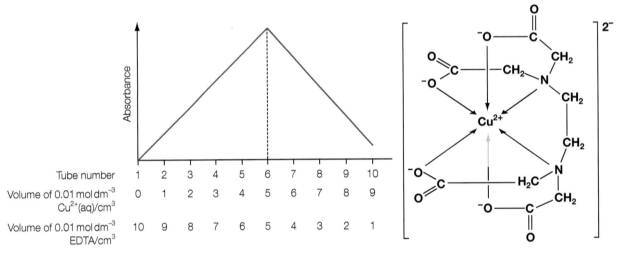

Tube number	1	2	3	4	5	6	7	8	9	10
Volume of $0.01\,mol\,dm^{-3}$ $Cu^{2+}(aq)/cm^3$	0	1	2	3	4	5	6	7	8	9
Volume of $0.01\,mol\,dm^{-3}$ EDTA/cm^3	10	9	8	7	6	5	4	3	2	1

■ **Figure 13.33** Plot of absorbance of ten mixtures of $0.01\,mol\,dm^{-3}$ $Cu^{2+}(aq)$ ions and $0.01\,mol\,dm^{-3}$ $EDTA^{4-}(aq)$

■ **Figure 13.34** Structure of the complex ion formed between copper(II) ions and $EDTA^{4-}$ ions

The peak of absorbance corresponds to mixing equal volumes of the two solutions, which both have the same concentration. Hence, copper(II) ions and $EDTA^{4-}$ react in a 1 : 1 molar ratio (Figure 13.34). The formula of the complex is $[Cu(EDTA)]^{2-}$.

EDTA is used in chelation therapy, where chelating agents are used to remove toxic heavy metals, such as mercury, lead and uranium, from the body. The ions of the heavy metals mercury, lead and silver have the ability to change the structure of proteins, including the active sites of enzymes. Major sources of mercury include the burning of coal and small-scale gold mining. A major source of mercury pollution used to be the production of sodium hydroxide solution using the Castner–Kellner process. This involved the electrolysis of sodium chloride solution using a flowing mercury cathode. In the past, lead was used for water pipes, and so lead(II) ions were present in the drinking water. A lead compound, tetraethyl lead(0), $Pb(C_2H_5)_4$, was added to petrol to improve its combustion properties, and lead compounds were present in car exhausts. This has now largely been stopped in many countries. Hence it is very important for the concentrations of transition metal ions, especially heavy metal ions, to be carefully monitored (see Chapter 22 on the accompanying website) in drinking water, fresh water, the air and soil (environmental systems).

13.2 Coloured complexes – *d-orbitals have the same energy in an isolated atom, but split into two sub-levels in a complex ion; the electric field of ligands may cause the d-orbitals in complex ions to split so that the energy of an electron transition between them corresponds to a photon of visible light*

■ The colours of complex ions

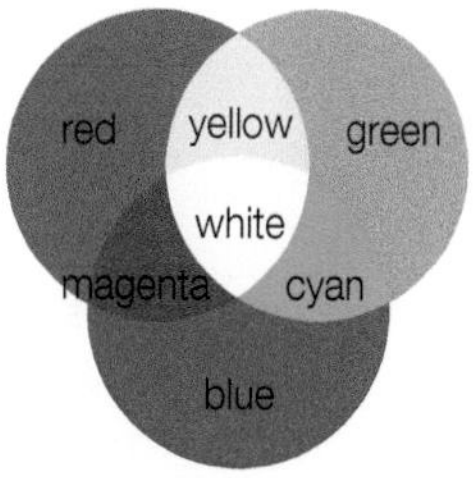

White light can result from the combination of only red, green and blue light. When equal brightnesses of these are combined and projected on a screen, white light is produced (Figure 13.35). The screen appears yellow when red and green light alone overlap. The combination of red and blue light produces the bluish-red colour of magenta. Green and blue produce the greenish-blue colour called cyan. Almost any colour can be made by overlapping light of three colours and adjusting the brightness of each colour. Red, green and blue light are known as primary colours since all other colours can be formed from them.

When white light is shone on a chemical substance, either as a solid or in solution, some light is absorbed and some is reflected.

- If all the light is absorbed then the substance appears 'black'.

- If only certain wavelengths are absorbed then the compound will appear coloured.

- If all the light is reflected then the colour of the substance will appear 'white'.

Most d-block metal compounds are coloured, both in solution and in the solid state. The colours of many (but not all) of these compounds are due to the presence of incompletely filled 3d sub-levels.

In an isolated gaseous d-block metal atom, the five 3d sub-levels all have different orientations in space (shapes), but *identical* energies. However, in a complex ion the 3d sub-levels are orientated differently relative to the ligands. The 3d electrons close to a ligand will experience repulsion and be raised in energy. The 3d electrons located further away from the ligand will be reduced in energy.

The 3d sub-level has now been 'split' into two energy levels. Octahedral complexes are very common and the splitting of the d sub-levels is as shown in Figure 13.36 for the hydrated titanium(III) ion. Two d-orbitals are raised in energy; three d-orbitals are lowered in energy. (Different d–d splitting patterns are observed in tetrahedral, square planar and linear complexes. The terms t_{2g} and e_g are used to describe the split 3d sub-levels and are based on symmetry considerations.)

■ **Figure 13.35** Primary and secondary colours

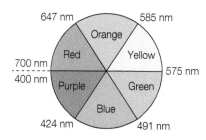

■ **Figure 13.36** The splitting of the 3d sub-levels in the titanium(III) ion in the octahedral $[Ti(H_2O)_6]^{3+}$(aq) complex

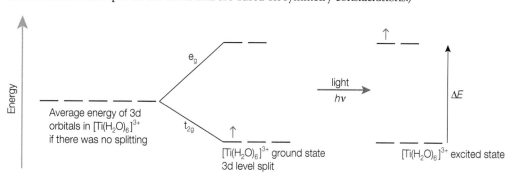

The energy difference or energy gap ΔE between the two sets of energy levels is related to the frequency of light necessary to cause an electron to be excited from the lower energy level to the higher energy level.

$$\Delta E = h\nu$$

where h is Planck's constant and ν is the frequency (Chapter 2).

The colour of hydrated titanium(III) ions, $[Ti(H_2O)_6]^{3+}$(aq), is violet because yellow-green light (of a particular frequency) is absorbed and the colour of the complex ions will be *complementary* to that (Figure 13.37).

When white light is absorbed by a solution of titanium(III) ions then some of the light waves will have energies that correspond to the energy gap or energy difference, ΔE, between the two groups of 'split' 3d energy levels. This light will be absorbed and a single 3d electron will become excited and be promoted to the higher energy level. This is known as a d–d transition.

■ **Figure 13.37** Colour wheel of complementary colours

The energy difference, and hence the colour of d-block metal complex ions, depends on three factors:

■ *The nuclear charge*
For example, vanadium(II) ions (3d^3) are lavender in colour, while chromium(III) ions (also 3d^3) are green.

■ *The number of d electrons*
d–d transitions occur only if there is an incomplete 3d sub-level, so there is an orbital for the 3d electron to be promoted into.

Scandium(III), copper(I) and zinc(II) compounds are all colourless due to either the absence of 3d electrons (Sc^{3+}, 3d^0) or the presence of a filled 3d sub-level (Cu$^+$ and Zn^{2+}, 3d^{10}).

■ *The nature of the ligand*
Different ligands, because of their different sizes and charges, produce different energy gaps between the two groups of 3d sub-level energy levels. For example, ammonia ligands produce a larger energy gap than water molecules, causing a colour change when aqueous ammonia solution is added to the solution of a copper(II) salt. This means that light of higher energy and frequency, and hence lower wavelength, is absorbed.

Table 13.9 displays the elements of the first row of the d-block elements, giving an example of one coloured simple ion for each, where there is one.

Transition metal ion	Sc^{3+}	Ti^{4+} Ti^{3+}	V^{2+}	Cr^{3+}	Mn^{2+}	Fe^{3+} Fe^{2+}	Co^{2+}	Ni^{2+}	Cu^{2+}	Zn^{2+}
Colour in aqueous solution	Colourless	Colourless Violet	Violet	Green	Very pale pink	Yellow-brown Pale green	Pink	Green	Pale blue	Colourless

■ **Table 13.9** Simple ions of the first-row d-block elements

14 The wavelength of light most strongly absorbed by nickel(II) ions, Ni^{2+}(aq), is 410 nm. Calculate the value of the energy gap or field splitting in hydrated nickel(II) ions in joules and in kilojoules per mole (to the nearest integer).

Determining the value of the energy gap, ΔE

Planck's equation and the wave equation (Chapter 2) can be used to determine an *approximate* value for the energy gap of a transition metal complex ion from the frequency or wavelength of the light *most strongly absorbed* by the ions of a complex ion. (This is an approximate value because the absorption spectrum is broad – it is not a single sharp peak.)

Factors affecting the size of crystal field splitting

As outlined previously the size of the crystal field splitting (ΔE) depends on a number of factors:

■ *The nature of the metal ion*
For ions belonging to the same sub-level, for example, 3d, the magnitude (size) of the crystal field splitting (ΔE) depends on the principal quantum number (n). It increases by 30% to 50% from 3d^n to 4d^n, etc.

■ *The oxidation state of the cation*
The higher the oxidation state of the metal ion, the larger is the value of the crystal field splitting (ΔE). This is because the central metal ion with the higher oxidation state has a smaller ionic radius and hence polarizes the ligands more effectively. As a result the ligand approaches the central transition metal cation more closely and hence a greater splitting is observed,

■ *The nature of ligand*
A stronger ligand has a greater or higher crystal field splitting power than a weak ligand. The common ligands are arranged in order of increasing splitting power in the spectrochemical series:

$$I^- < Br^- < S^{2-} < Cl^- < F^- < OH^- < H_2O < SCN^- < NH_3 < CN^- < CO$$

This is an experimentally determined series based on the absorption of light by complexes with different ligands.

■ *The geometry of the complex*
The value of crystal field splitting in tetrahedral complexes is about half of that in octahedral complexes.

The absorption spectrum for the hexaaquacopper(II) complex ion, $[Cu(H_2O)_6]^{2+}$, is shown in Figure 13.38. Although the maximum absorption occurs at about 800 nm, the band is very *broad* with measurable absorption down to a wavelength of about 600 nm. This broadening of the absorption band is caused by bond vibration; a similar effect is observed with ultraviolet spectra (see Chapter 23 on the accompanying website). As the ligands move with respect to the central metal ion, so the crystal field splitting energy will vary.

Figure 13.38 Visible spectra of **a** the hexaaquacopper(II) ion, $[Cu(H_2O)_6]^{2+}$, and **b** the tetraamminediaquacopper(II) ion, $[Cu(H_2O)_2(NH_3)_4]^{2+}$

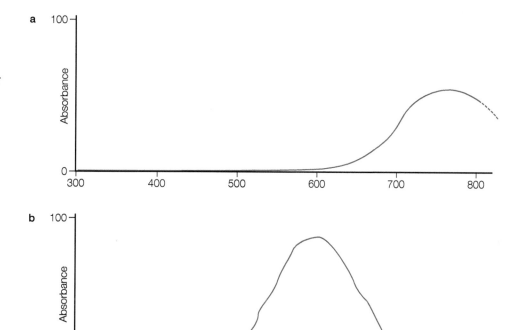

When an excess of concentrated ammonia solution is added to a solution containing hexaaquacopper(II) ions, $[Cu(H_2O)_6]^{2+}$, the colour changes from pale blue to a characteristic deep royal-blue owing to the formation of a new complex ion: diaquatetraamminecopper(II).

$$[Cu(H_2O)_6]^{2+}(aq) + 4NH_3(aq) \rightarrow [Cu(H_2O)_2(NH_3)_4]^{2+}(aq) + 4H_2O(l)$$

The complex is still octahedral in shape (albeit distorted) but four of the water ligands have been replaced by ammonia molecules (a more effective ligand) (Figure 13.39). Maximum absorption now occurs at around 600 nm, that is, at a shorter wavelength than for the hexaaquacopper(II) ion $[Cu(H_2O)_6]^{2+}$ (aq). This means that the crystal field splitting energy has been increased by substituting ammonia ligands for water (Figure 13.40).

Figure 13.39 Structure of the $[Cu(H_2O)_2(NH_3)_4]^{2+}$ ion

Figure 13.40 Absorption spectra and colours of selected copper(II) compounds showing the effect of a stronger ligand field

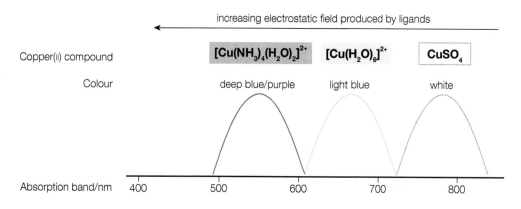

The spectrochemical series lists some common ligands in order of their d-orbital splitting ability. Much of the order can be accounted for by the basicity of the molecules or ions: *generally*, the more basic the ligand, the greater the d-orbital splitting power. For example, ammonia, NH_3, is a better ligand than nitrogen trichloride, NCl_3, but not as good as trimethylamine, $N(CH_3)_3$. Nitrogen trichloride is an example of the negative inductive effect operating, but in trimethylamine the positive inductive effect is operating (Figure 13.41). The inductive effect is the ability of a function group or atom to sigma electrons towards itself, or repel them, resulting in the formation of a dipole (Chapter 20). Methyl groups are electron releasing and 'push' electron density on to the nitrogen of trimethylamine, making it larger and more 'available'. In nitrogen trichloride the electronegative chlorine withdraws electron density from the nitrogen, making it smaller and less 'available'.

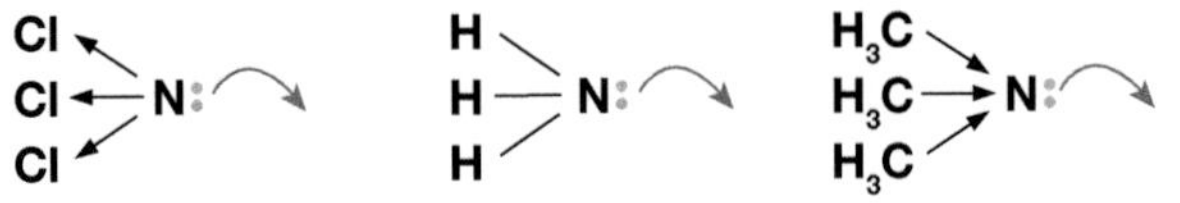

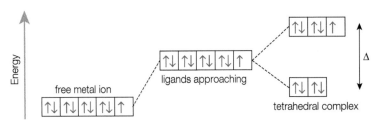

■ **Figure 13.41** Increasing electron density (lone pair availability) on the nitrogen atom improves its complexing ability

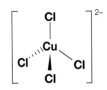

■ **Figure 13.42** Structure of the tetrachlorocuprate(II) ion, $[CuCl_4]^{2-}$

It is not only the type of ligand that affects the crystal field splitting energy, but also the coordination number and the shape of the complex. Addition of concentrated hydrochloric acid to a solution containing hexaaquacopper(II) ions, $[Cu(H_2O)_6]^{2+}$, causes a colour change from blue to yellow-green:

$$[Cu(H_2O)_6]^{2+}(aq) + 4Cl^-(aq) \rightleftharpoons [CuCl_4]^{2-}(aq) + 6H_2O(l)$$

The new complex ion, tetrachlorocuprate(II), has only four ligands, arranged tetrahedrally around the central copper(II) ion (Figure 13.42). The d-orbitals on the Cu^{2+} ion are again split into two sets but the arrangement of the energy levels is reversed, with three orbitals at a higher energy than the other two (Figure 13.43).

■ **Figure 13.43** Effect of tetrahedral complex ion formation on the energies of the 3d electrons in the copper(II) ion

As there are only four ligands here (causing repulsion), the crystal field splitting energy, Δ, is significantly less than in a hexa coordinate octahedral complex. Combined with the weaker splitting caused by chloride ions, Cl^-, compared to ammonia molecules, NH_3, and water molecules, H_2O, the maximum absorption moves to lower energy, i.e. a longer wavelength.

Charge transfer

A number of substances change their bonding when they absorb visible light. Some metal oxides have a different colour from their hydrated ions in aqueous solution. For example, copper(II) oxide, CuO, is black, but copper(II) ions in aqueous solution are blue. Lead(II) oxide (Figure 13.44) is orange, but lead(II) ions are colourless. Copper(II) and lead(II) oxides are essentially ionic, but the bonding has some covalent character (Chapter 4). The absorption of a photon of appropriate visible radiation promotes one of the electrons of the oxide ion into a partially covalent bond by a process called charge transfer (Figure 13.45).

■ **Figure 13.44** Lead(II) oxide

$$\mathbf{Pb^{2+}} \overset{\frown}{} \ddot{\mathbf{O}}^{2-} \qquad \mathbf{Pb^{2+}} \cdot \quad \cdot \mathbf{O}^{2-} \qquad \mathbf{Pb^{1.5+}} \cdot \quad \cdot \mathbf{O}^{1.5-}$$

ground state   charge transfer   excited state

Charge transfer also happens with the yellow chromate(VI) ion, CrO_4^{2-}(aq), and the purple manganate(VII) ion, MnO_4^-(aq). It helps to account for the very high intensity of light absorption by these ions.

■ The shapes of d-orbitals

The shapes of the 3d atomic orbitals that make up the 3d sub-level are shown in Figure 13.46. They all have the same energy (in the gas phase ions), but different orientations in space relative to one another. The + and − symbols in the lobes do *not* represent electrical charge. They represent the phases of the waves (Chapter 14).

■ **Figure 13.46**
The shapes of the 3d orbitals

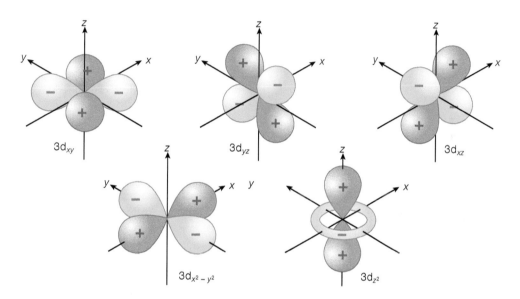

The model described here to account for colours of transition metal ions is a simplified version of crystal field theory. The theory is based on the idea that the bonding in complex ions is purely electrostatic and that the ligands behave as point negative charges. The most common type of complex ion is octahedral, where six ligands form an octahedron around the metal ion. In octahedral symmetry the d-orbitals split into two sets with an energy difference ΔE. The d_{xy}, d_{xz} and d_{yz} orbitals will be lower in energy than the d_{z^2} and $d_{x^2-y^2}$, because they are further from the ligands than the latter and therefore electrons in these orbitals experience *less repulsion* (Figure 13.47). The lobes of the d_{z^2} and $d_{x^2-y^2}$ orbitals point directly at the ligands so d electrons in these two orbitals will experience a significant degree of repulsion. In contrast the lobes of the d_{xy}, d_{xz} and d_{yz} orbitals have their lobes pointing between the ligands. The d-orbitals are split due to the electric field of the ligands; this is termed ligand field splitting.

■ **Figure 13.47**
Ligands at the ends of the *x*, *y* and *z* axes have weaker interactions with d_{xy}, d_{yz} and d_{xz} orbitals than with d_{z^2} and $d_{x^2-y^2}$ orbitals

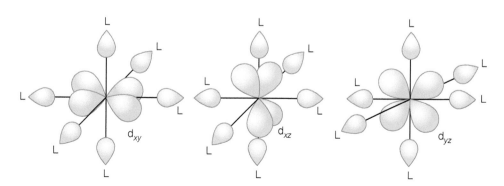

Nature of Science

Models and theories – explaining the colours of transition metal complexes

One of the most distinctive properties of transition metal complexes is their wide range of colours. This demonstrates that some part of the visible spectrum is being removed from white light as it passes through the sample of the coloured complex ion, so the light that emerges is no longer white. The colour of the complex ion is complementary to that which is absorbed.

The colour in transition metal complexes can readily be explained in terms of crystal field theory, which accounts for the colour of complex ions from d–d transitions resulting from the splitting of the d sub-level by the repulsive effect of ligands. The type of splitting depends upon the number of ligands and is determined by the shape of the five d-orbitals and their electron distributions in space.

The colour of a complex ion depends upon the magnitude of the crystal field splitting, which is dependent upon the nature of ligand (electric field of the ligand). For example, the octahedral complexes of chromium(III) all have the d^3 configuration but the colours of the complexes vary with the ligands (Table 13.10). The size of the splitting observed in each complex ion can be explained on the basis of the spectrochemical series.

■ **Table 13.10** Selected isomeric complexes of chromium(III), a d^3 system

Complex ion	Colour
$[Cr(H_2O)_6]^{3+}$	Violet
$[Cr(H_2O)_5Cl]^{2+}$	Blue-green
$[Cr(H_2O)_4Cl_2]^+$	Green
$[Cr(NH_3)_6]^{3+}$	Yellow
$[Cr(NH_3)_5Cl]^{2+}$	Purple
$[Cr(NH_3)_4Cl_2]^+$	Violet

It is important to note that in the absence of ligands, crystal field splitting does not occur and hence the substance is colourless. For example, anhydrous nickel(II) sulfate is almost colourless but hydrated nickel(II) sulfate is green. The influence of the ligand on the colour of a complex may be demonstrated by considering the $[Ni(H_2O)_6]^{2+}$ complex ion formed when nickel(II) chloride is dissolved in water. If the bidentate ligand 1,2-diaminohexane (en) is progressively added in the molar ratios en : Ni of 1 : 1, 2 : 1 and 3 : 1, the following series of reactions (ligand displacements) and their associated colour changes occur:

$$[Ni(H_2O)_6]^{2+}(aq) + en(aq) \rightleftharpoons [Ni(H_2O)_4(en)]^{2+}(aq) + 2H_2O(l)$$
green · pale blue

$$[Ni(H_2O)_4(en)]^{2+}(aq) + en(aq) \rightleftharpoons [Ni(H_2O)_2(en)_2]^{2+}(aq) + 2H_2O(l)$$
blue/purple

$$[Ni(H_2O)_2(en)_2]^{2+}(aq) + en(aq) \rightleftharpoons [Ni(en)_3]^{2+}(aq) + 2H_2O(l)$$
violet

The crystal field theory is successful in explaining the colours of complex ions to a large extent, on the basis of its assumption that ligands are point charges, and hence that the anion ligands should have the greatest splitting effect. However, the anion ligands are found at the low end of the spectrochemical series.

Crystal field theory does not take into account the covalent bonding between the ligand and the central transition metal cation. These are some of the weaknesses which are explained by ligand field theory, which is based on molecular orbital (MO) theory (Chapter 14).

Explaining the effect of the identity of the metal ion, its oxidation number and the identity of the ligand on the colour of transition metal ion complexes

■ *Identity of the metal ion*
For M^{n+} with constant charge, ΔE increases down a group because there is less overlap with larger and more diffuse d-orbitals.

■ *Oxidation number of the metal*
For a given metal, ΔE increases as the oxidation state increases (Table 13.11). Part of the interaction between the metal and the ligand is electrostatic. The greater the charge on the metal, the closer the approach of the ligand and the stronger the overlap between the metal and ligand orbitals.

Table 13.11 Number and geometry of ligands

Complex	$[Cr(H_2O)_6]^{2+}$(aq)	$[Cr(H_2O)_6]^{3+}$(aq)	$[Cr(NH_3)_6]^{2+}$(aq)	$[Cr(NH_3)_6]^{3+}$(aq)
$\Delta E/cm^{-1}$	14 100	17 400	10 200	22 900
Colour	Light blue	Purple/blue		Purple

The more ligands are coordinated to the metal, the larger is ΔE. The d-orbital splitting is greatest when the ligand geometry allows direct overlap between the ligand orbital and a metal d-orbital, such as occurs for linear, square planar and octahedral geometries.

Overlap in tetrahedral complexes is relatively poor, and consequently Δ_t (the splitting for a tetrahedral geometry) is less than Δ_o (the splitting for an octahedral geometry).

■ *Identity of the ligand*

Generally, the more basic the ligand, the higher the value of ΔE (Figure 13.48).

Figure 13.48
The effect of changing the ligands: chromium(III) complexes with six monodentate ligands

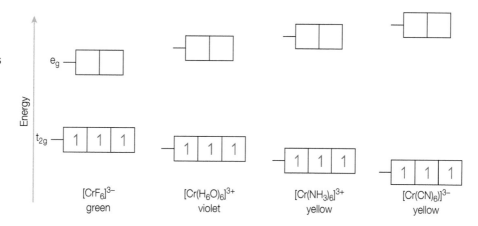

Explaining the effect of different ligands on the splitting of the d-orbitals in transition metal complexes and colour observed using the spectrochemical series

Studies have shown that, on the varying the ligands attached to a particular central metal atom, the magnitude of ΔE is different in each case. Ligands which cause only a small degree of splitting are termed weak-field ligands and those which cause a large splitting are called strong-field ligands. The common ligands are arranged in order of their strength and the series is called the spectrochemical series (Figure 13.49).

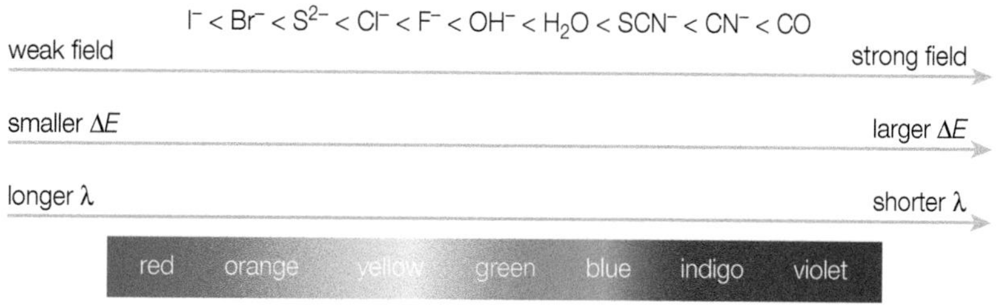

Figure 13.49
The spectrochemical series showing trends in effects

$$I^- < Br^- < S^{2-} < Cl^- < F^- < OH^- < H_2O < SCN^- < CN^- < CO$$

weak field → strong field

smaller ΔE → larger ΔE

longer λ → shorter λ

red   orange   yellow   green   blue   indigo   violet

As the ligands decrease in size, their ability to split the d-orbitals increases. The larger and bulkier ligands approach the metal less effectively; that is, they exhibit more steric hindrance. It might be expected that ligands with a negative charge might split the d-orbitals more, but this is not always the case. Notice that water is higher in the series than OH^-, even though the oxygen in OH^- has a high concentration of charge.

■ Ligand field theory

In crystal field theory the isolated transition metal ion is seen as being surrounded by point charges or simple charges. It is a very simple model but gives qualitatively correct predictions about magnetism and spectra.

Ligand field theory allows for coordinate bonding and gives the same description for the splitting of d-orbitals in complexes. For example, it predicts the d-orbitals in an octahedral complex will be split into t_{2g} and e_g.

When a complex is formed, the e_g orbitals being directed towards the ligands are used to form coordinate bonds by accepting lone pairs from the ligands. If there are any electrons already in these orbitals, they will be strongly repelled by the lone pairs of the ligands. These electrons must be accepted in orbitals of higher energy so that the e_g orbitals are available for bonding.

If the atom that donates an electron pair from the ligands is very electronegative, such as oxygen in water, the bonding between the ligand and the metal has a high degree of ionic character and the ligand field is weak. The two e_g^* anti-bonding orbitals are used to accept the highest energy electrons and a high-spin complex is formed. If the atom that donates an electron pair from the ligand is less electronegative, for example the carbon atom in the cyanide ion, the bonding between the ligand and the metal is essentially covalent and the ligand field is strong. The energy gap, ΔE, is greater than the electron repulsion when the electrons are paired in the t_{2g} orbitals and the result is the formation of a low-spin complex. These predictions are identical to those of crystal field theory.

■ Molecular orbital theory

Crystal field theory is a simple electrostatic model that treats the transition metal ion and the ligands as point charges. It is very successful in predicting in a very simple way the role of the 3d electrons in determining the properties of complex ions. Crystal field theory ignores the fact that the ligands form coordinate bonds with the transition metal ion via their lone pairs. In addition the stability of metal carbonyls, for example, $Ni(CO)_4$, cannot be explained using crystal field theory.

A deeper understanding of metal complex ions and complexes involves combining the idea of the splitting of the 3d orbitals in different geometries (shapes) but taking into account the overlap that occurs between atomic orbitals on the ligand and the transition metal or atom. This is a covalent model based on molecular orbital theory (Chapter 14).

First-row transition metals use their 4s, 4p and 3d orbitals in bonding with monodentate ligands to form an octahedral complex. Figure 13.50 shows that a 4s orbital in the transition metal overlaps with all six of the ligand orbitals. The three 4p orbitals will overlap with a pair of ligands. Only the $3d_{z^2}$ and $3d_{x^2-y^2}$ orbitals can overlap with ligands. The remaining 3d orbitals ($3d_{xz}$, $3d_{yz}$ and $3d_{zy}$) cannot overlap to form sigma bonds and so are lone pairs.

■ **Figure 13.50**
Bonding combinations of ligand σ orbitals with metal orbitals

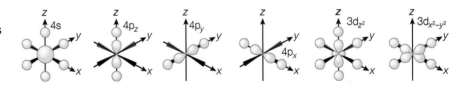

The molecular orbital diagram for an octahedral complex in which the metals and ligands form sigma bonds is shown in Figure 13.51. This provides a strong link between the molecular orbital (MO) approach and crystal field theory. The non-bonding t_{2g} and weakly anti-bonding e_g^* sets of orbitals correspond to the t_{2g} and e_g levels in the crystal field splitting diagram for an octahedral complex.

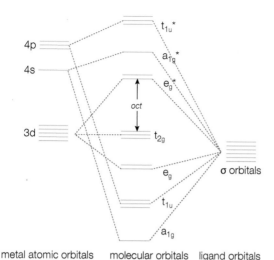

■ **Figure 13.51** Energy level diagram for an octahedral metal complex showing only sigma bond interactions

---

Colour linked to symmetry can be explored in the sciences, architecture and the arts

Symmetry is a fascinating phenomenon in nature. It is found in geometrical figures such as the cube, a sphere, a regular hexagon and the truncated icosahedron (C_{60} molecule). Its importance was recognized by ancient Greek philosophers such as Plato and Pythagoras. Symmetry is found in molecules, crystalline solids and orbitals. The mathematical study of symmetry is called group theory whose foundations were developed during the 19th century by the European mathematicians Galois and Abel among others. Murray Gell-Mann, the American theoretical physicist, was awarded the 1969 Nobel Prize in physics for applying symmetry to the classification of elementary particles and the postulation of quarks (Chapter 2).

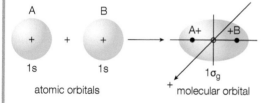

■ **Figure 13.52** The formation of the $1\sigma_g$ molecular orbital

Molecular orbitals and symmetry

A sigma molecular orbital in a hydrogen molecule is described as $1\sigma_g$ (Figure 13.52). It is a three-dimensional wave function which is said to be positive everywhere. This means that the electron wave is all in phase.

The subscript g stands for the German word *gerade*, meaning that the function is symmetric with respect to inversion in the centre of symmetry. In inversion, the x, y, and z coordinates are all replaced by their negatives.

The $1s_A$ and $1s_B$ atomic orbitals can also be combined in a different way to produce an electron density which is the same around each nucleus. This is an anti-bonding $1\sigma^*$ orbital, where the sign of the wave function is positive around one nucleus and negative around the other (Figure 13.53). These correspond to the electron waves having opposite phases.

This molecular orbital is described as $1\sigma_u$, where the subscript u, from the German word for odd *ungerade*, refers to the function being anti-symmetric – changing sign on inversion at the centre of the symmetry. In inversion, the x, y, and z coordinates are all replaced by their negatives.

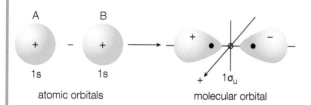

■ **Figure 13.53** The formation of the $1\sigma_u$ molecular orbital

The t_{2g} and e_g notations used previously in octahedral crystal field energy splitting diagrams have their origin in symmetry. The g in t_{2g} is from the term *gerade*, the t refers to a triply degenerate (same energy) set of d-orbitals and the 2 indicates that the sign of the wave function of the d_{xy} orbital changes upon rotation.

Symmetry in science, the arts and architecture

Symmetry underlies many of the ways we as knowers think about both the arts and the natural sciences. Of the four dimensions that we normally use to define the world we live in (up and down, in and out, left and right, and time), only time is inherently asymmetrical, moving forwards at a

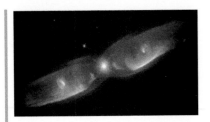

■ **Figure 13.54** A bipolar nebula

constant rate (entropy is time's arrow). Hence if we know the spatial properties of one-half of an object, such as an image of nebula (Figure 13.54), we can infer (in science) or anticipate (in art) what the other half may be like, even if it is unseen or inaccessible. This principle applies universally in the natural sciences and widely in the visual arts, in poetry and in literature and, especially, in music.

Also important in understanding the worlds of the natural sciences and the arts is colour. While artists and scientists 'see' the same colours, their interpretation and motivation for understanding them is totally different. The gap between the two areas of knowledge is nowhere greater than in the discussion of colour and symmetry. Almost as important as symmetry is its opposite, asymmetry.

Perfect symmetry, such as seen in the carbon-60 molecule, is beautiful and pleasing to the eye, but perhaps is also sterile. If the universe had failed to develop asymmetries billions of years ago following the Big Bang, humans would not be here to study it. In art it is often the deviations from symmetry that are aesthetically pleasing or disturbing and in the natural sciences, asymmetries are both revealing and informative.

To the artist, colour is a means of expression that can convey an emotion (mood) as well as a mental state. Artists talk of complementary colours as though there were real symmetries in the concepts and they are familiar with colours that convey warmth, for example red, yellow and orange, or distance, for example blue and violet. While scientists may be indifferent to those emotions, in the context of the natural sciences, colour is simply another diagnostic tool, providing more information about life and light.

However, the reds are the part of the visible spectrum accessed by thermal processes (as are the blues but their processes are different, hotter). The blues, violets and greys of objects in the distance are a statement about light scattering. So, the principle is artistic but with a scientific basis.

Figure 13.55 shows the beautiful mosque in Cordoba in Spain with its apparently endless rows of double arched columns that extend beneath a richly ornamented roof. In an inspired piece of artistic craftsmanship, the components of the arches are made of alternating grey stone and red tile sections. The columns are evenly spaced, and each one gives a new perspective on the striped arches with subtle shifts in colour; possibly relevant is the Islamic prohibition on pictures of animate objects, leading to an art based on symmetric, often abstract, patterns.

■ **Figure 13.55** Mosque in Cordoba, Spain

■ Chemistry of selected d-block metals

Vanadium

Vanadium can exist in four different oxidation states in compounds. In aqueous solution, ions containing vanadium in the different oxidation states have different colours (Table 13.12).

■ **Table 13.12**
Formulas, colours and oxidation numbers of some vanadium ions

Oxidation number	Formula of aqueous ion	Colour of aqueous ion
+2	V^{2+}	Lavender
+3	V^{3+}	Green
+4	VO^{2+}	Blue
+5	VO_2^+, VO_3^-	Yellow

■ **Figure 13.56**
The colour changes that can be seen here are due to reduction of the acidified solution of VO_2^+ (yellow), through VO^{2+} (blue), V^{3+} (green) to V^{2+} (lavender)

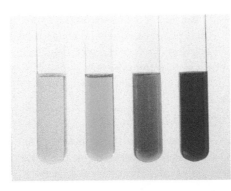

A common vanadium compound is ammonium vanadate(v), NH_4VO_3. In acidic conditions the trioxovanadate(v), VO_3^-(aq), ions are converted to dioxovanadium(v), VO_2^+(aq) ions:

$$2H^+(aq) + VO_3^-(aq) \rightarrow VO_2^+(aq) + H_2O(l)$$

These dioxovanadium(v) ions will react with zinc and dilute sulfuric acid (a powerful reducing agent) and undergo stepwise reduction to vanadium(II) ions, V^{2+}(aq), displaying the colours of the different ions as the reaction proceeds (Figure 13.56).

Vanadium(v) oxide, V_2O_5, is used as a catalyst in the Contact process (Chapter 7).

Chromium

Chromium has the oxidation number +6 both in chromate(vi), CrO_4^{2-}, and in dichromate(vi), $Cr_2O_7^{2-}$ (Figure 13.57). Yellow chromate(vi) ions can be converted to orange dichromate(vi) ions by the addition of dilute acid. This is an example of a condensation reaction (Chapter 10).

$$2CrO_4^{2-}(aq) + 2H^+(aq) \rightarrow Cr_2O_7^{2-}(aq) + H_2O(l)$$

Dichromate(vi) ions can be converted to chromate(vi) ions by the addition of dilute alkali:

$$Cr_2O_7^{2-}(aq) + 2OH^-(aq) \rightarrow 2CrO_4^{2-}(aq) + H_2O(l)$$

The structures of the chromate(vi) and dichromate(vi) ions are shown in Figure 13.58. The ions have resonance or delocalized bonding (Chapter 14), not shown in the diagram.

The dichromate(vi) ion is a powerful oxidizing agent. The half-equation below shows how it reacts with reducing agents in acidified aqueous solution. The reduction results in the formation of the green chromium(iii) ion:

$$Cr_2O_7^{2-}(aq) + 14H^+(aq) + 6e^- \rightarrow 2Cr^{3+}(aq) + 7H_2O(l) \qquad E^\ominus = +1.33 \text{ V}$$

The high positive value for the standard electrode potential ($E^\ominus$) indicates that the dichromate(vi) ion has a strong affinity for electrons under these conditions.

The reaction is used in redox titrations (Chapter 1 and Chapter 9), in which it can be used to find the concentrations of reducing agents. Acidified aqueous solutions of potassium dichromate(vi), $K_2Cr_2O_7$, are used to oxidize alcohols (Chapter 10).

In dilute acidified solutions, dichromate(vi) ions react with hydrogen peroxide solution (acting here as a reducing agent) to form green chromium(iii) ions. The two half-equations are:

$$Cr_2O_7^{2-}(aq) + 14H^+(aq) + 6e^- \rightarrow 2Cr^{3+}(aq) + 7H_2O(l)$$
$$H_2O_2(aq) \rightarrow 2H^+(aq) + O_2(g) + 2e^-$$

Another important chromium compound is chromium(vi) oxide, CrO_3, a covalent compound which is precipitated when concentrated sulfuric acid is added to solutions of chromate(vi) or dichromate(vi) ions. It is a red crystalline solid that reacts with water to form a solution of dichromate(vi) ions. Chromium(iii) oxide, Cr_2O_3, is a green solid (insoluble in water) that can be prepared by heating ammonium dichromate(vi):

$$(NH_4)_2Cr_2O_7(s) \rightarrow N_2(g) + Cr_2O_3(s) + 4H_2O(g)$$

The +2 oxidation state of chromium is unstable but can be prepared from the reduction of dichromate(vi) ions. Dichromate(vi) ions can be reduced by zinc and dilute acid to chromium(iii) and then chromium(ii). Hydrogen is produced from a side reaction between the zinc and the acid. This must be allowed to escape, and air should be kept out of the reaction mixture. Oxygen in the air rapidly re-oxidizes chromium(ii) to chromium(iii). A simple approach is to put a piece of cotton wool in the top of the flask (or test-tube). This allows the hydrogen to escape, but stops most of the air getting in against the flow of the hydrogen.

Manganese

Manganese can exist in four oxidation states: +2, +4, +6 and +7.

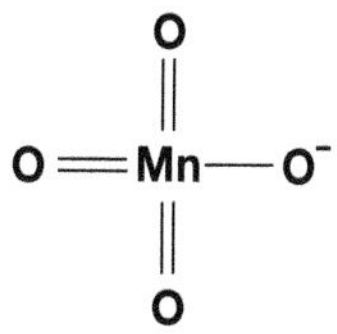

Manganese(vii) compounds

The most familiar manganese(vii) compound is potassium manganate(vii), which dissolves in water to give a deep purple solution that contains MnO_4^- ions (Figure 13.59). Potassium manganate(vii) is commonly used as an oxidizing agent in the presence of excess dilute sulfuric acid and under these conditions is usually reduced to the pale pink manganese(ii) ions (nearly colourless at low concentrations), and the purple solution is decolorized:

■ **Figure 13.57**
Aqueous solutions of chromate(vi) and dichromate(vi) ions

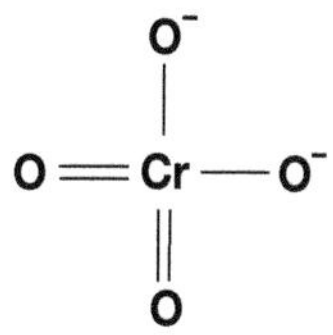

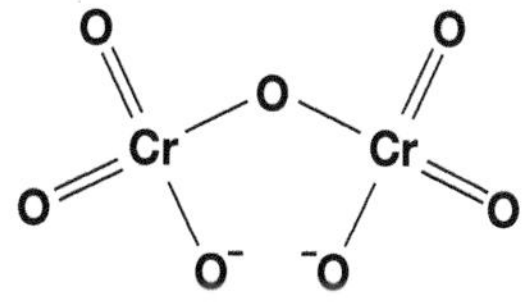

■ **Figure 13.58**
Structures of chromate(vi) and dichromate(vi) ions

■ **Figure 13.59**
Structure of the manganate(vii) ion

$$MnO_4^-(aq) + 8H^+(aq) + 5e^- \rightarrow Mn^{2+}(aq) + 4H_2O(l) \qquad E^\ominus = +1.52\,V$$

In neutral or slightly alkaline conditions the manganate(VII) ions are reduced to brown manganese(IV) oxide:

$$MnO_4^-(aq) + 4H^+(aq) + 3e^- \rightarrow MnO_2(s) + 2H_2O(l) \qquad E^\ominus = +1.67\,V$$

In very strong alkaline solutions, manganate(VII) ions are reduced to green manganate(VI) ions:

$$MnO_4^-(aq) + e^- \rightarrow MnO_4^{2-}(aq) \qquad\qquad E^\ominus = +0.56\,V$$

■ **Figure 13.60**
Manganese(IV) oxide powder

Manganese(IV) compounds

The most common manganese(IV) compound is manganese(IV) oxide (Figure 13.60). It is a strong oxidizing agent and is reduced to manganese(II) ions:

$$MnO_2(s) + 4H^+(aq) + 2e^- \rightarrow Mn^{2+}(aq) + 2H_2O(l) \qquad E^\ominus = +1.23\,V$$

Manganese (IV) oxide is a catalyst for the decomposition of hydrogen peroxide (Chapter 6).

Manganese(II) compounds

Manganese(II) salts are generally pale pink in colour. Manganese(II) chloride, $MnCl_2$, and manganese(II) sulfate, $MnSO_4$, are prepared by reacting manganese with dilute hydrochloric and sulfuric acids, respectively. Other manganese(II) salts are made via precipitation reactions, for example, manganese(II) carbonate (Figure 13.61).

■ **Figure 13.61**
Manganese(II) carbonate

Iron

The two most common oxidation states of iron are +2 and +3.

Iron(II) compounds

Soluble iron(II) salts, for example hydrated iron(II) sulfate, $FeSO_4.7H_2O$ (Figure 13.62), are green crystalline solids that release the hexaaquairon(II) ion, $[Fe(H_2O)_6]^{2+}$, in solution. The solutions of soluble iron(II) salts give (in the absence of air) a pale green precipitate of iron(II) hydroxide when treated with a base:

$$Fe^{2+}(aq) + 2OH^-(aq) \rightarrow Fe(OH)_2(s)$$

■ **Figure 13.62**
Hydrated iron(II) sulfate crystals, $FeSO_4.7H_2O$

Neutral solutions of iron(II) salts are readily oxidized to iron(III) by oxidizing agents, for example chlorine water, and are oxidized slowly by oxygen in the air:

$$[Fe(H_2O)_6]^{3+}(aq) + e^- \rightarrow [Fe(H_2O)_6]^{2+}(aq) \qquad E^\ominus = +0.77\,V$$

Iron(III) compounds

Soluble iron(III) salts, for example iron(III) chloride, $FeCl_3$, are usually yellow or brown crystalline solids that release the violet hexaaquairon(III) ion, $[Fe(H_2O)_6]^{3+}$, in strongly acidic solution.

Iron(III) salts are acidic in aqueous solution (see section 13.1). The solutions of soluble iron(III) salts give (in the presence of air) a rusty brown precipitate of iron(III) hydroxide on reaction with base:

$$Fe^{3+}(aq) + 3OH^-(aq) \rightarrow Fe(OH)_3(s)$$

Iron(III) salts are readily reduced to iron(II) salts by a variety of reducing agents, for example iodide ions, copper metal and copper(I) ions. Iron(II) salts are readily oxidized under alkaline conditions:

$$Fe(OH)_3(aq) + e^- \rightarrow Fe(OH)_2(aq) + OH^-(aq) \qquad\qquad E^\ominus = +0.77\,V$$

Copper

The common oxidation states of copper are +1 and +2. In water, the hydrated copper(II) ion is stable, but the hydrated copper(I) ion is unstable in water and is immediately converted into copper(II) ions and copper metal:

$$2Cu^+(aq) \rightarrow Cu^{2+}(aq) + Cu(s)$$

■ **Figure 13.63**
Copper(I) oxide

The reaction between copper(I) ions and water is an example of disproportionation (Chapter 9). Some copper(I) compounds are insoluble, for example copper(I) oxide, Cu_2O (Figure 13.63) and copper(I) chloride, CuCl.

Copper(I) chloride can be prepared by boiling copper(II) chloride with copper (a reducing agent) and pouring the complex ion mixture into air-free water to precipitate white copper(I) chloride. The overall equation for the reaction is:

$$CuCl_2(aq) + Cu(s) \rightarrow 2CuCl(s)$$

Copper(I) chloride is not stable in aqueous solution, but the reaction is slow. Copper(II) ions can be reduced to copper(I) ions by powerful reducing agents. For example, a solution of aqueous copper(II) ions reacts with potassium iodide solution to give a white precipitate of copper(I) iodide and iodine:

$$2Cu^{2+}(aq) + 4I^-(aq) \rightarrow 2CuI(s) + I_2(aq)$$

However, the yellow or brown colour of the iodine solution obscures the white precipitate. This can be made more obvious by the careful addition of thiosulfate ions.

Zinc

■ **Figure 13.64**
Zinc oxide powder

The only stable oxidation state of zinc is +2. The compounds of zinc are white (Figure 13.64). Zinc complexes usually have a coordination number of 4 and these are tetrahedral. Addition of alkali to an aqueous solution of a zinc salt initially produces a white precipitate of the hydroxide but this is amphoteric and dissolves in excess to give a colourless solution of zincate(II) ions:

$$Zn^{2+}(aq) + 2OH^-(aq) \rightarrow Zn(OH)_2(s)$$

$$Zn(OH)_2(s) + 2OH^-(aq) \rightarrow [Zn(OH)_4]^{2-}(aq)$$

■ Transition metals as catalysts

Transition metals and their compounds are often used as catalysts to increase the rates of industrial processes (Chapter 22 on the accompanying website). Their catalytic properties are due to their ability to exist in a number of stable oxidation states and the presence of empty orbitals for temporary bond formation.

The transition metal catalysts used in industry are heterogeneous catalysts, where the catalyst is in a different physical state from the reactants. Typically, the catalyst is a powdered solid (often on the surface of an inert support) and the reactants are a mixture of gases. Some examples of transition metal based catalysts are given in Table 13.13.

■ **Table 13.13**
Some transition metal based industrial catalysts

Process	Reaction catalysed	Products	Catalyst
Haber	$N_2(g) + 3H_2(g) \rightleftharpoons 2NH_3(g)$	Ammonia	Iron, Fe
Contact	$2SO_2(g) + O_2(g) \rightleftharpoons 2SO_3(g)$	Sulfuric acid	Vanadium(V) oxide, V_2O_5
Hydrogenation of unsaturated oils to harden them	$RCH=CHR' \rightarrow RCH_2CH_2R'$	Semi-solid saturated fat	Nickel, Ni
Hydrogenation	Alkene to alkane	Alkane	Nickel, Ni
Ziegler–Natta polymerization of alkenes	$nCH_2=CHR \rightarrow -[CH_2-CHR]_n-$	Stereoregular polymer	Complex of $TiCl_3$ and $Al(C_2H_5)_3$

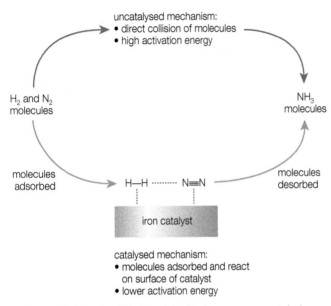

uncatalysed mechanism:
• direct collision of molecules
• high activation energy

H₂ and N₂ molecules

NH₃ molecules

molecules adsorbed

molecules desorbed

H—H ·········· N≡N

iron catalyst

catalysed mechanism:
• molecules adsorbed and react on surface of catalyst
• lower activation energy

■ **Figure 13.65** A simplified model of heterogeneous catalysis, using the Haber process as an example

Heated nickel can also be used in the laboratory to catalyse the reduction of nitriles to amines using hydrogen gas. The Haber and Contact processes are both examples of chemical equilibria (Chapter 7) and the resulting mixtures will contain both reactants and products.

Heterogeneous catalysis can be demonstrated in the laboratory by adding a small amount of manganese(IV) oxide, MnO_2, to a dilute solution of hydrogen peroxide (Chapter 6).

During heterogeneous catalysis, the liquid or gas molecules are adsorbed on the surface of the solid catalyst (Figure 13.65), where their bonds are weakened via complex formation so the products are produced more rapidly (Chapter 6).

The strength of the adsorption helps to determine the activity of a catalyst. Some transition metals adsorb very strongly, so products are released slowly. Others adsorb weakly so the concentration of reactants on the surface is low.

Transition metal ions also exhibit homogeneous catalysis, where they and the reactant(s) are in the same physical state; usually all are in solution. For example, iron(III) ions act as a homogeneous catalyst for the reaction between peroxodisulfate and iodide ions to form sulfate ions and iodine molecules (Chapter 16). Iron catalyses the reaction by interconverting between its two common oxidation states, iron(II) and iron(III). This facilitates the electron transfer processes that occur. Many metal-containing enzymes, especially those in the electron transport chain, act in a similar way inside cells.

Homogeneous catalysis is also exhibited in the reaction between manganate(VII) ions and ethanedioate ions. This is an example of autocatalysis, as manganese(II) ions, one of the products, are a catalyst for the reaction.

Biomolecules containing a metal

A number of molecules in living organisms contain one or more strongly bonded metal ions as part of their molecular structure. The metal ion will be attached to the biological molecule via donor atoms, usually nitrogen, oxygen or sulfur, present in the molecules. They act as ligands to the metal ion. The coordination number of the metal ion is usually 6 and the coordination geometry is often octahedral. The ligands may be the side-chains of amino acids or a porphyrin ring (Figure 13.66), a planar tetradentate ligand. Hemoglobin, myoglobin, chlorophylls a and b and vitamin B12 (which contains a related corrin ring) can all be regarded as complex ions containing a metal cation.

■ **Figure 13.66** Basic porphyrin structure

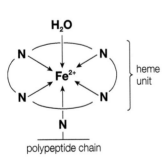

■ **Figure 13.67** Simplified structure of hemoglobin

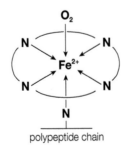

■ **Figure 13.68** Simplified structure of oxyhemoglobin

Hemoglobin

A hemoglobin molecule is made up of a heme unit covalently attached to a protein chain (globin). Each hemoglobin molecule contains four heme units and four globin chains. In the hemoglobin molecule the iron(II) ions are bonded to five nitrogen atoms and one oxygen atom (in a water molecule). A simplified structure of hemoglobin is shown in Figure 13.67.

Hemoglobin absorbs oxygen from the lungs by forming oxyhemoglobin (Figure 13.68). The oxygen molecule displaces the water molecule and forms a dative bond with the iron. This reaction is reversible and at low pressures the oxygen leaves, re-forming hemoglobin.

Catalysts in industry

Catalysts play a critical role in the chemical industry by increasing the rates of reaction and decreasing the time needed for a reaction to reach equilibrium. They increase the efficiency of industrial processes and help to reduce costs and so increase profits. The ammonia and sulfuric acid produced by the Haber and Contact processes are vital feedstocks for many other parts of the chemical industry. Considerable research is conducted to find cheaper, 'greener' and more effective catalysts for industrial reactions.

One reason for recent increases in the prices of metals such as platinum, rhodium and palladium is that they are used in catalytic converters in vehicles and as catalysts in some industrial processes. For example, a platinum–rhodium alloy can be used in the Contact process (Chapter 7).

■ Summary

Table 13.15 summarizes the important properties of transition elements and their compounds.

■ Identifying transition metal ions

The hydroxides of transition metal ions can be precipitated from their aqueous solution by the addition of sodium hydroxide solution. The colour of the precipitate (Figure 13.69) can be used to identify the transition metal present (Table 13.14).

■ **Figure 13.69** Precipitates of hydrated transition metal hydroxides. From left to right: cobalt(ii), zinc, iron(iii), iron(ii) and copper(ii)

Transition metal ion present	Formula of precipitate	Colour of precipitate
Chromium(iii)	$Cr(OH)_3$	Green
Manganese(ii)	$Mn(OH)_2$	Pale brown
Iron(ii)	$Fe(OH)_2$	Pale green (surface turns rusty brown)
Iron(iii)	$Fe(OH)_3$	Rusty brown
Cobalt(ii)	$Co(OH)_2$	Pink
Nickel	$Ni(OH)_2$	Green
Copper(ii)	$Cu(OH)_2$	Blue
Zinc	$Zn(OH)_2$	White

■ **Table 13.14** Colours and formulas of selected transition metal hydroxides

■ Acidity of transition metal ions

The acidity of hexaaqua transition metal ions (Chapter 8) can be expressed in a 'Brønsted–Lowry' proton transfer style equation:

$$[M(H_2O)_6]^{n+}(aq) + H_2O(l) \rightleftharpoons [M(H_2O)_5(OH)]^{(n-1)+}(aq) + H_3O^+(aq)$$

where $n = 2$ or 3. The overall charge on the complex falls by +1 for each proton transferred, as an electrically neutral water ligand is replaced by a charged hydroxide ion (OH^-) ligand. Water acts as the Brønsted–Lowry base (H^+ acceptor) and the hexaaqua ion acts as the Brønsted–Lowry acid (H^+ donor) in the deprotonation reaction. The forward reaction is favoured by polarizing transition metal cations that is, those with high charge and small ionic radius, since they strongly attract water molecules.

Transition element	Ti	V	Cr	Mn	Fe	Co	Ni	Cu
Electronic configuration	[Ar] $3d^24s^2$	[Ar] $3d^34s^2$	*[Ar] $3d^54s^1$	[Ar] $3d^54s^2$	[Ar] $3d^64s^2$	[Ar] $3d^74s^2$	[Ar] $3d^84s^2$	*[Ar] $3d^{10}4s^1$
	Across the period, the additional electron enters the 3d orbital. When forming cations, the 4s electrons are lost first before removal of the 3d electrons							
Atomic radius, M	Generally small increase across the period as the additional electron enters the 3d orbital, providing effective shielding between the nucleus and the outer 4s electrons. Thus the increase in nuclear charge is almost counterbalanced by the increase in shielding							
Ionic radius, M⁺	Smaller atomic and ionic radii than s-block elements due to greater nuclear charges							
First ionization energy	Greater first IE than s-block elements due to increase in nuclear charge and small change in atomic radius							
Third and higher ionization energies	Increases across the period as the 3d electrons are now outermost. Across the period the nuclear charge increases but the shielding does not increase significantly. The third IE of iron is unexpectedly low, as Fe^{2+} has a d^6 configuration and the electron is more easily removed from a filled d-orbital which experiences inter-electron repulsion							
Melting point	Higher than s-block elements, all melting points >1000 °C. Both the 4s and 3d electrons can be delocalized as they are close in energy to form stronger metallic bonding than in s-block elements which have fewer electrons for delocalization							
Density	Denser than s-block elements, gradual increase across the period. Greater relative atomic mass to radius ratio than s-block elements							
Electrical conductivity	Higher than s-block metals due to a larger mobile charge cloud (delocalized valence electrons) than in s-block elements as 3d and 4s electrons are delocalized. Tends to increase across the period							
Variable oxidation states	+1 to +4	+1 to +5	+1 to +6	+1 to +7	+1 to +6	+1 to +5	+1 to +4	+1 to +3
Colour of complexes	There are obvious colour changes when the transition metal changes its oxidation state since the number of 3d electrons is changed. The colour of complexes will also change as a result of ligand exchange reactions since the extent of interaction between the ligands and the 3d electrons will be different, that is, the d–d splitting will be different for different ligands (spectrochemical series)							
	The 3d orbitals of transition metals in octahedral complexes are split due to the presence of ligands, a process known as d–d splitting. An electron from the lower energy level is promoted to the upper level by absorbing energy from the visible region of the electromagnetic spectrum. This is known as a d–d transition. The frequency of light absorbed is determined by the degree of splitting. The complement of the colour absorbed is seen.							

■ **Table 13.15** Selected atomic and physical properties of the first-row transition metals

*These electron configurations are anomalous and do not follow the Aufbau principle.

■ *Examination questions – a selection*

Paper 1 IB questions and IB style questions

Q1 The electron configuration of atoms of a transition metal atom is $1s^22s^22p^63s^23p^63d^34s^2$. What is the maximum oxidation state?

    A +5   **C** +3
    B +4   **D** +2

Q2 Transition metals differ from group 1 and group 2 metals in all of the following respects except for:

    A being more chemically reactive
    B having higher melting points
    C being more likely to form coloured compounds
    D being more likely to form complex ions in aqueous solution

Q3 Which of these species involves the transition metal in one of its common oxidation states?

    I CrO_4^{2-}
    II MnO_4^{3-}
    III $FeBr_3$

    A I and II only
    B I and III only
    C II and III only
    D I, II and III

Q4 The cyanide ion, CN^-, can form two complex ions with iron ions. The formulas of these ions are $[Fe(CN)_6]^{4-}$ and $[Fe(CN)_6]^{3-}$. What is the oxidation state of iron in the two complex ions?

	$[Fe(CN)_6]^{4-}$	$[Fe(CN)_6]^{3-}$
A	−4	−3
B	+2	+3
C	+3	+2
D	−3	−4

Higher Level Paper 1, Nov 2004, Q8

Q5 Which statements about $[Ag(NH_3)_2]^+$ are correct?

    I NH_3 forms a dative covalent (coordinate) bond with Ag^+.

    II The formation of the bond between NH_3 and Ag^+ is an example of a Lewis acid–base reaction.

    III Ag^+ is the ligand in this complex ion.

    A I and II only

    B I and III only

    C II and III only

    D I, II and III

Higher Level Paper 1, May 2013, Q8

Q6 What is the overall charge on the complex ion formed by the reaction between a single iron(III) and six cyanide ions?

    A 3–   **C** 6–

    B 3+   **D** 0

Q7 Which species can act as ligands with transition metals?

    I $H_2N–CH_2–CH_2–NH_2$

    II Br^-

    III CH_4

    A I and II only

    B I and III only

    C II and III only

    D I, II and III

Q8 Which oxidation number is the most common among first-row transition elements?

    A +1   **C** +3

    B +2   **D** +5

Q9 The colours of the compounds of d-block elements are due to electron transitions:

    A between different d orbitals (within the same shell)

    B between d orbitals and p orbitals

    C among the attached ligands

    D from the metal ion to the attached ligands

Q10 In which one of the following reactions does the transition metal or compound not behave as a catalyst?

    A the formation of ethanal from ethanol, using acidified potassium dichromate(VI)

    B the formation of oxygen from hydrogen peroxide using manganese(IV) oxide

    C the formation of ammonia from its elements in the presence of iron

    D the use of vanadium(V) oxide in the Contact process

Q11 Transition metals can be distinguished from non-transition metals by the fact that:

    A non-transition metals have higher relative atomic masses than transition metals

    B non-transition metals only have +1 or +2 oxidation states

    C only the transition metals can form complex ions

    D transition metals have a greater tendency to form coloured compounds than non-transition metals

Q12 A metal ion M^{n+} forms a complex ion of formula $[ML_2]^{(n-4)+}$ where L represents a bidentate ligand. The charge on the ligand L is

    A +2   **C** –1

    B 0   **D** –2

Q13 The conversion of chromate ions, $CrO_4^{2-}(aq)$ to dichromate ions, $Cr_2O_7^{2-}(aq)$ is represented by the following equation:

$$2CrO_4^{2-}(aq) + 2H^+(aq) \rightleftharpoons Cr_2O_7^{2-}(aq) + H_2O(l)$$

Which statement is not true?

    A The $CrO_4^{2-}(aq)$ ion acts as a base.

    B There is a colour change.

    C None of the ions are complex ions.

    D The conversion of $CrO_4^{2-}(aq)$ to $Cr_2O_7^{2-}(aq)$ involves a change of oxidation state.

Q14 Which of the following has the greatest number of unpaired electrons?

    A Fe^{3+} **C** Cr^{3+}

    B Fe^{2+} **D** Co^{2+}

Q15 Which one of the following characteristics of transition metals is associated with their catalytic behaviour?

    A coloured ions

    B low standard electrode potentials

    C variable oxidation states

    D high melting and boiling points

Q16 The compound $[Co(NH_3)_5Cl]SO_4$ is isomeric with the compound $[Co(NH_3)_5SO_4]Cl$. What is the oxidation state of cobalt in these compounds?

	$[Co(NH_3)_5Cl]SO_4$	$[Co(NH_3)_5SO_4]Cl$
A	+2	+3
B	+3	+2
C	+2	+1
D	+3	+3

Paper 2 IB questions and IB style questions

Q1 Carboplatin used in the treatment of lung cancer has the following three-dimensional structure.

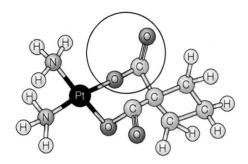

a Identify the name of the functional group circled in the structure of carboplatin. [1]

b State the type of bonding between platinum and nitrogen in carboplatin. [1]

c Elemental platinum has electrons occupying s, p, d and f atomic orbitals.

   i Draw the shape of an s orbital and a p_x orbital. Label the *x*, *y* and *z* axes on each diagram. [2]

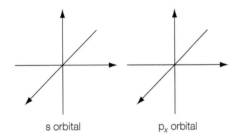

s orbital p_x orbital

   ii State the maximum number of orbitals in the $n = 4$ energy level. [1]

d A number of ruthenium-based anti-cancer drugs have also been developed. State the full electron configuration of the ruthenium(II) ion, Ru^{2+}. [1]

e Iron is in the same group in the periodic table as ruthenium. Construct the orbital diagram (using the arrow-in-box notation) for iron, showing the electrons in the $n = 3$ and $n = 4$ energy levels and label each sub-level on the diagram.

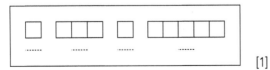

[1]

Q2 a State and explain what would be observed when aqueous ammonia is added to aqueous copper(II) nitrate, dropwise, until the aqueous ammonia is in excess. [4]

b The green MnO_4^{2-} ion, when treated with acid, forms a brown precipitate of MnO_2 in a purple solution of MnO_4^-.

   i Write a balanced equation for this redox reaction. [2]

   ii Deduce the oxidation numbers of manganese in all three manganese compounds. [3]

   iii What type of behaviour does MnO_2 exhibit when placed in hydrogen peroxide solution? [1]

c Explain why an aqueous and concentrated solution of zinc ions is colourless. [2]

Q3 Prussian blue is made by mixing together aqueous solutions of $FeCl_3$ and $K_4Fe(CN)_6$, which contains $[Fe(CN)_6]^{4-}$ ions.

a State the oxidation states of the iron ions in each of these solutions. [2]

b Describe the shape of the $[Fe(CN)_6]^{4-}$ ion. [2]

c Iron is a transition metal. Define the term *transition metal*. [1]

d Explain the activity of iron in hemoglobin. [2]

Q4 A hypothetical metal, M, forms the following complexes with the generalized ligands X, Y and Z.

Complex ion	Observed colour	Absorbed colour
$[M(X)_6]^{3+}$	green	red
$[M(Y)_6]^{3+}$	blue	orange
$[M(Z)_6]^{3+}$	yellow	violet

Order these ligands according to their ability to split d orbitals. Set up a spectrochemical series, from strongest to weakest ligand field strength. [3]

Q5 The hexachlorochromate(III) ion has a maximum in its absorption spectrum at 735 nm. Calculate the crystal field splitting energy (in $kJ\,mol^{-1}$) for this ion. [4]

Q6 Answer the following questions about the complex $[RhCl_6]^{3-}$, where Rh is rhodium $[Kr]4d^8 4s^1$.

a Deduce the oxidation state of rhodium in the complex ion. [1]

b Deduce the electron configuration of the metal cation. [1]

c Deduce the number of unpaired electrons present in the complex ion. [1]

d State the shape of the complex and show the arrangement of electrons. [5]

14 Chemical bonding and structure

ESSENTIAL IDEAS

- Larger structures and more in-depth explanations of bonding systems often require more sophisticated concepts and theories of bonding.
- Hybridization results from the mixing of atomic orbitals to form the same number of new equivalent hybrid orbitals that can have the same mean energy as the contributing atomic orbitals.

14.1 Further aspects of covalent bonding and structure – *larger structures and more in-depth explanations of bonding systems often require more sophisticated concepts and theories of bonding*

■ Shapes of molecules and ions

We have seen earlier (Chapter 4) that the valence shell electron pair repulsion theory (VSEPR theory) can be very usefully applied to explain the shapes of simple covalent molecules and polyatomic ions built around a central atom.

This theory can also be applied to molecules and ions that have five and six electron domains. The basic shapes (Figure 14.1) adopted by molecules with five or six electron pairs are trigonal bipyramidal and octahedral, respectively. These shapes minimize the repulsion between electron pairs in the valence shell. The trigonal bipyramid has three equatorial bonds and two axial bonds; the octahedron has six equivalent bonds.

Table 14.1 summarizes how the numbers of bonding and lone pairs of electrons determine the geometries of molecules with five and six electron domains.

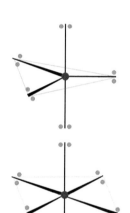

■ **Figure 14.1**
The basic shapes for molecules with five and six electron pairs

Total number of electron pairs	Number of electron domains		Molecular shape	Examples
	Bonding pairs	Lone pairs		
5	2	3	Linear	ICl_2^-, XeF_2 and I_3^-
5	3	2	T-shaped	ClF_3 and BrF_3
5	4	1	See-saw (distorted tetrahedral)	SF_4
5	5	0	Trigonal bipyramidal	PCl_5
6	6	0	Octahedral	SF_6 and PF_6^-
6	5	1	Square pyramidal	BrF_5 and ClF_5
6	4	2	Square planar	XeF_4 and ICl_4^-

■ **Table 14.1** Summary of molecular shapes for species with five and six centres of negative charge

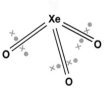

■ **Figure 14.2**
Structure and shape of the XeO_3 molecule

For species with five electron domains there are alternative positions for any lone pairs of electrons. The favoured positions will be those where the lone pairs are located furthest apart, thus minimizing the repulsive forces in the molecule. Consequently, lone pairs will *usually* occupy equatorial positions.

A multiple bond is still treated as if it is a single electron pair and the two or three electron pairs of a multiple bond are treated as a single pair. For example, the xenon trioxide molecule has a pyramidal shape (Figure 14.2). The valence shell of the xenon atom in xenon trioxide contains 14 electrons: eight from the xenon and two each from the three oxygen atoms.

Worked examples

Deduce the shape of PF₅.

> The valence shell of the phosphorus atom in phosphorus(v) fluoride contains ten electrons: five from the phosphorus and one each from the five fluorine atoms. The shape will be a trigonal bipyramid with bond angles of 120°, 180° and 90° (Figure 14.3).

Deduce the shape of SF₆.

> The valence shell of the sulfur atom in the sulfur(vi) fluoride molecule contains 12 electrons: six from the sulfur and one each from the six fluorine atoms. The shape will be an octahedron with bond angles of 90° and 180° (Figure 14.4).

Deduce the shape of SF₄.

> The valence shell of the sulfur atom contains ten electrons: six from the sulfur and one each from the four fluorine atoms. There are four bonding pairs and one lone pair. The basic shape adopted by the electron pairs in the molecule is trigonal bipyramidal. In this arrangement, the electron pairs at the equatorial positions experience less repulsion compared to axial electron pairs. Hence the lone pair occupies an equatorial position and thus the shape of the molecule itself resembles a see-saw (Figure 14.5). As a general rule, for a molecule where the electron domains adopt a trigonal bipyramidal structure, any lone pairs will occupy equatorial positions.

Deduce the shape of ClF₃.

> The valence shell of the chlorine atom contains ten electrons: seven from the chlorine and one each from the three fluorine atoms. There are three bonding pairs and two lone pairs. The basic shape adopted by the electron pairs in the molecule is a trigonal bipyramid. To minimize the repulsion between bonding pairs and lone pairs of electrons, the two lone pairs of electrons occupy the equatorial positions. Hence, the molecule has a T-shape (Figure 14.6).

Deduce the shape of XeCl₄.

> The valence shell of the xenon atom contains 12 electrons: eight from the xenon and one each from the four chlorine atoms. There are four bonding pairs and two lone pairs. The basic shape adopted by the molecule is octahedral. However, there are two possible arrangements for the lone pairs. The first structure, square planar, minimizes the repulsion (the lone pairs are at 180° to each other) and is hence adopted as the molecular shape (Figure 14.7). As a general rule, for a molecule where the electron domains adopt an octahedral structure, any lone pairs will occupy positions opposite to one another.

Deduce the shape of ICl₂⁻.

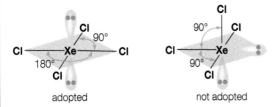

■ **Figure 14.7** Possible structures of XeCl₄

> The valence shell of the central iodine atom contains ten electrons: seven from the iodine atom, two from the two chlorine atoms and an additional electron responsible for the negative charge. There are two bonding pairs and three lone pairs. The basic shape adopted by the ion is a trigonal bipyramid (Figure 14.8). The three lone pairs occupy the equatorial positions to minimize the repulsion between the bonding pairs and the lone pairs of electrons, so the final shape is linear.

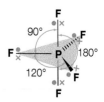

■ **Figure 14.3** Structure and shape of the PF₅ molecule

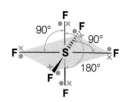

■ **Figure 14.4** Structure and shape of the SF₆ molecule

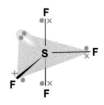

■ **Figure 14.5** Structure and shape of the SF₄ molecule

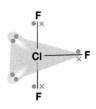

■ **Figure 14.6** Structure and shape of the ClF₃ molecule

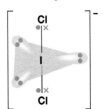

■ **Figure 14.8** Structure and shape of ICl₂⁻

Utilization: Drug action and its link to a molecule's structure

The properties of a drug are directly linked to its structure and shape. The main molecular targets for drugs are proteins (usually enzymes and proteins in cell membranes) or DNA. The interaction of a drug with its larger target macromolecule is a process known as binding. This occurs at a specific area known as the binding site, which is often a hollow on the surface of the macromolecule, allowing the drug ('key') to fit into its 'lock'.

Some drugs react with the binding site and become permanently attached via the formation of a strong covalent bond. However, most drugs interact through weaker forms of interaction: hydrogen bonds, dipole–dipole forces and London (dispersion) forces. Ionic bonds and hydrophobic interactions may also be involved. These are all weaker than covalent bonds and can be formed and then broken with small amounts of energy. This means there is an equilibrium between the bound drug and the free drug. Drugs having a large number of strong interactions will remain bound longer than those with few or weaker interactions. Functional groups (Chapter 10) present in the drug can also be important in forming intermolecular forces or ionic bonds with the target binding site.

Angiotensin II is an important hormone that causes blood vessels to constrict, causing a rise in blood pressure. A number of drugs have been developed to bind and inhibit the action of the peptide. Enalaprilate binds to the active site of angiotensin II as shown in Figure 14.9. Note that its shape and structure allow a number of interactions to be formed with the active site of the peptide.

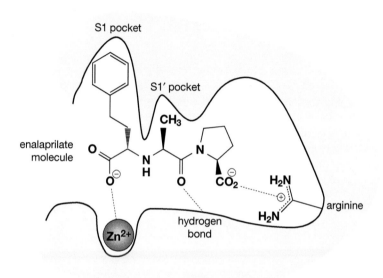

■ **Figure 14.9** Binding of enalaprilate to the active site of angiotensin II

■ Expansion of the octet and incomplete octets

Nitrogen forms one chloride, nitrogen trichloride, NCl_3. Phosphorus, however, forms two chlorides: phosphorus trichloride, PCl_3, and phosphorus pentachloride, PCl_5. Phosphorus can form five bonds since it has low-energy d-orbitals (in the third shell) to accommodate the extra electrons, while nitrogen has no such orbitals available (in the second shell). There are no 2d orbitals.

The energy required to promote a 3s electron in the phosphorus atom (Figure 14.10) to the empty 3d orbital to form five unpaired electrons is more than offset by an even larger amount of energy released when two extra P–Cl bonds are formed in PCl_5. Compounds with more than eight electrons in their outer or valence shell, such as PCl_5 and SF_6 (Figure 14.11), are termed hypervalent and are said to have 'expanded their octet'. There are also examples of molecules in which the central atoms has an incomplete octet (Chapter 4): $BeCl_2(g)$, $BCl_3(l)$, $BH_3(g)$ and $AlCl_3(g)$.

■ **Figure 14.10**
Expansion of the octet in phosphorus

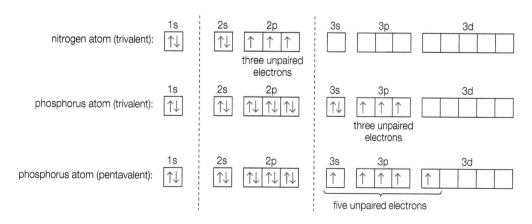

■ **Figure 14.11**
Molymod models
of phosphorus
pentachloride,
PCl₅, and sulfur
hexafluoride, SF₆

The VSEPR model is based upon Lewis structures which assume that all valence electrons are paired and a chemical bond requires two electrons. The model is limited to simple compounds of the main group elements (s- and p-blocks) and some transition metal ions (those with d^0 and d^{10} configurations). It can only predict exact bond angles for molecules with no lone pairs. It is theoretically unsatisfactory since electrons do not behave as static point charges and it provides no information about the stability of molecules. However, VSEPR theory is a simple and powerful model that satisfactorily predicts and explains the shapes of a large number of molecules and ions from the s- and p-blocks.

Using VSEPR theory to deduce the electron domain geometry and molecular geometry with five and six electron domains and associated bond angles

Table 14.2 summarizes the electron domain geometry and molecular geometry of molecules and ions with five electron domains as predicted by VSEPR theory. A is the central atom, the surrounding atoms are B, and a lone pair of electrons is represented by L.

Type of molecule	Number of bonding pairs	Number of lone pairs	Arrangement of electron pairs (bonding pairs and lone pairs)	Shape of molecule	Examples	Reason
AB_4L	4	1	$\begin{array}{c} B \\ | \\ :-A \overset{\diagup B}{\diagdown} B \\ | \\ B \end{array}$	See-saw	SeF_4 and ClF_4^+	The lone pair preferably occupies the equatorial position because repulsive interactions are less than those at the axial position
AB_3L_2	3	2	$\begin{array}{c} B \\ | \\ :-A-B \\ | \\ B \end{array}$	T-shape	BrF_3 and IF_3	The two lone pairs prefer to occupy equatorial positions at 120° to each other
AB_2L_3	2	3	$\begin{array}{c} B \\ | \\ :-A-: \\ | \\ B \end{array}$	Linear	Br_3^-	All three lone pairs occupy equatorial positions at 120° to each other

■ **Table 14.2** Summary of VSEPR theory for the electron domain geometry and molecular geometry of molecules and ions with five electron domains

Table 14.3 similarly summarizes the geometry of molecules and ions with six electron domains. Again, A is the central atom, the surrounding atoms are B, and a lone pair is represented by L.

Type of molecule	Number of bonding pairs	Number of lone pairs	Arrangement of electron pairs (bonding pairs and lone pairs)	Shape of molecule	Example	Reason
AB_5L	5	1	B B—|—B B—A—B ••	Square pyramidal	IF_5	
AB_4L_2	5	2	•• B—|—B B—A—B ••	Square planar	$XeCl_4$	The two lone pairs lie opposite each other at an angle of 180°

■ **Table 14.3** Summary of VSEPR theory for the electron domain geometry and molecular geometry of molecules and ions with six electron domains

■ Introduction to molecular orbital theory

Sigma bonding

Covalent bonding was previously described (Chapter 4) by means of 'dot-and-cross' diagrams where the electron pairs making the covalent bonds are represented by dots and crosses. A single bond is a shared pair of electrons, a double bond is two shared pairs of electrons and a triple bond is three shared pairs. A simple electrostatic model was used to describe molecules.

A *better* description of the nature of covalent bonding is derived from examining covalent bonding in terms of interactions between atomic orbitals (Chapter 2). A covalent bond is formed by the overlap and merging of two atomic orbitals on different atoms, each containing an unpaired electron. A molecular orbital is formed and is the region where the electron density is concentrated. This theory of bonding is known as molecular orbital theory (MO theory). The strength of a bond is directly related to the match in energy levels for the two atomic orbitals and to the degree of the overlap.

A coordinate covalent bond (Chapter 4) is formed by the similar merging of two atomic orbitals, but in this case one orbital initially contains both the electrons that will form the bond. This orbital merges with a vacant (empty) atomic orbital of appropriate orientation and energy level on the other atom.

The simplest molecule formed is that produced by the overlap of the 1s orbitals of two hydrogen atoms (Figure 14.12). Later in the chapter molecular orbital theory is used to describe the bonding in the diatomic molecules in the first and second periods of the periodic table. MO theory was mentioned briefly in Chapter 13 as a description of bonding in complex ions and complexes. An alternative model of covalent bonding is provided by the valence bond (VB) theory. VB theory was used in Chapter 13 to describe the bonding in complex ions, although it is not a very satisfactory model.

The electron density distribution for a hydrogen molecule, H_2, can also be illustrated by means of an electron density map. Figure 14.13 shows a contour map of the charge distribution for the hydrogen molecule. Imagine a hydrogen molecule cut in half by a plane which contains the nuclei. The amount of charge at every point in space is determined, and all points having the same value for the electron density in the plane are joined by a contour line. The electron density occupies the space between and around the two nuclei.

The single bond in the hydrogen molecule, and all other single covalent bonds in other molecules, are known as σ bonds. They are so named because, if you imagine looking down the bond, the electron density would appear to be circular (Figure 14.14). By analogy with the spherically symmetrical s orbitals, these bonds are termed sigma, σ being the Greek letter corresponding to s.

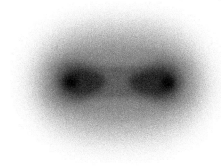

■ **Figure 14.12** Molecular orbital for the hydrogen molecule, H_2

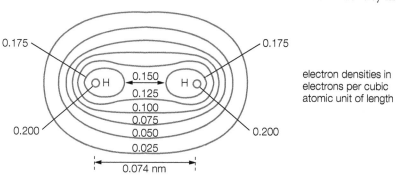

electron densities in electrons per cubic atomic unit of length

■ **Figure 14.13** Electron density map of a hydrogen molecule

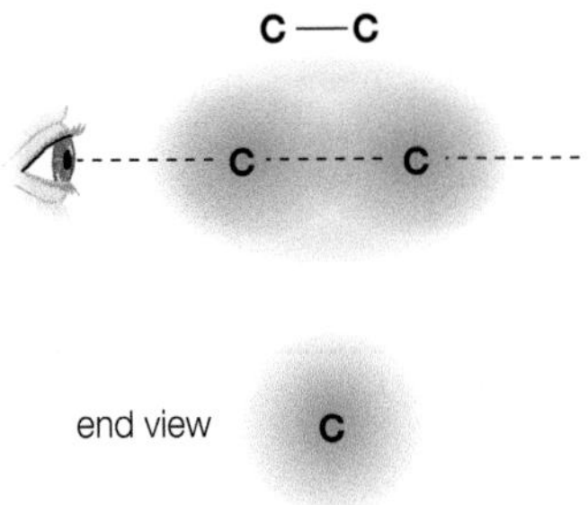

C —C

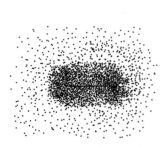

end view   C

■ **Figure 14.14** The carbon–carbon single bond (σ bond)

■ **Figure 14.15**
Overlap of two 1s orbitals to form two molecular orbitals, σ and σ*

■ **Figure 14.16**
The energy levels of the molecular orbitals σ and σ*

The distinguishing feature of a σ bond (or σ bonding orbital) is that the overlap region lies directly between the two nuclei.

Molecular orbitals in hydrogen

Consider the hydrogen molecule, H_2. Two hydrogen atoms, each with an electron in the 1s orbital, approach each other. The two 1s orbitals overlap and merge to form two new molecular orbitals: σ (sigma) and σ* (sigma star) (Figure 14.15).

The σ orbital is of lower energy than the original atomic orbital, and is known as a bonding orbital. The σ* orbital is of higher energy than the original atomic orbital and is known as an anti-bonding orbital. In a manner similar to the filling of electrons into the orbitals in atoms, the two 1s electrons enter the lower energy σ bonding orbital as a *spin pair* (Chapter 2). The potential energy of the hydrogen molecule is *lower* than the potential energy of the uncombined atoms and hence bond formation is exothermic (Figure 14.16).

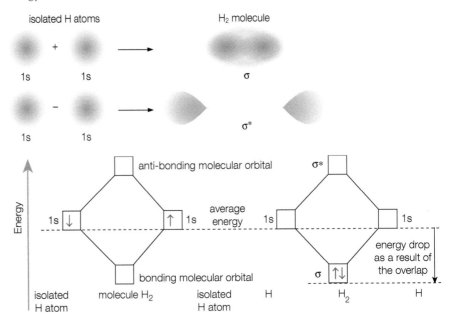

MO theory is based upon the quantum mechanical model which regards electrons as standing waves (Chapter 12). The bonding and anti-bonding σ orbitals correspond to in-phase and out-of-phase wave combinations. The electron density is a *minimum* in the centre of a σ* orbital because that is where the two electron waves *cancel*.

The two electrons in the bonding molecular orbital of H_2 are equivalent to a shared pair of electrons (single covalent bond). The bonding molecular orbital corresponds to an increase in electron density concentrated around the nuclei and on an imaginary axis, known as the inter-nuclear axis, connecting the two hydrogen nuclei (Figure 14.17). The electron density reduces the repulsion between the two nuclei and is the source of attractive forces that hold the two hydrogen atoms together (Chapter 4).

■ **Figure 14.17** An electron dot density plot for the bonding σ orbital of the hydrogen molecule

Pi bonding

Sigma bonds are formed in all the examples described by the axial (head-on) overlap of orbitals (Figure 14.18). Such σ bonds are relatively unreactive, but are important in determining the shape or 'skeleton' of a molecule or ion (Chapter 4). However, there is another way in which p orbitals can overlap if they are brought together in the correct orientation.

■ **Figure 14.18** Sigma molecular orbitals formed between **a** hydrogen atoms, **b** carbon and hydrogen atoms, **c** carbon atoms

Two parallel p orbitals can also undergo sideways overlap to produce a π bond (Figures 14.19). Pi bonds (Figure 14.20) occur in molecules containing double or triple covalent bonds. In practice the formation of a π bond requires the prior formation of a σ bond between the atoms concerned; the formation of the σ bond brings the p orbitals together so that they can overlap sideways. A double bond consists of one σ and one π bond; a triple bond consists of one σ bond and two π bonds.

■ **Figure 14.19**
Sideways overlap of two parallel p orbitals to form a π bond

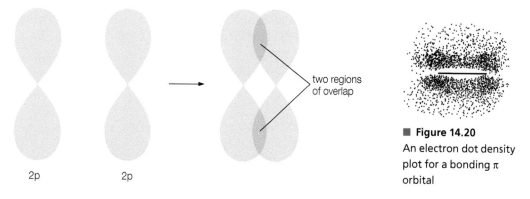

2p   2p

two regions of overlap

■ **Figure 14.20**
An electron dot density plot for a bonding π orbital

In a π bond the two nuclei are poorly shielded from each other and the electrons are further away from the nuclei than the electrons in the σ bond. As a consequence the π electrons are more *polarizable* (Figure 14.21) and hence chemically reactive. They are often involved in initiating chemical reactions, for example addition reactions of alkenes.

■ **Figure 14.21**
Polarization of the bromine molecule by the π bond of an ethene molecule

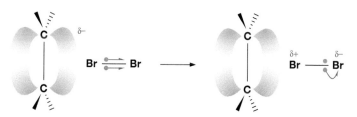

Bond	Bond enthalpy/ kJ mol⁻¹
C–C	346
C=C	614
C≡C	839

When a double bond forms between two atoms, the two bonds are different. There is a strong σ bond and a weaker π bond. Evidence supporting this model is derived from bond enthalpies (Table 14.4).

A double bond, although stronger than a single bond, is *not* twice as strong. If a carbon–carbon double bond consisted of two identical bonds, then its bond enthalpy would be $2 \times 346\,\text{kJ mol}^{-1}$ (= $692\,\text{kJ mol}^{-1}$).

■ **Table 14.4** Bond enthalpies of carbon

strength of carbon–carbon single bond (σ bond) = $346\,\text{kJ mol}^{-1}$

strength of carbon–carbon double bond (σ bond + π bond) = $614\,\text{kJ mol}^{-1}$

Hence, the extra strength due to the π bond
= $614\,\text{kJ mol}^{-1} - 346\,\text{kJ mol}^{-1} = 268\,\text{kJ mol}^{-1}$.

This is based on the assumption that the σ bond has the same strength in double and in single carbon–carbon bonds.

In a π bond the electron density is concentrated in two regions, one above and one below the inter-nuclear axis (Figure 14.22). The end-on view has the same symmetry as, and looks like, an atomic p orbital. The letter π is the Greek equivalent of p.

■ **Figure 14.22**
A carbon–carbon double bond showing the σ and π bond electron density

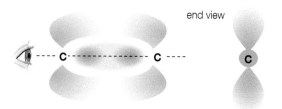

end view

π bond formation and the periodic table

The formation of strong π bonds only occurs in molecules formed by the elements carbon, nitrogen and oxygen from period 2 of the periodic table. Examples include CO_2, CO, N_2, O_2, HCN and NO_2.

In the larger atoms from period 3, strong π bonds are not formed between atoms of the *same element* because the p orbitals are larger and the electron density is more diffuse (spread out), hence the overlap is poor (Figure 14.23). This explains why there are no stable P_2 or S_2 molecules. (However, sulfur and phosphorus can form π bonds with oxygen. These double bonds are greatly strengthened by their polar character.)

■ **Figure 14.23**
Effective and ineffective overlap of p orbitals

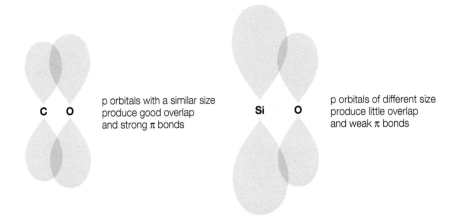

p orbitals with a similar size produce good overlap and strong π bonds

p orbitals of different size produce little overlap and weak π bonds

Silicon, also in period 3, has p orbitals significantly larger than those of oxygen. Their differences in size and energy mean that extensive overlap does not occur. Consequently silicon dioxide, SiO_2, has a giant covalent structure (see Chapter 4) where the bonds are –O–Si–O– bonds. No stable SiO_2 (O=Si=O) molecules are possible in the solid state.

Comparison of σ and π bonds

The different features of σ and π bonding are compared in Table 14.5. However, consideration of these two bonding types does not offer a complete explanation of covalent bonding, even in simple molecules such as methane, ethane and ethene. The explanation of the known spatial arrangements and shapes of these molecules has led to chemists developing the concept of hybridization.

Sigma (σ) bond	Pi (π) bond
This bond is formed by the axial overlap of atomic orbitals.	This bond is formed by the sideways overlap of atomic orbitals.
This bond can be formed by the axial overlap of s with s or of s with a hybridized orbital.	This bond involves the sideways overlap of parallel p orbitals only.
The bond is stronger because overlapping can take place to a larger extent.	The bond is weaker because the overlapping occurs to a smaller extent.
The electron cloud formed by axial overlap is symmetrical about the inter-nuclear axis and consists of a single electron cloud.	The electron cloud is discontinuous and consists of two charged electron clouds above and below the plane of the atoms.
There can be a free rotation of atoms around the σ bond.	Free rotation of atoms around the π bond is not possible because it would involve the breaking of the π bond.
The σ bond may be present between the two atoms either alone or along with a π bond.	The π bond is only present between two atoms with a σ bond, i.e. it is always superimposed on a σ bond.
The shape of the molecule or polyatomic ion is determined by the σ framework around the central atom.	The π bonds do not contribute to the shape of the molecule.

■ **Table 14.5** A summary of the differences between σ and π bonds

■ Valence bond theory

Valence bond theory was the first quantum mechanical theory of bonding. The valence bond approach to the bonding in the hydrogen molecule, H_2, involves considering how the 1s orbitals on two hydrogen atoms interact together to give the wave functions (ψ) for the hydrogen molecule as a whole (Figure 14.24).

The interactions between the 1s orbitals form a sigma bonding orbital, which lies directly between the two hydrogen atoms (along the inter-nuclear axis). Calculations show that, for an accurate description of the bonding in H_2, the ionic form $H^+ H^-$ needs to be considered as well as the covalent form (H–H).

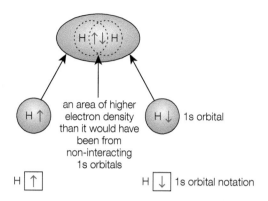

■ **Figure 14.24** Formation of the H_2 molecule: the separate s orbitals have in-phase wave functions that interact to build up electron density between the two nuclei

The real structure is a weighted average of the covalent and ionic forms. This leads to one of the most important concepts in valence bond theory, that of resonance (delocalization). The structure of hydrogen can be represented as

$$H–H \leftrightarrow H^+ H^- \leftrightarrow H^- H^+$$

with the double-headed arrow used to indicate resonance. The resonance forms are shown separately to give a complete 'picture' or description of the character of the actual bond. The three resonance forms of hydrogen do not have an independent existence and do not exist in rapid equilibrium with each other. There is only one wave function for the hydrogen molecule, H_2, which has both covalent and ionic contributions.

However, the resonance forms do not contribute equally to the characteristics of the bond, and the bonding in H_2 is a weighted average of the different resonance forms. The covalent resonance form has a larger contribution to the molecular wave function than the ionic resonance forms. The two ionic resonance forms are equally important, so overall H_2 is non-polar and does not have a permanent dipole, as it would if one of these were more important than the other.

14.2 Hybridization – *hybridization results from the mixing of atomic orbitals to form the same number of new equivalent hybrid orbitals that can have the same mean energy as the contributing atomic orbitals*

■ Hybridization

Atomic orbitals on adjacent atoms can overlap to form σ and π molecular orbitals. In addition, orbitals *of the same atom* can overlap, merge and undergo a process of hybridization to form a new set of *hybrid atomic orbitals*. The hybrid or hybridized orbitals formed have a specific shape and relative orientation depending on the number and type of atomic orbitals that have hybridized. The number of hybrid orbitals formed is equal to the number of atomic orbitals involved in the hybridization process. The three common types of hybridization are sp, sp^2 and sp^3. All atoms (except hydrogen) are *postulated* to undergo a process of hybridization prior to bonding.

The hybrid orbital has electron density concentrated on one side of the nucleus, i.e. it has one lobe relatively larger than the other. Hence, the hybrid orbitals can form stronger bonds compared to unhybridized atomic orbitals because they can undergo more effective overlap. The hybrid orbitals repel each other and adopt a configuration that minimizes the electron repulsion. Hybridization is simply a mathematical model that is convenient for describing localized bonds. It is *not* a phenomenon that can be studied or measured.

sp hybridization

A single s and a single p orbital will overlap and merge to form two identical sp hybridized orbitals (Figure 14.25). The orbitals will be orientated at 180° to each other and will have identical energies and shapes. The potential energy of the hybrid orbital will be intermediate between the energies of the s and p orbitals.

■ **Figure 14.25**
The formation of sp hybridized orbitals from an s orbital and a p orbital

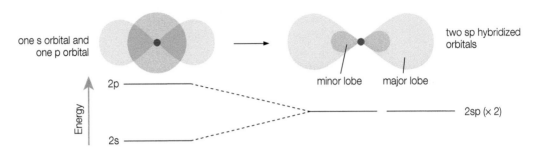

■ **Figure 14.26** sp hybrid orbitals in the beryllium fluoride molecule

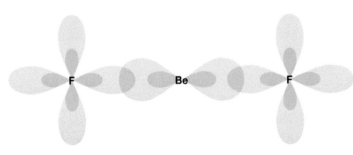

Beryllium in the beryllium fluoride molecule, $BeF_2(g)$, provides an example of sp hybridization (Figure 14.26). The beryllium atom has the electron configuration $1s^2 2s^2$. After hybridization the electrons in the outer shell of the beryllium atom are in two sp hybrid orbitals. Single bonds between the beryllium and fluorine atoms involve the sharing of the unpaired electrons in the sp hybrid orbital of beryllium and the sp^3 hybrid orbitals of the fluorine atom (Figure 14.27).

■ **Figure 14.27** Atomic orbitals in beryllium (ground state), beryllium (excited state) and beryllium fluoride (hybridized state)

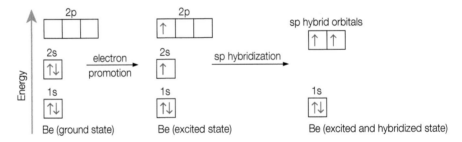

sp^2 hybridization

sp^2 hybridization involves the combination of *one* s and *two* p orbitals. These three hybrid orbitals have identical shapes and orientations. They point towards the corners of an equilateral triangle (Figure 14.28).

■ **Figure 14.28**
The formation of sp^2 hybridized orbitals from an s orbital and two p orbitals

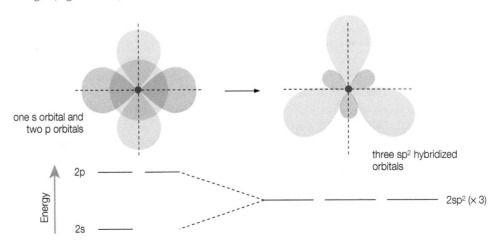

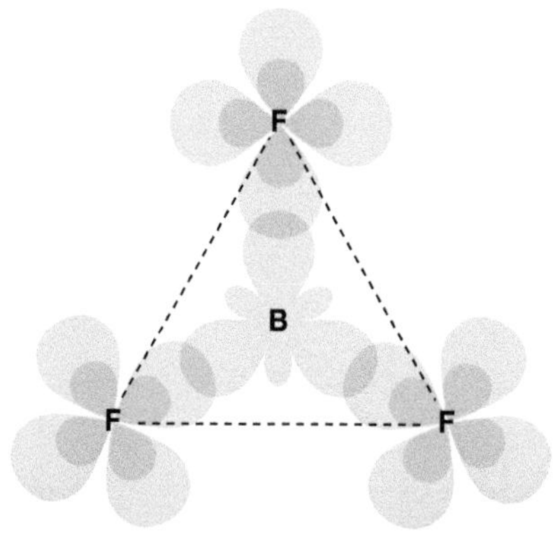

■ **Figure 14.29** sp^2 hybrid orbitals in the boron trifluoride molecule

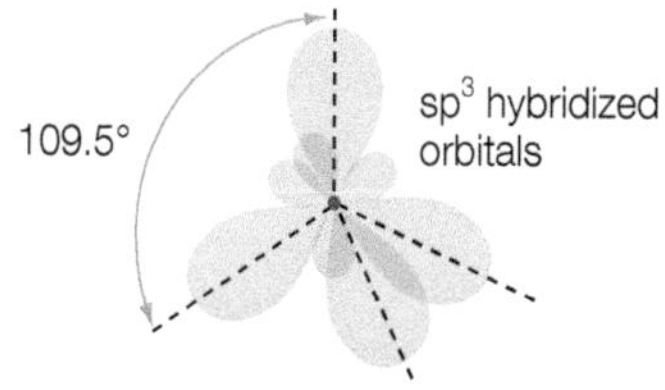

■ **Figure 14.31** The formation of sp^3 hybridized orbitals from an s orbital and three p orbitals

Boron in the boron trifluoride molecule, BF_3, provides an example of sp^2 hybridization (Figure 14.29). The boron atom has the electron configuration $1s^22s^22p^1$. After hybridization the electrons in the outer shell of the boron atom are in three sp^2 hybrid orbitals. Single bonds between the boron and fluorine atoms involve the sharing of the unpaired electrons in the sp^2 hybrid orbitals of boron and the sp^3 orbitals of the fluorine atoms (Figure 14.30).

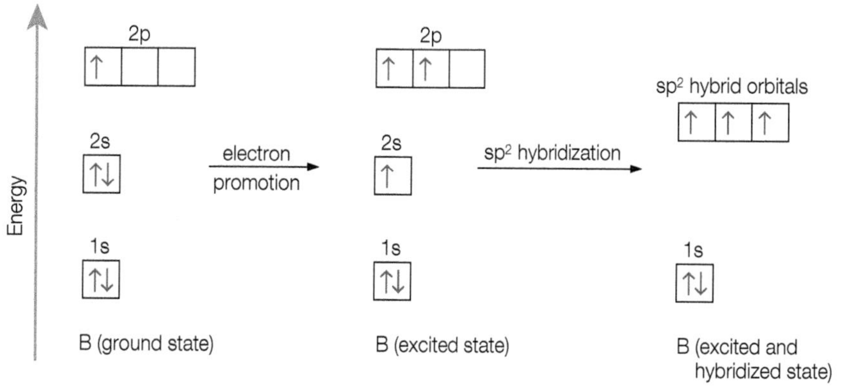

■ **Figure 14.30** Atomic orbitals in boron (ground state), boron (excited state) and boron trifluoride (hybridized state)

sp^3 hybridization

sp^3 hybridization involves the combination of one s orbital and three p orbitals (Figure 14.31). The sp^3 hybridized orbitals formed are arranged tetrahedrally (to minimize repulsion).

■ Hybridization in carbon

Carbon provides examples of all three types of hybridization: sp, sp^2 and sp^3. A detailed discussion follows on these three types in the context of organic molecules.

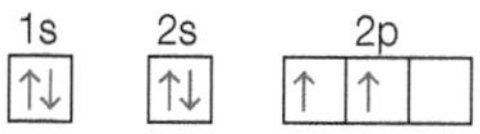

■ **Figure 14.32** Carbon atom in the ground state

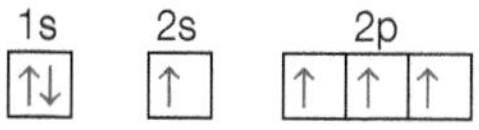

■ **Figure 14.33** Carbon atom in an excited state

sp^3 hybridization in alkanes

Carbon atoms have the configuration $1s^22s^22p^2$ in their ground state (Figure 14.32). Since the 2s sub-shell is full and there are two unpaired electrons in the 2p sub-shell, carbon might be expected to form *two* covalent bonds.

However, carbon always forms *four* bonds in familiar and stable compounds, such as methane, CH_4, and carbon dioxide, CO_2. To account for the ability of a carbon atom to form four bonds, a 2s electron has to be unpaired and promoted into an empty orbital of the 2p sub-shell (Figure 14.33). This is an endothermic process, but the excess energy is regained when the two extra bonds are formed (Figure 14.34).

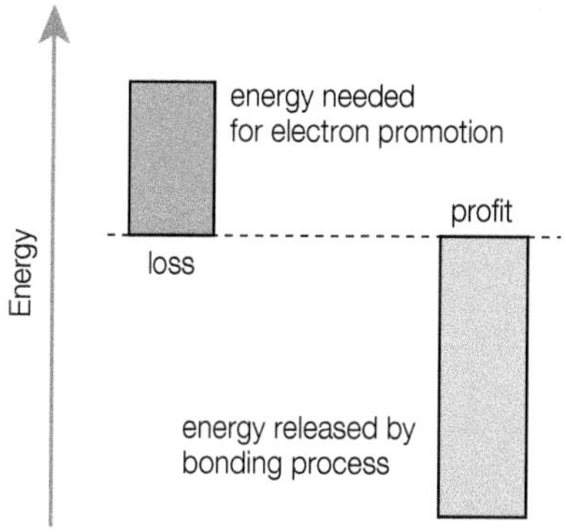

■ **Figure 14.34** The 'cost and benefit' of hybridization

The 2s orbital (now containing just an unpaired electron) and the three 2p orbitals undergo hybridization, which leads to the production of four identical sp^3 hybrid orbitals, each containing a single electron (Figure 14.35).

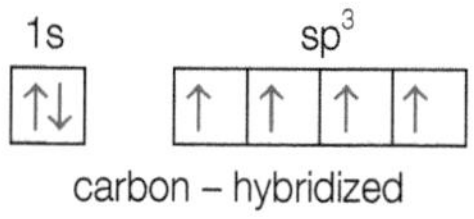

■ **Figure 14.35** Orbitals in an sp^3 hybridized carbon atom

The use of the idea of hybridization also explains the observed shape of the methane molecule. The four sp^3 hybridized carbon atoms can then overlap with the 1s electrons of four hydrogen atoms (Figure 14.36) to form four σ bonds arranged tetrahedrally around the central carbon atom. Atoms joined by single covalent bonds can usually rotate freely about the bond. The linear shape of BeF_2 and the trigonal planar shape of BF_3 can be understood similarly.

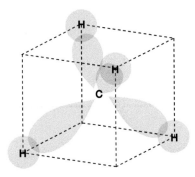

■ **Figure 14.36** sp³ hybrid orbitals in a methane molecule

sp² hybridization in alkenes

In many organic compounds, for example the alkenes and the carbonyl compounds (Chapter 10), carbon forms bonds with three other atoms: two single bonds and a double bond. An electron from the 2s sub-shell is again promoted into the 2p sub-shell. The 2s orbital hybridizes with *two* of the $2p^2$ hybrid orbitals to give *three* sp² hybrid orbitals (Figure 14.37). The $2p_z$ orbital does *not* participate in the hybridization process.

■ **Figure 14.37** Excited carbon atom and an sp² hybridized carbon atom

The hypothetical formation of ethene, C_2H_4, is summarized in Figure 14.38. One sp² hybrid orbital on each carbon atom overlaps and merges with its neighbour to form a carbon–carbon **σ** bond. The other four sp² hybrid orbitals overlap with the 1s orbitals on four hydrogen atoms to form four carbon–hydrogen bonds. The *unhybridized* 2p orbital on each carbon atom overlaps sideways with its neighbouring carbon atom to form the carbon–carbon **π** bond.

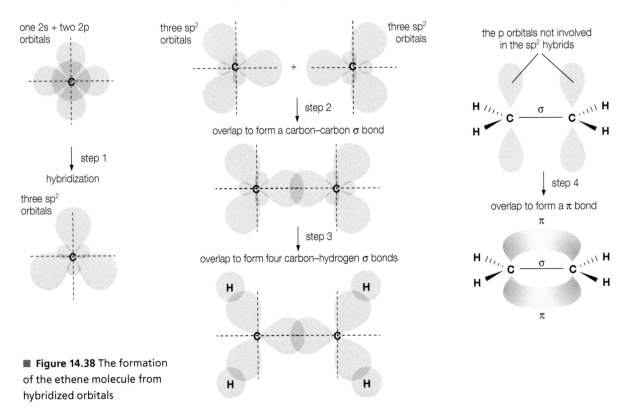

■ **Figure 14.38** The formation of the ethene molecule from hybridized orbitals

The two areas of orbital overlap in the **π** bond (above and below the plane of the molecule) cause ethene to be a rigid molecule: there is no rotation around the carbon–carbon bond. This is in contrast to ethane, and other non-cyclic alkanes, and leads to the existence of *cis–trans* (geometric) isomerism in alkenes (Chapter 20).

rotation possible around
the single bond

no rotation possible

■ **Figure 14.39**
The π bond in ethene
prevents free rotation
around the carbon–
carbon double bond

Any rotation about the σ bond of ethene joining the two carbon atoms would result in the reduction of p overlap and weaken the π bond (Figure 14.39). The breaking of the π bond will only occur at relatively high temperatures. There is a high activation energy barrier to π bond rotation. Hence *cis–trans* isomers will only interconvert at high temperatures, when a sufficient proportion of molecules have enough energy to overcome the π bond.

sp hybridization in alkynes

In the ethyne molecule, C_2H_2, the two carbon atoms form sp hybrid orbitals. An electron from the 2s sub-shell is again promoted into the 2p sub-shell. The 2s orbital hybridizes with *one* of the 2p orbitals to give *two* sp hybridized orbitals. The $2p_z$ and $2p_y$ orbitals do *not* participate in the hybridization process (Figure 14.40).

Triple bonds are formed in ethyne, C_2H_2, when *two unhybridized* p orbitals overlap sideways, forming two π bonds (Figure 14.41), in addition to the σ bond already present. The total electron density of the two combined π orbitals takes the shape of a cylinder that encircles the molecule.

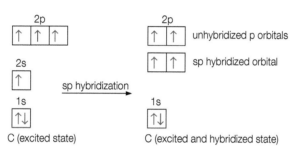

■ **Figure 14.40** Excited carbon atom and an sp hybridized carbon atom

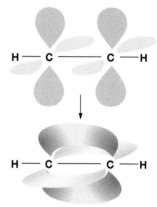

■ **Figure 14.41** Pi bond formation in ethyne

Type of hybridized orbital	sp³	sp²	sp
Atomic orbitals used	s, p, p, p	s, p, p	s, p
Number of hybridized orbitals	4	3	2
Number of atoms bonded to the carbon atom	4	3	2
Number of σ bonds	4	3	2
Number of unhybridized p orbitals	0	1	2
Number of π bonds	0	1	2
Bonding arrangement(s)	Tetrahedral; four single bonds only	Trigonal planar; two single bonds and a double bond	Linear; one single bond and a triple bond or two double bonds
Example	CH_4, C_2H_6 and CCl_4	$H_2C=CH_2$ and H_2CO	$H–C\equiv C–H$, $H_2C=C=CH_2$

■ **Table 14.6** Summary of hybridization in carbon

The concept of hybridization can be understood by the analogy of mixing paint. If red and white paints are mixed together in equal proportions, the colour of the resulting mixture is pink. A double quantity of pink paint has been produced. The pink paint is a hybrid of red and white paint because its shade is intermediate between red and white.

In biology the term hybridization may refer to the result of interbreeding between two animals or plants of different species. For example, the tigron is a hybrid cross between a female lion and a male tiger. Tigrons have a blend of lion and tiger features, for example, they may show spots and stripes.

The term sp³ hybridization indicates that the hybrid orbitals are derived from one s and three p orbitals. Each orbital is said to have 25% s character and 75% p character. The term sp hybridization indicates that the hybrid orbitals are derived from one s and one p orbital. Each orbital is said to have 50% s character and 50% p character. Consequently, sp hybrid orbitals look more like s orbitals and sp³ hybridized orbitals look more like p orbitals.

Relating a molecule's Lewis (electron dot) structure as determined by VSEPR theory to the hybridization of its central atom

The application of VSEPR theory (Chapter 4) to determine the shape of a simple molecule or polyatomic ion from its Lewis structure (Table 14.7) can also be used to quickly identify the hybridization state of the central atom in the structure.

- sp^3 hybridization can be used to describe the bonding in any structure where there are four electron domains around the centrally bonded atom. An electron domain is a lone pair or a covalent bond (whether single, double or triple).

- sp^2 hybridization can be used to describe the bonding in any structure where there are three electron domains around the centrally bonded atom.

- sp hybridization can be used to describe the bonding in any structure where there are two electron domains around the centrally bonded atom.

Hybridization state of central atom	Number of electron domains	Number of covalent bonds	Number of lone pairs	Shape	Examples
sp	2	2	0	Linear	BeF_2, CO_2
sp^2	3	3	0	Trigonal planar	BF_3, graphite, fullerenes, SO_3 and CO_3^{2-}
sp^2	3	2	1	V-shaped or bent	SO_2 and NO_2^-
sp^3	4	4	0	Tetrahedral	CH_4, diamond, ClO_4^- and SO_4^{2-}
sp^3	4	3	1	Pyramidal	NH_3, NF_3, PCl_3 and H_3O^+
sp^3	4	2	2	V-shaped or bent	H_2O, H_2S and NH_2^-

■ **Table 14.7** The relationship between the Lewis structure and the hybridization of the central atom

Hybridization models involving *d orbitals*, such as dsp^3 and d^2sp^3, have been used to explain molecules with an expanded octet of electrons, for example PCl_5 and SF_6. This is one model used to explain the observed shapes of certain molecules.

> ### Worked example
>
> Deduce the hybridization state of the central atoms of the following ions and molecules: CS_2, $AlCl_3$, PH_3 and NH_4^+.
>
> CS_2
>
> The carbon atom forms two double bonds; there are no lone pairs of electrons on the carbon atom, hence the hybridization is sp.
>
> $AlCl_3$
>
> The aluminium atom forms three single bonds; there are no lone pairs of electrons on the aluminium atom, hence the hybridization is sp^2.
>
> PH_3
>
> The phosphorus atom forms three single bonds; there is one lone pair of electrons on the phosphorus atom, hence the hybridization is sp^3.
>
> NH_4^+
>
> The nitrogen atom forms four single bonds; there are no lone pairs of electrons on the nitrogen atom, hence the hybridization is sp^3.

Explaining the formation of sp^3, sp^2 and sp hybrid orbitals in methane, ethene and ethyne

Methane

In sp^3 hybridization, the 2s orbital is mixed with all three of the 2p orbitals to give a set of four tetrahedrally arranged sp^3 hybrid orbitals as described previously. The valence electrons can now be fitted into the four sp^3 hybridized orbitals. A half-filled sp^3 hybridized orbital from one carbon atom can be used to form a sigma (σ) bond with a half-filled sp^3 hybridized orbital from another carbon atom. This leads to the formation of a strong sigma bond between two carbons atoms. Sigma bonds are also formed when each half-filled sp^3 hybridized orbital from the carbon atom overlaps with the half-filled 1s orbital of a hydrogen atom.

Ethene

sp^2 hybridization results in three half-filled sp^2 hybridized orbitals which are arranged in a trigonal planar manner. The C–H bonds are sigma bonds and formed when a half-filled 1s hydrogen orbital overlaps with a half-filled sp^2 hybrid orbital. A strong carbon–carbon sigma bond is also formed by the overlap of the remaining sp^2 hybrid orbitals. The alkene is 'locked' into its planar shape by the remaining half-filled $2p_z$ orbitals which overlap in a sideways manner to form a pi (π) bond, with one lobe above and one lobe below the plane of the molecule.

Ethyne

In ethyne the two carbon atoms are sp hybridized. The C–H bonds are strong sigma bonds where each hydrogen atom uses its half-filled 1s orbital to overlap with a half-filled sp orbital on the carbon atom. The remaining sp orbital on each carbon atom is used to form a strong sigma bond. Each carbon atom has two unhybridized p orbitals, $2p_y$ and $2p_z$, which overlap sideways to form two pi bonds arranged at 90° to each other.

ToK Link

Hybridization is a mathematical device that allows us to relate the bonding in a molecule to its symmetry. What is the relationship between the natural sciences, mathematics and the natural world? What role does symmetry play in the different areas of knowledge?

Hybridization is the use of a linear combination of atomic orbitals whose resultant matches the symmetry of the molecule in question. For example, the four linear combinations of the 2s and 2p orbitals that we call sp^3 hybridization give us four orbitals, each pointing to the corner of a tetrahedron. (It is only an approximate model and it breaks down when considering excited states, but it is a convenient model for electronic ground states.)

Symmetry is the geometric property of a molecule (or object), whereby the molecule has the same observed physical structure and appearance when viewed from different orientations in space. The different symmetry properties of molecules are described by a branch of mathematics called group theory.

Symmetry arguments provide a powerful tool for understanding atomic phenomena. The concepts of symmetry and group theory impact on a number of important areas of chemistry, such as optical activity, crystallography (the study of crystal lattices), chemical bonding and spectroscopy, especially infrared spectroscopy. Symmetry arguments can often be used to simplify complex chemical calculations.

Since nature seems to behave mathematically, what is the connection between mathematics and the natural world? The astronomer Galileo wrote that, *'Nature's great book is written in mathematical symbols.'* The description of natural phenomena in mathematical terms, rather than a search for causal explanations, was achieved by Newton, whose laws of motion and gravitational attraction brought previous work together in a unified mathematical system. Newton claimed to arrive at his knowledge of motions of the planets by deduction, making use of hypotheses or laws which had been established on the basis of his investigations. Modern physics takes this process even further, giving mathematical form to phenomena such as magnetic, electric and gravitational fields, and the behaviour of the electron and other sub-atomic particles.

Einstein wrote, *'Here arises a puzzle that has disturbed scientists of all periods. How is it possible that mathematics, a product of human thought that is independent of experience, fits so excellently the objects of physical reality? Can human reason without experience discover by pure thinking properties of real things?'*

There are a number of very different views on the relationship between mathematics and the natural world. According to the Platonic view, mathematics is eternally true and is therefore to be discovered rather than invented. Plato wrote, *'God eternally geometrises'*.

Another contrasting view is that the universe is mathematically structured and that, whether it was created by God or came into existence from nothing via the Big Bang, it is the task of mathematicians and scientists to *discover* the mathematical 'laws' by which nature works. Galileo wrote, *'The chief aim of all investigations of the external world should be to discover the rational order and harmony which has been imposed on it by God and revealed to us in the language of mathematics.'*

Yet another view suggests that mathematics is a product of human thinking that is independent of our experience in the natural world. This view holds that mathematics is an invention of the human mind rather than a discovery of something that is already there, either in the natural world (physical universe) or as an idea in the mind of God or as part of the natural order of the universe.

Nobel Prize winner Richard Feynman had this to say about mathematics: '*To those who do not know mathematics it is difficult to get across a real feeling as to the beauty, the deepest beauty, of nature ... If you want to learn about nature, to appreciate nature, it is necessary to understand the language that she speaks in.*'

Because nature is often intrinsically mathematical because of symmetries and geometry, any science that intends to describe nature is completely dependent on mathematics. It is impossible to overemphasize this point, and it is why Carl Friedrich Gauss called mathematics 'the queen of the sciences.'

1 Find out what roles symmetry plays in the other areas of knowledge (AOK), including physics and biology.

Nature of Science

The need to regard theories as uncertain hybridization

It should be understood that *hybridization is not a physical phenomenon*; it is simply a *mathematical operation* that combines the atomic orbitals in such a way that the new (hybrid) orbitals possess the geometric and other properties that are reasonably consistent with what we observe in a wide range (but certainly not in all) of molecules. In other words, hybrid orbitals are abstractions that describe reality fairly well in certain classes of molecules, especially organic, and are therefore a useful means of organizing a large body of chemical knowledge.

Although the hybrid orbital approach has proven very powerful, especially in organic chemistry, it does have some limitations. For example, it predicts that both the water molecule, H_2O, and the hydrogen sulfide molecule, H_2S, will be tetrahedrally coordinated, V-shaped or bent molecules with bond angles slightly less than the tetrahedral bond angle of 109° 28′ due to greater repulsion by the non-bonding or lone pair. This description is in good agreement with the water molecule (the observed H–O–H bond angle is 104.5°), but the bond angle in the hydrogen sulfide molecule is only 92°, suggesting that p orbitals (which are 90° apart) may give a better description of the electron distribution around the sulfur atom than an sp^3 hybrid model.

As with any scientific model, the hybridization model is useful only to the degree with which it can predict phenomena that are actually observed. All models contain weaknesses due to simplifications that place limits on their general applicability.

Quantum mechanics

Planck proposed that the minimum amount of electromagnetic radiation that an object can emit or absorb is related to the frequency of the radiation: $E = hv$. The smallest quantity is termed a quantum. In quantum mechanics, energy is quantized; this means that it can only have certain values (multiples of hv). Hence the mean energy in a system (for example, electrons in an atom) is restricted to certain values. The idea of a quantum – a certain definite amount of energy – provided the name for the theory.

Quantum mechanics deals with the mathematical description of the motion and interaction of sub-atomic particles, incorporating the concepts of quantization of energy, wave–particle duality, the uncertainty principle, and the correspondence principle.

De Broglie proposed that matter should show wave-like properties. The de Broglie hypothesis was supported by Davisson and Germer's studies of electron diffraction. Every object has a wavelength that depends on its momentum (the product of its mass and velocity).

Electrons will undergo diffraction when passed through a crystal since the distances between the particles are smaller than the wavelength of the electrons. The diffraction of electrons confirms wave behaviour with a wavelength given by the de Broglie equation.

Newton regarded light as a beam of particles but the interference and diffraction of light cannot be explained with this theory. These phenomena can only be explained on the basis of classical wave theory.

However, these experiments demonstrate that light exhibits wave–particle duality. Some experiments reveal the wave properties of light, but others demonstrate its particle behaviour. Only light (photons), electrons and some atoms with a very small mass will show their wave nature in experiments.

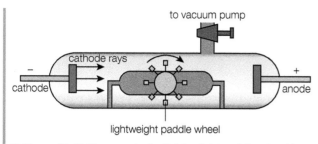

Figure 14.42 Movement of a lightweight paddle wheel in a cathode ray tube

However, electrons (in the form of cathode rays) can be shown to behave as particles and transfer momentum to a lightweight paddle wheel and make it move (Figure 14.42).

The discovery of the wave properties of electrons and other sub-atomic particles led to Heisenberg's uncertainty principle, which states that there is an inherent physical limit to the accuracy with which the position and velocity of any particle can be measured simultaneously.

In the quantum mechanical model of the hydrogen atom, the wave behaviour of the electron is described by a mathematical function known as the wave function, ψ. Each allowed wave function has a precisely known energy, but the location of the electron cannot be determined exactly, only the probability.

---

2   Find out about the photoelectric effect and the development of quantum mechanics.

■ Delocalization of electrons

Resonance

For some molecules and compound ions, it is possible to draw several Lewis structures that differ in the positions of the π-bonding electrons and lone (non-bonded) pairs. For example, we could draw the carbonate ion as in the first structure shown in Figure 14.43.

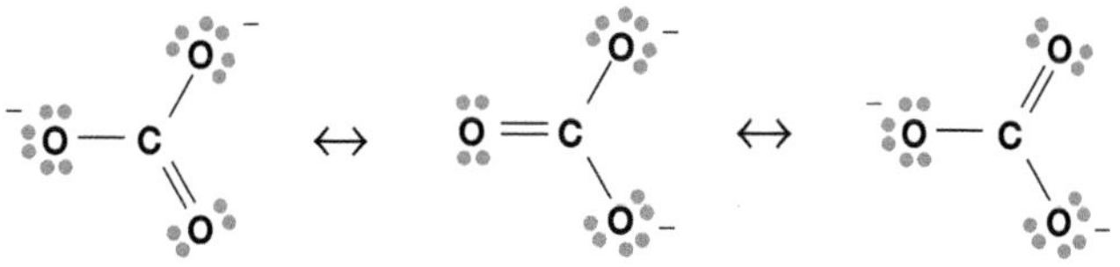

Figure 14.43
Three equivalent Lewis structures for the carbonate ion

However, we could also draw the carbonate ion as either of the other two structures shown in Figure 14.43 (assuming that none of the atoms have changed position).

The double-headed single arrow often drawn between the different forms represents resonance and is not to be confused with the double arrow symbol ($\rightleftharpoons$) for a reversible reaction at equilibrium (Chapter 7).

The carbonate ion is *not* correctly described by any of these structures, but exists as a form, known as a resonance hybrid, which is a 'blend' of all three structures (Figure 14.44). Each of the three structures, known as resonance structures, contributes to the resonance hybrid depending on its energy: the lower the energy of the resonance structure, the greater its contribution to the hybrid. In the case of the carbonate ion all three resonance structures are of equal energy (due to their symmetry) and make an equal contribution to the resonance hybrid. The concept of resonance was introduced in Chapter 2.

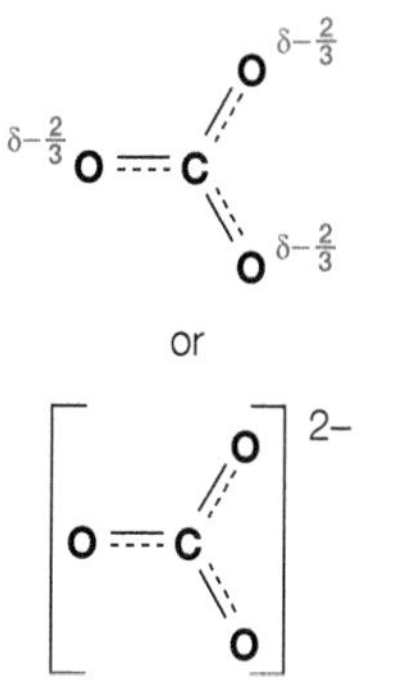

The dotted lines indicate that all three carbon–oxygen bonds are identical or equivalent to each other and that each has partial double bond character. Similarly, each of the three oxygen atoms has a partial negative charge. The real hybrid is thus a 'blend' with equal weighting from the three imaginary resonance structures that have the familiar single and double bonds with two of the oxygen atoms carrying a complete formal negative charge.

or

Figure 14.44
Resonance hybrid for the carbonate ion

Experimental evidence supports the resonance description of the carbonate ion. X-ray diffraction data (Chapter 4) of metal carbonate crystals reveals that all the carbon–oxygen bond lengths in this ion are equivalent, and are shorter than a single C–O bond but slightly longer than a C=O bond.

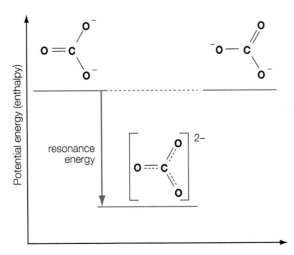

■ **Figure 14.45** A diagram illustrating the concept of resonance energy for the carbonate ion

When resonance occurs, the resonance hybrid is more stable than any of the resonance structures. The difference between the energy of the most stable form and the hybrid is known as the resonance energy. This concept is illustrated in Figure 14.45 for the carbonate ion.

For significant resonance stabilization to occur within a molecule or ion, the suggested resonance structures must meet all of the following requirements, as exemplified by the carbonate ion:

■ All resonance forms must have the same distribution of atoms or nuclei in space, that is, the same molecular shape.

All three resonance structures of the carbonate ion have the three oxygen atoms distributed around a central carbon atom in a trigonal planar arrangement.

■ No resonance form may have a very high energy. In particular, no resonance form containing carbon, oxygen or nitrogen (or other atom from the second row of the periodic table) may have more than eight valence electrons (or for hydrogen, two valence electrons). In other words, the octet (and duplet) rules must be obeyed.

The three oxygen atoms and one carbon atom of the carbonate ion each obey the octet rule – in all three resonance forms they each have eight valence electrons.

■ All resonance forms must contain the same number of electron pairs.

All the resonance structures of the carbonate ion have three σ pairs, one π pair and eight lone (non-bonded) pairs.

■ All resonance forms must carry the same total or net charge.

All the resonance structures of the carbonate ion have a total charge of –2.

To understand the importance of resonance in the stabilization of a structure, and the contribution of a particular resonance form, the following points must be considered:

■ In the case of ions, the most stable resonance structures will have negative charges on the electronegative atoms, usually oxygen and sulfur, and positive charges on the less electronegative atoms, usually carbon and nitrogen.

■ The most important resonance structures are those where as many atoms as possible obey the octet rule, have the maximum number of bonded electrons and have the fewest charges.

■ Resonance effects are always stabilizing and *generally* the greater the number of resonance structures that can be drawn, the greater the stability of the resonance hybrid.

The concept of formal charge can be used to identify the correct Lewis structure for a molecule or the most important resonance structure for a resonance-stabilized molecule or ion. The concept of formal charge is discussed later in this chapter.

Examples of resonance-stabilized ions and simple molecules

Two other inorganic ions that are stabilized by resonance and described by a series of symmetrical resonance structures are the nitrate(III) ('nitrite') ion, NO_2^-, and the nitrate(V) ('nitrate') ion, NO_3^- (Figure 14.46). Curly arrows may be used to show the movement of electron pairs to generate resonance structures.

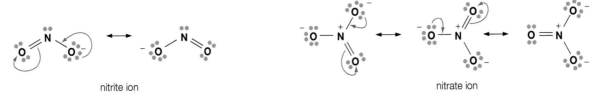

nitrite ion   nitrate ion

■ **Figure 14.46** Resonance structures and hybrids for the nitrite and nitrate ions

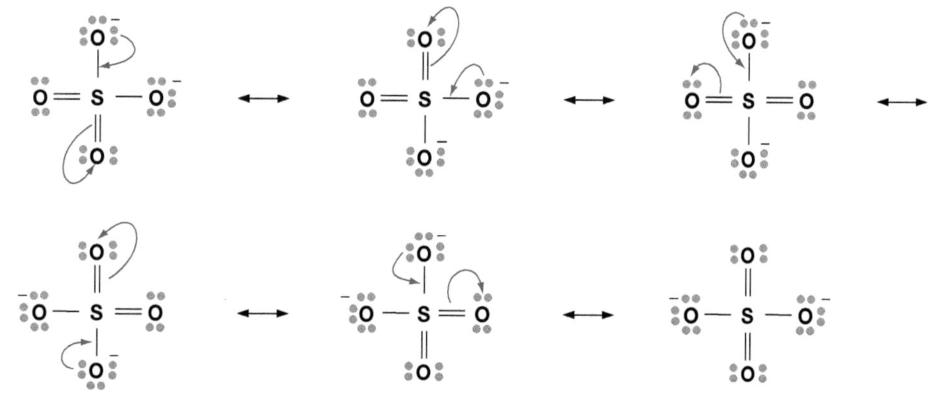

■ **Figure 14.47**
Resonance structures
for the sulfate(VI) ion

Another familiar ion extensively stabilized by resonance is the sulfate(VI) ('sulfate') ion, SO_4^{2-} (Figure 14.47).

Ozone (trioxygen, O_3) is an allotrope of oxygen that plays an important role in the ozone layer, protecting the Earth's surface from the harmful effects of ultraviolet radiation (Chapter 25 on the accompanying website). The ozone molecule is V-shaped and is a resonance hybrid described by two major resonance forms (Figure 14.48).

■ **Figure 14.48** Resonance structures for the ozone molecule

Many transition metal oxoanions (Chapter 13) are resonance stabilized, for example manganate(VII) ('permanganate'), MnO_4^-, and chromate(VI) ('chromate'), CrO_4^{2-} (c.f. sulfate).

Examples of resonance in organic chemistry

A number of organic molecules and ions exist as resonance hybrids, for example the ethanoate ion, CH_3COO^-, formed during the dissociation of ethanoic acid, CH_3COOH (Chapter 8). The ethanoate ion, like the carbonate ion, has symmetrical resonance involving equivalent resonance structures making equal contributions to the resonance hybrid (Figure 14.49). As with the carbonate ion, the two oxygens cannot be distinguished and the two carbon–oxygen bond lengths are identical.

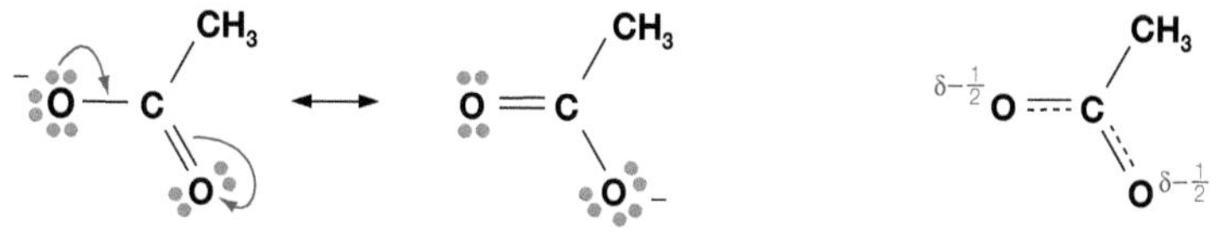

■ **Figure 14.49** Resonance structures and resonance hybrid of the ethanoate ion

Simple resonance theory can be used to explain why ethanoic acid, CH_3COOH, is a stronger acid than ethanol, C_2H_5OH. Neither the ethanol molecule nor the ethoxide ion ($C_2H_5O^-$) are stabilized by resonance, hence the low dissociation of ethanol into ions.

Although ethanoic acid itself is stabilized by resonance, this stabilization is not very effective compared with that in the ethanoate ion. In the latter, both the negative charge and the electrons are delocalized, and the resonance is symmetrical. However, in ethanoic acid (Figure 14.50) the charged form has unlike charges separated and is of relatively high energy. (We assume for the purposes of this argument that entropy (Chapter 15) and hydration effects are similar enough to be ignored.)

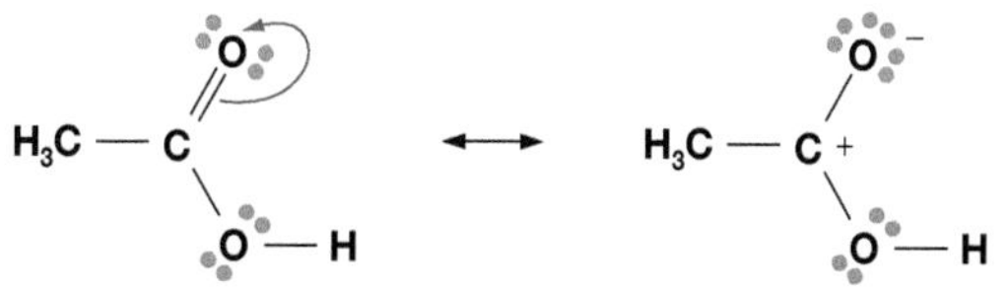

■ **Figure 14.50** Resonance in ethanoic acid

The concept of resonance and another electronic effect called the inductive effect can be used to explain and predict the differences in strength between other organic acids and bases.

Propanone, $(CH_3)_2CO$, the simplest ketone, can be described as a resonance hybrid of two resonance structures (Figure 14.51). The first resonance structure is known as the major resonance form and makes the largest contribution to the resonance hybrid; the second resonance structure, with the separation of charge, makes a smaller contribution to the resonance hybrid.

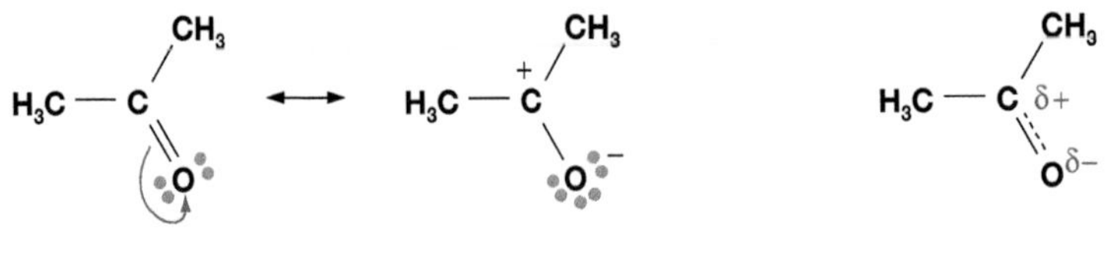

■ **Figure 14.51**
Resonance structures and hybrid for propanone

The second resonance structure in propanone makes a significant contribution because oxygen is appreciably more electronegative than carbon and is often found bearing a complete or formal negative charge and forming a single covalent bond, for example in the hydroxide ion, OH^-.

This description for propanone is consistent with the chemical reactions of ketones, which frequently involve nucleophilic attack on the carbon atom of the carbonyl group.

The best known example of resonance in organic chemistry concerns the cyclic hydrocarbon benzene, C_6H_6, which can be described by two major resonance structures called Kekulé structures (Figure 14.52).

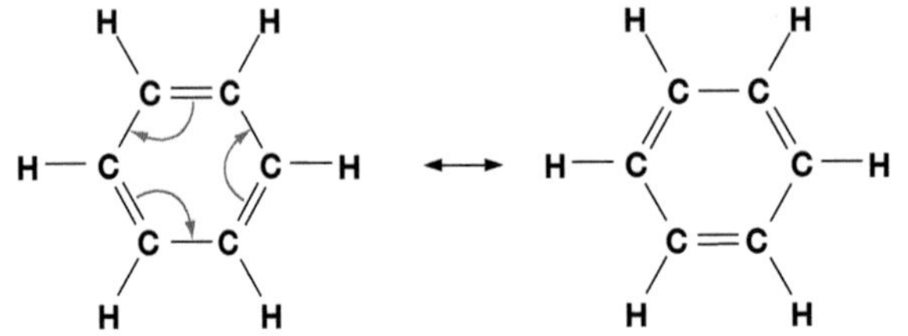

■ **Figure 14.52**
Major resonance structures for benzene

The two resonance structures are symmetrical and make equal contributions to the resonance hybrid where all the carbon–carbon bonds are equivalent, being intermediate between single and double carbon–carbon bonds, both in strength and in length (0.140 nm and 507 kJ mol^{-1}).

The difference in energy between the resonance hybrid (the 'real' benzene) and the resonance structures (Kekulé structures) is known as the resonance energy (Figure 14.53). An approximate value can be calculated from enthalpies of hydrogenation or combustion data.

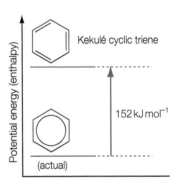

■ **Figure 14.53** The relative energetic stabilities of benzene and cyclohexatriene (the Kekulé structure)

■ Molecular orbital theory – delocalization

An alternative but equivalent model for describing benzene (and other resonance-stabilized structures) is molecular orbital theory. We have already seen how this theory can explain the formation of molecular structures such as methane, ethene and others. In 'localized' molecules like ethene, C_2H_4, two unhybridized p_z orbitals overlap to form a π molecular orbital in which a pair of electrons is shared between the nuclei of two carbon atoms. In molecular orbital theory, resonance-stabilized structures are described in terms of 'delocalized' π orbitals where the π electron clouds extend over three or more atoms.

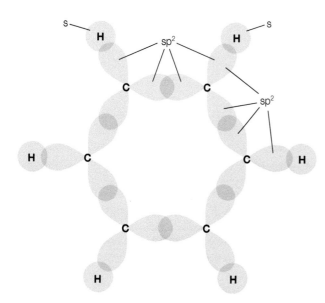

■ **Figure 14.54** Sigma framework of the benzene molecule

Delocalization in benzene

The benzene molecule has a distinctive structure in which the six carbon atoms (each with one hydrogen atom attached) are arranged in a planar hexagonal 'skeleton'. Each of the six carbon atoms is bonded to three other atoms (two carbons and one hydrogen) and so sp^2 hybridization can be used to describe the atomic orbitals of each carbon. Each of the six sp^2 hybridized carbon atoms forms three σ bonds with neighbouring atoms, forming the σ framework of the benzene ring (Figure 14.54).

Each carbon atom has an unhybridized 2p$_z$ orbital (with lobes above and below the ring) which overlaps with those of the carbon atoms on either side to give a delocalized cyclic π orbital above and below the plane of the benzene ring (Figure 14.55). The six π electrons are therefore delocalized over the six carbon atoms in a 'doughnut'-shaped π molecular orbital (a symmetrical torus – Figure 14.56). It is these π electrons which are responsible for the kinetic stability of benzene and its tendency to undergo substitution reactions, rather than addition reactions.

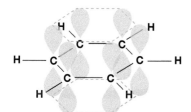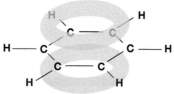

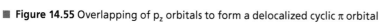

■ **Figure 14.55** Overlapping of p$_z$ orbitals to form a delocalized cyclic π orbital

Delocalization in ions

Another example of π delocalization occurs in the carboxylate ion, RCOO⁻ (e.g. the ethanoate ion). A lone pair of electrons in the 2p$_z$ orbital of the oxygen atom overlaps and merges with the π orbital of the adjacent carbonyl group (>C=O). This is an alternative but equivalent description to the resonance model described earlier. Four π electrons (two from the carbonyl group and two from the lone pair) are delocalized over three atoms. The resulting molecular orbital is known as a *three-centre delocalized* π orbital (Figure 14.57).

All molecules and ions in which the bonding can be represented by a series of resonance structures can also be described in terms of delocalized π orbitals. For example, in the carbonate ion, each of the lone pairs in 2p$_z$ orbitals can overlap with the π orbital of the >C=O group, creating a four-centre delocalized π orbital (Figure 14.58).

If there is to be delocalization of π electrons across a series of σ-bonded atoms, then the p$_z$ orbitals must be parallel for maximum overlap. Hence, the ion or molecule must be *flat* (planar).

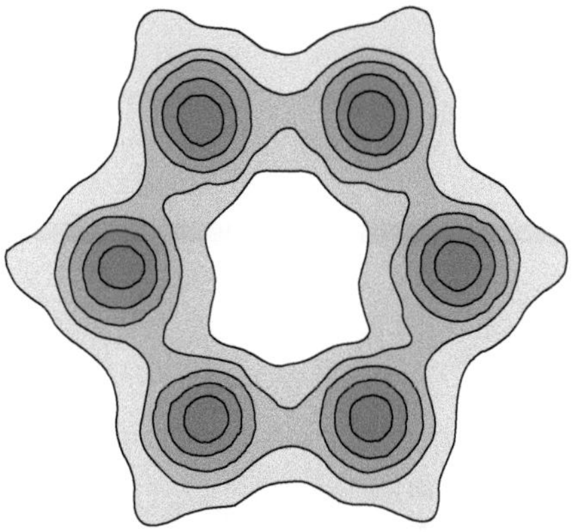

■ **Figure 14.56** Pi electron density map for benzene (in the plane of the molecular π orbital)

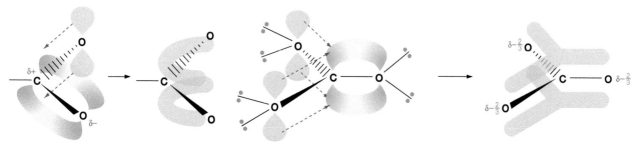

■ **Figure 14.57** Delocalization in a carboxylate ion

■ **Figure 14.58** Delocalization in a carbonate ion

■ Ozone – a case study in bonding theory and international environmental concern

Ozone (or, more strictly speaking, trioxygen) was first identified as a gaseous allotrope of oxygen (dioxygen) in 1840. The name derives from the Greek for 'to smell', reflecting the strong smell in the air after a lightning storm.

A molecule of ozone (O_3) consists of three oxygen atoms covalently bonded together in a V-shaped molecule. As such it provides an appropriate example for discussing different aspects of the various approaches to covalent bonding: resonance forms and bond order, formal charge and bond polarization, and the hybridization of molecular orbitals. Ozone is also of note in terms of its environmental significance both in the lower levels of the stratosphere and 'at ground level'.

Lewis (electron dot) structures of the resonance forms of ozone indicate that the central oxygen atom has three electron domains around it, which gives rise to a trigonal planar structure. Two of these electron domains are bonding pairs, while the third is a lone pair. The stronger repulsion of this lone pair results in a bond angle slightly less than 120° (around 117°). There are three pairs of electrons in two bonding positions so the bond order is 1.5, meaning that the bonds are of intermediate strength and length between oxygen–oxygen single and double bonds.

The structure of ozone can also be explained in terms of sp^2 hybridization of the atomic orbitals of the oxygen atoms. Sigma (σ) bonds are formed by overlap of the hybrid orbitals. The unhybridized p orbitals on each atom overlap to form a delocalized pi (π) bond above and below the plane of the molecule. Again the picture is of a molecule in which the oxygen–oxygen bonds are equal in strength, intermediate between that of a single and double bond.

The bonds in ozone are between oxygen atoms and so are in themselves non-polar. However, the molecule as a whole has a net dipole moment which can be explained by checking the formal charges on each atom (Figure 14.60). This shows the uneven distribution of electrons through the structure.

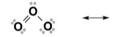

■ **Figure 14.59** Resonance forms and trigonal structure of the ozone molecule

■ **Figure 14.60** The formal charges on the atoms of the ozone molecule, showing the net dipole of the structure

Explaining the wavelength of light required to dissociate oxygen and ozone

This relative weakness of the bonds in ozone compared to the bonds in dioxygen (O_2) is significant in terms of the chemistry that takes place in the lower stratosphere and results in the phenomena of ozone generation and depletion. Throughout the millions of years of the Earth's existence it has always been subjected to ultraviolet (UV) radiation from the Sun. The early atmosphere, lacking any significant level of oxygen, offered little protection against this radiation, and this may have been a factor in the rapid mutation of early life forms. However, following the evolution of photosynthesizing organisms the levels of atmospheric oxygen increased, with the consequent generation of an ultraviolet-absorbing layer of ozone in the stratosphere.

The stratosphere is a layer of the Earth's atmosphere between 12 and 50 kilometres above the surface. The lower regions of the stratosphere (the ozone layer) contain around 90% of the atmospheric ozone at a concentration of less than 10 ppm. Ozone levels are maintained through a cycle of synthesis and breakdown reactions involving free radicals generated by the action of energy from UV-C and UV-B radiation (Table 14.8).

Oxygen dissociation:	$O_2(g) \rightarrow 2O\bullet(g)$	UV-A radiation
Ozone synthesis and dissociation:	$O_2(g) + O\bullet(g) \rightarrow O_3(g)$	exothermic
	$O_3(g) \rightarrow O_2(g) + O\bullet(g)$	UV-B radiation

■ **Table 14.8**
Comparison of oxygen (dioxygen) and ozone (trioxygen)

	Oxygen, O_2	Ozone, O_3
Bonding	$\ddot{O}=\ddot{O}$	O⋯O⋯O
Bond order	2	1.5
Bond energy/kJ mol^{-1}	498	364
Dissociation	UV-C $\lambda < 242\,nm$ higher energy radiation of shorter wavelength	UV-B $\lambda < 330\,nm$ lower energy radiation of longer wavelength

Note that the breakdown of oxygen requires ultraviolet radiation of a shorter wavelength than the breakdown of ozone. The key feature here is that these reactions, by using the higher energies of this radiation, protect the surface of the Earth from the highly damaging effects of UV-B and UV-C radiation (Figure 14.61). Most of the ultraviolet radiation reaching the Earth's surface is the least harmful UV-A form. Thus the ozone layer protects life on Earth from the radiation that would be most harmful to living tissue. Ozone also plays a role in establishing the temperature structure of the atmosphere. The generation of ozone is exothermic; this is a major source of heat at this altitude and results in the stratospheric temperature rising with increased altitude.

■ **Figure 14.61**
Absorption of UV-B and UV-C in the stratospheric ozone–oxygen cycle

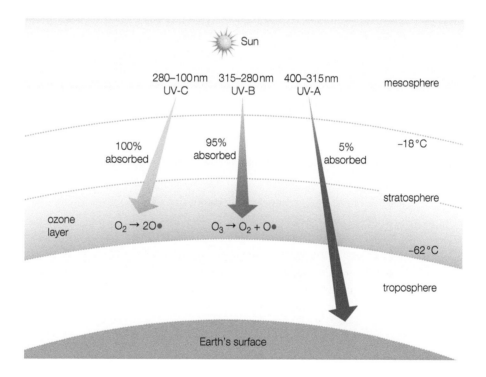

Describing the mechanism of the catalysis of ozone depletion by CFCs and NO$_x$

Earlier, in Chapter 6, we discussed the catalytic cycle involving chlorine free radicals generated by the effect of ultraviolet radiation on chlorofluorocarbons (CFCs). This cycle results in the phenomenon of ozone depletion and the consequent polar 'ozone holes'. CFCs are not the only compounds that cause this depletion. Nitrogen oxides (NO$_x$) are also responsible.

Both nitrogen monoxide (NO) and nitrogen dioxide (NO_2) are present in the exhaust fumes of vehicles and are themselves free radicals; their molecules both have a lone electron. The reaction of nitrogen monoxide with ozone is as follows:

$$NO\bullet(g) + O_3(g) \rightarrow NO_2\bullet(g) + O_2(g)$$
$$NO_2\bullet(g) + O\bullet(g) \rightarrow NO\bullet(g) + O_2(g)$$

$NO\bullet(g)$ is acting as a catalyst as it is regenerated during the overall reaction, which results in the breakdown of ozone:

$$O_3(g) + O\bullet(g) \rightarrow 2O_2(g)$$

This catalytic cycle is very similar to that shown with chlorine free radicals (Chapter 6).

Chemicals such as CFCs and nitrogen oxides that damage the ozone layer are known as ozone-depleting chemicals (ODCs). Concern about the use of chlorofluorocarbons in particular led to the signing of the Montreal Protocol and the subsequent search for alternatives, as discussed earlier. The concerted international effort to resolve this situation remains, despite setbacks and complexities, the most successful environmental intervention achieved to date.

■ Formal charge

A Lewis (electron dot) structure describes how the electrons are distributed in a molecule, polyatomic ion or resonance structure (Chapter 4). In some cases several different Lewis structures can be drawn that all obey the octet rule. The concept of formal charge provides one way of determining which is the most reasonable or important. Formal charge is a 'book keeping' of the valence electrons to determine the formal charge of each atom in each of the alternative Lewis structures. The formal charge of any atom in a molecule is the charge the atom would have if all the atoms in the molecule had the same electronegativity, i.e. if each bonding or shared pair of electrons was shared equally between its two atoms.

To calculate the formal charge on any atom in a Lewis structure, electrons are assigned (given) to the atom according to the following rules:

■ All unshared or non-bonding electrons (lone pairs) are assigned to the atom on which they are found.

■ For any covalent bond – single, double or triple – half of the bonding electrons are assigned to each atom in the bond.

■ The formal charge of each atom is then calculated by subtracting the number of electrons assigned to the atom from the number of valence electrons in the isolated atom.

■ The cyanide ion has the Lewis structure:

$$[:\!C \equiv N\!:]^-$$

For the carbon atom there are two non-bonding electrons (one lone pair) and three electrons from the six in the triple bond, making a total of five. The number of valence electrons on a neutral carbon atom is four, so $4 - 5 = -1$. For nitrogen, there are two non-bonding electrons (one lone pair) and three electrons from the triple bond. Because the number of valence electrons on a neutral nitrogen atom is five, its formal charge is $5 - 5 = 0$. Hence, the formal charges on the atoms in the Lewis structure of CN^- are:

$$[:\!\overset{-1}{C} \equiv \overset{0}{N}\!:]^-$$

Note that the sum of the formal charges equals the overall charge on the ion, −1. In general, the formal charges on a molecule add to zero, but those on an ion add to give the overall charge on the ion.

Using the concept of formal charge to determine which structure is preferred from different Lewis (electron dot) structures

The following are three possible Lewis structures for the thiocyanate ion, NCS⁻:

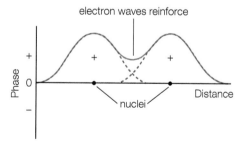

Determine the formal charges of the atoms in each Lewis structure. Determine the preferred Lewis structure.

Neutral nitrogen, carbon and sulfur atoms have five, four and six valence electrons, respectively. The formal charges are shown below using the rules previously outlined.

$$[\overset{-2}{\ddot{N}} - \overset{0}{C} \equiv \overset{+1}{S}]^- \qquad [\overset{-1}{N} = \overset{0}{C} = \overset{0}{\ddot{S}}]^- \qquad [\overset{0}{N} \equiv \overset{0}{C} - \overset{-1}{\ddot{S}}]^-$$

All the formal charges in all three Lewis structures sum to −1, the charge on the thiocyanate ion.

Since nitrogen (3.0) is more electronegative than carbon (2.6) or sulfur (2.6), the negative formal charge will be located on the nitrogen atom. In addition the Lewis structure is selected that produces the smallest formal charges. Based on these two criteria, the Lewis structure in the middle is the preferred description of the thiocyanate ion, SCN⁻.

■ Molecular orbital theory (diatomic molecules)

As described previously for the hydrogen molecule, molecular orbital (MO) theory takes the atomic orbitals of the atoms, and mathematically combines the wave functions that represent these atomic orbitals (using an approach known as the linear combination of atomic orbitals). This combination produces new molecular orbitals that describe the regions of space occupied by the bonding electrons. The number of new molecular orbitals formed is the same as the number of atomic orbitals combined. The wave functions that represent the new molecular orbitals can be used to calculate the energy of an electron in those molecular orbitals.

Bond energies can also be calculated and are found to be in good agreement with experimental values.

MO theory is based upon the quantum mechanical model which regards electrons as standing waves (see Chapter 12). The bonding and anti-bonding sigma orbitals correspond to in-phase (Figure 14.62) and out-of-phase wave combinations (Figure 14.63). The electron density is a minimum (a saddle point) in the centre of a bonding sigma molecular orbital but is zero at the centre of an anti-bonding sigma molecular orbital, since the waves cancel.

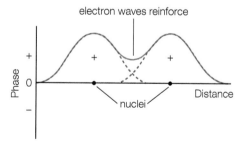

(margin note)

3 The nitronium ion, NO₂⁺, has three possible Lewis structures that obey the octet rule. Draw these three Lewis structures and assign formal charges to the atoms in each structure. Deduce the preferred Lewis structure.

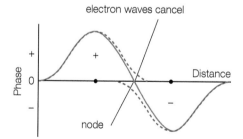

■ **Figure 14.62** In-phase combination of waves (constructive interference): amplitudes of wave functions added

■ **Figure 14.63** Out-of-phase combination of waves (destructive interference): amplitudes of wave functions subtracted

Linear combination of atomic orbitals

The basic concept of molecular orbital theory is that molecular orbitals may be constructed from a set of contributing atomic orbitals so that the molecular wave functions consist of linear combinations of atomic orbitals (LCAO).

In the case of the combinations of the two hydrogen 1s atomic orbitals to give two molecular orbitals, the two linear combinations are written below, in which atomic wave functions are represented by ψ (psi) and molecular wave functions by ϕ (phi):

$$\phi_1 = \psi_A + \psi_B$$
$$\phi_2 = \psi_A - \psi_B$$

where ψ_A and ψ_B are the two hydrogen 1s wave functions of the two hydrogen atoms, A and B. The first expression above represents the formation of a sigma bonding molecular orbital where there is a build-up of electron density along the inter-nuclear axis (electron waves sum). The second expression represents the formation of a sigma anti-bonding orbital (electron waves cancel each other out).

The equations above describing the linear combination of atomic orbitals are simplified since they imply that the atomic wave functions ψ contribute fully (100%) to both molecular wave functions ϕ_1 and ϕ_2. In practice, the functions are normalized with a function to represent the degree of overlap.

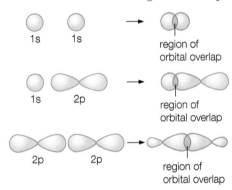

■ **Figure 14.64** Molecular orbitals formed by the overlap of 1s and 1s, 1s and 2p and 2p and 2p atomic orbitals

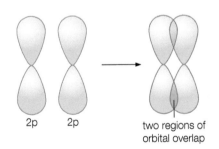

■ **Figure 14.65** Formation of a pi bond by sideways overlap of two $2p_x$ orbitals

A good approximation of the shape of a molecular orbital can be found by seeing where the maximum overlap occurs when the two isolated atoms with their atomic orbitals are brought close together. Figure 14.64 shows s–s, s–p and p–p overlap, three combinations that can occur in many molecules. For example:

■ The H–H bond in the H_2 molecule arises through the overlap of 1s orbitals on adjacent atoms (as previously described).

■ The C–H bond in alkanes, such as methane, can arise through the overlap of the 1s orbital on the hydrogen atom and the 2p orbital on a carbon atom. (An alternative model is based upon sp^3 hybridization of the carbon atom.)

■ Similar overlap, either between themselves or with the 1s atomic orbital of the hydrogen atom, occurs with the 2p orbitals of nitrogen, oxygen and fluorine. (Again there is an alternative model involving sp^3 hybridization of all the atoms except hydrogen.)

■ All of these orbitals are sigma (σ) orbitals and formed by the direct head-on or end-to-end overlap of atomic orbitals resulting in electron density concentrated between the nuclei of the atoms.

■ Two p orbitals can also undergo sideways overlap (as described previously in the section on hybridization) to produce a pi (π) orbital (Figure 14.65). These pi orbitals are often found in compounds with double or triple bonds.

■ The overlapping of s and p orbitals gives rise to sigma bonding (σ), sigma anti-bonding (σ^*), pi bonding (π) and pi anti-bonding (π^*) orbitals. The energy diagrams for σ and σ^* 1s and 2p orbitals are shown in Figure 14.66.

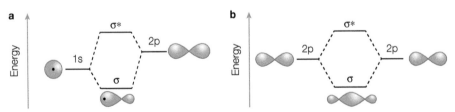

■ **Figure 14.66** Energy diagram for the formation of σ and σ^* orbitals from the axial overlap of **a** a 1s and 2p orbital and **b** two 2p orbitals

Figure 14.67 shows the energy diagram for the formation of the π and π^* orbitals. The attraction to the two nuclei experienced by the bonding pair of electrons (spin pair) is not as great as 2p for a σ

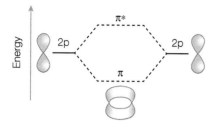

Figure 14.67 Energy diagram for the formation of π and π* orbitals from the sideway or lateral overlap of two 2p orbitals

orbital because the average distance between the electron pair and the nucleus is greater. The decrease in energy on forming the π orbital is therefore less, so the π bond is weaker than the σ bond (in the same sub-level).

It has been outlined earlier how s and p orbitals on adjacent atoms can overlap to form σ and π molecular orbitals. These types of atomic orbital overlap can occur at the same time, to form multiple bonds. This can be illustrated by the diatomic molecules, X_2, of the elements of the second row of the periodic table.

Most of these elements form diatomic molecules, although only N_2, O_2 and F_2 are stable at room temperature. The one 2s orbital and the three 2p orbitals on each atom in the pair overlap and produce four molecular bonding orbitals, and four anti-bonding orbitals (Figure 14.68).

As we fill these molecular orbitals with electrons, (according to the Aufbau principle), the type and approximate strength of the bonding between the atoms in the various X_2 molecules can be predicted.

In Li_2, for example, only the σ (2s) orbital is filled, giving a bond order of 1. This molecule only exists in the gas phase.

The bond order is given by the following expression:

$\frac{1}{2}$[(number of electrons in bonding molecular orbitals) − (number of electrons in anti-bonding orbitals)]

A bond order of 1 corresponds to one covalent bond.

In Be_2, both the bonding σ orbital (2s) and the anti-bonding σ* (2s) orbitals would be filled, giving an overall order of zero. Hence, we can predict that Be_2 is not stable. (Be_2 only exists at very low temperatures, as an unstable species held together by London (dispersion) forces.)

In N_2, four bonding orbitals and one anti-bonding orbital have been filled, giving an overall bond order of 4 − 1 = 3. Thereafter, in O_2 and F_2, further anti-bonding orbitals are being filled, reducing the bond orders to 2 and 1, respectively (see Table 14.9 and Figure 14.69).

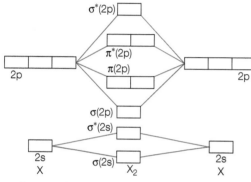

Figure 14.68 Bonding molecular orbitals for diatomic molecules, X_2, of elements in the second period of the periodic table

Molecule	Number of bonding electrons	Number of anti-bonding electrons	Net bond order	Bond enthalpy/kJ mol⁻¹
Li_2	2	0	1	105
Be_2	2	2	0	(0)
N_2	8	2	3	945
O_2	8	4	2	498
F_2	8	6	1	159
Ne_2	8	8	0	(0)

Table 14.9 Numbers of bonding and anti-bonding electrons for selected second-row diatomic molecules

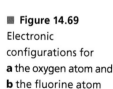

Figure 14.69 Electronic configurations for **a** the oxygen atom and **b** the fluorine atom

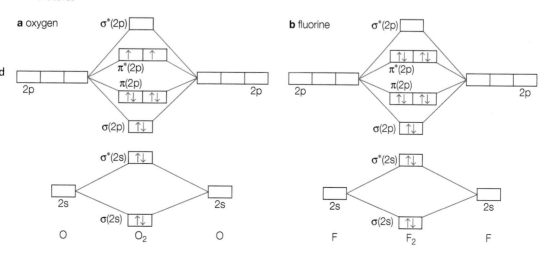

4 Write the electron configurations of H_2, H_2^+ and H_2^- in terms of molecular orbital theory.

5 Explain why He_2^+ exists but He_2 does not. Deduce bond orders for both species.

■ **Figure 14.70** Liquid oxygen is attracted to the poles of a powerful magnet (the liquid oxygen is inside a container surrounded by a blue insulator)

One of the successes of molecular orbital theory was to predict correctly the paramagnetic nature (Figure 14.70) of the O_2 molecule, due to its two unpaired electrons. Most molecules, e.g. N_2, contain fully paired-up electrons, and are not paramagnetic.

Predicting whether sigma (σ) or pi (π) bonds are formed from the linear combination of atomic orbitals

The overlap of two s orbitals always gives rise to a sigma orbital. The overlap of an s orbital with a p orbital always gives rise to a sigma orbital. p orbitals can overlap in two ways. If the atomic orbitals overlap along the inter-nuclear axis then a sigma bond is formed. Sigma bonds are formed by the axial overlapping of half-filled atomic orbitals.

The strengths of the three types of sigma bonds vary as follows:

p–p > p–s > s–s.

This is because p orbitals overlap to a greater extent than s orbitals.

A pi bond is only formed by the lateral or sideways overlap of p orbitals. The axes of the orbitals are parallel to each other but perpendicular to the inter-nuclear axis.

Worked example

Describe the formation of the oxygen molecule, O_2, in terms of the atomic orbitals.

The oxygen atom has the electron configuration $1s^2 2s^2 2p_x^2 2p_y 2p_z$ and hence has two half-filled p orbitals in its valence shell. One of the half-filled p orbitals overlaps axially (head-on) with the half-filled p orbital of the other oxygen atom to form the sigma (σ) bond. The other half-filled p orbitals of the two oxygen atoms overlap laterally (sideways) to form a pi bond (pπ–pπ bond). Figure 14.71 shows the formation of the sigma and pi bonds.

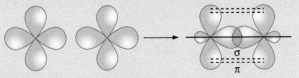

■ **Figure 14.71** Formation of the oxygen molecule, O_2

---

6 Describe the formation of the nitrogen molecule, N_2.

Nature of Science

Principle of Occam's razor – bonding theories have been modified over time to remain as simple as possible while maximizing explanatory power

Schrödinger developed the ideas of quantum (wave) mechanics in 1925. It was then applied to determine atomic and molecular structure. The idea of covalent bonding between two atoms based on the sharing of electron pairs was proposed by Lewis in 1916. The Lewis model (of 'dots and crosses' to represent electrons) is still relevant and useful, but the quantum mechanical model (Chapters 2 and 12), incorporating wave–particle duality, Pauli's exclusion principle and Heisenberg's uncertainty principle, gives a deeper understanding of chemical bonds.

Theoretical investigations into the nature of chemical bonding were centred around valence bond (VB) theory and molecular orbital (MO) theory.

The valence bond theory is a quantum mechanical model of the chemical bond that was proposed by Heitler and London in 1927. It uses Lewis's concept of a covalent bond as a shared pair of electrons and the idea that a molecule is described by a series of resonance structures.

Figures 14.72 and 14.73 shows the valence bond (VB) theory descriptions of the carbon dioxide and benzene molecules. Each resonance structure corresponds to a Lewis structure of the molecule, and each has its own characteristic energy. The wave functions of the two molecules are a linear combination of the wave functions corresponding to the resonance structures. The number of resonance structures to be included to describe the molecule increases very rapidly with an increase in the number of atoms in the molecule. This is one of the drawbacks of VB theory (in its original form).

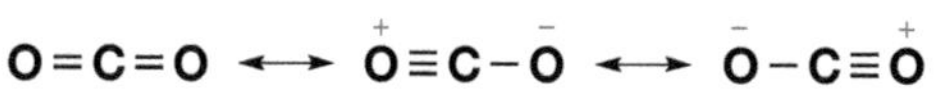

■ **Figure 14.72**
Resonance structures in carbon dioxide

$$O=C=O \longleftrightarrow \overset{+}{O}\equiv C-\overset{-}{O} \longleftrightarrow \overset{-}{O}-C\equiv \overset{+}{O}$$

■ **Figure 14.73**
Resonance structures in benzene

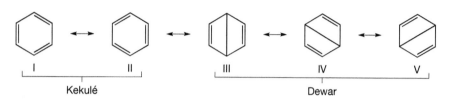

The concept of formal charge was introduced to help identify the more important resonance structures or correct Lewis structures for molecules.

An ideal bonding theory needs to be relatively simple while maximizing its ability to account for the structures and bonding types present in molecules. If there are two competing bonding theories, both of which are equally supported by empirical data, then the principle of Occam's razor needs to be applied. This is sometimes known as the principle of parsimony; it stops the adoption of a complicated explanation for a phenomenon when there is a competing but simpler theory.

Occam's razor does not claim that a simpler explanation is correct, merely that it is more likely to be true. Both the MO and VB models (when pushed to its mathematical limits) give identical descriptions of bonds, but simple VB theory also needs to be modified with the concept of hybridization before it can predict molecular shapes correctly. Organic chemists draw VB-like structures and use curly arrows to show the movements of relatively localized electron pairs from one place to another.

7   Find out about Pauling's electroneutrality principle for transition metal complex ions.

■ Valence bond theory versus molecular orbital theory

Similarities

According to both the theories, the atomic orbitals (AOs) of the two atoms overlapping each other must be of similar energy (and the same symmetry). According to both theories, the electrons are found in the region between the atomic nuclei, and both theories postulate (suggest) that a covalent bond possesses directional properties.

Differences

The differences between MO and VB theories are summarized in Table 14.10.

MO theory	VB theory
The molecular orbitals (MOs) are formed by the LCAO approximation method. The AOs involved in the formation of these MOs are from the valence shells of the two atoms.	Two atomic orbitals (AOs) with unpaired electrons overlap and merge to form a molecular orbital.
The atomic orbitals (AOs) of the resulting molecule lose their individual identity.	The resulting molecule consists of atoms which, although interacting, retain a large measure of their individual character.
MO theory starts with the nuclei of the constituent atoms.	VB theory starts with the individual atoms and considers the interaction between them.
MO theory explains the paramagnetic character of the O_2 molecule.	VB theory fails to explain the paramagnetic character of the O_2 molecule (unless resonance is invoked).
Resonance is not part of MO theory.	Resonance plays a critical role in VB theory.

■ **Table 14.10** The differences between the MO and VB theories of chemical bonding

ToK Link

Covalent bonding can be described using valence bond or molecular orbital theory. To what extent is having alternative ways of describing the same phenomena a strength or a weakness?

Molecular orbital (MO) theory is based on the idea that electrons are standing waves that add either constructively (to form bonding orbitals) or destructively (to form anti-bonding orbitals). Valence bond (VB) theory is an orbital-based model of bonding that includes the concept of hybridization and focuses on the bonds formed by the valence electrons of different atoms.

Both theories treat molecular bonds as a sharing of electrons between nuclei. Unlike the VB theory, which starts by treating the electrons as localized balloons of electron density, the MO theory suggests that the electrons are delocalized over the entire molecule.

A chemical bonding theory should accurately predict the physical and chemical properties of the molecule, for example magnetic properties (Chapter 13), spectra, shape, bond energy, bond length and bond angles. Additionally, it should describe correctly the changes that take place during any chemical reactions.

The VB model in its simplest form cannot adequately explain the fact that some molecules and ions contain two equivalent bonds intermediate between a single bond and a double bond. The best it can do is suggest that these molecules or ions are resonance hybrids of the Lewis structures that can be written for them. MO theory does not need resonance structures to describe such molecules, because the orbitals reflect the geometry of each particular molecule to which the model is applied. MO theory is also more straightforward for predicting electronic spectra and magnetic properties.

On the other hand, MO theory in its simplest form is less successful than VB theory for describing correctly the changes that take place to the bonding during a chemical reaction. Each model describes some properties better than the other does. Both models can be improved by well-defined schemes, and they do in fact then become equivalent.

For technical reasons, MO theory is much easier to implement for numerical calculations on computers than VB theory is. The final test for any chemical theory is its fit with experimental data and the ease with which it can predict the structure, properties and reactions of molecules. A good compromise for numerical calculations is to use MO theory, which takes less computer time, and then to turn the result into the language of VB theory, which can be easier to visualize. This is known as a 'VB reading' of MO theory.

The strength of having two bonding theories is that each theory has its own weakness and strengths and hence each theory has its own uses. The shared weakness is that bonding theories are approximate descriptions, and neither on its own is an ideal bonding model.

Utilization: Vision science and links to a molecule's structure

Vision begins when light rays (photons) are focused by the eye's lens on to the retina, the layer of cells lining the inside of the eye ball. The retina contains large numbers of photoreceptor cells known as rods and cones. The ends of the rods and cones contain a molecule called rhodopsin which consists of a protein (opsin) covalently bonded to a purple pigment molecule called retinal. Structural changes which occur around a carbon–carbon double bond in the retinal component of the rhodopsin trigger a series of chemical reactions that eventually result in vision.

Double bonds are not only stronger than single bonds, they also introduce stiffness or rigidity into molecules. Imagine taking the –CH$_2$– group of the ethene molecule, and rotating it relative to the other –CH$_2$– group as shown in Figure 14.74. This rotation results in the loss of overlap between the p orbitals, breaking the pi bond. This is a process that requires considerable energy that is not available at room temperature. Hence, the presence of a carbon–carbon double bond restricts the rotation of the bonds in a molecule. In contrast, molecules can rotate freely around the axis in carbon–carbon single bonds (sigma bonds) because this motion has no effect on the overlap for a sigma bond.

Human vision depends on the rigidity of double bonds in retinal. In its normal form, retinal is held rigid by its carbon–carbon double bonds, as shown in Figure 14.75. Light (photons) entering the eye is absorbed by rhodopsin, and the energy is used to break the pi-bond component of the indicated double bond. The molecule then freely rotates around this bond, changing its geometry (shape).

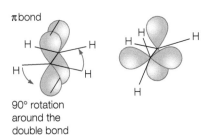

π bond

90° rotation around the double bond

■ **Figure 14.74** Rotation around the carbon–carbon double bond in ethene

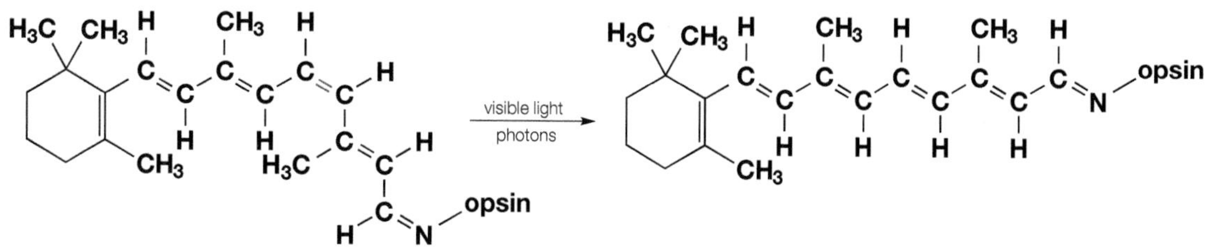

■ **Figure 14.75** The chemical basis of vision: the *cis–trans* isomerization of retinal

The retinal then separates from the opsin, triggering the reaction that produces a nerve impulse. It takes only five closely spaced molecules undergoing this conversion to produce the sensation of vision. Hence only five photons of light are necessary to stimulate the receptors of the eye. The retinal slowly reverts to its original form and re-attaches covalently to the opsin. The slowness of this process helps explain why intense bright light causes temporary blindness. The light causes all the retinal to separate from opsin, leaving no further molecules to absorb light.

■ *Examination questions – a selection*

Paper 1 IB questions and IB style questions

Q1 What are the hybridization states of carbon in ethyne (C_2H_2), in graphite and in diamond?
A sp, sp^2, sp^3 **C** sp^3, sp^2, sp
B sp, sp^3, sp^2 **D** sp, sp^3, sp^3

Q2 Which of the following species does *not* contain an sp^3 hybridized oxygen atom?
A H_2O_2 **C** H_2O
B H_3O^+ **D** CH_3CHO

Q3 Which of the following molecules does *not* have a π bond?
A CO_2 **C** H_2O_2
B CO **D** SO_3

Q4 What are the numbers of σ and π bonds in $(NC)_2C=C(CN)_2$?
A 5, 4 **C** 9, 4
B 6, 6 **D** 9, 9

Q5 Which one of the following species is octahedral?
A SF_6 **C** BF_4^-
B PF_5 **D** BO_3^{3-}

Q6 Which one of the following contains the largest number of lone pairs on the central atom?
A ClO_3^- **C** I_3^-
B XeF_4 **D** SF_4

Q7 The length of a carbon–carbon single bond is 0.154 nm and the length of a carbon–carbon double bond is 0.134 nm. What is the likely carbon–carbon bond length within the benzene molecule, C_6H_6?
A 0.164 nm **B** 0.124 nm **C** 0.139 nm
D 0.154 nm for three bonds and 0.134 nm for the other three bonds

Q8 Which one of the following statements is incorrect about the sulfur(VI) fluoride molecule?
A The oxidation number of the sulfur in the molecule is the same as the number of its electrons it uses in the covalent bonding.
B All the S–F bonds are equivalent.
C The molecule is octahedral.
D The sulfur atom has the electronic structure of argon.

Q9 Which statements correctly describe the NO_2^- ion ?
I It can be represented by resonance structures.
II It has two lone pairs of electrons on the N atom.
III The N atom is sp^2 hybridized.
A I and II only **C** II and III only
B I and III only **D** I, II and III
Higher Level Paper 1, Nov 2005, Q12

Q10 What is the hybridization of the carbon atoms in 1,3-butadiene, $CH_2CHCHCH_2$?
A sp^3 **C** sp
B sp^2 **D** s^2p

Q11 Which one of the following statements concerning resonance is *not* true?
A The contributing resonance structures differ only in the arrangement of the π electrons.
B The resonance hybrid is intermediate between the contributing resonance structures.
C Resonance describes the chemical equilibrium between two or more Lewis structures.
D A single Lewis structure does not provide an adequate representation of bonding.

Q12 When the carbon–carbon bonds in the compounds C_2F_2, C_2F_4 and C_2F_6 are arranged in order of increasing length, the correct order is:

A $C_2F_6 < C_2F_4 < C_2F_2$ **C** $C_2F_4 < C_2F_6 < C_2F_2$
B $C_2F_4 < C_2F_2 < C_2F_6$ **D** $C_2F_2 < C_2F_4 < C_2F_6$

Q13 The hybridization of the carbon atom in the carbonate ion, CO_3^{2-}, is best described as:

A sp   **C** sp^2
B sp^3 **D** unhybridized

Q14 For which one of the following species would one usually draw resonance structures?

A O_2 **C** $(CH_3)_2CO$
B CH_3COOH **D** $CH_3CH_2COO^-$

Q15 In the Lewis structure for the ion ClF_2^+, what is the number of lone pairs around the central atom?

A 3   **C** 1
B 2   **D** 0

Q16 How many sigma (σ) and pi (π) bonds are there in the following molecule?

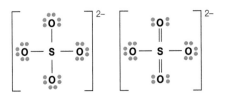

	σ bonds	π bonds
A	9	2
B	9	4
C	11	2
D	11	4

Higher Level Paper 1, May 2013, Q12

Q17 Which species have delocalized π electrons?

     I CH_3COOH **II** NO_2^- **III** CO_3^{2-}
A I and II only   **C** II and III only
B I and III only   **D** I, II and III

Higher Level Paper 1, May 2013, Q13

Q18 State the geometry of a molecule in which the bonding may be described using the valence–bond model as being made up of sp^3 hybrid orbitals on the central atom.

A tetrahedral
B trigonal planar
C square planar
D octahedral

Q19 Carbon monoxide has ten bonding electrons and four anti-bonding electrons. Deduce the bond order of the molecule.

A 3   **C** 1
B 7   **D** 2

Q20 Anti-bonding molecular orbitals are produced by:

A constructive interaction of atomic orbital wave functions
B destructive interaction of atomic orbital wave functions

C the overlap of the atomic orbital wave functions of two negative ions
D the overlap of the atomic orbital wave functions of two positive ions

Paper 2 IB questions and IB style questions

Q1 Two structures of the sulfate ion, SO_4^{2-}, are shown below.

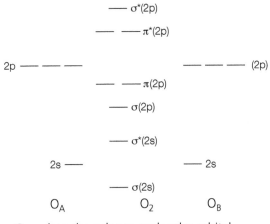

a State which of these structures obeys the octet rule. [1]
b Deduce the formal charges for the two structures. [2]
c State which structure is more stable based on formal charge. [1]

Q2 For a diatomic molecule of oxygen (O_2), we define the bond as lying along the *z* axis.

             — $\sigma^*(2p)$

         — — $\pi^*(2p)$

2p — — —   — — — (2p)

         — — $\pi(2p)$

            — $\sigma(2p)$

            — $\sigma^*(2s)$

2s —   — 2s

            — $\sigma(2s)$

    O_A O_2 O_B

a Complete the valence molecular orbital (MO) diagram for O_2. Include labels for the molecular orbitals. [2]
b Which valence atomic orbitals combine to form σ MOs in O_2? Be specific. [2]
c Which valence atomic orbitals combine to form π MOs in O_2? Be specific. [2]
d Write the valence orbital occupancy for O_2. [1]
e State whether O_2 is paramagnetic or diamagnetic. Explain your answer. [2]
f State the overall bond order for O_2. [2]
g State how many electrons must be added to O_2 to reduce the bond order to zero. If this number of electrons is added, state what product(s) will be formed. [1]

Q3 **a** For each of the molecules C_2H_2, C_2Cl_4 and SF_4, draw their Lewis (electron dot) structures, and use the valence shell electron pair repulsion (VSEPR) theory to predict their shape and bond angles. [10]

 b State the type of hybridization in C_2H_2 and C_2Cl_4. [2]

 c Draw two resonance structures for each of the ethanoate ion (CH_3COO^-) and the benzene molecule. [4]

Higher Level Paper 2, May 2001, Q8

Q4 **a** Explain what is meant by a σ bond and a π bond. Describe a double and a triple bond in terms of σ and π bonds. [4]

 b Define the term *delocalization*. [2]

Higher Level Paper 2, Nov 2001, Q6

Q5 Phosphorus(III) bromide is a colourless liquid. Phosphorus(V) bromide is a yellow solid which sublimes when heated.

The solid is ionic and consists of $[PBr_4]^+$ and Br^- ions, but in the gas phase PBr_5 molecules are present. Phosphorus(V) bromide is hydrolysed by water producing hydrogen bromide gas:

$$PBr_5(s) + 4H_2O(l) \rightarrow H_3PO_4(aq) + 5HBr(aq)$$

 a Write Lewis electron dot structures for PBr_3 and PBr_5 and sketch their molecular shapes. [4]

 b State the bond angles present in PBr_5 and account for the bond angle in PBr_3 being approximately 107°. [4]

 c Deduce the shape of the $[PBr_4]^+$ ion. [1]

 d Give the hybridization of the phosphorus in phosphorus(III) bromide and the oxygen in water. [2]

15 Energetics/thermochemistry

ESSENTIAL IDEAS

- The concept of the energy change in a single-step reaction being equivalent to the summation of smaller steps can be applied to changes involving ionic compounds.
- A reaction is spontaneous if the overall transformation leads to an increase in total entropy (system plus surroundings). The direction of spontaneous change always increases the total entropy of the universe at the expense of energy available to do useful work. This is known as the second law of thermodynamics.

15.1 Energy cycles – *the concept of the energy change in a single step being equivalent to the summation of smaller steps can be applied to changes involving ionic compounds*

Nature of Science   Making quantitative measurements with replicates to ensure reliability – energy cycles allow for the calculation of enthalpy changes

Hess's law states that if a reaction is carried out in a series of steps, ΔH for the overall reaction will equal the sum of the enthalpy changes for the individual steps. The overall enthalpy change for the process is independent of the number of steps or the particular path by which the reaction is carried out. This principle is a consequence of the fact that enthalpy is a state function. A state function is a property that depends only on the condition or 'state' of the system, and not on the path used to reach the current conditions. ΔH is therefore independent of the path between the initial and final states. Chemists can therefore calculate ΔH for any chemical reaction or physical process, as long as they can find a route for which ΔH is known for every step. This means that a relatively small number of experimental measurements (with replicates to ensure reliability) can be used to calculate ΔH for a huge number of different reactions. Hess's law provides a useful means of calculating enthalpy changes that are difficult to measure directly.

■ Enthalpy of atomization

The enthalpy change of atomization of an element is the heat change (at constant pressure) when one mole of separate gaseous atoms of the element is formed from the element in its standard state under standard conditions.

The following thermochemical equations each describe the enthalpy of atomization of an element. In each case the enthalpy change of the reaction is the enthalpy change of atomization.

$$Fe(s) \rightarrow Fe(g) \qquad \Delta H^{\ominus}_{at} = +418 \, kJ \, mol^{-1}$$

$$\tfrac{1}{2}Br_2(l) \rightarrow Br(g) \qquad \Delta H^{\ominus}_{at} = +96.5 \, kJ \, mol^{-1}$$

1 Write equations with state symbols showing the enthalpy of atomization for oxygen, white phosphorus, $P_4(s)$, and boron.

Note that the enthalpy change of atomization for a halogen or other diatomic gaseous molecule is equivalent to *half* the bond enthalpy (Chapter 5).

All the enthalpy changes of atomization of the noble gases are zero. This is because the elements are already in the form of separate gaseous atoms under standard conditions.

Enthalpy changes of atomization are always positive, because energy must be absorbed to pull the atoms apart and break the chemical bonds. Enthalpy changes of atomization are usually found indirectly by calculation from other enthalpy changes, using Hess's law. Enthalpy changes of atomization are used in Born–Haber cycle calculations.

Enthalpy of atomization and bonding

The enthalpy of atomization is an indication of the strength of bonding in a substance. For a solid to break up into atoms, it may first melt (accompanied by the standard enthalpy change of fusion), then evaporate (accompanied by the standard enthalpy change of vaporization) and finally, in the gas phase, any remaining bonds break to give individual atoms.

The size of the enthalpy changes associated with the different processes depends on the type of substance. For a metal, the enthalpy changes associated with melting and evaporation are the most important, while for a covalent substance, the bond enthalpies are the most important.

The concept of enthalpy of atomization can also be applied to compounds. For example, the following equation describes the enthalpy of atomization of methane:

$$CH_4(g) \rightarrow C(g) + 4H(g) \qquad \Delta H^\ominus = \Delta H^\ominus_{at}[CH_4(g)]$$

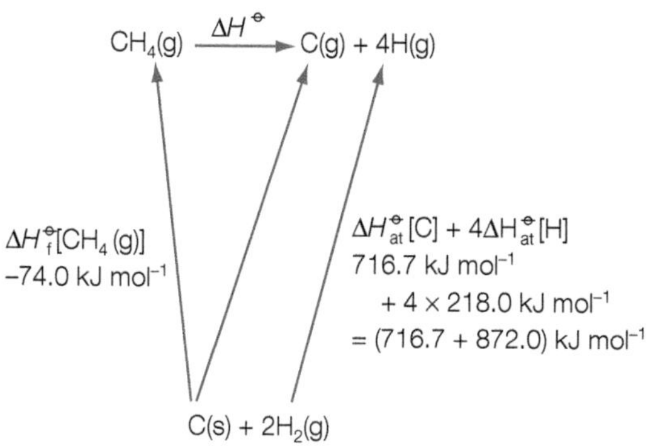

Dividing the standard enthalpy of atomization between four bonds gives an average value for the C–H bond enthalpy. The sum of all the bond enthalpies for a compound is the standard enthalpy of atomization of that compound in the gaseous state. The standard enthalpy of formation of a compound is composed of two terms: the bond enthalpies and the standard enthalpies of atomization of all the atoms, which are themselves derived from the bond enthalpy of the element.

The Hess's law cycle in Figure 15.1 can be used to calculate the average bond enthalpy in methane using the enthalpy of formation of methane and the enthalpies of atomization of carbon and hydrogen:

$$\Delta H^\ominus_f[CH_4(g)] + \Delta H^\ominus = \Delta H^\ominus_{at}[C] + 4\Delta H^\ominus_{at}[H]$$
$$-74.0\,kJ\,mol^{-1} + \Delta H^\ominus = 716.7\,kJ\,mol^{-1} + 872.0\,kJ\,mol^{-1}$$
$$\Delta H^\ominus = 1588.7\,kJ\,mol^{-1} - (-74.0\,kJ\,mol^{-1}) = +1662.7\,kJ\,mol^{-1}$$

■ **Figure 15.1** Hess's law cycle to calculate the average bond enthalpy in methane

Hence, the average C–H bond enthalpy for methane is 416 kJ mol⁻¹.

If similar calculations are performed on molecular liquids, for example tetrachloromethane, $CCl_4(l)$, then the cycle must show the bonds breaking in the gaseous state, rather than the liquid (Figure 15.2).

■ **Figure 15.2**
Hess's law cycle to calculate the average bond enthalpy in tetrachloromethane

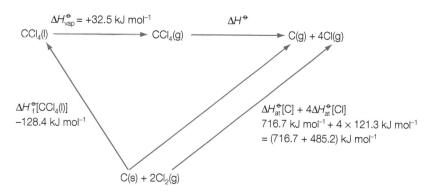

It is essential to include an enthalpy of vaporization term in the bond energy calculation:

$$\Delta H^\ominus_f[CCl_4(l)] + \Delta H^\ominus_{vap} + \Delta H^\ominus = \Delta H^\ominus_{at}[C] + 4\Delta H^\ominus_{at}[Cl]$$
$$-128.4\,kJ\,mol^{-1} + 32.5\,kJ\,mol^{-1} + \Delta H^\ominus = 716.7\,kJ\,mol^{-1} + 485.2\,kJ\,mol^{-1}$$
$$\Delta H^\ominus = 1201.9\,kJ\,mol^{-1} - (-95.9\,kJ\,mol^{-1}) = +1297.8\,kJ\,mol^{-1}$$

Hence, the average C–Cl bond enthalpy for tetrachloromethane is a quarter of this value, i.e. 324 kJ mol⁻¹.

■ Enthalpies of physical change

The standard enthalpy change that accompanies a change in physical state is called the standard enthalpy of transition. The standard enthalpies of fusion and vaporization are two examples of enthalpies of transition.

The standard enthalpy change of vaporization is the enthalpy change which occurs (at constant pressure) when one mole of a pure liquid is completely vaporized under standard conditions. The standard enthalpy change of fusion is the enthalpy change which occurs (at constant pressure) when one mole of a pure solid is completely melted under standard conditions.

The following two thermochemical equations represent the enthalpies of fusion and vaporization of benzene:

$$C_6H_6(s) \rightarrow C_6H_6(l) \quad \Delta H^{\ominus}_{fus} = 11\,kJ\,mol^{-1}$$
$$C_6H_6(l) \rightarrow C_6H_6(g) \quad \Delta H^{\ominus}_{vap} = 353\,kJ\,mol^{-1}$$

Hess's law can be applied to enthalpies of transition. For example, the conversion of ice to water vapour can be regarded as occurring by sublimation:

$$H_2O(s) \rightarrow H_2O(g) \quad \Delta H^{\ominus}_{sub}$$

or as occurring in two steps, first melting (fusion) and then vaporization of the liquid (Figure 15.3):

$$H_2O(s) \rightarrow H_2O(l) \quad \Delta H^{\ominus}_{fus}$$
$$H_2O(l) \rightarrow H_2O(g) \quad \Delta H^{\ominus}_{vap}$$

Overall:

$$H_2O(s) \rightarrow H_2O(g) \quad \Delta H^{\ominus}_{sub} = \Delta H^{\ominus}_{fus} + \Delta H^{\ominus}_{vap}$$

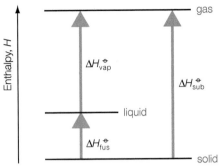

■ **Figure 15.3** The relationship between the enthalpies of fusion, vaporization and sublimation

Figure 15.3 shows that, because all enthalpies of fusion are positive, the enthalpy of sublimation of a substance is greater than its enthalpy of vaporization. Another consequence of Hess's law is that the enthalpy changes for a forward process and its reverse process differ in sign (Figure 15.4). For example, the enthalpy of vaporization of water is $+44\,kJ\,mol^{-1}$ (at 298 K), but the enthalpy of condensation is $-44\,kJ\,mol^{-1}$ (at 298 K).

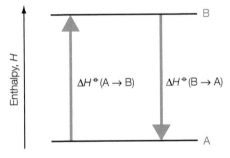

■ **Figure 15.4** A simple application of Hess's law

2 Calculate the enthalpy change when 2.38 g of carbon monoxide vaporizes at its normal boiling point. The enthalpy of vaporization of carbon monoxide is $6.04\,kJ\,mol^{-1}$.

Performing laboratory experiments to measure enthalpy changes, for example single replacement reactions in aqueous solutions

When $50.00\,cm^3$ of $0.100\,mol\,dm^{-3}$ silver(I) nitrate solution, $AgNO_3(aq)$, and $50.00\,cm^3$ of $0.100\,mol\,dm^{-3}$ aqueous hydrochloric acid, $HCl(aq)$, were mixed in an open polystyrene cup (which acted as a simple calorimeter) and the temperature of the reaction mixture was monitored by a data-logger, it was found to increase from 22.20 °C to 23.11 °C. The temperature change is caused by the following reaction:

$$AgNO_3(aq) + HCl(aq) \rightarrow AgCl(s) + HNO_3(aq)$$

Ionically,

$$Ag^+(aq) + Cl^-(aq) \rightarrow AgCl(s)$$

3 Calculate the enthalpy change, ΔH for this reaction in $kJ\,mol^{-1}$, assuming that the combined solution has a mass of 100.00 g and a specific heat capacity of $4.18\,kJ\,kg^{-1}\,K^{-1}$.

4 Calculate the percentage error if the accepted value is $-70\,kJ\,mol^{-1}$. Suggest how the percentage error can be reduced.

Other simple experiments include determining the enthalpy of melting (or crystallization) of ice. If a known mass of ice is introduced into a known mass of hot water at an initial temperature T_1, the system will end up at some new (lower) temperature T_2. Since the heat lost by the water equals the heat gained by the ice, you can calculate the amount of heat used in melting the ice if you know the specific heat capacity of water ($4.187\,kJ\,kg^{-1}\,K^{-1}$) (and assume the ice is at 0 °C). Obviously, if you know the enthalpy of fusion of ice ($+334\,kJ\,kg^{-1}$, as the enthalpy of crystallization is $-334\,kJ\,kg^{-1}$) you could use the same experiment to obtain the heat capacity of water.

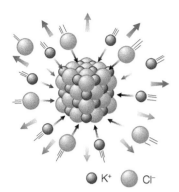

Figure 15.5 The *reverse* of lattice enthalpy is the energy which would be released to the surroundings (short red arrows) if one mole of an ionic compound could form directly from infinitely free gaseous ions rushing together (black arrows) and forming a lattice

Figure 15.6
The lattice energy of potassium chloride, $\Delta H^{\ominus}_{\text{lattice}}$

■ Born–Haber cycle

Lattice enthalpy

The lattice enthalpy ($\Delta H^{\ominus}_{\text{lattice}}$) of an ionic crystal is the heat energy absorbed (at constant pressure) when one mole of solid ionic compound is decomposed to form gaseous ions separated to an infinite distance from each other (under standard thermodynamic conditions). (This is the definition used in the IB *Chemistry data booklet*.)

Note that the sign of the lattice enthalpy must always be included in the thermochemical equation; the *reverse* of lattice enthalpy is the heat energy released (at constant pressure) when one mole of ionic solid is formed from gaseous ions (Figure 15.5).

For example, the lattice enthalpy of potassium chloride is the enthalpy change for the reaction:

$$KCl(s) \rightarrow K^+(g) + Cl^-(g) \qquad \Delta H^{\ominus}_{\text{lattice}} = +720 \, kJ \, mol^{-1}$$

The reaction is illustrated in Figure 15.6. Lattice energies are a measure of the stability of a crystal. The greater the value of the lattice energy, the more energetically stable the lattice. This results in higher melting and boiling points. The size of the lattice energy has an effect on the solubility (if any) of an ionic salt. The size of the lattice energy is controlled by the charges on the ions, their ionic radii and the packing arrangement of the ions (type of lattice).

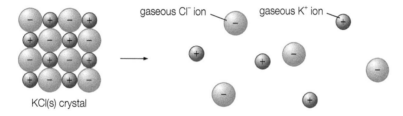

KCl(s) crystal   gaseous Cl⁻ ion   gaseous K⁺ ion

Electron affinity

When an electron is acquired by an atom, energy is released, for example:

$$Cl(g) + e^- \rightarrow Cl^-(g) \qquad \Delta H^{\ominus}_{EA(1)} = -349 \, kJ \, mol^{-1}$$

The **first electron affinity**, $\Delta H^{\ominus}_{EA(1)}$, is the energy released when one mole of gaseous atoms accepts one mole of electrons to form singly charged negative ions.

The **second electron affinity**, $\Delta H^{\ominus}_{EA(2)}$, is the energy absorbed when one mole of gaseous ions with a single negative charge accept one mole of electrons. For example:

$$O^-(g) + e^- \rightarrow O^{2-}(g) \qquad \Delta H^{\ominus}_{EA(2)} = +753 \, kJ \, mol^{-1}$$

5   Write equations with state symbols describing the third electron affinity of nitrogen and the lattice enthalpy for aluminium oxide. Explain why both processes are highly endothermic.

describes the second electron affinity of oxygen. It is always endothermic because energy is required to overcome the mutual repulsion between the negatively charged ion and the electron.

First electron affinities *generally* correlate with electronegativity (Chapter 3). The halogens show clear trends in electronegativity and electron affinity (with the exception of fluorine, which has an unexpectedly low electron affinity) (Table 15.1).

Halogen	Electronegativity (Pauling scale)	First electron affinity/kJ mol⁻¹
Fluorine	4.0	−328
Chlorine	3.2	−349
Bromine	3.0	−325
Iodine	2.7	−295

■ **Table 15.1** Values of electronegativity and first electron affinity for the halogens

 ## Temperature measurements, global warming and the usefulness of indirect measurements

Scientific discovery and evaluation are most often based on direct experimental evidence and determination. However, in certain circumstances the ability to extrapolate from known, defined situations to explore the otherwise inexplorable can be of significant usefulness.

■ **Figure 15.7** The 'calving' of a glacier is indicated by the light blue colour of the newly exposed ice

Historically, one of the key examples of this is the evaluation by Einstein of the significance of Brownian motion, which led to the substantiation of the ideas behind the atomic theory of matter. Atomic theory was under challenge at the time from well-established and prestigious names within the scientific community. The phenomenon of Brownian motion and its interpretation was one major factor in the acceptance of the theory. Yet this acceptance involved interpretation of the unseen atomic world – the motion of sub-microscopic atoms and molecules – in terms of the motion of the seen world – the motion of smoke or dust particles under the microscope.

The use of Hess's law and Born–Haber cycles to put values to otherwise non-achievable parameters of bond energies and chemical interaction is another example of the significant value of controlled interpretation and indirect extrapolation. Indirect evaluation of globally accumulated data is of great usefulness in assessing, and indeed combating, some of the major environmental challenges of our day. Direct temperature measurements across an array of weather stations worldwide have provided evidence for global warming – though some of that evidence has been challenged in recent years in terms of the siting and maintenance of these stations. The conviction that we are observing a real phenomenon, though, is bolstered by the wide range of indirect evidence indicating the reality of this warming. Indirect evidence from retreating glaciers (Figure 15.7), the disappearance of the polar ice sheets, borehole temperature measurements and changes in climate patterns all lend support to the concern that global warming (see Chapter 24 on the accompanying website) and its consequences are a reality.

The accumulation of this data is, and must continue to be, a global, multinational venture if we are to have the most reliable and comprehensive foundation for this indirect evaluation.

■ **Figure 15.8** Baseline biological assessment of the environment within the Arctic Circle

However, international cooperation must take place at a number of research, political, economic and government aid levels if we are to react wisely to prevent some of the consequences and react positively to events inherent in the playing out of the differing aspects of the consequences of global warming.

Island nations in the Pacific – the Maldives and Tuvalu for instance – are under threat from rising sea levels, whereas the prospect of the opening up of the legendary north-west passage in the Arctic has led to the proposal to build a new port on the shores of the Bathurst Inlet within the Arctic Circle. This port would serve as the export route for the minerals mined in some of the largest mines in the world that are located in the region – the Ekati diamond mine, for instance. The impact of the exploitation of the mineral resources of this region on both the lives of the local peoples and the environment requires careful assessment (Figure 15.8).

The issues facing the Arctic region in terms of balancing the interests of nations, peoples and the environment will be an interesting test-bed for those that will face the Antarctic when the treaty which has protected that region expires in the relatively near future.

Sustainable energy

'Sustainable Energy for All' is a United Nations initiative that aims to redress the imbalance of the supply of clean and efficient energy worldwide, to improve energy efficiency and thus reduce energy demand, and to increase the proportion of energy that comes from renewable energy resources.

There are three main objectives of the project that tackle the issues surrounding energy provision at different levels.

■ Ensuring universal access to modern energy services that will improve the economic and social well-being and life experience of peoples who currently have no access to reliable energy provision. Currently one-fifth of the world's population do not have electricity in their homes and 40% use fuel sources based on the burning of animal waste, wood or charcoal in the domestic situation. Provision of electricity in homes will reduce exposure to toxic fumes and enable the better storage of food through refrigeration. It will also have beneficial effects on education, and there are currently projects in various parts of the world for the setting up of basic science laboratories in schools that rely on solar power rather than a wired grid system.

- Improvements in the management of electrical power supplies and their usage will reduce the demand on resources, lengthening the lifetime of the natural resources and lowering the cost of energy to domestic and business users.

- The development of renewable energy resources will relieve the burden on, and use of, fossil fuels. The UN target is to double the share of renewable energy to overall global energy production by the year 2030. As the technology develops and the costs of renewable energy generation fall, then this form of energy can play an increasingly significant role in future government and business plans for energy provision. One key question here is whether nuclear energy has a role in these developments, given the sheer size of the energy demand, particularly in the developed world. No less an environmental advocate then James Lovelock, the major proponent of the 'Gaia hypothesis' has advocated that nuclear energy must play a part in modern energy resourcing.

■ Lattice enthalpies of ionic compounds

In an ionic compound, the lattice enthalpy depends on the attractive electrostatic forces operating between oppositely charged ions in the crystal. The larger the electrostatic forces of attraction, the larger the size of the lattice enthalpy.

According to Coulomb's law, the attractive force F operating between two adjacent oppositely charged ions in contact (Figure 15.9) can be expressed as follows:

$$F \propto \frac{\text{charge on positive ion} \times \text{charge on negative ion}}{d^2}$$

where d represents the distance between the nuclei of the two ions.

Ionic charge has a large effect on the size of the lattice enthalpy. For example, the lattice enthalpy of magnesium oxide, MgO, is about four times as great as the lattice enthalpy of sodium fluoride, NaF:

$$\Delta H^{\ominus}_{\text{lattice}}[\text{MgO(s)}] = +3791\,\text{kJ mol}^{-1}$$
$$\Delta H^{\ominus}_{\text{lattice}}[\text{NaF(s)}] = +930\,\text{kJ mol}^{-1}$$

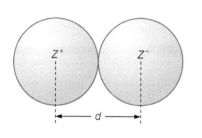

Figure 15.9 Ions with charges of Z^+ and Z^- separated by a distance of d

This is largely due to the doubling of the charges of the ions. The sum of the ionic radii and the lattice structures of magnesium oxide and sodium fluoride are similar.

The effect of ionic radius can be clearly seen in the sodium halides (Table 15.2). The smaller the distance between the centres of the ions (sum of the ionic radii), the larger the value of the lattice enthalpy.

■ Table 15.2 The effect of ionic radius on lattice enthalpy

Sodium halide	Radius of halide ion/nm	Distance between centres of ions/nm	Lattice enthalpy/kJ mol⁻¹
NaF (Na⁺)(F⁻)	0.133	0.235	+930
NaCl (Na⁺)(Cl⁻)	0.181	0.283	+790
NaBr (Na⁺)(Br⁻)	0.196	0.298	+754
NaI (Na⁺)(I⁻)	0.220	0.322	+705

Lattice type

The relative sizes of the cation and anion determine the type of lattice an ionic compound adopts. For example, although caesium and sodium are both in the same group of the periodic table, the chlorides crystallize with different types of lattice. Sodium chloride adopts the simple cubic structure (Chapter 4), whereas caesium chloride adopts the lattice shown in Figure 15.10. In caesium chloride, the caesium ions cannot get as close to the chloride ions as the smaller sodium ions. Eight caesium ions can pack around a chloride ion if they are positioned at the corners of a cube. The structure of ionic lattices is determined by X-ray crystallography (see Chapter 21, and Chapter 22 on the accompanying website).

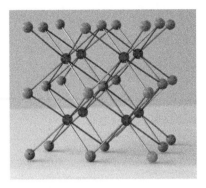

■ **Figure 15.10** A model of the caesium chloride lattice: red balls represent caesium ions; green balls represent chloride ions

Using Born–Haber cycles to calculate enthalpy changes

Lattice enthalpies *cannot* be found directly from experiments (partly because ionic crystals form ion pairs when heated, not free gaseous ions). Therefore lattice enthalpies must be calculated *indirectly* from other known enthalpy changes of reaction using a **Born–Haber cycle**. This is an enthalpy level diagram derived from Hess's law; it is used to follow the enthalpy changes which occur when an ionic compound is formed from its chemical elements and gaseous ions (Figure 15.11).

Consider the reaction between sodium metal and chlorine gas to form sodium chloride:

$$Na(s) + \tfrac{1}{2} Cl_2(g) \rightarrow NaCl(s) \qquad \Delta H_f^\ominus = -411\,kJ\,mol^{-1}$$

This reaction can be described by an equivalent pathway that involves a number of steps, each with its own individual enthalpy change.

■ **Figure 15.11**
The main features of a generalized Born–Haber cycle

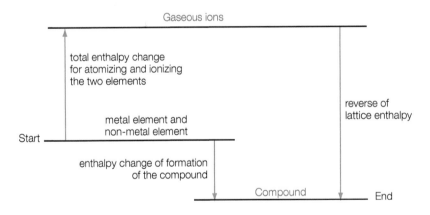

■ The atoms in the solid sodium must be converted into gaseous sodium atoms:

$$Na(s) \rightarrow Na(g) \qquad \Delta H_{at}^\ominus = +108\,kJ\,mol^{-1}$$

This is the enthalpy change of atomization of sodium.

■ The gaseous chlorine molecules are then dissociated into gaseous chlorine atoms:

$$\tfrac{1}{2} Cl_2(g) \rightarrow Cl(g) \qquad \Delta H_{at}^\ominus = +121\,kJ\,mol^{-1}$$

This is the enthalpy change of atomization of chlorine. It is equivalent to *half* the bond enthalpy of the chlorine molecule.

■ Once gaseous sodium and chlorine atoms are formed, electron transfer can take place. The sodium atom loses its outer electron and donates it to the chlorine atom, which forms the chloride ion:

$$Na(g) \rightarrow Na^+(g) + e^- \qquad \Delta H^{\ominus}_{IE(1)} = +496\,kJ\,mol^{-1}$$
$$Cl(g) + e^- \rightarrow Cl^-(g) \qquad \Delta H^{\ominus}_{EA(1)} = -349\,kJ\,mol^{-1}$$

These energy changes are the first ionization energy ($\Delta H^{\ominus}_{IE(1)}$) of sodium and the first electron affinity ($\Delta H^{\ominus}_{EA(1)}$) of chlorine.

■ The oppositely charged ions exert powerful attractive electrostatic forces and form an ionic lattice of solid sodium chloride.

$$Na^+(g) + Cl^-(g) \rightarrow NaCl(s) \qquad -\Delta H^{\ominus}_{lattice} = -790\,kJ\,mol^{-1}$$

or

$$NaCl(s) \rightarrow Na^+(g) + Cl^-(g) \qquad \Delta H^{\ominus}_{lattice} = +790\,kJ\,mol^{-1}$$

The reactions leading to the formation of sodium chloride from its elements are summarized in graphic form in Figure 15.12.

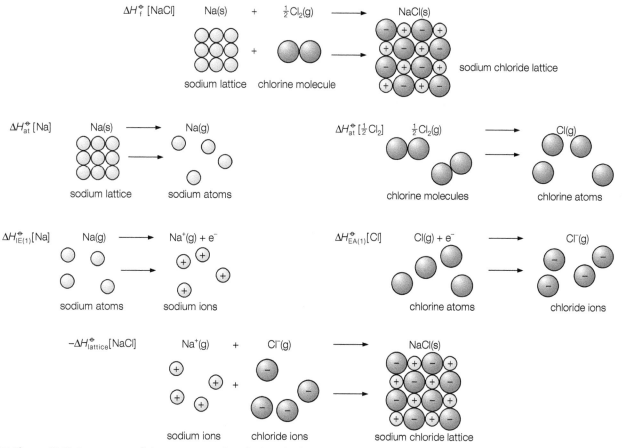

■ **Figure 15.12** A summary of the steps occurring during the formation of sodium chloride from sodium and chlorine in their standard states

The enthalpy changes described can be used to construct a Born–Haber cycle for sodium chloride (Figure 15.13). The Born–Haber cycle can be used to calculate an individual enthalpy change if all the others are known. The unknown value is usually the lattice enthalpy.

The Born–Haber cycle clearly shows that the principal reason why stable ionic compounds form from their elements is that the reverse of the lattice enthalpy is very exothermic. Large amounts of energy are released during lattice formation which more than compensate for a number of endothermic steps.

■ **Figure 15.13**
The Born–Haber cycle
for sodium chloride

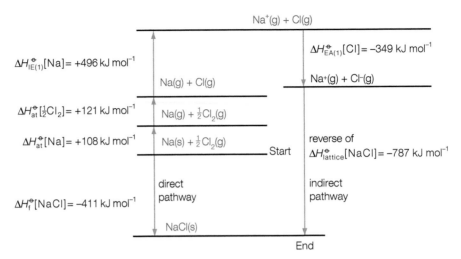

Note that polyatomic ions, such as NH_4^+, NO_3^-, CO_3^{2-}, OH^- and SO_4^{2-}, cannot be used in Born–Haber cycle calculations as they do *not* have atomization energies, ionization energies or electron affinities. Lattice energies for these compounds have to be calculated theoretically.

Constructing Born–Haber cycles for group 1 and 2 oxides and chlorides

Worked example

Use the Born–Haber cycle shown in Figure 15.14 to calculate the value of the lattice enthalpy for magnesium chloride.

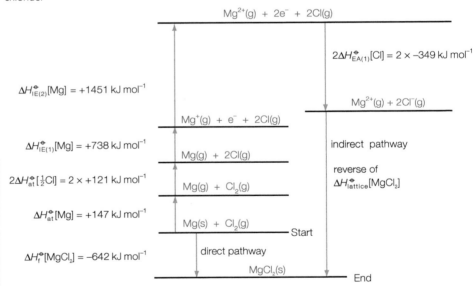

■ **Figure 15.14** The Born–Haber cycle for magnesium chloride

Applying Hess's law:

indirect pathway = direct pathway

$\Delta H^{\ominus}_{at}[Mg] + 2 \times \Delta H^{\ominus}_{at}[Cl_2] + \Delta H^{\ominus}_{IE(1)}[Mg] + \Delta H^{\ominus}_{IE(2)}[Mg] + 2 \times \Delta H^{\ominus}_{EA(1)}[Cl] + (-\Delta H^{\ominus}_{lattice}[MgCl_2]) = (\Delta H^{\ominus}_{f}[MgCl_2])$

where subscripts IE(1) and IE(2) represent the first and second ionization energies and EA(1) represents the first electron affinity.

$+147\,kJ\,mol^{-1} + (2 \times 121\,kJ\,mol^{-1}) + 738\,kJ\,mol^{-1} + 1451\,kJ\,mol^{-1} + (2 \times -349\,kJ\,mol^{-1}) + -\Delta H^{\ominus}_{lattice}[MgCl_2]$

$= -642\,kJ\,mol^{-1}$

$-\Delta H^{\ominus}_{lattice}[MgCl_2] = -642\,kJ\,mol^{-1} - 1880\,kJ\,mol^{-1} = 2522\,kJ\,mol^{-1}$

$\Delta H^{\ominus}_{lattice} = -2520\,kJ\,mol^{-1}$ (to 3 significant figures)

With ions possessing charges greater than 1 (+ or −), second ionization energies (or higher) are needed for the metal and second electron affinities (or higher) are needed for the non-metal. The need for more than one of a particular ion also multiplies the relevant enthalpy value by that number. This is illustrated in Figure 15.14 for magnesium chloride and in Figure 15.15 for calcium oxide.

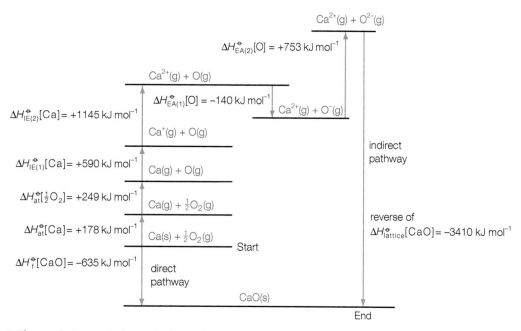

■ **Figure 15.15** Born–Haber cycle for calcium oxide

Large negative values of enthalpy of formation are typical of stable ionic compounds. This can be illustrated by examining the Born–Haber cycle for the hypothetical ionic compound, CaCl [Ca^+Cl^-] (Figure 15.16). Using a theoretically calculated lattice enthalpy in the Born–Haber cycle, CaCl has an *estimated* enthalpy of formation of −69 kJ mol⁻¹. In contrast, $CaCl_2$ has an enthalpy of formation of −795 kJ mol⁻¹.

6 Construct Born–Haber cycles for sodium and calcium oxides using the data below, and the IB *Chemistry data booklet* calculate their lattice energies.
Standard enthalpy of formation of sodium oxide: −416 kJ mol⁻¹
Standard enthalpy of formation of calcium oxide: −635 kJ mol⁻¹

7 The Born-Haber cycle can be used to calculate any missing energy term, not just the lattice enthalpy. Using the data below, calculate the first electron affinity of chlorine.

Standard enthalpy of formation of rubidium chloride: −431 kJ mol⁻¹

Lattice enthalpy of rubidium chloride: +695 kJ mol⁻¹

First ionization energy of rubidium: +403 kJ mol⁻¹

Standard enthalpy of atomization of rubidium: +86 kJ mol⁻¹

Bond dissociation energy of chlorine molecule: +242 kJ mol⁻¹

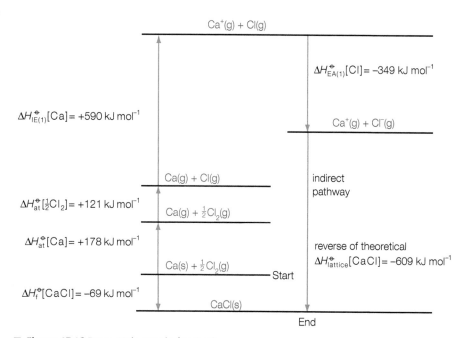

■ **Figure 15.16** Born–Haber cycle for CaCl

Utilization: Other energy cycles

The carbon cycle

 Carbon exists in its elemental form as diamonds and as graphite (Chapter 4). Coal contains up to 90% carbon and it is also present in fossil fuels (see Chapter 24 on the accompanying website), in carbonate minerals and in all living organisms. As carbon dioxide, carbon also accounts for about 0.046% by mass of the Earth's atmosphere. The carbon dioxide in the air forms an essential part of the carbon cycle (Figure 15.17), in which carbon dioxide is absorbed by plants during photosynthesis and regenerated by animals and plants during respiration and by the combustion of fossil fuels.

It had been assumed that the proportion of carbon dioxide remains constant and so it was put at the centre of the carbon cycle. However, there is increasing international concern about the increasing level of carbon dioxide in the atmosphere, which is believed by many scientists to contributing to the enhanced greenhouse effect and hence climate change (see Chapter 24 on the accompanying website).

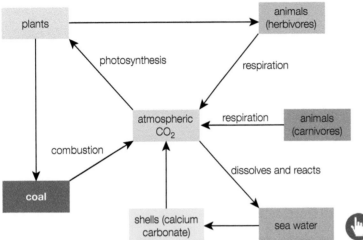

■ **Figure 15.17**

The Krebs cycle

The enzyme-catalysed reactions that living organisms use to generate the energy they need and to prepare the molecules they require, are collectively termed 'metabolism'. In anabolism, enzyme-catalysed reactions are used to make large complex molecules, for example the synthesis of starch, cellulose and proteins. Photosynthesis is an example of an anabolic reaction. These processes require an input of energy from ATP. In catabolism, nutrient molecules are hydrolysed under enzyme control to provide smaller and simpler molecules for synthesis and also to supply energy (to convert ADP back to ATP).

An important catabolic reaction in organisms that use molecular oxygen for respiration is the Krebs cycle (Figure 15.18). This is a series of nine enzyme-catalysed reactions that result in the formation of carbon dioxide, release of energy (via ATP synthesis) and the production of reducing power. They also result in the formation of metabolic intermediates that can be converted to a wide range of useful molecules. This cycle of reactions takes place in the mitochondria of plant and animal cells.

In the first step of the cycle, acetyl coenzyme A (a C_2 molecule formed from glucose) reacts with oxaloacetic acid (C_4) to form citric acid (C_6). This undergoes a series of eight reactions in a metabolic cycle that re-forms oxaloacetic and releases two molecules of CO_2 (in decarboxylation reactions).

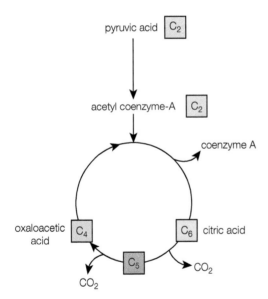

■ **Figure 15.18** Krebs cycle

Electron transfer in biology

Electron transfer reactions are central to many of the metabolic processes necessary for the survival of all living organisms. These reactions depend upon the approach of an electron donor and an electron acceptor. In biology, intermolecular electron transfer is common and occurs between sites on different proteins. This leads to electron-transfer chains that function as a series of consecutive electron-transfer reactions between metal sites within a protein or group of proteins (Chapter 9). Electron-transfer chains are important in photosynthesis and respiration (see Chapter 23 on the accompanying website).

■ Dissolving ionic solids in water

Many ionic compounds, such as sodium chloride, dissolve well in water to form solutions. Others, such as silver chloride, are almost insoluble. When an ionic substance dissolves, the lattice of the ionic crystal needs to be broken up (Figure 15.19). Lattice enthalpies are always endothermic, so if the compound is to dissolve the energy needed to achieve this must be supplied from enthalpy changes that occur during the dissolving process.

■ **Figure 15.19**
The formation of a sodium chloride solution from a sodium chloride lattice

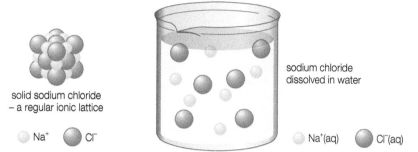

solid sodium chloride – a regular ionic lattice

Na$^+$ Cl$^-$

sodium chloride dissolved in water

Na$^+$(aq)   Cl$^-$(aq)

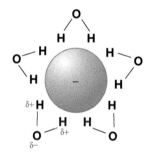

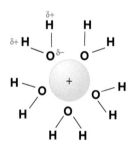

■ **Figure 15.20** Hydrated anion and cation

The ions in the crystal lattice become separated as they become hydrated by water molecules (Figure 15.20). Water molecules are polar (Chapter 4) and are attracted to both positive and negative ions. The hydration process involves the cations and anions being surrounded by a number of water molecules. Ion–dipole bonds are formed and hence the hydration process is an exothermic process.

The separation of the ions in the lattice is strongly endothermic and the hydration of the ions is an exothermic process. The enthalpy change of solution is the difference between these two enthalpy changes.

The enthalpy change of solution, $\Delta H^{\ominus}_{sol}$, is the enthalpy change when one mole of solute dissolves in an infinite volume of water. The value cannot be determined directly by experiment and must be found by a process of extrapolation. In practice, there comes a point when further dilution has no measurable effect on the value of the enthalpy change of solution, and this may be taken as infinite dilution.

The enthalpy change of hydration, $\Delta H^{\ominus}_{hyd}$, is the enthalpy change when a mole of gaseous ions becomes hydrated by a large excess of water and refers to the process

$$A^{n+}(g) \rightarrow A^{n+}(aq)$$

where the concentration of A^{n+} in the aqueous solution approaches zero. Enthalpies of hydration for ions are always negative because strong ion–dipole bonds are formed when the gas phase ion is surrounded by water. Small, highly charged ions have the most negative values.

The overall process of dissolving an ionic solid can be represented by a Hess's law cycle. Figure 15.21 shows the energy cycle for sodium chloride. Ionic substances that are soluble *generally* have a large negative value for the enthalpy change of solution. Conversely, insoluble ionic substances *generally* have a large positive value for the enthalpy of solution.

However, these are 'rules of thumb' and a number of exceptions occur. This is because free energy changes determine solubility and they include entropy changes. Figure 15.22 is an enthalpy level diagram that shows the processes which occur when silver chloride, an almost insoluble salt, is placed in water. Figure 15.23 is an energy level diagram that shows the processes which occur when silver fluoride, a very soluble salt, is placed in water. Note the larger positive enthalpy of solution for silver chloride compared to silver fluoride.

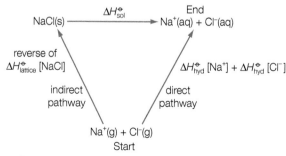

■ **Figure 15.21** Hess's law energy cycle summarizing the dissolving process for sodium chloride

■ **Figure 15.22** Enthalpy level diagram for the dissolving of silver chloride

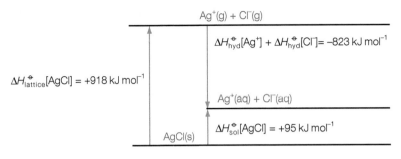

■ **Figure 15.23** Enthalpy level diagram for the dissolving of silver fluoride

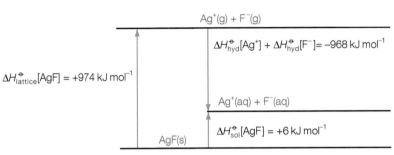

Constructing energy cycles from hydration, lattice and solution enthalpies

The hydration of ions promotes dissolving and helps to supply the energy needed to separate the ions from the lattice. The differences between the enthalpies of hydration of the ions and the lattice enthalpy gives the enthalpy of solution, which can be measured experimentally. Figure 15.24 represents a generalized dissolution energy cycle for an ionic compound.

Figure 15.25 shows the energy cycle applied to sodium hydroxide. Dissolving an ionic compound can be considered as two steps: step 1 is the breakdown of the lattice to form gaseous ions (the lattice enthalpy) and step 2 is the hydration of these ions, as polar water molecules are attracted to the ions. Step 3 involves the overall enthalpy of solution for sodium hydroxide.

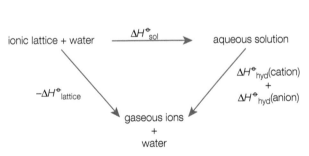

■ **Figure 15.24** A generalized energy cycle to show the dissolving (dissolution) of an ionic solid

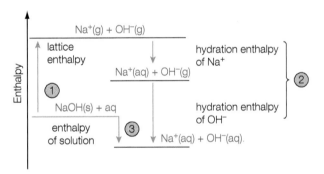

■ **Figure 15.25** An energy cycle for the dissolving (dissolution) of sodium hydroxide

---

8   Draw an energy cycle for the dissolving (dissolution) of ammonium chloride. It dissolves endothermically.

9   Given the following data, determine the enthalpy change, ΔH, for dissolving potassium iodide, KI, in water, $KI(s) \rightarrow K^+(aq) + I^-(aq)$. The lattice enthalpy for potassium iodide is $650\,kJ\,mol^{-1}$ and the enthalpies of hydration for the potassium and iodide ions are $-340\,kJ\,mol^{-1}$ and $-287\,kJ\,mol^{-1}$ respectively.

Relating the size and charge of ions to lattice and hydration enthalpies
Hydration enthalpy

The trend is that the smaller the ionic radius, the greater (more exothermic) is the hydration energy. One reason for this is that the water molecules can get closer to the centre of the charge so the attractive forces (ion–dipole forces) are increased. This trend can be clearly observed in group 1 elements (Table 15.3).

The greater the charge on the ion, the greater the affinity for water molecules and the more exothermic the hydration process will be. This is shown in Table 15.4 for the first three ions from period 3 elements.

■ **Table 15.3** Hydration enthalpies for group 1 cations

Cation	$\Delta H^\ominus_{hyd}$/kJ mol^{-1}
Li$^+$	−538
Na$^+$	−424
K$^+$	−340
Rb$^+$	−315
Cs$^+$	−291

Cation	$\Delta H^\ominus_{hyd}$/kJ mol^{-1}
Na$^+$	−418
Mg^{2+}	−1963
Al^{3+}	−4741

■ **Table 15.4** Hydration enthalpies for the sodium, magnesium and aluminium cations

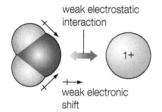
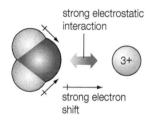

■ **Figure 15.26** The effect of charge density of a cation on the hydration enthalpy

The hydration enthalpy will depend on the charge density of the ion (Figure 15.26). Charge density increases with an increase in charge and a decrease in ionic radius.

Lattice enthalpy

The lattice enthalpy is an indication of the strength of the ionic bonds between the ions present – the more exothermic the value, the stronger the ionic bonding and the more stable the lattice.

There will be more attraction between 2+ and 2− ions in a lattice and so the values for lattice enthalpy should be more exothermic, resulting in a more stable lattice. For example, compare the lattice energies of the oxides and chlorides of magnesium and sodium:

$$\Delta H^\ominus_{lattice}[MgO] = 3791\,kJ\,mol^{-1} \qquad \Delta H^\ominus_{lattice}[MgCl_2] = 2540\,kJ\,mol^{-1}$$
$$\Delta H^\ominus_{lattice}[Na_2O] = 2478\,kJ\,mol^{-1} \qquad \Delta H^\ominus_{lattice}[NaCl] = 790\,kJ\,mol^{-1}$$

As the ionic radius increases, the charge is spread over a greater surface area. Therefore this will mean a decrease in the electrostatic forces of attraction between oppositely charged ions, a less exothermic lattice enthalpy and a less stable lattice.

For example, compare the lattice enthalpies of group 1 chlorides and group 2 oxides:

$$\Delta H^\ominus_{lattice}[NaCl] = 790\,kJ\,mol^{-1} \qquad \Delta H^\ominus_{lattice}[MgO] = 3791\,kJ\,mol^{-1}$$
$$\Delta H^\ominus_{lattice}[KCl] = 720\,kJ\,mol^{-1} \qquad \Delta H^\ominus_{lattice}[CaO] = 3401\,kJ\,mol^{-1}$$
$$\Delta H^\ominus_{lattice}[RbCl] = 695\,kJ\,mol^{-1} \qquad \Delta H^\ominus_{lattice}[SrO] = 3223\,kJ\,mol^{-1}$$

15.2 Entropy and spontaneity *– a reaction is spontaneous if the overall transformation leads to an increase in total entropy (system plus surroundings); the direction of spontaneous change always increases the total entropy of the universe at the expense of energy available to do useful work; this is known as the second law of thermodynamics*

■ Entropy

Entropy can be regarded (in a crude and simplified way) as a measure of the disorder or dispersal of energy in a system. Entropy is given the symbol S. The disorder refers to the arrangement of particles (atoms, ions or molecules) and the kinetic energies of the particles in a system.

For example, comparing an ionic solid and a gas (maintained at the same temperature), the gas has a significantly greater entropy because its particles are moving rapidly in all directions. In an ionic solid the particles are in fixed positions within a lattice.

A collection of particles with a larger range of kinetic energies has a greater entropy than a sample of the same amount of particles which have a smaller range of kinetic energies. (This corresponds to a high temperature and a lower temperature.)

Effect of a change in temperature

When the temperature is raised, disorder and hence entropy increases. For example, the particles of solids vibrate more, which makes the arrangement of their particles slightly less orderly. The particles in liquids and solutions move (on average) faster, increasing the disorder of the system. The reverse changes take place when the temperature is lowered (Figure 15.27).

Effect of a change of state

The disorder of the particles increases from solid to liquid to gas (of the same substance), increasing entropy (Figure 15.28). The particle arrangement becomes more orderly when a change in state occurs from gas to liquid to solid, hence the entropy decreases.

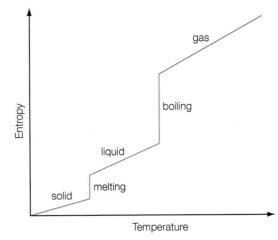

■ **Figure 15.27** Entropy changes with temperature

■ **Figure 15.28** Effect of changes in state on entropy

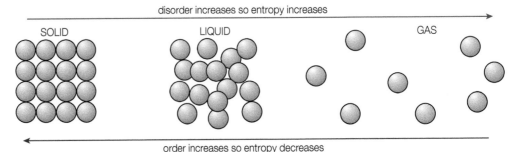

Effect of a change in the number of particles

If the number of particles increases, disorder and hence entropy increases. This is especially significant in reactions involving gases, for example the thermal decomposition of dinitrogen tetroxide:

$$N_2O_4(g) \rightarrow 2NO_2(g)$$

Conversely, the entropy decreases when the number of particles decreases, for example the hydrogenation of ethene:

$$CH_2{=}CH_2(g) + H_2(g) \rightarrow C_2H_6(g)$$

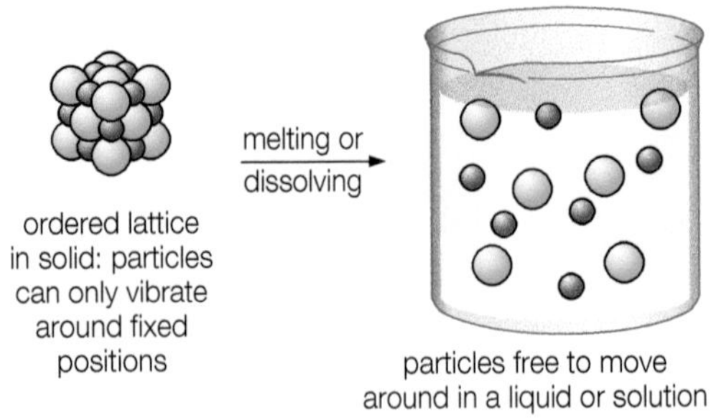

Effect of mixing of particles

The mixing of particles increases disorder, resulting in an increase in entropy (Figures 15.29 and 15.30). If the two sets of particles have different average kinetic energies (that is, different temperatures), then the kinetic energy is randomly dispersed in collisions until a new equilibrium temperature is attained.

ordered lattice in solid: particles can only vibrate around fixed positions

melting or dissolving

particles free to move around in a liquid or solution

■ **Figure 15.29** A generalized illustration showing that entropy increases when particles are mixed during melting or dissolving

■ **Figure 15.30** Two gas jars separated by a removable partition: the gas particles spread out between the two gas jars when the partition is removed, increasing disorder and hence increasing entropy

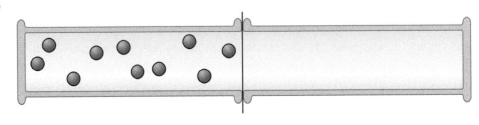

The second law of thermodynamics

The second law of thermodynamics states that the total entropy of the universe tends to increase. This usually means that for a chemical reaction or a physical change to take place, the entropy of the system (the reactants) and their surroundings must increase. Some chemical reactions and physical changes *appear* to have a decrease in entropy but this is because the entropy of the surroundings increases by a greater amount, giving an overall increase in entropy in the universe (Figure 15.31).

The system is the sample or reaction mixture. Outside the system are the surroundings, which include the apparatus. The universe is the system plus the surroundings (Figure 15.32).

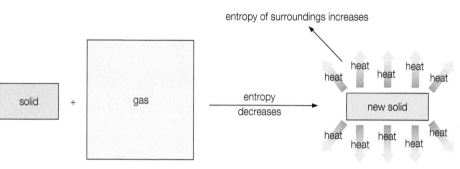

■ **Figure 15.31** A reaction involving the formation of a solid from a solid and a gas. The small decrease in entropy in the system is accompanied by an even larger increase in entropy in the surroundings

■ **Figure 15.32** A diagram illustrating the thermodynamic concepts of system and surroundings

Predicting the sign of a change in entropy

In many chemical reactions and physical processes it is possible to predict the sign of the entropy change (of the system), ΔS, by examining the reactants and products in the balanced equation.

If the products are more disordered than the reactants, then the entropy change (of the system), ΔS, is positive. If the products are less disordered than the reactants, then the entropy change (of the system), ΔS, is negative.

Some of the more common examples are summarized in Table 15.5. The largest entropy changes occur when a gas is produced from a liquid or solid (or vice versa) and when there is a change in the number of gas molecules.

■ **Figure 15.33** Ice cubes melting (a positive entropy change)

■ **Figure 15.34** Condensation of steam (a negative entropy change)

Chemical reaction or physical change	Entropy change	Example
Melting (Figure 15.33)	Increase	$H_2O(s) \rightarrow H_2O(l)$
Freezing	Decrease	$H_2O(l) \rightarrow H_2O(s)$
Boiling	Large increase	$H_2O(l) \rightarrow H_2O(g)$
Condensing (Figure 15.34)	Large decrease	$H_2O(g) \rightarrow H_2O(l)$
Sublimation	Very large increase	$I_2(s) \rightarrow I_2(g)$
Vapour deposition	Very large decrease	$I_2(g) \rightarrow I_2(s)$
Dissolving a solute to form a solution	Generally an increase (except with highly charged ions)	$NaCl(s) + (aq) \rightarrow NaCl(aq)$
Precipitation	Large decrease	$Pb^{2+}(aq) + 2Cl^-(aq) \rightarrow PbCl_2(s)$
Crystallization from a solution	Decrease	$NaCl(aq) \rightarrow NaCl(s)$
Chemical reaction: solid or liquid forming a gas	Large increase	$CaCO_3(s) \rightarrow CaO(s) + CO_2(g)$
Chemical reaction: gases forming a solid or liquid	Large decrease	$2H_2S(g) + SO_2(g) \rightarrow 3S(s) + 2H_2O(l)$
Increase in number of moles of gas	Large increase	$2NH_3(g) \rightarrow N_2(g) + 3H_2(g)$

■ **Table 15.5** Qualitative entropy changes (of the system) for some common reactions and physical changes

Predicting whether a change will result in an increase or decrease in entropy by considering the states of the reactants and products

Consider the following reaction:

$$CO(g) + H_2O(g) \rightarrow CO_2(g) + H_2(g)$$

The entropy change will be approximately zero, since there are equal amounts of gases on both sides of the equation. Gases have relatively high values of entropy compared to solids and liquids (Figure 15.35). Hence, the sign of the entropy change of a reaction can be deduced by simply considering changes in the amounts of gases.

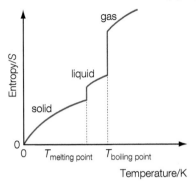

■ **Figure 15.35** Variation of entropy with temperature for a pure substance undergoing melting and boiling

10 Predict whether the following reactions and changes will result in an increase, decrease or little change in entropy. Consider the stoichiometry of the reaction and the physical state of the reactants and products.

a $H_2(g) + Br_2(g) \rightarrow 2HBr(g)$
b $H_2O_2(l) \rightarrow H_2O_2(s)$
c $Cr^{3+}(aq) + 6H_2O(l) \rightarrow [Cr(H_2O)_6]^{3+}(aq)$
d $Hg(l) \rightarrow Hg(g)$
e $AgNO_3(s) \rightarrow AgNO_3(aq)$
f $CaO(s) + CO_2(g) \rightarrow CaCO_3(s)$
g $H^+(aq) + OH^-(aq) \rightarrow H_2O(l)$
h $2HCl(g) + Br_2(l) \rightarrow 2HBr(g) + Cl_2(g)$
i $SO_2(g) + \frac{1}{2}O_2(g) \rightarrow SO_3(g)$
j $H_2(g) \rightarrow 2H(g)$

Calculating entropy changes

A change in entropy is represented by ΔS. The units of entropy, S, and of entropy change, ΔS, are both joules per kelvin per mole, $J\,K^{-1}\,mol^{-1}$. Entropy values are absolute values and can be measured experimentally (via specific heat capacities). (It is also possible to calculate entropy values theoretically, as for lattice enthalpy.)

The value of an entropy change can be calculated from absolute values of entropies using the following expression:

standard entropy change = sum of entropies of products − sum of entropies of reactants

In symbols this can be expressed as:

$$\Delta S^\ominus = \sum S^\ominus[\text{products}] - \sum S^\ominus[\text{reactants}]$$

Entropy values (under standard thermodynamic conditions) for selected organic compounds are listed on page 12 of the IB *Chemistry data booklet*.

Worked example

Calculate the entropy change that occurs during the complete combustion of ethane:

$$C_2H_6(g) + 3\tfrac{1}{2}O_2(g) \rightarrow 2CO_2(g) + 3H_2O(l)$$

$S^\ominus_{[C_2H_6(g)]} = 230\,J\,K^{-1}\,mol^{-1}$

$S^\ominus_{[O_2(g)]} = 205\,J\,K^{-1}\,mol^{-1}$

$S^\ominus_{[CO_2(g)]} = 214\,J\,K^{-1}\,mol^{-1}$

$S^\ominus_{[H_2O(l)]} = 70\,J\,K^{-1}\,mol^{-1}$

$\Delta S^\ominus = \sum S^\ominus[\text{products}] - \sum S^\ominus[\text{reactants}]$

$\Delta S = [(2 \times 214) + (3 \times 70)] - [230 + (3.5 \times 205)]$

$\quad = -310\,J\,K^{-1}\,mol^{-1}$

As expected, because of the decrease in the amount of gas (from 4.5 moles to 2 moles), there is an increase in the order of the system, hence the entropy change is negative. Note that, in contrast to standard enthalpy changes of formation, the absolute entropy values of elements, such as oxygen in this example, are *not* zero (under standard thermodynamic conditions).

Calculating values of entropy changes (ΔS) from given standard entropy values ($S^\ominus$)

The entropy change, ΔS, for a reaction is given by the following expression:

$$\Delta S^\ominus = \sum S^\ominus[\text{products}] - \sum S^\ominus[\text{reactants}]$$

11 Calculate the entropy change for the following reaction at 298 K:

$$4Fe(s) + 3O_2(g) \rightarrow 2Fe_2O_3(s)$$

$S^\ominus[Fe(s)] = 27.3\,J\,K^{-1}\,mol^{-1}$; $S^\ominus[O_2(s)] = 205.0\,J\,K^{-1}\,mol^{-1}$; and $S^\ominus[Fe_2O_3(s)] = 87.4\,J\,K^{-1}\,mol^{-1}$

■ Spontaneity and the Gibbs free energy

Chemists want to know whether a physical change or chemical reaction is spontaneous under standard conditions (1 atm pressure and 298 K). A spontaneous process has a natural tendency to occur. A spontaneous process involves an increase in the entropy of the universe.

Some spontaneous processes need no initiation, for example:

■ the evaporation of water

■ the dissolving of sucrose in water to form a solution

■ the diffusion of gases.

Some spontaneous chemical processes may need initiation, for example:

■ hydrogen reacts rapidly with oxygen to form water if a small brief spark is applied

■ carbon reacts with the oxygen in the air when ignited. The reaction then produces its own heat.

Spontaneous processes may occur very quickly or very slowly.

Some reactions and processes are non-spontaneous, for example copper does not react with dilute hydrochloric acid and water does not freeze (under standard thermodynamic conditions). A non-spontaneous process would result in a decrease in the entropy of the universe.

However, some processes and reactions which are non-spontaneous under standard conditions may become spontaneous when the temperature is increased or when energy is supplied continuously from an external source. For example, the decomposition of water into hydrogen and oxygen is a non-spontaneous process under standard thermodynamic conditions. However, water will undergo decomposition into hydrogen and oxygen when an electric current is passed through it (Chapter 19). The decomposition stops immediately when the electrical energy is no longer supplied.

The spontaneity of a process or chemical reaction is determined by the sign of the Gibbs free energy change, $\Delta G^\ominus$. It is calculated from the following relationship (Gibbs equation):

$$\Delta G^\ominus = \Delta H^\ominus - T\Delta S^\ominus$$

where T represents the absolute temperature, $\Delta S^\ominus$ represents the entropy change occurring in the system (chemicals) and $\Delta H^\ominus$ represents the enthalpy change (Chapter 5).

The Gibbs free energy change as a criterion of spontaneity is summarized as follows:

■ If the Gibbs free energy change, $\Delta G^\ominus$, is negative then the reaction or process will be spontaneous.

■ If the Gibbs free energy change, $\Delta G^\ominus$, is positive then the reaction or process will be non-spontaneous.

■ If the Gibbs free energy change, $\Delta G^\ominus$, is zero, then the reaction or process will be at equilibrium: the rate of the forward reaction will equal the rate of the backward reaction (see Chapter 7).

($\Delta G = \Delta G^\ominus$ when all the reactants and products are in their standard states, with any solutions having a concentration of $1\,mol\,dm^{-3}$.)

Worked example

Calculate the Gibbs free energy change for the following reaction under standard conditions:

$$N_2(g) + 3H_2(g) \rightarrow 2NH_3(g) \qquad \Delta H^{\ominus} = -95.4\,kJ\,mol^{-1}; \Delta S^{\ominus} = -198.3\,J\,K^{-1}\,mol^{-1}$$

$$\Delta G^{\ominus} = \Delta H^{\ominus} - T\Delta S^{\ominus}$$

$$\Delta G^{\ominus} = -95.4\,kJ\,mol^{-1} - 298\,K \times -0.1983\,kJ\,K^{-1}\,mol^{-1}$$

(Note the conversion from $J\,K^{-1}\,mol^{-1}$ to $kJ\,K^{-1}\,mol^{-1}$ for the entropy change – this is because the units of Gibbs free energy changes are $kJ\,mol^{-1}$.)

$$\Delta G^{\ominus} = -36.3\,kJ\,mol^{-1}$$

The negative sign indicates that the reaction is spontaneous at this temperature.

Calculate the temperature above which the reaction ceases to occur spontaneously.

$$\Delta G^{\ominus} = 0 = \Delta H^{\ominus} - T\Delta S^{\ominus}$$

$$\Delta H^{\ominus} = T\Delta S^{\ominus}$$

$$T = \frac{\Delta H}{\Delta S} = \frac{-95\,400\,kJ\,mol^{-1}}{198.3\,kJ\,K^{-1}\,mol^{-1}} = 481\,K = 208\,°C$$

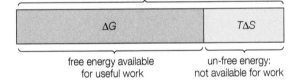

total energy change
at constant temperature
ΔH

| ΔG | $T\Delta S$ |

free energy available
for useful work

un-free energy:
not available for work

■ **Figure 15.36** A diagram showing how an enthalpy change can be split into two parts: $\Delta H = \Delta G + T\Delta S$

CaCO₃

CaO

■ **Figure 15.37** The decomposition of calcium carbonate (within a closed system) illustrating expansion work

The Gibbs energy change, ΔG, is often referred to as 'free energy'. Gibbs free energy changes refer to chemical reactions and physical processes which take place at constant temperature and *constant pressure*.

The Gibbs free energy, G, refers to the maximum amount of non-expansion work that can be done by the system. The non-expansion work is termed 'useful work' (Figure 15.36). $T\Delta S$ (which has units of energy) is *not* available to do work and can be regarded as 'un-free energy', that is, energy that is dispersed into the random motion of particles. A useful analogy is a game of squash or tennis. The heat energy lost through perspiration (sweat) is not useful energy; rather it is the energy to hit the ball which is 'free' to do useful work. Work is done when a force moves an object through a distance (in the direction of the force). An example of expansion work is shown in Figure 15.37. When the calcium carbonate decomposes, the carbon dioxide produced must push back the surrounding atmosphere (represented by the mass resting on the piston), and hence must do work on its surroundings.

Non-expansion work refers to any work done by the system other than that due to expansion. For redox reactions the maximum amount of work they can do can be easily measured by constructing an electrochemical cell and measuring the potential difference (voltage) generated (Chapter 19). The voltage can be converted to a Gibbs free energy change, ΔG.

Deriving the Gibbs equation

The total entropy change (in the system and surroundings) in a chemical reaction or physical process is given by the following expression:

$$\Delta S_{universe} = \Delta S_{system} + \Delta S_{surroundings}$$

The entropy change in the surroundings is given by the following relationship:

$$\Delta S_{surroundings} = -\frac{\Delta H}{T}$$

where ΔH represents the enthalpy change of the chemical reaction or physical process and T represents the absolute temperature (in kelvins). (Note the change of sign: the heat that leaves the system enters the surroundings, so a decrease in the enthalpy of the system corresponds to an addition of heat to the surroundings.)

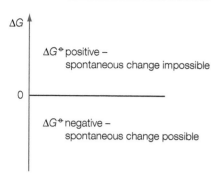

$\Delta G^{\ominus}$ positive –
spontaneous change impossible

$\Delta G^{\ominus}$ negative –
spontaneous change possible

■ **Figure 15.38** A diagram showing the possibility of change related to the value of $\Delta G^{\ominus}$

Hence:

$$\Delta S_{universe} = \Delta S_{system} - \frac{\Delta H}{T}$$

Multiplying both sides of the equation by $-T$ gives the expression

$$-T\Delta S_{universe} = \Delta H - T\Delta S_{system}$$

This means that, at constant temperature, the total entropy change is proportional to $\Delta H - T\Delta S$. The quantity $-T\Delta S_{universe}$ is defined as the Gibbs free energy change, ΔG. It is the free energy change for a chemical reaction or physical process. Hence:

$$\Delta G = \Delta H - T\Delta S$$

Under standard thermodynamic conditions:

$$\Delta G^{\ominus} = \Delta H^{\ominus} - T\Delta S^{\ominus}$$

The advantage of using $\Delta G^{\ominus}$ to predict whether or not a reaction will proceed spontaneously (Figure 15.38) is that only information about the chemical system is required and the entropy change in the surroundings need not be calculated.

Worked example

Calculate the entropy change of the surroundings when water condenses on a window at 25 °C:

$$H_2O(g) \rightarrow H_2O(l) \qquad \Delta H^{\ominus} = -44.0\,kJ\,mol^{-1} \qquad \Delta S^{\ominus} = -118\,J\,K^{-1}\,mol^{-1}$$

(where ΔS represents the entropy change of the system). Comment on the significance of the value you obtain.

$$\Delta S_{surroundings} = -\frac{\Delta H}{T}$$
$$= -\frac{(-44\,000\,J\,mol^{-1})}{298\,K}$$
$$= +147.7\,J\,K^{-1}\,mol^{-1}$$

(Note the conversion from $kJ\,mol^{-1}$ to $J\,mol^{-1}$ for the enthalpy change – this is because the units of entropy and entropy changes are $J\,K^{-1}\,mol^{-1}$.)

The entropy change in the surroundings is positive (favourable), but the entropy change in the system is negative (unfavourable) (Figure 15.39).

heat

exothermic process

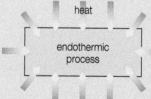

heat

endothermic process

energy released to surroundings, the entropy of which therefore increases

energy absorbed from surroundings, the entropy of which therefore decreases

■ **Figure 15.39** Changes in the entropy of the surroundings during exothermic and endothermic reactions

The overall entropy change in the universe can then be calculated:

$$\Delta S_{universe} = \Delta S_{system} + \Delta S_{surroundings}$$
$$\Delta S_{universe} = -118\,J\,K^{-1}\,mol^{-1} + 147.7\,J\,K^{-1}\,mol^{-1}$$
$$= +29.7\,J\,K^{-1}\,mol^{-1}$$

Hence, the overall entropy change in the universe is positive (favourable) and the process is spontaneous at this temperature.

Spontaneity can also be predicted by calculating the Gibbs free energy change, $\Delta G^{\ominus}$:

$$\Delta G^{\ominus} = \Delta H^{\ominus} - T\Delta S^{\ominus}$$
$$= -44.0\,kJ\,mol^{-1} - (298\,K \times 0.118\,kJ\,K^{-1}\,mol^{-1})$$
$$= -79.2\,kJ\,mol^{-1}$$

A negative value for the Gibbs free energy change, $\Delta G^{\ominus}$, and a positive value for the entropy change of the universe, $\Delta S_{universe}$, are equivalent criteria for spontaneity.

Gibbs free energy change of formation

Every compound has a Gibbs free energy change of formation, $\Delta G_f^\ominus$. This is the free energy change that occurs when one mole of the compound is formed from its elements in their standard states under standard conditions. (This is analogous to expressing the standard enthalpy of the reaction in terms of the standard enthalpies of formation of each chemical species taking part in the reaction.)

For example, the Gibbs free energy changes of formation of water and benzene are:

$$H_2(g) + \tfrac{1}{2}O_2(g) \rightarrow H_2O(l) \qquad \Delta G_f^\ominus = -237\,\text{kJ mol}^{-1}$$

$$6C(s) + 3H_2(g) \rightarrow C_6H_6(l) \qquad \Delta G_f^\ominus = +125\,\text{kJ mol}^{-1}$$

The Gibbs free energy changes of formation (under standard thermodynamic conditions) for a selection of organic compounds are listed on page 12 of the IB *Chemistry data booklet*. Note that the Gibbs free energy change of formation of an element (in its standard state) is zero.

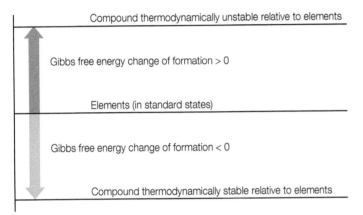

■ **Figure 15.40** A diagram illustrating compounds with negative and positive Gibbs free energy changes of formation

The Gibbs free energy change of formation can be regarded as a measure of a compound's thermodynamic stability relative to its elements. Compounds that have a negative Gibbs free energy change of formation are more thermodynamically stable than their elements. The compound can be synthesized from its elements and there is no tendency for it to decompose back into the elements (Figure 15.40). Compounds that have a positive Gibbs free energy change of formation are less thermodynamically stable than their elements. The compound cannot be synthesized from its elements and there is a tendency for it to decompose back into its constituent elements (Figure 15.40). However, compounds such as this, for example benzene, are often kinetically stable because there is a large activation energy barrier to decomposition.

Gibbs free energy changes of formation can be used to calculate the Gibbs free energy change, $\Delta G^\ominus$, for a reaction using the following relationship:

$$\begin{array}{ccc} \text{Gibbs free} \\ \text{energy change} \end{array} = \begin{array}{c} \text{sum of Gibbs free energies of} \\ \text{formation of products} \end{array} - \begin{array}{c} \text{sum of Gibbs free energies} \\ \text{of formation of reactants} \end{array}$$

In symbols:

$$\Delta G^\ominus = \sum \Delta G_f^\ominus(\text{products}) - \sum \Delta G_f^\ominus(\text{reactants})$$

12 Use the following Gibbs free energy changes of formation, $\Delta G_f^\ominus$, to calculate the free energy change, $\Delta G^\ominus$, for the decomposition of magnesium carbonate:

$$MgCO_3(s) \rightarrow MgO(s) + CO_2(g)$$

$\Delta G_f^\ominus(MgCO_3(s)) = -1012\,\text{kJ mol}^{-1}$

$\Delta G_f^\ominus(MgO(s)) = -569\,\text{kJ mol}^{-1}$

$\Delta G_f^\ominus(CO_2(g)) = -394\,\text{kJ mol}^{-1}$

Spontaneity and temperature

The Gibbs equation, $\Delta G^\ominus = \Delta H^\ominus - T\Delta S^\ominus$, gives rise to four different types of reaction, depending on whether the enthalpy change, $\Delta H^\ominus$, and the entropy change (of the system), $\Delta S^\ominus$, are positive or negative.

Positive entropy changes are favourable; negative enthalpy changes are favourable and hence help to 'drive' the reaction forwards. Negative entropy changes are unfavourable; positive enthalpy changes are unfavourable and hence help to 'drive' the reaction backwards.

The results for these four combinations on the sign of the Gibbs free energy change, ΔG, are shown in Table 15.6. The results are also summarized graphically in Figure 15.41. A reaction is only spontaneous if the sign of the Gibbs free energy change is *negative*.

■ **Table 15.6**
The four types of thermodynamic reactions

Enthalpy change, ΔH	Entropy change, ΔS	Gibbs free energy change, ΔG	Spontaneity
Positive (endothermic)	Positive (products more disordered than reactants)	Depends on the temperature	Spontaneous at high temperatures, when $T\Delta S > \Delta H$
Positive (endothermic)	Negative (products less disordered than reactants)	Always positive	Never spontaneous
Negative (exothermic)	Positive (products more disordered than reactants)	Always negative	Always spontaneous
Negative (exothermic)	Negative (products less disordered than reactants)	Depends on the temperature	Spontaneous at low temperatures, when $T\Delta S < \Delta H$

■ **Figure 15.41**
A graphical summary of the conditions for spontaneity (assuming that the values of entropy and enthalpy changes remain constant with a change in temperature)

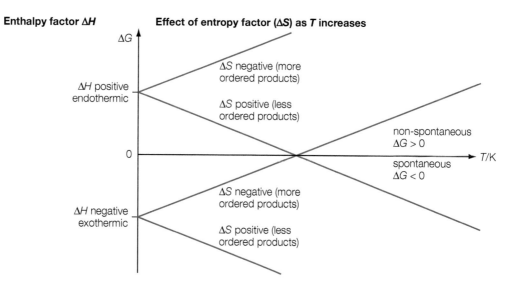

The relationship between free energy and temperature can also be modelled using a spreadsheet. One example of an interactive Excel model is shown in Figure 15.42; the user can alter the temperature using a set of buttons, which in turn dynamically updates a graph.

■ **Figure 15.42**
Spreadsheet showing free energy changes with temperature (Ian Bridgwood, Wyggeston and Queen Elizabeth I College, Leicester)

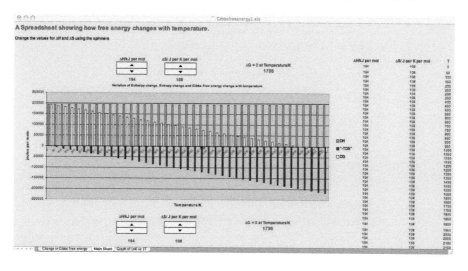

A change in temperature can alter the thermodynamics of the reaction. This dependence on temperature is shown by the presence of absolute temperature, T, in the Gibbs equation. However, temperature affects the spontaneity of exothermic and endothermic reactions in different ways.

For endothermic processes with a positive entropy change, the enthalpy change, ΔH, is positive (unfavourable and opposing the forward reaction) and hence, for the process to be spontaneous $T\Delta S$ must be positive and greater than the enthalpy change, ΔH. With an increase in temperature, $T\Delta S$ increases but ΔH remains constant. However, with a decrease in temperature $T\Delta S$ decreases and at a specific temperature will become less than ΔH. The Gibbs free energy change, ΔG, would become positive and the process would become non-spontaneous. So for an *endothermic process* or reaction a *higher temperature* favours the spontaneity of the process. Note that this is in agreement with what Le Châtelier's principle (Chapter 7) would suggest.

For exothermic processes with a negative entropy change, the enthalpy change, ΔH, is negative (favourable and favouring the forward reaction). For such reactions to be spontaneous, the enthalpy change, ΔH, must be greater than $T\Delta S$. With an increase in temperature, the opposing factor $T\Delta S$ increases but ΔH remains constant. As the temperature increases the opposing factor $T\Delta S$ will become greater than ΔH. The Gibbs free energy change, ΔG, would become positive and the process would become non-spontaneous. So for an *exothermic process* or reaction a *lower temperature* favours the spontaneity of the process – again, in agreement with Le Châtelier.

The effect of temperature on spontaneity

Using example values for ΔH and ΔS we can calculate the Gibbs free energy change for reactions at different temperatures (10 K and 10 000 K) for positive and negative values of ΔH and ΔS.

$\Delta H^{\ominus}$ and $\Delta S^{\ominus}$ both positive

$\Delta H^{\ominus} = 200\,\text{kJ mol}^{-1}$ and $\Delta S^{\ominus} = 200\,\text{J K}^{-1}\,\text{mol}^{-1}$

At $T = 10\,\text{K}$:

$\Delta G^{\ominus} = 200\,\text{kJ mol}^{-1} - (10\,\text{K} \times 0.2\,\text{kJ K}^{-1}\,\text{mol}^{-1}) = +198\,\text{kJ mol}^{-1}$

At $T = 10\,000\,\text{K}$:

$\Delta G^{\ominus} = 200\,\text{kJ mol}^{-1} - (10\,000\,\text{K} \times 0.2\,\text{kJ K}^{-1}\,\text{mol}^{-1}) = -1800\,\text{kJ mol}^{-1}$

This corresponds to the first row in Table 15.6: the sign of the Gibbs free energy change depends on the temperature and the reaction is spontaneous at high temperatures, when $T\Delta S > \Delta H$.

$\Delta H^{\ominus}$ positive and $\Delta S^{\ominus}$ negative

$\Delta H^{\ominus} = 200\,\text{kJ mol}^{-1}$ and $\Delta S^{\ominus} = -200\,\text{J K}^{-1}\,\text{mol}^{-1}$

At $T = 10\,\text{K}$:

$\Delta G^{\ominus} = 200\,\text{kJ mol}^{-1} - (10\,\text{K} \times -0.2\,\text{kJ K}^{-1}\,\text{mol}^{-1}) = +202\,\text{kJ mol}^{-1}$

At $T = 10\,\text{K}$:

$\Delta G^{\ominus} = 200\,\text{kJ mol}^{-1} - (10\,000\,\text{K} \times -0.2\,\text{kJ K}^{-1}\,\text{mol}^{-1}) = +2200\,\text{kJ mol}^{-1}$

This corresponds to the second row in Table 15.6: the sign of the Gibbs free energy is always positive and the reaction is never spontaneous.

$\Delta H^{\ominus}$ negative and $\Delta S^{\ominus}$ positive

$\Delta H^{\ominus} = -200\,\text{kJ mol}^{-1}$ and $\Delta S^{\ominus} = 200\,\text{J K}^{-1}\,\text{mol}^{-1}$

At $T = 10\,\text{K}$:

$\Delta G^{\ominus} = -200\,\text{kJ mol}^{-1} - (10\,\text{K} \times 0.2\,\text{kJ K}^{-1}\,\text{mol}^{-1}) = -202\,\text{kJ mol}^{-1}$

At $T = 10\,\text{K}$:

$\Delta G^{\ominus} = -200\,\text{kJ mol}^{-1} - (10\,000\,\text{K} \times 0.2\,\text{kJ K}^{-1}\,\text{mol}^{-1}) = -2200\,\text{kJ mol}^{-1}$

This corresponds to the third row in Table 15.6: the sign of the Gibbs free energy is always negative and the reaction is always spontaneous.

ΔH⁻ and ΔS⁻ both negative

$\Delta H^{\ominus} = -200\,\text{kJ}\,\text{mol}^{-1}$ and $\Delta S^{\ominus} = -200\,\text{J}\,\text{K}^{-1}\,\text{mol}^{-1}$

At $T = 10\,\text{K}$:

$\Delta G^{\ominus} = -200\,\text{kJ}\,\text{mol}^{-1} - (10\,\text{K} \times -0.2\,\text{kJ}\,\text{K}^{-1}\,\text{mol}^{-1}) = -198\,\text{kJ}\,\text{mol}^{-1}$

At $T = 10\,\text{K}$:

$\Delta G^{\ominus} = -200\,\text{kJ}\,\text{mol}^{-1} - (10\,000\,\text{K} \times -0.2\,\text{kJ}\,\text{K}^{-1}\,\text{mol}^{-1}) = +1800\,\text{kJ}\,\text{mol}^{-1}$

This corresponds to the fourth row in Table 15.6: the sign of the Gibbs free energy depends on the temperature and the reaction is spontaneous at low temperatures, when $T\Delta S < \Delta H$.

---

13 Determine whether it is possible to reduce magnesium oxide using carbon under standard thermodynamic conditions (298 K). If not, determine at what temperature it becomes spontaneous.

$$MgO(s) + C(s) \rightarrow Mg(s) + CO(g)$$

$\Delta H^{\ominus} = +491\,\text{kJ}\,\text{mol}^{-1}$ and $\Delta S^{\ominus} = 198\,\text{J}\,\text{K}^{-1}\,\text{mol}^{-1}$ at 298 K.

14 For the reaction: $\quad 2Fe_2O_3(s) + 3C(s) \rightarrow 4Fe(l) + 3CO_2(g)$

$\Delta H^{\ominus} = 457.9\,\text{kJ}\,\text{mol}^{-1}$ and $\Delta S^{\ominus} = +0.56\,\text{kJ}\,\text{K}^{-1}\,\text{mol}^{-1}$.

Calculate the temperature at which the value of ΔG becomes zero. Deduce the direction of the reaction above this temperature.

Voltaic cells

In a working voltaic cell (Chapter 19) a spontaneous change is occurring and hence the Gibbs free energy change, ΔG, must be negative. The relationship between the free energy change and the cell's potential is given by the following relationship:

$$\Delta G^{\ominus} = -nFE^{\ominus}_{cell}$$

where n represents the number of electrons transferred and F represents the Faraday constant ($96\,500\,\text{C}\,\text{mol}^{-1}$). A *negative* free energy change will only result from a *positive* cell potential. The measurement of cell potential provides one approach to the measurement of Gibbs free energy changes for redox reactions.

■ Entropy and the direction of change

Events happen by chance

If you spill some ethanol (alcohol) in an enclosed space, such as a sealed laboratory, you can soon smell its sweetness throughout the laboratory. The ethanol evaporates, and the ethanol molecules diffuse (spread out) to occupy all the available space. This is why ethanol is a fire risk; as the gas spreads out it mixes with the oxygen in the air to make a highly flammable mixture.

But why does the ethanol gas diffuse? Why does it not all stay in one part of the laboratory? It is the laws of chance and probability that cause it to diffuse (from a place of high concentration to a place of lower concentration).

Look at the diagram in Figure 15.43. The situation is simplified so that the molecules of ethanol are in one gas jar and can diffuse into the other when the partition is removed. The presence of air molecules has been ignored and only five ethanol molecules are shown.

Each ethanol molecule moves in a straight line until it collides (elastically) with another gas molecule or the wall of the container, when it changes direction. Figure 15.44 shows what can happen when the partition is removed. The molecules move around in an overall random manner and it is pure chance which container they end up in after a given length of time. Each of the molecules could end up in either of two places: the left-hand or the right-hand container. There are five molecules, each with two places once the partition is removed, i.e. a total of $2 \times 2 \times 2 \times 2 \times 2 = 2^5 = 32$ possible arrangements. Each of these arrangements is equally likely.

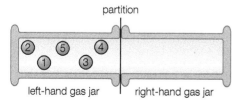

partition

left-hand gas jar | right-hand gas jar

■ **Figure 15.43** Five ethanol molecules confined to a container by a partition

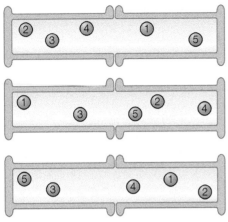

■ **Figure 15.44** Three arrangements of the five ethanol molecules after the partition between the two gas jars has been removed

■ **Figure 15.45** Peanuts at the bottom and cashew nuts on the top

Only one of these 32 arrangements has all the ethanol molecules where they are started, in the left-hand container. So the chance that they will all stay all in one container, instead of spreading out between the two, is 1 in 32. The ethanol molecules diffuse because there are more ways of them being spread out than being all in one place.

Now consider the real-life situation, when there are many millions of ethanol molecules instead of just five. The number of ways all these ethanol molecules can spread out to fill the containers is almost infinite, so the chance that they will all remain in one is virtually zero (negligible).

The idea that there is a number of ways of arranging is very important in chemistry because it decides whether chemical and physical changes are likely to take place. Events that happen are the ones that are most likely to occur. The more ways an event can occur, the more likely it is to happen.

The essential idea is that matter (atoms and molecules) and energy tend to spread out or disperse, provided they are not prevented from doing so. When energy is dispersed or spread out (including heat) there is an increase in entropy.

Why do miscible liquids mix?

The mixing of liquids is another example of where increases in entropy are favoured. If you have a jar half full of peanuts and you carefully pour half a jar of cashew nuts on top of them, you get two layers of different nuts. If you shake the jar, they will mix and you will have a jar of mixed nuts (Figure 15.45).

However much you shake them, the two types of nuts will be very unlikely to 'unmix' and produce two separate layers again. There are far more ways that the nuts can be mixed than unmixed. Each time you shake the jar, you nearly always produce another way of mixing them. Unmixing could in theory happen – the different nuts could by chance get shaken to the top and bottom. But this is very unlikely in practice, and almost never happens due to the low probability. The nuts effectively stay mixed.

If the different nuts represent molecules of different liquids you have the situation when two miscible liquids are mixed, for example when ethanol and water are mixed. The two liquids mix because there are more ways of being mixed than unmixed: the mixing results in an increase in entropy.

However, some pairs of liquids do not mix, for example petrol and water. This is because there is something that stops the natural mixing process (resulting in an increase in entropy) from happening. There are weak attractive forces between all molecules, but if the attractive forces between molecules of one liquid are stronger than those between the molecules in the other liquid and stronger than the intermolecular forces between the two different types of molecules, then mixing is less likely. It is as if the peanuts in Figure 15.45 had a sticky coating that makes them stay attracting one another rather than getting mixed up with the cashew nuts.

Entropy

Imagine a sample of chlorine gas inside a sealed metal container at room temperature. The container is then briefly heated. The molecules of the gas gain kinetic energy, which causes the molecules to move more quickly from one point to another, i.e. there is an increase in translational energy. The molecules will also rotate more rapidly, i.e. there is an increase in rotational energy. Finally, the bonds of the molecules will vibrate more rapidly and with greater amplitude. These changes are represented graphically in Figure 15.46 using the idea that covalent bonds behave as springs (Chapter 11).

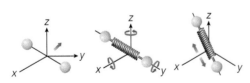

■ **Figure 15.46** Changes in kinetic energy in a diatomic gas molecule

$$\begin{array}{c}\text{Energy given to}\\\text{oxygen molecules}\end{array} = \begin{array}{c}\text{increase in translational}\\\text{kinetic energy}\end{array} + \begin{array}{c}\text{increase in rotational}\\\text{kinetic energy}\end{array} + \begin{array}{c}\text{increase in vibrational}\\\text{kinetic energy}\end{array}$$

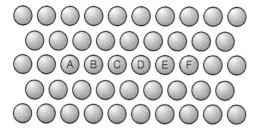

■ **Figure 15.47** Six of the helium atoms in a solid crystalline sample of helium, labelled A to F. They are identical to each other but distinguished from each other by their position in the lattice

(It is assumed that the energy of the electrons in the energy levels of the chlorine molecule is unchanged.)

It is absolutely essential to understand that not every chlorine molecule gains the same amount of these kinetic energies. It is also important to remember the kinetic energy is quantized (it comes in 'packets' or quanta, Chapters 2 and 12), that is, only specific kinetic energies of translation, rotation and vibration are allowed.

There is a distribution or 'spread' of translational, rotational and vibrational kinetic energies in a sample of gas molecules. There are many different ways in which the kinetic energy can be arranged between the translational, vibrational and rotational energy levels. As the temperature increases, more molecules are in the higher level states, so there is a larger number of arrangements at a higher temperature than there is at a lower temperature.

Consider a sample of frozen crystalline helium with a large number of atoms arranged into a lattice (Figure 15.47). Six of them are labelled A to F, and each is assumed to have a set of four evenly spaced vibrational energy levels. (In reality the vibrational energy levels converge in a similar way to electronic energy levels (Chapter 2)).

If the temperature is very low, close to absolute zero, the helium atoms will have the lowest possible vibrational energy, which is shown as E_0 (Figure 15.48). The six dots on the line for E_0 represent the six helium atoms. There is only one way of arranging the atoms if they all have kinetic energy E_0.

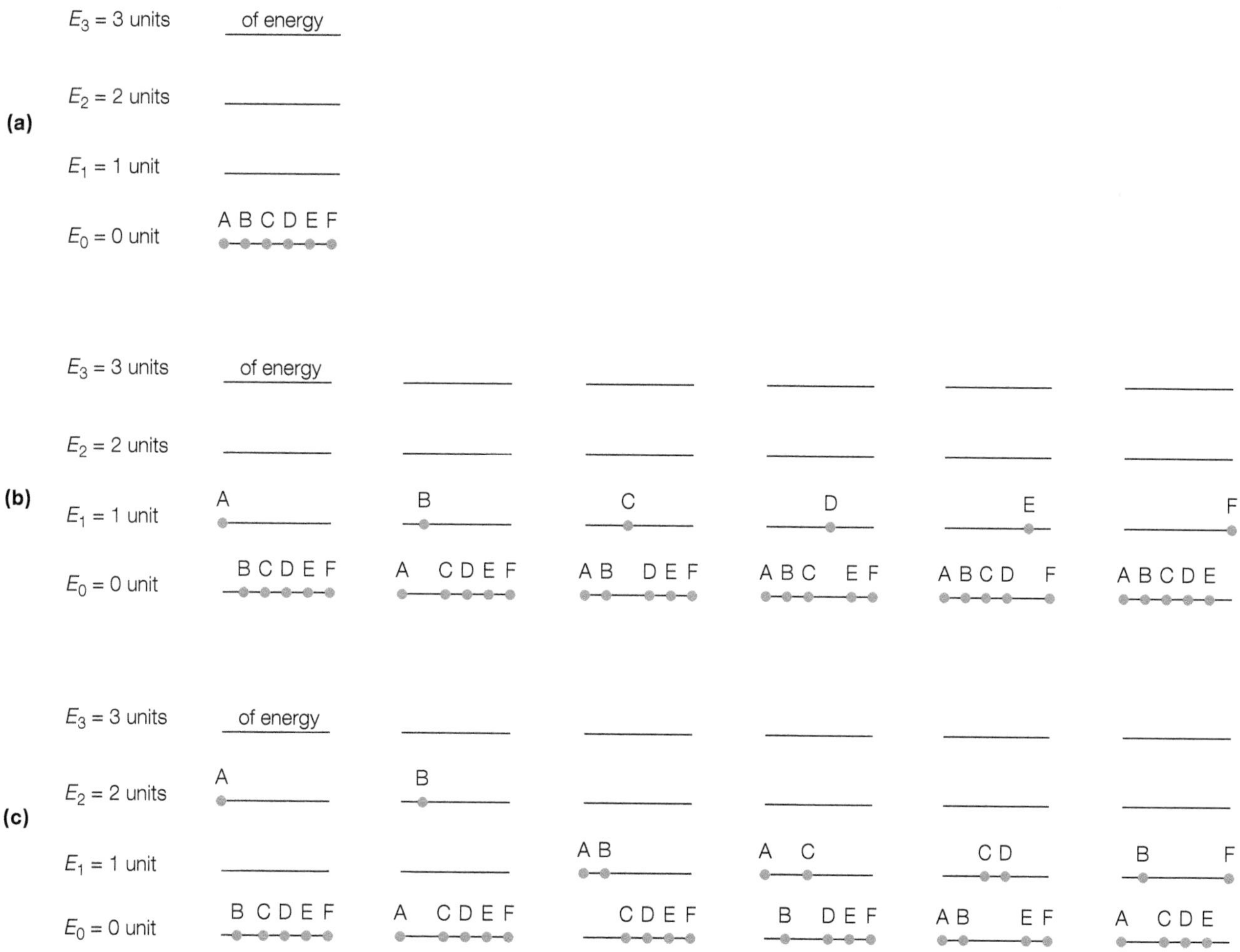

(a)

E_3 = 3 units	of energy
E_2 = 2 units	
E_1 = 1 unit	
E_0 = 0 unit	A B C D E F

(b)

E_3 = 3 units	of energy
E_2 = 2 units	
E_1 = 1 unit	A · · · · · · B · · · · · · C · · · · · · D · · · · · · E · · · · · · F
E_0 = 0 unit	B C D E F · A C D E F · A B D E F · A B C E F · A B C D F · A B C D E

(c)

E_3 = 3 units	of energy
E_2 = 2 units	A · · · · · · B
E_1 = 1 unit	A B · A C · C D · B F
E_0 = 0 unit	B C D E F · A C D E F · C D E F · B D E F · A B E F · A C D E

■ **Figure 15.48** Examples of how atoms can be arranged among vibrational energy levels: each arrangement is a microstate

If the atoms are given one extra unit of energy (equivalent to the energy difference between the vibrational energy levels), then only one of the atoms can reach the next highest vibrational energy level, E_1. However, because there are six helium atoms, there are six ways of arranging them so that one atom has kinetic energy E_1 and five atoms have kinetic energy E_0.

If the collection of helium atoms is given another single unit of energy, the number of arrangements greatly increases. For one atom with energy E_2, and the other five atoms with E_0, as before, there are six arrangements by which this could be achieved. Alternatively, two helium atoms could have kinetic energy E_1, with the other four atoms with E_0. There are 15 different ways this can be achieved, giving 21 different arrangements all together. As the total kinetic energy increases there is a rapid increase in the number of possible arrangements. The number of atoms with a particular kinetic energy is described by the Maxwell–Boltzmann distribution.

Each arrangement is called a **microstate**. Hence, at a higher temperature there is a greater number of vibrational microstates. When the number of microstates increases, entropy increases. When the number of microstates decreases, entropy decreases. Entropy is a measure of the number of ways that energy can be shared out among molecules. Entropy values calculated in this way are called statistical entropies.

A chemical system will adopt the 'arrangement' that offers the maximum statistical probability of microstates. This description of entropy is known as statistical thermodynamics.

The Austrian physicist Ludwig Boltzmann proposed the following relationship between entropy and the number of microstates:

$$S = k \ln W$$

in which S = entropy, k = the Boltzmann constant ($1.381 \times 10^{-23}\,\text{J K}^{-1}$) and $\ln W$ = the logarithm of the number of microstates possible for a system.

Worked example

Calculate the statistical entropy of four molecules of carbon monoxide.

Consider carbon monoxide molecules. There are two ways of arranging each of them. Two of the possible arrangements of the four molecules are:

| C=O | O=C | | C=O | C=O |

and

| C=O | O=C | | C=O | C=O |

This means there are $2^4 = 16$ possible orientations (microstates) of four molecules of CO. Bear in mind that all the oxygen and carbon atoms are chemically the same as each other but can be distinguished by their positions, e.g. C=O C=O is different from C=O C=O.

$$S = k \ln W$$
$$= 1.38 \times 10^{-23}\,\text{J K}^{-1} \ln 16$$
$$= 3.8 \times 10^{-23}\,\text{J K}^{-1}$$

Nature of Science — Theories can be superseded – development of the concept of entropy

The concept of entropy was developed so chemists could understand the concept of spontaneity in a chemical system. Entropy is a thermodynamic property that is often associated with the extent of randomness or disorder in a chemical system. In general if a system becomes more spread out, or more random, the system's entropy increases. This is a simplistic view, and a deeper understanding of entropy is derived from Ludwig Boltzmann's molecular interpretation of entropy. He used statistical thermodynamics (which uses statistics and probability) to link the microscopic world (individual particles) and the macroscopic world (bulk samples of particles). The connection between the number of microstates (arrangements) and its entropy is expressed in the Boltzmann equation, $S = k \ln W$, where W is the number of microstates and k is the Boltzmann constant, $1.38 \times 10^{-23}\,\text{J K}^{-1}$.

■ **Figure 15.49**
Boltzmann's tomb in
the Zentralfriedhof
(Central Cemetery)

Ludwig Boltzmann (1844–1906) was an Austrian physicist famous for developing statistical thermodynamics. He also made important contributions to kinetic theory, including the Maxwell–Boltzmann distribution for molecular speeds in a gas (Chapter 6). He was also a strong supporter of atomic theory when the model was still very controversial. He suffered from mental illness and committed suicide during an attack of depression. He is buried in Vienna and his tombstone (Figure 15.49) has the Boltzmann equation on it. This logarithmic connection between entropy and probability is the cornerstone of statistical thermodynamics. Statistical thermodynamics gives identical results to the simple thermodynamic approach in this chapter, but provides a deeper and more subtle description of entropy.

The relationship between K and ΔG

It is the Gibbs free energy change which determines whether a reaction proceeds (spontaneous) or not (non-spontaneous). The Gibbs free energy change, $\Delta G^{\ominus}$, and the equilibrium constant, K, are related by the following expression:

$$\Delta G^{\ominus} = -RT \ln K_c$$

This expression will be used in Chapter 17 to perform calculations.

This equation shows that:

- if $\Delta G^{\ominus}$ is zero, then $\ln K_c$ is zero and $K_c = 1$
- if $\Delta G^{\ominus}$ is negative, then $\ln K_c$ is positive and $K_c > 1$; equilibrium lies to the right
- if $\Delta G^{\ominus}$ is positive, then $\ln K_c$ is negative and $K_c < 1$; equilibrium lies to the left.

$K_c = 1$ for a simple reaction (e.g. A → B) where there are equal concentrations of reactants and products. If $K_c > 1$ then the products are favoured and if $K_c < 1$ then the reactants are favoured. The further away from zero the value of $\Delta G^{\ominus}$ is, the further the equilibrium lies to the right or left, until when the size of ΔG is greater than approximately $30 \, \text{kJ} \, \text{mol}^{-1}$, when the reaction can be regarded as essentially complete in the forward or the backward reaction.

Relating the value of ΔG to the position of equilibrium

When ΔG is equal to zero then the chemical reaction will be at equilibrium. When $\Delta G < 0$, i.e. negative, the reaction is spontaneous and the forward direction is favoured; K_c will be greater than 1. When $\Delta G > 0$, i.e. positive, the reaction is not spontaneous and the backward direction is favoured; K_c will be less than 1. The value of the equilibrium constant can be calculated from the expression $\Delta G^{\ominus} = -RT \ln K_c$ (Chapter 17).

ToK Link

Entropy is a technical term which has a precise meaning. How important are such technical terms in different areas of knowledge? Is their correct use a necessary or sufficient indicator of understanding?

Often entropy is described as being a measure of disorder. Disorder is, at best, a metaphor for entropy – it is *not* a definition. At worse it can cause profound misunderstanding.

Precisely defined technical terms are an important part of the 'language' of chemistry. The term 'entropy' encapsulates a complex concept that is important to all three natural sciences. The concept of entropy can only be applied once the concept has been correctly understood.

Entropy measures the spontaneous dispersal of heat energy: it measures how widely a specific quantity of heat is dispersed during a physical or chemical process. The random motion of particles and the random dispersion of energy mean that the configuration that a system adopts, in terms of the distribution of molecules and of energy, is the most probable one, based on these random chances.

Entropy values are associated with substances at particular temperatures, because energy has been spread out in them and increases their temperature. Entropy can be quantified using the Boltzmann equation, $S = k \ln W$, where k is the Boltzmann constant. Entropy's symbol S could be seen as a shorthand for 'spreading' and is a useful memory aid for students.

Examination questions – a selection

Paper 1 IB questions and IB style questions

Q1 Which reaction has the highest positive value of ΔS?
A $2Al(s) + 3S(s) \rightarrow Al_2S_3(s)$
B $CO_2(g) + 3H_2(g) \rightarrow CH_3OH(g) + H_2O(g)$
C $CH_4(g) + H_2O(g) \rightarrow 3H_2(g) + CO(g)$
D $S(s) + O_2(g) \rightarrow SO_2(g)$

Q2 Which is a correct equation to represent the lattice enthalpy of magnesium oxide?
A $MgO(s) \rightarrow Mg(g) + O(g)$
B $MgO(s) \rightarrow Mg(s) + O(s)$
C $MgO(s) \rightarrow Mg^+(g) + O^-(g)$
D $MgO(s) \rightarrow Mg^{2+}(g) + O^{2-}(g)$

Q3 Which reaction has the most negative $\Delta H^\ominus$ value?
A $LiF(s) \rightarrow Li^+(g) + F^-(g)$
B $Li^+(g) + F^-(g) \rightarrow LiF(s)$
C $NaBr(s) \rightarrow Na^+(g) + Br^-(g)$
D $Na^+(g) + Br^-(g) \rightarrow NaBr(s)$

Q4 Which of the following statements help(s) to explain why the value for the lattice enthalpy of lithium fluoride is less than that for strontium fluoride?
  I   The ionic radius of lithium is less than that of strontium.
  II The ionic charge of lithium is less than that of strontium.
A I only   C neither I nor II
B II only   D I and II

Q5 Consider the reaction
  $NH_4Br(s) \rightarrow NH_3(g) + HBr(g)$
Which response gives the correct signs for the values of ΔH and ΔS?
A ΔH +ve ΔS +ve   C ΔH −ve ΔS +ve
B ΔH −ve ΔS −ve   D ΔH +ve ΔS −ve

Q6 A Born–Haber cycle for the formation of potassium fluoride includes the steps below:
  I $K(g) \rightarrow K^+(g) + e^-$
  II $\frac{1}{2}F_2(g) \rightarrow F(g)$
  III $F(g) + e^- \rightarrow F^-(g)$
  IV $K^+(g) + F^-(g) \rightarrow KF(s)$
Which of these steps are exothermic?
A II and III only   C I, II and III only
B III and IV only   D I, III and IV only

Q7 When the substances $H_2(g)$, $O_2(g)$ and $H_2O_2(l)$ are arranged in order of increasing entropy values at 25 °C, what is the correct order?
A $H_2(g)$, $O_2(g)$, $H_2O_2(l)$ C $O_2(g)$, $H_2(g)$, $H_2O_2(l)$
B $H_2(g)$, $H_2O_2(l)$, $O_2(g)$ D $H_2O_2(l)$, $H_2(g)$, $O_2(g)$

Q8 In the reaction, $PbI_2(s) \rightarrow Pb^{2+}(aq) + 2I^-(aq)$, the solubility of PbI_2 is determined by the tendency of the reaction system to attain which of the following?
A maximum entropy and maximum enthalpy
B maximum entropy and minimum enthalpy
C minimum entropy and maximum enthalpy
D minimum entropy and minimum enthalpy

Q9 The standard enthalpy of formation of sodium fluoride corresponds to which reaction?
A $Na(g) + F(l) \rightarrow NaF(s)$ B $Na(g) + F(g) \rightarrow NaF(g)$
C $Na(s) + F(l) \rightarrow NaF(s)$ D $Na(s) + \frac{1}{2}F_2(g) \rightarrow NaF(s)$

Q10 For the reaction, $C(s) + CO_2(g) \rightarrow 2CO(g)$, which is spontaneous only at temperatures higher than 1100 K, one would conclude which of the following?
A ΔH is negative and ΔS is negative
B ΔH is positive and ΔS is negative
C ΔH is positive and ΔS is positive
D ΔH is negative and ΔS is positive

Q11 For the reaction $2NO(g) + O_2(g) \rightarrow 2NO_2(g)$ at one atmosphere pressure, the values of ΔH and ΔS are both negative and the process is spontaneous at room temperature. Which of the following is also true?
A ΔG is temperature dependent.
B The change in entropy is the driving force of the reaction.
C At high temperatures, ΔH becomes positive.
D The reaction is endothermic.

Q12 Which of the following processes would be expected to have an entropy change value close to zero?
A $2H_2(g) + O_2(g) \rightarrow 2H_2O(g)$
B $H_2O(s) \rightarrow H_2O(g)$
C $Br_2(g) + Cl_2(g) \rightarrow 2BrCl(g)$
D $CO_2(g) + (aq) \rightarrow CO_2(aq)$

Q13 For reaction systems at equilibrium, which of the following must always be true?
A $\Delta G = 0$ C $\Delta S = 0$
B $\Delta H = 0$ D $K_c = 0$

Q14 Which compound has the most positive lattice enthalpy of dissociation?
A NaCl   C $MgCl_2$
B NaBr   D $MgBr_2$

Paper 2 IB questions and IB style questions

Q1 When solid blue copper(II) sulfate pentahydrate, $CuSO_4.5H_2O$, loses water the white solid, copper(II) sulfate monohydrate, $CuSO_4.H_2O$, is produced as represented by the following equation:

$$CuSO_4.5H_2O(s) \rightleftharpoons CuSO_4.H_2O(s) + 4H_2O(g)$$

The thermodynamic data for the substances involved in the reversible process are:

Substance	$\Delta H_f^\ominus$/kJ mol^{-1}	$S^\ominus$/J K^{-1} mol^{-1}
$CuSO_4.5H_2O(s)$	−2278	305
$CuSO_4.H_2O(s)$	−1084	150
$H_2O(g)$	−242	189

a i Name and define the terms $\Delta H_f^\ominus$ and $S^\ominus$ and explain the standard symbol $\ominus$. [5]

 ii Explain why, in the case of $S^\ominus$, the symbol 'Δ' is not included. [1]

 iii What is the $\Delta H_f^\ominus$ value of elemental copper? [1]

b i Calculate the value of $\Delta H^\ominus$ for the above reaction and state what information the sign of $\Delta H^\ominus$ provides about this reaction. [4]

 ii Calculate $\Delta S^\ominus$ for the reaction and state the meaning of the sign of $\Delta S^\ominus$ obtained. [4]

 iii Identify a thermodynamic function that can be used to predict reaction spontaneity and state its units. [2]

c i Use the values obtained in **b** above to determine if the following reaction is spontaneous or non-spontaneous at 25 °C.
$CuSO_4.5H_2O(s) \rightleftharpoons CuSO_4.H_2O(s) + 4H_2O(g)$
Identify which compound is more stable at 25 °C, $CuSO_4.5H_2O(s)$ or $CuSO_4.H_2O(s)$. [5]

 ii Use the values obtained in **b** to determine the Celsius temperature above which the other compound in **c i** is more stable. [3]

Higher Level Paper 2, Nov 2000, Q6

Q2 a Define the term *lattice enthalpy*. [2]

 b State and explain the relationship between ionic radius and ionic charge and the size of the lattice enthalpy. [2]

c Draw a Born–Haber cycle for rubidium oxide, Rb_2O, and use the following data to calculate the lattice enthalpy.
$\Delta H_{at}^\ominus[Rb]$ = 80.9 kJ mol^{-1}
$\Delta H_{IE(1)}^\ominus[Rb]$ = 403.0 kJ mol^{-1}
$\Delta H_{at}^\ominus[O_2]$ = 249.2 kJ mol^{-1}
$\Delta H_{EA(1)}^\ominus[O]$ = −146.1 kJ mol^{-1}
$\Delta H_{EA(2)}^\ominus[O]$ = 795.5 kJ mol^{-1}
$\Delta H_f^\ominus[Rb_2O]$ = −339.0 kJ mol^{-1} [4]

d The experimental value of the lattice enthalpy for rubidium oxide is very similar to its theoretical value. However, there is a significant difference between the theoretical and calculated values of the lattice enthalpies of silver bromide. Explain these observations. [2]

e Explain why the lattice enthalpy of sodium oxide would be expected to be higher than that of rubidium oxide. (Assume both compounds have the same lattice structure.) [2]

Q3 The decomposition of solid barium carbonate is given by the following equation.

$$BaCO_3(s) \rightleftharpoons BaO(s) + CO_2(g)$$

Compound	$BaCO_3(s)$	$CO_2(g)$	$BaO(s)$
$\Delta H_f^\ominus$/kJ mol^{-1}	−1219	−394	−558
$S^\ominus$/kJ mol^{-1}	+112	+214	+70

a Calculate the value of $\Delta G^\ominus$ in kJ mol^{-1} at 25 °C. [6]

b State with a reason whether the reaction is spontaneous at 25 °C. [1]

c Determine the minimum temperature above which this reaction is spontaneous. Explain your answer. [4]

Higher Level Paper 2, May 2008, Q6

16 Chemical kinetics

ESSENTIAL IDEAS

- Rate expressions can only be determined empirically and these limit possible reaction mechanisms. In particular cases, such as a linear chain of elementary reactions, no equilibria and only one significant activation barrier, the rate equation is equivalent to the slowest step of the reaction.
- The activation energy of a reaction can be determined from the effect of temperature on reaction rate.

16.1 Rate expression and reaction mechanism
– rate expressions can only be determined empirically and these limit possible reaction mechanisms; in particular cases, such as a linear chain of elementary reactions, no equilibria and only one significant activation barrier, the rate equation is equivalent to the slowest step of the reaction

■ The rate expression and order of reaction

Many reactions that take place in solution have rates that are affected by changes in the concentrations of their reactants (Chapter 6). Similar behaviour is shown by reactions involving gases. The way in which the concentration of a reactant affects the rate of a chemical reaction, known as its order, can only be found by carrying out experiments, or by knowing the mechanism of the reaction.

You *cannot* deduce the order of a reaction from looking at a balanced equation for the reaction: any similarity is purely coincidental. It is experimental data that will show the relationship between the rate of a reaction and the concentrations of the reactants. The rate expression is a precise mathematical way of summarizing this information about concentration changes.

A very common rate expression is rate $\propto$ [A]. This means that if the concentration of the reactant A is *doubled*, the rate is *doubled*. Conversely, if the concentration of A is *halved*, the rate is *halved*. The equation specifies a *directly proportional* relationship between rate and concentration of the reactant A.

In a general reaction such as:

$$A + B \rightarrow C + D$$

where A and B represent reactants and C and D represent products, the generalized rate expression is:

$$\text{rate} \propto [A]^a[B]^b \qquad \text{or} \qquad \text{rate} = k[A]^a[B]^b$$

Square brackets indicate concentrations (as they do in an equilibrium expression – see Chapter 7), the exponents a and b are the individual orders of the reaction with respect to the reactants A and B, and k is the proportionality constant, known as the rate constant. The values of a, b and k have to be determined experimentally. The sum of the individual orders, $a + b$, is known as the overall order of the reaction. The order of reaction with respect to a particular reactant indicates precisely what happens to the rate of reaction if that concentration is changed.

The order of reaction with respect to a particular reactant is the power to which the concentration of that reactant is raised in the rate expression. The overall order of reaction is the sum of all the individual orders.

■ **Table 16.1**
The relationship
between order,
concentration and
rate of reaction

Order	Rate expression	Nature of dependence
Zero	Rate = $k[A]^0$	Rate is independent of the concentration of A; we could make any change to the concentration of A and the rate would remain the same
First	Rate = $k[A]^1$	Rate changes as the concentration of A changes; for example, if the concentration of A is doubled, the rate doubles
Second	Rate = $k[A]^2$	Rate changes as the square of the change in concentration of A; if the concentration of A is tripled (threefold increase), the rate increases by nine times (ninefold, as $3^2 = 9$)

Table 16.1 summarizes the common whole-number orders that you will need to be familiar with. Typically, orders with respect to reactants are either zero, first or second but, in fact, fractional orders do occur. For example, the reaction:

$$CH_3CHO(g) \rightarrow CH_4(g) + CO(g)$$

has an overall order of 1.5, the rate expression for this reaction being rate = $k[CH_3CHO]^{1.5}$. *Many reactions involving free radicals have fractional orders.*

However, the examples that are dealt with in the IB Chemistry syllabus all fall into one of the three categories shown in Table 16.1.

Rate expressions may not include *all* the reactants and they may include substances, such as acid and alkali, which although present in the reaction mixture do not appear in the equation because they act as catalysts. Rate expressions may contain products but *never* intermediates – chemicals that appear temporarily during the reaction.

Rate expressions have two main uses:

■ The rate expression (together with the rate constant) can be used to predict the rate of a reaction from a mixture of reactants of known concentrations.

■ A rate expression will help to formulate a mechanism for the reaction: this is a description of the intermediates and the simple reactions (known as elementary steps) by which many reactions occur.

Examples of rate expressions

■ $H_2(g) + I_2(g) \rightarrow 2HI(g)$

The rate expression is: rate = $k[H_2(g)][I_2(g)]$

■ $2N_2O_5(g) \rightarrow 4NO_2(g) + O_2(g)$

The rate expression is: rate = $k[N_2O_5(g)]$

This emphasizes that the order of reaction is *not* obtained from the stoichiometric coefficient in the chemical equation: it is obtained experimentally.

■ $CH_3COCH_3(aq) + I_2(aq) \rightarrow CH_2ICOCH_3(aq) + HI(aq)$

The rate expression is: rate = $k[CH_3COCH_3(aq)][H^+(aq)]$

The reaction between propanone and iodine is catalysed by hydrogen (H^+) ions. The rate expression includes propanone and the catalyst but does *not* include iodine, $I_2(aq)$, the other reactant in the equation. That is, the concentration of iodine does not affect the rate of reaction: the reaction is zero order with respect to iodine. This clearly indicates that the reaction does not occur via a one-step reaction involving iodine directly reacting with propanone. It consists of a number of individual reactions known as elementary steps.

Some rate expressions are shown in Table 16.2 for reactions that might be encountered during the IB Chemistry course.

Reaction	Rate expression
$H_2(g) + I_2(g) \rightarrow 2HI(g)$	Rate = $k[H_2(g)][I_2(g)]$
$2NO(g) + O_2(g) \rightarrow 2NO_2(g)$	Rate = $k[NO(g)]^2[O_2(g)]$
$H_2O_2(aq) + 2H^+(aq) + 2I^-(aq) \rightarrow 2H_2O(l) + I_2(aq)$	Rate = $k[H_2O_2(aq)][I^-(aq)]$
$S_2O_8{}^{2-}(aq) + 2I^-(aq) \rightarrow 2SO_4{}^{2-}(aq) + I_2(aq)$	Rate = $k[S_2O_8{}^{2-}(aq)][I^-(aq)]$
$BrO_3{}^-(aq) + 5Br^-(aq) + 6H^+(aq) \rightarrow 3Br_2(aq) + 3H_2O(l)$	Rate = $k[BrO_3{}^-(aq)][Br^-(aq)][H^+(aq)]$
$CH_3Br(aq) + OH^-(aq) \rightarrow CH_3OH(aq) + Br^-(aq)$	Rate = $k[CH_3Br(aq)][OH^-(aq)]$
$CH_3COOC_2H_5(aq) + OH^-(aq) \rightarrow CH_3COO^-(aq) + C_2H_5OH(aq)$	Rate = $k[CH_3COOC_2H_5(aq)][OH^-(aq)]$
$I_2(aq) + CH_3COCH_3(aq) \rightarrow CH_2ICOCH_3(aq) + HI(aq)$	Rate = $k[CH_3COCH_3(aq)][H^+(aq)]$
$CH_3COOH(aq) + C_2H_5OH(aq) \rightarrow CH_3COOC_2H_5(aq) + H_2O(l)$	Rate = $k[CH_3COOH(aq)][C_2H_5OH(aq)]$
$(CH_3)_3CCl(aq) + H_2O(l) \rightarrow (CH_3)_3COH(aq) + Cl^-(aq) + H^+(aq)$	Rate = $k[(CH_3)_3CCl(aq)]$

Worked example

The rate expression for the reaction:

$2A + B + C \rightarrow 2D + E$

is

rate = $k[A][B]^2$

Deduce the overall order and the individual orders for the reactants.

The overall order is 3 (1 + 2).

The reaction is first order with respect to A.

The reaction is second order with respect to B.

The reaction is zero order with respect to C.

A closer look at specific examples

Iodine reacts with thiosulfate ions as shown below:

$$I_2(aq) + 2S_2O_3{}^{2-}(aq) \rightarrow S_4O_6{}^{2-}(aq) + 2I^-(aq)$$

Experiments have shown that the reaction is first order with respect to the concentration of iodine and first order with respect to the concentration of thiosulfate ions. The overall order is therefore 2 (1 + 1).

First order with respect to the iodine concentration means that doubling the concentration of iodine would double the initial rate of the overall reaction. First order with respect to the thiosulfate ion concentration similarly means that doubling the concentration of thiosulfate ions would double the initial rate of the overall reaction. The initial rate of a reaction is the rate of reaction measured just after the reaction has started.

Halving the concentration of each reactant separately would reduce the rate of reaction by half. In a first-order reaction the initial rate of reaction is *directly proportional* to the concentration of that reactant. The overall order of 2 means that doubling the concentrations of both reactants, iodine and thiosulfate, would increase the overall rate of reaction fourfold: its initial rate would be four times faster. Halving the concentrations of both reactants would decrease the rate of reaction by a factor of 4: its initial rate of reaction would be four times slower.

The rate expression for this reaction is therefore:

rate = $k[I_2(aq)][S_2O_3{}^{2-}(aq)]$

In general a second-order rate expression will be:

rate = $k[A][B]$ or more simply   rate = $k[A]^2$

For the simpler rate expression, if the concentration of A is doubled then the initial rate of reaction would quadruple (2×2). Conversely, if the concentration of A were halved, then the initial rate of reaction would decrease by a factor of 4.

Some reactions have an overall order of 3 and are usually first order with respect to one reactant and second order with respect to another reactant:

$$\text{rate} = k[A]^2[B]$$

This means that if the concentration of A is doubled, then the initial rate will be quadrupled (2×2). If the concentrations of A and B are both doubled, then the initial rate will increase by a factor of 8 ($2 \times 2 \times 2$). For example:

$$\text{rate} = k[NO(g)]^2[O_2(g)]$$

However, another possibility that would result in a third-order reaction is:

$$\text{rate} = k[A][B][C]$$

where the rate is first order with respect to all three reactants, A, B and C. This means that if the concentration of any one of A, B or C is doubled, then the initial rate will be doubled. If the concentrations of two of the reactants are both doubled, then the initial rate will increase by a factor of 4 (2×2). If the concentrations of all three reactants are doubled, then the initial rate will be increased by a factor of 8 ($2 \times 2 \times 2$). An example of such a reaction is:

$$\text{rate} = k[BrO_3^-(aq)][Br^-(aq)][H^+(aq)]$$

A few reactions are zero order with respect to a particular reactant, which means that changing the concentration of that reactant has no effect on the initial rate of reaction. This occurs when the reactant does not participate until after the slowest step, or rate-determining step, of the mechanism.

The rate expression will then be:

$$\text{rate} = k[A] \qquad \text{or} \qquad \text{rate} = k \quad (\text{since } [A]^0 = 1)$$

For example, for the reaction:

$$(CH_3)_3CCl(aq) + H_2O(l) \rightarrow (CH_3)_3COH(aq) + Cl^-(aq)$$

the rate expression is:

$$\text{rate} = k[(CH_3)_3CCl(aq)]$$

Therefore for water:

$$\text{rate} = k[H_2O(l)]^0$$

Worked example

The following equation represents the oxidation of bromide ions in acidic solution.

$$BrO_3^-(aq) + 5Br^-(aq) + 6H^+(aq) \rightarrow 3Br_2 + 3H_2O$$

The rate expression is:

$$\text{rate} = k[BrO_3^-(aq)][Br^-(aq)][H^+(aq)]$$

Deduce the effect on the rate if the concentration of bromate is *halved*, but the concentration of hydrogen ions is *quadrupled* (at constant temperature and bromide concentration).

The quadrupling of the hydrogen ion concentration results in a quadrupling of the rate (first-order kinetic behaviour); the halving of the bromate concentration results in the rate being reduced by a factor of 2 (first-order kinetic behaviour). This is equivalent to the overall rate being doubled.

You may be asked to deduce the effect on the relative rate if two reactant concentrations are changed at the same time.

■ The rate constant

The rate of a reaction usually decreases during the reaction and is dependent on the concentrations of reactants. Hence, a reaction can exhibit many different rates depending on the concentrations and the extent of the reaction. Rate is proportional to an expression involving reactant concentrations and this is transformed into an equation by introducing a constant of proportionality, k.

The rate constant, k, is a numerical value included in the rate expression. It is characteristic of a particular reaction: each reaction has its own unique rate constant in terms of a value and associated units and it is constant at a particular temperature. The rate constant does *not* depend on the extent of the reaction or vary with the concentrations of the reactants.

Low values of rate constants are associated with slow reactions, while high values are associated with fast reactions. Since rate constants vary with temperature they are usually quoted for a specific temperature. Rate constants will also vary with a change in solvent if the reaction is performed in solution in different solvents.

Worked example

The rate expression for a reaction at 800 K is:

rate = $k[A]^2[B]$

The initial rate of reaction was $55.0 \times 10^{-5}\,mol\,dm^{-3}\,s^{-1}$ when the concentrations of A and B were $3.00 \times 10^{-2}\,mol\,dm^{-3}$ and $6.00 \times 10^{-2}\,mol\,dm^{-3}$. Calculate the rate constant (to 1 decimal place).

$$k = \frac{\text{rate}}{[A]^2\,[B]}$$

$$= \frac{55.00 \times 10^{-5}\,mol\,dm^{-3}\,s^{-1}}{(3.00 \times 10^{-2})^2\,(mol\,dm^{-3})^2 \times 6.00 \times 10^{-2}\,mol\,dm^{-3}}$$

$$= 10.2\,mol\,dm^{-3}\,s^{-1}$$

The units for the rate constant of a reaction depend on whether the reaction is first, second or third order overall. For example, in a first-order reaction:

rate = $k[A]$ and hence $k = \dfrac{\text{rate}}{[A]}$

Substituting the units for rate and concentration gives:

$$k = \frac{mol\,dm^{-3}\,s^{-1}}{mol\,dm^{-3}}$$

which cancels to s^{-1}.

However, for an equation with an overall order of 2:

rate = $k[A][B]$ and hence $k = \dfrac{\text{rate}}{[A] \times [B]}$

Substituting the units for rate and concentration gives:

$$\frac{mol\,dm^{-3}\,s^{-1}}{(mol\,dm^{-3})^2} \quad \text{which simplifies to} \quad \frac{mol\,dm^{-3}\,s^{-1}}{mol^2\,dm^{-6}}$$

before cancelling to $mol^{-1}\,dm^3\,s^{-1}$. These units are sometimes written as $dm^3\,mol^{-1}\,s^{-1}$.

For a third-order reaction:

rate = $k[A][B]^2$ and hence $k = \dfrac{\text{rate}}{[A] \times [B]^2}$

Substituting the units for rate and concentration gives:

$$k = \frac{mol\,dm^{-3}\,s^{-1}}{(mol\,dm^{-3})\,(mol\,dm^{-3})^2}$$

$$= \frac{mol\,dm^{-3}\,s^{-1}}{mol^3\,dm^{-9}}$$

$$= mol^{-2}\,dm^6\,s^{-1}$$

These units are sometimes written as $dm^6\,mol^{-2}\,s^{-1}$.

In general, for a reaction of nth order, the units of the rate constant are:

$$k = (mol\,dm^{-3})^{1-n}\,s^{-1}$$

The differing units for the rate constant, k, are summarized in Table 16.3.

■ **Table 16.3** The units of the rate constant for reactions of differing orders

Zero order	First order	Second order	Third order	nth order
Rate = $k[A]^0$	Rate = $k[A]$	Rate = $k[A]^2$	Rate = $k[A]^3$	Rate = $k[A]^n$
Units of rate = $mol\,dm^{-3}\,s^{-1}$	Units of $\dfrac{rate}{concentration}$ $= s^{-1}$	Units of $\dfrac{rate}{(concentration)^2}$ $= mol^{-1}\,dm^3\,s^{-1}$	Units of $\dfrac{rate}{(concentration)^3}$ $= mol^{-2}\,dm^6\,s^{-1}$	Units of $\dfrac{rate}{(concentration)^n}$ $= (mol\,dm^{-3})^{1-n}\,s^{-1}$

1 Deduce the overall order of the reaction and the units of the rate constant, k, for this reaction.

   $3NO(g) \rightarrow N_2O(g) + NO_2(g)$ rate = $k[NO(g)]^2$

2 If the rate constant and the rate expression are known for a reaction, then the initial rates of reaction can be calculated.

   Propene reacts with bromine to form 1,2-dibromopropane:

   propene + bromine → 1,2-dibromopropane:

   $CH_3CH=CH_2(g) + Br_2(g) \rightarrow CH_3CHBr–CH_2Br(l)$

   The rate equation for this reaction is:

   rate = $k[CH_3CH=CH_2(g)][Br_2(g)]$ and the rate constant is $30.0\,dm^3\,mol^{-1}\,s^{-1}$.

   Calculate the initial rate of reaction when the concentrations of propene and bromine are both $0.040\,mol\,dm^{-3}$.

3 Hydrogen iodide decomposes according to the equation:

   $2HI(g) \rightarrow H_2(g) + I_2(g)$

   The rate expression for the reaction is:

   rate = $k[HI(g)]^2$

   At a temperature of $700\,K$ and a concentration of $2.00\,mol\,dm^{-3}$, the rate of decomposition of hydrogen iodide is $25.0 \times 10^{-5}\,mol\,dm^{-3}\,s^{-1}$.

   Calculate the rate constant, k, at this temperature and calculate the number of hydrogen iodide molecules that decompose per second in $1.00\,dm^3$ of gaseous hydrogen iodide under these conditions. (Avogadro constant = $6.02 \times 10^{23}\,mol^{-1}$.)

The important differences between the rate and the rate constant are summarized in Table 16.4.

■ **Table 16.4** Differences between the rate and rate constant of a reaction

Rate of reaction	Rate constant, k
It is the speed at which the reactants are converted into products at a specific time during the reaction.	It is a constant of proportionality in the rate expression.
It depends upon the concentration of reactant species at a specific time.	It refers to the rate of reaction when the concentration of every reacting species is unity (one).
It generally decreases with time.	It is constant and does not vary during the reaction.

■ Experimental determination of the rate expression

Earlier we stressed that the orders of a reaction with respect to particular reactants, and therefore the overall order and rate expression, can only be determined experimentally. A variety of graphical and non-graphical methods are available that enable us to carry out these determinations.

Initial rates method (non-graphical)

For a reaction such as:

   $A + B \rightarrow C + D$

where A and B represent reactants and C and D represent products, the following procedure is used to establish the rate expression.

- Carry out the reaction with known concentrations of A and B and measure the initial rate of reaction.
- Repeat the experiment using double the concentration of A, but keeping the concentration of B the same as in the first experiment. Therefore any change in the rate of reaction can only be caused by the change in the concentration of A.

If the rate is doubled in the second experiment then the reaction is first order with respect to A, if the initial rate is increased four times, the reaction is second order with respect to A and if there is no change in the initial rate then the reaction is zero order with respect to A. Similar experiments can be carried out to establish the order with respect to B. This method of finding orders is known as the initial rates method, and the method is illustrated in the following example.

Worked example

Iodine reacts with propanone according to the following equation:

$$I_2(aq) + CH_3COCH_3(l) \rightarrow ICH_2COCH_3(aq) + HI(aq)$$

The kinetics of this reaction were investigated in four experiments carried out at constant temperature. The initial rate of reaction was measured at different concentrations of propanone, iodine and hydrogen ions (Table 16.5). Use these data to determine the individual orders and overall order of the reaction.

Experiment number	Propanone concentration/ $mol\,dm^{-3}$	Hydrogen ion concentration/ $mol\,dm^{-3}$	Iodine concentration/ $mol\,dm^{-3}$	Initial rate/ $mol\,dm^{-3}\,s^{-1}$
1	6.0	0.4	0.04	18×10^{-6}
2	6.0	0.8	0.04	36×10^{-6}
3	8.0	0.8	0.04	48×10^{-6}
4	8.0	0.4	0.08	24×10^{-6}

■ **Table 16.5** Initial rate data for the iodination of propanone

Comparing experiments 1 and 2 in Table 16.5, there is a doubling in the concentration of hydrogen ions, while the other two reactant concentrations are kept constant. There is a doubling in rate between experiments 1 and 2, indicating that the reaction is first order with respect to hydrogen ions. (Rate is proportional to the concentration of hydrogen ions.)

Comparing experiments 3 and 4, there is a doubling in the concentration of iodine, while the propanone concentration is kept constant and the hydrogen ion concentration is halved. The initial rate is also halved between experiments 3 and 4, which means the reaction is zero order with respect to iodine, since the halving of the initial rate is due to the change in concentration of hydrogen ions. (Rate is not affected by iodine concentration.)

Comparing experiments 2 and 3, there is an increase in the concentration of propanone of $\frac{4}{3}$. There is also an increase in rate between experiments 2 and 3 of $\frac{4}{3}$. Therefore, the rate is proportional to the propanone concentration, that is, it is first order with respect to propanone. Overall, therefore:

$$rate = k[H^+(aq)]^1[I_2(aq)]^0[propanone]^1$$

or, since $[I_2(aq)]^0 = 1$,

$$rate = k[H^+(aq)][propanone]$$

The overall order of the reaction is therefore 2.

Graphical methods – concentration versus time graphs

The order of a reaction with respect to a reactant can also be determined from a concentration–time graph. If the reaction is zero order with respect to a reagent, then the graph produced is a straight line (Figure 16.1).

In the case of first-order (Figure 16.2) and second-order reactions (Figure 16.3), the graph obtained is a curve. If the reaction is second order then a 'deeper' curve is obtained for the graph of concentration against time. The first-order curve is an exponential curve and the second-order curve is a quadratic curve. It can be hard to distinguish between these two types of kinetic behaviour using experimental data with random uncertainties.

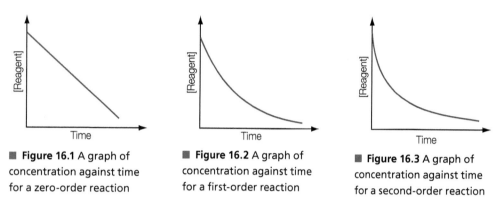

■ **Figure 16.1** A graph of concentration against time for a zero-order reaction

■ **Figure 16.2** A graph of concentration against time for a first-order reaction

■ **Figure 16.3** A graph of concentration against time for a second-order reaction

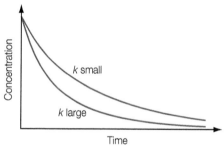

■ **Figure 16.4** First-order concentration–time graphs with different rate constant values

The greater the value of the rate constant, k, the more rapid the exponential decrease in the concentration of the reactant (Figure 16.4). Hence, a first-order rate constant is a measure of the rate: the greater the value of the rate constant, the faster the reaction.

Concentration–time graphs can be used to find the rate at a particular time or concentration during the course of the reaction by drawing the tangent at that point and finding the slope. If a series of tangents is drawn at different concentrations, and the rates found, then these rates can be plotted against concentration to determine the order of reaction. This process overcomes the difficulty of distinguishing first- and second-order reactions mentioned above. A slightly different analysis of such graphs can also be useful in distinguishing the different orders of reaction; this method involves considering successive half-lives of the reactant using the plot.

Worked example

Methanol reacts with hydrochloric acid at 25 °C to produce chloromethane and water:

$$CH_3OH(aq) + HCl(aq) \rightarrow CH_3Cl(g) + H_2O(l)$$

Equimolar amounts of methanol and hydrochloric acid are mixed at 25 °C and the progress of the reaction is followed by taking a small sample of the reaction mixture at time intervals. The samples are then titrated against a standard solution of sodium hydroxide. The results obtained are shown in Table 16.6.

Time/min	[HCl(aq)]/mol dm^{-3}	[CH$_3$OH(aq)]/mol dm^{-3}
0	1.84	1.84
200	1.45	1.45
400	1.21	1.21
600	1.04	1.04
800	0.91	0.91
1000	0.81	0.81
1200	0.72	0.72
1400	0.67	0.67
1600	0.60	0.60
1800	0.57	0.57
2000	0.54	0.54

■ **Table 16.6** Data for the reaction between hydrochloric acid and methanol at 25 °C

a Use these results to plot a graph of the concentration of HCl(aq) against time. By drawing tangents to the curve, find the rate ot the reaction at 200-minute intervals.

b Using the values for the rates of reaction, plot a graph of rate against concentration of HCl(aq) and determine the overall order of the rate of the reaction.

c Comment on how the individual orders of reaction could be determined experimentally.

a A graph of the concentration of HCl(aq) against time is shown in Figure 16.5. Note that the concentrations of both the acid and methanol fall at the same rate over time. Tangents can then be drawn to the curve to find the reaction rate. Figure 16.5 shows the tangent that corresponds to [HCl(aq)] = 1.04 mol dm^{-3}. Thus the rate at this concentration can be found from the slope of the tangent. The calculation is illustrated on the graph (note that the time in minutes is converted into seconds).

b Tangents can be drawn at various points and Table 16.7 shows the values calculated for the rate at five different concentrations of acid. These results are then plotted as a graph of rate against concentration graph. They produce a curve, indicating that the reaction is second order (Figure 16.6).

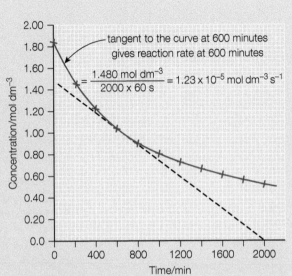

tangent to the curve at 600 minutes gives reaction rate at 600 minutes

$$= \frac{1.480 \text{ mol dm}^{-3}}{2000 \times 60 \text{ s}} = 1.23 \times 10^{-5} \text{ mol dm}^{-3}\text{ s}^{-1}$$

■ **Figure 16.5** A plot of concentration of HCl against time

Time/min	[HCl(aq)]/mol dm^{-3}	Rate from graph/ mol dm^{-3} min^{-1}	Rate from graph/ mol dm^{-3} s^{-1}
0	1.84	2.3×10^{-3}	3.83×10^{-5}
200	1.45	1.46×10^{-3}	2.43×10^{-5}
400	1.22	1.05×10^{-3}	1.75×10^{-5}
600	1.04	0.74×10^{-3}	1.23×10^{-5}
800	0.91	0.54×10^{-3}	0.90×10^{-5}

■ **Table 16.7** Results from the calculation of rates at different concentrations using tangents to the concentration–time graph

c A plot of the rate against [CH$_3$OH] would have produced an identical curve because, if you look at the data in Table 16.7, you will see that the concentration of CH$_3$OH is decreasing at the same rate as the decrease in concentration of HCl. Figure 16.6 shows an upward curve. This indicates that the reaction is second order; a first-order reaction would have produced a straight line (see later discussion). But the question remains, second order with respect to what? Since the concentrations of both HCl and CH$_3$OH are decreasing at the same rate, either of these may be second order. The possibilities are:

- rate = k[CH$_3$OH][HCl]
- rate = k[CH$_3$OH]^2
- rate = k[HCl]^2

Further experiments would have to be carried out to confirm one or other of these possibilities; carrying out the experiment in this way simply shows that the reaction is second order overall.

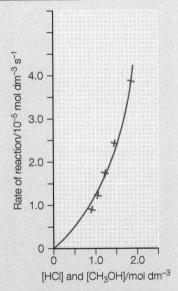

■ **Figure 16.6** A graph of rate of reaction against hydrochloric acid concentration

4   Suggest how the experiment for the reaction between methanol and hydrochloric acid might be re-designed to determine the effect of changing the hydrochloric acid (HCl) concentration while controlling the methanol (CH_3OH) concentration.

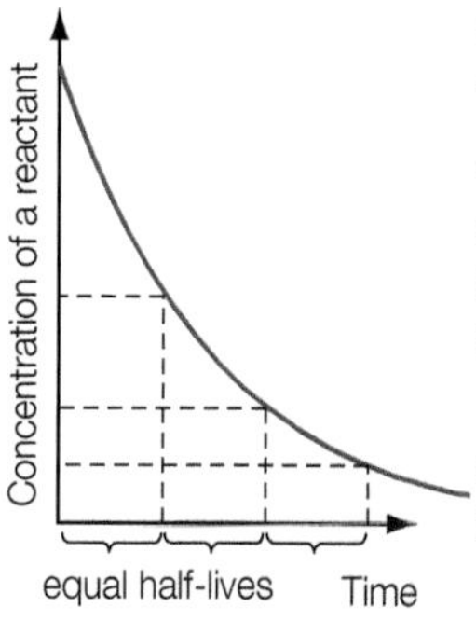

Concept of half-life for a first-order reaction

The time taken for the concentration of reactant to be halved during a chemical reaction is called the half-life. Identical kinetic behaviour is exhibited by substances undergoing radioactive decay (see Chapter 2), with the exception that this physical process is unaffected by changes in temperature. For a reaction that has an overall order of 1, the half-life is constant and is independent of the initial concentration of the reactants (see Figure 16.7).

For any other order the half-life is *not* constant: it will constantly change during the experiment. In first-order reactions, the half-life, $t_{1/2}$, is related to the rate constant k by the following equation:

$$t_{1/2} = \frac{\ln 2}{k} \text{ (where } \ln 2 = 0.693)$$

This expression is obtained by integrating the first-order differential equation

$$\frac{dx}{dt} = k(a - x)$$

Where a represents the initial amount of reactants and x represents the amount of products.

■ Figure 16.7
Concentration–time curve for a first-order reaction, showing how the half-life remains constant as concentration decreases.

Integration of a first-order differential equation

The half-life of a first-order rate expression can be obtained by integrating the first-order differential rate equation.

Let a represent the initial concentration of a reactant A, which is converted into products. After a time interval, t, a concentration of product represented by x has been formed:

	[A]	[Products]
At time = 0	a	0
At time = t	$a - x$	x

For a first-order reaction, the rate of formation of products is the product of the rate constant and the concentration of the reactant. Thus:

rate = k[A]

Using calculus notation, an expression can be written for the rate of formation of products at time t:

$$\frac{dx}{dt} = k(a - x)$$

Rearranging and integrating:

$$\int k \, dt = \int \frac{dx}{(a - x)}$$

$$kt = \ln\left(\frac{a}{a - x}\right)$$

Rearranging this equation using the exponential function yields:

$$\left(\frac{a}{a - x}\right) = \exp(kt) \quad \text{or} \quad a - x = a\exp(-kt)$$

If the equation $kt = \ln\left(\dfrac{a}{a - x}\right)$ is rearranged, then:

$$\ln a - \ln(a - x) = kt \quad \text{and}$$

$$\ln(a - x) = -kt + \ln a$$

A plot of $\ln(a - x)$ against t will generate a straight line whose slope is $-k$.

The half-life of a first-order reaction occurs when $x = \dfrac{a}{2}$. Substituting this into the equation demonstrates that $k \times t_{\frac{1}{2}} = \ln 2$, or $t_{\frac{1}{2}} = 0.693/k$, which does not depend on the initial concentration, a.

Figure 16.8 illustrates how the half-life varies for zero-, first- and second-order reactions. Note that it is only for first-order reactions that the value remains constant.

These findings are summarized as follows:

- The successive half-lives of a zero-order reaction decrease with time.
- The successive half-lives of a first-order reaction are constant.
- The successive half-lives of a second-order reaction increase with time.

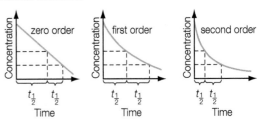

■ **Figure 16.8** The variation of successive half-lives for zero-, first- and second-order reactions

> **Worked example**
>
> The half-life of a first-order reaction is 100 seconds. Calculate its rate constant.
>
> $$k = \frac{\ln 2}{t_{1/2}} = \frac{0.693}{100\,\text{s}} = 6.93 \times 10^{-3}\,\text{s}^{-1}$$
>
> A first-order reaction has a rate constant of $0.100\,\text{s}^{-1}$. Calculate the half-life for this reaction.
>
> $$t_{1/2} = \frac{\ln 2}{k} = \frac{0.693}{0.100\,\text{s}^{-1}} = 6.93\,\text{s}$$

Radioactive decay

Radioactive decay is an important example of first-order kinetics that is worth mentioning here even though it is a nuclear reaction rather than a chemical change. The breakdown of the nucleus of a radioisotope is a spontaneous random process, and a significant reference parameter for different radioisotopes is their half-life values. Thus radiocarbon dating is based around the relatively long half-life of carbon-14, which is 5370 years. The half-lives of the different isotopes released into the atmosphere following accidents at nuclear power plants are one of the prime considerations in assessing the health risks in the aftermath of such events. Half-life values vary enormously, from milliseconds to many thousands of years.

Following the Chernobyl incident in 1986, many different radioisotopes were released. Some, such as iodine-131, had decayed almost completely in a matter of several weeks. However others, such as strontium-90 ($t_{\frac{1}{2}}$ = 29 years) and caesium-137 ($t_{\frac{1}{2}}$ = 30 years), will remain in food chains and the soil for over 300 years.

The more recent accident at Fukushima Daiichi in Japan in 2011 was different in its nature and has been internationally assessed as having released significantly lower levels of radiation. International monitoring is of crucial importance in these circumstances because of the potential for the contamination to spread across large areas of the globe.

Graphical methods – rate versus concentration graphs

The order of a reaction can also be determined by plotting the rate against different initial concentrations of a reactant, or the 'rate' for reactions like the iodine clock and that between thiosulfate ions and dilute acid (see Chapter 6).

For a first-order reaction, the initial rate of reaction is directly proportional to the concentration of the reactant and the resulting graph is a sloping straight line (Figure 16.9). For a second-order reaction, the initial rate of reaction increases with concentration in a quadratic manner and the resulting curve is known as a parabola. This method gives a clear graphical distinction between first- and second-order kinetics.

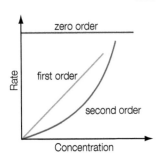

■ **Figure 16.9** Rate–concentration graphs for zero-order, first-order and second-order reactions

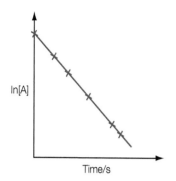

■ **Figure 16.10** Determining the rate constant for a first-order reaction by plotting the natural log of concentration against time

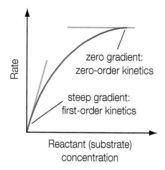

■ **Figure 16.11** Graph of the rate of an enzyme-catalysed reaction against substrate concentration

For a zero-order reaction, the rate remains constant as the reactant is depleted, leading to a horizontal line for the rate, but one with a definite end.

Another way of calculating the rate constant for a first-order reaction is to plot a graph of the natural logarithm of the concentration against the time. For a first-order reaction the graph (Figure 16.10) will take the form of a straight line with a slope (gradient) with a value of $-k$.

It should also be mentioned that apparent changes in the order of a reaction can take place under certain conditions. A change from first-order to zero-order kinetics is observed during the decomposition of gases on the surface of a homogeneous catalyst, for instance during the decomposition of ammonia on a tungsten catalyst. A simplified explanation is that at low concentrations the gas molecules are adsorbed onto the surface of the catalyst and the reaction exhibits first-order kinetics. However, at high concentrations of gas molecules all the catalytic surface sites are occupied. The number of available attachment sites on the metal surface becomes rate- limiting. The rate then becomes independent of the concentration of the reactant molecules and so the reaction exhibits zero-order kinetics.

Similar 'saturation' behaviour (Figure 16.11) is shown by enzymes (see Chapter 23 on the accompanying website). The enzyme interacts with the reactant, called the substrate, at a specific location in the enzyme called the active site. The three-dimensional shape of the active site fits the shape of the substrate.

A summary of the key aspects of the different graphical methods of determining orders of reaction is given in Table 16.8.

■ **Table 16.8** Summary of graphical methods of finding orders and half-lives

Overall reaction order	Zero order A → products	First order A → products	Simple second order* A → products A + B → products
Rate expression	Rate = $k[A]_0$**	Rate = $k[A]$	Rate = $k[A]^2$ Rate = $k[A][B]$
Data to plot for a straight-line graph	$[A]$ versus t	$\ln[A]$ versus t	$\dfrac{1}{[A]}$ versus t
Slope or gradient equals	$-k$	$-k$	$+k$
Changes in the half-life as the reactant is consumed	$\dfrac{[A]_0}{2k}$ $t_{1/2}$ becomes shorter	$\dfrac{\ln 2}{k}$ $t_{1/2}$ is constant	$\dfrac{1}{k[A]_0}$ $t_{1/2}$ becomes longer
Units of k	$mol\,dm^{-3}\,s^{-1}$	s^{-1}	$dm^3\,mol^{-1}\,s^{-1}$

* A simple second-order reaction is a reaction which is second order with respect to one reactant; that is, rate = $k[A]^2$.

** $[A]_0$ is the initial concentration (at time $t = 0$).

5   The progress of the isomerization of cyclopropane can be followed by measuring either the decrease in concentration of cyclopropane or the increase in concentration of propene.

$$H_2C-CH_2$$
$$\backslash\ /$$
$$CH_2 \qquad \rightarrow \qquad CH_3-CH=CH_2(g)$$
$$\qquad\qquad\qquad\qquad\qquad propene$$
cyclopropane

Table 16.9 shows these changes for the reaction carried out at 500 °C.

Time/min	[cyclopropane]/mol dm^{-3}	[propene]/mol dm^{-3}
0	1.50	0.00
5	1.23	0.27
10	1.00	0.50
15	0.82	0.68
20	0.67	0.83
25	0.55	0.95
30	0.45	1.05
35	0.37	1.13
40	0.33	1.17

■ **Table 16.9** Results for the experiment on the isomerization of cyclopropane

a Using the data in the table, calculate a value for the average rate of reaction over the first 5 minutes. (Note that you will need to convert minutes to seconds during your calculation.)

b The value calculated in part **a** is not the initial rate of reaction as – even over this relatively short time – the rate is slowing as the reactant is used up. Plot a graph of [propene] against time. Then find the initial rate of reaction by drawing the tangent to the curve at time 0 and finding its slope.

c By similarly drawing tangents, calculate the rate of reaction at propene concentrations of 0.30 mol dm^{-3}, 0.60 mol dm^{-3} and 0.90 mol dm^{-3}.

d Calculate the concentration of cyclopropane when the propene concentration is 0.00 mol dm^{-3}, 0.30 mol dm^{-3}, 0.60 mol dm^{-3} and 0.90 mol dm^{-3}.

e Plot a graph of the rate of reaction against the concentration of cyclopropane using these values and find the value of the rate constant, k, from your graph.

6 Benzenediazonium chloride ($C_6H_5N_2Cl$) decomposes at room temperature:

$$C_6H_5N_2Cl(aq) + H_2O(l) \rightarrow C_6H_5OH(aq) + N_2(g) + HCl(aq)$$

a How could the rate of this reaction be monitored experimentally?

b Using the data in Table 16.10, plot a graph of the concentration of $C_6H_5N_2Cl$ against time. From your graph find the value of two successive half-lives.

c Using this information, what is the order of the reaction with respect to benzenediazonium chloride?

Time/s	[$C_6H_5N_2Cl$]/mol dm^{-3}
0	5.8
200	4.4
400	3.2
600	2.5
800	1.7
1000	1.2
1200	0.8
1400	0.5
1600	0.3

■ **Table 16.10** Results for the decomposition of benzenediazonium chloride with time

Nature of Science

Controlling variables

Studies on reaction kinetics exemplify an essential part of the scientific approach to experimentation – the control of variables and the need to focus the analysis on one component of a possibly complex problem at any one time. In the above examples we have seen how the concentration of all of the reactants but one is kept constant so that the order of reaction with respect to the one under study is found. The overall order is then found as the sum of the individual orders. An alternative approach is embodied in establishing a pseudo first-order situation and using it to determine the order of reaction.

Pseudo first-order reactions

Chemists often change the concentration of reactants so that they can study the effect the change has on the rate of the reaction. For example, consider the reaction of manganate(VII) ions in an acidic solution with ethanol to form ethanoate ions. The balanced equation for this reaction is:

$$5C_2H_5OH(aq) + 4MnO_4^-(aq) + 17H^+(aq) \rightarrow 5C_2H_5O_2^-(aq) + 4Mn^{2+}(aq) + 11H_2O(l)$$

Five moles of ethanol molecules are needed to react with four moles of manganate(VII) ions to form five moles of ethanoate ions and four moles of the manganese(II) ions. If the concentrations of ethanol and acid are raised to a high level relative to the manganate(VII) concentration, the kinetics of the appearance of the manganese(II) ion can be studied. In a similar manner, if the concentration of the hydrogen ion is raised above the stoichiometric requirement of the reaction, then the interaction of the other two reactants can be studied.

Each participant in the reaction can be studied in turn using this technique. It is called a pseudo first-order reaction because the kinetics of the single reactant can be studied as for a first-order reaction while the other reactants are held almost constant because their concentration is so large relative to the species being studied.

The reaction is actually first order with respect to all the reactants:

$$\text{rate} = k[\text{C}_2\text{H}_5\text{OH(aq)}][\text{MnO}_4^-\text{(aq)}][\text{H}^+\text{(aq)}]$$

However, if this reaction is carried out with manganate(VII) and hydrogen ions present in large excess, only a small amount of these reactants will be consumed during the hydrolysis. The concentrations of these two species are then effectively constant, and the rate of reaction will depend only upon the concentration of the ethanol:

$$\text{rate} = k'[\text{C}_2\text{H}_5\text{OH(aq)}]$$

where $k' = k[\text{MnO}_4^-\text{(aq)}][\text{H}^+\text{(aq)}]$ and is termed an apparent first-order constant. Under these experimental conditions the reaction thus exhibits 'pseudo' first-order kinetics with respect to the ethanol.

Figure 16.12 illustrates how two reactant concentrations would vary in a reaction if B were present in a large excess (greater than ×10). The reaction between A and B occurs with a 1 : 1 stoichiometry and the concentration of B at the start of the reaction is 10 times greater than the concentration of A at the start of the reaction. The initial concentrations are represented by $[\text{A}]_0$ and $[\text{B}]_0$. The concentration of A rapidly approaches zero, but the concentration of B remains relatively constant during the reaction (it decreases by a much smaller proportion of its initial value).

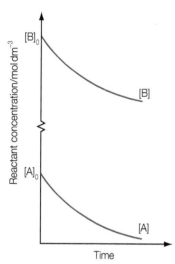

■ **Figure 16.12** The changes in concentrations for two reactants, A and B, where B is present in large excess

Super-fast reactions

The development of increasingly sophisticated analytical techniques has played a role in ensuring progress in kinetic studies and enhancing our understanding of very fast reactions. Femtochemistry is a term given to reactions that take place in a matter of 10^{-14} or 10^{-15} seconds (one femtosecond, $1\,\text{fs} = 10^{-15}\,\text{s}$). The Egyptian chemist, Ahmed Zewail, won the Nobel Prize in Chemistry in 1999 for his pioneering work studying such reactions using an ultra-fast laser technique. This technique allowed study of the vibrations of individual bonds and the analysis of bond-breaking and bond-making processes that are key to the ideas about transition states.

Flash photolysis can measure rates of reactions that are extremely fast. A very short but intense flash of light (often from a laser) is passed into the reaction mixture. After an equally brief period of time, another flash of light is passed through the mixture. The molecules produced in the reaction absorb some of the light from the second flash. By taking a photograph, the spectrum of the molecules can be recorded. The intensity of the lines in the spectrum gives a measure of the concentration of the molecules. If the time interval between the first and second flashes is changed, the intensity of the lines in the spectrum changes. A series of experiments allows the way the concentration of the molecules changes with time to be determined.

The complete course of some very fast reactions can be monitored using stopped-flow spectrophotometry. In this technique, very small volumes of reactants are driven at high speed into a mixing chamber. From here they go to an observation cell where the progress of the reaction is monitored (usually by measuring the transmission of ultraviolet radiation through the sample). A graph of rate of reaction against time can be generated automatically.

■ Reaction mechanism

Elementary steps

All chemical reactions, except the very simplest, actually take place via a number of simple reactions called elementary steps, or simply steps, which are collectively termed the mechanism of the reaction. The reaction mechanism is a hypothetical model of what chemists believe occurs during a chemical reaction at the molecular level.

Elementary steps are described as unimolecular if only one chemical species (atom, ion, radical or molecule) is involved, and bimolecular if two chemical species are involved. True termolecular steps in the gas phase, which would involve the simultaneous collision of three chemical species, are virtually *impossible*, since the statistical chance of three species colliding is considerably less than that of two particles colliding.

Unimolecular steps involve either the decomposition or dissociation of a molecule into two or more smaller molecules or ions, or the rearrangement of a molecule:

$$A \Rightarrow B \text{ (rearrangement)}$$

or

$$A \Rightarrow B + C \text{ (decomposition or dissociation)}$$

Bimolecular steps involve two species colliding and reacting with each other:

$$A + B \Rightarrow C \quad \text{or} \quad A + A \Rightarrow D$$

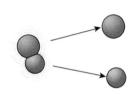

■ **Figure 16.13**
Unimolecular step

Unimolecular and bimolecular steps are illustrated in Figures 16.13 and 16.14.

It is important to distinguish between the elementary steps of a mechanism, indicated in this text by ⇒, and the overall chemical reaction, indicated by →. This is illustrated in the two specific examples of well-established mechanisms outlined below.

The thermal decomposition of dinitrogen oxide is given by:

$$2N_2O(g) \rightarrow 2N_2(g) + O_2(g)$$

This reaction is believed to occur via the following steps:

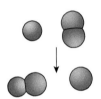

■ **Figure 16.14**
Bimolecular step

$$N_2O(g) \Rightarrow N_2(g) + O(g)$$
$$N_2O(g) + O(g) \Rightarrow N_2(g) + O_2(g)$$

The oxygen atoms are intermediates and are produced and consumed during the reaction.

However, the reaction:

$$2HI(aq) + H_2O_2(aq) \rightarrow I_2(aq) + 2H_2O(l)$$

has a more complex mechanism and is believed to occur via the following four bimolecular elementary steps:

$$I^-(aq) + H_2O_2(aq) \Rightarrow IO^-(aq) + H_2O(l)$$
$$H^+(aq) + IO^-(aq) \Rightarrow HIO(aq)$$
$$I^-(aq) + HIO(aq) \Rightarrow I_2(aq) + OH^-(aq)$$
$$H^+(aq) + OH^-(aq) \Rightarrow H_2O(l)$$

In these steps iodic(I) acid, HOI, and iodate(I) ions, IO⁻, are both intermediates.

Note that when the equations for the elementary steps are summed together, they give the overall stoichiometric equation for the reaction.

Much of the evidence for proposed mechanisms of reactions come from kinetic studies that identify the products and intermediates formed during a reaction, as well as determining the individual orders of reactants and overall order of the reaction. Other evidence for reaction mechanisms comes from stereochemical studies which follow the changes in shape that occur as the reactants are converted into intermediates and products. To find out which bonds are broken and formed, chemists frequently use isotopically labelled reactants that incorporate heavy oxygen, ^{18}O, or deuterium (heavy hydrogen), ^2H, which can be easily detected in the products and intermediates (Figure 16.15).

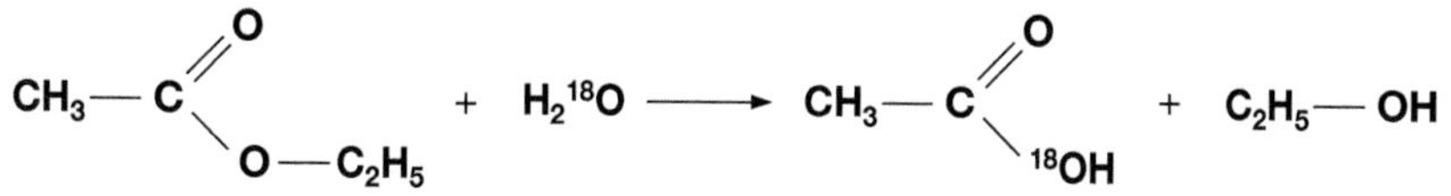

■ **Figure 16.15**
Use of labelling to investigate bond breaking during ester hydrolysis

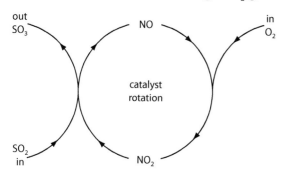

Kinetic studies only *suggest* a mechanism: they do not 'prove' that a particular mechanism is operating. They can perhaps disprove another candidate mechanism. Like any other chemical theory, a reaction mechanism may be revised or replaced as a result of later and more thorough investigations or more accurate calculations.

The elementary steps proposed for a mechanism must meet both of the following requirements:

■ The sum of the elementary steps must give the overall balanced equation for the reaction. For example, the reaction between sulfur dioxide and oxygen is:

$$2SO_2(g) + O_2(g) \rightarrow 2SO_3(g)$$

This reaction is catalysed by nitrogen monoxide via the following two elementary steps:

$$2NO(g) + O_2(g) \rightleftharpoons 2NO_2(g)$$
$$NO_2(g) + SO_2(g) \rightleftharpoons SO_3(g) + NO(g)$$

The sum of the first and second (multiplied through by 2) elementary steps is:

$$2NO(g) + O_2(g) + 2NO_2(g) + 2SO_2(g) \rightleftharpoons 2NO_2(g) + 2SO_3(g) + 2NO(g)$$

Cancelling the nitrogen dioxide intermediate and the nitrogen monoxide catalyst gives the overall reaction:

$$\cancel{2NO(g)} + O_2(g) + \cancel{2NO_2(g)} + 2SO_2(g) \rightarrow \cancel{2NO_2(g)} + 2SO_3(g) + \cancel{2NO(g)}$$

This and similar catalysed reactions can be represented by cyclical diagrams as shown in Figure 16.16. The catalyst remains 'rotating' within the middle, and the reactants and products enter and leave the cycle.

■ The mechanism must agree with the experimentally determined rate expression.

Each elementary step determines the order of the reaction with respect to the reactant or catalyst. Specifically, a bimolecular step will have second-order kinetics and a unimolecular reaction will have first-order kinetics.

However, these orders will *only* appear in the rate expression *if* they occur during the rate-determining step of the mechanism, *or* in an equilibrium directly before the rate-determining step. The rate-determining step (RDS) is the slowest step of the mechanism and determines the rate of the overall reaction.

Outlined overleaf are mechanisms of five reactions with their corresponding rate expressions. Intermediates do *not* appear in a rate expression.

■ **Figure 16.16** Catalytic cycle for the oxidation of sulfur dioxide by oxygen

Overall reaction: $A + B \rightarrow D$

Mechanism: $A + B \Rightarrow D$ rate $= k[A][B]$

Overall reaction: $P + Q \rightarrow R$

Mechanism: $P \Rightarrow S$ slow

                  $S + Q \Rightarrow R$ fast   rate $= k[P]$

Overall reaction: $K + 2M \rightarrow N$

Mechanism: $2M \rightleftharpoons M_2$ fast

                  $M_2 + K \Rightarrow N$ slow   rate $= k[M]^2[K]$

Overall reaction: $A + B \rightarrow C + D$

Mechanism: $A \Rightarrow M + D$ slow

                  $M + B \Rightarrow C$ fast   rate $= k[A]$

Overall reaction: $T + R \rightarrow P$

Mechanism: $T + H^+ \rightleftharpoons TH^+$ fast

                  $TH^+ + R \Rightarrow P + H^+$ slow   rate $= k[T][R][H^+]$

(Hydrogen ions are acting as a catalyst here.)

Note that in these mechanisms, the rate-determining step is not necessarily the first step in the sequence of reactions.

Molecularity

The number of particles participating in the rate-determining step (RDS) is known as the molecularity. (The term molecularity should be reserved for describing the elementary steps of a complex reaction. It should not be used to describe an overall reaction of a complex mechanism.) It may or may not be the same value as the overall order of the reaction and, unlike the order, it will always be a positive integer.

So, for example, a reaction may involve several elementary steps and yet still exhibit second-order kinetics. For example, consider the reaction:

$$2A + B \rightarrow C + D$$

This occurs via the following elementary steps:

     $A + B \Rightarrow X$ slow

     $X + A \Rightarrow C + D$ fast

where X is an intermediate in the reaction. The first and second steps are both bimolecular, but only the kinetics of the first step, the rate-determining step, will appear in the rate expression. The reaction will be first order with respect to A and first order with respect to B. The overall order of the reaction is 2. During the reaction all of the intermediate X formed reacts with A as fast as it is formed. The rate of formation of C and D under these conditions equals the rate of formation of X.

Only reactants that take part in the rate-determining step will appear in the final rate expression for a reaction (after intermediates have been removed). A reactant that does not appear in the rate-determining step will not appear in the rate expression. This means that changing the concentration of that reactant will have no effect on the rate of that reaction. It is said to have zero-order kinetics.

The reaction between iodine and propanone shows zero-order kinetics with respect to iodine. Changing the concentration of iodine has *no* effect on the rate of the reaction. The chemical equation for the reaction is:

$$CH_3COCH_3(aq) + I_2(aq) \rightarrow CH_3COCH_2I(aq) + HI(aq)$$

The rate expression is:

$$\text{rate} = k[CH_3COCH_3(aq)][H^+(aq)]$$

The accepted mechanism that explains this rate equation involves a mechanism with four elementary steps.

Step 1 Rate-determining step: rapid protonation

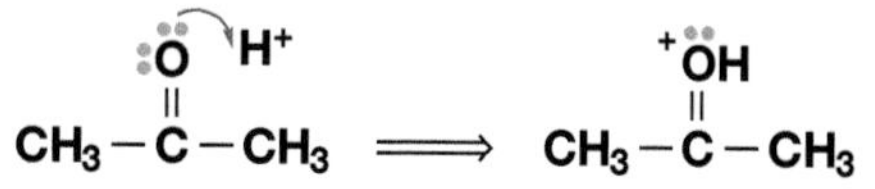

Step 2 Deprotonation and formation of propene-1,2-diol (an intermediate)

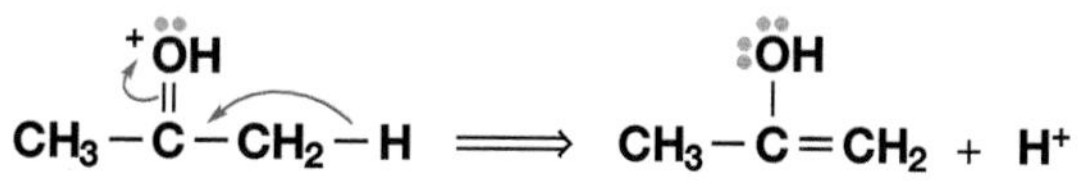

Step 3 Reaction of propene-1,2-diol with iodine to form a carbocation intermediate

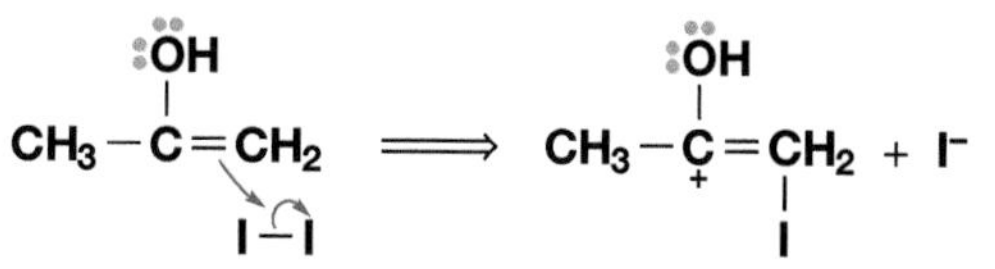

Step 4 Deprotonation and formation of product, iodopropanone

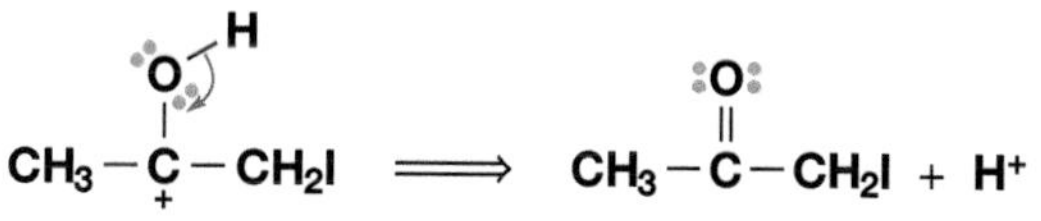

The first slow step of the mechanism is the rate-determining step. It has a molecularity of 2 since only propanone molecules and hydrogen ions are involved. The molecularity of 2 in the rate-determining step gives the reaction an order of 1 with respect to both the propanone and the acid. The iodine is *not* involved in the rate-determining step and therefore changing its concentration has *no* effect on the overall rate.

Kinetic studies provide much of the data required for proposing reaction mechanisms. Two organic examples (see also Chapter 20) are outlined below.

Bromoethane, C_2H_5Br, undergoes rapid hydrolysis in the presence of aqueous alkali. The products of the reaction are ethanol, C_2H_5OH, and bromide ions:

$$C_2H_5Br(aq) + OH^-(aq) \rightarrow C_2H_5OH(aq) + Br^-(aq)$$

Experimental investigations reveal that the reaction is first order with respect to the concentration of hydroxide ions and first order with respect to the amount of bromoethane:

$$\text{rate} = k[C_2H_5Br(aq)][OH^-(aq)]$$

This implies that bromoethane and hydroxide ions are both involved in the rate-determining step. The mechanism is thought to involve the transition state or activated complex shown below:

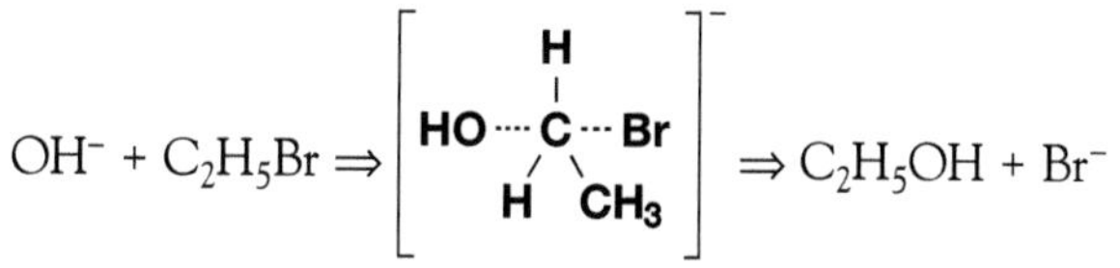

transition state

The reaction is therefore a bimolecular second-order reaction, termed S_N2, where the S indicates *substitution* (the replacement of one atom (or group) by another atom (or group), in this example a bromine atom by the hydroxyl group), the N indicates that the organic species is attacked by a *nucleophile* (an electron pair donor), in this example the hydroxide ion; and the 2 indicates a *molecularity* of 2. (The 2 *may* also indicate the order *but* if the reaction is carried out with a large excess of hydroxide ions then pseudo first-order kinetics are observed.)

The dotted lines in the transition state indicate partial bonds, and the negative charge is delocalized or 'spread out' over both the partial bonds. The transition state is preceded and followed by the two related structures shown below, which show the HO–C bond getting shorter and stronger as the C–Br bond gets longer and weaker:

$$[HO\cdots\cdots\cdots C_2H_5\cdots Br]^- \qquad \text{and} \qquad [HO\cdots\cdots C_2H_5\cdots\cdots\cdots\cdots Br]^-$$

In contrast, the hydrolysis of 2-bromo-2-methylpropane (tertiary-butyl bromide), $(CH_3)_3CBr$, exhibits first-order kinetics:

$$\text{rate} = k[(CH_3)_3CBr]$$

and so the initial rate is *independent* of the concentration of the alkali. In other words, it exhibits zero-order kinetics with respect to hydroxide ions. The kinetic data suggests a unimolecular mechanism that involves only the 2-bromo-2-methylpropane in a rate-determining step:

Step 1 $(CH_3)_3Br \Rightarrow (CH_3)_3C^+ + Br^-$

Step 2 $(CH_3)_3C^+ + H_2O \Rightarrow (CH_3)_3COH + H^+$

This hydrolysis is a unimolecular first-order reaction, termed S_N1, where the S indicates substitution, the N indicates that the organic species is attacked by a nucleophile (electron pair donor, in this example the hydroxide ion), and the 1 indicates a molecularity of 1.

(Note: a more detailed description of this mechanism using curly arrows to show electron pair movement is given in Chapter 20.)

Chain reactions

Reactions with very high rates often involve chemical species called radicals which contain one or more unpaired electrons. These are formed when a covalent bond is split homolytically. During this process each of the atoms or groups involved in the covalent bond accepts one of the bonding or shared pair of electrons:

$$A\!:\!B \rightarrow A\bullet + B\bullet$$

Homolytic cleavage of bonds frequently takes place at high temperatures, in the presence of ultraviolet light or when reactions are carried out in non-polar solvents. Homolytic cleavage in a molecule usually occurs in the weakest bond, which is often a single bond.

The explosive reaction between hydrogen and chlorine in the presence of sunlight is an example of a so-called chain reaction that involves free radicals as intermediates. The first step of the mechanism is an endothermic step involving the absorption of the ultraviolet light present in sunlight. The chlorine molecules dissociate into chlorine atoms, which contain seven valence electrons, one of which is unpaired:

$$Cl_2 \rightarrow 2Cl\bullet$$

(Note: for simplicity only the single unpaired electron is drawn to emphasize the radical nature of the chlorine atom.) This step of the mechanism is known as the initiation step.

The chlorine atoms or radicals then react with hydrogen molecules to release hydrogen atoms or radicals. This and the subsequent step in the mechanism are termed propagation steps, since in these steps the product, HCl, is formed along with another free radical:

$$Cl\bullet + H_2 \rightarrow HCl + H\bullet$$

The hydrogen atoms or radicals formed react with chlorine molecules to regenerate the chlorine atoms or radicals:

$$H\bullet + Cl_2 \rightarrow HCl + Cl\bullet$$

The two propagation steps often occur many times, constituting a chain reaction. The reaction rates of the two propagation steps are very high because of the relatively low activation energies for these two steps of the mechanism.

The chain reaction stops when two free radicals combine to form molecules. These steps are called chain termination steps and three operate in this mechanism:

$$2Cl\bullet \rightarrow Cl_2 \qquad 2H\bullet \rightarrow H_2 \qquad H\bullet + Cl\bullet \rightarrow HCl$$

 Free-radical chain reactions also occur during the chlorination of methane (Chapter 10) and of the methyl group of methylbenzene. Ozone depletion by chlorofluorocarbons (CFCs), acid rain formation and formation of photochemical smog (Chapter 25 on the accompanying website) also involve free-radical reactions. (Free-radical reactions are also operating in unpolluted atmospheres and play an important role in all chemical reactions that occur in the gas phase.) The combustion of hydrocarbons, such as petrol, also proceeds via a free-radical mechanism, which has important consequences for the smooth running and performance of combustion engines. Chain reactions may also have ions as intermediates, as opposed to free radicals.

■ Transition-state theory

Single-step reactions

This theory suggests that as molecules collide, and bond breaking and bond formation take place, the interacting molecules are temporarily in a high-energy and unstable state. This state is known as a transition state or activated complex. It is invariably of higher enthalpy or potential energy than either reactants or products and is inherently unstable. The transition state can either decompose to re-form the reactants, or it can undergo further changes to form the product molecules (or an intermediate). This is illustrated by the simple bimolecular reaction between hydrogen and iodine to form hydrogen iodide (see Figure 16.17):

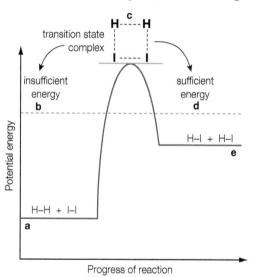

■ **Figure 16.17** Enthalpy or potential energy level diagram for the formation of hydrogen iodide

a represents the enthalpy of the individual reactant hydrogen and iodine molecules;

b weak covalent bonds start to form between the hydrogen and iodine atoms of the hydrogen and iodine molecules and, simultaneously, the hydrogen–hydrogen and iodine–iodine bonds start to lengthen and weaken;

c represents the formation of the transition state or activated complex;

d the two hydrogen–iodine bonds continue to shorten and strengthen, while the hydrogen–hydrogen and iodine–iodine bonds continue to lengthen and weaken; in other words, electron density steadily increases between the hydrogen and iodine atoms;

e represents the formation of the two hydrogen iodide molecules.

Hydrogen iodide is only formed if the colliding hydrogen and iodine molecules have sufficient kinetic energy to overcome the energy barrier, which corresponds here to the activation energy. A successful reaction also requires the hydrogen and iodine molecules to collide in a 'sideways' fashion: a so-called steric factor. Transition-state theory (TST) can be used to calculate reaction rates and transition states from a knowledge of the molecular structures and shapes of reactants.

Multi-step reactions

Many reactions involve a sequence of elementary steps, with the rate expression being determined by the nature of the rate-determining step (RDS). Only those species involved in this step are included in the rate expression for that reaction. The sequence of steps is referred to as the reaction mechanism. It is possible to link the ideas involved here with transition-state theory and develop potential energy level profiles that reflect the sequence of steps involved. Consider the reaction

$$2NO_2(g) + F_2(g) \rightarrow 2NO_2F(g)$$

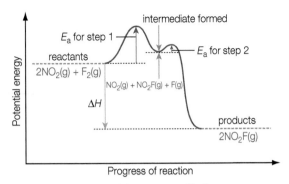

■ **Figure 16.18** Potential energy profile for a two-step reaction. The formation of an intermediate is represented by the potential energy well in the profile. Step 1 is the rate-determining step in this case.

For this reaction to happen in a single step would require three molecules to collide simultaneously and in the correct orientation – a highly unlikely event, particularly in the gas phase. Experiments show that the rate expression for this reaction is:

$$\text{rate} = k[NO_2][F_2]$$

and the suggested mechanism is:

Step 1 $NO_2 + F_2 \rightarrow NO_2F + F$ slow, rate-determining step
Step 2 $NO_2 + F \rightarrow NO_2F$ fast

The potential energy profile for this reaction is shown in Figure 16.18 and it can be seen that the rate-determining step (step 1) has a higher activation energy than the other step. The activation energy for the overall reaction is equal to the activation energy of the slow, rate-determining step.

More complex situations arise where the first step of a sequence is not the rate-determining step, for instance in the oxidation of nitrogen(II) oxide

$$2NO(g) + O_2(g) \rightarrow 2NO_2(g)$$

for which the following reaction mechanism has been proposed:

Step 1 $NO(g) + NO(g) \rightarrow N_2O_2(g)$ fast

Step 2 $N_2O_2(g) + O_2(g) \rightarrow 2NO_2(g)$ slow, rate-determining step

Consequently the rate of reaction depends on step 2 of the sequence, for which the rate expression is

$$\text{rate} = k[N_2O_2(g)][O_2(g)]$$

However, N_2O_2 is the intermediate product of step 1, and so the concentration of this intermediate depends on $[NO]^2$, since the first step is second order with respect to NO. Therefore this fact must be substituted into the rate expression, which then becomes

$$\text{rate} = k[NO(g)]^2[O_2(g)]$$

The overall order of this reaction is, therefore, 3.

---

7 a Check for yourself that the sum of the equations for the two steps of the mechanism proposed above for the oxidation of nitrogen(II) oxide is the same as the observed stoichiometric equation.
   b Sketch the potential energy profile of this reaction as an example of a case where the rate-determining step is not the first step of the mechanism.

8 Gaseous reaction mixtures can contain a complex mixture of molecular species. Nitrogen(V) oxide decomposes in the following reaction

$$2N_2O_5(g) \rightarrow 4NO_2(g) + O_2(g)$$

which is found experimentally to have the following rate expression:

$$\text{rate} = k[N_2O_5]$$

Figure 16.19 shows a suggested mechanism for this reaction. The rate equation suggests that a single N_2O_5 molecule is involved in the rate-determining step. This fits with the proposed mechanism, which suggests that the decomposition of N_2O_5 to form NO_2 and NO_3 is the slow step. The steps which follow the slow step are relatively fast and so have no effect on the reaction rate.

By suitably numbering or labelling the stages in a copy of the diagram, visually try to match the reaction steps with the illustrations to get a picture of what is happening.

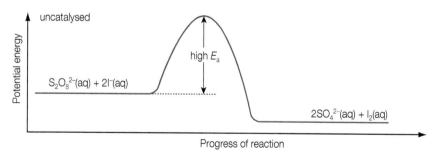

In the first step each
molecule breaks down.
They do not collide in pairs.

$$N_2O_5 \xrightarrow{\text{slow}} NO_2 + NO_3$$

$$NO_2 + NO_3 \xrightarrow{\text{fast}} NO + NO_2 + O_2$$

$$NO + NO_3 \xrightarrow{\text{fast}} 2NO_2$$

(Note that two molecules of N_2O_5 need to have reacted for subsequent steps to be completed)

■ **Figure 16.19** The proposed mechanism for the decomposition of N_2O_5

■ Reactions involving a catalyst

In our earlier discussion we saw that the reaction between propanone and iodine was a multi-step reaction catalysed by H^+ ions which participated in the first, rate-determining step. Catalysts change a reaction mechanism by providing an alternative pathway that has a lower activation energy. This will be reflected in the potential energy profile of the reaction, as the activation energy of this first catalysed step will be lower than that of the uncatalysed reaction.

The reaction in which iodide ions are oxidized by peroxodisulfate ions requires homogeneous catalysis by iron(II) ions (Figure 16.20). The uncatalysed reaction involving direct reaction between negatively charged iodide and peroxodisulfate ions has a high activation energy and hence a slow reaction rate. In order to collide and react, these ions need considerable energy to overcome the repulsive forces when ions of the same charge approach each other.

$$S_2O_8^{2-}(aq) + 2I^-(aq) \rightarrow 2SO_4^{2-}(aq) + I_2(aq)$$

The presence of iron(II) ions provides an alternative mechanism that involves two elementary steps involving reactions between oppositely charged ions, which have lower activation energies and hence higher rate constants:

$$2Fe^{2+}(aq) + S_2O_8^{2-} \rightleftharpoons 2Fe^{3+}(aq) + 2SO_4^{2-}(aq)$$

$$2Fe^{3+}(aq) + 2I^- \rightleftharpoons 2Fe^{2+}(aq) + I_2(aq)$$

■ **Figure 16.20**
Energy level diagrams
for the uncatalysed
and catalysed oxidation
of iodide ions and
peroxodisulfate ions.

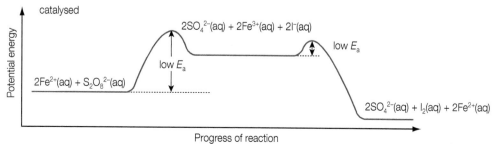

The iron(II) ion catalyst is consumed during the first elementary step, but is 'regenerated' in the second elementary step. The iron(III) ion intermediate is readily detected and studied by spectroscopic techniques.

---

9 Sketch the potential energy profile for the reaction between propanone and iodine. Simplify the diagram by combining the fast stages into one combined second stage.

10 The mechanism for a reaction is:

$$XY_2 + XY_2 \rightarrow X_2Y_4 \qquad \text{slow}$$
$$X_2Y_4 \rightarrow X_2 + 2Y_2 \qquad \text{fast}$$

   a What is the overall equation for the reaction?
   b What is the rate expression for the reaction?
   c What are the units of the rate constant, k, in this rate expression?
   d Sketch the potential energy profile for the reaction.

ToK Link

Theoretical developments

In science, theories are proposed and then tested, in various ways, over time. The story of the transition-state theory provides an interesting example.

The concept of a transition state originates from **transition-state theory**. Before transition-state theory, chemists had explained rates of reactions in terms of collision theory, which is based on the kinetic theory of gases. It treats collisions by regarding the reacting molecules as hard spheres colliding with one another. Transition-state theory does not conflict with collision theory. It assumes that reactions involve collisions but takes into account some of the details of the collision, such as how the reacting molecules must approach one another for a reaction to be possible and what the effect of a solvent might be. None of these factors are taken into account by simple collision theory.

One of the assumptions of transition-state theory is that the transition state is, in a certain sense, at equilibrium with the reacting molecules. This special kind of equilibrium is termed a quasi-equilibrium. Transition states do not exist except as the state corresponding to the highest energy value on a reaction coordinate plot: they cannot be captured or directly observed. However, the technique known as femtochemical infrared spectroscopy mentioned earlier allows chemists to probe molecular structure extremely close to the transition point. Transition-state theory was first proposed in a paper published in 1933 by an American chemist called Henry Eyring. The theory has withstood the test of time – so far – but it has not been successful in predicting, from first principles, the rates of chemical reactions.

Nature of Science

Establishing the mechanism – the principles behind the proposition

There are a number of ways of exploring the circumstances of a reaction in order to propose a reaction mechanism.

- Use sophisticated analytic techniques to discern the changes taking place and their sequence. These may possibly be able to detect the presence of the postulated intermediate in a reaction. For instance, the use of nuclear magnetic resonance (see Chapter 11) shows that acidified propanone contains about one molecule in around a hundred in the enol form $CH_2=C(OH)CH_3$ – an intermediate suggested by the proposed mechanism.
- It is possible in some cases to do experiments on the intermediate involved. Some intermediates are sufficiently stable for this. For example, some organic halides form tertiary carbocations that can be isolated.
- Use isotopic labelling – if an atom is labelled with an isotope (not necessarily a radioactive one) the label may indicate which bond has been broken in a reaction. For example, when some esters labelled with ^{18}O are hydrolysed, the ^{18}O appears in the alcohol and not in the acid group. This shows that the acyl oxygen bond, and not the alkyl oxygen bond, is the one that is broken.
- Change the solvent – the rate of ionic reactions changes with the polarity of the solvent. For example, the rate of hydrolysis of 2-bromo-2-methylpropane is raised by the addition of sodium chloride. The sodium chloride increases the polarity of the solvent and increases the ionization of the bromide.

There are some basic considerations to bear in mind when considering the validity of a proposed mechanism:

■ The mechanism must agree with the stoichiometric equation – the sum of the equations for the elementary steps must result in the overall equation.
■ No elementary step should involve more than two particles.
■ All the species in the rate expression must appear in the mechanism in or before the rate-determining step.
■ The power to which the concentration of a particular reactant is raised in the rate expression indicates the number of times it appears in the mechanism up to, and including, the rate-determining step.

When trying to establish a mechanism it is often useful to use the principle of Occam's razor when deciding between two conflicting possibilities which satisfy the above criteria. The simpler mechanism should be adopted until further evidence is found which falsifies the suggested sequence of reactions.

Additional Perspectives

One intriguing area of study for project work that highlights the interplay between competing intermediates in a reaction mechanism is the study of oscillating reactions such as the Briggs–Rauscher and Belousov–Zhabotinsky (BZ) reactions. The Briggs–Rauscher reaction shows periodic changes in colour: a sudden change from amber to dark blue, followed by a gradual change back from dark blue to amber. The solution ends up as a blue-black colour if the proportions quoted in the original method are used (it finishes colourless if a higher ratio of malonic acid to iodate(v) is used). The reaction occurs in a series of elementary steps but can be summarized as follows:

$$IO_3^-(aq) + 2H_2O_2(aq) + CH_2(COOH)_2(aq) + H^+(aq) \rightarrow ICH(COOH)_2(aq) + 2O_2(g) + 3H_2O(l)$$

The reaction mixture involves hydrogen peroxide, the iodate(v) ion, malonic acid, with Mn^{2+} ions as catalyst and sulfuric acid also present to provide H^+ ions. The complex mechanism has two component reactions:

• the slow consumption of free iodine by the malonic acid substrate in the presence of iodate(v); this process involves the intermediate production of iodide ions;
• a fast autocatalytic process involving manganese ions and radical intermediates that converts hydrogen peroxide and iodate(v) to iodine and oxygen; this process also can consume iodide up to a limiting rate. (An autocatalytic reaction is one in which an intermediate that is produced in the reaction catalyses a subsequent step in the reaction.)

It is important to emphasize that the oscillation in the reaction is not between the reactants and products, but rather it is the concentration of intermediates involved in the elementary reactions that are fluctuating. The overall reaction is always moving towards the minimum Gibbs free energy. The reaction can be followed using a colorimeter linked to a data-logging system and provides scope for investigating the interplay of the elementary steps in the mechanism, besides providing a visually fascinating reaction sequence.

16.2 Activation energy – *the activation energy of a reaction can be determined from the effect of temperature on reaction rate*

■ The effect of temperature

Svante Arrhenius (1859–1927) was a Swedish physical chemist who was awarded the Nobel Prize in Chemistry in 1903 for his work on ionic solutions. His theory of acids and bases defined acids as substances that produce hydrogen ions in solution (as the only positive ions) and bases as substances that produce hydroxide ions (as the only negative ions). In addition he explored the relationship between the rate of a chemical reaction and temperature. The equation which bears his name was originally proposed by the Dutch chemist J.H. van't Hoff, but it was Arrhenius who provided a physical interpretation and justification for it.

When the temperature increases, the rate of a chemical reaction increases very rapidly. It has been found that for many reactions, the initial rate and the rate constant,

■ **Figure 16.21** Svante Arrhenius

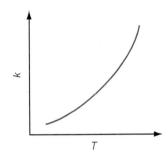

k, vary with temperature in an exponential manner (Figure 16.22). This relationship between absolute temperature and the rate constant can be approximately described or modelled by the Arrhenius equation:

$$k = Ae^{-E_a/RT}$$

The Arrhenius equation describes reactions involving gases, as well as those occurring in solution or on the surface of a catalyst. E_a and A are both constants characteristic of a particular reaction, R is a fundamental physical constant for all reactions and T and k are variables. None of the three constants change significantly with temperature. The expression $(e^{-E_a/RT})$ is known as the exponential factor and allows for the large effect of an increase in temperature in the Arrhenius equation.

A represents the Arrhenius constant or frequency factor (which has the same units as the rate constant, k, usually $dm^3 mol^{-1} s^{-1}$), E_a represents the activation energy (units of $kJ mol^{-1}$), T represents the absolute temperature (in kelvins) and R represents the gas constant $(8.31 J K^{-1} mol^{-1})$. The Arrhenius constant is a measure of the proportion of molecules that collide with enough kinetic energy to react and which also have the correct orientation to react.

The activation energy, E_a, is commonly interpreted as being a measure of the 'energy barrier' that a reaction has to overcome before it can proceed. Its value controls the 'sensitivity' of the reaction to changes in temperature. Low activation energies give rise to fast rates of reaction and a low sensitivity to changes in temperature. Large activation energies give rise to slow reactions at low temperatures and a high sensitivity to changes in temperature.

The Arrhenius equation is used to calculate the activation energy and the Arrhenius constant of a reaction. First you need to experimentally measure the rate constants of the reaction at several different temperatures. The modified form of the Arrhenius equation shown below is used to transform the data so that an Arrhenius plot can be produced (see below):

$$\ln k = \ln A - \frac{E_a}{RT}$$

■ Arrhenius temperature dependence

Some reactions have an activation energy of approximately $50 kJ mol^{-1}$ which means they exhibit a so-called Arrhenius temperature dependence: a rise in temperature of 10 °C will approximately double the initial rate and rate constant of the reaction over a range of temperatures (Figure 16.23). This is often stated as a general rule, but care is required since values of activation energies vary considerably, so reactions may be either much faster or much slower. Such considerations are of importance in materials research, where the temperature sensitivity of reactions is crucial. Research into the temperature dependence of memory devices such as flash drives is based on the Arrhenius equation, and such studies aid manufacturers in ensuring memory retention under a variety of conditions.

■ **Figure 16.23** Arrhenius temperature dependence

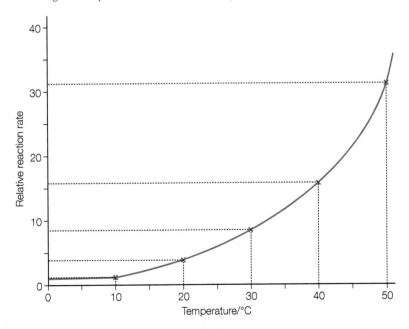

Utilization: The flashing of fireflies

Intriguingly, the Arrhenius equation has been applied to a range of biological phenomena that are chemically dependent. These include the frequency of flashing of fireflies, which depends on the activity of the enzyme luciferase. It has been found that the temperature dependence of the frequency of flashing fitted the equation and generated a value for the activation energy of this activity.

■ Calculating activation energies graphically

If you take natural logarithms of both sides of the original form of the Arrhenius equation and rearrange it, you get:

$$k = A \, e^{-E_a/RT}$$

$$\ln k = \ln A + \ln(e^{-E_a/RT})$$

$$\ln k = \ln A - \frac{E_a}{RT}$$

$$\ln k = \ln A - \left(\frac{E_a}{R}\right)\frac{1}{T}$$

This form of the Arrhenius equation fits the general formula for a straight line, that is, $y = mx + c$. Here $\ln k$ is analogous to y, m to $-E_a/R$, x to T^{-1} and $\ln A$ to c. Essentially, the original Arrhenius equation describing a curve has been transformed into a more useful linear or 'straight line' form (Figure 16.24).

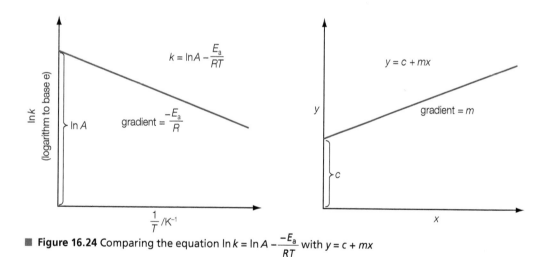

■ **Figure 16.24** Comparing the equation $\ln k = \ln A - \dfrac{-E_a}{RT}$ with $y = c + mx$

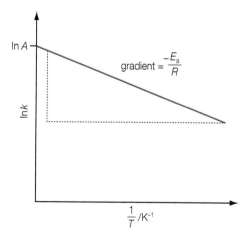

■ **Figure 16.25** An Arrhenius plot of $\ln k$ against T^{-1}

An **Arrhenius plot** is a graph of the natural logarithm of the rate constants, k, against the reciprocal of the corresponding absolute temperatures (T^{-1}). As the temperature, T, increases, $-E_a/RT$ becomes less negative, and $\ln k$ (and therefore the rate constant k) increases.

A sloping straight-line graph (Figure 16.25) is obtained, which can be used to calculate the experimental activation energy and Arrhenius factor. The slope or gradient has a value of $-E_a/R$ and the intercept on the rate constant axis is $\ln A$. Alternatively, once the activation energy, E_a, has been determined, the Arrhenius constant, A, can be calculated by substituting into the Arrhenius equation. The Arrhenius plot will give an initial value for the activation energy in $J\,mol^{-1}$, provided that temperatures are measured in kelvins and the gas constant is expressed in $J\,mol^{-1}\,K^{-1}$.

Worked example

The rate constant, k, was determined for a reaction at various temperatures. The results are given in the table.

Temperature/°C	Second-order rate constant, $k/\text{mol}^{-1}\,\text{dm}^3\,\text{s}^{-1}$
5	6.81×10^{-6}
15	1.40×10^{-5}
25	2.93×10^{-5}
35	6.11×10^{-5}

a   Plot a graph of $\ln k$ against T^{-1} where T must be expressed as an absolute temperature. (Take the $\ln k$ axis from −12 to −8 and the T^{-1} axis from 0.0030 to 0.0038.)

b   Calculate the gradient (slope) of your Arrhenius plot and use it to determine a value for the activation energy, E_a, in $\text{kJ}\,\text{mol}^{-1}$.

c   Calculate an approximate value for the Arrhenius constant, A, using the Arrhenius plot.

a   First, draw up a table showing T^{-1} and $\ln k$ values.

T^{-1}/K^{-1}	$\ln k$
3.597×10^{-3}	−11.90
3.472×10^{-3}	−11.18
3.356×10^{-3}	−10.44
3.247×10^{-3}	−9.70

Use these values to draw the Arrhenius plot (Figure 16.26).

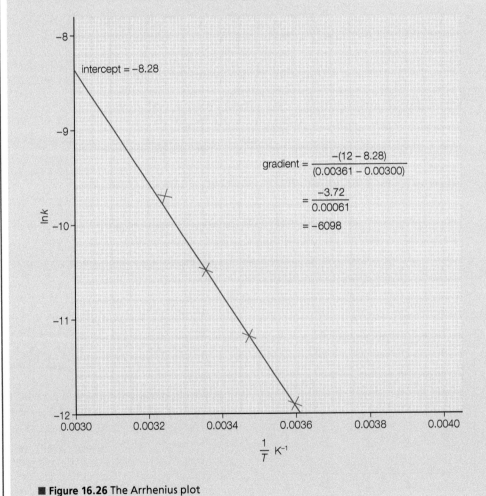

■ **Figure 16.26** The Arrhenius plot

b From the graph,

y-intercept = −8.28

gradient = −6098

So $\quad y = -6098x - 8.28$

The straight line gives:

$$\text{slope} = -\frac{E_a}{RT} = -6098\,\text{K}$$

$$-E_a = -6098\,\text{K} \times 8.31\,\text{J}\,\text{mol}^{-1}\,\text{K}^{-1}$$

$$E_a = 50.7\,\text{kJ}\,\text{mol}^{-1}$$

c Intercept $\quad \ln A = -8.28$

$$A \approx 2.5 \times 10^{-4}\,\text{mol}^{-1}\,\text{dm}^3\,\text{s}^{-1}$$

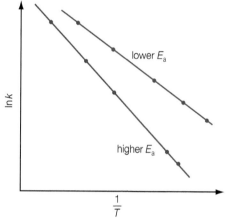

■ **Figure 16.27** Arrhenius plots for two reactions with different activation energies

If Arrhenius plots are drawn on the same axes for two reactions with different activation energies (Figure 16.27) you can see that the reaction with the higher activation energy has a steeper gradient. This indicates that the rate constant, and hence the initial rate, will change with temperature much more quickly than for the reaction with the lower activation energy. This is because the value of the activation energy is given by the expression $-R \times$ gradient.

Finding the activation energy non-graphically

The activation energy can also be calculated from two values of the rate constant, k_1 and k_2, at only two temperatures, T_1 and T_2, by using the following formula:

$$\ln k_2 - \ln k_1 = \frac{-E_a}{R}\left(\frac{1}{T_2} - \frac{1}{T_1}\right)$$

Worked example

The rate constant for a reaction increases by a factor of 1.65 when the temperature is increased from 20 °C to 40 °C. Calculate the activation energy.

$$\ln(1.65) = \frac{-E_a}{8.31 \times 10^{-3}}\left(\frac{1}{313} - \frac{1}{293}\right)$$

$$E_a = 19.1\,\text{kJ}\,\text{mol}^{-1}$$

■ Catalysis

Catalysts are substances that increase the rate constant of a particular chemical reaction but remain chemically unchanged. There are three types of catalysts: homogeneous catalysts, heterogeneous catalysts and enzymes.

Homogeneous catalysts are in the same physical state as the reactants. Often both the catalyst and the reactants are in solution.

Heterogeneous catalysts are in a different physical state or phase from the reactants. Often the reactants are gases and the catalyst is a solid, frequently a transition metal or a transition metal compound. Many industrial processes use heterogeneous catalysts (Chapter 13).

The action of catalysts may be modified by the presence of low concentrations of certain substances, which may be classified as either promoters, inhibitors or catalyst poisons. Promoters increase rates of reactions. For example, in the Haber process (Chapter 7) traces of the metal molybdenum act as a promoter for the iron catalyst. Inhibitors slow down the rates of catalysed reactions by reacting with and removing intermediates. Catalyst poisons greatly reduce the rates of catalysed reactions by binding to catalytic sites on the surface of the heterogeneous catalyst. Examples include arsenic, carbon monoxide and hydrogen cyanide.

The rate of catalysed reactions depends on the 'amount' of catalyst present. For a homogeneous catalyst the reaction rate depends on the concentration of the catalyst. The rate of a heterogeneous catalysed reaction depends on the surface area of the catalyst.

 Enzymes are biological catalysts present in living cells (see Chapter 23 on the accompanying website). They are large globular protein molecules, consisting of a large number of amino acid molecules polymerized together (Chapter 20). They frequently contain a metal ion in their active site, where the catalysis occurs. Unlike other catalysts, enzymes only increase reaction rates over a narrow pH range (typically about pH 5 to pH 8) and a narrow temperature range (typically about 20–40 °C). They are also very sensitive to the presence of various inhibitors which affect their kinetic behaviour.

Homogeneous catalysis

Homogeneous catalysis usually involves the formation of an intermediate during the reaction, which then decomposes to form the product and the unchanged catalyst (Figure 16.28). The presence of a catalyst provides an alternative pathway that is more energetically favourable. Generally, the rate is directly proportional to the concentration of the catalyst.

■ **Figure 16.28**
The principle of homogeneous catalysis

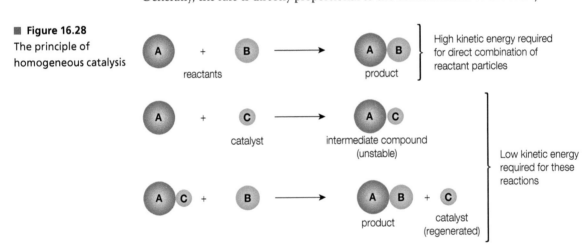

The homogeneous catalysis by iron(II) ions of the reaction between iodide and peroxodisulfate ions has been discussed earlier (see Figure 16.20). The uncatalysed reaction involving direct reaction between negatively charged iodide and peroxodisulfate ions has a high activation energy and hence a slow reaction rate, but the presence of iron(II) ions provides an alternative mechanism with two elementary steps that involve reactions between *oppositely charged* ions which have lower activation energies and hence higher rate constants.

Heterogeneous catalysis

Usually the process involves the reaction of two gases on the surface of a solid catalyst, which is often in the form of a powder. Such reactions are not only important in many industrial processes, but are also involved in acid rain formation and ozone depletion.

All heterogeneous catalysis occurs at a phase boundary, often involving the reaction of gas molecules on the surface of a solid. Figures 16.29 and 16.30 show the five steps that are thought to occur during heterogeneous catalysis, using the hydrogenation of ethene by hydrogen in the presence of a nickel catalyst as an example.

The *first* step in heterogeneous catalysis involves the diffusion of the reacting gas molecules onto the surface of the catalyst. The *second* step involves the adsorption (Figure 16.29) of the reacting gas molecules onto the surface of the metal, where they are temporarily bonded to the surface by weak intermolecular forces and/or dative or coordinate covalent bonds.

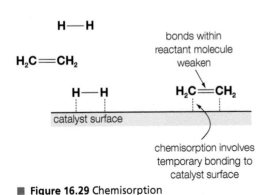

■ **Figure 16.29** Chemisorption

product molecule desorbed
(i.e. leaves the catalyst surface)

Figure 16.30 Desorption

The *third* step involves the breaking of and formation of chemical bonds to bring about the formation of the product molecules. The activation energy for the reaction is lowered (relative to the uncatalysed reaction) because the reaction follows a different pathway, one with lower activation energy barriers. During the *fourth* step, desorption, the product molecules break free from the surface of the catalyst; this is the reverse of the adsorption step (Figure 16.30).

Finally, in the *fifth* step the molecules of the gaseous product diffuse away from the surface of the catalyst. Their places on the catalytic surface are then occupied by unreacted gas molecules.

A great deal of knowledge has been gained into the mechanism of surface catalysis by studying examples of 'exchange reactions'. This is the term used to describe the substitution in a compound of one isotope for another of the same element, for example, deuterium for hydrogen.

When a mixture of ethane, C_2H_6, and deuterium, D_2, is exposed at moderate temperatures to the surfaces of transition metals which are efficient catalysts in hydrogenation reactions (nickel, copper or palladium, for instance), deuterium is exchanged for hydrogen in successive reactions, of which the first is:

$$C_2H_6(g) + D_2(g) \rightleftharpoons C_2H_5D(g) + HD(g)$$

It is found that the experimental data is explained by supposing that the metal surface covers itself with a layer of activated molecules of deuterium similar to the situation shown in Figure 16.29. The advantage of studying such exchange reactions is that the stabilities of hydrides and deuterides are equal, and hence attention may be focused exclusively on the surface conditions.

Enzymes

Enzymes catalyse a wide range of biochemical reactions inside cells. These reactions take place in dilute solution at 37 °C. An enzyme is a protein molecule, and is highly specific for a particular reaction. The substrate becomes bound to the active site by non-covalent interactions that depend very specifically on the three-dimensional shapes of the enzyme and substrate. The reaction then takes place in the active site. The products are less strongly bound and fit the active site less well, so they are released from the enzyme, which is then free to react with another substrate molecule. This is the 'lock and key' model of enzyme activity (Figure 16.31). Enzymes, like other catalysts, work by providing an alternative pathway (mechanism) with a lower activation energy. If the enzyme is heated above body temperature, the enzyme changes shape (it is denatured) and loses its activity.

Figure 16.31
The 'lock and key' model of enzyme catalysis

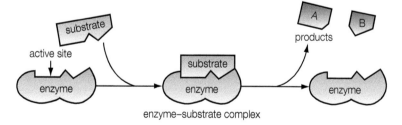

Enzymes are usually only present in very small amounts. If the substrate concentration is high enough, all the enzyme molecules will have substrates attached at any moment during the reaction. So, if the substrate concentration increases, no more enzyme–substrate complexes can be formed, and the rate of the enzyme-catalysed reaction is independent of the concentration of the substrate – the reaction is zero order with respect to the substrate.

Key industrial processes

The first time a catalyst was used in the chemical industry was in 1746 by J Roebuck, in the lead chamber process. The lead chamber process was the first approach to the industrial production of sulfuric acid. In it, sulfur dioxide is oxidized by nitrogen dioxide in the presence of water. This reaction was carried out in wooden chambers lined with lead. Both the lead chamber and the Contact process are catalytic, and both depend upon the oxidation of sulfur dioxide by atmospheric oxygen. The Contact process yields a purer and more concentrated sulfuric acid than the cheaper lead chamber process. The lead chamber process is now largely rendered obsolete on environmental grounds and has been largely replaced by the Contact process.

Sulfuric acid is manufactured on a very large scale and is used in many areas of the chemical industry. Sulfuric acid is used in lead–acid batteries, cellophane, detergents, paints, fertilizers, ore processing, steel production and water treatment and nylon production. In 1843 Justus von Liebig (see Chapter 8) suggested that the commercial prosperity of a country could be judged by the amount of sulfuric acid it produced. His reasons were a consequence of its use in a wide variety of industries and its being too hazardous to store in large quantities, meaning that it was only produced as required. This, in particular, makes it a very sensitive indicator of industrial activity. Sulfuric acid was the key industrial chemical until the first half of the 20th century. During those years, industry was dominated by metal products and natural fibres, with phosphate as the most important fertilizer. However, the chemical industry has changed and plastics are now the most important products and nitrogen compounds the most important fertilizers. A better guide to a country's prosperity may therefore be the production of ammonia or organic chemicals, especially ethene (which is widely used to make many plastics).

The American Chemical Council has developed CAB (a Chemical Activity Barometer – see www.americanchemistry.com/CAB). This is an economic indicator that predicts peaks and troughs in the overall economy in the USA and highlights trends in a range of industries using a number of different criteria. The website gives an insight into the importance of chemistry to the global economy.

■ Summary of factors affecting the rate of reaction

In general, other factors being similar, the higher the activation energy for a reaction the slower it will be. The value of the frequency factor, A, will be smaller for reactions between larger, more complex molecules because they can collide in more diverse ways and only a small proportion of them will be in the correct orientation for reaction. Collisions between individual atoms, however, will almost always be correctly orientated for reaction.

The effect of a catalyst on the rate equation is to increase the value of the rate constant. Table 16.11 summarizes the changes that affect the rate of reaction and the rate constant. Rate constants are unaffected by changes in concentration and are only affected by temperature (as described by the Arrhenius equation) or the presence of a catalyst, which provides a new pathway or reaction mechanism. Rates increase with concentration and pressure (if gaseous reactants are involved), which can be accounted for by simple collision theory (Chapter 6).

■ **Table 16.11**
Summary of the changes that affect the rate of reaction and the rate constant

Change	Effect on rate of reaction	Effect on rate constant, k	Notes
Increase in concentration	Increased	No change	
Increase in pressure	Increased	No change	Only applies to gaseous reactants
Increase in temperature	Increased	Increased	
Use of a catalyst	Increased	Increased	A catalyst changes the rate expression

■ *Examination questions – a selection*

Paper 1 IB questions and IB style questions

Q1 Under acidic conditions hydrogen peroxide oxidises iodide ions to iodine in the following reaction.

$$H_2O_2(aq) + 2H^+(aq) + 2I^-(aq) \rightarrow 2H_2O(l) + I_2(aq)$$

Kinetic studies of this reaction using different initial concentrations of reactants at a constant temperature

Initial [$H_2O_2(aq)$]/ mol dm^{-3}	Initial [$H^+(aq)$]/ mol dm^{-3}	Initial [$I^-(aq)$]/ mol dm^{-3}	Initial rate of reaction/ mol dm^{-3} s^{-1}
0.005	0.05	0.015	1.31×10^{-6}
0.01	0.05	0.015	2.63×10^{-6}
0.01	0.05	0.03	5.25×10^{-6}
0.01	0.1	0.03	5.25×10^{-6}

What is the overall order of the reaction?
A zero order
B first order
C second order
D third order

Q2 Which step in a multi-step reaction mechanism will be rate-determining?
A the first step
B the last step
C the step with the highest activation energy
D the step with the lowest activation energy
Higher level Paper 1, Nov 2012, Q21

Q3 For the reaction

$$(CH_3)_3CBr + OH^- \rightarrow (CH_3)_3COH + Br^-$$

it is experimentally found that doubling the concentration of $(CH_3)_3CBr$ causes the reaction rate to be increased by a factor of 2, but doubling the concentration of OH^- has no effect on the rate. What is the rate expression?
A rate = $k[(CH_3)_3CBr]^2[OH^-]$
B rate = $k[(CH_3)_3CBr][OH^-]$
C rate = $k[(CH_3)_3CBr]$
D rate = $k[(CH_3)_3COH][Br^-]$

Q4 To what does *A* refer in the Arrhenius equation $k = Ae^{-E_a/RT}$?
A activation energy
B rate constant
C gas constant
D collision geometry
Higher Level Paper 1, Nov 2005, Q21

Q5 The rate expression for a reaction is shown below:
rate = $k[A]^2[B]^2$
Which statements are correct for this reaction?
I The reaction is second order with respect to both A and B.
II The overall order of the reaction is 4.
III Doubling the concentration of A would have the same effect on the rate of reaction as doubling the concentration of B.
A I and II only
B I and III only
C II and III only
D I, II and III
Higher Level Paper 1, Nov 2003, Q20

Q6 Which graph would be produced by a second order reaction if the rate equation is rate = $k[X]^2$?

A
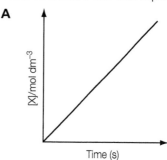

B
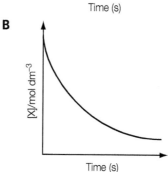

C
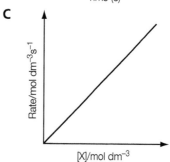

D
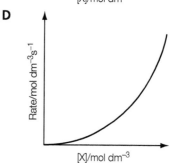

Higher level Paper 1, Nov 2012, Q20

Q7 In aqueous solution, iodine reacts with propanone as represented by the following stoichiometric equation:

$I_2 + CH_3COCH_3 \rightarrow CH_3COCH_2I + H^+ + I^-$

The experimental rate expression is:

rate $= k[H^+][CH_3COCH_3]$

From this information it can be concluded that increasing the iodine concentration will:

A decrease the value of the equilibrium constant.

B increase the value of the equilibrium constant.

C decrease the rate of the reaction.

D not affect the rate of reaction.

Paper 2 IB questions and IB style questions

Q1 Re-write

a The rate constant, k, for a reaction varies with temperature in an exponential manner according to the Arrhenius equation.

$k = Ae^{-E_a/RT}$

Describe what you understand by the term *frequency (pre-exponential) factor, A*. [1]

b The iodoalkane 1-iodoethane reacts with sodium hydroxide in a substitution reaction. The activation energy, E_a, for this reaction is found to be $87.0\,kJ\,mol^{-1}$, and the frequency (pre-exponential) factor, A, is $2.10 \times 10^{11}\,mol^{-1}\,dm^{-3}\,s^{-1}$.
Calculate the rate constant, k, of the reaction at 25 °C. State the units of k, and give the reason for your choice. [2]

Q2 Chemical kinetics involves an understanding of how the molecular world changes with time.
a i Define the term rate of reaction. [1]
ii Temperature and the addition of a catalyst are two factors that can affect the rate of a reaction. State two other factors. [2]
iii In the reaction represented below, state one method that can be used to measure the rate of the reaction.

$ClO_3^-(aq) + 5Cl^-(aq) + 6H^+(aq)$
$\rightarrow 3Cl_2(aq) + 3H_2O(l)$ [1]

b A catalyst provides an alternative pathway for a reaction, lowering the activation energy, E_a.
i Define the term activation energy, E_a. [1]
ii Sketch the two Maxwell–Boltzmann energy distribution curves for a fixed amount of gas at two different temperatures, T_1 and T_2 ($T_2 > T_1$). Label both axes. [3]

Higher level Paper 2, Nov 2012, QB6

Q3 Dinitrogen oxide decomposes to give nitrogen and oxygen according to the following equation:

$2N_2O(g) \rightarrow 2N_2(g) + O_2(g)$ $\Delta H = -82\,kJ\,mol^{-1}$

The decomposition is a first-order reaction in the presence of gold as a catalyst. The half-life of the catalysed reaction at 834 °C is 1.62×10^4 s.
i Calculate the rate constant (velocity constant), k, for the reaction at this temperature and give the units of k. [1]
ii Calculate the activation energy of the reaction at this temperature, given the Arrhenius constant, $A = 25\,s^{-1}$. [2]

Higher Level Paper 2, Nov 1999, Q3a

Q4 Evidence suggests that the reaction between the gases nitrogen dioxide and fluorine is a two-step process:

$2NO_2(g) + F_2(g) \rightarrow 2NO_2F(g)$

Step 1 $NO_2 + F_2 \rightarrow NO_2F + F$ (slow)
Step 2 $F + NO_2 \rightarrow NO_2F$ (fast)

a State and explain which step is the rate-determining step. [1]
b State and explain which of the two steps is expected to have the higher activation energy. [2]
c Give the rate expression of the reaction based on your answer to **a**. [1]

Higher Level Paper 2, Nov 2000, Q5

17 Equilibrium

ESSENTIAL IDEA

- The position of equilibrium can be quantified by the equilibrium law. The equilibrium constant for a particular reaction only depends on the temperature.

Physical equilibria

Evaporation and condensation

Systems that establish a functional equilibrium form a highly significant part of our lives and the world around us, from the biochemical reactions that sustain life to the way in which we generate major industrial chemicals. There are many different examples of physical equilibria that one could focus on but one relatively simple situation is the balance between evaporation and condensation that takes place at the surface of a liquid and the concept of the vapour pressure of a liquid. This equilibrium situation can be generalized for any liquid in a sealed container, and becomes:

$$\text{liquid} \underset{\text{condensation}}{\overset{\text{evaporation}}{\rightleftharpoons}} \text{vapour}$$

■ **Figure 17.1** An oil painting of the *SS Dunedin*, the first ship to complete the successful transport of refrigerated meat on a journey from New Zealand to Britain

The position of the equilibrium will depend on the liquid being used and the temperature. It is this equilibrium that forms the basis for modern refrigeration systems.

It is difficult to over-estimate the importance of the invention of the modern refrigerator in the context of food transportation and storage. The invention of refrigerated transport for food led to a revolution in the globalization of markets and the availability of important commodities across, and between, continents. Commercial organizations experimented with refrigerated shipping in the mid-1870s. The first commercial success came when William Davidson fitted a compression refrigeration unit to the New Zealand sailing vessel *SS Dunedin* in 1882 (Figure 17.1). These developments led to a meat and dairy boom in Australia, New Zealand and South America.

The first gas absorption refrigeration system was developed by Ferdinand Carré of France in 1859 and patented in 1860. He used gaseous ammonia dissolved in water (referred to then as '*aqua ammonia*'). Such systems were not developed for use in homes because of the toxicity of ammonia; however they were used to manufacture ice for sale. In the United States, the consumer public at that time still used the ice box with ice brought in from commercial suppliers, many of whom were still harvesting ice in winter (from frozen lakes, for instance) and storing it in icehouses. An original slant on the significance of the ice-making is highlighted in Paul Theroux's novel *The Mosquito Coast* (and the subsequent film starring Harrison Ford (Figure 17.2)). In his escape to nature from the trappings of affluence in the USA, the one item that Allie Fox, the central character of the book, takes with him is the engineering know-how to build an icehouse. The idiosyncratic inventor has frequent battles with his ammonia-based ice-making machine as he tries to establish his family in the inhospitable surroundings of the Honduran coast. The ice he produces from his refrigeration system based on the liquid–vapour equilibrium is clearly central to how he sees his family surviving and relating to the local people.

■ **Figure 17.2** Harrison Ford in the film *The Mosquito Coast*

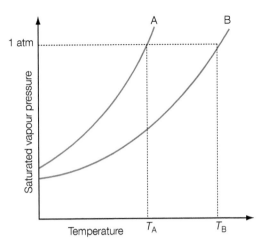

■ **Figure 17.3** Saturated vapour pressure curves for two liquids A and B, where A (e.g. ethanol, b.p. 78 °C) is more volatile than B (e.g. water, b.p. 100 °C)

'Dynamic' is a key word in our understanding of what is happening in liquid–vapour equilibria. It implies continuous activity and helps explain many everyday phenomena relating to the behaviour of liquids, including the variation of boiling point with atmospheric pressure.

Figure 17.3 shows how the saturated vapour pressure of a liquid increases with temperature. It also shows why two different liquids do not have the same boiling point. As a liquid is heated, its vapour pressure increases. When the temperature of the liquid is raised to the point at which the vapour pressure *equals* the external pressure, vaporization can occur throughout the liquid. Thus, bubbles of vapour form in the liquid and rise to the surface. Since vaporization no longer occurs only at the surface, it can proceed very rapidly. This situation we call 'boiling'; the temperature at which it occurs is the 'boiling point'. If the container is not sealed, then the liquid will boil when its vapour pressure is equal to that of the atmosphere.

Liquid A is more volatile than B. We can see on the graph that, at any temperature, liquid A (ethanol, for instance) has a higher vapour pressure than liquid B (say, water). Consequently, liquid A boils at a lower temperature than liquid B (Figure 17.3). So, at 1 atmosphere, ethanol boils at 78 °C, while water boils at 100 °C.

Looking more closely at these curves it is possible to see why water, for instance, boils at a lower temperature at a higher altitude. In Denver, Colorado – the mile-high city – water boils at 95 °C, while it would boil at 69 °C on the summit of Everest. As we rise above sea level, atmospheric pressure is reduced. As water is heated at altitude, its vapour pressure reaches equality with this reduced atmospheric pressure at a lower temperature. And so the water boils at this lower temperature.

■ **Figure 17.4** Iodine dissolved in a mixture of hexane (upper layer) and water (lower layer)

Partitioning

When a small quantity of iodine is shaken with a mixture of water and hexane (Figure 17.4), some iodine will dissolve in both liquids. The water and hexane do not mix and are said to be a pair of immiscible liquids. If the mixture is allowed to separate into two layers and left until equilibrium is established (Figure 17.5), the iodine concentration in each layer can be determined by titration with sodium thiosulfate (see Chapter 9).

$$I_2 (aq) \rightleftharpoons I_2 (hexane)$$

Experiments using different masses of iodine, water and hexane show that at a fixed temperature the ratio of the concentrations of the iodine in the two layers is constant:

$$K_D = \frac{\text{concentration of iodine in water}}{\text{concentration of iodine in hexane}}$$

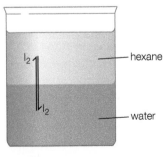

■ **Figure 17.5** Iodine molecules between the two layers – a dynamic equilibrium is set up

The constant K_D is called the partition coefficient or distribution coefficient for the solute distributed between two solvents at a given temperature. The partition or distribution law states that at a fixed temperature a solute distributes itself between two immiscible solvents so that the ratio of the concentrations of solute in each layer is *constant*.

Paper chromatography and other chromatographic techniques (see Chapter 21) depend on the principle of partitioning. It is also the basis for the separation technique of solvent extraction (see Chapter 20). We also need to know particular partition coefficients when developing pesticides and insecticides. Pesticides and insecticides need to be soluble in the fatty tissues of the animals that they are designed to kill, but much less soluble in water so that the chemicals are not simply washed away by rain.

Chemical equilibria

The importance of the equilibrium law is widespread throughout chemistry. We have seen in Chapter 7 that defining the optimum conditions for certain key industrial gas phase reactions is dependent on a thorough understanding of the factors that determine the proportions of reactants and products in an equilibrium mixture, and we will return to a consideration of the Haber process later in this chapter. However, chemists use the equilibrium law to represent the extent to which a weak acid or base ionizes or dissociates, defining terms such as the dissociation constants K_a and K_b in relation to these effects. The behaviour of acid–base indicators is also explained in terms of the equilibria involved and the application of Le Châtelier's principle.

One further area of increasing importance in our modern world, as we seek to develop alternative energy sources, is that of redox equilibria and the concept of electrode potential as used in electrochemical cell technology. These are just a few examples of how the ideas discussed in this chapter are of importance across a range of our understanding of chemistry.

Utilization: Equilibria in closed systems

The key feature of the chemical and physical equilibria described here and in Chapter 7 is the fact that they are established in closed systems where material cannot escape or enter to disturb the available components involved in establishing the equilibrium. The model is an attractive one and there have been many attempts to extend the notions involved to different areas of human understanding, ranging from the biological world and environmental systems to human sciences such as economics.

Although attractive, the application to these other areas of study stumbles at times when faced with defining what would be a truly closed system in these complex fields. In biology, it is possible to consider the compartmentalization within a cell, reactions within the mitochondria for instance, but there is transfer of molecules across membranes. On a larger scale one might begin to apply the idea to the distinctiveness of species found in the context of an isolated island group. Located some 2400 miles (4000 km) from the nearest continental shore, the Hawaiian Islands are the most isolated group of islands on the planet. The plant and animal life of the Hawaiian archipelago is the result of early, very infrequent colonizations of arriving species and the slow evolution of those species – in isolation from the rest of the world's flora and fauna – over a period of at least 70 million years. As a consequence, Hawaii is home to a large number of endemic species. Similar analyses have been applied to the generation of endemic flora and fauna on Madagascar and the Galapagos Islands. The extent to which the ideas of dynamic equilibrium can be applied to the populations on these islands is debatable but one possible applicable situation may be that of a particular species in this context.

Complex systems in nature – for example ecosystems – involve a dynamic interaction of many variables (e.g. animals, plants, insects and bacteria; predators and prey; climate, the seasons and the weather, etc.) These interactions can adapt to changing conditions but maintain a balance both between the various parts and as a whole; this balance is maintained through homeostasis. Human societies are complex systems – as it were, human ecosystems. Early humans, as hunter-gatherers, recognized and worked within the parameters of the complex systems in nature and their lives were circumscribed by the realities of nature. This they did without the need to elaborately theorize on their behaviour. Only in recent centuries did the need arise to define complex systems scientifically. Complex systems theories first developed in mathematics in the late 19th century, and then in biology in the 1920s to explain ecosystems.

■ **Figure 17.6** The common clownfish at home among the anemones of the Great Barrier Reef

Certainly the idea of equilibrium has been applied to populations of a particular species generally. Some species exhibit sequential hermaphroditism. In these species, such as many species of coral reef fishes, sex change is a normal anatomical process. Clownfish, wrasses, moray eels, gobies and other fish species are known to change sex, including reproductive functions. A school of clownfish is always built into a hierarchy with a female fish at the top (Figure 17.6). When she dies, the most dominant male changes sex and takes her place. In the wrasses (the family Labridae), sex change is from female to male, with the largest female of the harem changing into a male and taking over the harem upon the disappearance of the previous dominant male.

In some animal species the male–female equilibrium ratio is maintained at a fairly constant level. In fact, some animals change their sex in response to environmental stresses. For example, Atlantic silverside fish change sex as the temperature changes; others, like the female African reed frog and the Anihias squamipinnis fish, change sex if there is a decrease in the male population.

These population changes illustrate equilibrium as the balance between males and females in the population is adjusted in response to conditions.

The anthropologist Gregory Bateson is the most influential and earliest founder of systems theory in social sciences. In the 1940s he recognized its application to human societies with their many variables and the flexible, but sustainable, balance that they maintain. Bateson describes a system as 'any unit containing feedback structure and therefore competent to process information'. Thus an open system allows interaction between concepts and materiality, or the subject and the environment, and the abstract and the real.

In economics, general equilibrium theory attempts to explain the behaviour of supply, demand and prices in a whole economy with several or many interacting markets, by seeking to prove that a set of prices exists that will result in an overall (or 'general') equilibrium. General equilibrium theory contrasts to partial equilibrium theory, which only analyses single markets. As with all models, this is an abstraction from a real economy; it is proposed as being a useful model, both by considering equilibrium prices as long-term prices and by considering actual prices as deviations from equilibrium.

17.1 The equilibrium law – *the position of equilibrium can be quantified by the equilibrium law; the equilibrium constant for a particular reaction only depends on the temperature*

■ The equilibrium law and changes in concentration

Le Châtelier's principle can be used to predict the effect of changes in concentration (or pressure for gas phase reactions) and temperature on the position of an equilibrium in terms of the proportions of reactants and products in the equilibrium mixture. The equilibrium law can be used to explain and quantify the effect of concentration changes at a given temperature. Such explanations are based on the fact that the value of the equilibrium constant, K_c, is itself not affected by a change in concentration.

Consider a reaction,

$$A + B \rightleftharpoons C + D$$

for which the equilibrium expression is

$$K_c = \frac{[C]\,[D]}{[A]\,[B]}$$

Table 17.1 summarizes the predictions from Le Châtelier as to the adjustments that take place in the respective components of the mixture if reactant A is added to, or removed from, the mixture. The changes involve work to maintain the constant value of K_c.

■ Table 17.1

The changes involved in component concentrations when a reactant is supplemented or removed

If A is added to reaction	If A is removed from reaction
The forward reaction works to remove excess A.	The backward (reverse) reaction works to replace A.
A and B react together to produce more C and D.	C and D react together to produce more A and B.
At equilibrium, there will be more C and D but less B compared to the *original equilibrium*.	At equilibrium, there will be more B but less C and D compared to the *original equilibrium*.
Position of equilibrium shifts from *left* to *right*.	Position of equilibrium shift from *right* to *left*.
K_c remains the same.	K_c remains the same.

Using the example of the reaction that is the basis for Haber process, we can illustrate the changes graphically to gain a visual representation of the changes occurring.

$$N_2(g) + 3H_2(g) \rightleftharpoons 2NH_3(g)$$

Consider the changes when more nitrogen is added at constant volume. The concentration increases and, using arguments based on the equilibrium law, we can make the following statements regarding the consequent changes:

- Hydrogen reacts with the added nitrogen to form ammonia.
- $[NH_3]$ increases a lot; $[N_2]$ is increased and $[H_2]$ is decreased since K_c is unchanged.
- The position of equilibrium shifts to the right (favouring the products).
- Both forward and backward rates will be greater than before.

These changes in concentration are illustrated in Figure 17.7a while the argument regarding the changes in the rates of the forward and backward reactions is shown in Figure 17.7b.

■ **Figure 17.7**
The effect of the addition of nitrogen on: **a** the concentrations of the components of the equilibrium mixture and **b** the rates of the forward and backward reactions

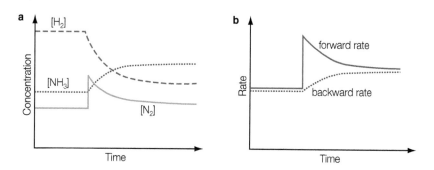

The addition of more nitrogen increases its concentration, which causes an increase in the rate of the forward reaction. This uses up nitrogen and hydrogen, so the forward rate decreases, and it makes more ammonia so the backward rate increases.

The decreasing forward rate and increasing backward rate finally become equal when a new equilibrium is re-established.

A similar sequence of arguments can be applied when considering the removal of some of the product, ammonia, from such an equilibrium mixture. Figure 17.8a shows the effect of reducing the ammonia concentration in this way, while Figure 17.8b illustrates the effect on the rates of the two reactions.

■ **Figure 17.8**
The effect of the removal of ammonia on **a** the concentrations of the components of the equilibrium mixture and **b** the rates of the forward and backward reactions

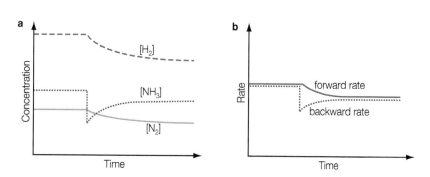

Again the consequences of removing ammonia can be summarized as a sequence of consequences which flow from the reduction in the concentration of ammonia:

- Firstly, nitrogen and hydrogen react to make up for the lost ammonia.
- Then the concentrations of all of the components of the mixture decrease, especially ammonia since K_c is unchanged.
- The position of equilibrium shifts to the right (favouring the products).
- Both rates will be slower than before.

The argument in terms of the rates of reactions runs as follows. The withdrawal of some ammonia decreases the backward rate. The forward reaction continues, making more ammonia quickly. Then the rate of the forward reaction slows, while the backward rate increases until they are again equal.

The changes discussed in these circumstances are consistent with both the predictive capacity of Le Châtelier's principle and the underlying condition that the value of K_c should remain constant at a particular temperature. It is possible to develop the arguments further by involving the ideas behind the reaction quotient, Q, introduced earlier in Chapter 7.

Consider the equilibrium established by the esterification reaction:

$$CH_3COOH(l) + C_2H_5OH(l) \rightleftharpoons CH_3COOC_2H_5(l) + H_2O(l)$$

At 373 K the equilibrium constant for this reaction is 4.0, and equilibrium will be established at this temperature such that the following condition is satisfied.

$$K_c = \frac{[CH_3COOC_2H_5(l)]\,[H_2O(l)]}{[CH_3COOH(l)]\,[C_2H_5OH(l)]} = 4.0$$

If some water is added to the system in equilibrium, then the concentrations of the other species will be decreased as the total volume of the reaction mixture has increased. The equilibrium will be disturbed such that the value of the reaction quotient, Q, will be greater than 4.0. The value of Q must decrease to bring it back to 4.0 – so some ethyl ethanoate must react with water (these concentrations are on the top of the expression for Q) to achieve this. The reverse (backward) reaction is favoured over the forward reaction until the new equilibrium is established.

This new equilibrium position will be such that the concentrations of ethanol and ethanoic acid are higher than in the original equilibrium mixture – the position of the equilibrium has shifted to the left to use up the added water. This exactly what Le Châtelier's principle would have predicted. From this discussion we can see that if a system in equilibrium is subjected to a change in concentration then the system will no longer be in equilibrium ($Q \neq K_c$). The reaction will adjust and shift position until $Q = K_c$ and a new equilibrium is established. These considerations mean that we could re-state Le Châtelier's principle to say that 'if a system in equilibrium is subjected to a change in concentration (or pressure, for a gas phase reaction) then the position of equilibrium will shift until the value of the reaction quotient, Q, is restored to the value of K_c again'.

■ The relation of equilibrium composition to reaction rate

The approach to understanding the nature of K_c in terms of competing reaction rates is one which, provided it is viewed carefully, gives an understanding of the dynamics of how equilibrium is achieved. The approach is based on the fact that equilibrium is achieved when the forward and backward (reverse) reactions taking place in a reaction mixture have the same rates. Since reaction rates depend on (and change with) concentration, then, at a particular temperature, there will be a unique set of reactant and product concentrations that correspond to these forward and backward rates of reaction. The equilibrium constant expresses the relationship between the concentrations that guarantee this equality of rates. To look at this more closely, consider a general reaction. Here the forward and backward (reverse) reactions are both single-step, bimolecular reactions with 1 : 1 stoichiometry.

$$A + B \rightleftharpoons C + D$$

Forward reaction:	$A + B \rightarrow C + D$	rate $= k_f[A][B]$
Backward reaction:	$C + D \rightarrow A + B$	rate $= k_r[C][D]$

At equilibrium these two rates are equal. Therefore:

$$k_f[A][B] = k_r[C][D]$$

This can be rearranged to give:

$$\frac{[C]\,[D]}{[A]\,[B]} = \frac{k_f}{k_r} = \text{constant}$$

This is the form of the equilibrium expression for K_c, and implies that the equilibrium constant is the ratio of the forward and reverse rate constants.

$$K_c = \frac{k_f}{k_r}$$

If the rate constant for the forward reaction is large relative to that of the reverse reaction, then the equilibrium constant is large and the production of products is favoured (Figure 17.9a). On the other hand, if the rate constant for the reverse reaction is relatively large compared to that of the forward reaction, then the reactants will be favoured and the equilibrium constant will be small (Figure 17.9b).

■ **Figure 17.9**
The relationship between the values of K_c, the position of the equilibrium and the rate constants of the forward and reverse reactions

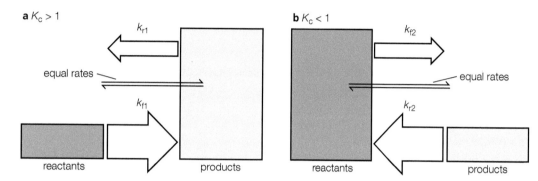

One apparent problem with this argument relating K_c to k_f and k_r is that it is only easily derived for a single-step reaction. In practice, many reactions have complex rate expressions (determined by experiment) where reaction orders are not related to reaction stoichiometry. Mechanisms may not be known, and where they are, they are often multi-step. Nevertheless, even in these cases, when the system is at equilibrium, we have a distinctive situation in which all the individual elementary steps of a reaction mechanism must be in equilibrium too (see Chapter 16 for the use of the idea of elementary steps in the context of reaction mechanisms). As a result, each elementary step of the reaction sequence can be treated as an equilibrium in itself. Equilibrium constants for each step can then be expressed in terms of the forward and reverse rate constants found for each elementary step. Using the relationship we discussed in Chapter 7 for finding the overall equilibrium constant of a sequence of connected equilibria, it can be demonstrated that it is valid to evaluate the expression for K_c directly from the overall stoichiometric equation, even though the reaction may take place in several steps.

In fact, the concept of the equilibrium constant for a reversible reaction in a closed system was discovered by analysing experimental data and has since been theoretically justified in terms of a thermodynamic approach involving consideration of $\Delta G^\ominus$ values, and we will return to this idea later in the chapter.

ToK Link

The equilibrium law can be deduced by assuming that the order of the forward and backward reactions matches the coefficient in the chemical equation. What is the role of deductive reasoning in science?

The idea that the equilibrium position established for a reversible reaction under particular conditions is the balanced position resulting from two competing reactions – the forward and backward reactions – has led to the useful deduction and explanation of the phenomenon based on equating the rate expressions for these two reactions. This has proved a useful approach, particularly for situations in which the opposing reactions are both simple single-step reactions where the order of reaction can be taken from the stoichiometric coefficients. As such, the deductions involved in this approach usefully support the more rigorous thermodynamic approach which provides the strongest theoretical validation of the equilibrium law.

Deductive reasoning has a key role to play in establishing generalizations that can then be tested by studying specific examples. The generalization only remains worthwhile if it can accommodate the detail generated by specific experiments. In this particular case, the application of the generalization from an immediate reaction to the simpler types of reversible reaction to those that involved multi-step sequences held true, and so the approach retains its merit as a mental and mathematical picture of the nature of reversible reactions.

It is worth remembering that the thermodynamic origins of the justification of the equilibrium law are the reason why equilibrium constants do not have units. When the equilibrium constant is derived from thermodynamic measurements it is defined, not in terms of concentrations (or partial pressures, for gases) but activities. For an ideal system, the activity of a substance is the ratio of the concentration (or partial pressure) to its standard value ($1\,mol\,dm^{-3}$ or $10^5\,Pa$). Thus if the concentration of a substance were, say, $0.4\,mol\,dm^{-3}$, its activity would be $0.4\,mol\,dm^{-3}/1\,mol\,dm^{-3}$; i. e. 0.4, as the units cancel. The activity of a substance is always the ratio to a standard state and therefore dimensionless (it has no units). The following guidelines apply to particular situations:

- For a dilute solution the activity is numerically equal to the concentration.
- For a solid or a solvent it is equal to 1.
- For an ideal gas it is numerically equal to the partial pressure.
- At this level, for all the examples dealt with, the systems can be treated as behaving ideally.

Calculating equilibrium constants from concentration data

In Chapter 7 we saw how it is possible to derive an equilibrium expression for K_c for a homogeneous equilibrium mixture produced by a reversible reaction in a closed system. The value of K_c is constant for a given reaction at a particular temperature. For example, K_c for the reaction

$$PCl_5(g) \rightleftharpoons PCl_3(g) + Cl_2(g)$$

is given by the expression

$$K_c = \frac{[PCl_3]\,[Cl_2]}{[PCl_5]}$$

The value of K_c is a very useful parameter as it gives an indication of the position of the equilibrium and the proportion of products in the equilibrium mixture. The next section of this chapter gives examples of some calculations based on K_c. Later we will develop ideas about different equilibrium situations.

Calculations on homogeneous equilibria

The fact that such a highly significant relationship as that of the equilibrium constant can be established for *any* reversible reaction occurring under conditions where equilibrium can be reached is very useful in quantitative chemistry. Whether dealing with an industrial process (Chapter 7), a biochemical interaction or a wide range of other important areas of chemistry including electrochemistry (Chapter 19), it is important that we can 'put numbers' to the process and calculate the shifting proportions of reactants and products during a reaction. The calculations involved at IB level are entirely confined to those relating to homogeneous equilibrium systems. Such calculations require knowledge of the relevant chemical equation and the ability to write equilibrium expressions confidently. The following discussion and series of worked examples illustrate the different levels of sophistication needed to solve such problems.

The most straightforward type of question would require the writing of an equilibrium expression, followed by the 'feeding in' of some equilibrium concentration values to find K_c.

Worked example

Nitrogen(II) oxide, NO, is a pollutant released into the atmosphere from car exhausts. It is also formed when nitrosyl chloride, NOCl, dissociates according to the following equation:

$$2NOCl(g) \rightleftharpoons 2NO(g) + Cl_2(g)$$

To study this reaction, different amounts of the three gases were placed in a closed container and allowed to come to equilibrium at 503 K and at 738 K.

The equilibrium concentrations of the three gases at each temperature are given in Table 17.2.

	Concentration/mol dm^{-3}		
Temperature/K	NOCl	NO	Cl$_2$
503	2.33×10^{-3}	1.46×10^{-3}	1.15×10^{-2}
738	3.68×10^{-4}	7.63×10^{-3}	2.14×10^{-4}

■ **Table 17.2** Equilibrium concentrations for the reaction $2NOCl(g) \rightleftharpoons 2NO(g) + Cl_2(g)$ at two different temperatures

> **a** Write the expression for the equilibrium constant, K_c, for this reaction.
>
> **b** Calculate the value of K_c at each of the two temperatures given.
>
> **c** Is the forward reaction endothermic or exothermic? (Explain your answer based on ideas covered in Chapter 7.)

a $K_c = \dfrac{[NO]^2 \, [Cl_2]}{[NOCl]^2}$

b At 503 K $\quad K_c = \dfrac{(1.46 \times 10^{-3})^2 \times 1.15 \times 10^{-2}}{(2.33 \times 10^{-3})^2}$

$\quad\quad\quad\quad\quad\quad = 4.5 \times 10^{-3}$

At 738 K $\quad K_c = \dfrac{(7.63 \times 10^{-3})^2 \times 2.14 \times 10^{-4}}{(3.68 \times 10^{-4})^2}$

$\quad\quad\quad\quad\quad\quad = 9.2 \times 10^{-2}$

c The value of K_c is greater at 738 K; K_c increases with temperature, with the forward reaction being favoured to increase the proportion of products in the equilibrium mixture. This suggests that the forward reaction is endothermic.

A slightly more difficult question depends on you being able to use the equation for the reaction to work out the concentrations of the various substances in the equilibrium mixture. The approach here is sometimes referred to as the 'ICE' method as it involves the tabulation of the initial numbers of moles, or concentrations, **I**; the change in numbers of moles, or concentrations, **C**; and the equilibrium numbers of moles, or concentrations, **E** (see the worked example that follows).

Worked example

The acid-catalysed hydrolysis of ethyl ethanoate can be achieved by mixing the ester with dilute hydrochloric acid.

$$CH_3COOC_2H_5(l) + H_2O(l) \overset{H^+}{\rightleftharpoons} CH_3COOH(l) + C_2H_5OH(l)$$

If 1.00 mole of ethyl ethanoate is mixed with 1.00 mole of water and the reaction is allowed to reach equilibrium at a particular temperature, then 0.30 moles of ethanoic acid is found in the equilibrium mixture.

Calculate the value of K_c at this temperature.

It is useful to set out the first stage of the calculation as follows, focusing on the information that can be worked out from the equation:

$$CH_3COOC_2H_5(l) + H_2O(l) \rightleftharpoons CH_3COOH(l) + C_2H_5OH(l)$$

(I) Starting amount (moles)	1.00	1.00	0.00	0.00
(E) Equilibrium amount (moles)				0.30

We need to fill in the gaps in the second line by applying the stoichiometry built into the equation. It is important to note that the coefficients in the equation are all '1'. The reaction has proceeded to produce 0.30 moles of ethanoic acid, and the molar ratio of ethanoic acid and ethanol is 1:1. This means that the amount of ethanol in the equilibrium mixture is also 0.30 moles.

If 0.30 moles of each product are present in the equilibrium mixture, then they must have been produced from the reaction of 0.30 moles of the ester and water. This means that the amounts of ester and water remaining at equilibrium must be (1.00 − 0.30) moles of each.

This means we can complete the table above as follows:

$$CH_3COOC_2H_5(l) + H_2O(l) \rightleftharpoons CH_3COOH(l) + C_2H_5OH(l)$$

(I) Starting amount (moles)	1.00	1.00	0	0
(C) Change (moles)	−0.30	−0.30	+0.30	+0.30
(E) Equilibrium amount (moles)	(1.00 − 0.30)	(1.00 − 0.30)	0.30	0.30
	= 0.70	= 0.70		

Many questions on equilibria will require the drawing up of a similar **'ICE'** table to this. It is important to get this line of equilibrium amounts correct.

However, there is still one more line to put in. To calculate K_c we need the equilibrium concentration values to put into the equilibrium expression. But we have not been given the volume of the reaction mixture. So let us say that the volume is $V\,dm^3$. Thus we have an additional, and final, line to our table:

Equilibrium concentration (mol dm^{-3})   0.70/V   0.70/V   0.30/V   0.30/V

We are now in a position to calculate K_c:

$$K_c = \frac{[CH_3COOH]\,[C_2H_5OH]}{[CH_3COOC_2H_5]\,[H_2O]}$$

$$K_c = \frac{(0.30/V)\,(0.30/V)}{(0.70/V)\,(0.70/V)} \quad \text{All the 'V' terms cancel out.}$$

$$= \frac{0.30}{0.70} \times \frac{0.30}{0.70}$$

$$= 0.18$$

In other examples you may be given the total volume of the reaction mixture (if the reaction is in the liquid phase or in solution) or the volume of the container (if the reaction is gaseous). In these cases you would need to use the numerical values provided in your calculations.

In the examples so far you have been asked to calculate K_c. Obviously it is possible that a question may be posed that provides you with that value and asks you to calculate the equilibrium concentrations of the reactants and/or products.

Worked example

An organic compound X exists in equilibrium with its isomer, Y, in the liquid state at a particular temperature.

$$X(l) \rightleftharpoons Y(l)$$

Calculate how many moles of Y are formed at equilibrium if 1 mole of X is allowed to reach equilibrium at this temperature, if K_c has a value of 0.020.

Let the amount of Y at equilibrium = y moles

	X(l) $\rightleftharpoons$	Y(l)
(I) Starting amount (moles)	1.00	0.00
(C) Change in amount (moles)	−y	y

The process now is similar to that we have used previously. From the equation, if y moles of the isomer Y are present then y moles of X must have reacted. Therefore, $(1.00 - y)$ moles of X must remain at equilibrium. Also, if we call the volume of liquid $V\,dm^3$, then we can complete the table as follows:

	X(l) $\rightleftharpoons$	Y(l)
(I) Starting amount (moles)	1.00	0.00
(E) Equilibrium amount (moles)	$(1.00 - y)$	y
Equilibrium concentration (mol dm^{-3})	$(1.00 - y)/V$	y/V

$$K_c = \frac{[Y]}{[X]}$$

$$0.020 = \frac{y/V}{(1.00 - y)/V} \quad \text{The 'V' terms cancel.}$$

$$0.020 = \frac{y}{(1.00 - y)}$$

$$0.020(1.00 - y) = y$$

$$0.020 - 0.020y = y$$

and so $\qquad 1.020y = 0.020$

therefore $\qquad y = \dfrac{0.02}{1.020} = 0.0196 = 0.020 \text{ moles}$

This type of calculation involves using some basic algebra. The chemical equation here was as simple as possible, involving just one reactant and one product. Most chemical reactions are more complicated than this! Equilibrium calculations similar to the one above can be solved for these more complex reactions, provided sufficient numerical information is given.

Worked example

Phosphorus(v) chloride undergoes thermal decomposition as follows:

$$PCl_5(g) \rightleftharpoons PCl_3(g) + Cl_2(g)$$

and therefore

$$K_c = \frac{[PCl_3][Cl_2]}{[PCl_5]}$$

Some PCl_5 was placed in an evacuated flask of volume 1.0 dm^3 at 500 K. An equilibrium was then established in which the concentration of PCl_5 was $4.0 \times 10^{-2} \text{ mol dm}^{-3}$. The value of K_c for this reaction at 500 K is 1.00×10^{-2}. Calculate the concentration of chlorine in the equilibrium mixture.

Let the concentration of Cl_2 at equilibrium $= x \text{ mol dm}^{-3}$

	$PCl_5(g)$	$\rightleftharpoons$	$PCl_3(g)$	$+$	$Cl_2(g)$
Equilibrium concentrations (mol dm^{-3})	4.0×10^{-2}		x		x

$$K_c = 1.0 \times 10^{-2} = \frac{x^2}{4.0 \times 10^{-2}}$$

therefore $\qquad 4.0 \times 10^{-4} = x^2$

so $\qquad x = 2.0 \times 10^{-2} \text{ mol dm}^{-3}$

This example is straightforward but there are problems where the solution generates a quadratic equation for working out the unknown concentration. The IB syllabus specifically states that calculations that would require the use of the formula for solving quadratic equations will not be asked (an example is given as extension work here).

Additional Perspectives

Calculations using the formula for quadratic solutions

For the esterification reaction

$$CH_3COOH(l) + C_2H_5OH(l) \rightleftharpoons CH_3COOC_2H_5(l) + H_2O(l)$$

what amount of ethyl ethanoate will be formed at equilibrium when 1.0 mole of ethanol is reacted with 2.0 moles of ethanoic acid at 373 K, given that the value of K_c is 4.0 at this temperature?

Let the amount of ethyl ethanoate at equilibrium $= x$ moles, and the volume of the reacting mixture $= V \text{ dm}^3$

	$CH_3COOH(l)$	$+ C_2H_5OH(l)$	$\rightleftharpoons CH_3COOC_2H_5(l)$	$+ H_2O(l)$
(I) Starting amount (moles)	2.00	1.00	0.00	0.00
(C) Change (moles)	$-x$	$-x$	x	x
(E) Equilibrium amount (moles)	$(2.0 - x)$	$(1.0 - x)$	x	x
Equilibrium concentration (mol dm^{-3})	$(2.0 - x)/V$	$(1.0 - x)/V$	x/V	x/V

$$K_c = \frac{[CH_3COOC_2H_5][H_2O]}{[CH_3COOH][C_2H_5OH]}$$

$$= \frac{(x/V)\,(x/V)}{((2.0 - x)/V)((1.0 - x)/V)} \quad \text{Note that the 'V' terms cancels.}$$

$$= \frac{x^2}{(2.0 - x)(1.0 - x)}$$

Therefore

$$4.0 = \frac{x^2}{(2.0 - x)(1.0 - x)}$$

$$= \frac{x^2}{x^2 - 3x + 2}$$

This rearranges to

$$3x^2 - 12x + 8 = 0$$

The solution of this quadratic equation requires the use of the general expression:

$$x = \frac{-b \pm \sqrt{b^2 - 4ac}}{2a}$$

for the general quadratic $ax^2 + bx + c = 0$

Using this expression gives possible values for x of 0.85 or 3.15 moles. The second of these solutions is impossible as we only started with 1.0 mole of ethanol. Therefore the number of moles of ethyl ethanoate at equilibrium is 0.85 moles.

Nature of Science

Making approximations

In the practical application of science it is often the case that calculated and appropriate approximations and assumptions are the key to making progress and developing new insights. Most gases do not behave ideally over the full range of available conditions but the assumptions intrinsic to ideal behaviour have proved immensely fruitful in moving our understanding of the kinetic model of matter forward. The Born–Oppenheimer approximation is an important tool of quantum chemistry; without it only the lightest molecule, H_2, could be handled, and all computations of molecular wave functions for larger molecules make use of it. Even in the cases where the approximation breaks down, it remains useful as a point of departure for the computations. First proposed in 1927 by Max Born and J. Robert Oppenheimer, the approximation is based on treating the protons and neutrons of the nuclei as static and thus isolating the behaviour of the electrons for separate mathematical treatment. The success of the approximation is due to the high ratio between the nuclear and electronic masses, and its implementation is still indispensable in quantum chemistry.

In the application of the equilibrium law to the behaviour of weak acids and bases, there are workable approximations made in deriving expressions for the dissociation constants K_a and K_b which are justified by the practical applicability of the derived equations for calculating these parameters. The approximations are based on the fact that the degree of dissociation in most cases is so small that the concentration of the acid or base molecules can be regarded as unchanged by the ionization. This leads to a simplification of the expressions for the constants that eases calculations based on their values. The key in all these situations is in being aware of the limitations of the assumptions and approximations being made and therefore being able to move on from them where understanding demands.

1   Sulfur dioxide, SO_2, reacts with oxygen in the presence of a catalyst (vanadium(v) oxide) to form sulfur trioxide. This reaction is carried out in a sealed container of volume $3.0\,dm^3$ by mixing $2.0\,mol$ of sulfur dioxide and $1.4\,mol$ of oxygen and allowing equilibrium to be established. A conversion rate of 15% is achieved at $700\,K$. Calculate the equilibrium constant K_c at this temperature for this reaction.

2   When carried out at a particular temperature, the equilibrium constant for the reaction

$$SO_3(g) + NO(g) \rightleftharpoons NO_2(g) + SO_2(g)$$

was found to be 6.78. The initial equimolar concentrations of SO_3 and NO were $0.030\,mol\,dm^{-3}$. What is the equilibrium concentration of each component in the mixture once equilibrium is established?

3   Hydrogen and carbon dioxide gases react according to the following equation:

$$H_2(g) + CO_2(g) \rightleftharpoons H_2O(g) + CO(g)$$

The reaction was carried out in a sealed vessel of volume $10\,dm^3$. The four components of the reaction were put into the vessel in the following proportions: $2.00\,mol$ of each of the reactants (H_2 and CO_2) and $1.00\,mol$ of each of the products (H_2O and CO). The system was then allowed to come to equilibrium at $1200\,K$. The equilibrium constant, K_c, for this reaction at $1200\,K$ is 2.10. Calculate the equilibrium concentration of each component of the reaction mixture.

[Note that while the IB syllabus states that examples of this type of calculation will not be set involving the solution of quadratic equations, both examples 2 and 3 above involve deriving equations that include perfect squares and so can be solved by taking the square root of each side of the expression. This seems an acceptable method of calculation and is worth remembering.]

ToK Link

We can use mathematics successfully to model equilibrium systems. Is this because we create mathematics to mirror reality or because the reality is intrinsically mathematical?

Mathematics is a universal language because the principles and foundations of mathematics are the same everywhere around the world. Chemists use mathematics to describe and explain the physical world. Mathematical concepts, such as differential equations and logarithms, which were developed for purely abstract reasons, turn out to explain real chemical phenomena. Their usefulness, as physicist Eugene Wigner once wrote, 'is a wonderful gift which we neither understand nor deserve'. He wrote about the 'unreasonable effectiveness of mathematics', while Einstein commented that 'the most incomprehensible thing about the universe is that it is comprehensible'. Is mathematics 'invented' (a creation of the human mind) or 'discovered' (something that exists independently of human thought) or both? What is beyond doubt is the astonishing power, precision and conciseness of mathematics. For example, James Clerk Maxwell's four equations of electromagnetism summarized the field of electromagnetism in the 1860s. They also predicted the existence of radio waves two decades before the German physicist Hertz detected them. Radio waves are now widely used in MRI scanners in hospitals and in mobile phones. There are further examples of the predictive power of mathematics. Most famously, British theorist Paul Dirac used pure mathematics to formulate an equation that led to the idea of antimatter several years before the first antiparticle (the positron) was found in 1932.

■ **Figure 17.10** The head of an ox-eye daisy, with the Fibonacci spirals drawn in to show the arrangement

Is the universe intrinsically mathematical? Symmetry is certainly a key feature and driving force in nature and one of the keys to the important process of self-assembly. Patterning and the presence of geometric shapes such as Fibonacci spirals (Figure 17.10) in structures and organisms demonstrate the underlying importance of mathematical order in the make-up of the world around us. Science is built on the notion that the universe is not anarchic, that there is a reproducibility to the fabric of existence and that that order can be approximated to in the linguistic and mathematical models with which we strive to describe the world as we find it. The order is there – atoms obey the same laws in distant galaxies as in the laboratory – the imprecision lies in the disjoint between the subtlety and precision of our models and reality. One purpose of science is to bring the two ever closer together.

Gaseous equilibria

For reactions involving gases, the equilibrium constant is often expressed in terms of the partial pressures of the gases in the equilibrium mixture rather than their concentrations. The equilibrium constant is then given the symbol K_p. The reason this approach is feasible is that it can be shown that the partial pressure of a gas in a mixture is directly proportional to its concentration. Note that the partial pressure of a gas, in a mixture of ideal gases (Chapter 1), is the pressure which that gas would exert if it alone occupied the container. The concept was introduced by John Dalton (Chapter 2), who stated that the total pressure of a mixture of gases is the sum of the partial pressures of the individual gases in the mixture (Dalton's law of partial pressures).

The partial pressure of a gas is related to the amount of gas by the ideal gas equation (Chapter 1):

$$PV = nRT$$

Hence

$$P = \frac{n}{V} RT$$

However, $\frac{n}{V} = c$, where c represents the concentration (in $mol\,dm^{-3}$) of the gas.

Therefore

$$P = cRT$$

Since R is the gas constant and T is a specific temperature, the multiple RT is numerically constant at a given temperature. This shows that the pressure of a gas is *directly proportional* to its concentration at a specific temperature and it is valid therefore to express an equilibrium constant in terms of partial pressures for reactions involving gases. The structure of the expression for the equilibrium constant is identical to that for K_c (see the following worked example).

Worked example

In an equilibrium mixture, the partial pressures of N_2, H_2 and NH_3 are as follows:

$P_{N_2} = 149\,atm$, $P_{H_2} = 40\,atm$ and $P_{NH_3} = 11\,atm$

Calculate K_p for the following equilibrium reaction.

$$N_2(g) + 3H_2(g) \rightleftharpoons 2NH_3(g)$$

$$K_p = \frac{(P_{NH_3})^2}{(P_{N_2})(P_{H_2})^3} = \frac{(11)^2}{(149)(40)^3} = 1.3 \times 10^{-5}$$

Relationship between the equilibrium constant, spontaneity and Gibbs free energy

You will be familiar from Chapter 15 with the relationship between Gibbs free energy ($\Delta G^{\ominus}$) and the enthalpy and entropy factors that determine the feasibility of a reaction. They are linked by the equation:

$$\Delta G^{\ominus} = \Delta H^{\ominus} - T\Delta S^{\ominus}$$

An exothermic reaction (where $\Delta H^{\ominus}$ is negative) will always be spontaneous under certain temperature conditions. If the reaction involves an increase in entropy (where $\Delta S^{\ominus}$ is positive) then the term $-T\Delta S^{\ominus}$ will be negative. In this case, because $\Delta H^{\ominus}$ is also negative, $\Delta G^{\ominus}$ will always be negative and the reaction will always be spontaneous.

If, however, the reaction involves a decrease in entropy ($\Delta S^{\ominus}$ negative), the reaction will be spontaneous at low temperatures, when $\Delta H^{\ominus}$ is more negative than the term $-T\Delta S^{\ominus}$ is positive. It will, however, become less spontaneous as the temperature increases (because $-T\Delta S^{\ominus}$ is positive and becomes progressively more positive as the temperature increases). At higher temperatures, $-T\Delta S^{\ominus}$ will be more positive than $\Delta H^{\ominus}$ is negative, and therefore $\Delta G^{\ominus}$ will be positive and the reaction will be non-spontaneous. Reactions in which $\Delta S^{\ominus}$ is positive become more spontaneous as temperature increases, but reactions in which $\Delta S^{\ominus}$ is negative become less spontaneous as temperature increases. Table 17.3 gives an overview of these considerations.

■ **Table 17.3**
Thermodynamic factors affecting whether or not a reaction is spontaneous

Value of $\Delta H^{\ominus}$	Value of $\Delta S^{\ominus}$	Value of term $-T\Delta S^{\ominus}$	$\Delta G^{\ominus}$	Spontaneous or not?
Negative	Positive	Negative	Negative	At all temperatures
Positive	Positive	Negative	Becomes increasingly negative as temperature increases	Becomes more spontaneous as temperature increases
Negative	Negative	Positive	Becomes decreasingly negative as temperature increases	Becomes less spontaneous as temperature increases
Positive	Negative	Positive	Positive	Never spontaneous

Earlier we discussed the derivation of the equilibrium constant K_c (or K_p) from a consideration of the rate expressions for the forward and backward reactions. It is important to realize that the value of the equilibrium constant does *not* give any information about those individual rates of reaction. Equilibrium constants are *independent* of the kinetics of the reaction. *However*, the chemical equilibrium constant, K, is directly related to the Gibbs free energy change, $\Delta G^{\ominus}$ (Chapter 15) by the following equation (van't Hoff's equation):

$$\Delta G^{\ominus} = -RT \ln K$$

where R represents the molar gas constant and T the absolute temperature in kelvins. For reactions in solution or the liquid phase, *the value of K derived is that of K_c.*

The relationship between K_c and $\Delta G^{\ominus}$ obtained from this expression is summarized in Table 17.4.

■ **Table 17.4**
A summary of the relationship between $\Delta G^{\ominus}$ and K_c

$\Delta G^{\ominus}$	$\ln K_c$	K_c	Position of equilibrium
Negative	Positive	>1	To the right – products favoured
Zero	Zero	=1	Equal proportions of reactants and products
Positive	Negative	<1	To the left – reactants favoured

Table 17.4 indicates the following broad relationship between $\Delta G^{\ominus}$ and the equilibrium constant, K_c:

■ If $\Delta G^{\ominus}$ is negative, K_c is greater than 1 and the products predominate in the equilibrium mixture.

■ Alternatively, if $\Delta G^{\ominus}$ is positive, K_c will be less than 1 and the reactants will predominate in the equilibrium mixture.

Exploring the relationship between Gibbs free energy and equilibrium further, consider again the Haber process for the production of ammonia (arguably one of the key industrial processes ever developed):

$$N_2(g) + 3H_2(g) \rightleftharpoons 2NH_3(g) \qquad \Delta G^{\ominus} = -33 \text{ kJ mol}^{-1}$$

Based on the discussion above, this reaction will proceed from left to right – nitrogen and hydrogen will spontaneously become ammonia – but the reverse reaction ($\Delta G^{\ominus} = +33 \text{ kJ mol}^{-1}$) will not occur spontaneously. However, equilibrium can be reached in either direction. If we start with nitrogen and hydrogen, the system will form an equilibrium mixture in which nitrogen, hydrogen and ammonia are present; if we start with pure ammonia, some will spontaneously react to form nitrogen and hydrogen so that all three are present in the equilibrium mixture. This would appear to contradict the arguments we used above about the spontaneity of reactions. However, this does not violate the second law of thermodynamics because the value of $\Delta G^{\ominus}$ quoted for the backward reaction ($+33 \text{ kJ mol}^{-1}$) was for the complete conversion of two moles of ammonia into one mole of nitrogen and three moles of hydrogen, whereas here we are talking of the reaction to produce an equilibrium mixture. The equilibrium mixture always has a lower Gibbs free energy (and higher entropy) than either the pure reactants or the pure products (a mixture has higher entropy than pure substances); therefore the conversion of either reactants or products into the equilibrium mixture results in a process in which $\Delta G^{\ominus}$ is negative (Figure 17.11).

■ **Figure 17.11**
The variation in the Gibbs free energy for a reaction for which the overall ΔG is negative

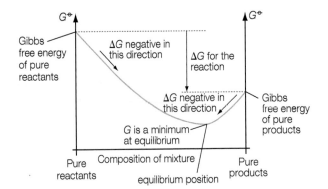

Note that the overall Gibbs free energy of a system ($G^\ominus$) depends on how much of each substance is present, and the equilibrium mixture represents the composition that gives the minimum value of the Gibbs free energy (maximum value of entropy). When the system is at equilibrium, the Gibbs free energy of the remaining amount of reactants present is the same as that of however much of the products has been formed. Thus $\Delta G^\ominus$ is zero at this point and there is no tendency to spontaneously move in either direction away from equilibrium. Any shift away from the equilibrium position results in an increase in G and therefore a process for which $\Delta G^\ominus$ is positive, i.e. non-spontaneous.

■ **Figure 17.12**
The influence of the value of $\Delta G^\ominus$ on the position of equilibrium:
a $\Delta G^\ominus$ is negative and the position of equilibrium lies closer to the products;
b $\Delta G^\ominus$ is positive and the position of equilibrium lies closer to the reactants

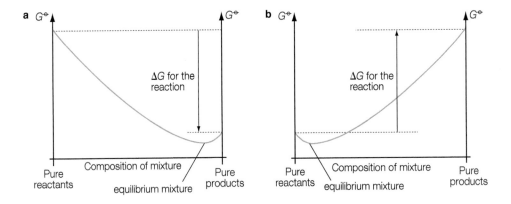

The value and sign of $\Delta G^\ominus$ give us information about the position of equilibrium. If $\Delta G^\ominus$ is negative then the position of equilibrium will be closer to the products than the reactants (Figure 17.12a). The more negative the value of $\Delta G^\ominus$, the closer the position of equilibrium lies towards the products. If $\Delta G^\ominus$ is numerically very large and negative then the position of equilibrium lies very close to pure products, which corresponds to the idea discussed above (see Tables 17.3 and 17.4) – a reaction for which $\Delta G^\ominus$ is negative proceeds spontaneously from reactants to products. If $\Delta G^\ominus$ is positive then the position of equilibrium lies more towards the reactants (Figure 17.12b) – the more positive the value, the closer the position of equilibrium lies towards pure reactants.

In summary, $\Delta G^\ominus$ can be used to predict the spontaneity of a reaction and position of equilibrium as follows:

■ A reaction that has a value of $\Delta G^\ominus$ that is both large and negative takes place spontaneously and reaches an equilibrium position to the right, favouring the products. The equilibrium mixture contains a large proportion of products.

■ A reaction with a value of $\Delta G^\ominus$ that is large and positive does not take place spontaneously and reaches an equilibrium position to the left favouring the reactants. The equilibrium mixture contains predominantly reactants, with only a limited amounts of the products formed.

The position of equilibrium corresponds to the mixture of reactants and products that produces the minimum value of the Gibbs free energy ($G^\ominus$) and the maximum value of entropy (S) and, as mentioned earlier, the relationship between Gibbs free energy and the equilibrium constant for reactions in solution is given by

$$\Delta G^{\ominus} = -RT \ln K_c$$

However, for reactions in the gas phase the value of equilibrium constant generated by this equation is that of K_p – the constant is expressed in terms of partial pressures of the gases in the equilibrium mixture. Earlier we derived the relationship between concentration and partial pressure as

$$P = cRT$$

from which the following relationship between K_p and K_c can also be derived:

$$K_p = K_c \times (RT)^{\Delta n}$$

where Δn = number of moles of products in the equation – number of moles of reactants
So for the Haber process reaction above, $\Delta n = 2 - 4 = -2$, and so $K_p \neq K_c$ for this reaction. However, for a reaction such as

$$H_2(g) + I_2(g) \rightleftharpoons 2HI(g)$$

$$n = 0 \quad \text{and so} \quad K_p = K_c$$

Worked example

The esterification reaction between ethanol and ethanoic acid has a free energy change ($\Delta G^{\ominus}$) of $-4.38\,kJ\,mol^{-1}$. Calculate the value of K_c for this reaction at 25°C (298 K). ($R = 8.31\,J\,K^{-1}\,mol^{-1}$)

$$CH_3COOH(l) + C_2H_5OH(l) \rightleftharpoons CH_3COOC_2H_5(l) + H_2O(l)$$

$$\Delta G^{\ominus} = -RT \ln K_c$$

$$-4.38 \times 1000 = -(8.31 \times 298 \times \ln K_c)$$

Note that the value for $\Delta G^{\ominus}$ is converted to $J\,mol^{-1}$ to be consistent with the units for R.

$$\ln K_c = -\frac{4380}{2478} = 1.77$$

Therefore $K_c = e^{1.77} = 5.9$

---

4 The gas phase reaction between hydrogen and iodine to produce hydrogen iodide has a value of $\Delta G^{\ominus}$ of $+1.38\,kJ\,mol^{-1}$ at 298 K.

$$H_2(g) + I_2(g) \rightleftharpoons 2HI(g)$$

a Calculate the value of the equilibrium constant at this temperature given the relationship
$\Delta G^{\ominus} = -RT \ln K_p$ for a gas phase reaction.
b What would be the value of K_c at this temperature for this reaction? Explain your reasoning.
c From your calculated value for the equilibrium constant predict whether the position of the equilibrium achieved is closer to the reactants or products side of the equation.

5 a What is the value of $\Delta G^{\ominus}$ for a reaction when $K = 1$?
b Nitrogen(II) oxide, NO, is oxidized in air to nitrogen(IV) oxide, NO_2:

$$2NO(g) + O_2(g) \rightleftharpoons 2NO_2(g)$$

The value of K_c for this reaction at 298 K is 1.7×10^{12}. Calculate the value of $\Delta G^{\ominus}$ for the reaction.

■ Coupled reactions

An equilibrium where the reactants are favoured over the products ($K_c < 1$) may be 'driven forward' by a reaction that is more spontaneous, that is, has a more negative value for the Gibbs free energy change, $\Delta G^{\ominus}$ (Chapter 15), and hence strongly favours the products over the reactants ($K_c > 1$).

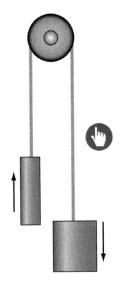

■ **Figure 17.13**
A mechanical analogy to illustrate the concept of a coupled reaction

A simple mechanical analogy is a pair of masses joined by a rope passing over a pulley (Figure 17.13). The smaller of the two masses will be pulled up as the heavier mass falls: its coupling to the heavier mass results in it being raised. The thermodynamic equivalent is a reaction with a small positive value of $\Delta G^{\ominus}$ being forced to occur by its coupling to a reaction with a very large negative value of $\Delta G^{\ominus}$. The sum of the two values of $\Delta G^{\ominus}$ is negative.

The role of adenosine triphosphate (ATP) in cells is to act as the short-term energy source. The function of the hydrolysis of ATP is to couple with non-spontaneous reactions, for example polymerization, and provide sufficient free energy to make them spontaneous (Chapter 24 on the accompanying website).

■ Homogeneous and heterogeneous equilibria

The IB syllabus specifies that questions will deal only with homogeneous equilibria. But it is still worthwhile understanding what this means, and indeed what type of reaction represents the alternative, heterogeneous, equilibria.

An equilibrium in which all the substances are present in the same phase is known as a homogeneous equilibrium. For example, the Haber process reaction,

$$N_2(g) + 3H_2(g) \rightleftharpoons 2NH_3(g)$$

is an example of a homogeneous equilibrium (Chapter 7).

An equilibrium in which the substances involved are present in different phases is known as a heterogeneous equilibrium. For example

$$H_2O(l) \rightleftharpoons H_2O(g) \quad \text{and} \quad AgCl(s) + (aq) \rightleftharpoons Ag^+(aq) + Cl^-(aq)$$

are examples of heterogeneous equilibria. It is worth noting that pure solids and pure liquids do *not* appear in the equilibrium expression for a heterogeneous reaction. For example, in the case of the thermal decomposition of limestone in a closed system,

$$CaCO_3(s) \rightleftharpoons CaO(s) + CO_2(g)$$

it is found that $K_c = [CO_2(g)]$. This situation occurs because the 'activity' of a pure liquid or solid is 1. We have already seen that the terms homogeneous and heterogeneous can also applied to catalysts (Chapter 6).

One example of heterogeneous equilibria relates to sparingly soluble salts, which will be discussed in Chapter 22 on the accompanying website.

Solubility equilibria

When a solute is added to a given amount of solvent at a given temperature, a point is finally reached when no more solute dissolves in the solvent. At that point, the solution is described as being saturated.

$$\text{solute + solvent} \underset{\substack{\text{crystallization or}\\\text{precipitation}}}{\overset{\text{dissolving}}{\rightleftharpoons}} \text{saturated solution}$$

In a saturated solution, a dynamic equilibrium is established between the dissolved solute in the solution and the undissolved solute. At equilibrium, the rate of the forward reaction (dissolving) equals the rate of the reverse reaction (crystallization or precipitation). The solubility of a substance is usually expressed as the mass or amount of solute present in 1 dm³ of solution.

Compounds are often regarded as being soluble *or* insoluble. However, many ionic compounds, such as silver chloride, are *sparingly soluble* in water. When increasing quantities of a sparingly soluble ionic solid are added to water, a saturated solution is eventually formed. There is a dynamic equilibrium between the undissolved salt and its dissolved ions:

$$AgCl(s) \rightleftharpoons Ag^+(aq) + Cl^-(aq)$$

The product of the concentrations of ions in a saturated solution of silver chloride is an equilibrium constant termed the *solubility product* (K_{sp}):

$$K_{sp} = [Ag^+(aq)] \times [Cl^-(aq)]$$

 Calculating a solubility product from the solubility and vice versa is discussed in Chapter 24 on the accompanying website.

Studies on such saturated solutions of sparingly soluble salts have provided evidence for our ideas on dynamic equilibria. Radioactive labelling experiments with lead(II) chloride solution have provided evidence for the exchange of ions in an equilibrium situation (Figure 17.14). Solid lead(II) chloride, $PbCl_2$, is only slightly soluble in cold water. Some solid lead(II) chloride is placed in a saturated solution of radioactive lead(II) chloride. The solution contains radioactive $Pb^{2+}(aq)$ ions. Although the solution is saturated and no more lead chloride can dissolve overall, the solid takes up some of the radioactivity. This shows that some of the radioactive lead ions in the solution have been precipitated into the solid, and an equal number of non-radioactive lead ions from the solid must have dissolved to keep the solution saturated.

■ **Figure 17.14**
If solid lead chloride is placed in a saturated solution of lead chloride labelled with radioactive lead ions, Pb^{2+} (shown in red), the solid becomes radioactive

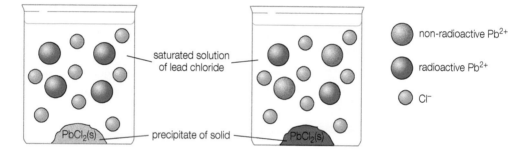

A 'barium meal' before an X-ray is used to diagnose cancers and ulcers in the intestine or stomach (Figure 17.15). The patient drinks a 'barium meal' (barium sulfate and water) before having the X-ray taken. Aqueous barium ions, $Ba^{2+}(aq)$, are highly toxic. However, the 'barium meal' is not poisonous because barium sulfate is highly insoluble – this is indicated by its very low solubility product ($K_{sp} = 1.08 \times 10^{-10}$ – IB *Chemistry data booklet*).

■ **Figure 17.15**
A coloured photograph of the entrance to the duodenum showing the blocking of the passage of the barium meal by an ulcer in the centre

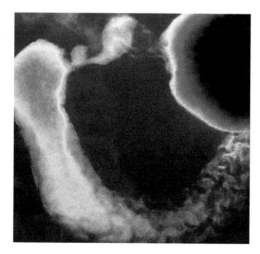

■ *Examination questions – a selection*

Paper 1 IB questions and IB style questions

Q1 Iron(III) ions, Fe^{3+}, react with thiocyanate ions, SCN^-, in a reversible reaction to form a red solution.

Which changes to the equilibrium will make the solution go red?

$Fe^{3+}(aq) + SCN^-(aq) \rightleftharpoons [FeSCN](aq)$ $\Delta H^\ominus = +ve$

      yellow   red

    I increasing the temperature
    II adding $FeCl_3$
    III adding a catalyst

    A I and II only   **C** II and III only
    B I and III only   **D** I, II and III

Higher Level Paper 1, Nov 2012, Q22

Q2 Consider the following reversible reaction:

$$2NO_2(g) \rightleftharpoons N_2O_4(g)$$

What is the value of K_c for the reaction when the equilibrium concentrations are $[NO_2] = 4.0\,mol\,dm^{-3}$ and $[N_2O_4] = 4.0\,mol\,dm^{-3}$?

    A 0.25   **C** 2.0
    B 0.50   **D** 4.0

Higher Level Paper 1, Nov 2012, Q23

Q3 Which change will shift the position of equilibrium to the right in this reaction?

$N_2(g) + 3H_2(g) \rightleftharpoons 2NH_3(g)$ $\Delta H = -92\,kJ\,mol^{-1}$

    A increasing the temperature
    B decreasing the pressure
    C adding a catalyst
    D removing ammonia from the equilibrium mixture

Q4 $N_2O_4(g) \rightleftharpoons 2NO_2(g)$ $K_c = 5.0 \times 10^{-3}$

In an equilibrium mixture of these two gases $[N_2O_4] = 5 \times 10^{-1}\,mol\,dm^{-3}$. What is the equilibrium concentration of NO_2 in $mol\,dm^{-3}$?

    A 5.0×10^{-1} **C** 5.0×10^{-3}
    B $5.0 \times 10^{-}$ **D** 2.5×10^{-4}

Higher Level Paper 1, Nov 2001, Q25

Q5 $2H_2O(l) \rightleftharpoons H_3O^+(aq) + OH^-(aq)$

The equilibrium constant for the reaction above is 1.0×10^{-14} at 25 °C and 2.1×10^{-14} at 35 °C. What can be concluded from this information?

    A $[H_3O^+]$ decreases as the temperature is raised.
    B $[H_3O^+]$ is greater than $[OH^-]$ at 35 °C.
    C Water is a stronger electrolyte at 25 °C.
    D The ionization of water is endothermic.

Standard Level Paper 1, May 2000

Q6 The sequence of diagrams shown represents the system as time passes for a gas phase reaction in which reactant X is converted to product Y.

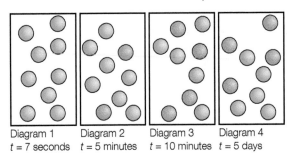

Diagram 1   Diagram 2   Diagram 3   Diagram 4
$t = 7$ seconds $t = 5$ minutes $t = 10$ minutes $t = 5$ days

Time, t

$X = \bigcirc$ $Y = \bigcirc$

Which statement is correct?

    A At $t = 5$ days the rate of the forward reaction is greater than the rate of the backward reaction.
    B At $t = 7$ seconds the reaction has reached completion.
    C At $t = 10$ minutes the system has reached a state of equilibrium.
    D At $t = 5$ days the rate of the forward reaction is less than the rate of the backward reaction.

Higher Level Paper 1, Specimen 2009, Q9

Q7 Consider the reversible reaction

$$N_2(g) + 3H_2(g) \rightleftharpoons 2NH_3(g)$$

The value of the equilibrium constant at a particular temperature is found to be $K_c = 2.0$.

The concentrations in the reaction mixture at a particular time are found to be:

    $[N_2(g)] = 1.0\,mol\,dm^{-3}$ $[H_2(g)] = 2.0\,mol\,dm^{-3}$
    $[NH_3(g)] = 1.0\,mol\,dm^{-3}$

Which of the following statements is true?

    A $Q = 0.50$ and the system is not at equilibrium.
    B $Q = 2.00$ and the system is not at equilibrium.
    C $Q = 1.30$ and the system is not at equilibrium.
    D $Q = 2.00$ and the system is at equilibrium.

Q8 Which of the following describes the relationship between the equilibrium constant, K, and the change in Gibbs free energy, $\Delta G^\ominus$, for a reaction?

    A If $K > 1$, then $\Delta G^\ominus > 0$
    B If $K > 1$, then $\Delta G^\ominus < 0$
    C If $K = 0$, then $\Delta G^\ominus = 0$
    D If $K < 1$, then $\Delta G^\ominus < 0$

Paper 2 IB questions and IB style questions

Q1 Hydrogen gas reacts with iodine gas to form hydrogen iodide gas. A 2.00 dm^3 flask was filled with 1.50×10^{-2} mol of hydrogen and 1.50×10^{-2} mol of iodine at a temperature, T.

The equilibrium constant, K_c, has a value of 53.0 at this temperature.

a Deduce the equilibrium constant expression, K_c, for the formation of HI(g). [1]

b Determine the equilibrium concentrations, in $mol\,dm^{-3}$, of hydrogen, iodine and hydrogen iodide. [4]

c Identify the intermolecular forces present in hydrogen iodide in the liquid state, HI(l). [1]

Higher Level Paper 2, May 2013, Q3

Q2 The reversible reaction involving the conversion of sulfur dioxide to sulfur trioxide is central to the industrial process for making sulfuric acid.

$$2SO_2(g) + O_2(g) \rightleftharpoons 2SO_3(g) \quad \Delta H = -198\,kJ$$

Consider the reaction at equilibrium and predict, giving reasons, in which direction the equilibrium position will shift for each of the changes in conditions listed below. [3]

Change	Shift	Reason
Increase in temperature		
Increase in pressure		
Addition of a catalyst to the mixture		

Q3 Methanol is an important industrial solvent and fuel. It can be produced from carbon monoxide and hydrogen according to the following equation:

$$CO(g) + 2H_2(g) \rightleftharpoons CH_3OH(g)$$
$$\Delta H^\ominus = -91\,kJ\,mol^{-1}$$

The effect of different catalysts on this reaction is investigated using the following apparatus:

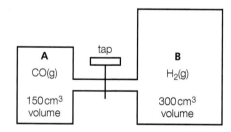

A contains 1 mole of carbon monoxide and **B** contains 2 moles of hydrogen. The gases in both containers are at the same temperature and pressure. The tap is closed at the start of the experiment.

a What pressure change will occur, if any, in the containers when the tap is opened

  i and the gases are allowed to mix (but before they start to react)? [1]

  ii as the reaction takes place? [1]

b i What will happen to the temperature as the gases begin to react? [1]

  ii What will happen to the concentration of methanol if the system is allowed to reach equilibrium at a lower temperature? [1]

c i Write the equilibrium expression for the above reaction. [1]

  ii Calculate a value for K_c if the maximum yield of methanol is 85%. [3]

  iii When this reaction is carried out on an industrial scale, the yield is about 60%. Suggest a reason for this. [1]

  iv Copper is a good catalyst for this reaction. What effect, if any, will the addition of copper have on the value of K_c? [1]

Higher Level Paper 2, Nov 2000, Q4

Q4 a An industrial gas mixture is produced by the catalytic re-forming of methane using steam.

$$CH_4(g) + H_2O(g) \rightleftharpoons CO(g) + 3H_2(g)$$
$$\Delta H^\ominus = +206\,kJ\,mol^{-1}$$

By choosing from the appropriate letter(s) below, identify the change(s) that would shift the position of equilibrium to the right.

  A increasing the temperature

  B decreasing the temperature

  C increasing the pressure

  D adding a catalyst

  E decreasing the pressure

  F increasing the concentration of H_2 [2]

b The following graph represents the change of concentration of reactant and product during the reaction.

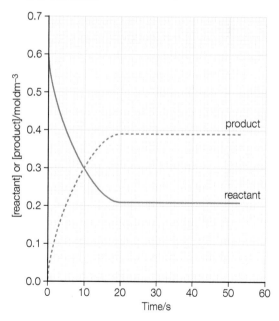

  i Calculate the average rate of reaction over the first 15 seconds, stating the units. [3]

  ii After 19 seconds the concentrations of the reactant and product do not change. State what this indicates about the reaction. [1]

Higher Level Paper 2, May 2003, Q3

18 Acids and bases

ESSENTIAL IDEAS

- The acid–base concept can be extended to reactions that do not involve proton transfer.
- The equilibrium law can be applied to acid–base reactions. Numerical problems can be simplified by making assumptions about the relative concentrations of the species involved. The use of logarithms is also significant here.
- pH curves can be investigated experimentally but are mathematically determined by the dissociation constants of the acid and base. An indicator with an appropriate end-point can be used to determine the equivalence point of the reaction.

18.1 Lewis acids and bases – *the acid–base concept can be extended to reactions that do not involve proton transfer*

Lewis theory (inorganic chemistry)

The Brønsted–Lowry theory defines an acid as a proton donor and a base as a proton acceptor. However, when a base accepts a proton it donates an electron pair to the proton. In general:

$$\text{B:} \qquad \text{H}^+ \rightarrow {}^+\text{BH}$$

where B: represents a base (with one or more lone pairs of electrons), H^+ represents the proton, BH^+ represents the conjugate acid and the curly arrow represents the movement of an electron pair to form a coordinate covalent bond (see Chapter 4). Simple examples include the reaction between the ammonia molecule and the proton to form the ammonium ion:

$$\text{H}_3\text{N:} \qquad \text{H}^+ \rightarrow {}^+\text{NH}_4$$

and between the water molecule and the proton to form the hydronium or oxonium ion:

$$\text{H}_2\ddot{\text{O}}: \qquad \text{H}^+ \rightarrow \text{H}_3\text{O}^+$$

The movement of an electron pair during an acid–base reaction is the basis of the Lewis theory of acidity developed by Gilbert Lewis (see Chapter 4). A Lewis acid is defined as a substance that can accept a pair of electrons from another atom to form a coordinate covalent bond. A Lewis base is defined as a substance that can donate a pair of electrons to another atom to form a dative covalent (coordinate) bond. In the simple examples above, the proton (H^+) is the Lewis acid and the ammonia molecule and water molecule are the Lewis bases.

However, the Lewis theory is *more general* than the Brønsted–Lowry theory: some reactions are classified as acid–base reactions under the Lewis definitions that are not regarded as acid–base reactions under the Brønsted–Lowry theory. Therefore the terms Lewis acid and Lewis base are often reserved for species which are Lewis acids and bases, but which are *not* Brønsted–Lowry acids and bases.

In these reactions no protons are involved, water is absent and the reactions frequently occur in the gas phase. For example, the gases ammonia and boron trichloride react together to form a solid adduct called ammonia boron trichloride:

$$\text{H}_3\text{N:} \qquad \text{BCl}_3 \rightarrow \text{NH}_3\text{BCl}_3$$

The ammonia is the Lewis base (electron pair donor) and boron trichloride is the Lewis acid (electron pair acceptor). The reaction is driven, in part, by the need for the boron in boron trichloride to overcome its electron deficiency: it only has six electrons in its outer shell. In

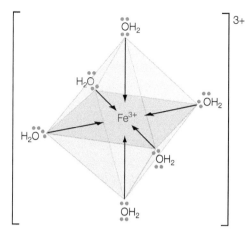

■ **Figure 18.1** The structure of the hexaaquairon(III) ion [Fe(H₂O)₆]³⁺

the adduct the boron has acquired a full outer shell of eight electrons (an octet).

An interesting example of Lewis acid–base behaviour is illustrated by the aluminium chloride dimer, Al_2Cl_6, formed when aluminium chloride, $AlCl_3$, undergoes sublimation. Each of the two aluminium chloride molecules forms a dative or coordinate bond to the aluminium of the other molecule using one of the lone pairs on its chlorine atoms, while accepting a lone pair of electrons from the chlorine of the other molecule. Each aluminium chloride molecule is thus acting simultaneously as both a Lewis acid and a Lewis base.

Transition metal complexes

Common examples of Lewis bonding are found in the complex ions formed by the transition metals (see Chapter 13). Charged metal ions become surrounded by water molecules in aqueous solution. Many transition metal ions become surrounded by six water molecules; for example; Fe^{3+} (aq), exists as the hexaaquairon(III) ion $[Fe(H_2O)_6]^{3+}$ (Figure 18.1). The six water molecules in this complex each donate a lone pair of electrons from the oxygen atoms of their water molecules to the empty 3d orbitals of the central iron(III) ion. The water molecules, known as ligands, are acting as Lewis bases (electron pair donors) and the iron(III) ion is acting as a Lewis acid (electron pair acceptor).

Investigation of transition metal complexes

Compounds with the same formula but that differ as to which anions are coordinated and which are present as counter ions, are described as ionization isomers. The isomers produce different ions when dissolved in solution, for example, $[Co(NH_3)_4Cl_2]NO_2$ and $[Co(NH_3)_4Cl(NO_2)]$ Cl. The first isomer releases $[Co(NH_3)_4Cl_2]^+$ and NO_2^- and the second isomer releases $[Co(NH_3)_4Cl(NO_2)]^+$ and Cl^-. The nitrate(v) and chloride ions are the counter ions.

Both of these salts contain different complex cations carrying a +1 charge, but the first complex has the nitrite ion, NO_2^- as the counter ion and the second complex has the chloride ion, Cl^-. The two isomers can be easily distinguished by adding silver nitrate solution: the first one will not give a precipitate, but the second one will give a white precipitate of silver(i) chloride.

The following three compounds with the formula '$CrCl_3.6H_2O$' are also ionization isomers: the violet $[Cr(H_2O)_6]Cl_3$, the green $[Cr(H_2O)_5Cl]Cl_2.H_2O$ and the green $[Cr(H_2O)_4Cl_2]Cl.2H_2O$. In these complexes the chloride ion can be analysed by quantitative silver(i) chloride formation with excess silver(i) nitrate solution. The non-coordinated 'extra water molecules' can be removed by dehydration with concentrated sulfuric acid. Conductivity measurements will show how many ions are present in solution and this will help distinguish the various ionization isomers: values of 4, 3 and 2 ions would be observed for $[Cr(H_2O)_6]Cl_3$, $[Cr(H_2O)_5Cl]Cl_2.H_2O$ and $[Cr(H_2O)_4Cl_2]Cl.2H_2O$, respectively.

Nature of Science

Theories can be supported, falsified or replaced by new theories – Lewis theory is an extension of Brønsted–Lowry theory

In 1932 Gilbert Lewis proposed a more general definition of acids and bases. A Lewis acid is a species capable of accepting an electron pair to form a coordinate covalent bond and a Lewis base is a species capable of donating a pair of electrons to form a coordinate covalent bond.

■ **Figure 18.2**
The reaction between ammonia and boron trifluoride

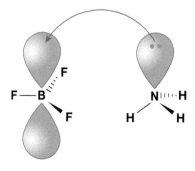

Figure 18.2 shows the reaction between boron trifluoride and ammonia to form a stable adduct. The donor orbital is a lone pair on the nitrogen atom of ammonia and the acceptor is the empty p orbital left over from the sp³ hybridization at boron in boron trifluoride.

The Lewis definition does not associate acidity with any particular element but rather to electronic arrangement. Lewis theory does not falsify Brønsted–Lowry theory but extends it: Brønsted–Lowry theory is a subset of Lewis theory. All Brønsted–Lowry bases are Lewis bases and all Brønsted–Lowry acids are Lewis acids. A Brønsted–Lowry base is an example of a Lewis base that uses an electron pair to bond specifically to a proton as opposed to another molecule or ion. When H^+ accepts a lone pair from the oxygen of a water molecule to form an oxonium ion, H_3O^+, H^+ is acting as a Lewis acid and water as a Lewis base.

Lewis theory (organic chemistry)

Nucleophiles and electrophiles

Lewis acids and bases are defined in terms of electron pair transfers. A Lewis base is an electron pair donor, and a Lewis acid is an electron pair acceptor. Like many reactions, an organic reaction results from a process of breaking covalent bonds and forming new ones. This process involves electron pair transfers. Ionic mechanisms, such as nucleophilic substitution and electrophilic substitution, also involve electron pair transfers and are therefore described by the Lewis acid–base theory.

The Lewis definition implies the presence of high electron density centres in Lewis bases, and low electron density centres in Lewis acids. In a reaction between a Lewis acid and a Lewis base the electron pair donated by the base is used to form a new sigma bond to the electron-deficient centre in the acid. The identification of Lewis bases follows basically the same guidelines as the identification of Brønsted–Lowry bases. They frequently contain atoms that have non-bonding electrons, or lone pairs. In contrast Lewis acids frequently contain atoms with an incomplete octet, a full positive charge, or a partial positive charge.

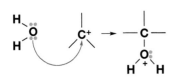

Figure 18.3 The reaction between a water molecule (Lewis base) and a carbocation (Lewis acid)

Water is an example of a Lewis base. Carbocations are examples of Lewis acids. When water reacts with a carbocation as shown in Figure 18.3, one of the electron pairs from the oxygen is used to form a new sigma bond to the central carbon in the carbocation. As with Brønsted–Lowry acid–base reactions, curly arrows are used to indicate the movement of electron pairs during the reaction process. The arrow always originates with the Lewis base and moves towards the area of electron deficiency in the Lewis acid (Figure 18.3).

To avoid confusion between the Lewis and the Brønsted–Lowry definitions of acids and bases, Lewis bases are sometimes called nucleophiles, and Lewis acids are called electrophiles. In the example above, water acts as a nucleophile (donates electrons), and the carbocation acts as an electrophile (receives electrons).

Since Brønsted–Lowry acids and bases are a subcategory of the more general Lewis definition, it can be said that most Brønsted–Lowry bases are also nucleophiles, and that the proton is a Lewis acid, or an electrophile.

Basic versus nucleophilic behaviour

There are some differences between Brønsted–Lowry bases and nucleophiles. First, the term 'base' is reserved for substances seeking acidic protons, whereas the term 'nucleophile' is used for substances seeking electron-deficient centres, protons or other atoms (most commonly carbon).

In acid–base reactions, the size (or bulk) of the base seldom matters. However, in nucleophilic reactions, the size of the nucleophile can be an important (steric) factor. Smaller nucleophiles are more effective. Thus, although the nucleophilic atom in the two species in Figure 18.4 is the same (oxygen) and they have similar structures, the methoxide ion is a more effective nucleophile than the *t*-butoxide ion (2-methylpropan-2-olate ion), even though they are about equally effective as bases. The larger *t*-butoxide ion has more difficulty reaching an electrophilic centre, which is often a carbon buried at the core of the molecular structure. That is not a problem when it acts as a base because acidic protons are usually found on the surface of the molecule and are easily accessible (Figure 18.4).

Figure 18.4 Structures of methoxide and tertiary-butoxide ions

Classification of Lewis acids

A Lewis acid must have at least one empty orbital in the valence (outer) shell of one of its atoms to accept an electron pair from a Lewis base. Lewis acids may be classified as:

- Molecules containing a central atom with an incomplete octet

  Typical examples of this class of Lewis acids are electron-deficient molecules such as the halides of boron, beryllium and aluminium, for example, BCl_3, $BeCl_2$ and $AlCl_3$.

■ Molecules containing a central atom with empty d orbitals

The central atom of the tetrahalides of silicon, germanium and titanium, phosphorus(v) chloride, phosphorus(iii) chloride and sulfur tetrafluoride all have empty d orbitals. These molecules can therefore accept an electron pair from the Lewis base to accommodate in their empty d orbitals and can therefore form adducts with halide ions and organic bases.

■ Simple cations

Theoretically all simple cations are potentially Lewis acids. The Lewis acid strength or coordinating ability of simple cations increases with an increase in the charge and increases with a decrease in ionic radius.

■ Molecules with a multiple bond between atoms of different electronegativity

Typical examples of molecules in this class of Lewis acids are carbon dioxide, sulfur dioxide and sulfur trioxide. In these compounds the oxygen atoms are more electronegative than the sulfur or carbon atoms. As a result, the electron density of the pi electrons is pushed away from the carbon or sulfur atoms, towards the oxygen atom. The carbon or sulfur atom becomes electron deficient and is able to accept an electron pair from a Lewis base.

---

1 Describe the following reactions with structural formulas and curly arrows. Label the reacting species as either a Lewis acid or a Lewis base. Show the lone pairs that form the coordinate bond.
   a Boron trifluoride reacting with ethoxyethane ($O(C_2H_5)_2$).
   b Aluminium chloride reacting with chloride ion to form the tetrachloroaluminate ion.
   c Silver(I) ions reacting with ammonia molecules to form the diamminesilver(I) complex.
   d Lithium ions reacting with four methanol molecules.
   e Boric acid, $B(OH)_3$, reacting with hydroxide ions to form $[B(OH)_4]^-$.
   f Two aluminium chloride molecules, $AlCl_3$, reacting to form an aluminium chloride dimer, Al_2Cl_6.

■ Solvents other than water

The Brønsted–Lowry theory can be applied to solvents other than water. Ammonia, like water, is amphiprotic and can behave as a Brønsted–Lowry acid or base:

As an acid: $NH_3 \rightarrow NH_2^- + H^+$

As a base: $NH_3 + H^+ \rightarrow NH_4^+$

So in liquid ammonia, ammonium chloride, $[NH_4^+ \, Cl^-]$, behaves as a strong acid, and sodium amide, $[Na^+ \, NH_2^-]$, behaves as a strong base.

In liquid ammonia solution, an acid may be defined as a substance that provides NH_4^+ ions, while a base produces amide ions, NH_2^-. More generally in a self-ionizing solvent, an acid is a substance that produces the cation characteristic of the solvent, and a base is a substance that produces the anion characteristic of the solvent.

Another solvent that may be used for acid–base reactions (proton transfer) is concentrated sulfuric acid. This is both an acid and a solvent for the nitration of benzene.

Sometimes an aprotic solvent is used for acid–base reactions, that is, a solvent whose molecules do not donate a proton. Under these conditions the more general Lewis theory of acids and bases is applied.

Levelling effect

Non-aqueous solvents that are good proton donors, for example liquid ammonia, encourage acids to ionize in them. Hence, in a basic solvent, all acids are strong. The solvent is said to show a levelling effect on the acid, since the strength of the dissolved acid cannot be greater than that of the protonated solvent.

For example, in aqueous solutions, no acidic species can exist that is a stronger acid than H^+/H_3O^+. In acidic solvents, for example, liquid sulfuric acid, ionization of bases is promoted or encouraged. Most acids are relatively weak under these conditions.

Development of acid–base theories

In the 1880s the Swedish scientist Arrhenius proposed that acids are substances which produce hydrogen ions in solution and bases are substances which produce hydroxide ions in solution. Neutralization occurs because hydrogen ions and hydroxide ions react to produce water. The theory was not totally satisfactory for several reasons. For example, some substances which had acidic properties did not contain hydrogen and some bases did not contain hydroxide ions. The theory also applied only to aqueous solutions.

The shortcomings of the Arrhenius theory led chemists to seek other explanations for the nature of acids and bases. The Brønsted–Lowry theory was introduced independently in 1923 by the Danish chemist Johannes Nicolaus Brønsted and the English chemist Thomas Martin Lowry, stating that any compound that can transfer a proton to any other compound is an acid, and the compound that accepts the proton is a base. Their theory explained the behaviour of all of the acids and bases covered by the Arrhenius theory, but also was able to resolve some of the problems with that theory. That is, they were able to explain why some salts are acidic *and* basic (due to salt hydrolysis) and why no free protons are found in the solutions of some acids.

Brønsted–Lowry theory does not require an aqueous solution or dissociation into ions as in the Arrhenius definition. The substance which accepts the H^+ from the acid is called the 'conjugate base'. This idea of conjugate acid–base pairs is an important part of the Brønsted–Lowry approach. Acid strength is defined in terms of the strength of the tendency to donate the hydrogen ion to the solvent (typically water). A strong acid has a high tendency to donate a proton to water, so the H_3O^+ concentration is high.

A more general definition of acids and bases is the approach of Gilbert Lewis in 1923. Lewis theory was developed because there was the problem of substances which exhibited acidic properties in solution (for example, CO_2) but did not contain a H^+. Lewis defined an acid as any compound that was a potential electron pair acceptor and a base as any compound that was a potential electron pair donor. In the Lewis scheme, H^+ itself is an acid. Usanovich (1939) developed an even more general approach to acid–base theory that consolidated the differing approaches of the previous theories. He defined an acid as any chemical species which is capable of combining with anions or electrons or giving up cations. Conversely, he defined a base as any chemical species which is capable of giving up anions or electrons or combining with cations. This definition includes all Lewis acids and bases and all redox reactions. For example, the redox reaction

$$Cl_2(g) + 2Na(s) \rightarrow 2NaCl(s)$$

is classified as an acid–base reaction under the Usanovich theory. The base, the sodium atom, loses an electron; the acid, the chlorine molecule, combines with this electron.

The various theories of acids and bases are summarized in Table 18.1.

■ **Table 18.1** Summary of the various acid and base theories

Theory	Basic principle
Traditional approach	Acid: a substance that has certain properties (for example, sour taste, turns litmus red)
Arrhenius	Acid: H^+ present in aqueous solution Base: OH^- present in aqueous solution At neutrality: $[H^+] = [OH^-]$
Brønsted–Lowry	Acid: H^+ donor Base: H^+ acceptor Conjugate acid–base pairs No concept of neutrality
Lewis	Acid: an electron pair acceptor Base: an electron pair donor
Usanovich	Acid: a substance that donates a cation, or accepts an anion or an electron Base: a substance that donates an anion or an electron, or accepts a cation

2 The following species can all be defined as acids: boron trichloride, BCl_3, bromine, Br_2, nitric(v) acid, HNO_3, hydrogen iodide, HI, and water, H_2O. Consider the chemical behaviour of each of these species in the following five reactions:

I $BCl_3(g) + KF(s) \rightarrow K^+BCl_4^-(s)$
II $Br_2(l) + 2K(s) \rightarrow 2K^+Br^-(s)$
III $HNO_3(aq) + NaOH(aq) \rightarrow NaNO_3(aq) + H_2O(l)$
IV $HI(g) + H_2O(l) \rightarrow H_3O^+(aq) + I^-(aq)$
V $H_2O(l) + C_3H_7NH_2(aq) \rightleftharpoons C_3H_7NH_3^+(aq) + OH^-(aq)$

Deduce which equation contains:
a The only acid that is described by the Lavoisier definition: an oxide of a non-metal in water.
b An acid that is described by the Arrhenius, Brønsted–Lowry, Lewis and Usanovich definitions of acidity.
c An acid that is described by the Brønsted–Lowry, Lewis and Usanovich definitions of acidity.
d An acid that is described by the Lewis and Usanovich definitions of acidity.
e An acid that is only described by the Usanovich definition of acidity.

3 Find out about the Lux–Flood definition of acids and bases.

ToK Link

The same phenomenon can sometimes be explored from different perspectives, and explained by different theories. For example, do we judge competing theories by their universality, simplicity or elegance?

Albert Einstein's theory of general relativity is over one hundred years old and is often suggested to be the archetype for a good scientific theory. Einstein's theory explained gravity as a geometric phenomenon: a force that results from the bending of space-time by matter, forcing objects and light to move along particular paths. The predictions of relativity have been verified many times, most famously in 1919 when the British physicist Arthur Eddington observed the Sun's gravity bending light during a solar eclipse.

Einstein was not worried if the results did not support his theory. '*Then,*' said Einstein, '*I would have been sorry for the dear Lord, for the theory is correct.*' The reason Einstein felt general relativity must be right was that it was too elegant (beautiful) a theory to be wrong. Ultimately theories are judged by how they explain experimental data and observations. However, Einstein believed that elegance or beauty in a scientific theory is a good guide to accepting a theory.

Simplicity, as distinct from elegance, is another criterion to establish scientific truth. Occam's razor is used to distinguish between competing theories by suggesting that the simpler theory is more likely to be a more accurate description of the phenomenon. However, it is a logical assumption all else being equal, and it is rare in science that all else is equal. Often some experimental results support one theory and others another.

The theory of general relativity is a universal theory and is believed to apply to all objects in the universe. The theory of relativity is useful and universal because it relates to phenomena that pervade the cosmos and it is intellectually compelling to have a theory that is as unified as possible. However, universal chemical theories, such as Usanovich's concepts of acids and bases may be less useful; they can become so all-encompassing as to lack definition and hence fail to clarify the area of science under consideration. It includes many reactions, such as redox reactions, which can perhaps best be considered as a separate type of reaction involving electron transfer.

Applying Lewis' acid–base theory to inorganic and organic chemistry to identify the role of the reacting species

The following inorganic reactions illustrate Lewis acid–base reactions, showing the Lewis acid (electron pair donor) and the Lewis acid (electron pair acceptor):

■ Carbon dioxide molecules reacting with hydroxide ions to form hydrogencarbonate ions:

- Copper(II) ions in aqueous solution reacting with ammonia molecules to form the complex tetramminecopper(II) ion:

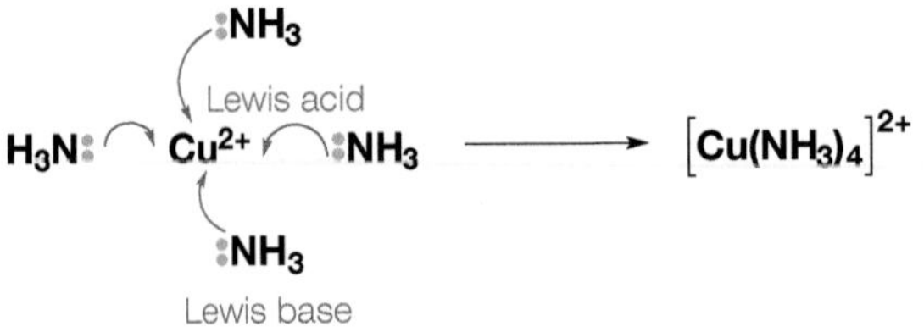

(The water molecules have been ignored for simplicity).

- Fluoride ions reacting with a silicon tetrafluoride molecule to form the silicon hexafluoride ion:

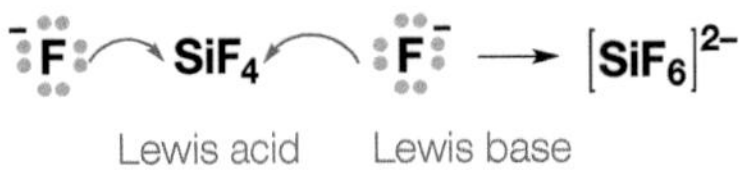

- The pi bond of an ethene molecule reacting with a proton (electrophile) to form an ethyl carbocation:

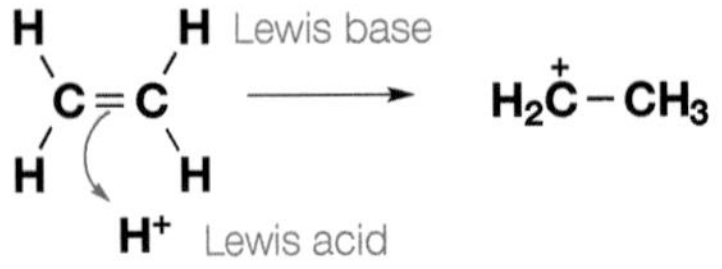

- A cyanide ion (nucleophile) reacting with the carbon atom of the carbonyl group of a methanal molecule (to form a tetrahedral intermediate):

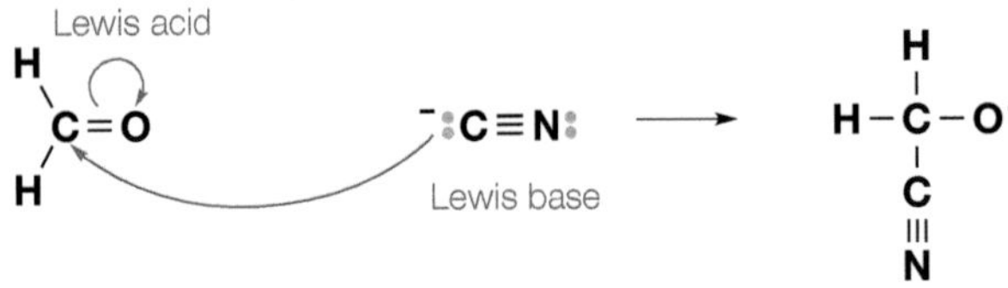

18.2 Calculations involving acids and bases – the equilibrium law can be applied to acid–base reactions; numerical problems can be simplified by making assumptions about the relative concentrations of the species involved; the use of logarithms is also significant here

Acid–base reactions as equilibria

Most acidic and basic substances are weak and are therefore partially ionized in aqueous solution. Chemists can therefore use the equilibrium law to represent the extent to which a weak acid or base ionizes or dissociates.

For example, for a weak acid the equilibrium can be represented in either of the following ways, depending on whether the hydrated proton is represented as H_3O^+ (oxonium) or H^+:

$$HA(aq) + H_2O(l) \rightleftharpoons H_3O^+(aq) + A^-(aq)$$

or

$$HA(aq) \rightleftharpoons H^+(aq) + A^-(aq)$$

Because water is a solvent, it is omitted from the equilibrium expression, which can be written as either

$$K_a = \frac{[H_3O^+][A^-]}{[HA]}$$

or

$$K_a = \frac{[H^+][A^-]}{[HA]}$$

The magnitude (size) of K_a indicates the tendency of the acid to ionize or dissociate in water. The larger the value of K_a, the stronger the acid. $pK_a = -\log_{10}K_a$ is another measure of acid strength. The smaller the value of pK_a, the stronger the acid.

The value of K_a can be easily calculated from the pH of the solution of the weak acid (as described later). The small magnitude of K_a allows chemists to use approximations to simplify the problem, without losing accuracy. Proton-transfer reactions are usually rapid and the measured pH value always represents equilibrium conditions.

Nature of Science

Obtaining evidence for scientific theories – applying the equilibrium law to acid–base equilibria allows strengths of acids and bases to be determined and related to their molecular structure

The value of K_a can be related to the molecular structure of the acid. For example, choric(I) acid, HClO, is a stronger acid than iodic(I) acid, HIO (Figure 18.5). The acidity of oxyacids increases with the increasing electronegativity of the halogen atom. As the electronegativity of the atom bonded to an –OH group increases, the ease with which the hydrogen is ionized or dissociated increases. The movement of electron density towards the electronegative atom further polarizes the –O–H bond, which favours ionization or dissociation. In addition, the electronegative atom stabilizes the conjugate base, which also leads to a stronger acid.

■ **Figure 18.5**
The acidity of oxyacids increases with increasing electronegativity of the halogen atom

shift of electron density

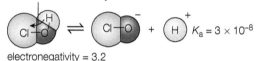

electronegativity = 3.2

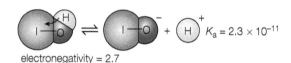

electronegativity = 2.7

Calculations involving acids and bases

The ionic product of water

When water is purified by repeated distillation (Figure 18.6) its electrical conductivity falls to a very low, constant value. This is evidence that pure water dissociates to a very small extent to form ions:

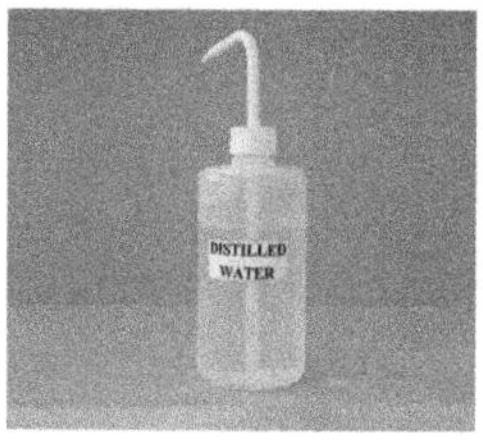

$$H_2O(l) \rightleftharpoons H^+(aq) + OH^-(aq) \qquad \text{or} \qquad 2H_2O(l) \rightleftharpoons H_3O^+(aq) + OH^-(aq)$$

If the equilibrium law is applied to the first equation:

$$K_w = [H^+(aq)] \times [OH^-(aq)]$$

where K_w represents a constant known as the ionic product constant of water. At 298 K (25 °C) the measured concentrations of $H^+(aq)$ and $OH^-(aq)$ in pure water are 1.00×10^{-7} mol dm^{-3}. Therefore:

$$K_w = [H^+(aq)] \times [OH^-(aq)] = 1.00 \times 10^{-7} \times 1.00 \times 10^{-7} = 1.00 \times 10^{-14} \, \text{mol}^2 \, \text{dm}^{-6}$$

This is a key equation in acid–base chemistry. Note that the product of $[H^+(aq)]$ and $[OH^-(aq)]$ is a *constant* at a given temperature. Thus, as the hydrogen ion concentration of a solution increases, the hydroxide ion concentration decreases (and *vice versa*).

The solution is described as neutral when the concentration of hydrogen ions equals the concentration of hydroxide ions, so that at 298 K (25 °C) the value of K_w is $1.00 \times 10^{-14} \, \text{mol}^2 \, \text{dm}^{-6}$.

■ **Figure 18.6** Distilled water (prepared by laboratory distillation apparatus) in a plastic dispenser

4 Calculate the hydroxide ion concentration of an aqueous solution whose hydrogen ion concentration at 25 °C is 5.4×10^{-4} mol dm^{-3}.

The values of K_w at different temperatures are tabulated in Table 18.2 and in section 23 of the IB *Chemistry data booklet*.

This data indicates that water becomes increasingly dissociated and hence acidic as the temperature rises (Figure 18.7). The increase in the ionic product of water, K_w, with temperature accounts for the corrosive action of hot pure water on iron pipes: this behaviour is caused by the increase in concentration of hydrogen ions. The pH decreases with an increase in temperature but the solution is still described as chemically neutral since the concentrations of hydroxide and hydrogen ions remain *equal*.

■ **Table 18.2** Values of the ionic product of water at different temperatures

Temperature (°C)	K_w value	Temperature (°C)	K_w value
0	0.113×10^{-14}	55	7.24×10^{-14}
5	0.185×10^{-14}	60	9.55×10^{-14}
10	0.292×10^{-14}	65	12.4×10^{-14}
15	0.453×10^{-14}	70	15.9×10^{-14}
20	0.684×10^{-14}	75	20.1×10^{-14}
25	1.00×10^{-14}	80	25.2×10^{-14}
30	1.47×10^{-14}	85	31.3×10^{-14}
35	2.09×10^{-14}	90	38.3×10^{-14}
40	2.92×10^{-14}	95	46.6×10^{-14}
45	4.02×10^{-14}	100	56.0×10^{-14}
50	5.43×10^{-14}		

■ **Figure 18.7**
The relationship between temperature and the ionic product constant of water

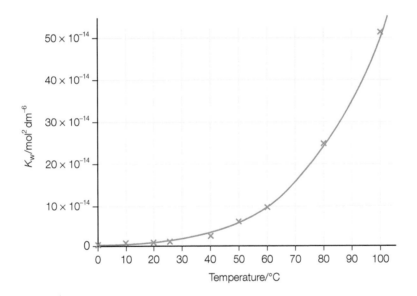

The dissociation of water is expected to be an endothermic process (Chapter 5) because energy is needed to separate oppositely charged ions. It can also be deduced that the dissociation of water is an endothermic process since applying Le Châtelier's principle (Chapter 7) predicts that increasing the temperature will favour the reaction that absorbs the heat, that is, the endothermic reaction. The increasing values of K_w also show that increasing the temperature favours the dissociation of water molecules, thereby producing more hydrogen and hydroxide ions.

The ionic product constant of water can be used to calculate the concentration of hydroxide or hydrogen ions at any specified temperature.

5   At 60 °C, the ionic product constant of water is $9.55 \times 10^{-14} \, mol^2 \, dm^{-6}$. Calculate the pH of a neutral solution at this temperature.

The pH of an aqueous solution is a measure of its hydrogen ion concentration; it depends on temperature because the degree of dissociation of an acid does, i.e. K_a changes. Values of the pH of pure water at $0\,°C$ and $100\,°C$ are approximately 7.5 and 6.1. Both the solutions are, however, *neutral*. The definition of neutrality is pH independent: a neutral solution is one where the concentration of hydrogen ions equals the concentration of hydroxide ions. This corresponds to pH 7 only at $25\,°C$.

The pH and pOH scales

pH and pOH are formally defined as the negative logarithms to the base 10 of the concentration in $mol\,dm^{-3}$ of the hydrogen and hydroxide ion concentrations, respectively. That is:

$$pH = -\log_{10}([H^+(aq)]/mol\,dm^{-3}) \quad \text{and} \quad pOH = -\log_{10}([OH^-(aq)]/mol\,dm^{-3})$$

(You can only take logarithms of a pure number and not of a quantity.)

The logarithmic pH and pOH scales reduce the extremely wide variation in concentrations of hydrogen ions, $H^+(aq)$, and hydroxide ions, $OH^-(aq)$, in dilute aqueous solutions of acids and bases (typically 1 to 10^{-14}) to a narrower range of pH (typically 1 to 14) (Figure 18.8). pH values of solutions are measured with a pH meter or narrow-range indicator paper (Figure 18.9).

■ **Figure 18.8**

The variation of pH with $[H^+(aq)]$

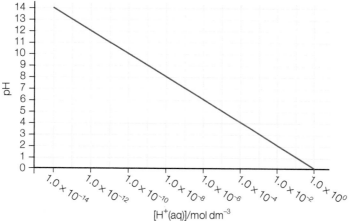

■ **Figure 18.9** Narrow-range indicator paper

The *negative* sign of the logarithmic function produces pH and pOH values that are *positive* for most dilute solutions.

It can also be shown that pH + pOH = 14:

$$K_w = [H^+(aq)] \times [OH^-(aq)] = 1.00 \times 10^{-14}\,mol^2\,dm^{-6}$$

Taking negative logarithms to the base 10 of both sides:

$$-\log_{10} K_w = -\log_{10}([H^+(aq)] \times [OH^-(aq)]) = -\log_{10}(1.00 \times 10^{-14})$$
$$= -\log_{10}[H^+(aq)] - \log_{10}[OH^-(aq)] = -\log_{10} 10^{-14}$$

$$pK_w = pH + pOH = 14$$

Calculating the pH values of aqueous solutions of strong acids and bases is relatively easy since the concentration of hydrogen ions is *directly related* to the concentration of the acid or base.

---

6   Calculate the pH of:
   a $0.01\,mol\,dm^{-3}$ hydrochloric acid, $HCl(aq)$
   b $0.01\,mol\,dm^{-3}$ aqueous sodium hydroxide, $NaOH(aq)$
   c $0.01\,mol\,dm^{-3}$ aqueous barium hydroxide, $Ba(OH)_2(aq)$
   d $0.01\,mol\,dm^{-3}$ sulfuric acid, $H_2SO_4(aq)$, a diprotic acid.

To calculate pH or pOH values from hydrogen or hydroxide ion concentrations on a calculator, type in the hydrogen or hydroxide ion concentration, press the log function key, then multiply by -1 to change the sign.

To calculate hydrogen ion concentrations from pH values on a calculator, type in the pH value, insert a negative sign and then press the 10^x or antilog function key. Mathematically this is expressed as:

$$[H^+(aq)] = 10^{-pH} \qquad \text{and} \qquad [OH^-(aq)] = 10^{-pOH}$$

7 Calculate the hydrogen ion concentration of a solution whose pH is 2.80.

8 A solution of nitric acid, $HNO_3(aq)$, contains 1.26 g of the pure acid in every 100.00 cm³ of aqueous solution. Calculate the pH of the solution.

Another common type of calculation is calculating the pH of a strong acid after dilution.

9 10.00 cm³ of an aqueous solution of a monoprotic (monobasic) strong acid is added to 990.00 cm³ of water. Calculate the change in pH.

The pH scale is used to describe *both* alkaline and acidic solutions. Alkaline solutions will contain a low concentration of hydrogen ions derived from the dissociation of water.

The pOH scale can also be used to describe acidic and alkaline solutions.

10 Calculate the pOH of a solution with a hydroxide ion concentration of 0.100 mol dm⁻³.

11 Calculate the hydroxide ion concentration of a solution with a pOH of 2.

12 Calculate the pH of a solution with a pOH of 1.

13 Calculate the pOH of a solution with a pH of 2.

 The pH of very dilute solutions and negative pH values are discussed as extension on the website that accompanies this book.

Acid dissociation constant

A weak monobasic acid, HA, reacts with water according to the equation

$$HA(aq) \rightleftharpoons H^+(aq) + A^-(aq)$$

The equilibrium constant for this reaction is known as the acid dissociation constant, K_a, (and has units of mol dm⁻³):

$$K_a = \frac{[H^+(aq)] \times [A^-(aq)]}{[HA(aq)]}$$

The acid dissociation constant is a measure of the strength of a weak acid. The larger the value of K_a, the stronger the acid and the greater the extent of ionization or dissociation.

Since acid dissociation constants, K_a, tend to be small and vary considerably, they are often expressed as pK_a values, where:

$$pK_a = -\log_{10} K_a \qquad \text{(cf. } [H^+(aq)] \text{ and pH)}$$

Values of pK_a are also a measure of acid strength, but now the *smaller* the value of pK_a, the *stronger* the acid. A change of 1 in the value of the pK_a means a change in acid strength of a factor of 10 (cf. pH and $[H^+(aq)]$).

(Acid dissociation constants are not usually quoted for strong acids because these effectively undergo *complete* ionization or dissociation in water. Their dissociation constants are very large and tend towards *infinity* in dilute solutions. It is difficult to measure them accurately because the concentration of undissociated acid molecules is so low.)

Values of K_a and pK_a are equilibrium constants and, like other equilibrium constants, are not affected by changes in concentrations, only by changes in temperature. This means that acid strengths vary with temperature and that the order of acid strengths can vary with temperature.

The pH of a solution of a weak acid can only be calculated if the acid dissociation constant, K_a (or pK_a), is known.

$$K_a = \frac{[H^+(aq)] \times [A^-(aq)]}{[HA(aq)]}$$

but since $[H^+(aq)] = [A^-(aq)]$ in a solution where only the acid is present,

$$K_a = \frac{[H^+(aq)]^2}{[HA(aq)]}$$

Rearranging:

$$[H^+(aq)] = \sqrt{[HA(aq)] \times K_a}$$

and then

$$pH = -\log_{10}[H^+(aq)]$$

You can also use this approach to calculate the K_a (and hence the pK_a) of a weak acid if you know the pH of the solution and its concentration.

---

14 The pH of $0.01\,mol\,dm^{-3}$ benzenecarboxylic acid solution, $C_6H_5COOH(aq)$, is 3.10. Calculate the acid dissociation constant, K_a, at this temperature.

15 Calculate the pH value of a $0.1\,mol\,dm^{-3}$ solution of ethanoic acid, $CH_3COOH(aq)$, given that its K_a value is $1.8 \times 10^{-5}\,mol\,dm^{-3}$.

Base dissociation constant

A weak base may be either a molecule, such as ammonia, or an anion, such as ethanoate. A weak base forms a weakly basic solution:

$$B(aq) + H_2O(l) \rightleftharpoons BH^+(aq) + OH^-(aq)$$

$$B^-(aq) + H_2O(l) \rightleftharpoons BH(aq) + OH^-(aq)$$

The equilibrium constant for this reaction is known as the base dissociation constant, K_b:

$$K_b = \frac{[BH^+(aq)] \times [OH^-(aq)]}{[B(aq)]} \quad \text{or} \quad \frac{[BH(aq)] \times [OH^-(aq)]}{[B^-(aq)]}$$

To calculate the pH of a solution containing a weak base, a similar approximation to that for a weak acid is used, giving:

$$[OH^-(aq)] = \sqrt{K_b \times [B(aq)]} \quad \text{or} \quad [OH^-(aq)] = \sqrt{K_b \times [B^-(aq)]}.$$

---

16 Calculate the pH of a $0.50\,mol\,dm^{-3}$ aqueous solution of ammonia for which $K_b = 1.8 \times 10^{-5}\,mol\,dm^{-3}$.

Solving problems involving $[H^+(aq)]$, $[OH^-(aq)]$, pH, pOH, K_a, pK_a, K_b and pK_b

The various equations derived from acid–base equilibria allow a wide range of acid–base problems to be solved. Acid–base problems are usually one of four types: strong acid/base, weak acid/base, buffers (see Chapter 23 and 25 on the accompanying website) and salt hydrolysis.

17 The pH of pure water at 37 °C is 6.80. Calculate K_w and [OH⁻(aq)].

18 The pH of a solution is 3.20 at 298 K. Calculate [H⁺(aq)] and [OH⁻(aq)].

19 Calculate the mass of sodium hydroxide needed to prepare 200.0 cm³ of NaOH solution with a pOH of 1.0.

20 Calculate the concentrations of H⁺(aq) and OH⁻(aq) in 0.05 mol dm⁻³ H_2SO_4.

21 Calculate the pH of 50 cm³ of 0.25 mol dm⁻³ $Ba(OH)_2$.

22 The pK_a of ethanoic acid is 4.76. Calculate the K_a of ethanoic acid and the pH of a 0.125 mol dm⁻³ solution.

23 The pK_b of phenylamine is 9.13. Calculate the K_b of phenylamine and the pH of a 0.50 mol dm⁻³ solution.

24 The pH of 0.025 mol dm⁻³ phenol is 5.74. Calculate K_a.

25 The K_a of hydrofluoric acid is 1.8×10^{-4}. Calculate K_b for the conjugate base, F⁻.

26 The solubility of $Sr(OH)_2$(aq) at 298 K is 19.23 g per dm⁻³ of solution. Calculate the concentration of strontium ions and the pH of the solution.

27 Calculate the pH of a solution prepared by mixing 25.0 cm³ of 0.1 mol dm⁻³ HCl with 15.0 cm³ of 0.1 mol dm⁻³ NaOH.

Discussing the relative strengths of acids and bases using values of K_a, pK_a, K_b and pK_b

Figure 18.10 shows a simple model of the relative strength of Brønsted–Lowry acids and bases that is easy to interpret and recall. It clearly illustrates the inverse relationship between K_a (or K_b) and pK_a (or pK_b).

■ **Figure 18.10**
Measures of Brønsted–Lowry acid and base strength

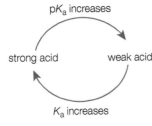
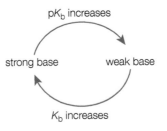

Base	K_b
$C_6H_7O_6^-$	1.3×10^{-10}
$(CH_3)_3N$	4.8×10^{-5}
C_5H_5N	1.7×10^{-9}

■ **Table 18.3** The K_b values of some organic bases

Table 18.3 shows the K_b values of three organic bases.

The *conjugate acids* of these bases can be arranged in order of increasing acidity as follows:

$$(CH_3)_3NH^+ < C_5H_5NH^+ < C_6H_7O_6H$$

This can be explained from the order of base strength, which increases with an increase in K_b: $C_6H_7O_6H < C_5H_5N < C_6H_7O_6^-$. The weaker the base, the stronger the conjugate acid.

Assumptions and simplifications

For weak acids we assume that there is no dissociation or ionization and that none of the acid molecules react with water to release ions. This is not far from reality since the dilute acid solutions used in the laboratory are typically about 1% dissociated. However, as indicated previously this becomes less true as the solution is progressively diluted.

We can take the dissociation of the acid into consideration when we perform a calculation with an aqueous solution of a weak acid. However, a quadratic equation results and the slight increase in accuracy rarely justifies the additional mathematical effort required.

Worked example

Calculate the pH of a $1.00\,mol\,dm^{-3}$ aqueous solution of hydrofluoric acid, HF(aq) ($K_a = 7.2 \times 10^{-4}\,mol\,dm^{-3}$).

$$HF(aq) \rightleftharpoons H^+(aq) + F^-(aq)$$

$$K_a = \frac{[H^+(aq)] \times [F^-(aq)]}{[HF(aq)]}$$

Before any dissociation has occurred:

$$[HF(aq)] = 1.00\,mol\,dm^{-3}; [F^-(aq)] = 0\,mol\,dm^{-3} \text{ and } [H^+(aq)] = 10^{-7}\,mol\,dm^{-3} \approx 0$$

(We ignore the very small concentration of hydrogen ions formed from the dissociation of water.) Once equilibrium has been reached and dissociation of the acid has occurred:

$$[HF(aq)] = (1.00 - x)\,mol\,dm^{-3}; [F^-(aq)] = x\,mol\,dm^{-3}; [H^+(aq)] = x\,mol\,dm^{-3}$$

where x represents the concentration of hydrofluoric acid that dissociates, which at the present is unknown. We now substitute these equilibrium concentrations into the expression for the acid dissociation constant:

$$K_a = 7.2 \times 10^{-4} = \frac{[H^+(aq)] \times [F^-(aq)]}{[HF(aq)]}$$

$$= \frac{x^2}{(1.00 - x)}$$

This expression can be rearranged to give a quadratic equation:

$$x^2 + (7.2 \times 10^{-4})x - (7.2 \times 10^{-4} \times 1.00) = 0$$

Comparing this expression with the general form of a quadratic equation:

$$ax^2 + bx + c = 0; \qquad a = 1, b = 7.2 \times 10^{-4} \text{ and } c = -7.2 \times 10^{-4}$$

One method of finding the two values of x that satisfy a quadratic equation is to use the quadratic formula:

$$x = \frac{-b \pm \sqrt{(b^2 - 4ac)}}{2a}$$

Substituting the values of a, b and c into the quadratic formula and evaluating the expression will give an accurate value for the concentration of hydrogen ions in this solution of hydrofluoric acid.

This approach is not demanded by the IB Chemistry programme, but you do need to know how to simplify this type of calculation so that a lengthy quadratic formula calculation can be avoided, and when such an approximation is valid.

To simplify the calculation and to avoid the tedious task of solving a quadratic, we assume (as in previous calculations) that the amount of acid dissociated, x, is negligible compared to the concentration of the hydrofluoric acid. In other words:

$$1.00 - x \approx 1.00 \text{ (where } \approx \text{ means approximately equal to).}$$

The equilibrium expression now simplifies to:

$$7.2 \times 10^{-4} = \frac{x^2}{1.00}$$

$$x^2 = (7.2 \times 10^{-4}) \times 1.00$$

$$x = \sqrt{(7.2 \times 10^{-4})} = 2.7 \times 10^{-2}$$

Solving a quadratic equation is only necessary when the two calculated pH values differ by more than 5%, since typically K_a values for weak acids and weak bases are known to an accuracy of about ±5%. The example above with hydrofluoric acid can be examined to see whether it fits this 5% 'rule'.

Writing out the simplified equilibrium expression and making x the subject:

$$K_a = \frac{x^2}{[HF(aq)]}$$

$$x = \sqrt{K_a \times [HF(aq)]}$$

Then compare the relative sizes of x and $[HF(aq)]$ as a percentage:

$$\frac{x}{[HF(aq)]} \times 100 = \frac{2.7 \times 10^{-2}}{1.00} \times 100 = 2.7\%$$

If the expression above is less than or equal to 5% (as here, and as it will be for IB questions), the value of x is such that the approximation is valid and the pH can be calculated. Hence:

$$[HF(aq)] - x \approx [HF(aq)]$$

$$pH = -\log_{10}(2.7 \times 10^{-2}) = 1.6$$

Relationship between K_a for a weak acid and K_b for its conjugate base

The relationship between K_a for a weak acid HA and K_b for its conjugate base A^- is

$$K_a(HA(aq)) \times K_b(A^-(aq)) = K_w = 1.0 \times 10^{-14}$$

Since $pK_a = -\log_{10}K_a$ and $pK_b = -\log_{10}K_b$, the logarithmic form of the equation above is

$$pK_a(HA(aq)) + pK_b(A^-(aq)) = pK_w = 14.00$$

The stronger the acid, the larger the value of K_a and the smaller the value of pK_a. Likewise the stronger the base, the larger the value of K_b and the smaller the value of pK_b. The two equations show that as the value of K_a increases (and the value of pK_a decreases), the value of K_b decreases (and the value of pK_b increases). These equations give quantitative support to the statement 'the stronger the acid, the weaker the conjugate base' (Chapter 8).

The justification for the first equation follows from the equations below. Recall from Chapter 7 that if two chemical equilibria are added together then the equilibrium constant for the reaction is the product of the two equilibria.

Weak acid:

$$HA(aq) + H_2O(l) \rightleftharpoons H_3O^+(aq) + A^-(aq) \qquad K_a(HA(aq)) = \frac{[H_3O^+(aq)][A^-(aq)]}{[HA(aq)]}$$

Conjugate base:

$$\underline{A^-(aq) + H_2O(l) \rightleftharpoons HA(aq) \quad + OH^-(aq)} \qquad K_b(A^-(aq)) = \frac{[HA(aq)][OH^-(aq)]}{[A^-(aq)]}$$

$$2H_2O(l) \rightleftharpoons H_3O^+(aq) + OH^-(aq) \qquad K_w = [H_3O^+(aq)][OH^-(aq)]$$

($[H_3O^+(aq)] = [H^+(aq)]$, remembering that each hydrogen ion, H^+, will be attached to a water molecule, H_2O.)

Relationship between K_b for a weak base and K_a for its conjugate acid

Analogous equations can be written to describe the relationship between K_b for a weak base B and K_a for its conjugate acid HB^+:

$$K_b(B(aq)) \times K_a(BH^+(aq)) = K_w = 1.0 \times 10^{-14}$$
$$pK_b(B(aq)) + pK_a(BH^+(aq)) = pK_w = 14.00$$

The equations below provide justification for these results.

Weak base:

$$B(aq) + H_2O(l) \quad \rightleftharpoons BH^+(aq) + OH^-(aq) \qquad K_b(BH^+(aq)) = \frac{[BH^+(aq)][OH^-(aq)]}{[B(aq)]}$$

Conjugate acid:

$$\underline{BH^+(aq) + H_2O(l) \rightleftharpoons H_3O^+(aq) + B(aq)} \qquad K_a(BH^+(aq)) = \frac{[H_3O^+(aq)][B(aq)]}{[BH^+(aq)]}$$

$$2H_2O(l) \rightleftharpoons H_3O^+(aq) + OH^-(aq) \qquad K_w = [H_3O^+(aq)][OH^-(aq)]$$

Successive acid dissociation constants

A number of important acids, such as carbonic acid, sulfuric acid and phosphoric(v) acid, release more than one proton per molecule and are called polyprotic acids. Their stepwise equilibria are discussed as extension on the website that accompanies this book.

◼ Buffer solutions

A buffer solution is an aqueous solution whose pH (and hence hydrogen ion concentration) remains unchanged by dilution with water or when relatively small amounts of acid or base are added to it. Buffers *resist* changes in pH.

Buffer solutions find many uses in chemistry, chemical products and the chemical industry – whenever it is helpful to have a controlled pH. For example, buffers are necessary in electrophoresis and are used to calibrate pH meters. They are an ingredient in shampoos and dyes. In addition, physiological systems are always buffered; the action of enzymes is heavily pH dependent.

Types of buffers

There are three types of buffer:

- ◼ acidic buffers, which are prepared from a weak acid and a salt of the acid, for example ethanoic acid and sodium ethanoate
- ◼ basic or alkaline buffers, which are prepared from a weak base and a salt of the base, for example ammonia and ammonium chloride
- ◼ neutral buffers, which are usually prepared from phosphoric acid and its salts.

Action of buffer solutions

Acidic buffers

Since ethanoic acid is only slightly dissociated and sodium ethanoate is completely dissociated, a mixture of the two contains a relatively low concentration of hydrogen ions, but a large proportion of ethanoic acid molecules and ethanoate ions:

$$CH_3COONa(aq) \rightarrow CH_3COO^-(aq) + Na^+(aq)$$
$$CH_3COOH(aq) \rightleftharpoons CH_3COO^-(aq) + H^+(aq)$$

If an acid is added to the buffer, the additional hydrogen ions will be removed by combination with the ethanoate ions to form undissociated acid molecules. The presence of sodium ethanoate ensures there is a large 'reservoir' of ethanoate ions to 'mop up' the additional hydrogen ions from an acid.

If an alkali is added, the hydroxide ions combine with the hydrogen ions to form water molecules:

$$H^+(aq) + OH^-(aq) \rightarrow H_2O(l)$$

The removal of hydrogen ions via neutralization results in the dissociation of ethanoic acid molecules to replenish the hydrogen ions removed. The presence of ethanoic acid ensures that there is a large 'reservoir' of undissociated ethanoic acid molecules that will dissociate following the addition of an alkali.

Basic buffers

Since ammonia is only slightly dissociated and ammonium chloride is completely dissociated, a mixture of the two contains a relatively low concentration of hydroxide ions, but a large proportion of ammonia molecules and ammonium ions:

$$NH_4Cl(aq) \rightarrow NH_4^+(aq) + Cl^-(aq)$$
$$NH_3(aq) + H_2O(l) \rightleftharpoons NH_4^+(aq) + OH^-(aq)$$

If an acid is added, the hydrogen ions will combine with hydroxide ions to form water:

$$H^+(aq) + OH^-(aq) \rightarrow H_2O(l)$$

As a result more ammonia molecules react with water to release hydroxide ions and restore the equilibrium.

If an alkali is added, the hydroxide ions react with the ammonium ions from ammonium chloride to form ammonia and water. The presence of ammonium chloride ensures that there is a large 'reservoir' of ammonium ions to cope with the addition of an alkali.

Calculations involving buffer solutions

The calculation of pH in buffer solutions will only be assessed in Options B and D (see Chapters 23 and 25 on the accompanying website), but the derivation of the relevant equations and worked examples of calculations are presented here for completeness.

Two assumptions are made to simplify calculations involving buffer solutions:

- In the buffer solution, the weak acid or weak base is not dissociated. This is because the presence of ions from the dissociation of its salt will prevent dissociation of the acid or base molecules.
- It is assumed that all the ions present in the buffer solution are produced by the dissolution of the salt: none originate from the acid or base.

Acidic buffers

Consider the equilibrium for a weak acid:

$$HA(aq) \rightleftharpoons H^+(aq) + A^-(aq)$$

$$K_a = \frac{[H^+(aq)] \times [A^-(aq)]}{[HA(aq)]}$$

Rearranging:

$$[H^+(aq)] = \frac{K_a \times [HA(aq)]}{[A^-(aq)]}$$

Taking negative logarithms to the base 10 of both sides:

$$pH = pK_a - \log_{10} \frac{[HA(aq)]}{[A^-(aq)]}$$

or

$$pH = pK_a + \log_{10} \frac{[A^-(aq)]}{[HA(aq)]}$$

This equation is often called the Henderson–Hasselbalch equation. It indicates that:

- the pH of a buffer solution depends on the K_a of the weak acid
- the pH of a buffer solution depends upon the ratio of the concentrations of the acid and its conjugate base and not on their actual concentrations.

Basic buffers

The Henderson–Hasselbalch equation described above can be readily applied to basic buffers since $pK_w = pK_a + pK_b$.

For example, ammonia has a base dissociation constant, K_b, of $1.78 \times 10^{-5}\,mol\,dm^{-3}$. Hence, the pK_b value is 4.75 and the pK_a value is 9.25.

However, the Henderson–Hasselbalch equation can also be applied to a basic buffer:

$$K_b = \frac{[B^+(aq)] \times [OH^-(aq)]}{[BOH(aq)]}$$

Taking negative logarithms of both sides of the equation:

$$-\log_{10} K_b = -\log_{10}[OH^-(aq)] - \log_{10}\frac{[B^+(aq)]}{[BOH(aq)]}$$

$$pK_b = pOH - \log_{10}\frac{[B^+(aq)]}{[BOH(aq)]}$$

$$pOH = pK_b + \log_{10}\frac{[B^+(aq)]}{[BOH(aq)]}$$

Calculating the pH of a buffer system

Worked example

Calculate the pH of a buffer containing 0.20 moles of sodium ethanoate in 500 cm³ of 0.10 mol dm⁻³ ethanoic acid. K_a for ethanoic acid is 1.8×10^{-5}.

(Assume complete dissociation of sodium ethanoate and that the dissociation of ethanoic acid is insignificant, so that the equilibrium concentration of ethanoic acid is the same as the initial concentration.)

$$[CH_3COO^-(aq)] = 0.20 \times \frac{1000}{500} = 0.40 \text{ mol dm}^{-3}$$

$$\frac{[H^+(aq)] \times [CH_3COO^-(aq)]}{[CH_3COOH(aq)]} = 1.8 \times 10^{-5}$$

$$[H^+(aq)] = x$$

$$1.8 \times 10^{-5} = \frac{(x) \times (0.40)}{0.10}$$

$$x = 4.5 \times 10^{-6} = [H^+(aq)]$$

$$pH = -\log_{10}[H^+(aq)] = -\log_{10}(4.5 \times 10^{-6}) = 5.3$$

Calculating the mass of a salt required to give an acidic buffer solution with a specific pH

Worked example

Calculate the mass of sodium propanoate ($M = 96.07$ g mol⁻¹) that must be dissolved in 1.00 dm³ of 1.00 mol dm⁻³ propanoic acid ($pK_a = 4.87$) to give a buffer solution with a pH of 4.5. (Let x represent the concentration of propanoate ions and y represent the amount of sodium propanoate.)

$$[H^+(aq)] = 10^{-pH} = 1 \times 10^{-4.5} = 3.16 \times 10^{-5} \text{ mol dm}^{-3}$$

$$K_a = 1 \times 10^{-4.87} = 1.35 \times 10^{-5}$$

$$K_a = \frac{[H^+(aq)][CH_3COO^-(aq)]}{[CH_3CH_2COOH(aq)]} = 1.35 \times 10^{-5}$$

$$1.35 \times 10^{-5} = \frac{(3.16 \times 10^{-5}) \times (x)}{1.00}$$

$$x = 0.427 \text{ mol dm}^{-3}$$

$$0.427 \text{ mol dm}^{-3} = \frac{y}{1.00 \text{ dm}^3}$$

$$y = 0.427 \text{ mol}$$

$$96.07 \text{ g mol}^{-1} \times 0.427 \text{ mol} = 41.0 \text{ g}$$

Calculating the pH of a buffer after base is added

> **Worked example**
>
> A buffer contains 0.20 mol of sodium ethanoate (CH_3COONa) in 500 cm^3 of 0.10 mol dm^{-3} ethanoic acid. K_a for ethanoic acid is 1.8×10^{-5}. Calculate the pH after 0.025 mol of sodium hydroxide is added.
>
> The addition of hydroxide ions will cause the acid dissociation to shift to the right. So the amount of hydroxide ions added must be *subtracted* from the ethanoic acid and *added* to the amount of ethanoate ions.
>
> $$K_a = \frac{[H^+(aq)]\,[CH_3COO^-(aq)]}{[CH_3COOH(aq)]} = 1.8 \times 10^{-5}$$
>
> $$[H^+(aq)] = x$$
>
> $$[CH_3COO^-(aq)] = \frac{(0.20\ mol + 0.025\ mol)}{(0.500\ dm^3)} = 0.45\ mol\,dm^{-3}$$
>
> $$[CH_3COOH(aq)] = \left(0.1\ mol\,dm^{-3} - \frac{0.025\ mol}{0.500\ dm^3}\right) - x = 0.050\ mol\,dm^{-3} - x \approx 0.050\ mol\,dm^{-3}$$
>
> $$1.8 \times 10^{-5} = \frac{(x) \times (0.45)}{0.050} - x \approx \frac{(x) \times (0.45)}{0.050}$$
>
> $$x = 2.0 \times 10^{-6} = [H^+(aq)]$$
>
> $$pH = -\log_{10}[H^+(aq)] = -\log_{10}(2.0 \times 10^{-6}) = 5.7$$
>
> Note that if *acid* is added to an acidic buffer composed of ethanoic acid and sodium ethanoate, then the addition of hydrogen ions will cause the acid dissociation to shift to the left. Hence the amount of hydrogen ions must be *added* to the ethanoic acid and *subtracted* from the amount of ethanoate ions.

Characteristics of buffer solutions

Dilution

The Henderson–Hasselbalch equation indicates that the pH of a buffer solution will depend only on the ratio of the concentrations of the acid and its conjugate base, so that dilution of the buffer solution should have no effect. This is because when you add distilled water to a buffer solution you dilute both components of the buffer to the same degree.

Buffering capacity

Buffer solutions have a limited capacity to resist pH changes. If too much strong acid or strong base is added, no more buffering action is possible. The buffering capacity is the ability of the buffer to resist changes in pH. The buffering capacity increases as the concentration of the buffer salt/acid solution increases. The closer the buffered pH is to the pK_a, the greater the buffering capacity. The buffering capacity is expressed in terms of the concentration of sodium hydroxide required to increase the pH by 1.0.

For example, consider the addition of a strong acid such as HCl to a buffer composed of ethanoic acid (a weak acid) and sodium ethanoate (the conjugate base). (Remember that weak acids have strong conjugate bases.)

Initially, the HCl donates its proton to the conjugate base (CH_3COO^-) through the reaction

$$CH_3COO^- + HCl \rightarrow CH_3COOH + Cl^-$$

This changes the pH by lowering the ratio [CH_3COO^-]/[CH_3COOH], but as long as there is still a lot of CH_3COO^- present, the change in pH will be relatively small. But if we keep adding HCl, the conjugate base CH_3COO^- will eventually run out. Once the CH_3COO^- is gone, any additional HCl will donate its proton to water:

$$HCl + H_2O \rightarrow H_3O^+ + Cl^-$$

This will dramatically increase the concentration of H_3O^+ ions and so the pH decreases significantly.

This is termed 'breaking the buffer solution', and we call the amount of acid a buffer can absorb before it breaks the 'buffer capacity for addition of strong acid'. A solution of this buffer with more conjugate base, CH_3COO^-, has a higher buffer capacity for addition of strong acid.

Similarly, a buffer will 'break' when the amount of strong base added is so large it consumes all the weak acid, through the reaction

$$CH_3COOH + OH^- \rightarrow CH_3COO^- + H_2O$$

A solution with more weak acid, CH_3COOH, has a higher buffer capacity for addition of strong base.

So although the pH of this buffer is determined only by the ratio $[CH_3COO^-]/[CH_3COOH]$, the ability of the buffer to absorb strong acid or base is determined by the individual concentrations of CH_3COO^- and CH_3COOH.

Preparation of buffers

Buffer solutions can be prepared either by mixing a weak acid or base with a solution of a salt containing its conjugate, or by partial neutralization of a weak acid or base with a strong acid or base.

The most common preparation method for an acidic buffer solution is combining a weak acid with its conjugate base. The conjugate base comes from an aqueous salt which dissociates in water to give the base. A basic buffer solution can be prepared by combining a weak base with its conjugate acid.

An alternative approach to making an acidic buffer solution is to start with a weak acid and add half as many moles of strong base. A basic buffer can also be prepared by starting with a weak base and adding half as many moles of strong acid.

The important point with any of the above preparation methods is that the *initial* solution must be a weak acid or base, otherwise the starting acid or base would already be 100% dissociated or ionized. Both components of a conjugate acid–base pair must remain in the solution to be able to neutralize any added acid or base. Regardless of the method of buffer production, the nature of the acid–base buffer always remains the same – a constant pH is maintained following any additions of small amounts of acid or base.

ToK Link

Mathematics is a universal language. The mathematical nature of this topic helps chemists speaking different native languages to communicate more objectively.

'Mathematics is invaluable to science as a strong grammar for didactic discourse; it is the ideal vehicle for precise intersubjective communication. The clarity and universality of mathematic language is of the greatest practical importance. A mathematically phrased statement in the archive is the best form for consultation, comprehension or critical assessment. A further special advantage of mathematic messages is that they may be symbolized, manipulated and transformed according to precise rules, without loss of meaning. The rules of arithmetic, algebra, trigonometry, calculus, group theory, analytic function theory etc. permit us to generate an infinite variety of unambiguous statements, of varying degrees of complexity, all of which are logically equivalent to the original message'.

John Ziman, *Reliable Knowledge* (Cambridge University Press, Cambridge, 1978)

18.3 pH curves – *pH curves can be investigated experimentally but are mathematically determined by the dissociation constant of the acid and base; an indicator with an appropriate end-point can be used to determine the equivalence point of the reaction*

■ Salt hydrolysis

A **salt** is defined as a compound formed when the hydrogen of an acid is completely or partially replaced by a metal (Table 18.4). If all the hydrogen is replaced, a normal salt is formed; if the hydrogen is not completely replaced, then an acidic salt is formed. Acid salts can only be formed by diprotic and triprotic acids; monoprotic acids can only form normal salts.

■ **Table 18.4** Salts of some selected acids

Acid	Salt	Example(s)	Classification
Hydrochloric acid, HCl	Chlorides	Sodium chloride, NaCl	Normal
Nitric acid, HNO_3	Nitrates	Sodium nitrate, $NaNO_3$	Normal
Ethanoic acid	Ethanoates	Sodium ethanoate, CH_3COONa	Normal
Sulfuric acid, H_2SO_4	Sulfates and hydrogensulfates	Sodium sulfate, Na_2SO_4, and sodium hydrogensulfate, $NaHSO_4$	Normal and acidic
Carbonic acid, H_2CO_3	Carbonates and hydrogencarbonates	Sodium carbonate, Na_2CO_3, and sodium hydrogencarbonate, $NaHCO_3$	Normal and acidic
Cyanic acid, HCN	Cyanides	Sodium cyanide, NaCN	Normal

Acid salts, if they are soluble in water, dissolve to form acidic solutions; for example sodium hydrogensulfate ionizes to release hydrogen, sulfate and sodium ions:

$$NaHSO_4(s) + (aq) \rightarrow Na^+(aq) + H^+(aq) + SO_4{}^{2-}(aq)$$

The resulting solution is acidic and exhibits typical acidic properties; for example it turns blue litmus red.

Normal salts, if they are soluble in water, often dissolve to form neutral solutions; for example sodium chloride ionizes to release sodium and chloride ions, neither of which react with water:

$$NaCl(s) + (aq) \rightarrow Na^+(aq) + Cl^-(aq)$$

This occurs when the salt has been formed by the neutralization of a strong acid by a strong base. In the case of sodium chloride the corresponding acid is hydrochloric acid, a strong acid, and the base is sodium hydroxide, a strong base or alkali:

$$NaOH(aq) + HCl(aq) \rightarrow NaCl(aq) + H_2O(l)$$

■ **Figure 18.11** Universal indicator solution added to a concentrated solution of sodium carbonate: the colour shows that it is alkaline

However, some normal salts dissolve in water to form either acidic or alkaline solutions. This is because one of the ions reacts with the water to release an excess of either hydroxide or hydrogen ions. This phenomenon is called salt hydrolysis and occurs when the salts are formed from weak acids or weak bases.

An example of the hydrolysis of a salt of a weak acid and a strong base is that of sodium carbonate solution, $Na_2CO_3(aq)$:

$$CO_3{}^{2-}(aq) + H_2O(l) \rightleftharpoons HCO_3{}^- (aq) + OH^-(aq)$$

The sodium ions are spectator ions (Chapter 1) and do not participate in the hydrolysis. The resulting solution will contain an excess of hydroxide ions and is alkaline. Its pH will be greater than 7 (Figure 18.11).

Similar reactions will occur between water and the anion of the salt formed from a weak acid and a strong base, for example sodium ethanoate, sodium hydrogencarbonate and sodium fluoride.

An example of the hydrolysis of a salt of a strong acid and a weak base is that of ammonium chloride solution, $NH_4Cl(aq)$:

$$NH_4{}^+(aq) + H_2O(l) \rightleftharpoons NH_3(aq) + H_3O^+(aq)$$

■ **Figure 18.12** Universal indicator solution added to a concentrated solution of aqueous ammonium chloride: the colour shows that it is acidic

The chloride ions are spectator ions and do not participate in the hydrolysis. The resulting solution will contain an excess of hydrogen ions and is acidic. Its pH will be less than 7 (Figure 18.12).

An example of the hydrolysis of a salt of a weak acid and a weak base is that of ammonium ethanoate, $CH_3COONH_4(aq)$:

$$NH_4{}^+(aq) + H_2O(l) \rightleftharpoons NH_3(aq) + H_3O^+(aq)$$

and

$$CH_3COO^-(aq) + H_2O(l) \rightleftharpoons CH_3COOH(aq) + OH^-(aq)$$

■ Figure 18.13
Hydrated iron(III)
chloride, $FeCl_3.6H_2O$

Both ions react with water and undergo hydrolysis: the final pH of the solution depends on the equilibrium constants for the two reactions. In this example, the two values are approximately the same, the two processes cancel each other out and the solution is neutral.

The two equations above can be summed together:

$$NH_4^+(aq) + CH_3COO^-(aq) + 2H_2O(l) \rightleftharpoons NH_3(aq) + H_3O^+(aq) + CH_3COOH(aq) + OH^-(aq)$$

Additional examples of salt hydrolysis occur with salts whose metal cation is small and highly charged. Examples include copper(II) sulfate, $CuSO_4$, aluminium sulfate, $Al_2(SO_4)_3$ and iron(III) chloride, $FeCl_3$ (Figure 18.13).

For example, in iron(III) chloride solution the hydrated iron(III) ions are $Fe[(H_2O)_6]^{3+}(aq)$. An equilibrium is set up between the hydrated iron(III) ions and water molecules, leading to the release of hydrogen ions (oxonium ions):

$$Fe[(H_2O)_6]^{3+}(aq) + H_2O(l) \rightleftharpoons Fe[(H_2O)_5OH]^{2+}(aq) + H_3O^+(aq)$$

This type of hydrolysis occurs very readily with trivalent cations, e.g. $Fe^{3+}(aq)$, much less with $Cu^{2+}(aq)$ and not at all with unipositive ions, e.g. $Ag^+(aq)$. The acidity also varies with the ionic radius: the smaller the ion, the greater the hydrolysis.

Small highly charged cations are described as polarizing. This may be expressed quantitatively as the charge on the cation divided by its ionic radius. The greater the polarizing power of the cation, the stronger the bond formed between the cation and the oxygen, weakening the O–H bond of the attached water molecule and favouring release of a proton (Figure 18.14).

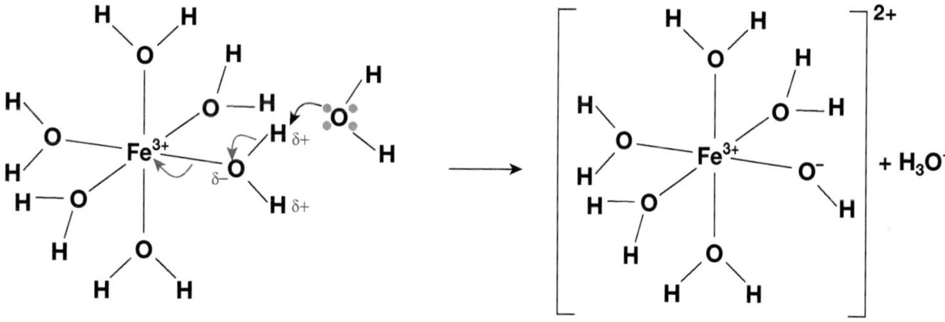

■ Figure 18.14
The polarization of
the hydrated iron(III)
ion by a water
molecule

Predicting the relative pH of aqueous salt solutions formed by the different combinations of strong and weak acid and base

Worked example

Sodium fluoride, NaF, is a salt formed when a strong base, NaOH, is reacted with hydrofluoric acid, HF. Predict and explain the pH of the NaF solution.

Sodium fluoride undergoes dissociation in aqueous solution:

$$NaF(aq) \rightarrow Na^+(aq) + F^-(aq)$$

The sodium ion, Na^+ (aq), does not hydrolyse because Na^+ is a very weak conjugate acid of the strong base, NaOH. The fluoride ion, F^-, hydrolyses because it is the conjugate base of the weak acid, HF, and is basic enough to remove a proton from water:

$$F^-(aq) + H_2O(l) \rightleftharpoons HF(aq) + OH^-(aq)$$

Since excess hydroxide ions are produced, the solution will be basic and the pH will be less than 7.

■ Acid–base titrations – titration curves for strong and weak acids and bases

The changes in pH that occur during an acid–base titration can be measured using the apparatus shown in Figure 18.15. The pH of the solution in the titration flask is measured with a pH probe and meter (which may be connected to a data-logger). The aqueous alkali is added in 0.5 or 1.0 cm³ portions and the pH is measured and recorded. A table of pH against volume of alkali is obtained and a graph is drawn.

Titration of a strong acid against a strong alkali

If we have $0.1 \, \text{mol dm}^{-3}$ aqueous hydrochloric acid in the flask at the beginning of the titration, then the pH will be $-\log_{10} 0.1$, i.e. 1. Let us now calculate the pH after $22.5 \, \text{cm}^3$ of $0.100 \, \text{mol dm}^{-3}$ aqueous sodium hydroxide is added to $25.0 \, \text{cm}^3$ of $0.100 \, \text{mol dm}^{-3}$ aqueous hydrochloric acid.

The addition of the alkali has removed $\frac{22.5}{25.0}$ or, if we divide the ratio by 2.5, $\frac{9}{10}$ (90%) of the hydrogen ions. In other words, after the neutralization $\frac{1}{10}$ (10%) of the original number of moles of hydrogen ions is left. This ratio can be termed the reaction factor.

An *approximate* pH for the resulting solution is calculated as follows:

$$[\text{H}^+(\text{aq})] = 0.100 \times \frac{1}{10} = 0.0100 \, \text{mol dm}^{-3}; \qquad \text{pH} = -\log_{10} 0.0100 = 2.00$$

So when 90% of the hydrogen ions have been neutralized, the pH has only changed by one unit, from 1 to 2.

However, this simple calculation ignores the 'dilution effect' which follows from the fact that the addition of aqueous sodium hydroxide not only adds hydroxide ions, but also changes the volume and hence the concentration of the resulting solution.

We can modify the previous equation to include the dilution factor and slightly improve the accuracy of the calculation:

'new' H⁺(aq) concentration = 'old' H⁺(aq) concentration × reaction factor × dilution factor

$$[\text{H}^+(\text{aq})] = 0.100 \times \frac{1}{10} \times \frac{25.0}{(25.0 + 22.5)} = 5.26 \times 10^{-3} \, \text{mol dm}^{-3}$$

pH = 2.28

Now repeat the above calculation (without the dilution factor) with greater volumes of NaOH(aq).

■ $24.75 \, \text{cm}^3$ of $0.100 \, \text{mol dm}^{-3}$ sodium hydroxide added to $25.0 \, \text{cm}^3$ of $0.100 \, \text{mol dm}^{-3}$ hydrochloric acid gives a pH of 3.00:

$$\text{reaction factor} = \frac{(25.0 - 24.75)}{25.0} = 0.0100$$

$$[\text{H}^+(\text{aq})] = 0.100 \times 0.0100 = 0.001\,00 \, \text{mol dm}^{-3}$$
$$\text{pH} = -\log_{10} 0.001\,00 = 3.00$$

■ $24.975 \, \text{cm}^3$ of $0.100 \, \text{mol dm}^{-3}$ sodium hydroxide added to $25.0 \, \text{mol dm}^{-3} \text{cm}^3$ of $0.100 \, \text{mol dm}^{-3}$ hydrochloric acid gives a pH of 4.00:

$$\text{reaction factor} = \frac{(25.0 - 24.975)}{25.0} = 0.001\,00$$

$$[\text{H}^+(\text{aq})] = 0.100 \times 0.001\,00 = 0.000\,100 \, \text{mol dm}^{-3}$$
$$\text{pH} = -\log_{10} 0.000\,100 = 4.00$$

■ 24.9975 cm³ of 0.100 mol dm⁻³ sodium hydroxide added to 25.0 cm³ of 0.100 mol dm⁻³ hydrochloric acid gives a pH of 5.00:

$$\text{reaction factor} = \frac{(25.0 - 24.9975)}{25.0} = 0.000\,100$$

$$[H^+(aq)] = 0.100 \times 0.000\,100 = 0.000\,010\,0\,\text{mol dm}^{-3}$$

$$pH = -\log_{10} 0.000\,010\,0 = 5.00$$

■ 24.9999 cm³ of 0.100 mol dm⁻³ sodium hydroxide added to 25.0 cm³ of 0.100 mol dm⁻³ hydrochloric acid gives a pH of 6.00:

$$\text{reaction factor} = \frac{(25.0 - 24.9999)}{25.0} = 0.000\,010\,0$$

$$[H^+(aq)] = 0.100 \times 0.000\,010\,0 = 0.000\,001\,00\,\text{mol dm}^{-3}$$

$$pH = -\log_{10} 0.000\,001\,00 = 6.00$$

These simplified calculations show that the pH rises *very rapidly* near the end-point or equivalence point where the reacting volumes will be equal. The end-point or equivalence point can also be found using an acid–base indicator.

Finally, when exactly 25 cm³ of sodium hydroxide is added to 25 cm³ of 0.100 mol dm⁻³ hydrochloric acid, it gives a pH of exactly 7, since the hydroxide and hydrogen ions are in an exactly reacting molar ratio of 1 : 1. Neither sodium nor chloride ions react with water and the solution of sodium chloride is neutral with a pH of exactly 7.

If we continue adding aqueous sodium hydroxide beyond the end-point, the hydroxide ions are now present in excess since all the acid has been removed by neutralization. The hydroxide ion concentration begins to rise as quickly after the end-point as the hydrogen ion concentration decreased before the end-point. The titration curve (Figure 18.16) is symmetrical around an imaginary horizontal axis that runs through pH 7 at the equivalence or end-point.

■ **Figure 18.16**
The titration curve for the titration of 25.0 cm³ of 0.100 mol dm⁻³ hydrochloric acid with 0.100 mol dm⁻³ sodium hydroxide

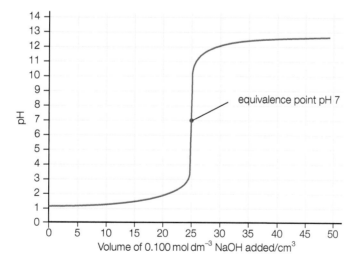

Let us calculate the pH after 25.5 cm³ of 0.100 mol dm⁻³ sodium hydroxide has been added to 25.0 cm³ of 0.100 mol dm⁻³ hydrochloric acid:

$$\text{reaction factor} = \frac{(25.5 - 25.0)}{25.0} = 0.02$$

An approximate pH (ignoring the dilution factor) for the resulting solution is calculated as follows:

$$[OH^-(aq)] = 0.100 \times 0.0200 = 0.002\,00\,\text{mol dm}^{-3}$$
$$pOH = -\log_{10} 0.002\,00 = 2.69; \quad pH = 11.3$$

Now calculate the pH after 27.5 cm³ of 0.100 mol dm⁻³ sodium hydroxide has been added to 25.0 cm³ of 0.100 mol dm⁻³ hydrochloric acid:

$$\text{reaction factor} = \frac{(27.5 - 25.0)}{25.0} = 0.100$$

An approximate pH (ignoring the dilution factor) for the resulting solution is calculated as follows:

$[OH^-(aq)] = 0.100 \times 0.100 = 0.0100 \, \text{mol dm}^{-3}$

$pOH = -\log_{10} 0.0100 = 2.00; \qquad pH = 12.0$

Titration of a weak acid against a strong alkali

25.00 cm³ of 0.100 mol dm⁻³ ethanoic acid requires exactly 25.00 cm³ of 0.100 mol dm⁻³ sodium hydroxide to reach the end-point or equivalence point. When these volumes react together 'neutralization' has occurred and only sodium ethanoate and water will be present:

$$CH_3COOH(aq) + NaOH(aq) \rightarrow CH_3COONa(aq) + H_2O(l)$$

However, the resulting solution will *not* be neutral. Ethanoic acid is a weak acid and exists mainly as molecules:

$$CH_3COOH(aq) \rightleftharpoons CH_3COO^-(aq) + H^+(aq)$$

At the beginning of the titration the pH will be about 3 since the acid is a weak acid and is only slightly dissociated into ions. (The exact pH of the ethanoic acid can be calculated if the value of K_a or pK_a is known.)

The addition of sodium hydroxide adds hydroxide ions to this equilibrium, which is 'pulled over' to the right as hydroxide ions remove the hydrogen ions via formation of water:

$$H^+(aq) + OH^-(aq) \rightarrow H_2O(l)$$

As alkali is added the ethanoic acid molecules undergo increasing dissociation to replace the hydrogen ions removed:

$$CH_3COOH(aq) \rightarrow CH_3COO^-(aq) + H^+(aq)$$

The overall reaction as an ionic equation is therefore:

$$CH_3COOH(aq) + OH^-(aq) \rightarrow H_2O(l) + CH_3COO^-(aq)$$

Note that the sodium ions are spectator ions and do not participate in the neutralization reaction, nor do they react with water molecules.

As a consequence of ethanoic acid being a weak acid, the line of the titration curve (Figure 18.17) (compared to hydrochloric acid) starts at a higher value of pH and stays higher because most of the hydrogen ions are kept 'in reserve' in undissociated ethanoic acid molecules. The dissociation of ethanoic acid gradually occurs as the alkali is added, hence the steady increase in pH with total volume of alkali added.

The equivalence point, where there are equal amounts of ethanoic acid and sodium hydroxide, will be at a pH *above* 7 due to salt hydrolysis since sodium ethanoate is the salt of a weak acid and strong base.

Ethanoate ions are a stronger base than water molecules and the following equilibrium is established:

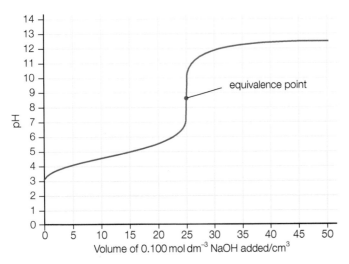

Figure 18.17 The titration curve for the titration of 25.0 cm³ of 0.100 mol dm⁻³ ethanoic acid with 0.100 mol dm⁻³ sodium hydroxide

$$CH_3COO^-(aq) + H_2O(l) \rightleftharpoons CH_3COOH(aq) + OH^-(aq)$$

with the forward reaction heavily favoured.

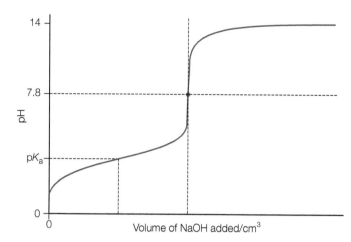

Figure 18.18 The determination of the pK_a of ethanoic acid from its titration curve

The relatively flat portions of titration curves are where the pH changes most slowly on addition of acid or alkali. These flat portions are, therefore, where the best buffering action occurs. They are known as the buffer regions.

The production of a titration curve for a weak acid such as ethanoic acid is helpful, as it allows the pK_a and hence K_a to be calculated graphically (Figure 18.18) since the pH of the *half-neutralized* acid (at 12.5 cm³ of alkali) corresponds to the pK_a of the acid.

During the titration of ethanoic acid by sodium hydroxide, the hydroxide ions gradually convert ethanoic acid molecules into ethanoate ions, so halfway to the end-point half of the ethanoic acid molecules will have been converted to ethanoate ions.

So specifically for the *half-neutralized* solution:

$$[CH_3COOH(aq)] = [CH_3COO^-(aq)]$$

However, in general:

$$K_a = [H^+(aq)] \times \frac{[CH_3COO^-(aq)]}{[CH_3COOH(aq)]}$$

Hence

$$K_a = [H^+(aq)] \times \frac{1}{1} \text{ since the two concentrations are equal}$$

So

$$K_a = [H^+(aq)]$$

Taking logarithms to the base 10 of both sides:

$$pK_a = pH$$

Titration of a strong acid against a weak alkali

If 0.100 mol dm⁻³ hydrochloric acid, HCl(aq), is titrated against 0.100 mol dm⁻³ aqueous ammonia, NH_3(aq), then the pH changes very little until near the equivalence point, when it changes rapidly (Figure 18.19). The pH levels off again, but at a relatively low pH since aqueous ammonia is a weak base.

Figure 18.19 The titration curve for the titration of 25.0 cm³ of 0.100 mol dm⁻³ hydrochloric acid with 0.100 mol dm⁻³ ammonia

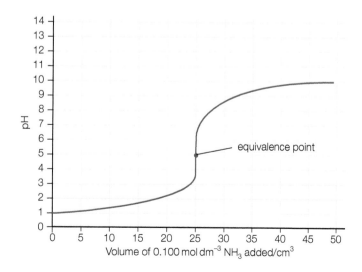

Titration of a weak acid against a weak alkali

If $0.100\,mol\,dm^{-3}$ ethanoic acid is titrated against $0.100\,mol\,dm^{-3}$ aqueous ammonia solution then a very different titration curve results (Figure 18.20). There is no sharp or abrupt change in pH and hence no vertical section in the titration curve; the pH changes gradually during the titration process. No indicator is suitable for following this type of neutralization. A pH probe and meter are often used to identify the end-point in this type of titration.

■ **Figure 18.20**
The titration curve for the titration of $25.0\,cm^3$ of $0.100\,mol\,dm^{-3}$ ethanoic acid with $0.100\,mol\,dm^{-3}$ ammonia

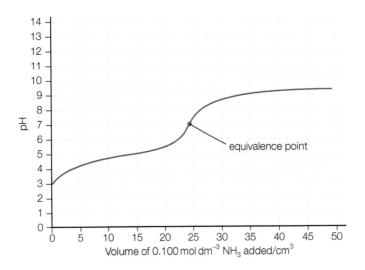

Simulation of a titration

An Excel spreadsheet can be constructed with appropriate formulas (to include the effects of dilution of the sample by titrant) to simulate the titration of weak and strong acids and bases (Figure 18.21). Some simulations use a 'master' equation to calculate all points on the titration; others use separate equations for different regions of the curve, for example before the equivalence point, at the equivalence point and after the equivalence point. The concentration of different species at a particular pH is calculated from $[H^+(aq)]$, and the volume of titrant required to produce that amount of each species is calculated.

■ **Figure 18.21**
Excel simulation of an acid–base titration and generation of a pH curve

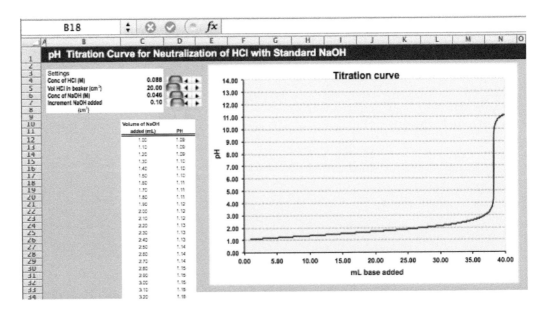

Increased power of instrumentation – development of the pH meter

Apart from the chemical balance, the pH meter is probably the most widely used piece of chemical instrumentation and has contributed to the progress of chemistry. There were three research tracks that led to the discovery and development of the pH meter: researchers interested in improving the quality of telegraphic signals, investigators interested in acid–base chemistry and physicists interested in the electrical properties of glasses. However, none of these had goals that included the manufacture of a pH meter. In 1935 German chemists had developed cells used to determine the concentration of redox substances (Chapter 19). These cells contained three elements: a reference electrode, an indicating electrode and a device for measuring the voltage developed by the cell. Two indicating electrodes – the standard hydrogen electrode (SHE) and the glass electrode – played important roles in the development of the pH meter. The SHE has a platinized metal surface which is easily 'poisoned' so the glass electrode is used in pH meters. The glass electrode is an ion-specific electrode made from a special glass containing group 1 cations that is sensitive to H^+ and sets up a small voltage across the surface.

Indicators

Nature of indicators

Acid–base indicators are soluble dyes that change colour according to the hydrogen ion concentration, that is, the pH. They are usually weak acids whose acid and conjugate base forms are different colours. The wavelength of the light absorbed by the acid changes greatly when a proton is lost to form the conjugate base (Chapter 2).

Common acid–base indicators include litmus, methyl orange, screened methyl orange, bromothymol blue, bromophenol blue, phenol red (Figure 18.22) and phenolphthalein. Figure 18.23 shows the structural formulas of the dissociated or ionized and undissociated or un-ionized forms of the indicator phenolphthalein.

■ **Figure 18.22** Phenol red: acidic (yellow) and alkaline (red) forms

■ **Figure 18.23** Phenolphthalein is colourless in acid, but pink in alkaline conditions

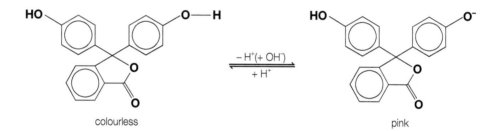

colourless   pink

Phenolphthalein is slightly unusual for an indicator as one of its two forms is colourless. (Since they are brightly coloured, only small quantities of indicators need to be used and their addition to a solution will not significantly alter the concentration of hydrogen ions already present.)

Action of indicators

Using HIn(aq) for the acid form of an indicator and In⁻(aq) for its conjugate base, the equilibrium for the dissociation of the indicator can be generalized to

$$HIn(aq) \rightleftharpoons In^-(aq) + H^+(aq)$$

or

$$HIn(aq) + H_2O(l) \rightleftharpoons In^-(aq) + H_3O^+(aq)$$

Consider the indicator bromophenol blue, whose colours are yellow (undissociated form, HIn(aq)) and blue (dissociated form, In⁻(aq)), respectively.

In a neutral solution, very few of the acid molecules dissociate since indicators are weak acids. The solution therefore appears yellow due to the relatively high concentration of HIn(aq). This means nearly all the indicator molecules will exist as the undissociated yellow form.

■ *Addition of an acid*: If an excess of an acidic solution is added to a solution of the indicator, the increase in hydrogen ion concentration will, according to Le Châtelier's principle, shift the equilibrium to the left so that the concentration of HIn(aq) is very high. This means that almost all the indicator molecules will exist as the undissociated yellow form.

■ *Addition of an alkali*: If an excess of an alkaline solution is added to a solution of the indicator, the hydroxide ions will combine with the hydrogen ions to form water, thereby removing them from the equilibrium. The removed hydrogen ions will be partly replaced by the dissociation of HIn(aq). A relatively high concentration of In⁻(aq) will be produced and the solution will be blue.

Since indicators are generally weak acids, an equilibrium expression for the acid dissociation constant, K_a, can be written for them. In general:

$$K_a = \frac{[H^+(aq)] \times [In^-(aq)]}{[HIn(aq)]} \qquad \text{or} \qquad K_a = \frac{[H_3O^+(aq)] \times [In^-(aq)]}{[HIn(aq)]}$$

The acid dissociation constant, K_a, is sometimes known as the dissociation constant for the indicator and given the symbol K_{In}.

The equation can be rearranged to make the ratio of the concentrations of the two coloured forms the subject:

$$\frac{[HIn(aq)]}{[In^-(aq)]} = \frac{[H^+(aq)]}{[K_a]}$$

This equation shows that the colour of an indicator depends not only on the hydrogen ion concentration, that is the pH, but also on the value of the acid dissociation constant, K_a. This means that different indicators change colour over different pH ranges.

$$K_a = \frac{[H^+(aq)] \times [In^-(aq)]}{[HIn(aq)]}$$

The equilibrium expression above can also be transformed into the Henderson–Hasselbalch equation previously derived, by rearranging it to:

$$\frac{1}{[H^+(aq)]} = \frac{1}{K_a} \times \frac{[In^-(aq)]}{[HIn(aq)]}$$

Taking logarithms to the base 10 of both sides:

$$pH = pK_a + \log_{10}\frac{[In^-(aq)]}{[HIn(aq)]}$$

This equation allows the calculation of any of the four variables, given the other three.

pH range of indicators

As shown previously, the colour of a solution to which the indicator has been added depends on the ratio of [HIn(aq)]/[In⁻(aq)] or [yellow] to [blue], which in turn depends on the hydrogen ion concentration or pH.

If the ratio for bromophenol blue is 10, the solution is yellow as the colour of HIn(aq) predominates. This happens, as shown previously, when the pH is low; that is, when the hydrogen ion concentration is high. The human eye cannot detect the small concentration of the blue In⁻(aq) form present. At this point:

$$pH = pK_a + \log_{10}\frac{[In^-(aq)]}{[HIn(aq)]}$$

$$= pK_a + \log_{10}\frac{1}{10}$$

$$= pK_a - 1$$

If the ratio [HIn(aq)]/[In⁻(aq)], or yellow to blue, is equal to 1 the solution is green, as the blue and yellow forms of the indicator are present in equal concentrations. At this point:

$$pH = pK_a + \log_{10} \frac{[In^-(aq)]}{[HIn(aq)]}$$

$$= pK_a + \log_{10} \frac{1}{1}$$

$$= pK_a$$

If the ratio [HIn(aq)]/[In⁻(aq)] is less than $\frac{1}{10}$, that is 0.1, then the solution is blue, as the colour due to the In⁻(aq) form predominates. The human eye cannot detect the small concentration of the yellow HIn(aq) form present.

$$pH = pK_a + \log_{10} \frac{[In^-(aq)]}{[HIn(aq)]}$$

$$= pK_a + \log_{10} \frac{10}{1}$$

$$= pK_a + 1$$

In general for indicators (Table 18.5) the colour change takes place over a range of about 2 pH units, specifically, from pH = pK_a − 1 to pH = pK_a + 1. This generally corresponds to the change described above, that is, going from 10% of one form of the indicator to 10% of the other form (Figure 18.24).

■ **Table 18.5**
The pH ranges of some common acid–base indicators

Indicator	'Acid colour'	'Alkaline colour'	pH range and pK_a
Methyl orange	Red	Yellow	3.1–4.4 and 3.7
Bromothymol blue	Yellow	Blue	6.0–7.6 and 7.0
Bromophenol blue	Yellow	Blue	3.0–4.6 and 4.2
Phenolphthalein	Colourless	Pink	8.3–10.0 and 9.6
Thymol blue	Red	Yellow	1.2–2.8 and 1.6
	Yellow	Blue	8.0–9.6 and 8.9
Methyl red	Red	Yellow	4.4–6.2 and 5.1
Litmus	Red	Blue	5.0–8.0 and 6.5

■ **Figure 18.24**
A diagram illustrating the behaviour of a typical acid–base indicator: bromothymol blue is placed into a transparent plastic box diagonally divided into halves

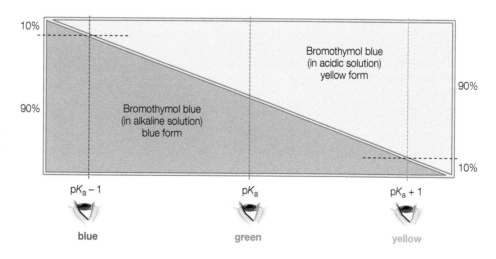

■ **Figure 18.25** Bottle of universal indicator solution

A few indicators undergo more than one change. Thymol blue, for example, changes colour in the pH range 1.2 to 2.8 and again in the range 8.0 to 9.6. This is because the undissociated acid is in equilibrium with *two* ionized forms. Universal indicators (Figure 18.25) are composed of mixtures of carefully selected indicators so as to give a series of gradual colour changes over a relatively large range of pH values.

Indicators as weak bases

Methyl orange (Figure 18.26), unlike most indicators, is a weak base which can be represented as BOH(aq). In aqueous solution the following equilibrium is set up:

$$BOH(aq) \rightleftharpoons B^+(aq) + OH^-(aq)$$

yellow   red

base   conjugate acid

Application of Le Châtelier's principle predicts that in alkaline solution the yellow form, BOH(aq), will predominate and in acidic solution the red $B^+(aq)$ will predominate (Figure 18.27).

■ **Figure 18.26** Methyl orange indicator in acidic and alkaline solutions

- ■ *Addition of an acid*: If an excess of an acidic solution is added to a solution of the indicator, the increase in hydrogen ion concentration will, according to Le Châtelier's principle, shift the equilibrium above to the right so that the concentration of the conjugate acid, $B^+(aq)$, is very high. This means that almost all the indicator molecules will exist as the ionized red form. This shift occurs because the hydrogen ions will combine with hydroxide ions to form water molecules.

- ■ *Addition of an alkali*: If an excess of an alkaline solution is added to a solution of the indicator, the hydroxide ion concentration will increase. The reaction will shift to the left to lower their concentration. A relatively high concentration of the base, BOH(aq), will be produced and the solution will be yellow.

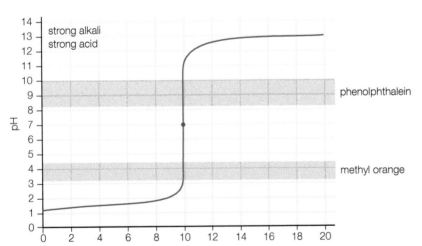

■ **Figure 18.27** The structure of methyl orange in acidic and alkaline conditions

 ### Selecting an appropriate indicator for a titration, given the equivalence point of the titration and the end-point of the indicator

An indicator used for any acid–base titration should ideally change colour at the pH corresponding to the mid-point of the almost vertically straight portion of the titration curve. (However, there is little loss in accuracy if the indicator changes colour anywhere within the range of the almost vertically straight portion of the curve, since the pH change is relatively *large* for the addition of a relatively *small* amount of acid or base.)

For a strong acid/strong base titration, any of the indicators could be used since all of them change colour within the almost vertical straight portion of the titration curve between about pH 4 and pH 11. In other words, the pK_a values of suitable indicators must lie between 4 and 11, and preferably be centred around 7.

Two common indicators are methyl orange and phenolphthalein. Methyl orange changes colour over the pH range 3.1 to 4.4 and phenolphthalein changes over the pH range 8.3 to 10.0. Both indicators are suitable for titrations involving a strong acid and a strong base (Figure 18.28).

■ **Figure 18.28** Titration curve starting with 100 cm³ of 0.100 mol dm⁻³ strong acid and adding 1.0 mol dm⁻³ strong alkali

However, the choice of indicator is more limited if a weak acid or a weak base is used in the titration, since the pH range of the almost straight portion is much smaller and fewer indicators change colour completely over this range.

For a strong acid/weak base titration, such as that between $0.1\,mol\,dm^{-3}$ aqueous ammonia and $0.1\,mol\,dm^{-3}$ hydrochloric acid, the indicator needs to change between pH values 4 and 7. Methyl orange is a suitable indicator, but phenolphthalein is not.

As Figure 18.29 shows, phenolphthalein would *not* be a suitable indicator because it will change colour at the wrong volume (not at the end-point) and over a large volume change of aqueous ammonia solution. It would therefore be impossible to find the end-point accurately using phenolphthalein as the indicator.

■ **Figure 18.29**
Titration curve starting with $100\,cm^3$ of $0.100\,mol\,dm^{-3}$ strong acid and adding $1.0\,mol\,dm^{-3}$ weak alkali

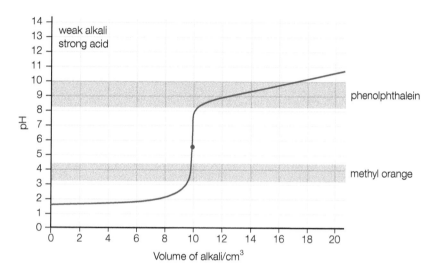

For a weak acid/strong base titration, such as that between $0.1\,mol\,dm^{-3}$ ethanoic acid and $0.1\,mol\,dm^{-3}$ sodium hydroxide, the indicator needs to change between pH values 6 and 10. Phenolphthalein is a suitable indicator, but methyl orange is not.

Figure 18.30 shows that methyl orange would *not* be a suitable indicator because it will change colour very slowly over a relatively large volume of sodium hydroxide so that it would be very difficult to locate the end-point accurately. In addition, the colour change would occur at the wrong volume.

■ **Figure 18.30**
Titration curve starting with $100\,cm^3$ of $0.100\,mol\,dm^{-3}$ weak acid and adding $1.0\,mol\,dm^{-3}$ strong alkali

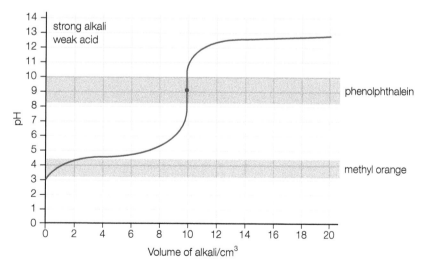

No indicator is suitable for the titration of a weak acid with a weak base, for example $0.1\,mol\,dm^{-3}$ ethanoic acid and $0.1\,mol\,dm^{-3}$ aqueous ammonia, since there is no almost straight portion present in the titration curve (Figure 18.31). In other words, the pH changes *gradually* throughout the titration.

If bromothymol blue, whose pK_a is approximately 7, was used as an indicator, it would change colour over a relatively large volume of ammonia. Hence it would not be possible to find the end-point accurately.

■ **Figure 18.31**
Titration curve
starting with 100 cm³
of 0.100 mol dm⁻³
weak acid and adding
1.0 mol dm⁻³ weak
alkali

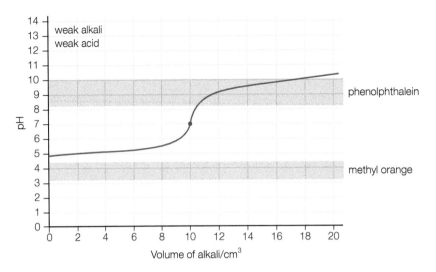

Table 18.6 summarizes the use of phenolphthalein and methyl orange as acid–base indicators. The principles described here can be used to select other suitable indicators for acid–base titrations.

No indicator can be used for an accurate titration of a weak acid with a weak base since the colour change of any indicator is going to be gradual. Such titrations are therefore often performed using a pH probe and meter or a conductivity probe and meter (Figure 18.33).

■ **Table 18.6**
The suitability of
methyl orange and
phenolphthalein as
indicators

Alkali	Acid	Indicator
Strong	Strong	Methyl orange or phenolphthalein
Strong	Weak	Phenolphthalein (Figure 18.32)
Weak	Strong	Methyl orange
Weak	Weak	None

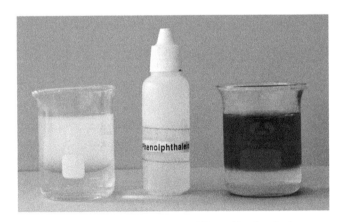

■ **Figure 18.32** Phenolphthalein in acidic and basic solutions

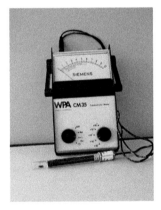

■ **Figure 18.33** Conductivity
probe and meter

ToK Link

Is a pH curve an accurate description of reality or an artificial representation? Does science offer a representation of reality?

A pH curve is described by a series of equations based on acid–base equilibria. There is nothing unusual about the mathematical features of a pH curve. The distinctive features that you should be able to identify are the starting pH, the buffer region and its mid-point, the equivalence point pH and the final asymptotic pH. All of these have been explained in the text in terms of chemical reactions and acid–base equilibria equations. The calculations used in the text to model pH curves are artificial representations of reality. They do not provide an exact model of pH curves, and they differ slightly from accurate experimental pH curves.

Science does attempt to offer a representation of reality, but it is always an approximate representation of reality. For example, it is predicted that if ethanoic acid is diluted (at constant temperature) and the pH is measured, the calculated K_a values will remain constant. However, in practice K_a values are found to decrease upon dilution (at constant temperature). These observations can be explained by using the Ostwald dilution law.

Consider the ionization of a weak acid in water. Let c be the concentration of the electrolyte in solution and α the degree of ionization.

$$HA(aq) \rightleftharpoons H^+(aq) + A^-(aq)$$

Initial concentrations:	c	0	0
Equilibrium:	$c - c\alpha$	$c\alpha$	$c\alpha$

Applying the law of chemical equilibrium:

$$K_a = \frac{[H^+(aq)] \times [A^-(aq)]}{[HA\,(aq)]}$$

$$= \frac{(c\alpha)(c\alpha)}{c(1 - \alpha)} = \frac{c\alpha^2}{(1 - \alpha)}$$

(c cancels)

For weak electrolytes the degree of ionization, α, is very small, and hence $1 - \alpha$ approximates to 1:

$$K_a = c\alpha^2; \qquad \alpha = \sqrt{\frac{K_a}{c}}$$

Hence the degree of ionization of an electrolyte is inversely proportional to the square root of the concentration. The degree of ionization of a weak acid therefore increases upon dilution. This relationship is known as the Ostwald dilution law and applies reasonably well if α is less than 10%. For ethanoic acid ($pK_a = 4.6$) this implies that the ethanoic acid concentration should not fall below approximately $2.5 \times 10^{-3}\,mol\,dm^{-3}$. (If $pK_a = 4.6$, then $K_a = 2.51 \times 10^{-5}\,mol\,dm^{-3}$.) Taking α as 0.1 (i.e. 10% dissociation) then $c = K_a/\alpha^2 = 2.51 \times 10^{-3}\,mol\,dm^{-3}$ which is taken to be the concentration for a 10% dissociated solution of ethanoic acid.

Consider the dissociation of a weak acid, such as ethanoic acid:

$$CH_3COOH\,(aq) + H_2O\,(l) \rightleftharpoons CH_3COO^-\,(aq) + H_3O^+\,(aq)$$

$$K_a = \frac{[H_3O^+(aq)] \times [CH_3COO^-(aq)]}{[CH_3COOH(aq)]}$$

Obviously, $[CH_3COOH(aq)] = [CH_3COOH(aq)]_0 - [H_3O^+(aq)]$ (where $[CH_3COOH(aq)]_0$ is the concentration of ethanoic acid before dissociation), and for electroneutrality

$$[CH_3COO^-(aq)] + [OH^-(aq)] = [H_3O^+(aq)]$$

But

$$[OH^-(aq)] = \frac{K_w}{[H_3O^+(aq)]}$$

and so

$$[CH_3COO^-(aq)] + \frac{K_w}{[H_3O^+(aq)]} = [H_3O^+(aq)]$$

Therefore

$$[CH_3COO^-(aq)] = [H_3O^+(aq)] - \frac{K_w}{[H_3O^+(aq)]}$$

$$K_a = \frac{[H_3O^+(aq)]\left([H_3O^+(aq)] - \left(\frac{K_w}{[H_3O^+(aq)]}\right)\right)}{[CH_3COOH(aq)]_0 - [H_3O^+(aq)]}$$

The simpler and less accurate model (as specified by the Chemistry IB syllabus), which ignores the ionization of water, gives instead:

$$K_a = \frac{[H_3O^+(aq)]^2}{[CH_3COOH(aq)]}$$

or, taking into account the ionization of the weak acid

$$K_a = \frac{[H_3O^+(aq)]^2}{[CH_3COOH(aq)]_0 - [H_3O^+(aq)]}$$

Conductometric titrations

The end-point of an acid–base titration can be found by monitoring the conductivity (Figure 18.34a) of the solution as the alkali is progressively neutralized by the addition of acid. For example, during the titration of barium hydroxide and dilute sulfuric acid, the electrical conductivity is zero at the end-point (Figure 18.34b).

$$Ba(OH)_2(aq) + H_2SO_4(aq) \rightarrow BaSO_4(s) + 2H_2O(l)$$

or ionically,

$$2OH^-(aq) + 2H^+(aq) \rightarrow 2H_2O(l)$$

At the end-point the electrical conductivity is zero because the ions of barium hydroxide and sulfuric acid are replaced by insoluble barium sulfate and water molecules.

Similar results are obtained when any base (strong or weak) is titrated against any acid (weak or strong). A V-shaped graph is obtained whose trough corresponds to the volume of acid required to achieve neutralization. Weak bases and acids, of course, have *shallower* gradients than strong acids or bases, and finish at *lower* points on conductivity graphs since their concentrations of ions are relatively smaller.

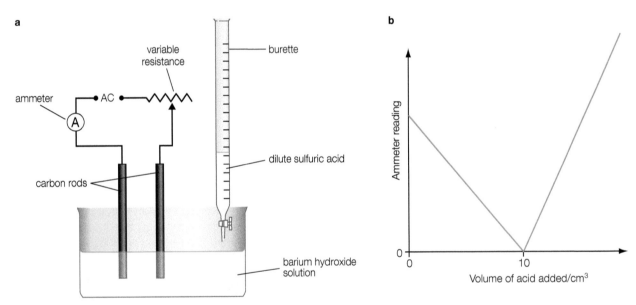

■ **Figure 18.34** Neutralization of barium hydroxide with dilute sulfuric acid: **a** apparatus to monitor the neutralization by measuring conductivity changes and **b** a graph of sample results

Examination questions – a selection

Paper 1 IB questions and IB style questions

Q1 An aqueous solution has a pH of 10. Which concentrations are correct for the ions below?

	$[H^+(aq)]/mol\,dm^{-3}$	$[OH^-(aq)]/mol\,dm^{-3}$
A	10^4	10^{-10}
B	10^{-4}	10^{-10}
C	10^{-10}	10^{-4}
D	10^{-10}	10^4

Higher Level Paper 1, Nov 2005, Q26

Q2 Which compound will dissolve in water to give a solution with a pH greater than 7?
  A rubidium chloride   **C** ammonium nitrate
  B sodium carbonate   **D** calcium sulfate

Q3 A buffer solution can be prepared by adding which of the following to $50\,cm^3$ of $0.20\,mol\,dm^{-3}$ $CH_3COOH(aq)$?
  I $50\,cm^3$ of $0.20\,mol\,dm^{-3}$ $CH_3COONa(aq)$
  II $25\,cm^3$ of $0.20\,mol\,dm^{-3}$ $NaOH(aq)$
  III $50\,cm^3$ of $0.20\,mol\,dm^{-3}$ $NaOH(aq)$
  A I only   **C** II and III only
  B I and II only **D** I, II and III

Q4 An acid–base indicator, HIn, dissociates according to the following equation:

$$HIn(aq) \rightleftharpoons H^+(aq) + In^-(aq)$$

colour A   colour B

Which statement about this indicator is correct?

    I In a strongly acidic solution colour A would be seen.

    II In a neutral solution the concentrations of HIn(aq) and In⁻(aq) must be equal.

    III It is suitable for use in titrations involving weak acids and bases.

A I only   **C** III only

B II only   **D** none of the above

Q5 When the following 2.0 mol dm⁻³ aqueous solutions are arranged in order of decreasing pH, which is the correct order?

    I ammonium chloride

    II ammonium ethanoate

    III potassium ethanoate

A I, II, III   **C** III, I, II

B II, I, III   **D** III, II, I

Q6 The hydrogen ion concentration of a 0.050 mol dm⁻³ solution of lactic acid (a weak monobasic organic acid) is 2.62×10^{-3} mol dm⁻³. The acid dissociation constant, K_a, is 1.37×10^{-4}. What is the pH of this solution?

A 1.30   **C** 5.94

B 2.58   **D** 3.86

Q7 The pH of a 0.10 mol dm⁻³ solution of a weak monobasic acid represented by HA is 4.20. What is the value of K_a for HA?

A 4.0×10^{-8} **C** 4.0×10^{-5}

B 2.5×10^{-7} **D** 2.5×10^{-9}

Q8 What is the pH in a titration when 20.0 cm³ of 0.011 mol dm⁻³ sodium hydroxide, NaOH, has been added to 25.0 cm³ of 0.014 mol dm⁻³ hydrochloric acid, HCl?

A 2.28   **C** 2.54

B 1.85   **D** 3.46

Q9 Pyridine is a weak base that reacts with water according to the equation:

$$pyridine(aq) + H_2O(l) \rightarrow pyridineH^+(aq) + OH^-(aq)$$

What is the pH of a 0.050 mol dm⁻³ solution of pyridine if the base dissociation constant, K_b, is 1.4×10^{-9}?

A 5.1   **C** 8.9

B 4.4   **D** 9.6

Q10 Which of the following statements correctly describes a *weak* acid?

    I It has a low pK_a value.

    II It has a strong conjugate base.

    III It has a relatively high electrical conductivity in dilute aqueous solutions.

A II only   **C** I and III

B II and III   **D** I, II and III

Q11 The dissociation of water is an endothermic reaction. Which of the statements is *false* when 1000 cm³ of pure water is heated from 25 °C to 60 °C?

A The concentration of hydrogen ions increases.

B The pH of the water decreases.

C The water becomes acidic.

D The concentration of hydroxide ions decreases.

Q12 What is the pH of a solution which is 0.0100 mol dm⁻³ in HA (a weak monobasic acid) and also 0.0020 mol dm⁻³ in NaA (its sodium salt) ($K_a = 9.0 \times 10^{-6}$)?

A 4.35   **C** 6.65

B 3.75   **D** 5.65

Q13 Which graph shows how the pH changes when a weak base is added to a strong acid?

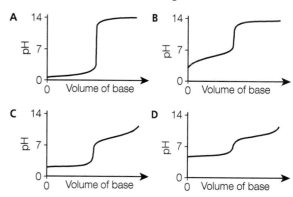

Higher Level Paper 1, Nov 2005, Q27

Q14 Which of the following is an example of a Lewis acid–base reaction, but not a Brønsted-Lowry acid–base reaction?

A $2CrO_4{}^{2-}(aq) + 2H^+(aq) \rightarrow Cr_2O_7{}^{2-}(aq) + H_2O(l)$

B $[Co(H_2O)_6]^{2+}(aq) + 4HCl(aq)$
$\rightarrow [CoCl_4]^{2-}(aq) + 4H^+(aq) + 6H_2O(l)$

C $NH_3(aq) + H^+(aq) \rightarrow NH_4{}^+(aq)$

D $CH_3COO^-(aq) + H_2O(l)$
$\rightarrow CH_3COOH(aq) + OH^-(aq)$

Higher Level Paper 1, May 2013, Q26

Q15 The pK_b value of ammonia is 4.75 at 298 K. What is the pK_a value of ammonia?

A $\dfrac{10^{-14}}{4.75}$ C 14.00 − 4.75

B $\dfrac{14.00}{4.75}$ D $\dfrac{10^{-14}}{10^{-4.75}}$

Higher Level Paper 1, May 2013, Q28

Q16 Which species can act as an acid according to the Lewis theory but not according to the Brønsted–Lowry theory?

A NCl_3 C H_2O
B HBr   D BCl_3

Q17 An acid-base indicator has a pK_a value of 4.00. At what pH will this indicator change colour?

A 12.00   C 4.00
B 8.00   D 2.00

Paper 2 IB questions and IB style questions

Q1 a i Define the term pH. [1]
    ii A 25.0 cm³ sample of 0.100 mol dm⁻³ hydrochloric acid is placed in a conical flask, and 0.100 mol dm⁻³ sodium hydroxide is added until a total of 50.0 cm⁻³ has been added. Sketch a graph of pH against volume of NaOH(aq) added, clearly showing the volume of NaOH(aq) needed for complete reaction and the pH values at the start, the equivalence point and finish. [4]
    iii The experiment in **a ii** was repeated but with a 25.0 cm³ sample of 0.100 mol dm⁻³ ethanoic acid in the conical flask instead of the hydrochloric acid. Use information from Table 21 on page 19 of the IB *Chemistry data booklet* to calculate the pH at the start of the experiment. State the approximate pH value at the equivalence point. [5]
   b i Describe how an indicator, HIn, works. [3]
    ii Name a suitable indicator for the reaction between ethanoic acid and sodium hydroxide. Use the information in the IB *Chemistry data booklet* to explain your choice. [2]

c i Identify *two* substances that can be added to water to form a basic buffer solution. [1]
    ii Describe what happens when a small amount of acid solution is added to the buffer solution prepared in **i**. Use an equation to support your explanation. [2]
   d Define the terms *Brønsted–Lowry acid* and *Lewis acid*. For each type of acid, identify one example other than water and write an equation to illustrate the definition. [5]
   e Predict and explain whether an aqueous solution of 0.10 mol dm⁻³ $AlCl_3$ will be acidic, alkaline or neutral. [2]

Higher Level Paper 2, May 2006, Q8

Q2 A mixture of benzoic acid (C_6H_5COOH) and sodium benzoate ($NaC_6H_5CO_2$) can act as a buffer solution.
   a Define the term *buffer solution* and describe what happens when an acid is added to a buffer solution. [5]
   b Calculate the pH of a solution containing 7.2 g of sodium benzoate in 1.0 dm³ of 3.0×10^{-2} mol dm⁻³ benzoic acid ($K_a = 6.3 \times 10^{-5}$ mol dm⁻³), stating any assumptions you have made. [5]
   c Benzoic acid is a *weak monoprotic* acid. Explain these terms. [2]

Q3 a In the reaction
$$2H_2O(l) \rightarrow H_3O^+(aq) + OH^-(aq)$$
use the Brønsted–Lowry theory to discuss the acidic and/or basic nature of water. [2]
   b What is the conjugate base of the hydroxide ion, OH^-? [1]
   c Define the term *pH* and give the pH of pure water (at 25 °C). [2]
   d i Write an expression for the ionic product of water, K_w. [1]
    ii The value of K_w increases with temperature. Explain with reasoning whether the dissociation of water is endothermic or exothermic. [3]

19 Redox processes

ESSENTIAL IDEA

- Energy conversions between electrical and chemical energy lie at the core of electrochemical cells.

Electrochemistry is concerned with the interconversion of electrical and chemical energy. Electrical effects occur as a result of the movement of electrical charge, either as mobile ions in an aqueous solution or melted liquid or as delocalized electrons in a conductor. Electrolytic and voltaic cells are the two types of electrochemical cells.

19.1 Electrochemical cells – *energy conversions between electrical and chemical energy lie at the core of electrochemical cells*

■ Redox equilibria and electrochemical cells

A chemical equilibrium (Chapter 7) known as a redox equilibrium is established when a piece of metal is placed in an aqueous solution of its cations. The forward reaction involves some of the atoms of the metal entering the solution as hydrated metal ions, leaving behind a layer of electrons on the surface of the metal. This oxidation process (at an anode) can be represented by

$$M(s) \rightarrow M^{n+}(aq) + ne^-$$

where n represents 2, for example for copper or 3, for example for aluminium. (The more reactive metals in groups 1 and 2 will also be involved in a direct reaction with water.)

The reverse reaction involves hydrated metal ions in the solution accepting electrons from the surface of the metal and being deposited as metal atoms on the surface of the piece of metal. This reduction process (at a cathode) can be represented by

$$M^{n+}(aq) + ne^- \rightarrow M(s)$$

Equilibrium (Figure 19.1) is established when the rates of the forward and backward reactions are equal:

$$M(s) \rightleftharpoons M^{n+}(aq) + ne^-$$

■ **Figure 19.1**
The establishment of a redox equilibrium

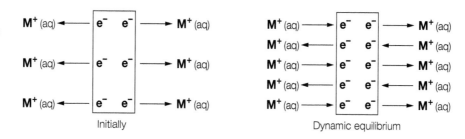

The position of equilibrium depends on a number of factors, but in particular on the *reactivity* (reducing strength) of the metal. For example, when a piece of zinc, a relatively reactive metal, is placed in an aqueous solution of zinc ions, the equilibrium lies to the right-hand side:

$$Zn(s) \rightleftharpoons Zn^{2+}(aq) + 2e^-$$

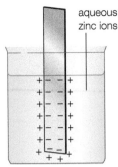

aqueous
zinc ions

zinc metal rod

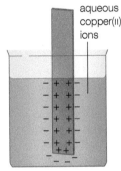

aqueous
copper(II)
ions

copper metal rod

■ **Figure 19.2** Redox
equilibria for zinc in
a solution of zinc(II)
ions and copper in a
solution of copper(II)
ions

with the overall change being the dissolution of zinc, leaving the surface with a *negative* charge due to the presence of a layer of electrons. The mass of the original piece of zinc has decreased slightly and the concentration of zinc ions in solution has increased slightly. (However, there is a clear distinction between reactivity, which is a kinetic concept, and position of equilibrium, a thermodynamic concept, which is discussed later in this chapter.)

The opposite process occurs when copper, a relatively unreactive metal, is placed in an aqueous solution of copper(II) ions. In this reaction the equilibrium lies to the left-hand side:

$$Cu(s) \rightleftharpoons Cu^{2+}(aq) + 2e^-$$

The overall reaction involves the deposition of copper(II) ions as copper atoms and so as a consequence the surface of the piece of copper gains a *positive* charge. The mass of the original piece of copper has increased slightly and the concentration of copper(II) ions in solution has decreased slightly. These two redox equilibria are illustrated in Figure 19.2. (The numbers of charges shown in the diagram should not be taken literally, but the numbers of positive and negative charges will be equal.)

In both the redox equilibria described above, the solution and the surface of the metal develop opposite electrical charges. A potential difference (measured as a voltage), known as an electrode potential, is said to exist between the surface of the metal and the solution because of this charge separation. The piece of metal dipping in the solution is referred to as an electrode and when immersed in its own ions it forms a half-cell.

A voltaic cell, such as the Daniell cell (Chapter 9), can be constructed by connecting two half-cells (anode and cathode) using an external circuit and a salt bridge. The cell potential can be measured by introducing a high-resistance voltmeter into the external circuit.

Types of half-cells

The potential difference between an electrode and a solution of aqueous ions is not limited to metals but also applies to non-metals. There are three types of commonly encountered half-cell:

■ A metal immersed in a solution of its own ions.

■ An inert electrode (for example, graphite or platinum which does not take part in the redox equilibrium) immersed in an aqueous solution containing two ions of the same element in *different* oxidation states, e.g. $Fe^{2+}(aq)/Fe^{3+}(aq)$.

■ A gas bubbling over an inert electrode immersed in an aqueous solution containing the ions of the gas, for example the standard hydrogen electrode, which has an equilibrium between hydrogen ions and hydrogen molecules.

Any two different half-cells can be combined together to form a voltaic cell and allow the electrons to flow from the reducing agent to the oxidizing agent. The resulting movement of electrons allows useful work to be done and also allows chemists to measure the tendency for a redox reaction to occur.

The electrode potential of an element depends on three factors:

■ the nature of the element

■ the concentration of its ions in solution

■ the temperature of the solution.

Note that the amount of metal present does *not* influence the electrode potential of a metal.

Hence, the concentrations and temperature of the electrolytes have to be stated when comparing the electrode potentials of different elements. Standard thermodynamic conditions are usually stated (standard conditions are 298 K (25 °C), 100 kPa for all gases and all concentrations 1 mol dm^{-3}).

The salt bridge

A simple salt bridge consists of a strip of filter paper soaked in saturated potassium nitrate solution, KNO_3(aq). The function of the salt bridge is to complete the circuit and to allow for the balancing of ionic charges in the two solutions of the Daniell cell and other simple voltaic cells.

The dissolution of zinc from the zinc electrode in the Daniell cell will result in an increase in the concentration of zinc ions in the zinc sulfate(VI) solution. The deposition of copper(II) ions from the copper(II) sulfate(VI) solution as copper atoms will cause a decrease in the concentration of copper(II) ions in the copper(II) sulfate(VI) solution.

These processes will lead to a *surplus* of positive ions in the zinc sulfate(VI) and a *deficiency* of positive ions in the copper(II) sulfate(VI). Unless the concentrations of these positive ions are kept constant, the two redox reactions will gradually slow and stop, and the current will drop to zero.

The imbalances in the concentrations of the two positive ions are restored by flows of ions from the salt bridge. Negatively charged nitrate ions leave the salt bridge and their place is taken up by zinc ions. For every two nitrate ions that enter the zinc sulfate(VI), one zinc ion enters the salt bridge. In the copper(II) sulfate(VI) solution, positive potassium ions leave the salt bridge and are replaced by sulfate ions. For every *two* potassium ions that enter the copper(II) sulfate(VI), *one* sulfate(VI) ion enters the salt bridge (Figure 19.3).

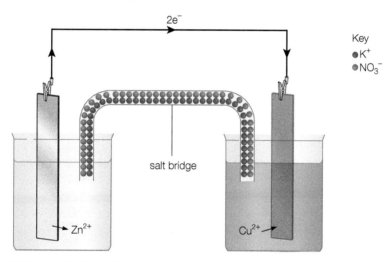

■ **Figure 19.3** Flow of ions in a salt bridge containing potassium and nitrate(V) ions

These flows of ions maintain the overall net positive charges of metal ions in both solutions. Potassium nitrate(V) is chosen for the salt bridge because neither potassium ions nor nitrate(V) ions react chemically with the other ions present in the two solutions. They also move at similar speeds to copper(II), zinc and sulfate(VI) ions in solution.

The standard hydrogen electrode (SHE)

The voltage of a *single* metal electrode in the half-cell of an electrochemical cell, such as the copper and zinc electrodes of the Daniell cell, cannot be measured. If the metal electrode is connected to a voltmeter using a wire and the wire placed in the solution to complete the circuit, another redox equilibrium and electrode potential will be generated. The voltage will be the difference of the two electrode potentials, not the voltage of the first metal electrode in equilibrium with its ions in aqueous solution.

The solution to this problem is to choose a *standard reference electrode* and measure the potentials of all other electrodes relative to this. In principle any electrode system could be used as a standard reference electrode, but metals, especially the reactive ones, tend to undergo corrosion, which reduces their accuracy.

The internationally agreed reference electrode is the standard hydrogen electrode (SHE) (Figure 19.4), which has hydrogen gas in equilibrium with hydrogen ions. In this system hydrogen is behaving as a metal since positively charged hydrogen ions are present. It is relatively easy to prepare pure hydrogen gas and solutions of hydrogen ions of known concentrations. The standard hydrogen electrode is arbitrarily given an electrode potential of *zero* volts, so all redox systems measured relative to it will be given either a positive or negative value.

■ **Figure 19.4**
The standard hydrogen
electrode

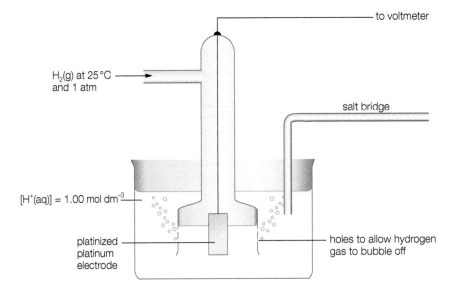

The standard hydrogen electrode is maintained by a stream of pure hydrogen gas bubbling over a platinum electrode coated with platinum black (finely divided platinum) and immersed in a solution of hydrochloric acid.

The platinum electrode has these functions:

■ It acts as an *inert* metal connector to the hydrogen gas/hydrogen ion equilibrium. There is no tendency for the very unreactive platinum itself to ionize and to act as an electrode.

■ The platinized surface acts as a heterogeneous *catalyst* for the adsorbed hydrogen gas on its surface. This allows standard electrode potentials to be measured quickly.

■ An equilibrium is set up between the gas adsorbed on the electrode and the hydrogen ions in the acid solution.

The electrode potential of this electrode is fixed at zero under the following standard conditions:

■ temperature at 298 K (25 °C)

■ pressure of hydrogen gas at standard atmospheric pressure (100 kPa)

■ hydrogen ion concentration at one mole per cubic decimetre ($1\,\text{mol}\,\text{dm}^{-3}$).

ToK Link

The standard hydrogen electrode is an example of an arbitrary reference. Would our scientific knowledge be the same if we chose different references?

The standard hydrogen electrode is the universal and internationally agreed IUPAC (International Union of Pure and Applied Chemistry) reference for reporting relative half-cell potentials. It is a type of gas electrode and was widely used in early studies as a reference electrode, and as an indicator electrode (Chapter 18) for the determination of pH values. It is an arbitrary reference and in principle any metal/metal ion system could be used as reference electrode. To use an analogy, heights are measured using sea level as an arbitrary zero. Any level above or below sea level could be used as the reference point.

It is the nature of electric potential that the voltage of zero is arbitrary; it is the *difference* in potential which has practical consequence. Tabulating all electrode potentials with respect to the same standard electrode (SHE) provides a practical working framework for a wide range of calculations and predictions.

However, the standard hydrogen electrode is often inconvenient to use as a reference electrode experimentally. It has to have

freshly made platinum electrodes, a solution of HCl with a very accurately determined concentration corresponding to a concentration of 1.18 M (corresponding to unit activity), and the safe provision of a hydrogen gas source at 100 kPa pressure at a temperature of 25 °C (298 K). It is generally much more convenient in practice to use other electrodes, for example the calomel electrode, as the reference electrode. A correction to the measured voltage is applied and the results obtained will then be the same as if the standard hydrogen electrode were used.

The standard hydrogen electrode is therefore a practical, if not a convenient, reference, whereas some references in chemistry are theoretical references, for example the absolute or thermodynamic scale. Zero kelvin is experimentally unobtainable. Absolute zero is not just a reference – it is a fundamental rather than arbitrary point. This fact is not devalued by practical difficulties in making matter at absolute zero as a standard reference, and it could be said that the true standard hydrogen electrode reference is also unobtainable as, in principle, equilibrium takes forever to establish.

Standard thermodynamic conditions are exactly the same – essentially, whether you are measuring $E^\ominus$, $\Delta H^\ominus$ or $\Delta G^\ominus$ it is an energy change and energy always needs an arbitrary zero point.

In thermodynamic data, chemists can choose to tabulate $\Delta H^\ominus_f$ and $S^\ominus$ and use them to calculate $\Delta G^\ominus$ (note that entropy *does* have an absolute reference, albeit hypothetical in practice) or can choose to tabulate $\Delta G^\ominus_f$ taking the elements as zero. It does not matter because chemists are always looking at differences.

In a broader sense, of course, all measurements are arbitrary – they are ratios of a measurement to a defined standard. The basic physical or chemical laws do not change but the values of the constants do. The important issue is not what reference we choose but that it be precisely defined and accepted by scientists.

■ Standard electrode potentials

Standard electrode potentials of metals are measured relative to the standard hydrogen electrode. The redox half-equation for the standard hydrogen electrode is:

$$2H^+(aq) + 2e^- \rightleftharpoons H_2(g) \qquad E^\ominus = 0.00\,V$$

Thus, if the standard half-cell is connected to a standard hydrogen electrode to form a voltaic or electrochemical cell, the measured voltage, called the electromotive force (EMF), is the standard electrode potential of that half-cell.

The standard electrode potential is defined as the potential difference between a standard hydrogen electrode and a metal (the electrode) which is immersed in a solution containing metal ions at $1\,mol\,dm^{-3}$ concentration at 298 K (25 °C) and 100 kPa.

Figure 19.5 shows the arrangement used to measure the standard electrode potential of a zinc half-cell. The electromotive force is −0.76 V.

■ **Figure 19.5**
Measuring the standard electrode potential of a zinc half-cell

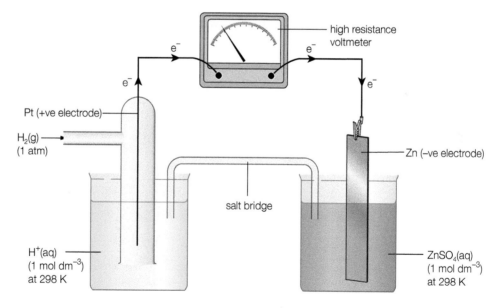

The voltmeter shows that the electrons flow from the zinc electrode to the standard hydrogen electrode in the external circuit. This means that at the zinc electrode, the following reaction occurs:

$$Zn(s) \rightarrow Zn^{2+}(aq) + 2e^-$$

That is, oxidation occurs and the zinc electrode acts as the negative pole, the anode.

Conversely, the hydrogen electrode acts as the positive pole, the cathode, and the reaction of the half-cell is:

$$2H^+(aq) + 2e^- \rightarrow H_2(g)$$

The overall cell reaction is:

$$Zn(s) + 2H^+(aq) \rightarrow Zn^{2+}(aq) + H_2(g)$$

According to IUPAC, the standard electrode potential for the zinc half-cell (Zn^{2+}(aq)/Zn(s)) is -0.76 V. The negative sign is used to show that the electrode is the negative pole if it is connected to a standard hydrogen electrode.

Sign convention

By convention, the oxidized species is written first when a particular half-equation and its standard electrode potential are being referred to. In other words, the half-equation is written as a *reduction* process:

$$\text{oxidized species} + ne^- \rightleftharpoons \text{reduced species}$$

Thus, Ag^+(aq)/Ag(s), $E^\ominus = +0.80$ V means that the silver half-cell reaction has a standard electrode potential of $+0.80$ V.

$$\underset{\text{oxidized species}}{Ag^+(aq)} + e^- \rightarrow \underset{\text{reduced species}}{Ag(s)} \qquad E^\ominus = +0.80 \text{ V}$$

The IB *Chemistry data booklet* contains standard electrode potentials of half-cells recorded in this format in Section 24.

In summary:

- If $E^\ominus > 0$, then *reduction* takes place at the electrode (electrons being used up) when it is connected to the standard hydrogen electrode (Figure 19.6). It is positive because electrons (negatively charged) are a reactant and are being used up. It is the cathode.

- If $E^\ominus < 0$, then *oxidation* takes place at the electrode (electrons being produced) when it is connected to the standard hydrogen electrode (Figure 19.7). It is negative because electrons are being produced on the surface of the electrode. It is the anode.

- The zero value of $E^\ominus$ for the standard hydrogen electrode indicates that the redox equilibrium is at 'perfect' equilibrium ($K_c = 1$): $2H^+$(aq) $+ 2e^- \rightleftharpoons H_2$(g)

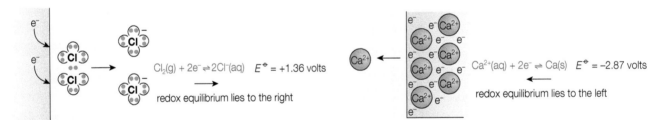

Cl_2(g) $+ 2e^- \rightleftharpoons 2Cl^-$(aq) $E^\ominus = +1.36$ volts

redox equilibrium lies to the right

Ca^{2+}(aq) $+ 2e^- \rightleftharpoons Ca$(s) $E^\ominus = -2.87$ volts

redox equilibrium lies to the left

■ **Figure 19.6** Reduction at the cathode   ■ **Figure 19.7** Oxidation at the anode

Cell potential and the electromotive force

The measurement of the electrode potential must be carried out without any flow of electric current so that the concentrations of the solutions in the half-cells do not change. A change in concentration of the solutions will affect the electrode potential of the half-cell. Hence, a high-resistance voltmeter is used for the measurement of the electromotive force of the electrochemical cell. This means that the current in the external circuit is virtually zero and the electrochemical cell registers its maximum potential difference.

The cell potential is the difference in electrode potentials of the two electrodes when the cell is passing current through the circuit. It is measured by a voltmeter, ideally with a high resistance. It is *less* than the maximum voltage obtainable from the cell (the electromotive force of the cell).

The electromotive force (EMF) is the potential difference between the two terminals of the voltaic cell when no current is flowing, that is, in an open circuit. The EMF is the *maximum* voltage obtainable from the voltaic cell. Strictly speaking, it should only be measured using a potentiometer and not a voltmeter (since voltmeters have a high but finite resistance). However, a good high-resistance voltmeter will give a value very close to the EMF.

The electrochemical series

The standard electrode potentials for some common metals are given in Table 19.1. Note that the half-cell reactions are written as *reduction* processes: the metal ions are gaining electrons. The standard electrode potentials are therefore sometimes known as standard reduction potentials. This arrangement of metals (and hydrogen) in order of decreasing standard electrode potential is known as the electrochemical series. It is very similar in arrangement to the activity series (Chapter 9).

Metals towards the top of the electrochemical series, that is, those metals with large *negative* electrode potentials, are very reactive and readily give up electrons in solution. In other words, they are powerful *reducing* agents: they have the greatest tendency to form positive ions in aqueous solution.

Towards the bottom of the electrochemical series the metals become progressively weaker reducing agents, *but* conversely their oxidizing power increases. Unreactive metals at the very bottom of the electrochemical series behave as weak oxidizing agents (Figure 19.8).

■ **Table 19.1** Standard electrode potentials for some common metals (all data taken from the IB *Chemistry data booklet*)

Oxidized species	$\rightleftharpoons$	Reduced species	$E^{\ominus}/V$
$Li^+(aq) + e^-$	$\rightleftharpoons$	$Li(s)$	−3.04
$K^+(aq) + e^-$	$\rightleftharpoons$	$K(s)$	−2.93
$Ca^{2+}(aq) + 2e^-$	$\rightleftharpoons$	$Ca(s)$	−2.87
$Na^+(aq) + e^-$	$\rightleftharpoons$	$Na(s)$	−2.71
$Mg^{2+}(aq) + 2e^-$	$\rightleftharpoons$	$Mg(s)$	−2.37
$Al^{3+}(aq) + 3e^-$	$\rightleftharpoons$	$Al(s)$	−1.66
$Mn^{2+}(aq) + 2e^-$	$\rightleftharpoons$	$Mn(s)$	−1.18
$Zn^{2+}(aq) + 2e^-$	$\rightleftharpoons$	$Zn(s)$	−0.76
$Fe^{2+}(aq) + 2e^-$	$\rightleftharpoons$	$Fe(s)$	−0.45
$Ni^{2+}(aq) + 2e^-$	$\rightleftharpoons$	$Ni(s)$	−0.26
$Sn^{2+}(aq) + 2e^-$	$\rightleftharpoons$	$Sn(s)$	−0.14
$Pb^{2+}(aq) + 2e^-$	$\rightleftharpoons$	$Pb(s)$	−0.13
$H^+(aq) + e^-$	$\rightleftharpoons$	$\frac{1}{2}H_2(g)$	0.00
$Cu^{2+}(aq) + 2e^-$	$\rightleftharpoons$	$Cu(s)$	+0.34
$Cu^+(aq) + e^-$	$\rightleftharpoons$	$Cu(s)$	+0.52
$Ag^+(aq) + e^-$	$\rightleftharpoons$	$Ag(s)$	+0.80

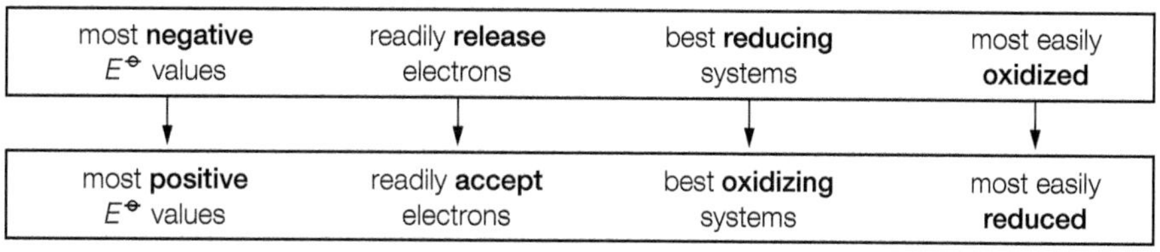

■ **Figure 19.8** Summary of the trends in the electrochemical series

most **negative** $E^{\ominus}$ values	readily **release** electrons	best **reducing** systems	most easily **oxidized**

↓

most **positive** $E^{\ominus}$ values	readily **accept** electrons	best **oxidizing** systems	most easily **reduced**

Worked example

Use the standard electrode potentials on page 23 of the IB *Chemistry data booklet* to arrange the following oxidizing agents in increasing order of oxidizing strength (under standard conditions):

Potassium manganate(VII) (in acidic solution)

Iodine

Iron(III) ions

Oxygen (in acidic solution)

1 Use the standard electrode potentials in Section 24 of the IB *Chemistry data booklet* to arrange the following species in decreasing order of reducing strength (under standard conditions):
Zinc atoms
Iodide ions
Acidified sulfate(VI) ions
Lead(II) ions

The standard electrode potentials are:

$MnO_4^-(aq) + 8H^+(aq) + 5e^- \rightarrow Mn^{2+}(aq) + 4H_2O(l)$ $E^\ominus = +1.51\,V$

$Fe^{3+}(aq) + e^- \rightarrow Fe^{2+}(aq)$ $E^\ominus = +0.77\,V$

$\frac{1}{2}I_2(s) + e^- \rightarrow I^-(aq)$ $E^\ominus = +0.54\,V$

$\frac{1}{2}O_2(g) + 2H^+(aq) + 2e^- \rightarrow H_2O(l)$ $E^\ominus = +1.23\,V$

Oxidizing agents undergo reduction (gain of electrons). The more positive the value of the standard electrode potential, the greater the oxidizing power of the chemical species on the left-hand side of the reduction potential.

Hence, the order of increasing oxidizing power (under standard conditions) is:
iodine, iron(III) ions, oxygen (in acidic solution) and potassium manganate(VII) (in acidic solution).

The reactivity series versus the electrochemical series

Note that the activity series (Chapter 9) and the electrochemical series, although they are very similar, are based upon different branches of chemistry. The activity series is derived from *kinetic* studies and the electrochemical series is based upon *thermodynamic* measurements.

The activity series is based upon the reactivities of the pure metals with water, dilute acid or metals ions: the faster the reaction, the more reactive the metal. In contrast, the electrochemical series is based upon the measurement of potentials (voltage – a thermodynamic quantity) of metals against a standard reference electrode (the SHE).

There is not necessarily a correlation between kinetics ('how fast') and thermodynamics ('how far'), although there happens to be one for many metals and their reactions. Hence the order of metals in the electrochemical and activity series is very similar.

The distinction between the activity series and the electrochemical series can be illustrated by adding lithium and potassium to water. Lithium reacts more slowly with water than potassium does, despite the former having a more negative electrode potential. The reaction between lithium and water to form lithium ions is more thermodynamically favourable than that between potassium and water, but the reaction is slower.

The standard electrode potentials for active metals, such as calcium and sodium, are not measured experimentally since they undergo a direct reaction with water to release hydrogen. The values of their electrode potentials are calculated indirectly using Hess's law.

Predicting cell reactions and voltages

Predictions of cell potentials for spontaneous reactions of any combination of metals and their ions can be easily calculated. The two half-cells are both written as reduction potentials. However, it is not possible for both reactions to accept electrons: one half-cell must be reversed so it releases electrons. The half-cell that is always reversed is the one with *more negative* (or least positive) electrode potential. The cell potential is then the sum of the electrode potentials (including their signs).

Worked example

A voltaic cell is constructed using magnesium and copper electrodes. Deduce the cell potential for the spontaneous reaction.

The electrode potentials are:
$Mg^{2+}(aq) + 2e^- \rightarrow Mg(s)$ $E^\ominus = -2.37\,V$
$Cu^{2+}(aq) + 2e^- \rightarrow Cu(s)$ $E^\ominus = +0.34\,V$

The magnesium half-cell has the more negative electrode potential, hence the equation and the sign of the electrode potential are reversed:
$Mg(s) \rightarrow Mg^{2+}(aq) + 2e^-$ $E^\ominus = +2.37\,V$
$Cu^{2+}(aq) + 2e^- \rightarrow Cu(s)$ $E^\ominus = +0.34\,V$

The two half-equations are added and the electrons cancelled to generate the ionic equation for the spontaneous reaction:

$$Mg(s) + Cu^{2+}(aq) \rightarrow Mg^{2+}(aq) + Cu(s)$$

$$E^{\ominus}_{cell} = (2.37\,V) + (0.34\,V) = +2.71\,V$$

Note that this is a larger voltage than that obtained from the Daniell cell (1.10V). In general, the larger the difference in positions between metals in the electrochemical series, the greater the voltage produced by them in a voltaic cell.

This voltage is only obtained under standard conditions, that is, when 1 mol dm⁻³ solutions are used at a temperature of 25 °C and 100 kPa. Changing the conditions will alter the voltage and maybe even the direction of the reaction.

The magnesium electrode acts as the cathode and the copper electrode acts as the anode. Reduction always takes place at the cathode and oxidation always takes place at the anode in any electrochemical cell (both voltaic and electrolytic cells).

2 A voltaic cell is made from a Co²⁺(aq)/Co(s) half-cell and a Cu²⁺(aq)/Cu(s) half-cell. The cell potential was +0.62 V, with the copper half-cell positive. Calculate the standard electrode potential of the cobalt half-cell.

Calculating cell potentials using standard electrode potentials

A slightly different, but equivalent, approach to determining the cell potential of a voltaic cell involves subtracting the standard electrode potentials:

$$E^{\ominus}_{cell} = E^{\ominus}_{C} - E^{\ominus}_{A}$$

where $E^{\ominus}_{C}$ = E of the cathode (reduction) and $E^{\ominus}_{A}$ = E of the anode (oxidation). The $E^{\ominus}$ values used must be 'as given' in the IB *Chemistry data booklet*: do *not* change the sign. The electrode with the more positive $E^{\ominus}$ value is more oxidizing and so will undergo reduction, i.e. the half-cell is on the right. (This is the approach adopted by the IUPAC.)

The other approach, described previously, is to find the two half-equations in the IB *Chemistry data booklet*. They are always written as *reduction* potentials. Reverse the half-equation with the *more negative* (or *less positive*) electrode potential and add it to the other half-equation. Since the half-equation is reversed, the sign must be reversed (cf. Hess's law in energetics). The number of electrons in the two half-equations must be adjusted so that they can be added together.

The standard electrode potential of a half-cell is *not* changed if the stoichiometry is changed. The voltage is a measure of the energy of an electron. Current is a measure of the number of electrons that flow past a point. The voltage of a simple voltaic cell does not depend on the amounts of chemicals used.

3 Calculate cell potentials and write ionic equations for voltaic cells made from the following half-cells:
a Fe²⁺(aq)/Fe(s) and Ni²⁺(aq)/Ni(s)
b I₂(s)/I⁻(aq) and MnO₄⁻(aq)/Mn²⁺(aq)
c F₂(aq)/F⁻(aq) and Cr₂O₇²⁻(aq)/Cr³⁺(aq)
d Cu²⁺(aq)/Cu(s) and Ag⁺(aq)/Ag(s)

Nature of Science

Employing quantitative reasoning – electrode potentials and the standard hydrogen electrode

A reaction in which there is a transfer of electron(s) from one species to another is called a redox reaction. Any redox reaction can be represented as the difference of two half-reactions. The overall chemical reaction taking place in an electrochemical is described in terms of two half-equations which describe the chemical changes that occur at the two electrodes. Each half-equation corresponds to the potential difference at the corresponding electrode. Oxidation occurs at the anode and reduction occurs at the cathode.

By convention the half-equations in each half-cell are written as reductions. For example:

Anode:

$$H^+(aq) + e^- \rightarrow \tfrac{1}{2}H_2(g) \qquad E^{\ominus} = 0.00\,V$$

Cathode:

$$Cu^{2+}(aq) + 2e^- \rightarrow Cu(s) \qquad E^{\ominus} = +0.34\,V$$

The potential of the cell can be calculated from the following expression:

$$E^{\ominus}_{cell} = E^{\ominus}_{C} - E^{\ominus}_{A}$$

$$E^{\ominus}_{cell} = (+0.34\,V) - (0.00\,V) = +0.34\,V$$

The overall reaction of the cell is:

$$Cu^{2+}(aq) + 2H^+(aq) \rightarrow Cu(s) + H_2(g)$$

A positive $E^{\ominus}_{cell}$ value implies that the reaction is favoured thermodynamically. This reaction will proceed as shown: the copper(II) ions are reduced and the hydrogen ions are oxidized (under standard conditions). Copper(II) ions are a good electron acceptor or oxidizing agent relative to the standard hydrogen electrode.

Under standard conditions the $E^{\ominus}_{cell}$ is determined relative to the standard hydrogen electrode. Hydrogen ions at $1\,mol\,dm^{-3}$ (actually unity activity) are in equilibrium with hydrogen gas at one atmosphere and 298 K. The equilibrium potential is detected with a platinum electrode that is coated with fine black (finely divided platinum) to enlarge the effective surface area. The potentials of electrodes are compared to the standard hydrogen electrode, where the standard hydrogen electrode is at the anode and the second electrode is at the cathode.

Cell diagrams

Electrochemical or voltaic cells can be represented by cell diagrams. For example, the Daniell cell is represented as

$$Zn(s) \mid Zn^{2+}(aq) \mid\mid Cu^{2+}(aq) \mid Cu(s)$$

The double line in the centre of the cell diagram represents the salt bridge while the single lines represent so-called phase boundaries between the metal electrodes and their ions. It has been agreed that the electrode with the more positive (or less negative) standard electrode potential is placed on the right-hand side of the diagram.

For this cell the electrode potentials are:

$$Zn^{2+}(aq) + 2e^- \rightarrow Zn(s) \qquad E^{\ominus} = -0.76\,V$$
$$Cu^{2+}(aq) + 2e^- \rightarrow Cu(s) \qquad E^{\ominus} = +0.34\,V$$

If this convention is followed then the cell potential or voltage can be calculated using the following equation:

$$E^{\ominus}_{cell} = E^{\ominus}(RH\ electrode) - E^{\ominus}(LH\ electrode)$$

Hence for the Daniell cell:

$$E^{\ominus}_{cell} = (0.34\,V) - (-0.76\,V) = +1.10\,V$$

A positive value for a cell potential indicates that the cell reaction is thermodynamically spontaneous under standard thermodynamic conditions; in other words, 'it will go'.

The cell reaction that corresponds to this voltage is easily found by replacing the | symbols with arrows and then balancing with electrons:

$$Zn(s) \mid Zn^{2+}(aq) \mid\mid Cu^{2+}(aq) \mid Cu(s)$$

$$Zn(s) \rightarrow Zn^{2+}(aq) + 2e^- \quad and \quad 2e^- + Cu^{2+}(aq) \rightarrow Cu(s)$$

or

$$Zn(s) + Cu^{2+}(aq) \rightarrow Zn^{2+}(aq) + Cu(s)$$

(Cell potentials are related to values of Gibb's free energy changes, $\Delta G^{\ominus}$ (Chapter 15).)

Utilization: Electrochemical processes in dentistry

Dentists need to consider the possibility of redox reactions when placing gold caps over teeth next to teeth with mercury amalgam fillings. An amalgam (Figure 19.9) is an alloy containing mercury. Atmospheric oxygen oxidizes some of the gold cap to gold(III) ions. Since the metals, such as tin, in the amalgam are more active than gold (higher up the activity series), contact between the amalgam fillings and the gold(III) ions results in the following replacement reaction occurring:

$$3Sn(s) + 2Au^{3+}(aq) \rightarrow 3Sn^{2+}(aq) + 2Au(s)$$

This can be described by the following cell diagram:

$$Sn(s) \mid Au^{3+}(aq) \mid\mid Sn^{2+}(aq) \mid Au(s)$$

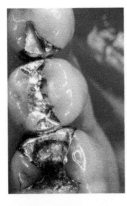

■ **Figure 19.9** Dental amalgam filling

As a result of this electrochemical cell, the dental fillings slowly dissolve and the patients are left with a constant metallic taste in their mouth.

■ Non-standard conditions

Electrode potential values can only be used to predict the feasibility of a redox reaction under *standard conditions*. Electrode potentials for oxidizing agents in acidic conditions refer to $1.0 \, mol \, dm^{-3}$ concentrations of hydrogen ions, $H^+(aq)$ (pH = 0). Increasing the $H^+(aq)$ concentration increases the oxidizing strength of the oxidizing agent, thus increasing the electrode potential of the half-cell.

Consider the following reaction:

$$MnO_2(s) + 4H^+(aq) + 2Cl^-(aq) \rightarrow Mn^{2+}(aq) + 2H_2O(l) + Cl_2(g)$$
$$E^{\ominus}_{cell} = 1.23 - (+1.36) \text{ or } (1.23 + (-1.36)) = -0.13 \, V$$

Since the cell potential, $E^{\ominus}_{cell}$, is negative, the reaction is *not* spontaneous under standard conditions. However, when *concentrated* hydrochloric acid is heated with manganese(IV) oxide, the cell potential becomes positive and the reaction can occur, and it can oxidize chloride ions. This is the standard laboratory preparation of chlorine. An additional factor is the shifting of the equilibrium to the right by the loss of chlorine gas.

In general, for a redox equilibrium:

$$Ox + ne^- \rightleftharpoons Red$$

increasing the concentration of the oxidized species, [Ox], or decreasing the concentration of the reduced species, [Red], will shift the position of the equilibrium to the right, reducing the number of electrons transferred and hence making the cell potential more positive. Similarly, the cell potential will become more negative if the concentration of the oxidized species, [Ox], is decreased or the concentration of the reduced species, [Red], is increased. These shifts can all be predicted from an application of Le Châtelier's principle (Chapter 7).

A Daniell cell consists of a zinc half-cell connected to a copper half-cell. Under standard conditions, electrons spontaneously flow from the zinc electrode to the copper electrode. The cell potential is 1.10 V. However, if the concentration of zinc ions in the zinc half-cell is decreased, then the equilibrium

$$Zn^{2+}(aq) + 2e^- \rightleftharpoons Zn(s) \qquad E^{\ominus} = -0.76 \, V$$

is shifted to the left and the negative charge on the electrode is increased. This also can be predicted from Le Châtelier's principle: the removal of zinc ions will cause some of the zinc atoms to ionize and replace the zinc ions. This will increase the voltage of the Daniell cell to a value above 1.10 V.

If the concentration of zinc ions in the half-cell of the Daniell cell is increased, then the equilibrium is shifted to the right and the negative charge on the electrode is decreased: the addition of zinc ions will cause some of the zinc ions to gain electrons. This will decrease the voltage of the Daniell cell to a value below 1.10 V.

The Nernst equation

The Nernst equation (see Chapter 24 on the accompanying website) allows chemists to calculate the cell potentials of non-standard half-cells, where the concentrations of ions are *not* $1 \, mol \, dm^{-3}$. The mathematical relationship between the electrode potential and the concentration of aqueous ions is known as the Nernst equation. It describes the relationship between cell potential and concentration (at constant temperature). It also describes the relationship between cell potential and temperature (at constant concentration).

For the general case of a metal/metal ion system:

$$M^{n+}(aq) + ne^- \rightleftharpoons M(s)$$

$$E_{cell} = E^{\ominus} + \frac{2.3RT}{nF} \log_{10} \frac{[M^{n+}(aq)]}{[M(s)]}$$

where R represents the gas constant ($8.31 \, J \, mol^{-1} \, K^{-1}$), F the Faraday constant (the product of the charge on an electron and the Avogadro constant), T the absolute temperature (in kelvins) and n the number of electrons transferred. The value of the Faraday constant is $96\,500 \, C \, mol^{-1}$, so at $T = 298 \, K$, $2.3RT/F = 0.059$. Since the 'concentration' of a solid is constant (taken as unity, 1) the expression can be simplified to:

$$E_{cell} = E^{\ominus} + \frac{0.059}{n} \log_{10}[M^{n+}(aq)] \text{ (if the electrode is solid, [M] = 1)}$$

which implies a logarithmic relationship between cell potential and concentration.

$$E_{cell} = E^\ominus + \frac{2.3RT}{nF} \log_{10} \frac{[\text{oxidized form}]}{[\text{reduced form}]}$$

is a generalized form of the Nernst equation that can be used to calculate the cell potentials of voltaic cells under non-standard conditions.

Worked example

Use the Nernst equation to calculate the cell potential at 298 K of a Daniell cell where the zinc ion concentration is 0.005 mol dm^{-3} and the copper(II) ion concentration is 1.5 mol dm^{-3}.

$$E_{cell} = 1.10 - \frac{0.059}{2} \log_{10} \frac{0.005}{1.5} = (1.10\,V) - (-0.07\,V) = +1.17\,V$$

Concentration cells

Concentration cells are voltaic cells that have electrodes of the same element (typically a metal), but different concentrations of the electrolyte in the cathode and the anode. The potential difference across the two electrodes is developed because of the difference in the concentrations of electrolytes.

The cell potential can be calculated by applying the Nernst equation:

$$E = E^\ominus + \frac{0.059}{n} \log_{10} \frac{C_2}{C_1}$$

where C_2 and C_1 represent the concentrations of electrolyte in the half-cells containing the anode and cathode. For the concentration cell to exhibit a positive voltage, C_2 must be greater than C_1.

---

4   Calculate the EMF of the following voltaic cell:

$Ag(s) \mid Ag^+(aq)\ (0.001\,mol\,dm^{-3}) \parallel Ag^+(aq) \mid Ag(s)\ (0.100\,mol\,dm^{-3})$

$E^\ominus = Ag^+(aq)/Ag(s) = +0.80\,V.$

■ **Table 19.2** Part of the redox series for metals at 298 K (25 °C)

Electrode reaction	$E^\ominus$/V
$H^+(aq) + e^- \rightarrow \frac{1}{2}H_2(g)$	0.00
$Cu^{2+}(aq) + 2e^- \rightarrow Cu(s)$	+0.34
$Cu^+(aq) + e^- \rightarrow Cu(s)$	+0.52
$Fe^{3+}(aq) + e^- \rightarrow Fe^{2+}(aq)$	+0.77
$Ag^+(aq) + e^- \rightarrow Ag(s)$	+0.80

■ The redox series

The electrochemical series has been extended to give the redox series (Table 19.2), which includes the standard electrode potentials of redox systems in which transition metals are present in different oxidation states.

$$Fe^{3+}(aq) + e^- \rightarrow Fe^{2+}(aq)$$

is the half-equation for a half-cell formed by dipping a platinum wire into an aqueous solution containing a mixture of 1 mol dm^{-3} iron(II) ions and 1 mol dm^{-3} iron(III) ions (Figure 19.10). Electrical contact is made with the mixture of two ions by means of the platinum wire, which acts as an *inert* conductor. As with all half-cells, a redox equilibrium is established:

$$Fe^{2+}(aq) \rightarrow Fe^{3+}(aq) + e^-$$

and

$$Fe^{3+}(aq) + e^- \rightarrow Fe^{2+}(aq)$$

or

$$Fe^{2+}(aq) \rightleftharpoons Fe^{3+}(aq) + e^-$$

Electrons produced by the forward reaction are transferred to the surface of the platinum, making it negatively charged, whereas the backward reaction removes electrons from the surface of the platinum wire. The resultant charge therefore depends on the relative balance between these two opposing processes.

■ **Figure 19.10** The half-cell system used to measure the standard electrode potential for the Fe^{3+}(aq)/Fe^{2+}(aq) system

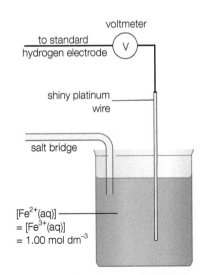

voltmeter
to standard hydrogen electrode
V
shiny platinum wire
salt bridge
[Fe^{2+}(aq)]
= [Fe^{3+}(aq)]
= 1.00 mol dm^{-3}

Worked example

Calculate the cell potential for a voltaic cell constructed from the following half-cells

$Fe^{3+}(aq)/Fe^{2+}(aq)$ and $Ag^+(aq)/Ag(s)$

$Fe^{3+}(aq) + e^- \rightarrow Fe^{2+}(aq)$ $E^\ominus = +0.77\,V$

$Ag+(aq) + e^- \rightarrow Ag(s)$ $E^\ominus = +0.80\,V$

The iron(III)/iron(II) half-cell is the least positive, so the half-equation and the sign of the electrode potential are reversed:

$Fe^{2+}(aq) \rightarrow Fe^{3+}(aq) + e^-$ $E^\ominus = -0.77\,V$

$Ag^+(aq) + e^- \rightarrow Ag(s)$ $E^\ominus = +0.80\,V$

The silver half-cell half-equation is multiplied through by 2 before it is added to the iron(III)/iron(II) half-equation. This is done to make the number of electrons equal, so they cancel to generate the ionic equation:

$2Ag^+(aq) + Fe^{2+}(aq) \rightarrow Fe^{3+}(aq) + 2Ag(s)$

The cell potential is then the sum of the electrode potentials (including their signs):

$E^\ominus_{cell} = (-0.77\,V) + (0.80\,V) = +0.03\,V$

Note that the standard electrode potential is not doubled when the stoichiometry is doubled. The standard electrode potential is an example of an intensive property, that is, it is independent of quantity or amount. Density and boiling point are other examples of intensive properties. This is in contrast to extensive properties, for example, mass and volume, which do depend on quantity or amount. The redox series can be extended to include the standard electrode potentials of non-metals and ions (Table 19.3).

■ **Table 19.3** The redox series

Oxidized species	$\rightleftharpoons$	Reduced species	$E^\ominus/V$
$Li^+(aq) + e^-$	$\rightleftharpoons$	$Li(s)$	−3.04
$K^+(aq) + e^-$	$\rightleftharpoons$	$K(s)$	−2.93
$Ca^{2+}(aq) + 2e^-$	$\rightleftharpoons$	$Ca(s)$	−2.87
$Na^+(aq) + e^-$	$\rightleftharpoons$	$Na(s)$	−2.71
$Mg^{2+}(aq) + 2e^-$	$\rightleftharpoons$	$Mg(s)$	−2.37
$Al^{3+}(aq) + 3e^-$	$\rightleftharpoons$	$Al(s)$	−1.66
$Mn^{2+}(aq) + 2e^-$	$\rightleftharpoons$	$Mn(s)$	−1.18
$H_2O(l) + e^-$	$\rightleftharpoons$	$\frac{1}{2}H_2(g) + OH^-(aq)$	−0.83
$Zn^{2+}(aq) + 2e^-$	$\rightleftharpoons$	$Zn(s)$	−0.76
$Fe^{2+}(aq) + 2e^-$	$\rightleftharpoons$	$Fe(s)$	−0.45
$Ni^{2+}(aq) + 2e^-$	$\rightleftharpoons$	$Ni(s)$	−0.26
$Sn^{2+}(aq) + 2e^-$	$\rightleftharpoons$	$Sn(s)$	−0.14
$Pb^{2+}(aq) + 2e^-$	$\rightleftharpoons$	$Pb(s)$	−0.13
$H^+(aq) + e^-$	$\rightleftharpoons$	$\frac{1}{2}H_2(g)$	0.00
$Cu^{2+}(aq) + e^-$	$\rightleftharpoons$	$Cu^+(aq)$	+0.15
$SO_4^{2-}(aq) + 4H^+(aq) + 2e^-$	$\rightleftharpoons$	$H_2SO_3(aq) + H_2O(l)$	+0.17
$Cu^{2+}(aq) + 2e^-$	$\rightleftharpoons$	$Cu(s)$	+0.34
$\frac{1}{2}O_2(g) + H_2O(l) + 2e^-$	$\rightleftharpoons$	$2OH^-(aq)$	+0.40
$Cu^+(aq) + e^-$	$\rightleftharpoons$	$Cu(s)$	+0.52
$\frac{1}{2}I_2(s) + e^-$	$\rightleftharpoons$	$I^-(aq)$	+0.54
$Fe^{3+}(aq) + e^-$	$\rightleftharpoons$	$Fe^{2+}(aq)$	+0.77
$Ag^+(aq) + e^-$	$\rightleftharpoons$	$Ag(s)$	+0.80
$\frac{1}{2}Br_2(l) + e^-$	$\rightleftharpoons$	$Br^-(aq)$	+1.09
$\frac{1}{2}O_2(g) + 2H^+(aq) + 2e^-$	$\rightleftharpoons$	$H_2O(l)$	+1.23
$Cr_2O_7^{2-}(aq) + 14H^+(aq) + 6e^-$	$\rightleftharpoons$	$2Cr^{3+}(aq) + 7H_2O(l)$	+1.36
$\frac{1}{2}Cl_2(g) + e^-$	$\rightleftharpoons$	$Cl^-(aq)$	+1.36
$MnO_4^-(aq) + 8H^+(aq) + 5e^-$	$\rightleftharpoons$	$Mn^{2+}(aq) + 4H_2O(l)$	+1.51
$\frac{1}{2}F_2(g) + e^-$	$\rightleftharpoons$	$F^-(aq)$	+2.87

Worked example

Use the electrode potential data below to write equations for the two half-reactions that occur if the half-cells are connected. Write a balanced equation for the overall reaction and hence predict the reaction, if any, when chlorine gas is bubbled into aqueous chromium(III) ions.

$$6e^- + Cr_2O_7^{2-}(aq) + 14H^+(aq) \rightarrow 2Cr^{3+}(aq) + 7H_2O(l) \qquad E = +1.36\,V$$

$$\tfrac{1}{2}Cl_2(aq) + e^- \rightarrow Cl^-(aq) \qquad E = +1.39\,V$$

The dichromate(VI)/chromium(III) half-cell is the least positive, so the half-equation and the sign of the electrode potential are reversed:

$$2Cr^{3+}(aq) + 7H_2O(l) \rightarrow 6e^- + Cr_2O_7^{2-}(aq) + 14H^+(aq) \qquad E = -1.36\,V$$

$$\tfrac{1}{2}Cl_2(aq) + e^- \rightarrow Cl^-(aq) \qquad E = +1.39\,V$$

The chlorine/chloride half-cell half-equation is multiplied through by 6 before it is added to the dichromate(VI)/chromium(III) half-equation.

The cell potential is then the sum of the electrode potentials (including their signs):

$$E_{cell} = (-1.36\,V) + (1.39\,V) = +0.03\,V$$

The E_{cell} is positive, so the reaction can take place:

$$2Cr^{3+}(aq) + 7H_2O(l) + 3Cl_2(g) \rightarrow Cr_2O_7^{2-}(aq) + 14H^+(aq) + 6Cl^-(aq)$$

Utilization: Rusting of metals

The rusting of iron and steel is an important redox reaction. The overall reaction involves the formation of hydrated iron(III) oxide from iron, water and oxygen. However, the first step of the reaction involves the formation of iron(II) hydroxide and can be derived from the following half-equations:

$$Fe^{2+}(aq) + 2e^- \rightarrow Fe(s) \qquad E^\ominus = -0.45\,V$$

$$\tfrac{1}{2}O_2(g) + H_2O(l) + 2e^- \rightarrow 2OH^-(aq) \qquad E^\ominus = +0.40\,V$$

We apply the rule that the more negative half-cell gives up electrons. Hence the iron half-cell is written as an oxidation process (the sign of the electrode potential is reversed) and added to the other half-cell:

$$Fe(s) \rightarrow Fe^{2+}(aq) + 2e^- \qquad E^\ominus = +0.45\,V$$

$$\tfrac{1}{2}O_2(g) + H_2O(l) + 2e^- \rightarrow 2OH^-(aq) \qquad E^\ominus = +0.40\,V$$

$$\tfrac{1}{2}O_2(g) + H_2O(l) + Fe(s) \rightarrow Fe^{2+}(aq) + 2OH^-(aq)$$

$$E^\ominus_{cell} = 0.45\,V + 0.40\,V = +0.85\,V$$

In this process the iron metal is oxidized to iron(II) ions at the centre of a water drop, where the oxygen concentration is low (due to slow diffusion), and the electrons released reduce the oxygen molecules at the surface of the water, where the oxygen concentration is high (Figure 19.11). The iron(II) and hydroxide ions formed diffuse away from the surface of the iron object. Further oxidation by dissolved oxygen in the air results in the formation of rust, hydrated iron(III) oxide.

■ **Figure 19.11**
Summary of the rusting
process

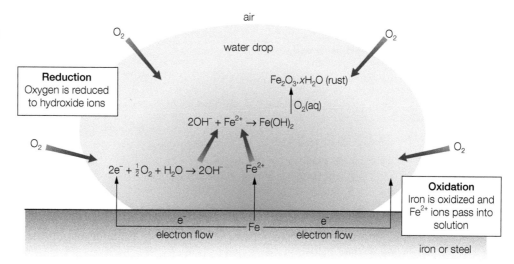

■ Cell spontaneity

An electrochemical cell, such as the Daniell cell, operates by the oxidation reaction producing electrons in the zinc anode, which are then 'pulled round' the external circuit (wires, bulbs, voltmeter, etc.) by the reduction reaction at the copper cathode. As long as the overall reaction is *not* at equilibrium, the oxidation reaction 'pushes' electrons into the external circuit, and the reduction reaction 'pulls' them out. The cell is described as doing work since it produces a force that moves electrons around the external circuit. This work can light a bulb, drive an electric motor, etc.

The amount of work done by an electrochemical cell depends on the cell potential or voltage between its two electrodes: the greater the cell potential, the greater the amount of work the cell can do. A cell in which the overall reaction is at equilibrium can do no work and its cell potential or voltage, as well as its current, are zero.

The maximum amount of electrical work that can be done by an electrochemical cell is equal to the Gibb's free energy change (Chapter 15), $\Delta G^\ominus$ (provided the temperature and pressure remain constant). The equation below gives the exact relationship between the Gibb's free energy and the cell potential:

$$\Delta G^\ominus = -nFE^\ominus_{cell}$$

where n represents the amount of electrons (in moles) transferred between the electrodes for the given equation, F represents the Faraday constant ($96\,500\,C\,mol^{-1}$), the amount of electrical charge carried by one mole of electrons, and $E^\ominus_{cell}$ represents the cell potential or voltage of the cell.

For example, in the Daniell cell, the cell reaction is

$$Zn(s) + Cu^{2+}(aq) \rightarrow Zn^{2+}(aq) + Cu(s)$$

and n is 2 because 2 moles of electrons are transferred from the zinc atoms to the copper(II) ions in the above equation.

$$Zn(s) + 2e^- \rightarrow Zn^{2+}(aq); \qquad Cu^{2+}(aq) \rightarrow Cu(s) + 2e^-$$

$$\Delta G^\ominus = -nFE^\ominus$$
$$= -2 \times 96\,500\,C\,mol^{-1} \times 1.1\,V$$
$$= 212\,300\,J\,mol^{-1}$$
$$= -212\,kJ\,mol^{-1}$$

This relatively large negative value for $\Delta G^\ominus$ means that the reaction is thermodynamically *spontaneous* and will take place under standard thermodynamic conditions (namely, $100\,kPa$ pressure, $298\,K$ ($25\,°C$) and both solutions with a concentration of $1\,mol\,dm^{-3}$).

By contrast, if we apply Hess's law (Chapter 5), the reverse reaction has an equally large, but positive, value for $\Delta G^{\ominus}$ and is not thermodynamically spontaneous under standard conditions. In other words, 'it will not go'.

$$Zn^{2+}(aq) + Cu(s) \rightarrow Zn(s) + Cu^{2+}(aq) \qquad \Delta G^{\ominus} = +212 \, kJ \, mol^{-1}$$

For any chemical reaction at equilibrium ΔG is zero, so

$$Zn(s) + Cu^{2+}(aq) \rightleftharpoons Zn^{2+}(aq) + Cu(s) \qquad \Delta G = 0 \, kJ \, mol^{-1}$$

Here, the concentration of $Cu^{2+}(aq)$ will be well below $1 \, mol \, dm^{-3}$ and the concentration of $Zn^{2+}(aq)$ will be much higher; that is, the system has shifted far enough to the right-hand side to reduce E_{cell} and ΔG to zero.

Predicting whether a reaction is spontaneous or not using $E^{\ominus}$ values

The standard free energy changes ($\Delta G^{\ominus}$) can be determining by using standard electrode potentials. Table 19.4 summarizes the relationship between $\Delta G^{\ominus}$ and $E^{\ominus}$.

■ **Table 19.4** Summary of the relationship between $\Delta G^{\ominus}$ and $E^{\ominus}$

$\Delta G^{\ominus}$	$E^{\ominus}$	Reaction under standard thermodynamic conditions
Negative	Positive	Forward reaction is spontaneous, formation of products favoured, $K_c > 1$
Positive	Negative	Forward reaction is non-spontaneous, formation of reactants favoured, $K_c < 1$
Zero	Zero	Reactants and products favoured equally, $K_c = 1$

5 Use the standard electrode potentials given in Table 19.3 (page 655) to calculate the $E^{\ominus}$ and $\Delta G^{\ominus}$ values for the following reaction:

$$4Ag(s) + O_2(g) + 4H^+(aq) \rightarrow 4Ag^+(aq) + 2H_2O(l)$$

State whether the reaction is spontaneous under standard conditions.

6 Calculate and comment on the values of $E^{\ominus}$ and $\Delta G^{\ominus}$ for the related reaction:

$$2Ag(s) + \tfrac{1}{2}O_2(g) + 2H^+(aq) \rightarrow 2Ag^+(aq) + H_2O(l)$$

Kinetically unfavourable reactions

Electrode potentials, when used to predict the feasibility of a reaction, give *no* indication of the kinetics or rate of the reaction. A positive $E^{\ominus}_{cell}$ value suggests that the reaction is possible from energy considerations under standard conditions only. However, the reaction may be so slow that it effectively does not occur. This may be due to the reaction having a high activation energy. Such a reaction, which has a positive $E^{\ominus}_{cell}$ but yet occurs very slowly, is said to be energetically favourable but kinetically unfavourable. Consider the following reaction:

$$H_2(g) + Cu^{2+}(aq) \rightarrow Cu(s) + 2H^+(aq) \qquad E^{\ominus}_{cell} = +0.34 \, V$$

The positive value suggests that hydrogen gas should displace copper from copper(II) salts in solution under standard conditions. In practice, the rate of reaction is so slow that the reaction is kinetically non-feasible. This is because a relatively large amount of energy is needed to break the strong hydrogen–hydrogen covalent bond before the reaction can start.

Microbial fuel cells

A microbial fuel cell (MFC) or biological fuel cell is a biochemical system that drives a current by using and copying bacterial interactions found in nature. It is a device that converts chemical energy to electrical energy by the catalytic reaction of micro-organisms, usually bacteria.

MFCs can be classified into two groups: those that use a mediator and those that do not. The first MFCs used a mediator, a chemical that transfers electrons from bacteria in the cell to the anode. Mediators include humic acid, methylene blue and thionine. Many mediators are toxic and expensive. In MFCs without mediators the bacteria have electron transfer proteins, such as cytochromes, on their outer membrane that can transfer electrons directly to the anode.

■ **Figure 19.12**
A generalized microbial
fuel cell

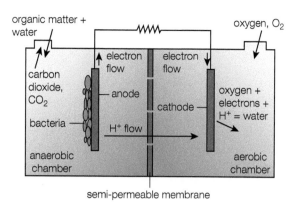

A typical MFC (Figure 19.12) consists of anode and cathode compartments separated by a cation-specific membrane. In the anode compartment, fuel is oxidized by micro-organisms, generating carbon dioxide, electrons and protons. Electrons are transferred to the cathode compartment through an external electrical circuit, while protons are transferred to the cathode compartment through the membrane. Electrons and protons combine with oxygen in the cathode compartment to form water molecules.

When micro-organisms respire in aerobic conditions they produce carbon dioxide and water. However, when oxygen is not present, they produce carbon dioxide, protons and electrons, as described below for the respiration of sucrose:

$$C_{12}H_{22}O_{11} + 13H_2O \rightarrow 12CO_2 + 48H^+ + 48e^-$$

Microbial fuel cells use inorganic mediators to access the electron transport chain of the cells and accept electrons. The mediator crosses the outer cell membrane and bacterial cell wall and releases electrons from the electron transport chain that normally react with oxygen at the end of the electron transport chain.

The reduced mediator leaves the cell with electrons that are transferred to an electrode, where they are deposited; this electrode then becomes negatively charged (anode). The release of electrons means that the mediator returns to its original oxidized state and is able to repeat the electron transfer process. In order to generate a useful current it is necessary to create a complete circuit.

Brewery and food manufacturing wastewater can be treated by microbial fuel cells because this wastewater is rich in organic compounds that can serve as respiratory substrates for the micro-organisms. Breweries are ideal for microbial fuel cells, as their wastewater composition is always the same; these constant conditions allow bacteria to adapt and become more efficient.

■ **Figure 19.13** Waste water treatment plant in Singapore (currently ultrafiltration and ultraviolet radiation, but microbial fuel cells are under investigation at the National University of Singapore)

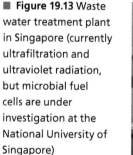

Sewage wastewater (Figure 19.13) can also be converted via microbial fuel cells to decompose the waste organic material present. Research has shown that MFCs can reduce the amount of organic material present in sewage wastewater by up to 80%. The process is very similar to brewery wastewater treatment, the difference being that the water must first be pre-treated to remove toxins. This is important because sewage wastewater often varies in composition and may require extensive treatment before it can be cleaned by the MFC. However, this extensive treatment is justified by the electricity produced while cleaning the wastewater. The electricity production from MFCs will help to offset the high costs of processing wastewater.

 ## Technology and ethics

Teleological ethics refers to ethical theories based on an assumption that what makes an action right or wrong is its outcome. If an action has good consequences, it is the right thing to do. If it has bad consequences, it is the wrong thing to do. According to teleological ethics, hydrogen fuel cells are an ethically acceptable form of energy since the consequences of hydrogen fuel cells are good, i.e. they are pollution free at their point of use, since water is their only product. The choice to use hydrogen fuels is morally right as the consequences are more favourable than unfavourable, as their use could potentially reduce global warming. However, other fuel cells, such as the methanol fuel cell, do generate carbon dioxide. Although there are safety risks associated with hydrogen (due to its flammability), these are minor and are outweighed by the potential reduction in climate change. The development of fuel cells is an active research area and involves collaboration between electrochemists, material chemists, physicists and engineers.

Priorities for government and international funding are often decided based on potential benefits for the populations of that country and the international community. However, such an approach may neglect the funding and development of fundamental and basic research that may have few immediate benefits to the national and international community.

■ Electrolysis

Electrolysis of aqueous solutions

The electrolysis of aqueous solutions of ionic compounds is more complicated than the electrolysis of molten ionic compounds (Chapter 9) since the water itself will undergo electrolysis. This occurs because water is slightly dissociated into hydrogen and hydroxide ions (Chapter 8):

$$H_2O(l) \rightleftharpoons H^+(aq) + OH^-(aq)$$

The hydrogen and hydroxide ions migrate with the ions from the ionic compound and compete with them to accept or release electrons at the cathode and anode, respectively. For example, an aqueous solution of sodium chloride contains the following ions:

$H^+(aq)$ and $OH^-(aq)$ from the water
$Na^+(aq)$ and $Cl^-(aq)$ from the sodium chloride

Both positive ions migrate to the negative cathode and both negative ions to the positive anode. At each electrode, depending upon the conditions, one or both of the ions may be discharged as atoms or molecules. Although the concentrations of hydrogen and hydroxide ions from the dissociation of water are very small, they will be rapidly restored via a shifting of the equilibrium if they are removed from the water via reactions with the electrodes.

If the solution of sodium chloride is concentrated, chlorine is produced at the anode and hydrogen is produced at the cathode:

Anode
$2Cl^- \rightarrow Cl_2 + 2e^-$

Cathode
$2H^+ + 2e^- \rightarrow H_2$

If the solution of sodium chloride is *dilute* then hydrogen is produced at the cathode and oxygen is produced at the anode:

Anode
$4OH^- \rightarrow 2H_2O + O_2 + 4e^-$

Cathode
$2H^+ + 2e^- \rightarrow H_2$

In both of these electrolyses inert graphite (carbon) or platinum electrodes are used, and in neither case are sodium ions discharged as sodium metal.

These and other observed results (Table 19.5) suggest the following 'rules' regarding the electrolysis of aqueous solutions (Figure 19.14):

■ Metals, if produced, are discharged at the cathode.

■ Hydrogen is produced at the cathode only.

■ Non-metals, apart from hydrogen, are produced at the anode.

■ Reactive metals, that is, those above hydrogen in the activity series (Chapter 9), are not discharged (unless special cathodes are used).

■ The products can depend upon the *concentration* of the electrolyte in the solution and the nature of the electrode.

■ If halide ions are present in reasonable concentrations they will be discharged more readily than hydroxide ions, *but* if no halide ions are present, hydroxide ions are discharged more readily than other anions.

■ **Figure 19.14**
Electrolytic cell with graphite electrodes and ignition tubes in which any gases released at the electrodes are collected

Table 19.5 Examples of electrolysis of solutions

Electrolyte	Electrodes	Cathode half-equation	Anode half-equation
Potassium bromide, KBr(aq)	Graphite/platinum	$2H^+ + 2e^- \rightarrow H_2$	$2Br^- \rightarrow Br_2 + 2e^-$
Magnesium sulfate, MgSO$_4$(aq)	Graphite/platinum	$4H^+ + 4e^- \rightarrow 2H_2$	$4OH^- \rightarrow 2H_2O + O_2 + 4e^-$
Concentrated hydrochloric acid, HCl(aq)	Graphite/platinum	$2H^+ + 2e^- \rightarrow H_2$	$2Cl^- \rightarrow Cl_2 + 2e^-$
Dilute sulfuric acid, H$_2$SO$_4$(aq)	Graphite/platinum	$2H^+ + 2e^- \rightarrow H_2$	$4OH^- \rightarrow 2H_2O + O_2 + 4e^-$
Dilute sodium hydroxide, NaOH(aq)	Graphite/platinum	$2H^+ + 2e^- \rightarrow H_2$	$4OH^- \rightarrow 2H_2O + O_2 + 4e^-$
Copper(II) sulfate, CuSO$_4$(aq)	Graphite/platinum	$Cu^{2+} + 2e^- \rightarrow Cu$	$4OH^- \rightarrow 2H_2O + O_2 + 4e^-$
Copper(II) sulfate, CuSO$_4$(aq)	Copper	$Cu^{2+} + 2e^- \rightarrow Cu$	$Cu \rightarrow Cu^{2+} + 2e^-$
Copper(II) chloride, CuCl$_2$(aq)	Graphite/platinum	$Cu^{2+} + 2e^- \rightarrow Cu$	$2Cl^- \rightarrow Cl_2 + 2e^-$
Potassium iodide, KI(aq)	Graphite/platinum	$2H^+ + 2e^- \rightarrow H_2$	$2I^- \rightarrow I_2 + 2e^-$

Figure 19.15 BAE Hawks (Red Devils Acrobatic Team): the aircraft are composed mainly of aluminium alloy with some magnesium

Utilization: Applications of electrolysis

The use of lightweight alloys containing lithium and magnesium makes the extraction of these metals increasingly important. Aluminium is a particularly useful metal, since in addition to its low density and high tensile strength, it does not suffer corrosion like iron (Figure 19.15).

The conductivity of copper increases by a factor of 10 when it is more than 99.9% pure. The impure copper is made the anode of an electrolysis cell and pure copper is the cathode. Impure copper contains small amounts of gold and silver. They drop off the anode as the copper around them dissolves, and fall to the bottom as 'anode sludge'. Gold and silver can be extracted from the filtered sludge.

Important chemicals, such as sodium hydroxide and sodium chlorate(I) (bleach) are made by the electrolysis of brine (saturated salt solution). The electrolysis of brine results in the formation of chlorine, hydrogen and sodium hydroxide, which are all useful raw materials for a variety of industrial processes (Figure 19.16).

Figure 19.16 Important products from the electrolysis of salt solution

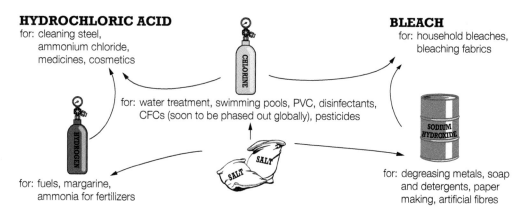

HYDROCHLORIC ACID
for: cleaning steel, ammonium chloride, medicines, cosmetics

BLEACH
for: household bleaches, bleaching fabrics

for: water treatment, swimming pools, PVC, disinfectants, CFCs (soon to be phased out globally), pesticides

for: fuels, margarine, ammonia for fertilizers

for: degreasing metals, soap and detergents, paper making, artificial fibres

The electrolysis of water

When very dilute sulfuric acid is electrolysed, one volume of oxygen gas is collected over the anode, and two volumes of hydrogen gas are collected over the cathode (Figure 19.17). At the anode, the hydroxide ions (from the dissociation of water) are discharged in preference to the sulfate ions. They give up electrons and form water and oxygen molecules. At the cathode, hydrogen ions are discharged by accepting electrons to form hydrogen molecules:

Anode: $4OH^-(aq) \rightarrow 2H_2O(l) + 1O_2(g) + \mathbf{4e^-}$
Cathode: $\mathbf{4e^-} + 4H^+(aq) \rightarrow 2H_2(g)$

The second half-equation has been adjusted to show that the ratio of the amounts or volumes of oxygen molecules to hydrogen molecules is $1:2$, so in effect, water is being electrolysed. As the electrolysis proceeds, more water molecules dissociate to replace the ions that have been discharged. Thus, although the *quantity* of sulfuric acid is unchanged, its *concentration* increases as the water is consumed.

■ **Figure 19.17**
Apparatus for the decomposition of water (Hoffman voltameter)

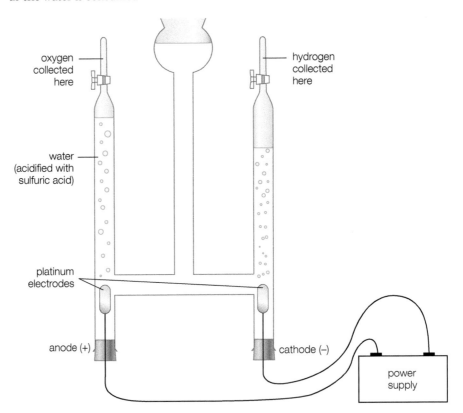

The electrolysis of copper(II) sulfate solution using copper electrodes

No gases are released during this electrolysis. However, if both the anode and cathode are weighed before and after passing the current, it is found that the mass of the anode decreases while that of the cathode increases, the two changes being equal.

At the anode, hydroxide ions are present (in low concentration) from the dissociation of water. However, it requires less energy to remove electrons from the copper atoms of the anode than to remove them from the hydroxide ions. Hence, the anode slowly dissolves.

At the cathode, copper(II) ions are discharged in preference to hydrogen ions because hydrogen is below copper in the activity series, and so the cathode becomes plated with copper.

Anode: $Cu(s) \rightarrow Cu^{2+}(aq) + 2e^-$
Cathode: $2e^- + Cu^{2+}(aq) \rightarrow Cu(s)$

The concentration of the copper(II) sulfate solution remains unchanged, but copper atoms are transferred from the anode to the cathode.

Alternative theory to explain the electrolysis of aqueous solutions

In the electrolysis of dilute sulfuric acid using inert electrodes, the formation of oxygen at the anode can be explained in terms of the discharge of hydroxide ions from the dissociation of water molecules. Similarly, the formation of hydrogen gas at the cathode in the electrolysis of sodium chloride solution was accounted for by the discharge of hydrogen ions from the dissociation of water. The degree of ionization in water is extremely small (Chapter 18) and pure water is virtually a non-conductor. The theory assumes that hydrogen and hydroxide ions are discharged from solution much more rapidly than from pure water.

An alternative but equivalent theory (common in North American textbooks) suggests that electrons can be taken or released at the electrodes by water *molecules*. Molecules of water are present in far greater concentration than any of the ions in solution. The observed results for the electrolysis of water can be readily accounted for by this theory:

Anode: $2H_2O(l) \rightarrow 4H^+(aq) + O_2(g) + 4e^-$

Cathode: $4H_2O(l) + 4e^- \rightarrow 4OH^-(aq) + 2H_2(g)$

Using standard electrode potentials to explain hydrolysis products

A more rigorous approach to predicting and accounting for electrolysis products uses standard electrode potentials.

During electrolysis, cations are discharged at the cathode:

$M^{n+}(aq) + ne^- \rightarrow M(s)$

If hydrogen ions are discharged, then hydrogen gas is produced:

$2H^+(aq) + 2e^- \rightarrow H_2(g)$

Since discharge at the cathode involves reduction, ions that accept electrons readily will be reduced first. Therefore, strong oxidizing agents with more positive standard electrode potential values will be preferentially discharged compared to those with less positive values. For example, it is easier to discharge copper(II) ions than zinc ions at the cathode:

$Zn^{2+}(aq) + 2e^- \rightarrow Zn(s)$ $E^{\ominus} = -0.76\,V$

$Cu^{2+}(aq) + 2e^- \rightarrow Cu(s)$ $E^{\ominus} = +0.34\,V$

Anions are discharged at the anode during electrolysis:

$2X^{n-}(aq) \rightarrow X_2(g) + 2ne^-$

Since this is an oxidation reaction, ions that lose electrons readily will be oxidized first. Therefore, an anion with a more negative standard electrode potential will be discharged instead of one with a less negative standard electrode potential.

For example, it is easier to discharge bromide ions than chloride ions:

$Br_2(aq) + 2e^- \rightarrow 2Br^-(aq)$ $E^{\ominus} = +1.09\,V$

$Cl_2(aq) + 2e^- \rightarrow 2Cl^-(aq)$ $E^{\ominus} = +1.36\,V$

Another way of understanding this is to look at the *oxidation* potential of both bromide and choride ions. Oxidation potentials are the electrode (reduction) potentials with the *sign reversed*.

$2Br^-(aq) \rightarrow Br_2(aq) + 2e^-$ $E^{\ominus}_{oxidation} = -1.09\,V$

$2Cl^-(aq) \rightarrow Cl_2(aq) + 2e^-$ $E^{\ominus}_{oxidation} = -1.36\,V$

As the oxidation potential of bromide is more positive, it also indicates that the oxidation of bromide ions to bromine molecules is energetically more favourable. Therefore, if chloride and bromide ions migrate to an inert platinum electrode, the bromide ions will be preferentially discharged:

$2Br^-(aq) \rightarrow Br_2(aq) + 2e^-$

In summary, when inert electrodes are used during electrolysis:

- Cations with more positive $E^\ominus_{\text{reduction}}$ values will be discharged first at the cathode.
- Anions with more negative $E^\ominus_{\text{reduction}}$ values will be discharged first at the anode.

or

- Anions with more positive $E^\ominus_{\text{oxidation}}$ values will be discharged first at the anode.
- Cations with more negative $E^\ominus_{\text{oxidation}}$ values will be discharged first at the cathode.

Worked example

Deduce the relevant half-equation for the electrolysis of copper(II) sulfate solution using inert electrodes.

Step 1 Write the ions present in the electrolyte used:

$Cu^{2+}(aq)$, $SO_4^{2-}(aq)$, $H^+(aq)$ and $OH^-(aq)$ (from the dissociation of water, $H_2O(l) \rightleftharpoons H^+(aq) + OH^-(aq)$)

Step 2 Write the possible reduction reactions that could occur at the cathode. Refer to page 23 of the IB *Chemistry data booklet* and quote the necessary standard electrode potential values ($E^\ominus_{\text{reduction}}$):

$Cu^{2+}(aq) + 2e^- \rightarrow Cu(s)$ $\quad\quad\quad\quad E^\ominus_{\text{reduction}} = +0.34\,V$

For the case of water molecules versus hydrogen ions, the IBO accepts the use of either

$2H^+(aq) + 2e^- \rightarrow H_2(g)$ $\quad\quad\quad\quad\quad E^\ominus_{\text{reduction}} = 0.00\,V$

or

$H_2O(l) + e^- \rightarrow \frac{1}{2}H_2(g) + OH^-(aq)$ $\quad\quad E^\ominus_{\text{reduction}} = -0.83\,V$

Step 3 Decide which reaction will take place by comparing the $E^\ominus_{\text{reduction}}$ values.

The copper(II) ion discharge half-equation has the more positive electrode potential and hence copper(II) ions will be preferentially discharged.

Step 4 Repeat the procedure for the possible reactions occurring at the anode.

$S_2O_8^{2-}(aq) + 2e^- \rightarrow 2SO_4^{2-}(aq)$ $\quad\quad E^\ominus_{\text{reduction}} = +2.01\,V$

For the case of water molecules versus hydroxide ions, the IBO accepts the use of either

$\frac{1}{2}O_2(g) + H_2O(l) + 2e^- \rightarrow 2OH^-(aq)$ $\quad E^\ominus_{\text{reduction}} = +0.40\,V$

or

$\frac{1}{2}O_2(g) + 2H^+(aq) + 2e^- \rightarrow H_2O(l)$ $E^\ominus_{\text{reduction}} = +1.23\,V$

Or, if you prefer looking at values of $E^\ominus_{\text{oxidation}}$:

$2SO_4^{2-}(aq) \rightarrow S_2O_8^{2-}(aq) + 2e^-$ $\quad\quad E^\ominus_{\text{oxidation}} = -2.01\,V$

$4OH^-(aq) \rightarrow O_2(g) + 2H_2O(l) + 4e^-$ $\quad E^\ominus_{\text{oxidation}} = -0.40\,V$

$2H_2O(l) \rightarrow O_2(g) + 4H^+(aq) + 4e^-$ $\quad E^\ominus_{\text{oxidation}} = -1.23\,V$

Step 5 Decide which reaction will take place by comparing either the $E^\ominus_{\text{reduction}}$ or $E^\ominus_{\text{oxidation}}$ values.

The most negative (or least positive) $E^\ominus_{\text{reduction}}$ value is for the discharge of water molecules or hydroxide ions. They also have the least negative (or most positive) $E^\ominus_{\text{oxidation}}$ values. Hence, sulfate ions will remain in solution and *not* be discharged.

So the relevant half-equations are:

Cathode: $Cu^{2+}(aq) + 2e^- \rightarrow Cu(s)$

Anode: $2OH^-(aq) \rightarrow \frac{1}{2}O_2(g) + H_2O(l) + 2e^-$

or

$H_2O(l) \rightarrow \frac{1}{2}O_2(g) + H^+(aq) + 2e^-$

7 Write appropriate half-equations to describe the following examples of electrolysis. Explain and justify these half-equations by reference to standard electrode potentials, the nature of the electrode (inert or active) and the concentration of the electrolyte (dilute or concentrated):
  a lithium iodide, LiI(aq), with graphite electrodes
  b dilute barium hydroxide, $Ba(OH)_2$(aq), with graphite or platinum electrodes
  c copper(II) nitrate, $Cu(NO_3)_2$(aq), with copper and with graphite electrodes
  d sodium chloride, NaCl(aq), both concentrated and dilute, with graphite electrodes

■ Faraday's laws

When a solution of aqueous copper(II) sulfate is electrolysed using copper electrodes (Figure 19.18), the copper anode slowly dissolves away and the copper cathode slowly gains a deposit of copper. Any impurities present in the copper anode collect at the bottom of the electrolytic cell. This method is used on the industrial scale to purify copper.

Cathode: $Cu^{2+} + 2e^- \rightarrow Cu$
Anode: $Cu \rightarrow Cu^{2+} + 2e^-$

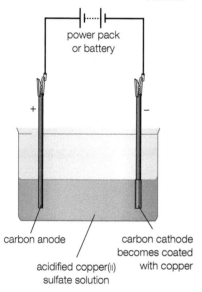

■ **Figure 19.18** Apparatus for the electrolysis of copper(II) sulfate solution

Experiments have shown that the amount of copper deposited depends on both the length of time for which the current flows and the size of the current. Results have shown *directly proportional* relationships: if the time is doubled, the mass of copper deposited on the cathode is doubled, and if the size of the current is doubled, then again, the mass of copper deposited is doubled.

The amount of copper deposited therefore depends upon the size of the current and the length of time it is allowed to flow. An electric current is a flow of negatively charged electrons and is measured in units called *amperes* (amps (A), for short). The tiny electrical charge on each electron can be expressed in units called coulombs (C).

The total charge carried by an electric current is given by this expression:

charge in coulombs (C) = current (A) × time (s)

Experiments have shown that a mole of electrons carries a charge of 96 500 coulombs. This is known as the Faraday constant in honour of the English physicist and chemist, Michael Faraday, and is given the symbol F with a value of 96 500 C mol^{-1}. Faraday's investigations into the factors controlling the amounts of products formed during electrolysis are summarized in Faraday's laws of electrolysis.

Faraday's first law

Faraday's first law states that the mass of an element produced during electrolysis is directly proportional to the quantity of electricity (charge) passed during the electrolysis. The quantity of electricity (charge), as measured in coulombs, depends on both the current and the time.

Faraday's second law

Faraday's second law states that the masses of different elements produced by the same quantity of electricity form simple whole number ratios when divided by their relative atomic masses.

Here is some experimental data that supports Faraday's second law. During an electrolysis experiment, 2.16 grams of silver are deposited and 0.64 grams of copper (for equal amounts of charge in coulombs). The relative atomic masses of silver and copper are 107.87 and 63.55, respectively.

	Silver	*Copper*
Amount	$\dfrac{2.16}{107.87} = 0.02\,\text{mol}$	$\dfrac{0.6355}{63.55} = 0.01\,\text{mol}$
Divide through by smallest	$\dfrac{0.02}{0.01} = 2$	$\dfrac{0.01}{0.01} = 1$

The results can be accounted for in terms of the relevant half-equations and molar quantities of ions, atoms and electrons:

$$Ag^+ \quad + \quad e^- \quad \rightarrow \quad Ag$$
$$\text{0.02 mol} \qquad \text{0.02 mol} \qquad \text{0.02 mol}$$
$$Cu^{2+} \quad + \quad 2e^- \quad \rightarrow \quad Cu$$
$$\text{0.01 mol} \qquad \text{0.02 mol} \qquad \text{0.01 mol}$$

The quantity of electricity consumed in each cell is the same. The amount of copper formed is half of the amount of silver formed because each mole of copper(II) ions needs two moles of electrons for discharge, whereas each mole of silver ions needs only one mole of electrons for discharge. A modern statement of Faraday's law is therefore that the number of moles of electrons required to discharge one mole of an ion at an electrode equals the charge on the ion.

Faraday's laws of electrolysis can be illustrated by three electrolytic cells with aqueous solutions (cell I, cell II and cell III) joined in series (Figure 19.19). This arrangement means all three cells receive the same current (number of electrons).

■ **Figure 19.19**
Electrolytic cells in series

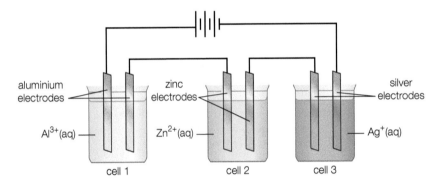

aluminium electrodes — zinc electrodes — silver electrodes

$Al^{3+}(aq)$ — $Zn^{2+}(aq)$ — $Ag^+(aq)$

cell 1   cell 2   cell 3

The results of passing 3 moles of electrons or 289 500 coulombs of electricity ($96\,500\,C\,mol^{-1} \times 3\,mol = 289\,500\,C$) through the three electrolytic cells are shown in Table 19.6.

Cell I	Cell II	Cell III
Anode: $Al(s) \rightarrow Al^{3+}(aq) + 3e^-$	Anode: $Zn(s) \rightarrow Zn^{2+}(aq) + 2e^-$	Anode: $Ag(s) \rightarrow Ag^+(aq) + e^-$
Cathode: $Al^{3+}(aq) + 3e^- \rightarrow Al(s)$	Cathode: $Zn^{2+}(s) + 2e^- \rightarrow Zn(s)$	Cathode: $Ag^+(aq) + e^- \rightarrow Ag(s)$
• 3 mol of electrons will deposit 1 mol of aluminium atoms • 3 mol of electrons will deposit 1 mol of aluminium atoms, Al	• 2 mol of electrons will deposit 1 mol of zinc atoms • 3 mol of electrons will deposit 1.5 mol of zinc atoms, Zn	• 1 mol of electrons will deposit 1 mol of silver atoms • 3 mol of electrons will deposit 3 mol of silver atoms, Ag

■ **Table 19.6** Electrolysis of aqueous solution in series

Determining the relative amounts of products formed during electrolytic processes

Faraday's laws and the relationships between charge, time, current and amount allow a variety of types of quantitative problems involving electrolysis to be solved.

8   Deduce the charge on an aluminium ion if 5.4 grams of aluminium is deposited by a current of 5.00 A flowing for 3 hours and 13 minutes.

9   Calculate the mass of copper that would be plated on the cathode from an aqueous solution of copper(II) sulfate by a current of 2.00 A flowing for 15 minutes.

10   Calculate the volume of hydrogen gas (in cm³) produced at STP when a current of 4.00 A is passed for 6 minutes and 10 seconds through a solution containing dilute aqueous sulfuric acid.

11   A current of 3.00 A was passed for 30 minutes through molten lead(II) bromide. Lead of mass 5.60 grams was obtained. Determine the value of the Avogadro constant.

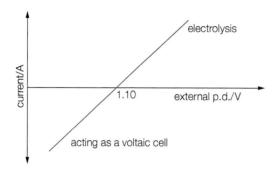

■ **Figure 19.20** Voltage–current graph for a Daniell cell (copper/zinc voltaic cell)

Reversing the flow

If the electrodes of a voltaic cell are connected together, electrons flow from the negative electrode to the positive terminal. If the two electrodes are instead connected to an external voltage supply (power pack) and the applied voltage is increased, electrons still flow as before until the external voltage equals the cell potential, $E^{\ominus}_{cell}$. At this voltage, no current flows, but if the external voltage is increased still further, current flows in the opposite direction and electrolysis takes place (Figure 19.20). For example, when an external voltage greater than 1.10 volts is applied to a Daniell cell, the reaction runs in reverse:

$$Zn^{2+}(aq) + Cu(s) \rightarrow Zn(s) + Cu^{2+}(aq)$$

1.10 volts is the minimum voltage required to bring about electrolysis in the Daniell cell. However, in practice the voltage used for electrolysis is always greater than this minimum. The voltaic cell has resistance and the cell discharge reactions require energy to overcome the activation energy associated with discharge of ions. The charging and discharging of batteries is discussed in Chapter 24 on the accompanying website.

Utilization: Electroplating

Metals are electroplated to improve their appearance or to prevent corrosion. The most commonly used metals for electroplating are copper, chromium, silver and tin. Familiar examples of electroplated objects include chromium-plated car bumpers and kettles, jewellery, for example gold bracelets, and cutlery (Figure 19.21) including EPNS (electroplated nickel silver) cutlery.

Figure 19.22 shows an electrolytic cell used to perform silver plating. At the cathode the silver ions undergo reduction to form silver atoms:

$$Ag^+(aq) + e^- \rightarrow Ag(s)$$

At the anode the silver atoms undergo oxidation:

$$Ag(s) \rightarrow Ag^+(aq) + e^-$$

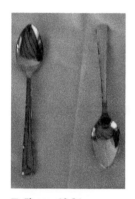

■ **Figure 19.21**
Gold-plated spoons

■ **Figure 19.22**
Electroplating
apparatus: silver
plating

As the current flows through the circuit, the anode slowly dissolves and replaces the silver ions in the electrolyte.

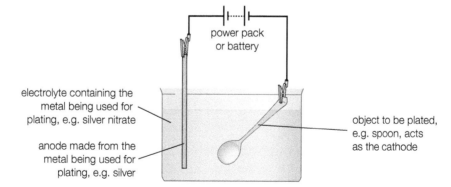

The object to be electroplated must be made the cathode. The cathode is the negative electrode and attracts metal ions (cations). The anode must be the metal used for the plating process. The electrolyte solution must contain ions of the metal for plating.

In order to obtain a good coating of metal during electroplating:

■ the object to be plated must be clean and free of grease

■ the object should be rotated to give an even coating

■ the current must not be too large or the 'coating' will form too rapidly and flake off

■ the temperature and concentration of the electrolyte must be carefully controlled, otherwise the 'coating' will be deposited too rapidly or too slowly.

In order to produce a thin, even layer of metal during electroplating, the metal needs to be deposited slowly. This means that the concentration of free ions must be kept low. In chromium plating (Figure 19.23), the electrolyte is a mixture of chromium(III) ions, $Cr^{3+}(aq)$ and chromate(VI) ions, $CrO_4^{2-}(aq)$. As the chromium(III) ions are deposited, they are replenished by the reduction of chromate(VI) ions at the cathode.

■ **Figure 19.23** Chrome-plated bumper from a Renault car

Cathode: $Cr^{3+}(aq) + 3e^- \rightarrow Cr(s)$

$$CrO_4^{2-}(aq) + 8H^+(aq) + 3e^- \rightarrow Cr^{3+}(aq) + 4H_2O(l)$$

In silver plating, a solution containing the complex ion $Ag(CN)_2^-(aq)$ is often used. This is a stable complex and produces a very low concentration of silver ions, $Ag^+(aq)$:

$$Ag(CN)_2^-(aq) \rightarrow Ag^+(aq) + 2CN^-(aq)$$

Cathode: $Ag^+(aq) + e^- \rightarrow Ag(s)$

Electroplating has become less important recently, as stainless steel has replaced chromium-plated steel. However, many items are chromium, gold or silver plated. Tin cans are steel cans that have been tin plated.

Explaining the process of electroplating

Copper plating requires a piece of copper (as a source of copper atoms), a power supply (battery or power pack), and a soluble copper(II) salt to act as an electrolyte. Copper(II) nitrate or copper(II) sulfate(VI) are both suitable electrolytes. The object to be plated must be connected to the negative terminal so it acts as an electrolytic cathode and attracts copper(II) ions present in the electrolyte. The following half-equation will occur on the surface of the metal object (cathode):

$$Cu^{2+}(aq) + 2e^- \rightarrow Cu(s)$$

The copper anode will replace the copper(II) ions via the action of the following half-equation:

$$Cu(s) \rightarrow Cu^{2+}(aq) + 2e^-$$

The mass gain of the cathode will be balanced by the mass loss at the anode. The overall result is a transfer of copper atoms from the anode to the cathode. The concentration of copper(II) ions in the electrolyte remains constant. The sulfate(VI) or nitrate(V) ions are spectator ions and undergo no change during the electroplating. The external circuit connecting the two electrodes allows the transfer of electrons from the anode to the cathode.

■ *Examination questions – a selection*

Paper 1 IB questions and IB style questions

Q1 Which one of the following factors does not influence the voltage in the reaction shown below?

$$Fe(s) + Cu^{2+}(aq) \rightarrow Cu(s) + Fe^{2+}(aq)$$

A the concentration of copper(II) ions, $Cu^{2+}(aq)$
B the concentration of iron(II) ions, $Fe^{2+}(aq)$
C the temperature of the solutions
D the size of the anode

Q2 A student constructs a voltaic cell using tin and lead electrodes immersed in $1\,mol\,dm^{-3}$ solutions of tin(II) and lead(II) ions. What is the EMF for the spontaneous reaction? The electrode potentials are:

$$Sn^{2+}(aq) + 2e^- \rightarrow Sn(s) \quad E^\ominus = -0.14\,V$$
$$Pb^{2+}(aq) + 2e^- \rightarrow Pb(s) \quad E^\ominus = -0.13\,V$$

A $-0.27\,V$ **C** $+0.01\,V$
B $-0.01\,V$ **D** $+0.27\,V$

Q3 For which of the reactions below will $\Delta G^\ominus$ be the most negative?

A $Cu(s) + 2Ag^+(aq) \rightarrow 2Ag(s) + Cu^{2+}(aq)$
$E^\ominus = 0.46\,V$

B $Co(s) + Cu^{2+}(aq) \rightarrow Cu(s) + Co^{2+}(aq)$
$E^\ominus = 0.62\,V$

C $Fe^{2+}(aq) + Cu^{2+}(aq) \rightarrow Fe^{3+}(aq) + Cu^+(aq)$
$E^\ominus = -0.61\,V$

D $H_2(g) + Cr^{2+}(aq) \rightarrow Cr(s) + 2H^+(aq)$
$E^\ominus = -0.74\,V$

Q4 One mole of electrons was passed through electrolytic cells in series containing solutions of $Ag^+(aq)$, $Ni^{2+}(aq)$ and $Cr^{3+}(aq)$. What mass of Ag, Ni and Cr will be deposited?
[A_r values: Ag = 108, Ni = 59, Cr = 52]

A 36 g, 29.5 g and 52 g
B 108 g, 59 g and 52 g
C 108 g, 29.5 g and 17.3 g
D 108 g, 118 g and 156 g

Higher Level Paper 1, Nov 2002, Q34

Q5 Given the standard reduction potentials

$Ni^{2+}(aq) + 2e^- \rightarrow Ni(s)$ $\quad E^\ominus = -0.23\,V$

$Cd^{2+}(aq) + 2e^- \rightarrow Cd(s)$ $\quad E^\ominus = -0.40\,V$

$2H^+(aq) + 2e^- \rightarrow H_2(g)$ $\quad E^\ominus = 0.00\,V$

which pair of substances will react spontaneously?

A nickel ions with cadmium ions
B nickel atoms with cadmium ions
C nickel ions with hydrogen ions
D cadmium atoms with nickel ions

Q6 Consider an electrochemical cell constructed from standard Ni/Ni^{2+} and Cu/Cu^{2+} half-cells. Which one of the following pairs of changes would be expected to increase the measured value of $E^\ominus_{cell}$?

$Cu^{2+}(aq) + 2e^- \rightarrow Cu(s)$ $\quad E^\ominus = +0.34\,V$

$Ni^{2+}(aq) + 2e^- \rightarrow Ni(s)$ $\quad E^\ominus = -0.23\,V$

A increase the $[Ni^{2+}(aq)]$ and increase the $[Cu^{2+}(aq)]$
B decrease the $[Ni^{2+}(aq)]$ and increase the $[Cu^{2+}(aq)]$
C decrease the $[Ni^{2+}(aq)]$ and decrease the $[Cu^{2+}(aq)]$
D increase the $[Ni^{2+}(aq)]$ and decrease the $[Cu^{2+}(aq)]$

Q7 Which statement is correct for the electrolysis of aqueous copper(II) sulfate using copper electrodes?

A Copper(II) ions move towards the cathode (negative electrode).
B Oxygen molecules are produced at the cathode (negative electrode).

C The anode gains in mass due to deposition of copper atoms.
D The blue colour of the copper(II) sulfate solution becomes lighter.

Q8 Which of the following statements is not correct about the charge on a mole of electrons?

A It always deposits one mole of an element during electrolysis.
B It equals the charge on 6×10^{23} electrons.
C It is approximately equivalent to 96 500 C of charge.
D It deposits half a mole of copper atoms during electrolysis.

Q9 Which of the following is an *incorrect* statement about the electrolysis of concentrated sodium chloride solution with graphite electrodes?

A The anode (positive electrode) attracts hydroxide and chloride ions.
B Sodium metal is produced at the cathode.
C Hydrogen ions undergo reduction at the cathode.
D More energy is required to discharge chloride ions compared to hydroxide ions.

Q10 Two standard zinc and silver half-cells are connected via a salt bridge. The two electrodes are connected by a wire and a high-resistance voltmeter. Select the *incorrect* statement.

A Electrons are flowing along the wire from the zinc electrode to the silver electrode.
B Electrons are flowing through the salt bridge to complete the circuit.
C If the salt bridge is lifted out of the solutions the voltmeter will read zero volts.
D If hydrochloric acid is added to the $Ag(s)/Ag^+(aq)$ half-cell, the reading on the voltmeter will change.

Q11 Which of the following will affect the mass of gold deposited on the cathode (negative electrode) during an electroplating process?

I the concentration of gold ions in the electrolyte
II the size of the current used
III the time of the electroplating process

A I and II $\qquad$ **C** I and III
B II and III $\qquad$ **D** I, II and III

Q12 Which of the following changes would take place at the positive electrode (cathode) in a voltaic cell?

I $Zn^{2+}(aq)$ to $Zn(s)$
II $Br_2(g)$ to $Br^-(aq)$
III $Mg(s)$ to $Mg^{2+}(aq)$

A I and II only $\qquad$ **C** II and III only
B I and III only $\qquad$ **D** I, II and III

Q13 The same quantity of electricity was passed through separate molten samples of potassium bromide, KBr, and calcium chloride, $CaCl_2$. Which statement is true about the amounts (in mol) that are formed?

  A The amount of calcium formed is twice the amount of chlorine formed.

  B The amount of calcium formed is equal to the amount of chlorine formed.

  C The amount of calcium formed is equal to the amount of potassium formed.

  D The amount of calcium formed is twice the amount of potassium formed.

Paper 2 IB questions and IB style questions

Q1 **a** Redox equations may be balanced using changes in oxidation number. For the following redox equation calculate the oxidation numbers of copper and nitrogen. Use these values to balance the equation. [5]

$$Cu(s) + HNO_3(aq) \rightarrow$$
$$Cu(NO_3)_2(aq) + NO(g) + H_2O(l)$$

  b **i** Draw a diagram for the voltaic cell formed by connecting the following standard half-cells: [3]

$$Ni(s) \mid Ni^{2+}(aq) \parallel Mn^{2+}(aq) \mid Mn(s)$$

  ii Describe the key features of the standard hydrogen electrode (SHE). [3]

  c **i** Write an equation for the reaction in each half-cell, identifying the species which is oxidized and the oxidizing agent. [4]

  ii State which electrode is the anode and state the direction of electron flow in the external circuit. [2]

  iii For the overall cell, calculate its voltage and state the sign of ΔG. [2]

  d An aqueous solution of gold nitrate is electrolysed. Predict the product formed at each electrode. [2]

Q2 A pale blue aqueous solution of copper(II) sulfate, $CuSO_4$, is electrolysed using copper electrodes.

  a Write balanced half-equations for the reactions occurring at the:

  i cathode (negative electrode) [1]

  ii anode (positive electrode). [1]

  b Explain why there is no change in the intensity of the pale blue colour or the pH when a current flows. [2]

  c Write a balanced equation for the products formed if the reactive copper anode is replaced by an inert platinum or graphite electrode. [2]

  d Calculate the mass of copper produced in grams when a current of 0.360 amperes is passed through a $1.0\,mol\,dm^{-3}$ copper(II) sulfate solution for 10 minutes. [4]

20 Organic chemistry

ESSENTIAL IDEAS

- Key organic reaction types include nucleophilic substitution, electrophilic addition, electrophilic substitution and redox reactions. Reaction mechanisms vary and help in understanding the different types of reaction taking place.
- Organic synthesis is the systematic preparation of a compound from a widely available starting material or the synthesis of a compound via a synthetic route that often can involve a series of different steps.
- Stereoisomerism involves isomers which have different arrangements of atoms in space but do not differ in connectivity or bond multiplicity (i.e. whether single, double or triple) between the isomers themselves.

Within our earlier discussion of organic chemistry (Chapter 10) we introduced some of the chemistry that prevails in the natural world and has revolutionized our lives in terms of the materials available for us to use. There are many arguments for halting the destruction of the world's rainforests. One reason relates to the possibility of deriving useful pharmaceutical compounds from rainforest resources. A number of important medicinal drugs are derived from plants, including salicin, the forerunner to aspirin, and the anti-cancer drug Taxol. Many medicinal drugs are either natural products or are derived from compounds found in plants growing in tropical rainforest. An example is calanolide A, an anti-HIV drug derived from *Calophyllum lanigerum* var *austrocoriaceum*, which is an exceedingly rare member of the *Guttiferae* or mangosteen family. This species is found only in Sarawak, Malaysia, and in the Botanic Gardens in Singapore (Figure 20.1). Fortunately, calanolide A is a relatively simple molecule so it can also be made by total synthesis from simple organic molecules. Reactions involving Grignard reagents are useful in a number of stages in these syntheses.

■ **Figure 20.1**
a Primary rainforest in the Singapore Botanic Gardens. **b** The structure of calanolide A, an anti-HIV drug

This illustrates one aspect of how important organic chemistry is to our lives. Further study of organic chemistry involves looking in more detail at how reactions happen at the molecular level – the mechanisms of reactions. Such study involves a breakdown of reactions into a sequence of steps, each involving the making or breaking of covalent bonds – the movement of pairs of electrons, represented using 'curly arrows'. Studies in reaction kinetics are useful because they provide data that can demonstrate consistency with a proposed reaction mechanism. Alternatively, they can suggest that a proposed mechanism should be revised. Understanding organic reactions at the molecular level makes it possible for research chemists to devise the most efficient conditions for synthetic reactions. Later in this chapter you will see how organic reactions are interlinked and can be developed as possible routes for the synthesis of some organic products. This includes the creative approach to devising synthetic routes based on retrosynthesis – starting from the desired product and imaginatively working back to devise the most efficient route to its synthesis.

This approach is made possible by the systematic structure built into organic chemistry. Organic molecules contain certain characteristic hydrocarbon structures, with the properties of the molecules then being determined by the functional group(s) present in the molecule. Some key features of organic reactions dealt with earlier and in this chapter are summarized in Tables 20.1a, b, c and d.

■ **Table 20.1a**

Types of hydrocarbon skeletons in target organic molecules

Saturated Compounds with only carbon–carbon single bonds		Unsaturated Compounds with carbon–carbon multiple bonds	
Alkanes	**Alkenes**	**Alkynes**	**Arenes**
Aliphatic Compounds not containing a benzene ring or related structure			**Aromatic** Compounds containing a benzene ring or similar ring structure involving a delocalized π system

■ **Table 20.1b**

Types of attacking species

Free radicals	Neutral reactive species containing a lone electron Produced by homolytic fission and participating in chain reactions Examples are Cl•, CH_3•, •$CClF_2$
Electrophiles	Electron-deficient species with a positive charge (+) or a partial positive charge ($\delta+$) Attracted to regions of target molecules that are electron rich Examples are $H^{\delta+}$ from HBr, $Br^{\delta+}$ from Br_2, NO_2^+, CH_3^+ and CH_3CO^+
Nucleophiles	Electron-rich species with at least one lone pair of electrons – may also have a negative charge (–) or a partial negative charge ($\delta-$) Attracted to regions of target molecules that are electron deficient Examples are $\overset{\cdot\cdot}{\underset{\cdot\cdot}{Cl}}^-$, $\overset{\cdot\cdot}{\underset{\cdot\cdot}{O}}H^-$, $H_2\overset{\cdot\cdot}{\underset{\cdot\cdot}{O}}$ and NH_3

■ **Table 20.1c**

Types of organic reactions

Addition	Reaction in which two reactants combine to make a single product Usually involves a reactant that has a multiple bond, such as C=C or C=O
Substitution	Reaction in which one atom or functional group replaces another Usually involves saturated or aromatic compounds
Elimination	Reaction in which a small molecule is lost from a larger molecule Usually results in the formation of a double or triple bond Dehydration is a particular example of this type of reaction, where water is lost
Addition–elimination (condensation)	Reaction in which two molecules join to make a larger molecule, accompanied by the loss of a small molecule such as H_2O or HCl Reaction involves functional groups on both molecules Initial step is often nucleophilic attack of one molecule on the other

■ **Table 20.1d**

Types of bond breaking in organic reactions

Homolytic fission (homolysis)	**Heterolytic fission (heterolysis)**
Is when a covalent bond breaks by splitting the shared pair of bonding electrons between the two products	Is when a covalent bond breaks with both the shared electrons going to one of the products
Produces two free radicals, each having an unpaired electron	Produces two oppositely charged ions
Depicting the movement of electrons	
Uses a single-barbed arrow (fish-hook) to show the movement of a single electron	Uses a curly arrow to depict the movement of an electron pair

20.1 Types of organic reactions – *key organic reaction types include nucleophilic substitution, electrophilic addition, electrophilic substitution and redox reactions; reaction mechanisms vary and help in understanding the different types of reaction taking place*

■ Nucleophilic substitution reactions

The S$_N$2 reaction

Towards the end of Chapter 10 we introduced a classic example of a nucleophilic substitution reaction, namely the hydrolysis of a halogenoalkane by a warm aqueous solution of sodium hydroxide. As a result of the polarization of the carbon–halogen bond, the carbon atom is an electron-deficient centre susceptible to attack by a nucleophile such as the hydroxide ion (OH$^-$). Primary halogenoalkanes are thought to undergo a substitution mechanism that involves a single reaction step. This one-stage reaction involves the simultaneous attack of the nucleophile and departure of the halide ion. We will use as an example the reaction between bromomethane and sodium hydroxide solution:

$$CH_3Br(aq) + OH^-(aq) \rightarrow CH_3OH(aq) + Br^-(aq)$$

Kinetic studies show that this reaction is a single-step reaction in which the halogenoalkane and hydroxide ion are both involved. The rate expression for the reaction is found experimentally to be:

$$rate = k[CH_3Br(aq)][OH^-(aq)]$$

In addition to hydroxide ions, other common nucleophiles are water molecules, ammonia molecules, amine molecules and cyanide ions. Each of these nucleophiles reacts to replace the halogen atom, which leaves as the halide ion.

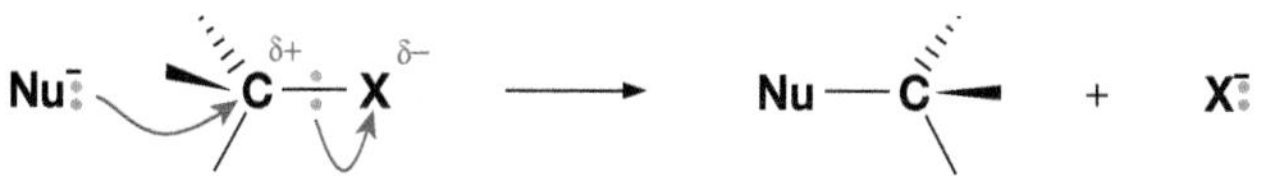

■ **Figure 20.2** Diagrammatic representation of nucleophilic substitution

In Figure 20.2, Nu represents a nucleophile (e.g. OH$^-$, CN$^-$, NH$_3$ or H$_2$O), and X represents a halogen atom (Cl, Br or I). We can see from this that a nucleophile is essentially a species with a lone pair of electrons and it can therefore attack an electron-deficient centre in the target molecule. As you can see from the list of examples, nucleophiles may also be negatively charged.

The mechanism is a concerted reaction where the nucleophile binds to the target carbon atom, simultaneously breaking the carbon–halogen bond to release the halogen atom as a negative halide ion. This type of bond breakage, where both electrons from the bond go to one of the products, is known as heterolytic fission. The halide ion detached during the reaction is known as the leaving group.

As mentioned above, for primary halogenoalkanes this reaction is a single-step reaction in which two species are involved in the one rate-determining step, and therefore the reaction is said to be bimolecular. The nucleophile (OH$^-$) is attracted to the electron-deficient carbon atom and a transition state is formed in which the carbon–bromine bond is broken at the same time as a new carbon–oxygen bond is formed. The bromine atom then leaves as a bromide ion, and the alcohol (in this case methanol) is formed (Figure 20.3). This mechanism is fully described as an S$_N$2 (substitution nucleophilic bimolecular) reaction.

■ **Figure 20.3**
The single-step mechanism envisaged for an S$_N$2 reaction

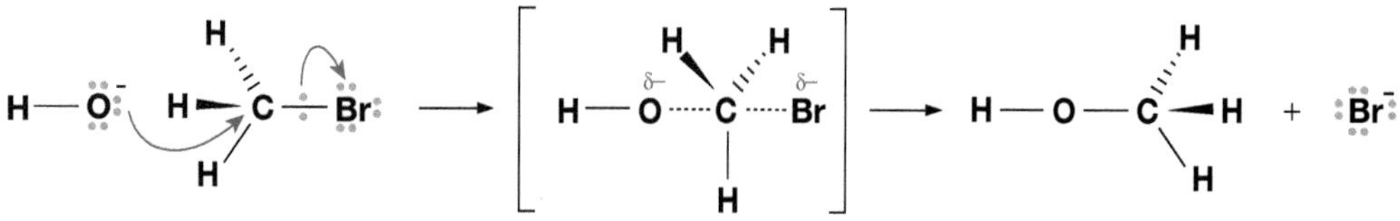

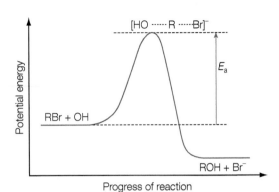

■ **Figure 20.4** The reaction profile for an S$_N$2 mechanism

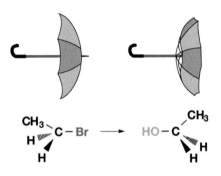

■ **Figure 20.5** The inversion of the structure of groups around the carbon atom during an S$_N$2 reaction has been likened to an umbrella being blown inside-out in the wind

If the concentration of either bromomethane molecules or hydroxide ions is doubled then the rate of reaction is also doubled. We can therefore deduce that the reaction is first order with respect to both bromomethane molecules and hydroxide ions, and that both these species are involved in the **rate-determining step** – that is the step in the overall reaction that is the slowest and so limits the overall rate of reaction. The reaction is thought to be a continuous, one-step process. The chemical structure shown in square brackets in Figure 20.3 is not an intermediate (as the carbocation in the S$_N$1 reaction discussed later is) but a **transition state**. It is a halfway stage in the reaction, where covalent bonds on the carbon atom are being simultaneously broken and made – each of these half-formed bonds has a bond order of 0.5. The transition state is believed to have a trigonal bipyramidal shape (see Chapter 14).

The reaction profile of the S$_N$2 reaction is shown in Figure 20.4. Do note the absence of an intermediate dip in the curve that would have corresponded to the existence of a reaction intermediate. Note also that the nucleophile attacks the electron-deficient carbon atom on the opposite side from the halogen – sometimes referred to as 'backside (or rear-side) attack' – and this causes the inversion of the arrangement of the other groups or atoms around the carbon atom. This is known as a Walden inversion after the Latvian chemist who first described this process using stereoisomers of the target halogenoalkane (see later in the chapter). This inversion process has been likened to an umbrella being blown inside-out in a strong wind (Figure 20.5).

The stereochemistry observed in the S$_N$2 mechanism can be explained by molecular orbital (MO) theory (Chapter 14). The theory suggests that the orbital from the incoming nucleophile starts to overlap with the empty anti-bonding orbital of the C–X bond, where X is a halogen (Figure 20.6). As this interaction increases, the bonding interaction between the carbon and the halogen decreases until the transition state is reached, where the incoming nucleophile and outgoing leaving group are both partially bonded (bond order 0.5). The orbital geometry requires the nucleophile and the leaving group to be on opposite sides of the molecule.

■ **Figure 20.6** Orbital interactions in the S$_N$2 mechanism

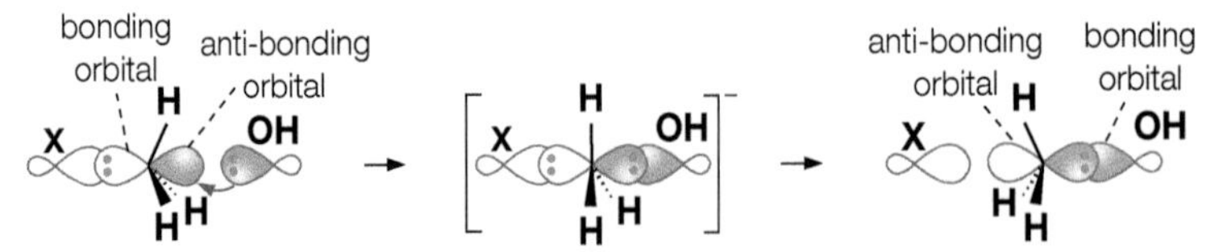

There is in fact another mechanism by which the nucleophilic substitution of halogenoalkanes can be achieved. The major factor that determines which mechanism takes place in a particular case is thought to depend primarily on the structure of the halogenoalkane.

The S$_N$1 reaction

Tertiary halogenoalkanes also undergo a substitution reaction, but kinetic studies show that the mechanism is different from that occurring with primary halogenoalkanes. For example, consider the reaction between 2-bromo-2-methylpropane and hydroxide ions (Figure 20.7).

■ **Figure 20.7** An S$_N$1 reaction

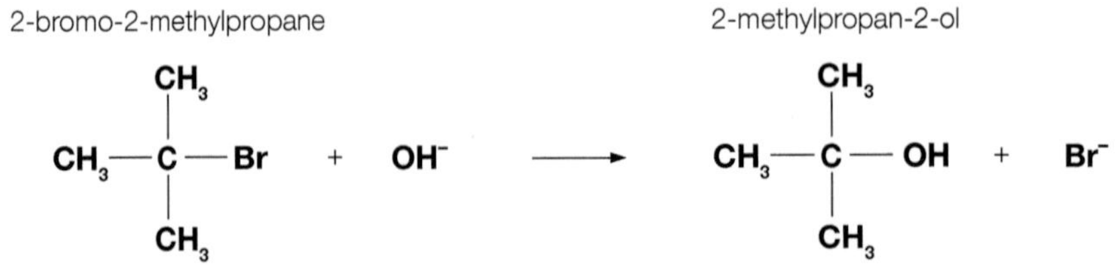

rate = k[CH$_3$C(CH$_3$)$_2$ Br(aq)]

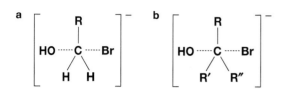

a

$$\left[\begin{array}{c} R \\ | \\ HO \cdots C \cdots Br \\ | \quad | \\ H \quad H \end{array} \right]^{-}$$

b

$$\left[\begin{array}{c} R \\ | \\ HO \cdots C \cdots Br \\ | \quad | \\ R' \quad R'' \end{array} \right]^{-}$$

■ **Figure 20.8** The structure of the intermediate (transition structure) in an S_N2 reaction involving **a** a primary halogenoalkane, and **b** a tertiary halogenoalkane (the bulky R groups make this mechanism difficult)

Kinetic studies show that this reaction is unimolecular, with the rate-determining step involving just the halogenoalkane molecule.

This reaction has a different mechanism for several reasons. The presence of the three alkyl groups around the carbon of the carbon–halogen bond (see Figure 20.8b) causes what is called steric hindrance, meaning that these bulky groups make it difficult for an incoming group to attack this carbon atom. Note the difference when compared with the situation involving a primary molecule, where hydrogen atoms are attached to the carbon atom (Figure 20.8a).

Instead, the first step of the reaction with a tertiary halogenoalkane involves ionization of the halogenoalkane through the breaking of its carbon–bromine bond. This is an example of heterolytic fission. The pair of electrons in the bond both end up on the halogen, forming the bromide ion. This leaves a temporary positive charge on the electron-deficient carbon atom, and the species produced is a type of carbocation (see Figure 20.9).

■ **Figure 20.9**
The S_N1 mechanism for the hydrolysis of 2-bromo-2-methylpropane

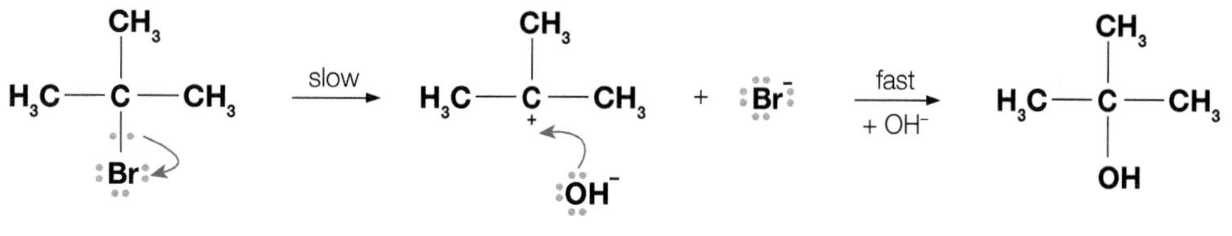

$$H_3C-\underset{\underset{Br}{|}}{\overset{\overset{CH_3}{|}}{C}}-CH_3 \quad \xrightarrow{\text{slow}} \quad H_3C-\underset{\underset{+}{|}}{\overset{\overset{CH_3}{|}}{C}}-CH_3 \quad + \quad Br^{-} \quad \xrightarrow[+ OH^{-}]{\text{fast}} \quad H_3C-\underset{\underset{OH}{|}}{\overset{\overset{CH_3}{|}}{C}}-CH_3$$

$$OH^{-}$$

2-Bromo-2-methylpropane is a tertiary halogenoalkane and the hydrolysis of this compound proceeds by an S_N1 mechanism (Figure 20.7). The hydrolysis is a first-order reaction, which means that the rate doubles if we double the concentration of the halogenoalkane, for instance. However, if we double the concentration of hydroxide ions, OH^{-}, the rate does not change at all. The rate depends only on the concentration of the bromoalkane and is independent of the hydroxide ion concentration. Kinetically this means that hydroxide ions cannot be involved in the rate-determining step. The mechanism is shown in Figure 20.9.

The first step of the reaction involves only the heterolysis of the C–Br bond, forming the carbocation intermediate and a bromide ion. The original halogenoalkane is tetrahedral in shape around the target carbon atom. This is the slowest (rate-determining) step in the reaction, and the hydroxide ions do not participate in it. If the concentration of hydroxide ions were increased, the rate of the second step would also increase. But this second step is already faster than the first one, so the rate of the overall reaction is unaffected.

Following the detachment of the Br^{-} ion, the intermediate carbocation is trigonal planar in shape. This contributes to the speed of the second step – the attachment of the OH^{-} ion – as it can attack from either side of the planar carbocation. The reaction profile of the S_N1 reaction is shown in Figure 20.10.

■ **Figure 20.10**
The reaction profile for an S_N1 mechanism

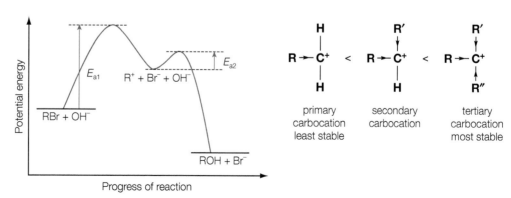

The first step in this reaction involves bond breaking, which is an endothermic process. This results in the relatively high activation energy of the first step, E_{a1}. The activation energy of the second step, E_{a2}, is lower as oppositely charged ions attract each other strongly.

Another factor which favours this mechanism is that the carbocation is stabilized by the presence of the three alkyl groups, each of which have an electron-donating effect (sometimes called a positive inductive effect), shown by the arrows in the structures on the right in Figure 20.10.

As the slow step of this reaction is determined by the concentration of only one reactant (the halogenoalkane), it is described as a unimolecular reaction. This reaction mechanism is therefore described as an S_N1 (substitution nucleophilic unimolecular) reaction.

The mechanism of nucleophilic substitution in secondary halogenoalkanes is less easy to define as the data show that they usually undergo a mixture of both S_N1 and S_N2 mechanisms, depending on the reaction conditions, or, possibly, some mechanism in between the two.

The relative reactivity of the different halogens in these reactions depends on the strength of their bonds with carbon, and this decreases as we go down the halogen group. The iodoalkane with the longest, and hence weakest, carbon–halogen bond is the most reactive and the fluoroalkane is the least reactive. Kinetic studies on these reactions can be carried out by a variety of methods. One interesting method, which establishes the S_N1 mechanism for tertiary halogenoalkanes, is to follow the increase in conductivity of the reaction mixture when 2-chloro-2-methylpropane is hydrolysed by water.

As the reaction proceeds, the conductivity of the reaction mixture increases as the chloride ion (Cl^-) is released from the halogenoalkane molecule. The hydrogen ion (H^+) is also produced. Figure 20.11 shows one trace of the increase in conductivity obtained using a conductivity sensor linked to a data-logger. A series of such traces at different concentrations of halogenoalkane can demonstrate that the reaction is first order (there is just one molecule involved in the rate-determining step – see Chapter 16):

$$CH_3C(CH_3)_2Cl + H_2O \rightarrow CH_3C(CH_3)_2OH + HCl$$

$$\text{rate} = k[CH_3C(CH_3)_2Cl]$$

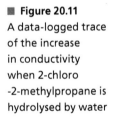

■ **Figure 20.11**
A data-logged trace of the increase in conductivity when 2-chloro -2-methylpropane is hydrolysed by water

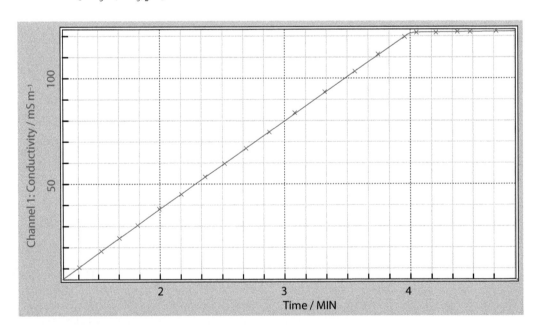

Factors affecting the rate of nucleophilic substitution

There are various factors that affect the rate of a nucleophilic substitution reaction involving a halogenoalkane:

■ the nature of the nucleophile
■ the identity of the halogen involved

- the structural type of the halogenoalkane
- the solvent involved, which can favour a particular substitution mechanism and also determine whether a nucleophilic substitution or an elimination reaction takes place.

We will look at the influence of these factors in the next sections.

The nature of the nucleophile

In this context a nucleophile is a species that is attracted to the partially positive carbon atom ($\delta+$) that is bonded to the electronegative halogen atom. Effective nucleophiles are neutral or negatively charged structures that have a lone pair of electrons which they can donate to make a new bond to the carbon atom. The more dense the negative charge on the ion or molecule is, the better it will act as a nucleophile. As a result, the negative anions tend to be more reactive than the corresponding neutral species. For example, the rate of substitution with hydroxide ions is faster than with water molecules; water is a weaker nucleophile than the hydroxide ion.

Where species have the same charge, the controlling factor seems to be the electronegativity of the atom carrying the lone pair of electrons. The less electronegative the atom carrying the non-bonded lone pair of electrons, the better the nucleophile. Thus ammonia is a better nucleophile than water, as nitrogen is less electronegative than oxygen.

The reason for this is that the less electronegative the atom is, the more easily it can donate its pair of electrons to make the new bond, as they are being held less strongly to that atom. Cyanide ions are the most effective common nucleophile. The effectiveness of nucleophiles follows the order below:

$$CN^- > OH^- > NH_3 > H_2O$$

decreasing nucleophilic strength

The identity of the halogen

An essential part of the substitution mechanism is that the halogen group in the target molecule must be able to leave. The carbon–halogen bond must be weak enough to allow this to happen. This consideration seems to be the most important factor in determining which is the best leaving group of the halogens. The reactivity of halogenoalkanes seems to depend on the ability of the carbon–halogen bond to break heterolytically and for the halogen to then leave as a halide ion; this is the reason that the halogen is referred to as the leaving group. Iodine is the best leaving group, and fluorine is the worst (Figure 20.12).

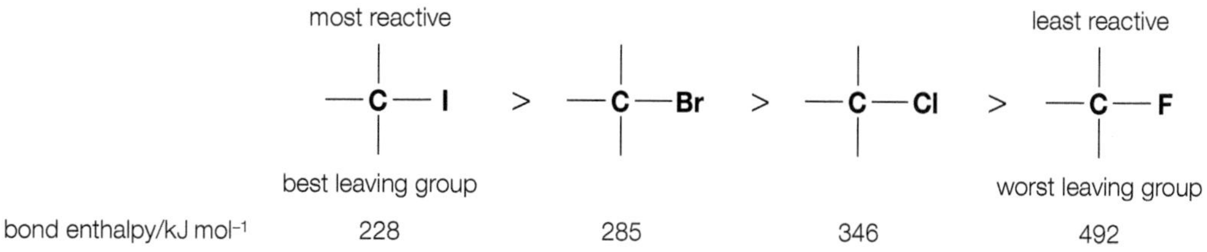

■ **Figure 20.12**
The bond enthalpy of the carbon–halogen bond determines how easily the halogen atom leaves the halogenoalkane molecule

	most reactive					least reactive
	$-\overset{|}{\underset{|}{C}}-I$	$>$	$-\overset{|}{\underset{|}{C}}-Br$	$>$	$-\overset{|}{\underset{|}{C}}-Cl$	$>$ $-\overset{|}{\underset{|}{C}}-F$
	best leaving group					worst leaving group
bond enthalpy/kJ mol^{-1}	228		285		346	492

This does raise an interesting point, because fluorine is the most electronegative of the halogens and therefore the carbon–fluorine bond will be the most polar: that is, it will have the most ionic character. Given that nucleophiles are attracted to the electron-deficient ($\delta+$) carbon atom, we might have predicted that fluoroalkanes would in fact be the most reactive. However, the practical evidence that fluoroalkanes are unreactive suggests that the polarity of the carbon–halogen bond in the molecule is not nearly as important a factor as the *strength* of the carbon–halogen bond. This is borne out by the fact that iodoalkanes, where the bonds are the least polarized, are the most reactive, as the carbon–iodine bond is the longest and, therefore, the weakest.

Looked at from a different perspective, the best leaving groups are those that form the most stable molecules or ions after they depart. This means that, in general, the best leaving groups are the ions or molecules that are the weakest bases. Of the halogens, an iodide ion is the best leaving group and a fluoride ion is the poorest:

$$I^- > Br^- > Cl^- \gg F^-$$

So the effect of the leaving group on the rate of reaction in both S_N1 and S_N2 reactions is:

$$R–I > R–Br > R–Cl > R–F$$

Nature of Science

Communicating the specifics

Different branches of science have to communicate particular ideas in a very specific way. To do this they develop a specific 'language' with a precise vocabulary and set of symbols. In the field of organic mechanism we have seen the use of 'curly' and 'half' arrows to depict the movement of electrons during a reaction. The use of this symbolism and the words that accompany it is, of necessity, very precise because it defines our understanding of the progress of reactions.

The meaning of the term 'leaving group' is reasonably self-evident in this context: it is the species that detaches from the electron-deficient carbon atom to make way for the nucleophile to bond to that carbon atom. A further factor that influences the ease of 'leaving', other than those that have already been discussed, is the stability of the group once it has detached from the carbon atom. The more stable the molecule or ion, the better it functions as a leaving group. The less stable, or more reactive, the leaving group is, the more it is likely to act as a nucleophile. If this happens then the reaction simply goes round in circles.

Neutral molecules are better leaving groups than negative ions. Thus a water molecule is a better leaving group than an OH^- ion. Within the halogens, the iodide ion (I^-) is the most stable ion and therefore the best leaving group.

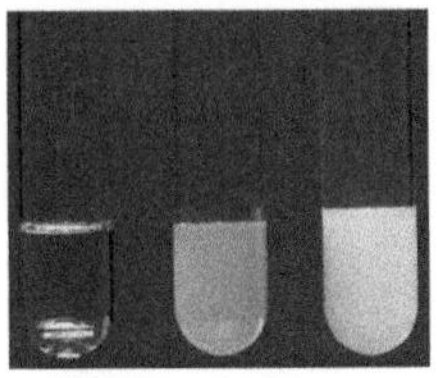

Some of the experimental evidence on which halogenoalkanes are most susceptible to nucleophilic attack has been gained using an aqueous silver nitrate solution as the source of the nucleophile. The solvent, water, is the nucleophile. The usefulness of this approach is that the appearance of the released halide ion is immediately detected by precipitation with the silver ions. Figure 20.13 shows the precipitates produced as a result of adding halogenobutanes (RCl, RBr and RI) separately to silver nitrate solution. The precipitates seen here are (left to right) silver chloride, silver bromide and silver iodide. The time taken for the precipitate to appear may be used as a comparative measure of the ease with which the substitution occurs.

The structural type of the halogenoalkane

Kinetic studies demonstrate that substitution reactions with primary halogenoalkanes proceed by an S_N2 mechanism. Substitution reactions with tertiary halogenoalkanes, however, proceed by an S_N1 mechanism in which an intermediate carbocation is formed. The reaction is first order with respect to the halogenoalkane, and is independent of the concentration of the nucleophile. It involves two steps. A similar experimental approach to that described above using aqueous silver nitrate solution can be used as part of an investigation to determine the relative rate of substitution of primary, secondary or tertiary bromoalkanes.

In these experiments the precipitate of silver bromide appears fastest when a tertiary bromoalkane is being substituted (Figure 20.14). Experimentally, S_N1 reactions are generally found to be faster than S_N2 reactions. This may be because the activation energy required to form the tertiary carbocation intermediate is less than the activation energy required to form the transition state of the S_N2 reaction.

■ **Figure 20.13**
Using silver nitrate solution to indicate the release of halide ions during nucleophilic substitution: the white precipitate of silver chloride is yet to appear in the left-hand tube, showing that this substitution is the slowest of the three

■ **Figure 20.14**
The timing of the appearance of the off-white precipitate of silver bromide indicates the rate of substitution of the halogenoalkane

after 10 minutes faint precipitates of AgBr(s)
getting denser

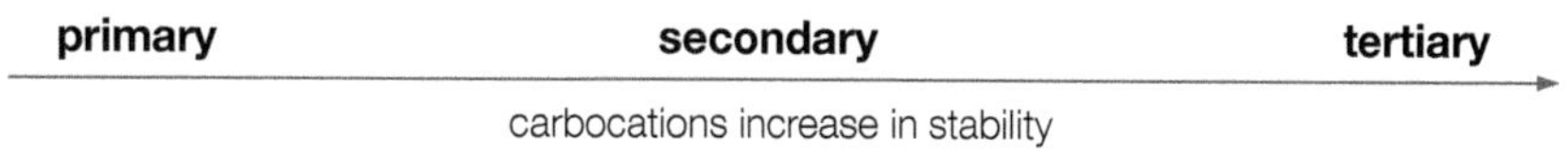

■ **Figure 20.15**
The relative stability of primary, secondary and tertiary carbocations

primary	secondary	tertiary

carbocations increase in stability

The more alkyl groups there are attached to the positively charged carbon at the centre of the carbocation, the more energetically stable the ion. Therefore the stability of carbocations increases in the order shown in Figure 20.15. As the carbocation becomes more stable, the activation energy for the reaction leading to its formation also decreases (see Figure 20.10). Consequently we would expect that the rate of the S_N1 reaction will increase in the order primary < secondary < tertiary. Table 20.2 gives an indication of the relative rates of reaction for the nucleophilic substitution of different bromoalkanes under identical experimental conditions.

■ **Table 20.2**
The relative rates of the S_N1 reactions for different types of bromoalkane

Type of halogenoalkane	Compound	Relative rate of S_N1 reaction
Primary	CH_3CH_2Br	1
Secondary	$(CH_3)_2CHBr$	26
Tertiary	$(CH_3)_3CBr$	60 000 000

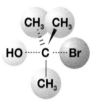

■ **Figure 20.16**
Different transition states for S_N2 reactions; the presence of more –CH_3 groups makes the second example more 'crowded' (sterically hindered)

The additional energetic stability of the tertiary carbocation arises because of the electron-donating effect (positive induction effect) of an alkyl group in such structures, mentioned earlier. An alkyl group, such as a methyl or ethyl group, affects the electron density of a structure in a way that a hydrogen atom does not. A hydrogen atom has no electrons associated with it other than those in its bond. A methyl group, however, has the three electron pairs in the carbon–hydrogen bonds in the group. In a carbocation, these electrons can be attracted towards the positive charge. Electron density is fed towards the charge, tending to lower the overall value of the charge and stabilizing the ion. Thus a methyl group, and other alkyl groups, are said to be electron-donating. This enhanced stability of the tertiary or secondary carbocation when compared to a primary carbocation is influential not only in the context of nucleophilic substitution mechanisms, but also in determining the major product of electrophilic addition reactions to asymmetric alkenes (see later in this chapter).

No intermediate carbocations are formed during an S_N2 reaction, so other factors must now come into play in determining the rate of reaction. The transition state in this type of reaction has five groups arranged around the central carbon atom in a trigonal bipyramid structure. It is therefore more crowded than either the starting bromoalkane or the alcohol product, each of which has only four groups around the central carbon atom. Hydrogen atoms are much smaller than alkyl groups. We therefore expect that the more alkyl groups there are around the central carbon atom, the more crowded will be the transition state (Figure 20.16), and the higher will be the activation energy, E_a (Figure 20.4). This will slow down the reaction (Table 20.3).

■ **Table 20.3**
The relative rates of the S_N2 reactions for different types of bromoalkane

Type of halogenoalkane	Compound	Relative rate of S_N2 reaction
Primary	CH_3CH_2Br	1000
Secondary	$(CH_3)_2CHBr$	10
Tertiary	$(CH_3)_3CBr$	1

■ **Figure 20.17**
The relative rates of reaction for S_N1 and S_N2 reactions for primary, secondary and tertiary halogenoalkanes

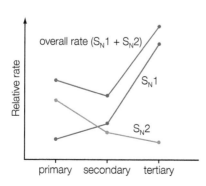

These two effects we have discussed here reinforce each other. The S_N1 reaction is faster for tertiary halogenoalkanes than for primary halogenoalkanes, whereas the S_N2 reaction is faster with primary molecules than with tertiary molecules under the same conditions in the same solvent. Overall, therefore, we would expect primary halogenoalkanes to react predominantly by the S_N2 mechanism, tertiary halogenoalkanes to react predominantly by the S_N1 mechanism, and secondary halogenoalkanes to react by a mixture of the two (Figure 20.17).

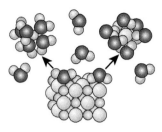

■ **Figure 20.18** Water molecules form 'shells' around sodium (yellow) and chloride (blue) ions when the salt dissolves. Note the difference in orientation of the water molecules around the cations and anions

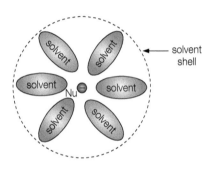

■ **Figure 20.19** Depending on the type of solvent used, the nucleophile may become surrounded by a solvent shell

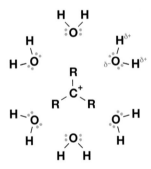

■ **Figure 20.20** Solvation of a carbocation by water. The ion is stabilized by ion–dipole interactions with the O atoms of water

The influence of the solvent on substitution

The solvent used to carry out a reaction can have a clear influence on the type of mechanism favoured and the rate of the reaction precisely because it provides the environment in which the reactant species are functioning. When molecules or ions are dissolved in a solvent they interact with the solvent molecules. Thus, for example, sodium and chloride ions gain hydration shells when the salt dissolves (Figure 20.18).

In these substitution reactions, the molecules and ions involved, including the intermediate species, are not necessarily 'naked' in a given environment, they can become solvated (Figure 20.19). This will, in turn, influence their interaction with the target molecule (sometimes referred to as the substrate). This means that they become surrounded by a shell of solvent molecules in the same way that sodium and chloride ions have hydration shells when dissolved in water.

There are a range of different solvents that can be used for these reactions, with the key property in this context being their polarity, and particularly their ability to form hydrogen bonds. Solvents can be divided into two broad categories – polar and non-polar. Non-polar solvents include hydrocarbons such as hexane or cyclohexane, and compounds such as tetrachloromethane. Non-polar solvents are not useful in a context where we are dealing with polarized and ionic species. Polar solvents are more useful in this context and can themselves be subdivided into protic and aprotic solvents:

- Protic polar solvents have molecules containing a hydrogen atom bonded to a highly electronegative nitrogen or oxygen atom. They can therefore participate in hydrogen bonding. Examples of protic polar solvents are water, ethanol, carboxylic acids and ammonia.
- Aprotic polar solvents may contain hydrogen atoms but they are not bonded to nitrogen or oxygen atoms and so cannot participate in hydrogen bonding. Examples of aprotic polar solvents are propanone (CH_3COCH_3), ethoxyethane ($C_2H_5OC_2H_5$), ethanenitrile (CH_3CN) and dimethyl sulfoxide (DMSO, ($CH_3)_2SO$).

The key difference is that protic polar solvents are capable of forming a solvation shell around both positive and negative ions. The interaction with a positive ion is through the nitrogen or the oxygen atom in the molecule (which has a $\delta-$ charge) (Figure 20.20), whereas the interaction with a negative ion is with the hydrogen atom(s) attached to the nitrogen or oxygen atoms through hydrogen bonding. Conversely, aprotic solvent molecules are able to solvate positive ions well but do not interact well with negative ions because of the absence of hydrogen atoms that are $\delta+$.

Consider now the action of the solvent in the context of the two different mechanisms of nucleophilic substitution. Any formation of a solvent shell around the nucleophile is in the way, holding back the nucleophile from attacking the halogenoalkane. For the nucleophile to do its job, the nucleophile must first shed this solvent shell. This is always the case when a nucleophile is dissolved in a polar protic solvent, but not so when a polar aprotic solvent is used.

As we have seen polar aprotic solvents are not very good at forming solvent shells around negative charges. So if a nucleophile is dissolved in a polar aprotic solvent, the nucleophile is said to be a 'naked' nucleophile, not having a solvent shell. Therefore, it does not need to first shed a solvent shell before it can react with the target molecule. This effect is very marked. As you can imagine, a nucleophile with a solvent shell is going to be slower in attacking the target molecule. By using an aprotic solvent and allowing the nucleophile to react all of the time, we are greatly speeding up the reaction. S_N2 reactions performed with nucleophiles in polar aprotic solvents occur about 1000 times faster than those in regular protic solvents.

- S_N2 reactions are favoured by using aprotic, polar solvents.

In the S_N1 mechanism the attack of the nucleophile is not the rate-determining step. That step involves the formation of the positively charged intermediate and the halide ion. Both these ions can be stabilized by the molecules of a polar protic solvent, whereas a polar aprotic solvent would not be as effective at stabilizing the negative ion formed in the rate-determining step. So this mechanism is favoured by using a protic polar solvent.

- S_N1 reactions are favoured by using protic, polar solvents.

1 Classify the following solvents as non-polar, polar aprotic or polar protic solvents.
  a methylbenzene, $C_6H_5CH_3$
  b methanol, CH_3OH
  c dimethyl sulfoxide, $(CH_3)_2S=O$
  d liquid ammonia, NH_3
  e propanone, CH_3COCH_3
  f dimethylformamide, $H(CO)N(CH_3)_2$
  g tetrachloromethane, CCl_4
  h tetrahydrofuran($TH(CH_2)_4O$)

2 1-bromoethane reacts with sodium hydroxide.
  a Explain the mechanism of this type of reaction, representing the movement of any electron pairs and describing any stereochemical features of the mechanism.
  b State the rate expression for this reaction and identify the molecularity of the rate-determining step (RDS). Explain why it is referred to as an S_N2 reaction.
  c Suggest why polar aprotic solvents are more suitable for S_N2 reactions whereas polar protic solvents favour S_N1 reactions.
  d Deduce, with a reason, if water or DMF (*N,N*-dimethylformamide), $HCON(CH_3)_2$) is a better solvent for this reaction.

Competition between nucleophilic substitution and elimination

A close look at the nature of a nucleophile will emphasize that it shares common features with a Lewis base (see Chapter 18). Indeed, a nucleophilic species can act as such a base if the reaction conditions are appropriate – it can remove a proton (H^+ ion) from a halogenoalkane and thereby initiate an elimination reaction. In this type of reaction HX is eliminated from the halogenoalkane and an alkene is produced. It is essential to realize that, given the similarity of the reagents involved, the two processes of nucleophilic substitution and elimination are generally in competition with each other. If a primary halogenoalkane is reacted with aqueous alkali (OH^-(aq)) then the substitution reaction we have discussed earlier is favoured. However, if ethanolic alkali (OH^-(ethanol)) is used, then the elimination reaction is favoured.

This is particularly true where tertiary halogenoalkanes are involved, as the E1 mechanism favoured in these reactions involves the same first step – the production of the intermediate carbocation. As a result of this competition between the two processes going on simultaneously, it is very difficult to obtain 'clean' products in these reactions. A single product will always have to be separated from a number of by-products.

Table 20.4 provides a summary of the major features of the two nucleophilic substitution mechanisms.

■ **Table 20.4**
A comparison of the S_N2 and S_N1 mechanisms of nucleophilic substitution

	S_N1	S_N2
Kinetics	First order (two-step mechanism)	Second order (one-step mechanism)
Nature of mechanism	Two-step reaction via a carbocation intermediate	Concerted one-step mechanism with unstable transition state
Substrate (R–L), where R represents an alkyl group and L represents the leaving group	Tertiary halogenoalkane, as R–L that forms the most stable carbocation favoured	Primary halogenoalkane: methyl > primary > secondary (there should not be any bulky alkyl groups at the carbon centre)
Nucleophile	Not important	Non-bulky strong nucleophile favoured
Solvent	Polar, protic solvent favoured	Polar, aprotic solvent favoured
Stereochemistry	Racemization	Inversion
Leaving group (L)	Good leaving group favoured	Good leaving group favoured
Reaction profile		

Nitrogen-containing nucleophiles

Ammonia as a nucleophile

As mentioned earlier, ammonia can act as a nucleophile through its lone pair of electrons on the nitrogen atom. Ammonia reacts with bromoethane by an S_N2 mechanism to form ethylamine and hydrogen bromide:

$$CH_3CH_2Br + \overset{\cdot\cdot}{N}H_3 \rightarrow CH_3CH_2\overset{\cdot\cdot}{N}H_2 + HBr$$
bromoethane   ethylamine

However, the product ethylamine is also a nucleophile, because the nitrogen atom still has a non-bonding pair of electrons. Thus the reaction can proceed further. The product, ethylamine, can react with more bromoethane to produce diethylamine – a secondary amine:

$$CH_3CH_2Br + CH_3CH_2\overset{\cdot\cdot}{N}H_2 \rightarrow (CH_3CH_2)_2\overset{\cdot\cdot}{N}H + HBr$$
bromoethane   ethylamine   diethylamine

Indeed, further substitution is possible to produce the tertiary amine triethylamine, $(CH_3CH_2)_3N$. The fact that these successive substitutions take place means that this is not a 'clean' way to prepare a particular amine and that there may be other, preferable, routes if a particular amine is the target of a synthesis.

In fact there are four possible substitution products possible in the reaction between ammonia and a halogenoalkane. Triethylamine itself still has a nitrogen atom with an unbonded pair of electrons at its centre. As such it can again act as a nucleophile and gain a fourth ethyl group to form the equivalent of an ammonium salt, tetraethylammonium bromide, $(CH_3CH_2)_4N^+Br^-$ (Figure 20.21).

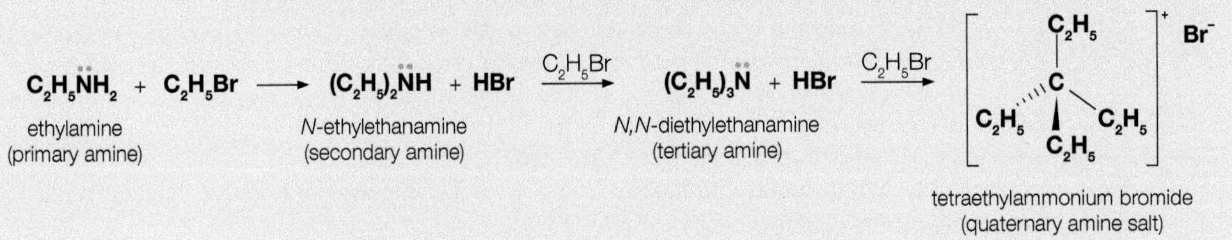

■ **Figure 20.21** The reaction sequence of successive substitutions when ammonia reacts with excess bromoethane. Note the use of alternative IUPAC names for the products

The cyanide ion as a nucleophile

Nucleophilic substitution reactions are important in organic synthesis because the halogen atom on halogenoalkanes can be replaced by other functional groups. The reaction with potassium cyanide is a good illustration of this. The cyanide ion reacts to form a nitrile. For example, bromoethane reacts by an S_N2 mechanism with a solution of potassium cyanide in ethanol to form propanenitrile:

$$CH_3CH_2Br + K\overset{\cdot\cdot}{C}N \rightarrow CH_3CH_2\overset{\cdot\cdot}{C}N + KBr$$
bromoethane   propanenitrile

A comparison of the names of the reactant and organic product here gives an indication of the potential significance of this particular reaction. With the introduction of the nitrile group into the molecule we have effectively extended the carbon chain.

Both the nucleophilic substitution reactions we have just considered proceed by an S_N2 mechanism. Figure 20.22 shows the mechanism involved, with the lone pair on the nitrogen of the ammonia molecule forming a bond to the electron-deficient carbon atom in bromoethane, for instance.

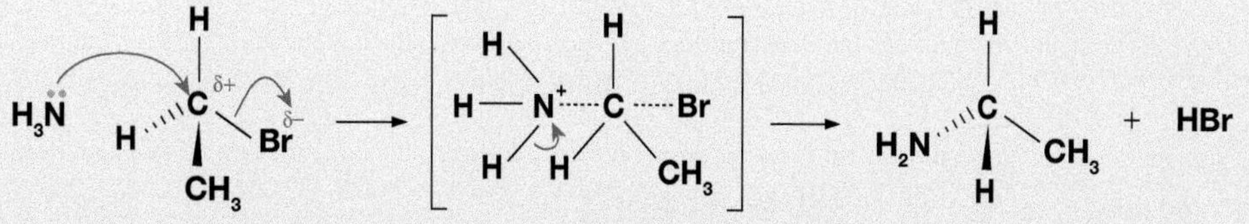

■ **Figure 20.22**
The S_N2 mechanism of substitution for the reaction between ammonia and bromoethane

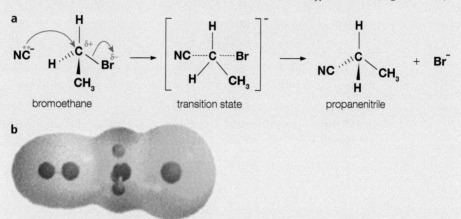

The reaction of cyanide ions with bromoethane is also an S_N2 reaction (Figure 20.23).

■ **Figure 20.23**
a The S_N2 mechanism for the reaction between cyanide ions and bromoethane molecules
b A computerized model of the transition state, showing the central trigonal planar arrangement around the carbon atom

a

bromoethane   transition state   propanenitrile

b

Nitriles as intermediates in organic synthesis

As we indicated above, the formation of a nitrile from a halogenoalkane is useful in devising synthetic pathways because it is a way of extending the carbon chain (an alternative method of achieving this uses Grignard reagents). However, this would be of little use to organic and industrial chemists if the nitrile produced could not be converted into useful organic products. Fortunately, nitriles can be reduced using hydrogen gas and a heated nickel catalyst to form amines:

$$CH_3CH_2CN + 2H_2 \xrightarrow[\text{catalyst}]{\text{Ni}} CH_3CH_2CH_2NH_2$$

They can also be hydrolysed in acid solution to form carboxylic acids, which can then be reacted to form many other compounds (Figure 20.24).

■ **Figure 20.24**
Two useful reactions of organic nitriles

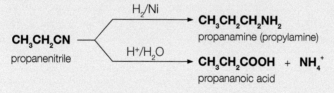

CH₃CH₂CN
propanenitrile

H₂/Ni → **CH₃CH₂CH₂NH₂**
propanamine (propylamine)

H⁺/H₂O → **CH₃CH₂COOH + NH₄⁺**
propananoic acid

■ Electrophilic addition reactions

Electrophilic addition to alkenes

Alkenes are unsaturated molecules and they are important compounds in many synthetic pathways because of their readiness to undergo addition reactions. The structure of alkenes makes these molecules particularly susceptible to electrophilic attack. Each carbon atom involved in the carbon–carbon double bond makes three σ bonds with bond angles of 120°, so the region immediately around the double bond is planar. The remaining shared pair of electrons which complete the double bond between the two carbon atoms are contained in a molecular orbital that lies above and below this plane, forming a localized π bond above and below this plane. Electrophiles are attracted to this pair of electrons. The fact that all alkenes are planar in this region of their molecules helps in making the polarizable π electrons readily accessible for interaction with an approaching electrophile (Figure 20.25).

■ **Figure 20.25**
Molecular models of ethene and propene showing the localized π bond characteristic of these compounds

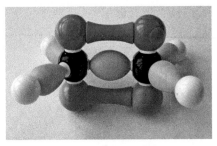 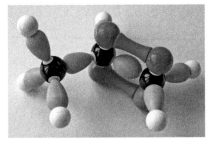

ethene   propene

Unlike alkanes, alkenes react with bromine at room temperature, and even in the dark. The reaction takes place either with bromine water or with a solution of bromine in an inert organic solvent such as hexane. For example, the reaction of ethene with bromine in hexane is:

$$CH_2=CH_2 + Br_2 \xrightarrow[\text{in hexane}]{\text{room temperature}} Br-CH_2-CH_2-Br$$

The reaction is an electrophilic addition, like most of the reactions of alkenes. The π bond of ethene is an electron-rich area ($\delta-$). Repulsion of the electrons of the Br–Br bond by the π electron cloud induces a temporary dipole in an approaching bromine molecule (Figure 20.26a).

■ **Figure 20.26**
The mechanism of electrophilic addition of bromine to ethene.
a The induction of a temporary dipole in a bromine molecule and electrophilic attack on the ethene molecule.
b Attachment of the bromide ion to the newly formed carbocation

Heterolytic fission of the Br–Br bond eventually takes place to form a bromide ion, Br^-. The π electrons move to form a σ bond between one of the carbon atoms and the nearest bromine atom. The movement of a pair of electrons away from the other carbon atom results in the production of an electron-deficient carbocation. Finally, the bromide ion acts as a nucleophile and forms a (dative) bond to the carbocation intermediate (Figure 20.26b). The product of this reaction is 1,2-dibromoethane (CH_2BrCH_2Br).

Other alkenes undergo similar reactions with bromine in solution in hexane. For example, propene reacts to give 1,2-dibromopropane, and but-2-ene to form 2,3-dibromobutane:

$$CH_3CH=CH_2(g) + Br_2(\text{inert solvent}) \rightarrow CH_3CHBrCH_2Br(l)$$
propene   1,2-dibromopropane

$$CH_3CH=CHCH_3(g) + Br_2(\text{inert solvent}) \rightarrow CH_3CHBrCHBrCH_3(l)$$
but-2-ene   2,3-dibromobutane

Evidence for the mechanism of electrophilic addition

Other nucleophiles can also attack the carbocation produced as an intermediate in electrophilic addition. In bromine water, for example, the water molecule is present in a much higher concentration than the bromide ion, and so is the nucleophile more likely to attach to the carbocation (Figure 20.27).

■ **Figure 20.27**
The latter part of the mechanism by which 2-bromoethanol is produced in the reaction between ethene and bromine water

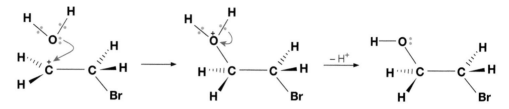

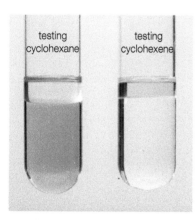

testing cyclohexane   testing cyclohexene

■ **Figure 20.28** The reaction of an alkene with bromine water serves as a test for unsaturation

Bromine water is frequently used as the test for an alkene, with the bromine water being decolorized as the positive outcome of the test (Figure 20.28). The major product of the test is 2-bromoethanol rather than 1,2-dibromoethane.

Similar products are produced with other alkenes. The incorporation of a water molecule, and the consequent production of the bromoalcohol, is good evidence for this suggested mechanism via an intermediate carbocation. Further evidence supporting the two-step mechanism is the incorporation of 'foreign' competing anions when bromination is carried out in an aqueous solution containing a mixture of various salts. For instance, if ethene is reacted with bromine water that also contains dissolved sodium chloride and sodium nitrate, then a mixture of products is formed (Figure 20.29).

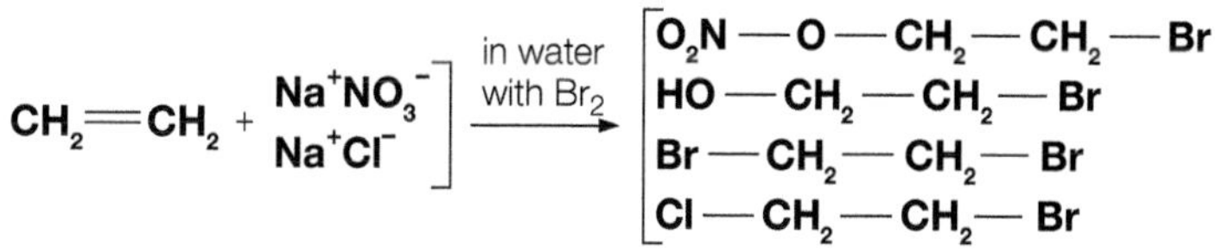

$$CH_2{=}CH_2 + \left.\begin{matrix} Na^+NO_3^- \\ Na^+Cl^- \end{matrix}\right] \xrightarrow[\text{with } Br_2]{\text{in water}} \left[\begin{matrix} O_2N{-}O{-}CH_2{-}CH_2{-}Br \\ HO{-}CH_2{-}CH_2{-}Br \\ Br{-}CH_2{-}CH_2{-}Br \\ Cl{-}CH_2{-}CH_2{-}Br \end{matrix}\right.$$

■ **Figure 20.29** The products formed when ethane reacts with bromine water containing salts

The ratio $(ClCH_2CH_2Br):(O_2NOCH_2CH_2Br)$ in the mixture is found to correspond to the $[Cl^-]:[NO_3^-]$ ratio in the original solution, indicating that the carbocation reacts with the first anion it successfully collides with – as would be expected for a cation of such high reactivity.

It should also be noted that, for instance, no 1,2-dichloroethane is detected in the products. This indicates that the initial attacking species is not the chloride ion (Cl^-) – indeed there is no reaction between ethene and sodium chloride solution itself. This, and the fact that all the products contain bromine, is consistent with bromine being involved in the first step of the mechanism to produce the carbocation – then the anions present react with that carbocation.

An intriguing and colourful angle on the addition of bromine to carbon–carbon double bonds is the reaction between bromine and tomato juice. Bromination of a normal unhindered double bond is usually a very rapid reaction – hence its usefulness as a test for unsaturation. In this experiment, fresh tomato juice is poured into a graduated measuring cylinder, and bromine water is then carefully layered on the top. A rainbow-like coloration develops in the tomato juice layer. This results from the reaction of bromine with lycopene, a carotenoid present in tomato juice that contains 13 conjugated double bonds! A stable charge transfer complex with a blue colour is formed. Upon further reaction with bromine water, lycopene essentially becomes pale yellow. The mixture of the blue colour with the reddish-orange of the tomato juice and the pale yellow colour cause the appearance of a rainbow to form progressively down the measuring cylinder.

The addition of HBr to alkenes

Molecules such as hydrogen bromide are permanently polar because of the higher electronegativity of bromine compared with hydrogen. The mechanism of electrophilic addition of hydrogen bromide is similar to that involving bromine. The electron pair of the π bond forms a bond with the hydrogen atom, which is polarized δ+, releasing a bromide ion in the process. This can be shown using curly arrows to represent the movement of pairs of electrons. During the process, a carbocation intermediate is formed, which reacts with a bromide ion to form the product (Figure 20.30).

The overall equation for the reaction is:

$$CH_2=CH_2(g) + HBr(g) \rightarrow CH_3–CH_2Br(l)$$
bromoethane

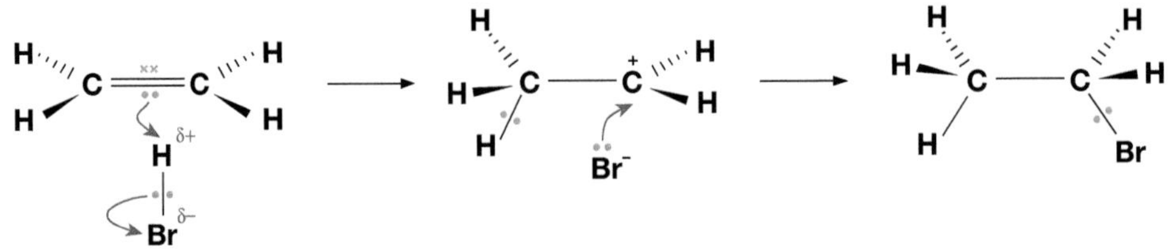

■ **Figure 20.30**
The mechanism of electrophilic addition of hydrogen bromide to ethene

Electrophilic addition to asymmetrical alkenes

An interesting situation arises in the case of asymmetrical alkenes such as propene and but-1-ene. Consider the addition of hydrogen bromide to propene: two possible carbocation intermediates can be formed, leading to two different products (Figure 20.31).

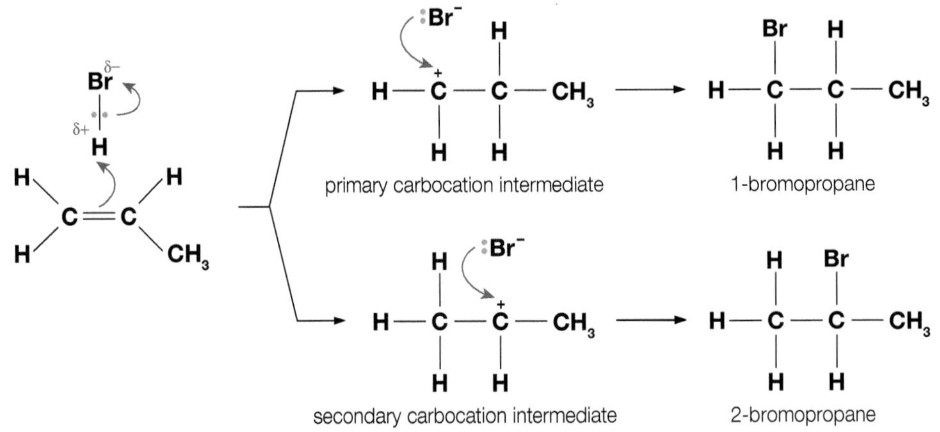

■ **Figure 20.31**
The possible reaction products when propene reacts with hydrogen bromide

primary carbocation intermediate   1-bromopropane

secondary carbocation intermediate   2-bromopropane

The Russian chemist Markovnikov proposed a rule to predict which isomer is formed in the greatest amount. Markovnikov's rule states that when hydrogen halides add to asymmetrical alkenes, the hydrogen atom always adds to the carbon atom that already has the most hydrogen atoms bonded to it. This rule is only predictive – indicating *which* product is formed but not explaining *why* it is formed. The mechanistic explanation lies in the relative energetic stabilities of the carbocation intermediates and was first proposed in 1959 by Edwin Gould.

The electron-deficient carbon in a carbocation is bonded to three other atoms. The positively charged, and electron deficient, carbon is sp²-hybridized (Chapter 14). There is an empty p orbital perpendicular to the plane with one lobe above the plane and the other below the plane (Figure 20.32).

As we have seen earlier when considering the S$_N$1 mechanism for the nucleophilic substitution of halogenoalkanes, carbocations can be characterized as primary, secondary or tertiary. Tertiary carbocations are the most energetically stable, with primary carbocations being

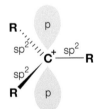

■ **Figure 20.32**
Structure of a generalized carbocation

the least energetically stable. This is because the alkyl groups tend to 'push' bonding electrons towards the positive (electron-deficient) carbon atom at the centre of the ion – this is known as a positive inductive effect. When propene reacts with hydrogen bromide, the secondary carbocation will be formed in preference to the primary carbocation – hence, the major product will be 2-bromopropane not 1-bromopropane.

A similar argument applies to the reaction between but-1-ene and hydrogen bromide. The enhanced energetic stability of the possible secondary carbocation will result in the formation of 2-bromobutane as the major product:

$$CH_3CH_2CH{=}CH_2 + HBr \rightarrow CH_3CH_2CHBrCH_3$$

but-1-ene   2-bromobutane

---

3   a   Describe the polarization of the interhalogen compound Br–Cl.
      b   Give the names and structures of the two possible products of the addition reaction between Br–Cl and propene.
      c   State which product is the more likely of the two, and explain why you think this is the case.

4   Pent-1-ene and pent-2-ene both undergo an addition reaction with hydrogen bromide. In each case, state what you think will be the major product and explain why.

Nature of Science

Prediction not explanation

It is important to realize that Markovnikov's rule is a pragmatic rule that is based on systematic observation and characterization, and as such it is capable of predicting the outcome of a reaction based on knowledge of the reactants. It is a predictive rule, and very useful as such, but is not an explanation of why the reaction happens as it does. In that sense it is similar to Le Châtelier's principle which predicts the outcome of a change of conditions on a dynamic equilibrium.

Such predictive rules and principles do have their rightful place in the practice of science, despite their lack of capacity to explain. They reflect an essential part of the observational and classification aspects of the development of any scientific discipline. We need a clear view of what we are explaining before we can even begin to evaluate why something is as it is.

■ Electrophilic substitution reactions

The distinctive nature of the bonding in benzene was discussed earlier in Chapter 10. The evidence presented there described a ring structure in which all the carbon–carbon bonds of the ring are intermediate between a double bond and a single bond – having a bond order of 1.5. Evidence for this came from X-ray crystallographic analysis of the benzene ring showing a planar, regular hexagon in which all the C–C bond lengths are 139 pm, intermediate between that of the single bond in ethane (154 pm) and that of the double bond in ethene (134 pm) (Figure 20.33). Note that methyl groups had to be attached to each of the carbons in the ring as hydrogen atoms are not 'seen' in X-ray crystallography (see Chapter 21).

■ **Figure 20.33**
An electron density map of benzene generated from X-ray crystallographic data

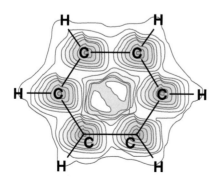

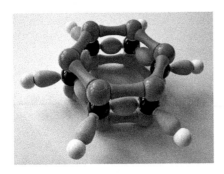

■ **Figure 20.34** A model of the benzene ring showing the delocalized π cloud above and below the ring

The delocalized π bonding system confers stability on the structure and also gives benzene and related compounds a particular chemistry. The presence of a stable structure means that reactions involving benzene will tend to retain or restore this structure where possible. As in alkenes, the presence of such an electron-rich region in the molecule makes arenes susceptible to electrophilic attack. However, alkenes undergo electrophilic addition, but the interaction of benzene and other arenes with electrophiles results in electrophilic substitution reactions, in which the structure of the aromatic ring is preserved (Figure 20.34).

Electrophilic substitution reactions in arenes

Given the earlier reference to the nitration and chlorination of the benzene ring in Chapter 10, we will concentrate on those reactions here. They involve the electrophiles $^+NO_2$ and Cl^+ – though there are a range of other important electrophiles such as $^+CH_3$ (and other examples of R^+) and CH_3C^+O (and other examples of RC^+O) which are very useful in synthetic organic chemistry. The generation of these electrophiles is one aspect of the mechanism that must be considered. The other aspect, which is essentially common to all these reactions, is the interaction of the electrophile with the benzene ring to bring about the substitution (Figure 20.35).

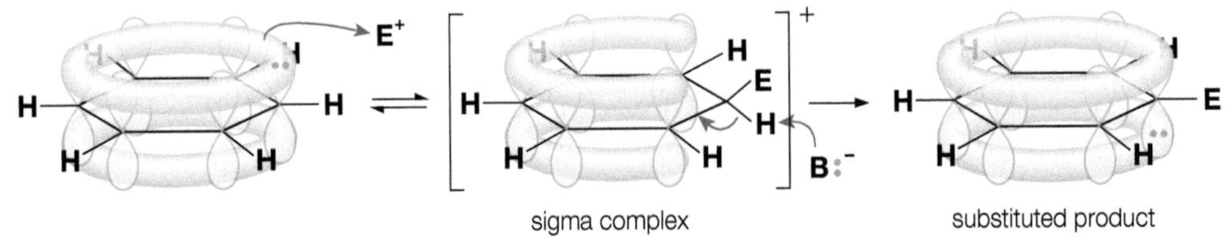

sigma complex   substituted product

■ **Figure 20.35** The common mechanism for the substitution of an electrophile (E^+) into the benzene ring, and the subsequent restoration of the stable ring structure involving a base

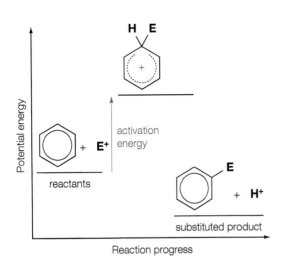

■ **Figure 20.36** The potential energy profile of an electrophilic substitution reaction in benzene

Although the six π electrons are in a stable aromatic system in benzene, they are still available for reaction with *strong* electrophiles. In Figure 20.35 the generalized strong electrophile is represented by E^+. Two electrons move from the π cloud system to form a bond to the electrophile. This creates a carbocation intermediate which is resonance stabilized (but not aromatic). This carbocation can be referred to as a sigma (σ) complex because the electrophile is joined to the benzene ring through a new σ bond. The σ complex is not aromatic because it contains an sp³ hybridized carbon (which disrupts the required overlap of p orbitals). The loss of aromatic stability involved in the formation of the intermediate carbocation explains the highly endothermic nature of the first step (Figure 20.36) and the need for a strong electrophile to bring about the reaction.

The final step is the restoration of the stable benzene ring structure by the loss of a proton (H^+ ion) from the carbocation. The pair of electrons from the carbon–hydrogen bond return to the delocalized π electron cloud. This second step is exothermic because it regenerates the aromatic π system. The hydrogen ion combines with a base (shown in Figure 20.35 as the anion B^-). The precise nature of this base depends on the particular substitution reaction being considered.

The nitration of benzene

The nitration of benzene involves the substitution of a nitro group, $-NO_2$, into the benzene ring, replacing one of the hydrogen atoms. This reaction involves the use of a nitrating mixture of concentrated sulfuric and nitric acids. The two acids react to produce the active electrophile for the subsequent substitution reaction – the highly reactive nitronium ion, $^+NO_2$ ($O=N^+=O$):

$$2H_2SO_4 + HNO_3 \rightarrow NO_2^+ + 2HSO_4^- + H_3O^+$$

The NO_2^+ electrophile forms a σ bond with the benzene ring by accepting a pair of delocalized π electrons, generating a positively charged intermediate (Figure 20.37).

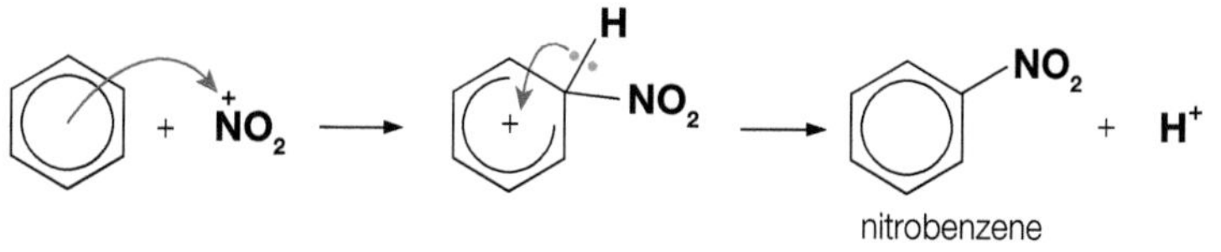

■ **Figure 20.37**
The nitration of benzene

nitrobenzene

The charged intermediate then loses a proton, H^+, to form the main product. The proton combines with a hydrogensulfate ion, HSO_4^-, to regenerate the sulfuric acid molecule:

$$H^+ + HSO_4^- \rightarrow H_2SO_4$$

The nitrobenzene produced is a yellow, oily substance. The reaction is carried out at a temperature between 45 °C and 55 °C. Restricting the temperature to below 55 °C helps to minimize the formation of multi-substitution products such as di- or tri-nitrobenzene.

The chlorination of benzene

The other substitution reaction of benzene discussed in Chapter 10 was the chlorination of benzene. The mechanism of the chlorination of benzene also involves the formation of an active electrophile, Cl^+. Anhydrous aluminium chloride, $AlCl_3$, is electron deficient because there are only six electrons around the central aluminium atom. This means it can act as a Lewis acid and attract a non-bonding pair of electrons from a molecule such as chlorine. The aluminium atom forms a dative covalent bond with one of the chlorine atoms in a chlorine molecule (Figure 20.38a). This triggers electron shifts to form a tetrachloroaluminate ion $[AlCl_4]^-$ and a positively charged chlorine ion (Cl^+, a chloronium ion) – the aluminium chloride acts as a halogen carrier in this reaction.

The powerful Cl^+ electrophile interacts with the π electrons of the benzene ring (Figure 20.38b) in the way described previously. The hydrogen ion formed reacts with the tetrachloroaluminate ion, forming hydrogen chloride and regenerating the halogen-carrier catalyst (Figure 20.38c). The whole process is an electrophilic substitution reaction with the overall equation:

$$C_6H_6 + Cl_2 \rightarrow C_6H_5Cl + HCl$$

Aluminium chloride requires anhydrous conditions and the reaction takes place with heating under reflux. Iron(III) chloride can be used instead, and works in exactly the same way.

Bromination can be achieved in a similar way by using bromine, $Br_2(l)$, and either aluminium bromide or iron(III) bromide as the halogen carrier. Iron(III) bromide can be generated *in situ* by the reaction between iron and bromine.

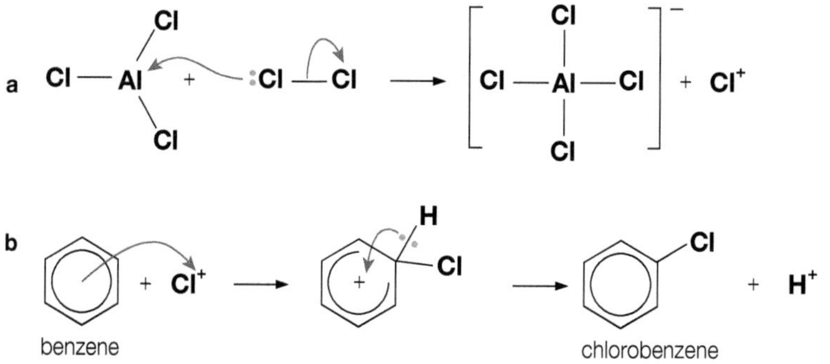

benzene

chlorobenzene

■ **Figure 20.38** The different stages in the chlorination of benzene

Developing an idea to maximum potential

A French chemist, Charles Friedel (1832–1899), collaborating with an American chemist, James Crafts (1839–1917), realized the significance of halogen carriers such as aluminium chloride and reasoned that by reacting them with halogenated organic compounds they could produce a range of electrophiles with positively charged, and hence electron-deficient, carbon atoms. These could react to substitute alkyl and acyl groups into the benzene ring. Such reactions are known as Friedel–Crafts reactions, and they provide a useful way of synthesizing a whole range of organic compounds.

The alkylation of benzene

The alkylation of a benzene ring involves the electrophilic substitution of a hydrogen atom on the benzene ring by an alkyl group, such as $-CH_3$. This reaction is synthetically important because it increases the length of the carbon skeleton by the formation of a carbon–carbon bond. The reaction requires the use of a halogen carrier to generate the active electrophile. The electrophile is a positively charged alkyl ion (a carbocation, $CH_3CH_2^+$ for instance) formed in the reaction of a halogenoalkane with anhydrous aluminium chloride. Figure 20.39 shows how benzene can be converted into ethylbenzene by this method.

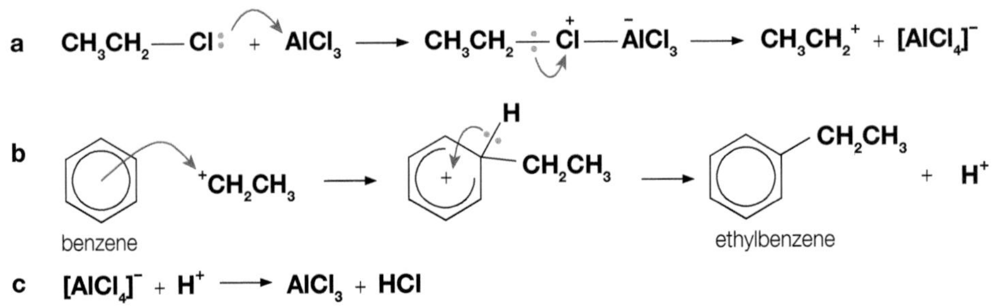

■ **Figure 20.39**
The Friedel–Crafts alkylation of benzene

The first step is the production of the necessary carbocation, in this case the ethyl ion, $CH_3CH_2^+$, from the reaction between chloroethane and aluminium chloride (Figure 20.39a). The powerful electrophile $CH_3CH_2^+$ then attacks the benzene ring to form a positively charged intermediate. This loses a proton to $AlCl_4^-$ to restore the stable delocalized electron structure of the ring system (Figure 20.39b). The proton eliminated reacts with the tetrachloroaluminate ion to re-form the aluminium chloride halogen carrier (Figure 20.39c).

The acylation of benzene

Acylation of the benzene ring is the electrophilic substitution of a hydrogen atom on the benzene ring by an acyl group, $R-C^+=O$. Once again, the production of an electrophile is achieved using a Friedel–Crafts halogen-carrier catalyst. In order to substitute a CH_3CO- group onto a benzene ring, the starting materials used should be ethanoyl chloride and anhydrous aluminium chloride. The electrophile produced would then, on heating under reflux, go on to interact with the benzene ring to form a positively charged intermediate (Figure 20.40). The usefulness and versatility of these reagents shows how a particular idea in science can be developed imaginatively from the original application to encompass a range of useful uses.

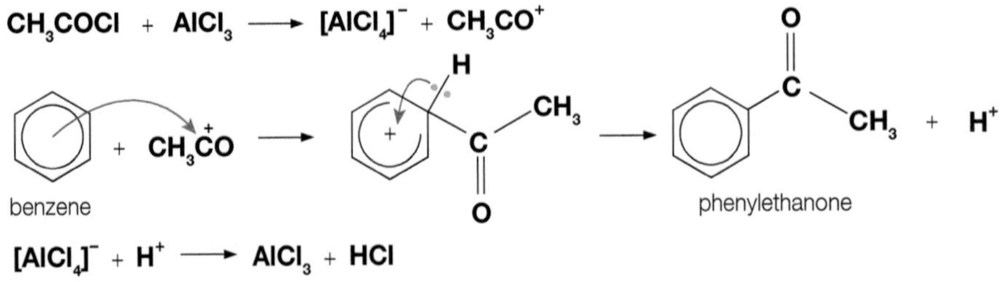

■ **Figure 20.40**
The Friedel–Crafts acylation of benzene

■ **Figure 20.41**
Methyl magnesium iodide – a Grignard reagent – and polarization of the carbon–magnesium bond. Red indicates areas of partial positive charge; areas of partial negative charge are blue

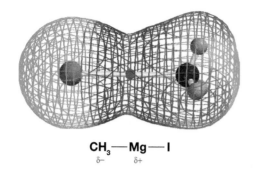

$$CH_3 \underset{\delta-}{\text{———}} Mg \underset{\delta+}{\text{———}} I$$

The Friedel–Crafts halogen carriers are one type of reagent that found a widespread usefulness in organic synthesis. Grignard reagents are another important group of compounds used widely in organic synthesis. We have mentioned that a carbon chain can be extended by one carbon atom by forming a nitrile as an intermediate step in a synthetic route. Grignard reagents enable a carbon chain to be increased by several carbon atoms. They consist of an alkyl group covalently bonded to a magnesium atom and have the general formula R–Mg–X, where X is a halogen, for example CH_3–Mg–I (Figure 20.41).

■ Reduction reactions

Reduction of carbonyl compounds

We saw earlier (Chapter 10) that the oxidation of alcohols to carbonyl compounds (containing the C=O group) takes place in the presence of a suitable oxidizing agent. The oxidation yields different products depending on whether the alcohol is primary, secondary or tertiary, and on the specific conditions used. The oxidation sequences can be summarized as follows:

■ primary alcohol → aldehyde → carboxylic acid

■ secondary alcohol → ketone

■ tertiary alcohol – no reaction.

These reactions can be reversed using a suitable reducing agent – usually one of two that are used frequently in organic chemistry:

■ sodium borohydride, $NaBH_4$, in aqueous or alcoholic solution, or

■ lithium aluminium hydride, $LiAlH_4$, in anhydrous conditions, such as dry ether followed by the addition of aqueous acid.

Both these reagents produce the hydride ion, H^-, which acts as a nucleophile on the electron-deficient carbonyl carbon (Figure 20.42). $NaBH_4$ tends to be the less hazardous reagent to use, but is not powerful enough to reduce carboxylic acids, so $LiAlH_4$, the stronger reducing agent, must be used for this.

■ **Figure 20.42**
a The carbonyl group contains an electron-deficient C atom.
b Reduction begins with the nucleophilic attack of an H^- ion

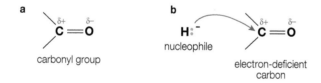

We can show these reactions using [H] to represent reduction by the addition of hydrogen. Some examples are given below.

■ Ethanoic acid to ethanol using $LiAlH_4$ (reflux in dry ether, then add dilute acid):

$$CH_3COOH + 4[H] \rightarrow CH_3CH_2OH + H_2O$$

Note that this reduction cannot be stopped at the halfway stage (the aldehyde) as the lithium aluminium hydride is too powerful a reducing agent. If it is necessary to convert carboxylic acid to an aldehyde then it would have to be reduced to the primary alcohol and then partially oxidized back to the aldehyde.

■ Ethanal to ethanol using $LiAlH_4$ or $NaBH_4$:

$$CH_3CHO + 2[H] \rightarrow CH_3CH_2OH$$

■ Propanone to propan-2-ol using $LiAlH_4$ or $NaBH_4$:

$$CH_3COCH_3 + 2[H] \rightarrow CH_3CH(OH)CH_3$$

Reduction of nitrobenzene

Nitrobenzene, $C_6H_5NO_2$, can be converted into phenylamine (aniline), $C_6H_5NH_2$, in a two-stage reduction process.

nitrobenzene

phenylammonium ion

Stage 1: $C_6H_5NO_2$ is reacted with a mixture of tin, Sn, or zinc, Zn, and concentrated hydrochloric acid, HCl. The reaction mixture is heated under reflux in a boiling water bath. The product is $C_6H_5NH_3^+$, the phenylammonium ion. The product of this stage is protonated because of the acidic conditions.

$$C_6H_5NO_2(l) + 3Zn(s) + 7H^+(aq)$$
$$\rightarrow C_6H_5NH_3^+(aq) + 3Zn^{2+}(aq) + 2H_2O(l)$$

phenylamine

Stage 2: Phenylamine (old, non-systematic name, aniline) is formed by the deprotonation of the phenylammonium ions using sodium hydroxide solution:

$$C_6H_5NH_3^+(aq) + OH^-(aq) \rightarrow C_6H_5NH_2(l) + H_2O(l)$$

Nature of Science

Noting the surprise outcome

We noted in Chapter 10 that some scientific discoveries take place 'by accident', for example the discovery of poly(ethane) and PTFE in the polymer industry, and of cyanoacrylate superglues. The skill of exploiting an unexpected, but possibly significant, outcome must credited to the scientists involved.

Phenylamine (aniline) was the chemical that generated the artificial dye industry. The traditional name of the compound lives on in the name of the world's biggest industrial chemistry company, BASF. The initials originally stood for *Badische Anilin- und Soda-Fabrik* in German, though they are now a registered trademark in their own right.

At the age of 18, William Perkins was already involved in chemical research and was given the task of making the anti-malarial drug, quinine, from aniline. He attempted to oxidize the aniline using acidified potassium dichromate(VI) and produced a black sludge! However, when washing up, he noticed a purple colour and pursued it further. He had produced mauve (or aniline purple) – the first organic dye that was to become the basis of a huge industry. The story is interestingly told by Simon Garfield in the book *Mauve: How One man Invented a Color That Changed the World*. The book convincingly argues that Perkin's invention of this chemical dye became a major turning point in the history of Western science and industry. Purple had always been a royal colour, in part because it was so difficult (and hence expensive) to achieve a good shade out of the natural raw materials from which all dyes were derived to that point.

Phenylamine is an important compound in other ways as it is used in the manufacture of anti-oxidants, the vulcanization of rubber and the synthesis of many pharmaceuticals.

20.2 Synthetic routes – *organic synthesis is the systematic preparation of a compound from a widely available starting material or the synthesis of a compound via a synthetic route that often can involve a series of different steps*

■ Reaction pathways

The development of new organic compounds – from drugs to dyes, clothing to construction materials – represents a major part of modern industrial chemistry. The oil industry remains the major source of feedstock for these processes, but there is increasing need for ingenuity in developing new sources and synthetic routes as this source alone does not yield the required proportion of desired compounds. Therefore organic chemists need to explore the conversion of one type of compound into another, with the pressure on to work with readily available starting materials and to use as few reactions as possible in the sequence, given that the product of one reaction is the reactant of the next and therefore the overall yield will progressively fall at each stage.

The series of discrete organic steps involved is known as a synthetic route. Functional group interconversions are the basis of a synthetic route, but there can also be a need to shorten or lengthen a carbon chain. Here we will look at examples of functional group interconversions using the reactions we have studied. We have already mentioned possible ways of altering the length of the carbon chain, but do note that these reactions are not required for the current IB syllabus.

Figure 20.43 summarizes the reactions and mechanisms covered here and in Chapter 10.

■ **Figure 20.43**
A summary of the reaction pathways and mechanisms discussed here and in Chapter 10

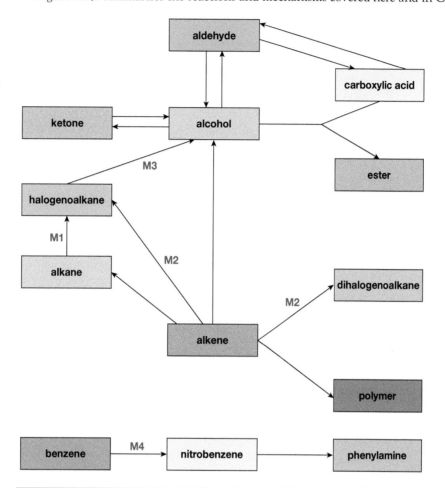

Worked example

Devise two-step synthetic routes to produce the following products from the given starting compound. Give the necessary conditions and equations for the reactions involved.

a propanone from propene   **b** pentan-1-ol from pentane   **c** ethyl ethanoate from ethanol

a propene $\xrightarrow{\text{conc. H}_2\text{SO}_4/\text{heat}/\text{H}_2\text{O}}$ propan-2-ol $\xrightarrow{\text{Na}_2\text{Cr}_2\text{O}_7/\text{H}^+/\text{reflux}}$ propanone

$CH_3CH{=}CH_2 + H_2O \rightarrow CH_3CH(OH)CH_3$

$CH_3CH(OH)CH_3 + [O] \rightarrow CH_3COCH_3 + H_2O$

b pentane $\xrightarrow{\text{Cl}_2/\text{UV radiation}}$ 1-chloropentane $\xrightarrow{\text{NaOH(aq)/reflux}}$ pentan-1-ol

$CH_3(CH_2)_3CH_3 + Cl_2 \rightarrow CH_3(CH_2)_3CH_2Cl + HCl$

$CH_3(CH_2)_3CH_2Cl + NaOH \rightarrow CH_3(CH_2)_3CH_2OH + NaCl$

c ethanol $\xrightarrow{\text{Na}_2\text{Cr}_2\text{O}_7/\text{H}^+/\text{reflux}}$ ethanoic acid $\xrightarrow{\text{more C}_2\text{H}_5\text{OH/H}^+/\text{reflux}}$ ethyl ethanoate

$C_2H_5OH + 2[O] \rightarrow CH_3COOH + H_2O$

$CH_3COOH + C_2H_5OH \rightarrow CH_3COOC_2H_5 + H_2O$

5   Identify the reaction mechanisms labelled M1, M2, M3 and M4 in the summary in Figure 20.43.

6   State broadly the essential conditions and reagents needed to carry out the following conversions.
    a   a carboxylic acid to a primary alcohol
    b   a ketone to a carboxylic acid
    c   an alkane to a bromoalkane
    d   an alkene to a dihalogenoalkane
    e   propene to propan-2-ol
    f   benzene to nitrobenzene
    g   nitrobenzene to phenylamine
    h   a primary alcohol to an aldehyde

■ Retrosynthesis – thinking in reverse

In devising new synthetic routes, chemists use a strategy involving retrosynthesis. Starting with knowledge of the target molecule (the TM), they think in reverse to determine possible pathways to produce it.

The strategy then involves progressively breaking down the target molecule into fragments, known as precursors. Each precursor then itself becomes the target of further analysis, eventually yielding a familiar and accessible starting molecule from which to begin the synthetic route:

target molecule (TM) → precursor 1 → precursor 2 → starting material

There are two aspects to the approach that help establish the nature of the fragments to be considered for the synthetic route, and these address the basic make-up of any organic molecule – the chain/ring structure and the functional group(s) present in the molecule.

The first aspect of the approach is disconnection. Disconnection is a paper exercise involving the imagined cleavage of bonds to produce fragments from which the molecule can be built. These fragments, known as 'synthons' are usually positive or negative ions produced by the heterolytic cleavage of a covalent bond. Usually synthons do not actually exist, but they help in making the correct choice of reagent. An analogy to the disconnection process would be examining the different sections of a partially completed jigsaw to see how they fitted together to make the whole.

The second aspect is to consider the functional groups present in the TM and the 'synthons' to see how these fragments could be related to known, available compounds capable of participating in known reactions. This is functional group interconversion (FGI) and draws on the types of reaction, and more, that we have mentioned in this chapter. Examining how the synthons can be produced from or related to real compounds gives the synthetic equivalents, or reagents, that are the starting point of the synthetic route.

The exact use of these two aspects of strategy varies with the problem being considered.

Nature of Science   ### A backward approach

This branch of organic chemistry became established essentially on the basis of the influential work of the American chemist E.J. Corey (awarded the Nobel Prize in Chemistry in 1990). The approach evidences the creative nature of science. Corey's work is an example of creative thinking and intuition. From the initial idea, using deductive reasoning and logic, he then developed a set of principles and guidelines which could be applied to a range of synthetic problems.

The retrosynthetic protocol was developed in the 1960s with the advent of computers that allowed an iterative algorithmic approach to considering synthesis in a backwards sense. Thus, it was considered that if the computer was given all the scientific facts (knowledge of chemical transformations, selectivities, fragment polarities, strategic bonds, efficiencies, etc.), a program could be developed to enable a dispassionate assessment of each forward synthetic step.

There is one big drawback to this over-simplistic approach. The 'retrosynthetic tree' that is formed from simply considering the breaking of any bond in the molecule to generate a series of precursor targets, and then any bond in each of the precursor targets, and so on, rapidly becomes far too large and unwieldy for even the most complex computer. Thus it was necessary to teach the computer to take each retrosynthetic step and consider the viability of the forward, synthetic, step. Furthermore, additional rules were introduced to identify 'strategic bonds' – those bonds most likely to yield greatest simplification if broken. Immediately this required the opinion of the program to be involved and so the program started to lose the element of impartiality.

So, at the end of the day, even with the computing power available today, it is impossible to use a totally dispassionate computational approach to retrosynthetic design. Human intuition, predilection and bias is always involved in decision making in retrosynthetic analysis. The nearest analogy is the development of computers to play chess – humans still have the edge. The difference between a purely computer-generated synthesis and one originating in the mind of the synthetic chemist – albeit inspired and led by the fundamental guidelines of retrosynthetic analysis – is like comparing a 'painting by numbers' with an 'old master'. The human element adds finesse.

The approach has been remarkably successful in terms of the number and extent of the compounds synthesized, and the research is ongoing. *'Synthesis remains a dynamic and central area of chemistry. There are many new principles, strategies and methods of synthesis waiting to be discovered'* (E.J. Corey, 1989). Imagination, intuition and reasoning all play their part in scientific innovation. From Kekulé's 'dream' of the structure of benzene through to Schrödinger's imaginative application of mathematics to the structure of the hydrogen atom and the innovative cross-over of ideas from different subject areas, imagination transcends the limitations of the routine acquisition of knowledge and opens the way to ground-breaking possibilities. There is a distinctive creative element to the progression of scientific ideas.

Worked examples

How could phenylamine be synthesized from benzene in a two-stage process?

Inspection of the functional groups suggests that an amine group could be generated from a nitro group (FGI) – a known reaction.

The disconnection suggests that the nitration of benzene would be a first step – again a known reaction. This sequence is one discussed earlier in the chapter.

Establish a sequence of reactions that could be used to synthesize the compound $(CH_3)_2CHOOCCH_3$ from starting molecules that are alkenes.

Firstly, consider the fragmentation (disconnection) of the TM – noting that the TM is an ester. The fact that the target molecule is an ester helps in suggesting the most useful disconnection of the molecule into positive and negative fragments (synthons) – see below.

Then consider the synthetic equivalents (reagents) that relate to these fragments.

The ester could indeed be synthesized from propan-2-ol and ethanoic acid. However the question asks us to start from alkenes only.

Propan-2-ol can be synthesized by the hydration of propene:

$$CH_3CH=CH_2 + H_2O \xrightarrow{\text{conc. } H_2SO_4/\text{heat }/H_2O} CH_3CH(OH)CH_3$$

Ethanoic acid cannot be made directly from ethene. We would have to make ethanol from ethene and then oxidize the ethanol to ethanoic acid:

$$CH_2=CH_2 + H_2O \xrightarrow{\text{conc. } H_2SO_4/\text{heat }/H_2O} CH_3CH_2OH$$

$$CH_3CH_2OH + 2[O] \xrightarrow{Na_2Cr_2O_7/H^+/\text{reflux}} CH_3COOH + H_2O$$

The following example draws on reactions mentioned in this chapter as part of the extension material. However, the example illustrates the usefulness of the retrosynthetic approach.

Use retrosynthetic analysis to devise a two-stage synthesis for phenylethanoic acid.

The strategy is illustrated in the following diagram which shows firstly the disconnection made and the fragments suggested. Secondly, it shows the synthetic equivalents that could be used to generate these fragments. (The first fragment here is a synthon, but the other fragment is technically known as an 'umpole' as its polarity is not the natural polarity of the carbon in a carbonyl group.)

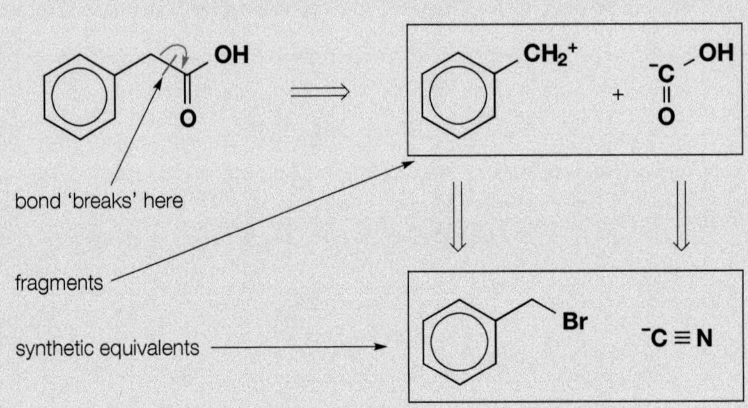

The reaction used to replace the bromine substituent is nucleophilic substitution with the nitrile anion acting as a nucleophile. We mentioned earlier in the chapter that the nitrile anion can then be converted into a carboxylic acid group.

The overall reaction scheme showing the conversion sequence is:

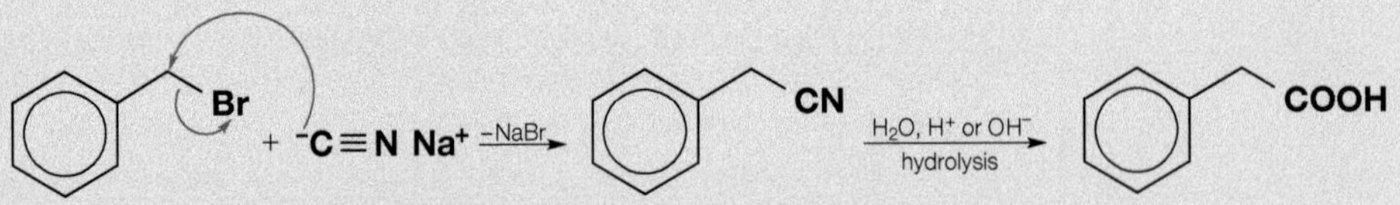

Earlier in the chapter we mentioned Grignard reagents as organometallic compounds that were very useful reagents for extending the hydrocarbon chain. We are including here an example of their use in synthetic pathways because they are so significant. The problem posed is how to synthesize the ketone $C_6H_5COCH_3$.

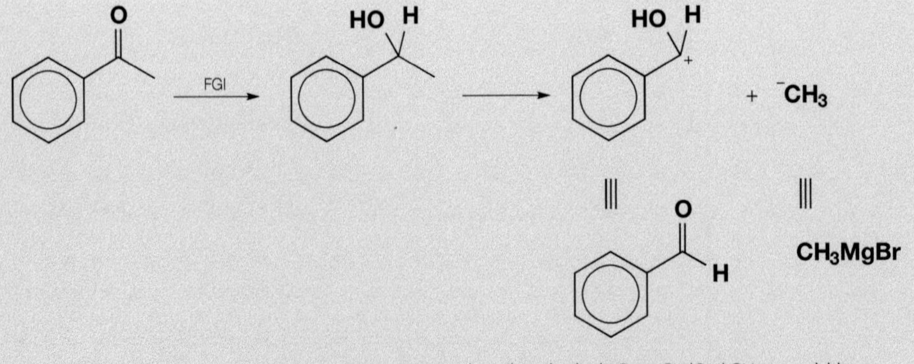

Here, a functional group interconversion suggests that the alcohol, $C_6H_5CH(OH)CH_3$, would be a useful intermediate.

Disconnection then suggests the two synthons on the right, and the synthetic equivalents of these two synthons are written underneath. One is the aldehyde, C_6H_5CHO, and the other is the Grignard reagent CH_3MgBr which we discussed earlier. This reagent will release the nucleophile, $^-CH_3$, which will attack the electron-deficient carbon of the carbonyl group, producing the desired alcohol.

The alcohol, $C_6H_5CH(OH)CH_3$, can then be reduced with lithium aluminium hydride to give the required target molecule (TM).

One of the most important reactions in organic synthesis is the Diels–Alder reaction, since it involves the formation of a ring (with well-defined stereochemistry). It is not currently a syllabus requirement but is used in a number of the total syntheses of Taxol (see Chapter 25 on the accompaning website).

general Diels–Alder reaction

or, emphasizing how the two components fit together:

new σ bond

1,3-diene →

new π bond   new σ bond

Three curly arrows are needed to show the cyclic movement of electron pairs because three π bonds break and two σ bonds and one π bond form. Because each new σ bond is stronger than a π bond that is broken, a typical Diels–Alder reaction is exothermic. The reaction is concerted (like the S_N2 mechanism); that is, all old bonds are broken and all new bonds are formed in a single step.

Otto Paul Hermann Diels and Kurt Alder first documented the novel reaction in 1928, for which they were awarded the Nobel Prize in Chemistry in 1950. The Diels–Alder reaction is generally considered one of the more useful reactions in organic chemistry since it requires very little energy to create a *cyclohexene* ring, which is useful in many other organic reactions.

Predict the starting materials you would need to synthesize the following product:

$CO_2CH_2CH_3$

Recognizing the cyclohexene ring in the structure helps you place the disconnections and suggests that a Diels–Alder reaction would be useful. Then look at the fragment that would react with the diene, and ask how it should look to achieve that reaction.

$CO_2CH_2CH_3$

+

It may well be that you could break down this other fragment and make that from simpler reagents.

The principles and approach of retrosynthesis have proved immensely successful. '*Contemporary activity in organic synthesis is impressive by any standard. Each year scores of new syntheses are described which are remarkable for the ingenuity underlying their design, the elegance and effectiveness with which known and new chemistry are applied, and the effectiveness of laboratory execution*' (E.J. Corey, 1987). Some of the key points to be borne in mind include:

■ The starting materials should be readily available.

■ The techniques involved should be as straightforward as possible.

■ The number of stages required should be as few as possible to enable as high a yield as feasible.

In complex synthetic routes, the technique of 'protecting' a required functional group can be important and the stereochemistry of the reactants and the final product may well need to be borne in mind. The strategy for complex molecules may well involve designing pathways to generate starting reagents for the route to the final target molecule but the approach to each pathway is still as summarized in Figure 20.44.

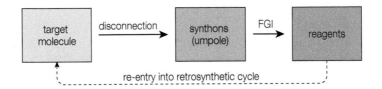

■ **Figure 20.44** The flow of events in a retrosynthetic analysis.

Retrosynthesis essentially involves looking at a target molecule and considering the bonds that can reasonably be made, and then generating a sub-structure and so working backwards. There are a number of structural fragments which are often indicative of reasonable starting materials or synthetic reactions. Knowledge of the relationship between different functional groups is also an important guide in retrosynthesis strategies.

Utilization: Drugs and natural products

Drugs are any compounds that lead to a biological response (see Chapter 25 on the accompaning website). Drugs interact with the cells in the human body via intermolecular forces or via chemical reactions. An understanding of the properties and reactions of the various functional groups present in drug molecules is critical as they control the kinds of reactions and response that a drug molecule participates in.

One possible source of starting materials for drug development is natural products such as those referred to in the introduction to this chapter. We also refer to some other compounds derived from natural sources which find commercial use during our later discussion of optical isomerism. In the early 1960s, the National Cancer Institute (NCI) in the United States initiated a programme of biological screening of extracts taken from a wide variety of natural sources. One of these extracts was found to exhibit marked anti-tumour activity against a broad range of rodent tumours. Although this discovery was made in 1962, it was not until five years later that researchers isolated the active compound from the bark of the Pacific yew tree (*Taxus brevifolia*). In 1971, the structure of this promising new anti-cancer compound, a complex poly-oxygenated diterpene, was published (Figure 20.45).

The generic name for this compound is now paclitaxel but it is often referred to by its registered trade name of Taxol. Taxol proved to have a unique anti-cancer mode of action, stabilizing the assembly of the microtubules in cells and therefore disrupting cell division. It gave rise to a new class of anti-tumour agents. The significance of this finding put pressure on the supply from its natural source. The Pacific yew is an environmentally protected species and isolation of the compound from the bark involves killing the tree. In any case the quantities available by this method are pitifully small. It would take six 100-year-old trees to provide enough Taxol to treat just one patient. The situation demanded the development of a pathway for total synthesis of Taxol, representing an enormous challenge to the ingenuity and creativity of synthetic organic chemistry. Three total syntheses have been carried out to date, involving complex sequences of steps. Many groups worldwide are continuing to carry out research in this area, in order to develop newer and shorter routes to this natural product, but also with a view to creating modified structures which may be more biologically active.

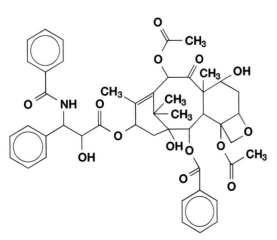

■ **Figure 20.45** The structure of Taxol

The highly significant work done in connection with Taxol illustrates the importance of screening natural sources for possible medically useful and active compounds. It stresses the need for international cooperation in the preservation of natural resources and collaboration in the identification, development and testing of potential new pharmaceuticals and other chemicals. Natural products are compounds isolated from natural sources and include Taxol, mescaline and capsaicin. Many of the drugs derived from natural sources are chiral, including nicotine, dopamine, thyroxine and naproxen, and this is the topic we now move on to consider.

7 Outline the steps in a method for synthesizing the ketone, butanone, starting from an alkene. There may be more than one possible route; comment on these possibilities and on which route may give the best yield of the ketone.

8 How would you convert the halogenoalkane, 1-chlorobutane, into butanoic acid? Outline the steps used giving the reagents, conditions and equations for each.

20.3 Stereoisomerism – *stereoisomerism involves isomers which have different arrangements of atoms in space but do not differ in connectivity or bond multiplicity (i.e. whether single, double or triple) between the isomers themselves*

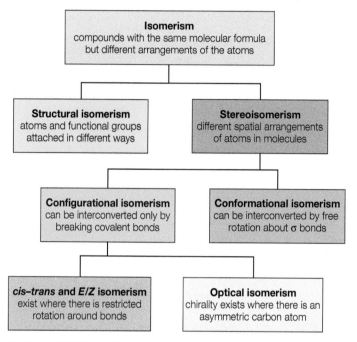

■ **Figure 20.46** The different types of isomerism

Where two compounds have the same molecular formula but different structural formulas (or different atom connectivities) they are said to be structural isomers. For example, propan-1-ol and propan-2-ol both have the molecular formula C_3H_8O, but the carbon atom to which the alcohol functional group (–OH) is attached in the hydrocarbon chain is different in the two molecules. We have also seen that hydrocarbon chains can be branched or straight, giving rise to structural isomerism; for example, butane and 2-methylpropane are isomers with the same molecular formula (C_4H_{10}) (see Chapter 10). Here we introduce a further category of isomerism known as stereoisomerism, in which the molecules concerned have the same molecular formula *and* structural formula, but their atoms are arranged differently in space. There are three types of stereoisomerism – conformational isomerism, *cis–trans* isomerism and optical isomerism (Figure 20.46).

Configurational isomers have permanent differences in their structural geometry and cannot be interconverted without bond breaking and rearrangement. Conformational isomers, on the other hand, usually interconvert spontaneously at normal temperatures by internal rotation about single bonds and cannot usually be isolated separately. The term 'geometric isomerism' used to be used for *cis–trans* isomerism but this is now obsolete and should not be used.

Nature of Science

Tetrahedral molecules – a paradigm shift

Jacobus van't Hoff (1852–1911) was the winner of the first ever Nobel Prize in Chemistry. He was a Dutchman, born in Rotterdam in the Netherlands, and one of the pre-eminent scientists of his day. He was a physical and organic chemist who contributed original ideas in the fields of reaction kinetics and equilibria, osmotic pressure and crystallography. He was a professor of chemistry at the University of Amsterdam for almost 18 years before moving to finish his career at the University of Berlin. In 1901 he gained the Nobel Prize for his work on aqueous solutions.

Even before he received his doctorate he had published work on the stereochemistry of organic compounds. He accounted for the phenomenon of optical isomerism with his ideas on the tetrahedral arrangement of the bonding around a carbon atom. He shares the honour of this original idea with the French chemist Joseph Le Bel who independently came up with the same idea.

Joseph Le Bel (1847–1930) was best known for his work on stereochemistry. He lived and worked for most of his life in Paris. He put forward his ideas on the spatial arrangement of atoms in molecules in 1874, the same year as van't Hoff. His ideas helped to explain the phenomenon of the optical activity of certain organic chemicals.

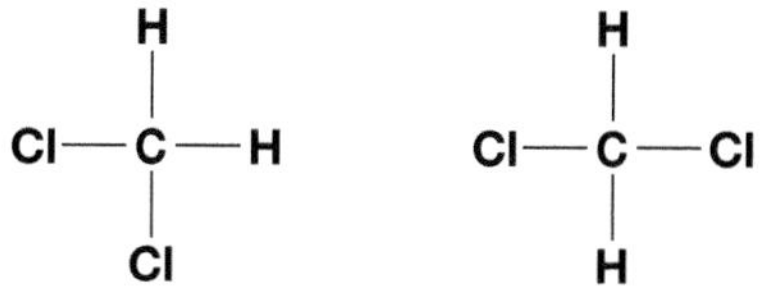

If a carbon atom formed four planar (flat) bonds then dichloromethane, for example, would exist in two isomeric forms (Figure 20.47). However, there is only one form of dichloromethane and this type of isomerism is unknown.

It is for this reason that van't Hoff and Le Bel independently suggested that the four bonds from a carbon atom were equivalent, and arranged *tetrahedrally*. This was a *paradigm shift* in chemical thinking and this idea was used to explain the existence of optical isomers. Together, van't Hoff and Le Bel were responsible for developing a new area of chemistry known as stereochemistry, which deals with the effects produced by the organization of atoms and functional groups in space.

■ **Figure 20.47** Possible isomers of dichloromethane if the bonds from carbon were all in one plane. This is not the case and this type of isomerism does not exist

■ *Cis–trans* isomerism

Cis–trans isomerism occurs when the arrangement of the bonds prevents free internal rotation about bonds within the molecule. Such restricted rotation occurs, for example, in alkenes and many cyclic compounds. Consider the structures of but-1-ene and but-2-ene (Figure 20.48).

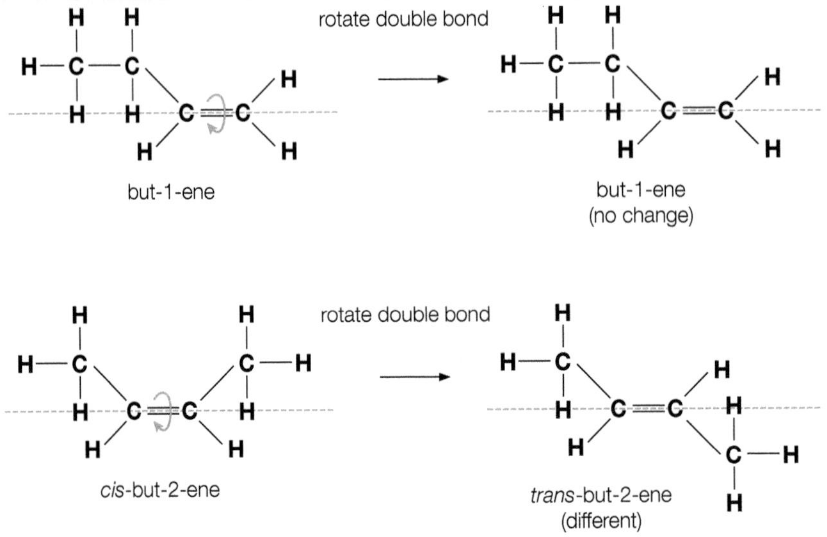

■ **Figure 20.48**
The different spatial arrangements possible for but-1-ene and but-2-ene

rotate double bond

but-1-ene

but-1-ene
(no change)

rotate double bond

cis-but-2-ene

trans-but-2-ene
(different)

But-1-ene and but-2-ene are structural isomers because the double bond is in a different place in the hydrocarbon chain. If we were to rotate the double bond in but-1-ene then the outcome would be the same: the two hydrogen atoms on the right-hand carbon atom simply exchange places. But-1-ene, therefore, does not show *cis–trans* isomerism; there is only one structure for but-1-ene.

However, if we were to rotate the double bond in but-2-ene, the resulting structure is different from the original. In the original structure the two methyl groups are on the same, upper, side of the molecule. After rotation the methyl groups are on opposite sides of the axis through the carbon–carbon double bond. Clearly the distance between the two carbon atoms in the methyl groups is different in the two molecules. When the methyl groups are on the same side of the molecule, the compound is known as the *cis* isomer. Conversely, when they are on opposite sides (across the molecule), the compound is known as the *trans* isomer.

The *cis* and *trans* isomers of but-2-ene exist because there cannot be rotation around the carbon–carbon double bond. The carbon atoms involved in the double bond are sp² hybridized.

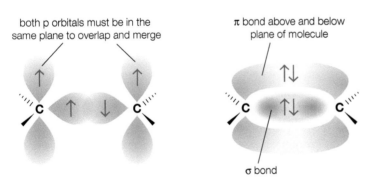

both p orbitals must be in the same plane to overlap and merge

π bond above and below plane of molecule

σ bond

■ **Figure 20.49** The nature of the carbon–carbon double bond in an alkene prevents rotation about the carbon–carbon axis. Single bonds are sigma (σ) only, and so rotation can take place without bond breaking (except in cyclic compounds)

One of the bonds between the two carbon atoms is a sigma (σ) bond formed by the end-on overlap of two sp² hybrid orbitals. The other bond is a pi (π) bond formed by the sideways overlap of the unused 2p atomic orbitals on each carbon atom (Chapter 14). To achieve this overlap the 2p orbitals must be in the same plane and, once formed, any rotation around the axis through the carbon atoms would mean the breaking of the pi (π) bond (Figure 20.49). As this would require a considerable amount of energy, the *cis* and *trans* isomers exist independently and are not easily interconvertible. The high activation energy for the conversion between the two isomeric forms is generally prohibitive except at very high temperatures. The use of molecular models that represent the formation of sigma (σ) and pi (π) bonds illustrates clearly the restriction placed on rotation in alkene-based molecules, for example 1,2-dichloroethene (Figure 20.50).

■ **Figure 20.50**
Molecular models
of *cis-* and *trans-*
1,2-dichloroethene
showing how the
presence of the pi (π)
bond restricts rotation
around the carbon–
carbon axis

One further situation where rotation about a carbon–carbon axis is restricted occurs in cyclic alkanes. *Cis–trans* isomerism is possible here, even though there are only single bonds between the carbon atoms. The rigid structure of the ring prevents free rotation. Thus, for example, 1,2-dichlorocyclopropane exists as *cis* and *trans* isomers (Figure 20.51).

■ **Figure 20.51**
Simplified
representations of the
cis and *trans* isomers of
1,2-dichlorocyclopropane

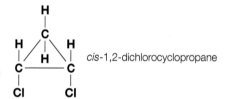 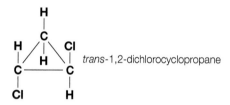

For more complex structures the situation can become quite complicated. Thus there are four isomers of dichlorocyclobutane. Firstly there are two structural isomers of this compound, that is 1,2-dichlorocyclobutane and 1,3-dichlorocyclobutane (Figure 20.52). Each of these structural isomers then has two *cis–trans* isomers. The *cis* and *trans* isomers of 1,3-dichlorocyclobutane are particularly intriguing as the chlorine atoms involved are not on adjacent carbon atoms. Consideration of these isomers reminds us of how the large number of organic compounds so readily arises.

■ **Figure 20.52**
The *cis–trans*
isomers of
dichlorocyclobutane

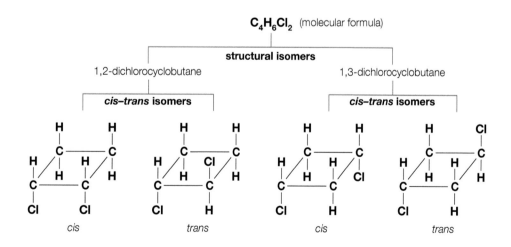

Differences in properties between *cis–trans* isomers

A consideration of the melting points and boiling points of the *cis–trans* isomers of various compounds illustrates some interesting aspects of the influence of intermolecular forces on these physical properties. Table 20.5 gives the melting and boiling points of two pairs of *cis–trans* isomers.

■ **Table 20.5**
The melting and boiling points of the *cis* and *trans* isomers of but-2-ene and 1,2-dichloroethene

Isomer	Condensed structure	Melting point/K	Boiling point/K
cis-but-2-ene	$CH_3CH=CHCH_3$	134	277
trans-but-2-ene	$CH_3CH=CHCH_3$	167	274
cis-1,2-dichloroethene	$CHCl=CHCl$	193	333
trans-1,2-dichloroethene	$CHCl=CHCl$	223	321

You will note from these figures that in each case:

■ the *trans* isomer has the higher melting point, whereas
■ the *cis* isomer has the higher boiling point.

As illustration of this, *cis*-1,2-dichloroethene boils at 333 K, which is higher than the boiling point of *trans*-1,2-dichloroethene (321 K). This suggests that there must be stronger intermolecular forces between the molecules of the *cis* isomer than between the *trans* isomer molecules. Both of these isomers have exactly the same atoms bonded together in the same order, which means that the London (dispersion) forces between the molecules will be identical. However, where the substituent groups in the isomers contain highly electronegative atoms the *cis–trans* isomers can differ significantly in their polarity. For instance, *cis*-1,2-dichloroethene has a dipole moment since the two polar C–Cl bonds are on the same side of the molecule and their effects do not cancel out. There will, therefore, be dipole–dipole attractions between molecules of *cis*-1,2-dichloroethene. In contrast, *trans*-1,2-dichloroethene is non-polar because the two polar C–Cl bonds are arranged symmetrically on either side of the carbon–carbon double bond. The effects of the two polarized bonds cancel each other in this isomer and the overall molecule is non-polar. The lower boiling point of the *trans* isomer results from this difference in polarity between the two isomers.

In the case of the boiling points of *cis*- and *trans*-but-2-ene a similar argument holds, although the degree of the effect is slighter. The methyl groups in but-2-ene, like other alkyl groups, are electron releasing. This polarizes the bond to the carbon atoms at either end of the double bond. The same argument then applies: while *cis*-but-2-ene is a polar molecule, *trans*-but-2-ene is not. Hence the boiling point of the *cis* isomer is higher than that of the *trans* isomer.

The fact that the same pattern is not observed with the melting points indicates that another factor has an effect in this case. When molecules assemble into the solid state they must form a lattice in which the molecules are packed closely together. The shape of the *trans* isomer of a compound means that the molecules pack together better than those of the *cis* isomer. The poorer packing of the *cis* isomer means that the intermolecular forces are not as effective as they could be, and so the melting point of the *cis* isomer is lower than that of the *trans* isomer.

In some cases there are very marked differences in melting point between two *cis–trans* isomers. This is often due to the nature of the functional groups attached to the carbon–carbon double bond and their proximity to each other in the *cis* form. The melting points of *cis*-but-2-ene-1,4-dioic acid and *trans*-but-2-ene-1,4-dioic acid are very different indeed, one being much higher than the other. In the *trans* isomer there is strong intermolecular hydrogen bonding between different molecules, because of the polarity of the carboxylic acid groups. However, in the *cis* isomer these groups are adjacent to each other and much of this hydrogen bonding occurs internally between the two carboxylic acid groups (intramolecular hydrogen bonding). Consequently the intermolecular forces between molecules of the *cis* form are significantly weaker in this case, and so the melting point of this isomer is much lower (Figure 20.53).

■ **Figure 20.53**
The structural
difference between the
cis–trans isomers of
but-2-ene-1, 4-dioic
acid, and the
consequences for
the melting points
and chemistry of the
isomers

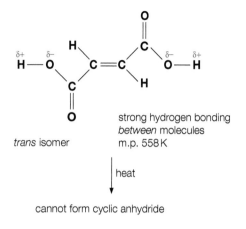

strong hydrogen bonding
between molecules
m.p. 558 K

trans isomer

strong hydrogen bonding
within molecules
m.p. 403–404 K (with
decomposition)

cis isomer

cannot form cyclic anhydride

cis-but-2-ene-1,4-dioic anhydride

These two *cis–trans* isomers of but-2-ene-1,4-dioic acid are also very different chemically. In the *cis* isomer the two carboxylic acid functional groups are close enough together to react. When this isomer is heated, a water molecule is eliminated between the two carboxylic acid groups and a cyclic acid anhydride is formed (Figure 20.53). In the *trans* isomer the two groups are distant from each other and no such reaction is possible.

---

9 Which of the following will exhibit *cis–trans* isomerism? Draw the two different forms for those you think show this type of isomerism.
 a 2,3-dimethylpent-2-ene
 b 1,3-dimethylcyclobutane
 c 1,2,3-trichlorocyclopropane

10 Draw and name the *cis–trans* isomers of butenedioic acid.

Acidity, biochemistry and *cis–trans* isomerism

Butene-2,3-dioic acid contains two carboxylic acid functional groups and undergoes stepwise ionization according to the following equation:

$$C_2H_2(COOH)_2(aq) \rightleftharpoons C_2H_2(COOH)(COO^-) + H^+(aq) \rightleftharpoons C_2H_2(COO^-)_2 + H^+(aq)$$

The *cis* isomer of butene-2,3-dioic acid is a much stronger acid than the *trans* isomer. The first pK_a of *cis*-butene-2,3-dioic acid is 1.92 whereas the first pK_a of *trans*-butenedioic acid is 3.02 (Chapter 18). This is because the –COO⁻ group formed in the *cis* isomer can be stabilized by hydrogen bonding from the adjacent –COOH group, which is on the same side of the double bond. This stabilization is not possible in the *trans* isomer because the two groups are too far apart.

 Biochemists know these two forms of butenedioic acid by different (non-systematic) names. Fumaric acid (*trans*-butenedioic acid) is an intermediate in the Krebs cycle, an essential part of aerobic respiration for energy release in cells (Chapter 15, and Chapter 23 on the accompanying website). Maleic acid (*cis*-butenedioic acid) is an inhibitor of reactions involved in the interconversion of amino acids in the liver. These different biological roles are a consequence of the molecules' different shapes and their interactions with the enzymes involved in metabolic pathways.

The molecular conversion that helps us see

The activation energy needed to convert one *cis–trans* isomer to the other is generally high enough to prevent interconversion. However, there is one crucially important case where this can be achieved with a photon of light! It relates to the mechanism by which we see.

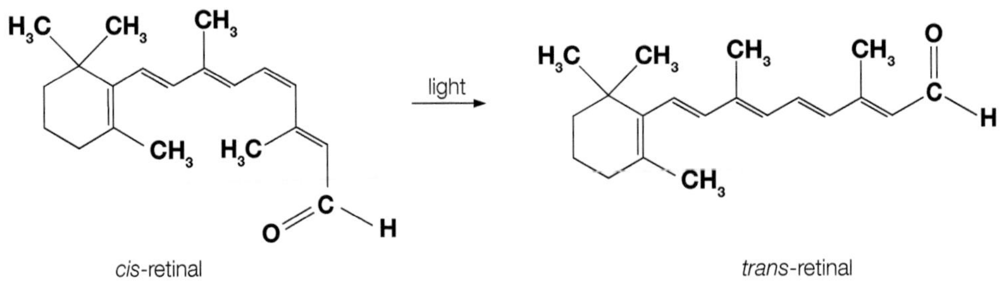

■ **Figure 20.54**
The conversion of *cis*-retinal to *trans*-retinal by light

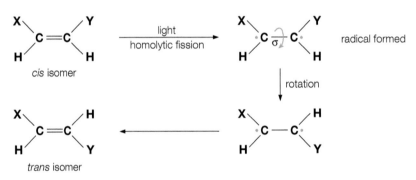

cis-retinal   *trans*-retinal

The light-sensitive cells of the retina, the inner lining at the back of the human eye, contain a compound known as retinal. When light falls on the retina it converts molecules of retinal from the *cis* form to the *trans* form (Figure 20.54).

Light energy promotes this photochemical reaction. The energy is sufficient to cause the homolytic fission of the pi (π) bond to form a free radical. Rotation can then take place around the remaining single sigma (σ) bond and the pi (π) bond is then re-formed, converting one isomer into the other. The energy released by the re-formation of the pi (π) bond causes a nerve impulse to be transmitted, sending a signal to the brain via the optic nerve (Figure 20.55). The *trans*-retinal is then converted back to *cis*-retinal by an enzyme, RPE isomerohydrolase, so that it can function again in response to a light stimulus.

■ **Figure 20.55**
Detail of the reaction involved in the conversion of *cis*-retinal to *trans*-retinal by light

The *E/Z* system (the CIP method)

Sometimes, in the case of more complicated alkenes, deciding which isomer to label as the *cis* isomer and which the *trans* isomer can be difficult – the *cis*–*trans* designation breaks down when there are more than two different substituents around the carbon–carbon double bond. In order to facilitate the naming of substituted alkenes, three chemists, Cahn, Ingold and Prelog, devised a method for prioritizing substituents on a double bond. Their method, sometimes called the CIP method or the *E/Z* system, is based on atomic number, and is as follows. For each group attached to the double bond, apply the following rules, in order:

Rule 1   If one of the atoms joined to the carbon–carbon double bond has a higher atomic number than the other one, then that atom has the higher priority. For example:

I > Br > Cl > F

Rule 2   If both the atoms joined to the carbon–carbon double bond have the same atomic number, for example if they were both carbon atoms, the next atom(s) in the groups are compared.

These rules mean that the substituents with the longer hydrocarbon chains have higher priority:

C_3H_7 > C_2H_5 > CH_3 > H

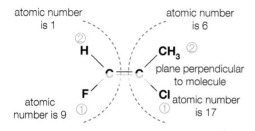

■ **Figure 20.56** The structure of (Z)-1-fluoro-2-chloropropene. Note that the high priority groups (labelled 1) are both on the same side of the double bond

The position of an atom such as oxygen (O) in the substituent can be significant – the closer it is to the carbon–carbon double bond, the higher the priority of the group containing it. For example:

$$-CH(OH)CH_2CH_3 > -CH_2CH_2CH_2(OH)$$

Also double-bonded atoms, such as an oxygen, count twice, thus

$$-COOH > -CHO > -CH_2OH$$

Once the order of priority of the groups on each carbon of the double bond has been decided, the letters E or Z can be assigned, depending on whether the groups of higher priority at each end of the carbon–carbon double bond are on *opposite sides* (E) or the *same side* (Z) of the molecule (Figure 20.56).

Worked example

a For the following isomers of but-2-ene, make sure you understand why they have been designated E or Z.

E-but-2-ene
(*trans*-but-2-ene)

Z-but-2-ene
(*cis*-but-2-ene)

b For the following four molecules, make sure you understand why they have been labelled as the E or Z isomer.

E   Z   Z   E

---

11 Draw the structures of the two isomers (E and Z forms) of 1-bromo-2-methylbut-1-ene.

12 Draw and name, using the E/Z system, the two stereoisomers of 3-methylpent-2-ene.

On a linguistic note, we now have two systems for naming what used to be termed geometric isomers – the *cis*–trans system and the E/Z system. In the first case the terms are derived from the Latin: *cis* meaning 'on this side' and *trans* meaning 'across'. In the E/Z system, which is most useful for complex alkenes, the letters come from German: E stands for *entgegen*, meaning 'opposite', while Z stands for *zusammen*, meaning 'together'.

■ Conformational isomers

We have seen how important rotation about the axis along a hydrocarbon molecule can be, and indeed the significance of the energy barrier to any possible internal rotation. Usually there is free rotation around a carbon–carbon single bond, but if the two carbon atoms that are joined by the bond have bulky groups attached to them, not every position of rotation will have the same potential energy. Conformational isomers are the different arrangements that correspond to energy minima as one atom (with its attached groups) is rotated with respect to the other.

Normally, the energy barriers are low enough for molecules to have enough kinetic energy at room temperature to overcome them, and hence one conformer (conformational isomer) easily changes into another. However, if the energy barriers to rotation are high enough, because of very large bulky groups, it is possible to observe the different conformers separately. Different conformations will quite often interact with drug receptors in different ways, or at different rates. They can also be modelled in computer-based simulations.

The simplest molecule to illustrate conformational isomerism is ethane. If we rotate one methyl group around the carbon–carbon single bond axis, keeping the other fixed, and imagine looking along the axis of the bond, there will be times when the hydrogen atoms on the front carbon atom obscure ('eclipse') the atoms on the far carbon, and times when they do not.

■ **Figure 20.57**
The different
conformations of
ethane

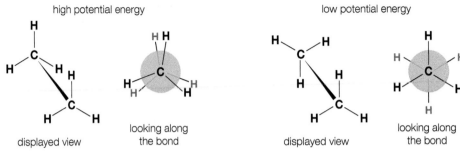

high potential energy

low potential energy

displayed view — looking along the bond

The eclipsed conformer of ethane

displayed view — looking along the bond

The staggered conformer of ethane

■ **Figure 20.57**
The different
conformations of
ethane

The two extremes are, on the one hand, total eclipsing, and on the other hand, the situation where the front hydrogens are exactly in between the back hydrogens, which is the 'staggered' conformation (Figure 20.57).

A further common example of conformational isomerism is the chair and boat forms of cyclohexane (Figure 20.58). The two forms are able to flip between each other but the boat form is under more strain. The bond angles are close to tetrahedral, so there is little angle strain, but the boat form of cyclohexane does have eclipsed bonds on four of its carbon atoms. This eclipsing produces a significant amount of torsional strain. More importantly, the close contact of the 'flagpole' hydrogens at either end of the molecule destabilizes the boat conformation.

■ **Figure 20.58**
a The chair and
b the boat forms of
cyclohexane

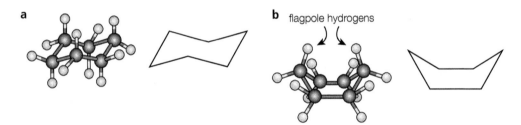

a

b flagpole hydrogens

■ Optical isomerism

Optical isomerism (or **enantiomerism**) arises from the inherent asymmetry of the molecules that make up each isomer. If you look at the everyday objects pictured in Figure 20.59 you see that these objects have a vertical plane of symmetry down through the centre of the object. Some molecules have a similar plane of symmetry. The benzene molecule is one such example (Figure 20.60).

■ **Figure 20.59** Everyday objects (a drinking glass and a fork) with a vertical plane of symmetry through the object concerned

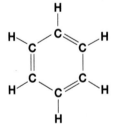

■ **Figure 20.60** Benzene is a molecule with seven planes of symmetry; the six shown here and the plane of the molecule itself

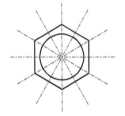

However, other molecules have no plane or centre of symmetry and they are referred to as **chiral** (pronounced 'kai-ral', from the Greek word meaning 'handed') molecules. The most common cases of chirality occur when a molecule contains a tetrahedral carbon atom surrounded by four

■ **Figure 20.61** Models of two tetrahedral carbon-containing molecules with four different groups around the central carbon atom

different atoms or groups of atoms; the feature which leads to the chirality, is called a chiral centre or centre of chirality.

Figure 20.61 shows two three-dimensional models of such a carbon atom, which is an example of a chiral centre (or stereogenic centre). The first model has four different groups around the central carbon atom, and the other model has just two of the groups interchanged. The two models, as you can see, are mirror image forms of each other. Molecules containing a chiral centre are said to be chiral molecules. No matter how we try, it is impossible to superimpose one model upon the other without breaking and re-making bonds. These molecules are said to be non-superimposable. The only way in which you can superimpose them is by reflection in a mirror: they are mirror images of each other. These two mirror images are known as enantiomers.

Figure 20.62 shows representations on paper of the enantiomers of butan-2-ol and 2-bromobutane. The chiral centre in each molecule is indicated here using an asterisk. We saw in Chapter 10 how three-dimensional structures can be represented in two dimensions by using a dotted line for bonds going behind the plane of the paper and wedge-shaped lines for bonds coming out from the plane of the paper.

■ **Figure 20.62** The enantiomers of butan-2-ol and 2-bromobutane

Enantiomers are also referred to as optical isomers because different enantiomers rotate the plane of polarized light in equal but opposite directions. Optical isomerism is the second form of stereoisomerism. In these molecules the groups in the optical isomers are the same; they differ in their arrangement in space, in this case around the central carbon atom.

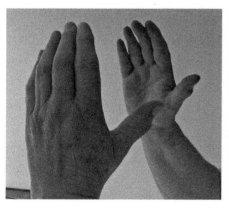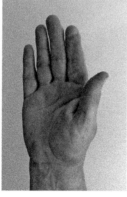

■ **Figure 20.63** Photographs of the 'hand' experiment demonstrating chirality

Chiral is derived from the Greek word *kheir*, which means 'hand'. The mirror image of the left hand is the right hand, and it cannot be superimposed on the left hand. If molecules (enantiomers) cannot be superimposed on their mirror images, they are showing 'handedness'. They are behaving rather like left and right hands – hence the word 'chiral'. The word 'enantiomer' is derived from the Greek *enantion* meaning 'opposite'.

There is a simple experiment with a flat mirror to show that your hands are chiral. Hold your left hand, outstretched and palm away from you, in front of a mirror. Now hold your right hand, outstretched and palm towards you, next to the mirror. The image of your left hand now looks identical to (is superimposable on) your real right hand (Figure 20.63)!

Nature of Science   Painstaking research

Scientific research is not always straightforward or instantly rewarding. Perhaps one of the most noteworthy examples of patient and thorough research is that of the French chemist Louis Pasteur (1822–1895). He started his career studying the various isomers of tartaric acid (2,3-dihydroxybutanedioic acid) isolated from the deposits from wine fermentation. Previously it had been found that there were two isomers: one, called racemic acid, had no effect on the plane of polarized light. The other, called tartaric acid, rotated it to the right. Chemically, however, the two acids had identical reactions.

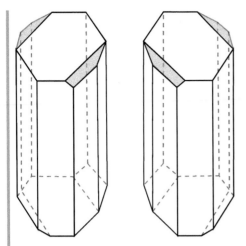

■ **Figure 20.64** Mirror image forms of sodium ammonium tartrate crystals

Pasteur carefully examined crystals of the sodium ammonium salt of racemic acid that he had prepared by allowing a saturated solution to evaporate slowly. He noticed there were two types of crystal that were mirror images of each other (Figure 20.64). Painstakingly, using a hand lens and a pair of tweezers, he separated the crystals into two piles. He then dissolved each sample of crystals in water and examined them in a polarimeter. He found that a solution of one pile of crystals rotated the plane of polarized light to the right (just as the same salt of tartaric acid had), but the other rotated it to the left, to an equal extent. He had become the first person to separate the enantiomers from a racemic mixture.

Only later did it become apparent how lucky he had been. Above the transition temperature of 22 °C the racemic salt crystallizes as symmetrical crystals containing equal amounts of both enantiomers. If he had recrystallized the salt in the usual way, by cooling a hot saturated solution, he would never have obtained the mixture of crystals.

Pasteur's remarkably patient isolation of mirror-image crystalline forms of an optically active compound serves to emphasize that chirality is first and foremost a property of the whole molecule. We have since developed that view and applied the language to a specific chiral centre in a molecule.

Pasteur's work was linked to that of his older friend and colleague, the physicist Jean Baptiste Biot (1774–1862). He was a pioneer of polarimetry and showed that certain solid quartz crystals, and later solutions of sugars, rotated the plane of polarized light in opposite directions. He realized this must be a molecular property and suggested the term 'optical activity' for the phenomenon. The work of these two scientists complemented each other and the phenomenon has immense significance, particularly in a biological context.

The defining physical property that distinguishes the optical isomers of a compound from each other is that they rotate the plane of plane-polarized light in equal but opposite directions. Normal light is electromagnetic radiation that is oscillating in every plane (Figure 20.65). Light passing through a polarizing filter only oscillates in one particular plane and is referred to as plane-polarized light. The filter shown in Figure 20.66 only allows through light waves oscillating in a vertical plane.

■ **Figure 20.65** A representation of how a polarizing filter works

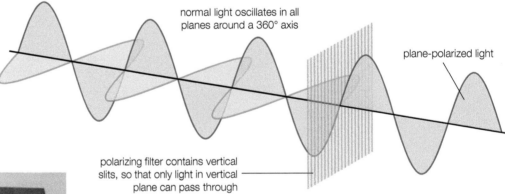

normal light oscillates in all planes around a 360° axis

plane-polarized light

polarizing filter contains vertical slits, so that only light in vertical plane can pass through

The polarizing filter acts as if it contains a series of narrow and closely spaced vertical slits, so that only the light oscillating in the same vertical plane can pass through it.

Our eyes are unable to distinguish between normal light and plane-polarized light. However, if another polarizing filter is placed in the path of plane-polarized light, rotated at right angles relative to the first filter, it will completely block the passage of all light (Figure 20.66). Polarizing filters are used in sunglasses and in camera lenses to cut down glare and reflections.

The ability of enantiomers to rotate the plane of plane-polarized light can be shown in practice by using a polarimeter. This consists of a light source, two polarizing lenses, and a tube to hold the sample of the enantiomer located between the lenses.

■ **Figure 20.66** If two pieces of Polaroid filter are laid at right angles to each other, the light is cut out. This is what is happening at the overlap of the filters here

■ **Figure 20.67**
The various stages
of a polarimeter for
analysing optical
isomers

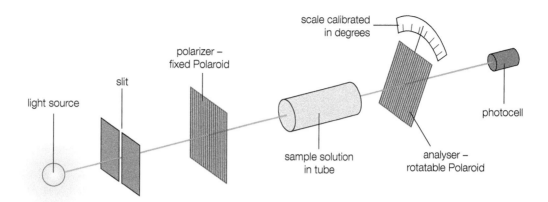

A polarimeter is an instrument used to distinguish optical isomers. The device consists of six parts, shown in Figure 20.67. Light from a monochromatic light source (which produces light of a single wavelength) passes through a slit to produce a thin beam of light. This beam of light then passes through a Polaroid filter. The polarized beam now enters and passes through the sample solution being tested. After the sample, the beam then passes through another piece of Polaroid, the analyser, and then into the photocell, which produces an electric current proportional to the intensity of light that falls upon it.

The instrument is initially calibrated using pure solvent. The output from the photocell is set to a minimum, at which point the analyser filter is at right angles to the polarizer filter. The angle on the scale is recorded. One of the samples is then placed in the sample tube and the analyser is rotated until the output from the photocell is again a minimum. The new angle on the scale is recorded. The rotation caused by the compound is the difference between the two measured angles.

A sample of the other enantiomer is then analysed in a similar way using a solution of the same concentration. In one case the analyser will have been rotated clockwise. This means that the enantiomer is dextrorotatory (from the Latin *dexter*, meaning 'right'). The other enantiomer will rotate the plane of the light anticlockwise and is said to be laevorotatory (from the Latin *laevus*, meaning 'left'). The two enantiomers rotate the plane of plane-polarized light by the same amount, but in opposite directions. One of the enantiomers is thus known as the (+)-form (formerly the d-form) and the other as the (−)-form (formerly the l-form). If both enantiomers are present in equal amounts the two rotations cancel each other out, and the mixture appears to be optically inactive. Such a mixture is known as a racemic mixture (or racemate).

Naming enantiomers

As we have just seen, enantiomers can be distinguished in their naming by referring simply to the direction in which they rotate the plane of polarized light, namely their optical activity. In this case they are known as the (+)-form and the (−)-form. The method of naming the optically active isomers using the symbols d- and l- is now obsolete and should not be used. There is no general way of predicting which of a pair of enantiomers will rotate the plane of polarized light in a particular direction, and there is no relationship between the configuration of a molecule and the direction or extent of rotation.

Various systems for naming the two isomers on the basis of their absolute configuration (the arrangement of the groups round the chiral centre) have been proposed, with the two main systems using the designations D/L or *R*/*S*, but it would be useful to have a system that was generally applicable and could be consistently applied as a means by which absolute configuration may be expressed in a manner which is dependent upon structure alone, and not upon physical or chemical properties. The most widely applicable method of describing the configurations of enantiomers, and the one approved by IUPAC, is the *R*/*S* convention based on the priority rules of Cahn, Ingold and Prelog. Chiral centres are designated *R*- or *S*- depending upon priority rules (Figure 20.68).

R- configuration

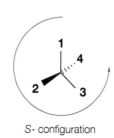

S- configuration

■ **Figure 20.68** The assignment of the configuration prefix based on CIP priority rules

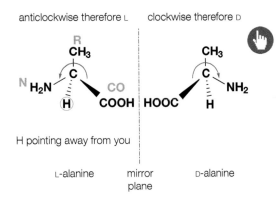

anticlockwise therefore L   clockwise therefore D

H pointing away from you

L-alanine   mirror   D-alanine
                   plane

■ **Figure** 20.69 The D- and L-stereoisomers of alanine

The D and L convention for naming enantiomeric forms of a molecule is discussed in Chapter 23 on the acompanying website; it tends to be used for carbohydrates and amino acids. It is rather an old-fashioned system and was developed before X-ray crystallography allowed the determination of the absolute configuration of molecules. For sugars, when the D and L system is used, it is based on the Fischer projection of the molecule and everything is compared to glyceraldehyde (2,3-dihydroxypropanal).

The application of the D and L system to amino acids uses the 'CORN' rule. This looks at the positions of the COOH, R and NH₂ groups around the chiral centre. The molecule is drawn in the tetrahedral form with the single hydrogen atom pointing away from you. If, moving from the COOH to R to NH₂, you go in a clockwise direction, the structure is the D-form; if you go anticlockwise it is the L-form (Figure 20.69).

All amino acids are chiral, except glycine which has only three different groups around the central carbon. All the amino acids found in naturally occurring proteins are L-amino acids, emphasizing again the importance of shape in biological systems.

Properties of optical isomers

The optical isomers of a compound differ in only one defining physical property: they rotate the plane of plane-polarized light in opposite directions. All their other physical properties, such as density and melting point, are identical. Not only are the physical properties of the two enantiomers identical, their general chemical properties are also identical. The exception to this is when they interact with biological sensors. Thus, in the body, the different enantiomers can have completely different physiological effects. For example, one of the enantiomers of the amino acid asparagine (H₂N–CH(CH₂CONH₂)–COOH) tastes bitter, whereas the other optical isomer tastes sweet. This relates to the fact that biological sensors, and indeed many biochemical reactions, are sensitive to molecular shape.

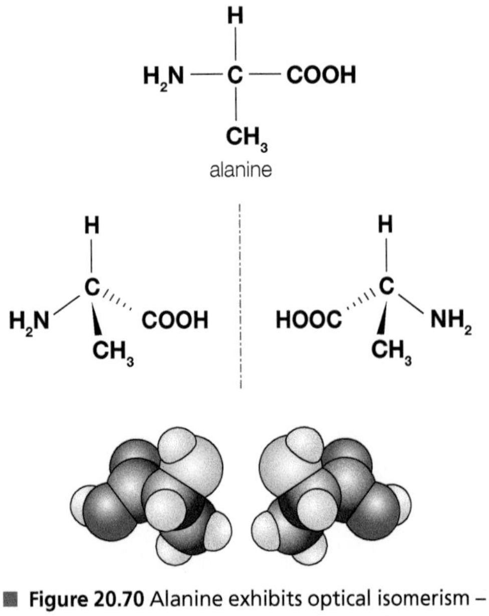

Utilization: The biochemical importance of shape

One group of compounds that exhibit optical isomerism is the 2-amino acids that are used in cells to synthesize proteins. Of the 20 amino acids utilized for this purpose, all but glycine (2-aminoethanoic acid) are chiral molecules. It is interesting to realize that it is the L-form of all these amino acids that is exclusively used by the protein-synthesizing machinery of the cell. Alanine (2-aminopropanoic acid) illustrates the optical isomerism shown by the 2-amino acids (Figure 20.70).

Biological systems are geared to the importance of shape recognition; it is the basis of self-assembly, enzyme–substrate interactions, the immune response, the significance of receptors and sensors, and many other aspects of living systems. There are several relatively simple examples of the differential activity of a molecule with one chiral centre. Carvone forms two mirror image forms or enantiomers: *R*-(−)-carvone smells like spearmint but its mirror image, *S*-(+)-carvone, smells like caraway. The fact that the two enantiomers are perceived as smelling differently is proof that olfactory receptors must contain chiral groups, allowing them to respond more strongly to one enantiomer than to the other. Recognition of this is of vital importance to the perfume industry; a highly significant and lucrative global industry. The art of making perfumes has been traced back to ancient Egypt, and the extraction of perfumed oils from natural sources encouraged the development of important chemical practical techniques such as the various forms of distillation.

alanine

■ **Figure** 20.70 Alanine exhibits optical isomerism – the two enantiomers rotate the plane of polarized light in opposite directions

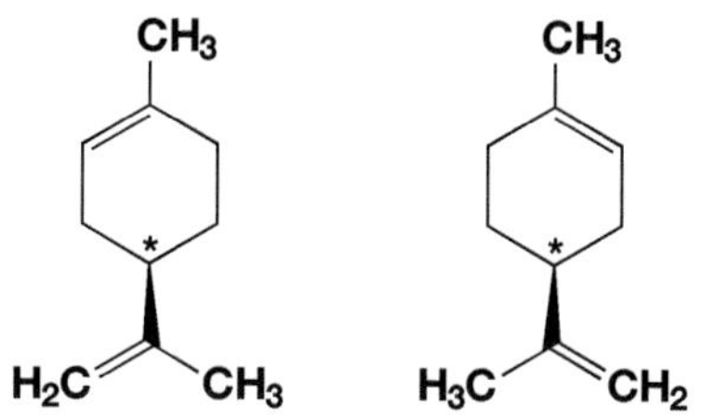

Figure 20.71 The enantiomers of limonene. The isomer found in the peel of citrus fruit is (+)-limonene. The chiral centre is shown by the asterisk

Materials can be extracted from plants and herbs in three ways: by applying pressure, by steam distillation, or by solvent extraction using an organic solvent. A modern version of the last method uses supercritical CO_2 because its volatility means that residual solvent is not a problem. Roses use small, fragrant molecules, synthesized in the petals, to attract pollinators. These compounds are formed by enzymatic oxidation of the carotenoid pigments, which give the petals their colour. Huge numbers of rose petals are used to make rose oil; it is estimated that around 1400 flowers are needed to get 1 g of the rose oil. Until the late 19th century, perfumes were based on available materials such as those that could be extracted from flowers and spices, but the growth of synthetic organic chemistry has brought with it the availability of new compounds with new odours. Today, virtually all perfumes involve some man-made molecules.

Limonene is a colourless liquid hydrocarbon classified as a cyclic terpene. The isomer found in orange peel is (+)-limonene (Figure 20.71). It is thought that its high abundance in this part of the fruit is connected with the fact that it is an insecticide. As well as its smell, limonene also contributes to the flavour of the fruit and as such has been used as a food additive for many years. Limonene is an important precursor in the biosynthesis of (−)-menthol, which is the major component of mint and the molecule responsible for the herb's refreshing taste. It is used in chemical synthesis as a precursor to carvone and as a renewably based solvent in cleaning products. It is readily prepared in the laboratory by steam distillation of the zest of an orange or lemon.

Menthol itself can be prepared in the laboratory by steam distillation of chopped mint, removing the water by drying, and then chilling the resulting oil to crystallize the menthol. The oil from corn mint is up to 85% (−)-menthol. It occurs naturally in peppermint oil. The ability of menthol to chemically trigger the cold-sensitive receptors in the skin is responsible for the well-known cooling sensation it provokes when inhaled, eaten, or applied to the skin. In this sense, it is similar to capsaicin, the chemical responsible for the spiciness of hot chillies (which stimulates heat sensors, also without causing an actual change in temperature). Because of its 'cooling' action, menthol is found in a wide range of medicines for treating sore throats and mouth irritations. It is also used in treatments for minor aches and sprains, and in nasal decongestants. It is found in some oral hygiene products, including toothpaste and mouthwashes, and will combat 'bad breath'.

The two optical isomers (enantiomers) of menthol have identical chemical properties. They differ in those properties that depend upon the chiral carbon, like smell. The (−) isomer can be described as 'fresh, sweet, minty, cooling, refreshing'. The (+) isomer is similar, but less minty, more herby, with 'musty, bitter, phenolic and herbaceous notes', and is less refreshing. The (−) isomer also has about four times the cooling power of the (+) isomer.

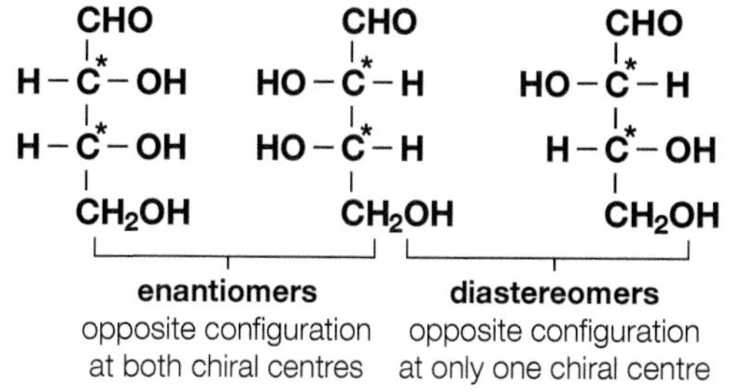

Figure 20.72 Illustration using linear 2D-structures of two four-carbon sugars showing the difference between enantiomers and diastereomers

Diastereomers

Many molecules have more than one chiral centre, and so can give rise to different configurations at every position. Enantiomers have opposite configurations at each chiral centre, which gives rise to the molecules being mirror images of each other (see Figure 20.70). But when molecules have different configurations at one or more, but not all, chiral centres, they are known as diastereomers (shortened from diastereoisomers) and are not mirror images of each other (Figure 20.72). Common sugars are often diastereomers of each other, such as glucose and galactose. In contrast to enantiomers, diastereomers have different physical and chemical properties.

Chiral molecules without chiral centres

Chirality is a property of the entire molecule and there are molecules that are chiral but do not contain a chiral centre. For example, 1,3-dimethylallene is a chiral molecule since it has no plane of symmetry, and it can exist as a pair of mirror images (Figure 20.73). The molecule has a *chiral axis* rather than a *chiral centre*. The presence of two rigid π bonds prevents free rotation around the three central carbon atoms.

■ **Figure 20.73**
The enantiomers of
1,3-dimethylallene

ToK Link

The ability to use reasoning based on physical evidence and to link that to our mental models of the microscopic 'world' is an essential part of scientific thinking. Modern scanning tunnelling microscopy has recently allowed us to gain a 'view' of atoms, and X-ray crystallography enables us to deduce the distances between atoms, yet we cannot ultimately *prove* the shapes of simple molecules or the mechanisms of organic reactions. The existence of optical isomers does provide good evidence to support our picture of chemistry at the molecular level. The ability to use optical isomerism and its effects on polarized light has provided us with physical evidence that these do represent the true shapes of these molecules and that our ideas regarding reaction mechanism are along the right lines.

Important in this was the application of polarimetry to studies on the S_N2 mechanism for nucleophilic substitution. This was first demonstrated by the Latvian chemist, Paul Walden. Walden reasoned that if he could find an optically active halogenoalkane that underwent nucleophilic substitution by an S_N2 mechanism, then the product should rotate the plane of light in the opposite direction to the starting material because the reaction mechanism suggests that an 'inversion' of the tetrahedral arrangement around the target carbon atom should occur (Figure 20.74).

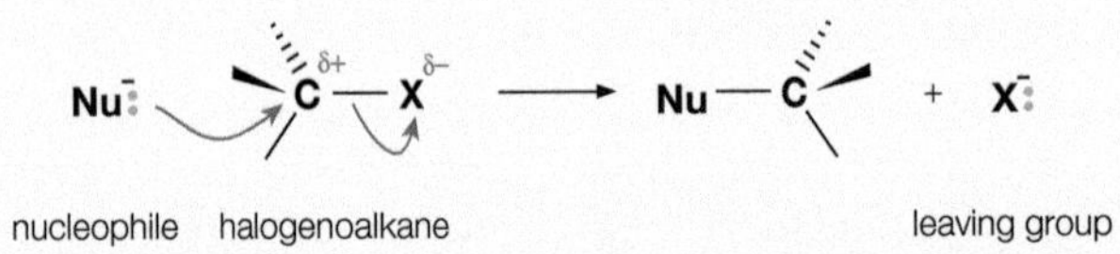

■ **Figure 20.74** The S_N2 mechanism suggests that inversion of the tetrahedral molecule should occur – the umbrella should blow open the wrong way!

In the S_N2 mechanism described in Figure 20.3, the nucleophile is shown approaching the halogenoalkane from the side of the molecule *opposite* the halogen atom – this is known as backside attack (Chapter 6). The nucleophile could also have been shown to be approaching the halogen from the same side. However, experiments strongly support the idea of backside attack. The halogenoalkane used in these experiments needs to have a chiral centre. The secondary halogenoalkane 2-bromooctane is suitable since it has a chiral centre and can exist in two optically active forms (enantiomers) (Figure 20.75).

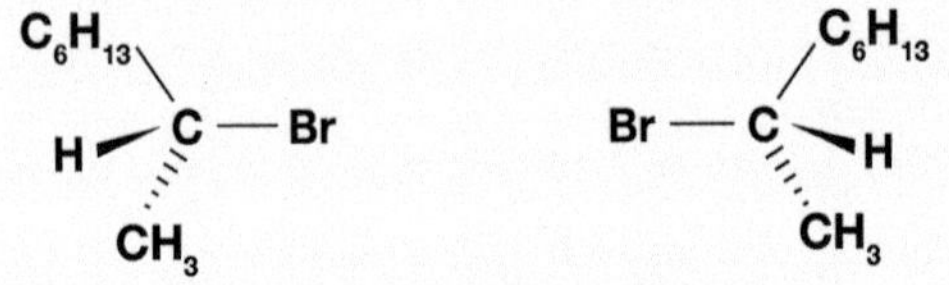

■ **Figure 20.75** The enantiomers of 2-bromooctane

Hydrolysis experiments show that each enantiomer gives the alcohol, octan-2-ol, of *opposite* configuration, showing that substitution involves *inversion* of configuration at the carbon atom that was bonded to the halogen. This observation is consistent with the approach of the hydroxide ion (nucleophile) from the opposite side of the molecule to the halogen atom (Figure 20.76).

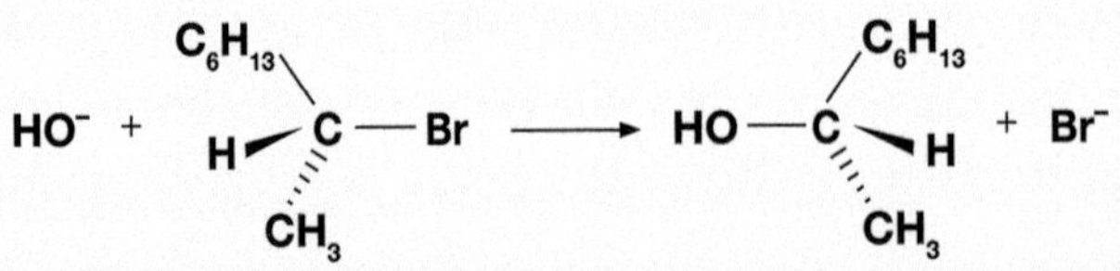

■ **Figure 20.76** The inversion of 2-bromooctane during nucleophilic substitution (sometimes referred to as a Walden inversion)

There is also strong stereochemical evidence in support of the S_N1 mechanism described in Figure 20.9. It has been found that when an optically active sample of a chiral tertiary halogenoalkane undergoes hydrolysis, all of the optical activity is lost. This observation is consistent with the suggested mechanism. VSEPR theory (Chapter 4) predicts that the three bonds from the positively charged carbon are in the form of a trigonal planar arrangement (Figure 20.77).

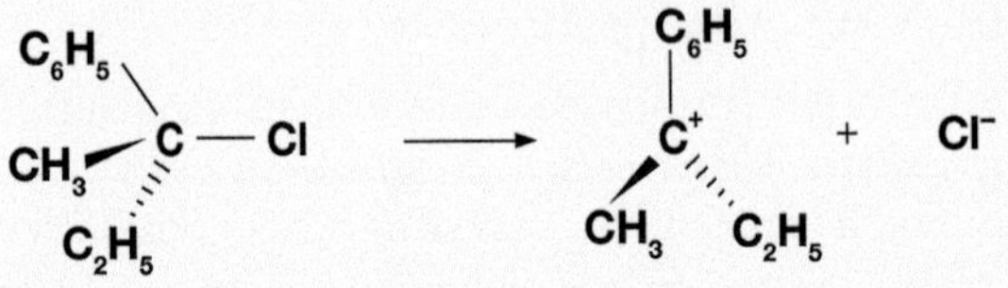

■ **Figure 20.77** The formation of a trigonal planar carbocation intermediate from an optically active halogenoalkane

The planar nature of the intermediate means that when the carbocation from an optically active halogenoalkane is attacked by a nucleophile from *either side* (with equal probability), a mixture of the two enantiomers of the alcohol is obtained (Figure 20.78). This gives a 50:50 racemic mixture of the two optical isomers. The planar shape of carbocations has been confirmed experimentally by X-ray diffraction (Chapter 4).

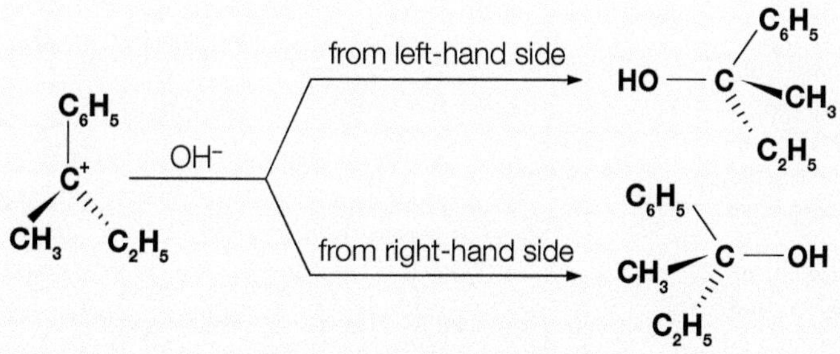

■ **Figure 20.78** The racemization of an optically active halogenoalkane during nucleophilic substitution (S_N1)

Chirality and the therapeutic activity of drugs

The design, development and supply of new pharmaceutical drugs is a global and economically highly important industrial concern. There are a range of issues involved, from some that are essentially scientific concerns through to highly charged commercial and political concerns. That this is so is hardly surprising given the importance of the therapeutic effects and the heavy financial implications of the development and marketing of new pharmaceuticals.

We have seen from the earlier discussion of the importance of shape in biological systems that issues surrounding the chirality of biological-targeted molecules are highly significant. This is an important aspect of pharmaceutical drug design and usage. There are several key examples here that illustrate the issues involved. One situation that can occur is that the opposite enantiomers of a compound can have differing effects on the human body. For the commercial compound, propoxyphene, one isomer is an analgesic while the other has anti-coughing (antitussive) properties (Figure 20.79). Intriguingly, even the commercial names are mirror images of each other!

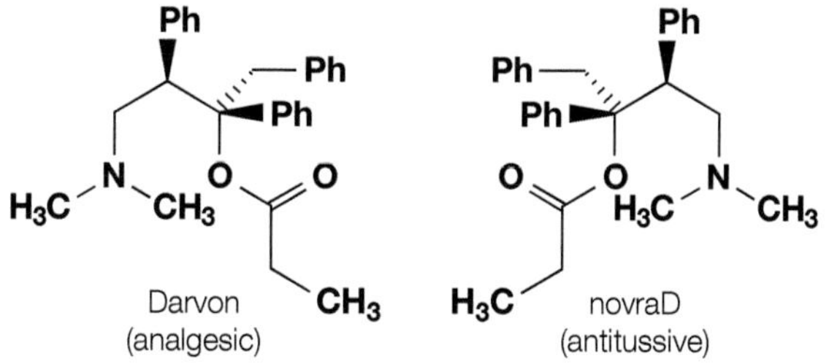

Darvon
(analgesic)

novraD
(antitussive)

■ **Figure 20.79** The enantiomers of propoxyphene have different effects in the human body

DOPA (dihydroxyphenylalanine) is a drug used to treat the neurodegenerative condition known as Parkinson's disease. It is of particular interest in this context as the form that is active in the body is actually achiral. However, one of the chiral forms – the D-isomer – causes harmful side effects and so the compound must be administered as the L-enantiomer. This is then converted to the active achiral form in the brain by the enzyme, L-DOPA decarboxylase (Figure 20.80).

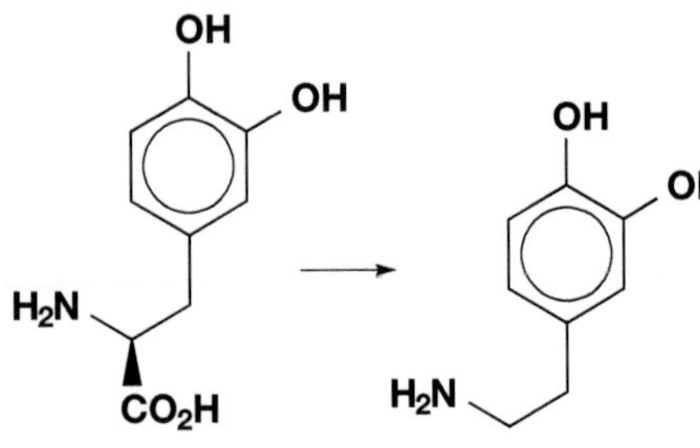

■ **Figure 20.80** The conversion of the chiral L–DOPA in the brain by the enzyme, L-DOPA decarboxylase

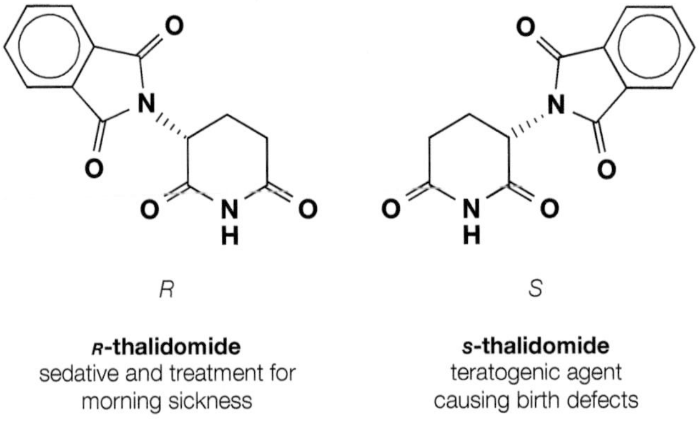

■ **Figure 20.81** The two enantiomers of thalidomide

The gravest and farthest reaching example of the importance of chirality and therapeutic effectiveness is the thalidomide story. This drug came to prominence in the 1950s. It was marketed extensively around the world as a sedative and, more specifically, as relief for morning sickness in pregnant women. It was marketed and administered as the racemic mixture and was effective as a treatment. However, it transpired that while one enantiomer, *R*-thalidomide, performed well in relieving morning sickness, the other proved to have teratogenic effects (toxicity to the fetus, causing severe birth defects) (Figure 20.81). Thousands of children worldwide were born with missing or malformed limbs, with significant numbers dying in infancy.

The two forms do interconvert in the body, so while this was a concern that grew out of these events, in this particular case treatment with a stereospecific enantiomer would not have avoided the problem. The situation arose because of a lack of stringency in the testing – the drug was not tested for teratogenic effects. Indeed, thalidomide was never approved for use by the FDA (Federal Drugs Administration) in the USA because of this. The situation led to legal cases being brought in several countries and compensation packages being agreed for the families concerned. It also led to more stringent regimes of drug testing, an increased awareness of the issues around chirality and, indeed, the need for stereospecific synthesis methods in drug production. Today thalidomide is marketed as a treatment for some cancers and for leprosy.

The concerns surrounding stereospecificity and testing that surfaced in the thalidomide case highlight the broader issues of the economic costs of the development and evaluation of new pharmaceutical products. Pharmaceutical companies are major players globally, with large multinational companies tending to dominate the world market. There are concerns over patent law and the balance between availability at reasonable cost and the proper return for a company investing in producing a new drug. Questions arise in national health services as to which drugs can be afforded for particular illnesses, while in other countries there are tensions over the availability of generic as opposed to branded preparations. These concerns have been popularly highlighted in films such as *The Constant Gardener*, based on the book by John Le Carré. There are international movements concerned to see that the distribution of health-promoting medications is more fair and equitable.

Nature of Science   Finding 'greener' synthetic routes

Green chemistry is targeted at changing the way in which we exploit our chemical knowledge of reactions and products so as to reduce the overuse of resources and the levels of hazardous waste, thus leading to a more sustainable chemical industry and a healthier environment. Throughout this chapter we have talked of various aspects of organic chemistry that are of importance to the chemical industry. Here we give an example of an important synthesis where the application of the ideas of green chemistry has led to an improved method of production.

Ibuprofen (2,4-isobutyl-phenylpropanoic acid) (Figure 20.82) is a popular over-the-counter drug that has pain-relief and anti-inflammatory properties. It was originally developed in the 1960s and at that time its synthesis involved a six-step process that generated a large amount of unwanted waste. A solution to this problem developed a new, greener synthesis of ibuprofen

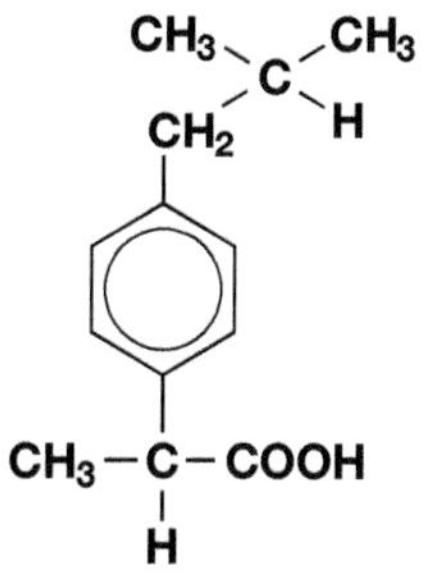

■ **Figure 20.82**
The structure of ibuprofen, a commercial pain reliever

that only required three steps and was implemented in the early 1990s. This process also incorporated most of the reactants into the final product, reducing or eliminating most of the waste by-products. The older synthetic route for ibuprofen had an atom economy of only 40%, whereas the new method runs at an atom economy of 99%.

The new synthetic route to ibuprofen is an important example of how ideas of 'green chemistry' can influence for the better the industrial synthetic methods used, not only from the point of view of economic efficiency, but also by introducing more effective methods of science and technology. Improved methods of synthesis for hexan-1,6-dioic acid (adipic aid) and *cis*-butenediol acid (maleic anhydride) – important for the industrial synthesis of nylon and polyesters respectively – are two other examples of the impact of a greener synthetic approach to industrial chemistry.

Aspects of the 'green' approach to chemical synthesis can be seen in the laboratory. One such possibility is the use of microwave ovens as the heating supply, and a method for synthesizing aspirin (2-ethanolyoxybenzoic acid) has been devised using such an oven. The method starts from 1-hydroxybenzoic acid and the esterification procedure used is outlined in Figure 20.83.

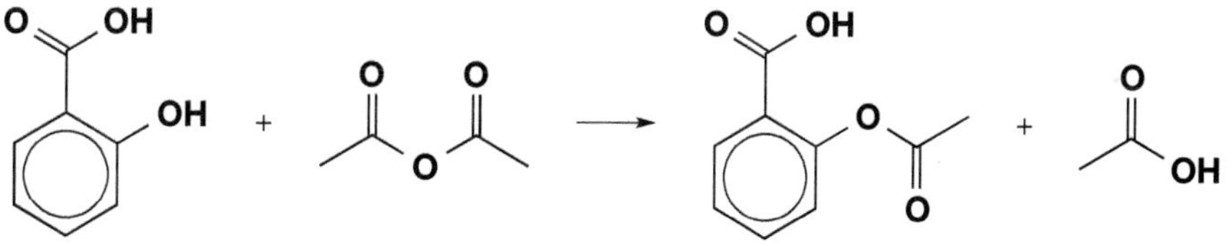

■ **Figure 20.83**
The esterification of 2-hydroxybenzoic acid to form the painkiller, aspirin

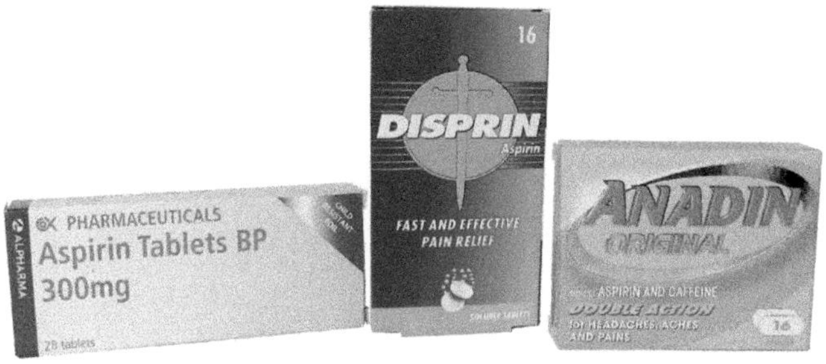

Weigh 5 g of salicylic acid (1-hydroxybenzoic acid) into a 250 cm³ beaker. Add 5 cm³ of ethanoic anhydride so as to wet the salicylic acid uniformly. Place a beaker containing 200 cm³ of cold water alongside the reaction mixture to absorb excess microwave energy. Cover the beaker with a Petri dish and irradiate at full power for 60 seconds. Carefully remove the beaker and swirl the contents gently to mix. Check the temperature, which should be between 120 and 130 °C. If the temperature is lower than this, continue heating the mixture until the proper temperature has been reached, noting that temperatures above 130 °C may generate by-products and reduce the yield of aspirin.

Carefully remove the beaker from the microwave oven (it will be hot) and allow the contents to cool to about 95–100 °C before pouring into cold water (50 cm^3). The mixture will oil out, and should be stirred until solid starts separating out. Keep stirring the mixture to prevent clumping and cool in a bath of ice-cold water. Filter the mixture when cold, and wash the product with ice-cold water. Air dry using vacuum suction. The melting point of the product should be 134–135 °C. If necessary, the aspirin may be recrystallized from a hot mixture of 5–7 ml of 2-propanol and 1–2 cm^3 of water.

■ Summary

Table 20.6 summarizes the key reagents for the types of reaction covered in this chapter.

■ **Table 20.6**
Summary of key organic reagents

Reagent	Use	Example
H_2, Pt catalyst	Reduction	$C_6H_5NO_2 \rightarrow C_6H_5NH_2$
$NaBH_4(aq)$	Reduction of >C=O, but not >C=C< or –COOH	$RCHO \rightarrow RCH_2OH$ $R_2C=O \rightarrow R_2CHOH$
$LiAlH_4(ether)$	Reduction	$RCOOH \rightarrow RCHO \rightarrow RCH_2OH$ $R_2C=O \rightarrow R_2CHOH$
$OH^-(aq)$	Nucleophilic substitution of halogenoalkane	$CH_3CH_2Br \rightarrow CH_3CH_2OH$
$Br_2(CCl_4)$ or $Br_2(aq)$	Test for unsaturation	$H_2C=CH_2 \rightarrow CH_2Br–CH_2Br$
HBr, BrCl	Electrophilic addition to an alkene	$CH_3CH=CH_2 \rightarrow CH_3CHBrCH_3$
Cl_2, $FeCl_3$, $FeBr_3$(anhydrous)	Friedel–Crafts reaction/ electrophilic substitution in an arene	$C_6H_6 \rightarrow C_6H_5Cl$
Concentrated HNO_3 and concentrated H_2SO_4	Nitration of an arene	$C_6H_6 \rightarrow C_6H_5NO_2$

■ *Examination questions – a selection*

Paper 1 IB questions and IB style questions

Q1 Which compound would decolourize bromine water in the dark?

- **A** $CH_3COCH_2CH_3$
- **B** $CH_3(CH_2)_4OH$
- **C** $CH_3CHCHCH_3$
- **D** $CH_3(CH_2)_3CH_3$

Higher Level Paper 1, Nov 2012, Q35

Q2 Which halogenoalkane will react most quickly with sodium hydroxide?

- **A** $CH_3CH_2CH_2CH_2Cl$
- **B** $CH_3CH_2CH_2CH_2Br$
- **C** $(CH_3)_3CCl$
- **D** $(CH_3)_3CBr$

Higher Level Paper 1, Nov 2012, Q37

Q3 Halogenoalkanes can undergo S_N1 and S_N2 reactions with aqueous sodium hydroxide. Which halogenoalkane will not react with a 0.1 mol dm^{-3} solution of aqueous sodium hydroxide?

- **A** iodobenzene
- **B** 1-iodobutane
- **C** 2-iodo-2-methylpropane
- **D** 2-iodobutane

Q4 Which two molecules are *cis-trans* isomers of each other?

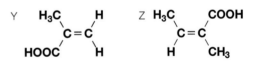

- **A** X and Z
- **B** X and Y
- **C** W and Y
- **D** W and Z

Higher Level Paper 2011, May 11, Q37

Q5 Which compound could rotate the plane of polarization of polarized light?

- **A** $(CH_3)_2CHCH_2Cl$
- **B** $CH_3CH_2CH_2CH_2Cl$
- **C** $CH_3CH_2CHClCH_3$
- **D** $(CH_3)_3CCl$

Higher Level Paper 1, Nov 2009, Q35

Q6 Which of the molecules would be able to rotate a plane-polarized light?

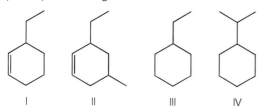

I	II	III	IV

A I and II
B III and IV

C I, II and III
D I, II and IV

Q7 What is the type of mechanism and an important feature of the reaction between $C(CH_3)_3Br$ and aqueous NaOH?

	Mechanism	**Feature**
A	S_N1	a transition state
B	S_N1	an intermediate
C	S_N2	a transition state
D	S_N2	an intermediate

Q8 Which molecule exhibits optical isomerism?
A 3-iodopentane
B 2-iodo-2-methylpropane
C 1,3-diiodopropane
D 2-iodobutane

Higher Level Paper 1, Nov 2011, Q36

Q9 Which compound is optically active?

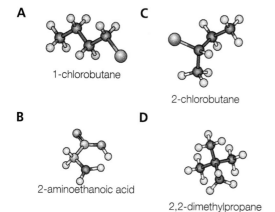

A 1-chlorobutane

C 2-chlorobutane

B 2-aminoethanoic acid

D 2,2-dimethylpropane

Higher Level Paper 1, May 2011, Q35

Q10 Which statement about stereoisomers is correct?
A 1,2-dichloroethane has two *cis–trans* isomers.
B 1,2-dichloroethane has two optical isomers.
C 1,2-dichloroethene has two *cis–trans* isomers.
D 1,2-dichloroethene has two optical isomers.

Higher Level Paper 1, Nov 2010, Q35

Paper 2 IB questions and IB style questions

Q1 But-1-ene undergoes an electrophilic addition reaction with iodine chloride, ICl. The major product of this reaction is 2-chloro-1-iodobutane.

a Show the mechanism of this reaction, using curly arrows to represent the movement of electron pairs. [4]
b Deduce the name of the minor product of this reaction and explain why only a small amount of it is formed. [3]

Higher Level Paper 2, Nov 2007, Q4

Q2 The compound methylbenzene, $C_6H_5CH_3$, was reacted with chlorine under two different conditions.

In the presence of aluminium chloride two organic products, **F** and **G**, were formed, both with the molecular formula C_7H_7Cl.

Under the other set of conditions three organic products, **J**, **K** and **L**, were formed, with molecular formulas of C_7H_7Cl, $C_7H_6Cl_2$ and $C_7H_5Cl_3$, respectively.

a State the type of mechanism that occurs in the formation of **F** and **G**. [1]
b Write equations, using curly arrows to represent the movement of electron pairs, to show the mechanism of the reaction in which either **F** or **G** is formed. Use Cl^+ to represent the attacking species. [3]
c Deduce the structures of compounds **J**, **K** and **L**. [3]
d State the type of mechanism that occurs in the formation of **J**, **K** and **L**. [1]
e Write an equation to show the initiation step that occurs before either **J**, **K** or **L** can be formed, and state the condition needed. [2]
f Write equations to show **two** propagation steps in the mechanism for the formation of compound **K**. [2]
g Write an equation to show a termination step in which compound **L** is formed. [1]

Higher Level Paper 2, Nov 2004, Q5

Q3 This question is based on this reaction scheme:
$$C_6H_{12} \rightarrow C_6H_{13}Br$$
W   **X** and **Y**

a The molecule **W** has the structure

$$\begin{array}{ccc} H_3C & & (CH_2)_2CH_3 \\ & C=C & \\ H & & H \end{array}$$

i Give the structure of the *cis–trans* isomer of **W**. [1]
ii Explain why **W** has a *cis–trans* isomer. [2]
iii State the full name of **W**. [2]
b i State the name of the reaction mechanism by which **W** is converted to **X** and **Y**. [1]

ii The product **Y** can exist as optical isomers. Deduce the structure of **Y** and explain why it shows optical isomerism. [2]

iii Write equations (using 'curly arrows' to represent the movement of electron pairs) to show the mechanism of the reaction in which **X** is formed. [4]

iv Markovnikov's rule is sometimes useful in predicting the major product in this type of reaction. Explain why this empirical rule cannot be used to predict whether **X** or **Y** would be the major product. [2]

Q4 Below are four structural isomers with molecular formula C_4H_9Br.

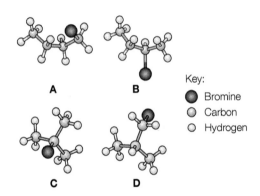

Key:
● Bromine
◉ Carbon
○ Hydrogen

a State the names of the four isomers. [4]

b i Identify the isomer(s) which will react with aqueous sodium hydroxide almost exclusively by S_N1 mechanism. State the meaning of the symbols in the term S_N1 mechanism. [2]

ii Using the formula RBr to represent a bromoalkane, write an equation for the rate-determining step of this S_N1 reaction. [2]

iii Identify one isomer that will react with aqueous sodium hydroxide almost exclusively by S_N2 mechanism. Draw

the mechanism for this reaction using curly arrows to represent the movement of electron pairs. Include the structural formulas of the transition state and the organic product. [4]

c State and explain how the rates of the reactions in parts **b i** and **b iii** are affected when the concentration of the sodium hydroxide is doubled. [2]

d State and explain how the rate of reaction of 1-bromobutane with sodium hydroxide compares with that of 1-chlorobutane with sodium hydroxide. [2]

e Identify the isomer of C_4H_9Br that can exist as stereoisomers. Outline how a polarimeter will distinguish between the isomers, and how their physical and chemical properties compare. [5]

Higher Level Paper, May 2010, Q5

Q5 The following molecules **A**, **B** and **C** all show stereoisomerism. State and explain whether each example is the *E*- or *Z*-form of the isomeric pair.

A

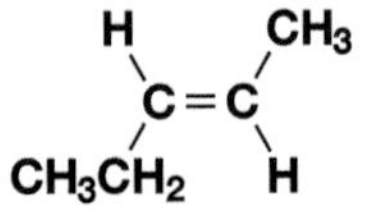

$$\begin{array}{ccc} H & & CH_3 \\ & C=C & \\ CH_3CH_2 & & H \end{array}$$

B

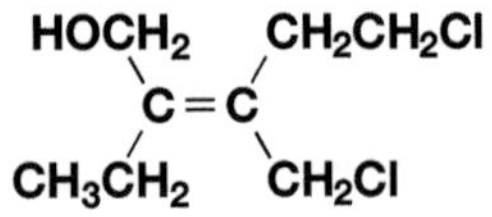

$$\begin{array}{ccc} HOCH_2 & & CH_2CH_2Cl \\ & C=C & \\ CH_3CH_2 & & CH_2Cl \end{array}$$

C

$$\begin{array}{ccc} & & O \\ & & \parallel \\ ClCH_2 & & C \\ & C=C & \diagdown OCH_3 \\ CH_3 & & CH_2OH \end{array}$$

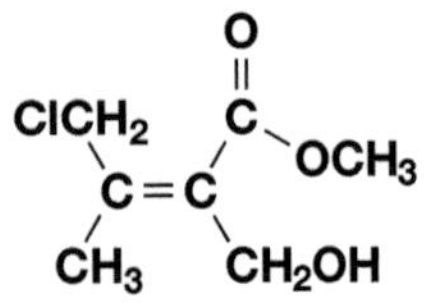

[9 (3 marks each)]

21 Measurement and analysis

ESSENTIAL IDEA

- Although spectroscopic characterization techniques form the backbone of structural identification of compounds, typically no one technique results in a full structural identification of a molecule.

Mass spectrometry and a variety of spectroscopic techniques, including nuclear magnetic resonance (NMR) and infrared (IR) spectroscopy are used to elucidate the structure of organic compounds. The full structural identification of complex organic molecules requires a combined application of all these techniques. X-ray crystallography can be used to determine the bond lengths and the bond angles of a molecule.

21.1 Spectroscopic identification of organic compounds – *although spectroscopic identification techniques form the backbone of structural identification of compounds, typically no one technique results in a full structural identification of a molecule*

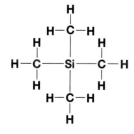

■ **Figure 21.1** Structure of tetramethylsilane (TMS)

■ Nuclear magnetic resonance (NMR) spectroscopy

Use of tetramethylsilane (TMS) as the reference standard

To ensure reproducibility and to set up a scale, the positions of NMR absorption peaks are measured relative to the signal of an internal standard, known as TMS. Tetramethylsilane (TMS), $(CH_3)_4Si$ (Figure 21.1), has 12 hydrogens in an identical chemical environment and it therefore produces a sharp single peak which is located away from the majority of the peaks found in many organic molecules. A small amount of this substance is added to a sample before it is introduced into the NMR machine. It is non-toxic, unreactive and can be readily removed after analysis by evaporation.

Explaining the use of tetramethylsilane (TMS) as the reference standard

The use of parts per million (ppm) on the horizontal axis of an NMR spectrum was introduced in Chapter 11, but its use rather than the expected units of frequency (Hz) was not explained. NMR instruments of many different applied magnetic field strengths are used in chemistry laboratories, and the proton's resonance frequency range depends on the strength of the applied magnetic field. For example, on an NMR instrument with an applied field of approximately 7.1 tesla, the protons resonate in the region of 300 million Hz (chemists refer to this as a 300 MHz instrument). If the NMR spectrum of the same molecule is recorded using an instrument with a 2.4 tesla magnet, the protons will resonate at around 100 million Hz (a 100 MHz instrument). One tesla is about 10 000 times as strong as the Earth's magnetic field.

It would be inconvenient and confusing to always have to convert NMR data according to the magnetic field strength of the instrument used. Therefore, chemists report resonance frequencies not as absolute values in hertz, but rather as values relative to a common standard: the signal generated by the protons in TMS. Regardless of the magnetic field strength of the instrument being used, the resonance frequency of the 12 equivalent protons in TMS is defined as a zero point. The resonance frequencies of protons in the sample molecule are then reported in terms of how much higher they are, in ppm, relative to the TMS signal (almost all hydrogens in organic molecules have a higher resonance frequency than those in TMS).

Analysing high-resolution ¹H NMR spectra

If the magnetic field generated by the NMR spectrometer is homogeneous and accurately controlled then it is possible to obtain high-resolution NMR spectra. The high-resolution NMR spectrum provides more information about the structure of molecules.

In high-resolution NMR spectra the single peak generated by a group of equivalent hydrogens is often observed to split into a cluster of peaks (Table 21.1). An analysis of this spin–spin splitting or coupling gives further structural information.

■ **Table 21.1**
Descriptions of simple peak clusters in a high-resolution ¹H NMR spectrum

Number of hydrogens on carbon adjacent to resonating hydrogen	Number of lines in cluster (multiplet)	Relative intensities
1	2	1 : 1
2	3	1 : 2 : 1
3	4	1 : 3 : 3 : 1
4	5	1 : 4 : 6 : 4 : 1

The spin–spin splitting occurs because hydrogens on *adjacent* carbon atoms may affect each other's NMR signals. A high-resolution ¹H NMR spectrum is interpreted using the $n + 1$ rule: spin–spin splitting by an adjacent group of n hydrogens will cause the signal to split into $n + 1$ peaks (Figure 21.2).

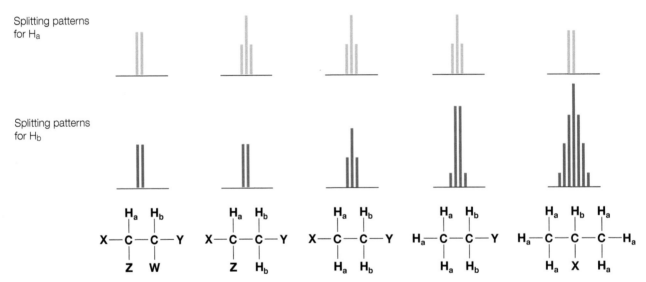

■ **Figure 21.2** Commonly observed splitting patterns

Pascal's triangle

The relative intensities of the lines in an NMR coupling pattern are given by a binomial expansion or more conveniently by Pascal's triangle (Table 21.2). To derive Pascal's triangle, start at 1 and generate each lower row by adding together the two numbers above and to either side in the row above.

■ **Table 21.2**
Pascal's triangle

$n = 0$				1				singlet
$n = 1$			1		1			doublet
$n = 3$		1		2		1		triplet
$n = 4$	1		3		3		1	quartet
$n = 5$	1	4		6		4	1	quintet

■ **Figure 21.3** Structure of propanal showing hydrogen atoms that undergo spin–spin splitting

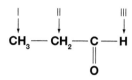

Note that a peak in a high-resolution ^{1}H NMR spectrum can be split *twice* by hydrogen atoms on two neighbouring atoms. For example, in the spectrum of propanal (Figure 21.3), the peak for the hydrogen atoms labelled II is split into four by the hydrogen atoms labelled I and then split again by the hydrogen atom labelled III. The peak for II is thus split into a doublet of quartets.

Spin–spin splitting is illustrated in Figure 21.4, which shows the high-resolution ^{1}H NMR spectrum of ethanol (in the presence of a small amount of water or acid). (The –OH group *will* undergo coupling, but only if the ethanol is dry and all traces of acid are excluded.)

■ **Figure 21.4** High-resolution NMR spectrum of ethanol, CH_3–CH_2–OH

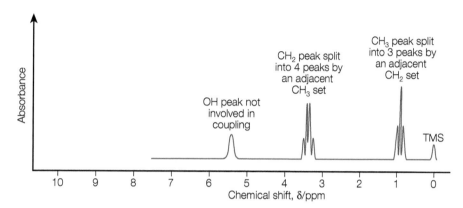

Worked example

Deduce the structure of the compound which has the molecular formula C_4H_8O, from its high-resolution ^{1}H NMR spectrum shown in Figure 21.5.

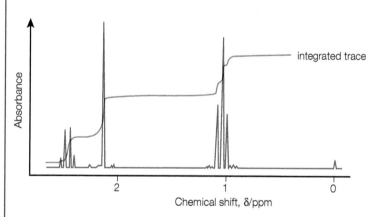

■ **Figure 21.5** High-resolution ^{1}H NMR spectrum for C_4H_8O

The single peak at $\delta = 2.1$ is not experiencing spin–spin splitting and therefore has no hydrogens immediately adjacent to it. The peak at $\delta = 2.5$ is the methylene group, $-CH_2-$ and is split into a quartet by the adjacent methyl group, $-CH_3$. The peak at $\delta = 1.0$ is the methyl group split into a triplet and so must be adjacent to the methylene group, $-CH_2-$.

This information suggests that the compound is butanone: CH_3–CO–CH_2–CH_3.

1 Sketch the predicted high-resolution ^{1}H NMR spectrum of ethyl ethanoate.

Worked example

The low-resolution ^{1}H NMR spectrum for ethanal is shown in Figure 21.6. Account for the number of peaks and their ratio. Predict the high-resolution spectrum for ethanal. Account for the splitting pattern predicted.

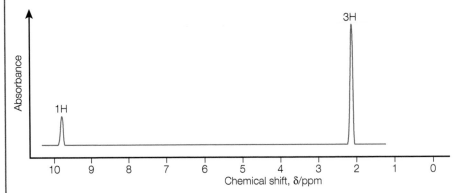

■ **Figure 21.6** Low-resolution ^{1}H NMR spectrum for ethanal

The ethanal molecule contains hydrogen in two types of chemical environment: the hydrogen attached to the carbonyl group and the hydrogen atoms forming the methyl group. The hydrogen forming the aldehyde group is very downfield (the peak is in the high chemical shift end of the spectrum) due to the presence of the electronegative oxygen atom. The two peaks will be in a 1:3 ratio. The ($n + 1$) rule predicts that the peak near 2 ppm will be split into 2 (1 + 1) peaks: a doublet. The peak near 10 ppm will be split into 4 (3 + 1) peaks: a quartet.

2   The diagram below shows the NMR spectrum of an organic compound with the formula $C_8H_8O_2$. It reacts rapidly with sodium to release hydrogen gas. Deduce its structure, explaining your reasoning.

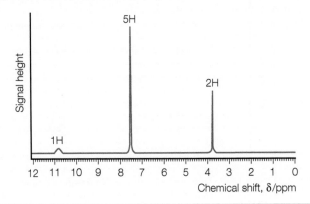

Spin–spin splitting

Spin–spin splitting (or spin–spin coupling) occurs in ^{1}H NMR whenever hydrogens (protons) on adjacent carbon atoms are in different chemical environments. The splitting of the peak arises because the magnetic field experienced by a hydrogen is slightly altered due to the orientations of the magnetic moments (spin states) of the hydrogens on the adjacent carbon atoms. Consider the hydrogens in the methyl group, $-CH_3$, of an ethyl group in a molecule (such as ethyl ethanoate). The magnetic field they experience will depend on the orientations of the magnetic moments of the $-CH_2-$ hydrogens, as shown in Figure 21.7.

In situations 2 and 3, the magnetic moments of the two $-CH_2-$ hydrogens cancel each other out, so the magnetic field experienced by the $-CH_3$

■ **Figure 21.7** The directions of the magnetic moments of the $-CH_2-$ hydrogens have an effect on the $-CH_3$ hydrogens

hydrogens will be the same as the applied magnetic field. In situations 1 and 4, however, the magnetic moments of the $-CH_2-$ hydrogens reinforce each other. Consequently, the magnetic field experienced by the hydrogens of the $-CH_3$ group will be higher and lower, respectively, than the applied magnetic field. There should therefore be a total of three radio wave frequencies at which these methyl ($-CH_3$) hydrogens absorb. The probabilities of the four states are equal, so overall there is twice the chance of the methyl ($-CH_3$) hydrogens experiencing no change in magnetic field (states 2 and 3) as there is for them to experience either an increased or decreased magnetic field (states 1 and 4). We therefore expect the intensities of the lines in the triplet to be in the ratio $1:2:1$.

---

3 By considering the different combinations of the ↑ and ↓ magnetic moments of the $-CH_3$ hydrogens, explain how the ratio $1:3:3:1$ arises.

Spin–spin splitting between adjacent hydrogen atoms is measured by spin–spin coupling constants measured in hertz (Hz). For example, >C=CH–CH=C< and >C=CH$_2$ have spin–spin coupling constants in the ranges 10–13 Hz and 1–2 Hz, respectively, but knowledge of these is not a syllabus requirement.

High-resolution NMR is a very powerful technique and can be used in a modified form (known as two-dimensional NMR) to establish the structures of proteins (see Chapter 23 on the accompanying website). Figure 21.8 shows the structure of a small protein known as LysM, which binds to bacterial cell walls. It is shown running from blue at the nitrogen terminus, and it has an antiparallel beta sheet and three alpha helices.

Figure 21.9 is a two-dimensional heteronuclear single quantum coherence (HSQC) spectrum of the protein. This is an NMR spectrum that shows H–N pairs in the protein (hydrogen along the horizontal axis and nitrogen on the vertical axis). There is one N–H per amino acid, so there is one peak per amino acid residue (numbered in the spectrum). Some of the side chains of the amino acid residue also contain N–H pairs.

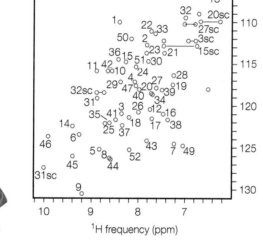

■ **Figure 21.9** Two-dimensional heteronuclear single quantum coherence (HSQC) spectrum of the protein LysM (supplied by Professor Michael Williamson, University of Sheffield)

■ **Figure 21.8** Ribbon structure of LysM

ToK Link

The intensity ratio of the lines in the high-resolution NMR spectrum is given by the numbers in Pascal's triangle, a mathematical pattern known independently by a number of different cultures over a thousand years ago. Why is mathematics such an effective tool in science? Is mathematics the science of patterns?

The relative peak intensities for multiple peaks appearing in a high-resolution ^{1}H NMR spectrum can be determined using Pascal's triangle:

Pascal's triangle is named after the French mathematician Blaise Pascal, but it was studied by many other mathematicians centuries before him in India, Greece, Iran and China. Pascal's triangle is a triangular array of the binomial coefficients. Each number is simply the two numbers above it added together, except for the edges, which are all '1'. Pascal's triangle can also be seen in nature and in the curves of string instruments, for example in the curve of a grand piano.

Some of the most beautiful shapes in nature, on close examination, are found to be governed by a simple series of numbers. For example, a pineapple has eight spirals of bumps going in the clockwise direction and 13 in the anticlockwise direction. Pine cones are built up in a similar pattern: five spirals go clockwise and eight anticlockwise. If we start with the number 1, and create a sequence of numbers built up so that each number is the sum of the previous two numbers, we obtain the Fibonacci sequence:

1, 1, 2, 3, 5, 8, 13, 21, 34,...

This sequence includes all the pairs of numbers found in pineapples, pine cones and many other examples in nature, including the way in which successive leaves grow round the stems of many plants and trees. The numbers on the diagonals of Pascal's triangle add to generate the Fibonacci sequence.

This raises the philosophical question: is mathematics invented (created) to mirror reality, or discovered because reality is intrinsically mathematical? Are numbers in some sense 'given' so that there comes a point at which any attempt to find a more basic definition is useless? To what extent, if any, are the numbers, symmetries and geometries found in the natural world, and the relations between those numbers, directing the way in which the biological and physical world evolves? Is mathematics the science of patterns?
G.H. Hardy wrote, *'A mathematician, like a painter or poet, is a master of pattern'*.

■ Combined techniques

NMR is a very powerful technique for determining the structure of organic compounds, but is often used in conjunction with other analytical techniques, including X-ray crystallography, to provide an unambiguous structure for an unknown organic compound.

The first step in determining the structure of an unknown organic compound is to establish which chemical elements are present and their percentages by mass. This process is performed in a machine called an elemental analyser. The organic sample undergoes complete combustion and the gaseous products are analysed by a gas chromatographic system. The areas under the individual peaks are proportional to the masses of each of the gases produced. Carbon dioxide and water are produced if hydrocarbons or organic compounds containing carbon, hydrogen and oxygen are introduced into the elemental analyser. The empirical formula can then be determined.

From a mass spectrum, the molecular ion can be identified and compared with the empirical formula to establish the molecular formula (Chapter 1). The functional groups present can be established from the infrared spectrum. The NMR spectrum and the fragmentation pattern of the mass spectrum will establish or confirm the structural formula.

Deducing the structure of a compound using information from a range of analytical characterization techniques

Elemental analysis of compound X gave the following percentage composition by mass: carbon (66.7%), hydrogen (11.1%) and oxygen (22.22%). The empirical formula can be determined using the relative atomic masses (integers).

	Carbon		Hydrogen		Oxygen
Amounts of atoms	5.56 mol		11.11 mol		1.39 mol
Integer ratio of amounts of atoms	4	:	8	:	1

Hence, the empirical formula of X is C_4H_8O. The mass spectrum (Figure 21.10a) shows a molecular ion at 72. This means that the molecular formula is C_4H_8O.

The infrared spectrum (Figure 21.10b) shows a strong absorption band at $1718\,cm^{-1}$. This is due to the presence of a carbonyl group from an aldehyde or ketone. The bands in the region of $2900\,cm^{-1}$ suggest the presence of several C–H bonds.

The high-resolution ^1H NMR spectrum (Figure 21.10c) shows three sets of peaks. The triplet of peaks is from the protons of a methyl group, $-CH_3$, that has been split by the protons of an adjacent methylene group, $-CH_2-$. The single peak is due to a methyl group that is adjacent to a carbonyl group. The quartet of peaks is due to the protons of a $-CH_2-$ group split by an adjacent $-CH_3$ group.

■ **Figure 21.10a**
The mass spectrum of compound X

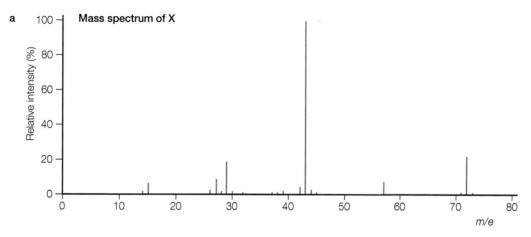

■ **Figure 21.10b**
The IR spectrum of compound X

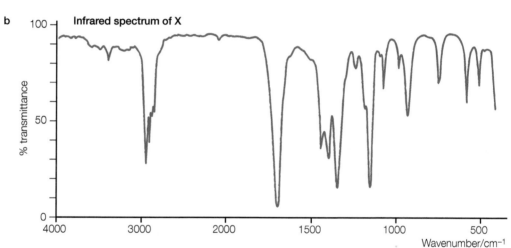

■ **Figure 21.10c**
The NMR spectrum of compound X

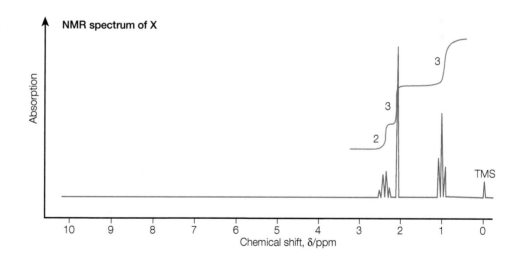

■ **Figure 21.11**
The correlation between the structure of butanone and the chemical shifts of the NMR spectrum of X

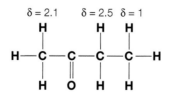

The combined analytical information suggest that X is butanone. Figure 21.11 shows the correlation between the structure of butanone and the NMR spectrum. The presence of a carbonyl group could be confirmed chemically by reacting X with 2,4-dinitrophenylhydrazine.

Nature of Science ■ Developments in spectroscopy

Improvements in modern instrumentation – spectroscopic techniques and mass spectrometry – have resulted in detailed knowledge of compounds, both organic and inorganic. Infrared spectroscopy gives information about the bonds present in organic molecules, and the fingerprint region can be used to uniquely identify a molecule. High-resolution NMR can give detailed information about the structure of molecules and even their conformations. The technique of NMR can be used to study a wide variety of atoms, including ^{13}C, ^{31}P and ^{11}B, etc. Mass spectrometry will fragment organic molecules, and these fragment ions can be used to determine the structure of the organic molecule under analysis. A combination of all these techniques gives the most detailed information about the structures of molecules (Figure 21.12).

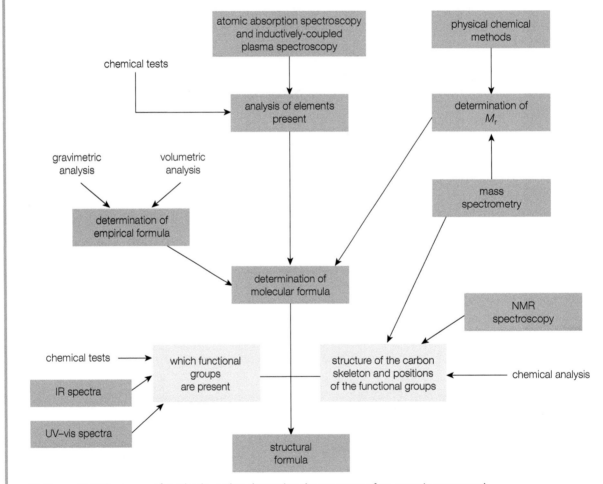

■ **Figure 21.12** Summary of methods used to determine the structure of an organic compound

Utilization: Magnetic resonance imaging and computerized tomography

Magnetic resonance imaging (MRI) was discussed in Chapter 11 and is based on the fact that the soft tissue of the human body is largely composed of water. By suitable scanning with radio waves, an image of the water distribution in the body can be built up, which is used in the diagnosis of various illnesses, including cancer and brain disorders.

As described in Chapter 11 the hydrogen nucleus behaves like a tiny bar magnet since it has an intrinsic magnetic moment (due to the spinning proton). In a strong external magnetic field, the hydrogen nuclei either line up in the direction of the magnetic field (lower energy state), or in the opposite direction (higher energy state). Each nucleus behaves like a gyroscope and its magnetic moment precesses about the external magnetic field. Precession occurs when a particle spins around its axis at an angle. A superconducting magnet is usually used to generate such a strong magnetic field in an MRI scanner (Figure 21.13).

■ **Figure 21.13**
The MRI scanner and its effect on hydrogen nuclei

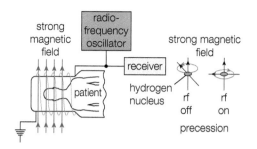

If radio waves are directed at the hydrogen nuclei at right angles to the external magnetic field, the hydrogen nuclei rotate (flip) through 90° and resonate by precessing in phase with each other in a plane at right angles to the external strong magnetic field. The energy absorbed from a short pulse of radio waves is released as a longer signal after the pulse has ended. This process is known as relaxation.

By applying magnetic field gradients in the x, y and z directions, the exact location where the radio signal is emitted from can be located in the body. The magnetic field gradients are varied continuously so the point of location of the radio signal changes systematically. The strength of the signal is a measure of the concentration of water molecules, which varies between tissues and between healthy and unhealthy tissue.

As the frequency of the radio waves is changed, hydrogen atoms in the water molecules at different depths inside the body respond to the radio waves and resonate. The direction of the magnetic field gradient is rotated through 360°, which enables the computer to produce a two-dimensional image – a 'slice'. A typical MRI brain scan contains over 30 slices and can be obtained within a few minutes. Analysis of data by a skilled technician makes it possible to distinguish between water in the grey or white tissue of the brain, or in cancerous (malign) or normal cells. It has the great advantage of being non-invasive, and the radio waves are of very low energy compared to the X-rays used in computerized tomography (CT).

4 Find out about the technique of functional NMR (fNMR).

Advantages of MRI

■ MRI scans do not involve ionizing radiation. As far as is known there are no harmful effects.

■ The ability to distinguish different types of soft tissue is better than that of a CT scan.

■ The resolution for soft tissue is better than a CT or ultrasound scan.

■ It can show both three-dimensional and cross-sectional images.

■ It is non-invasive and there are no known harmful effects of magnetic fields.

Disadvantages of MRI

■ MRI scans cannot be used if the patient has any metallic implants, such as a pacemaker.

■ The patient might have to be still for up to an hour; it is noisy and claustrophobic.

■ Bone does not show up on this type of scan.

■ The cost is greater than for any other scan.

Computerized tomography was developed in the 1970s and is a significant improvement on traditional X-ray imaging techniques. A narrow beam of X-rays is rotated around the patient and after passing through the body is detected electronically. The body is surrounded by several hundred X-ray photon detectors, whose outputs are transmitted to a computer. This analyses the data and forms an image of a narrow 'slice' of the body on a monitor screen: a CT scan (Figure 12.14). This technique rapidly produces images with good resolution and changes in 'real time' can be observed. A CT scan is particularly useful for diagnosing damage (lesions) to the brain, where surgery is not possible.

Advantages of CT

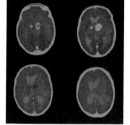

■ **Figure 21.14** CT scans of the brain of a patient with a cerebral lymphoma (orange)

■ Good for investigating critical bone fractures and calcification of organs; will also give good images of the brain and abdominal organs.

■ Better resolution compared to ultrasound.

■ Gives full cross-sectional image.

■ It is non-invasive.

Disadvantages of CT

- X-rays are highly ionizing.
- Limited contrast between tissues of similar density: images of the brain can be distorted by nearby bone.
- It is more expensive than a conventional X-ray picture.
- It often requires patients to hold their breath, which some find difficult.

■ Chromatography

It is very important that drugs, foods and water are free of harmful impurities or contaminants. The most reliable approach to establishing the purity of a substance is to show that it is not a mixture, that is, it cannot be separated into two or more distinct components (analytes). Various forms of chromatography are often used to establish the purity of a substance and to separate the components of a mixture. Some forms of chromatography can also give quantitative information, that is, concentrations or amounts of the components (analytes). Preparative chromatography seeks to separate the components of a mixture for further use (and is thus a form of purification). Analytical chromatography normally operates with smaller amounts of material and seeks to measure the relative proportions of analytes in a mixture.

The theory of chromatography

Separation by chromatography involves placing a sample on a liquid or solid stationary phase and passing a liquid or gaseous mobile phase through or over it. This process is known as elution. The components or analytes present in the mixture will move or migrate (be eluted) at different speeds. This differential rate of migration leads to their separation over a period of time and distance.

Chromatographic techniques can be classified (Table 21.3) according to whether the separation takes place on a flat surface (planar) or in a column. They can be further sub-divided into gas and liquid chromatography, and whether the stationary phase is a solid or a liquid.

■ Table 21.3
A classification of chromatographic techniques

Technique	Stationary phase	Mobile phase	Format	Mechanism of separation
Paper chromatography	Paper (cellulose)	Liquid	Flat	Partition
Thin-layer chromatography (TLC)	Silica, cellulose	Liquid	Flat	Adsorption or partition
Gas–liquid chromatography (GLC)	Liquid	Gas	Column	Partition
High-performance liquid chromatography (HPLC)	Solid	Liquid	Column	Modified partition

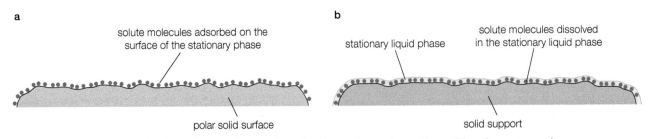

■ Figure 21.15 The two mechanisms of separation: **a** adsorption chromatography and **b** partition chromatography

A further very important classification involves the nature of the interactions between the mobile and stationary phases. The two main forms of interaction between the analyte and the stationary and mobile phases are adsorption and partition (Figure 21.15).

Adsorption (Figure 21.15a) involves the electrostatic interactions between chemical species and a surface. In adsorption chromatography, the solute molecules are held on the surface of the stationary phase. Generally, the stationary phase is a polar solid and the solutes are polar molecules. Strongly polar stationary phases attract and retain the polar solutes. Hence the separation of the solutes depends on their difference in polarity: the more polar solutes are more readily adsorbed than less polar solutes.

■ Figure 21.16 Bromine partitioned between water and tribromomethane

two liquid layers, each containing some of the solute

Partition can be demonstrated by adding bromine to a mixture of water and tribromomethane (Figure 21.16). These two liquids are immiscible and do not mix, but the bromine distributes itself in both liquids. Equilibrium is reached when the rates of movement of bromine up and down between the two liquids are equal. At equilibrium the solute molecules are distributed between the two liquids in a definite ratio (for a specific temperature); the solute has been partitioned between the two liquids. The bromine equilibrium favours the tribromomethane: the 'like dissolves like' principle (Chapter 4).

During the separation process in forms of partition chromatography, the solutes move between the stationary phase and the mobile phase and are partitioned between them (Figure 21.15b). Solutes in the mobile phase move forward with it. When the mobile phase is a gas, the rate of movement of solutes depends on their *volatility* and their *relative solubility*.

Paper chromatography

Paper chromatography is the simplest of the chromatographic techniques, and is often used to separate dyes in a mixture. In this technique the stationary phase is made up of water molecules that are trapped in the cellulose fibres of paper. The mobile phase is the aqueous or organic solvent that moves up the paper by capillary action. This capillary action is caused by the forces between the cellulose fibres of the paper and the solvent. Dyes that are more soluble in the solvent than they are in the water molecules of the stationary phase move rapidly up the paper, while those that are more soluble in the water are not carried as far up the paper (Figure 21.17).

■ Figure 21.17
The principles of paper chromatography

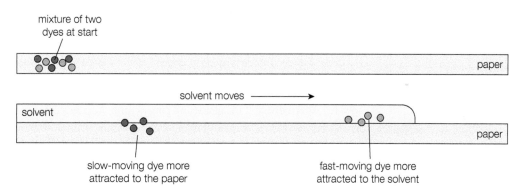

mixture of two dyes at start

paper

solvent moves ⟶

solvent

paper

slow-moving dye more attracted to the paper

fast-moving dye more attracted to the solvent

When the solvent front has almost reached the top, the paper is removed and left to dry in a fume cupboard (Figure 21.18). For each of the different components a retention factor (or R_f value) can be calculated:

$$R_f = \frac{\text{distance moved by component}}{\text{distance moved by solvent}}$$

Standard retention factors are tabulated for a wide variety of substances, using particular solvents under standard conditions. These allow the identification of unknown components by comparison with these standard retention factor values. Note that the retention factor is not dependent on the distance travelled by the solvent. It is dependent on the nature of the mobile and stationary phases as well as on the components of the substance being separated.

It is sometimes necessary in these cases to carry out a variation of simple chromatography. After the initial separation process the paper is allowed to dry and then rotated 90 degrees. A different solvent is used to repeat the process after the paper has been rotated. This technique is known as two-way or two-dimensional chromatography and allows the separation of complex mixtures.

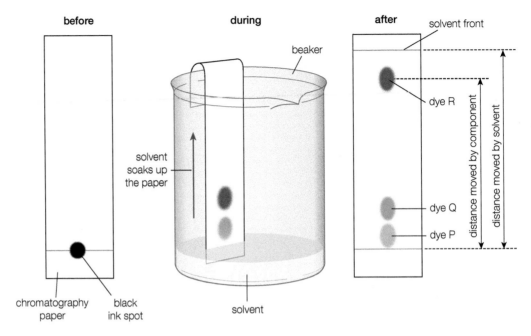

■ **Figure 21.18**
Ascending paper
chromatography

before   during   after

solvent front

beaker

solvent
soaks up
the paper

dye R

distance moved by component

distance moved by solvent

dye Q

dye P

chromatography
paper

black
ink spot

solvent

Thin-layer chromatography

The basis of thin-layer chromatography (TLC) is similar to that of paper chromatography. The paper stationary phase is replaced by a TLC plate (Figure 21.19), which is a thin layer of a substance such as silica (SiO_2) or alumina (Al_2O_3) coated on a glass, aluminium foil or plastic plate.

A spot of the sample solution is placed near the bottom of the plate. The plate is placed in a closed vessel containing solvent (the mobile phase) so that the liquid level is below the spot. The solvent ascends the plate by capillary action, the liquid filling the spaces between the solid particles. The technique is usually carried out in a closed vessel to ensure the atmosphere is saturated with solvent vapour and that evaporation from the plate is minimized.

The components may be recovered by scraping the areas containing the spots into a suitable solvent. Alternatively, TLC plates and paper chromatograms can be scanned by a device known as a densitometer to give quantitative information about the components of the mixture.

To prepare TLC plates, the silica or alumina is first heated to a high temperature so that all the water is removed from it. The compounds then act as polar solids and the solutes are transferred from the liquid mobile phase by adsorption on the surface. However, both these stationary phases attract water molecules and the surfaces become hydrated: $SiO_2.xH_2O$ (silica gel) and $Al_2O_3.xH_2O$ (hydrated alumina). The water present then forms the stationary phase and the solutes are separated by partition (Figure 21.20). A thin layer of cellulose can also be used as the stationary phase, but, since it retains water, the separation is by partition.

■ **Figure 21.19** Thin-layer
chromatography plates

■ **Figure 21.20**
The principles of TLC

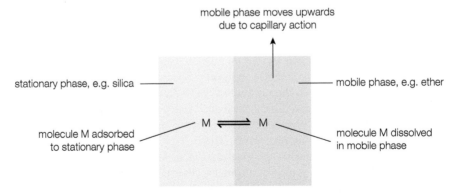

mobile phase moves upwards
due to capillary action

stationary phase, e.g. silica

mobile phase, e.g. ether

M ⇌ M

molecule M adsorbed
to stationary phase

molecule M dissolved
in mobile phase

Thin-layer chromatography is faster than paper chromatography and will work with smaller samples. Since the thin layer can be made from different solids, a wide range of mixtures can be separated. Thin-layer chromatography is mainly used for the separation of organic compounds. It is a simple, reliable and low-cost technique that is often used to select the conditions for larger-scale separations.

Gas–liquid chromatography

Gas–liquid chromatography (GLC) is a very powerful and sensitive form of partition chromatography. It is used to separate and identify very small samples of gases, liquids and *volatile* solids. The stationary phase is a non-volatile liquid, often adsorbed onto the surface of a solid packing material, contained within a long narrow coiled metal tube or column (Figure 21.21), which is kept at a controlled temperature in an oven. The stationary phase often consists of a long-chain alkane (with a high boiling point) coated on the surface of silica (SiO_2). The mobile phase is an inert **carrier gas**, such as dry nitrogen or dry argon, which is passed through the column at a constant measured rate. Unwanted organic solvents can be removed by passing the gas through activated charcoal.

■ **Figure 21.21**
Inside a GLC column
(usually coiled so it fits
into the oven)

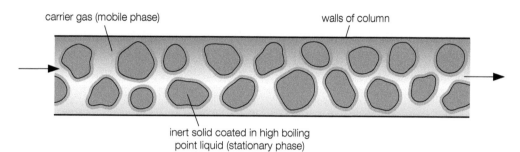

The sample mixture is injected using a microsyringe through a self-sealing silicone-rubber diaphragm. Once the sample has been injected into the instrument it is vaporized before it is carried through the column by the carrier gas (Figure 21.22). The mobile phase in gas chromatography is inert and does not interact with the solute.

■ **Figure 21.22**
The main components
of gas–liquid
chromatography

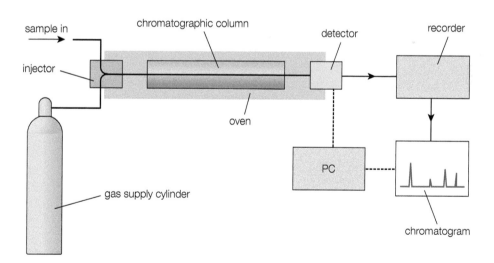

The components of the mixture distribute or partition themselves between the liquid and the gas and hence emerge from the column at different times. The more volatile (lower boiling point) components tend to remain largely in the gas phase and therefore emerge more quickly. The time for the component to travel through the column is known as the **retention time**. For a particular column at a given temperature with a specified flow rate of carrier gas, the retention time for a particular component is fixed. However, by programming the temperature of the column to rise at a constant rate, higher boiling components can be separated more rapidly. This approach also helps to separate components with similar boiling points.

The GLC chromatogram (Figure 21.23) also indicates how much of each component is present in the mixture, since the area under a component peak in the chromatogram is proportional to the amount of that component in the mixture.

■ **Figure 21.23** A GLC chromatogram: plot of peak of height against retention time

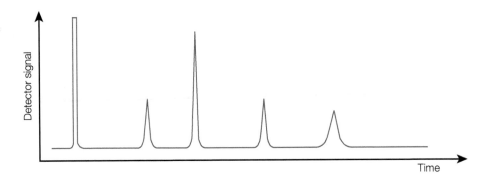

High-performance liquid chromatography

High-performance liquid chromatography (HPLC) (Figure 21.24) is similar in principle to GLC, except that the mobile phase is a solvent or mixture of solvents rather than a gas. The support is usually silica-based. Decreasing the particle size of the stationary phase in the column increases the efficiency of traditional column chromatography (larger surface area). The smaller the particle size, the higher the efficiency and hence resolution. However, it is harder to force a liquid through a mass of small particles, so a high pressure pump is required to overcome this and achieve reasonable flow rates. This is how the HPLC technique originated. The components are usually detected by measuring the absorbance of ultraviolet radiation at the end of the column.

■ **Figure 21.24** The HPLC system

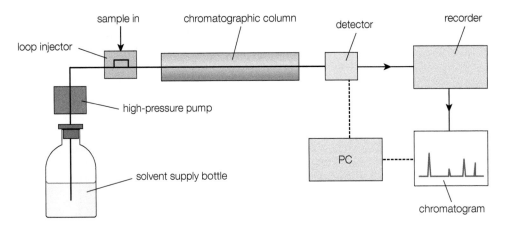

The mobile phase of HPLC is usually a mixture of two miscible solvents. In gas chromatography the carrier gas plays no role in determining retention times, but in HPLC the mobile phase controls retention times and selectivity.

HPLC is used to separate small samples of non-volatile substances and determine the amount of each component present in the mixture. HPLC can identify compounds that are temperature-sensitive and hence not readily analysed by GLC. No special treatment is required since aqueous solutions can be used in HPLC.

Uses of HPLC include: analysis of oil; alcoholic beverages; antioxidants, sugars and vitamins in foods; pharmaceuticals; polymers; biochemical and biotechnology research; presence of the stimulant caffeine in competing athletes and quality control of insecticides and herbicides.

Utilization: Detecting drug abuse in high-performance athletes

The majority of drugs that might be used by athletes can be detected in samples of urine. An athlete at an event will be informed by a drug control officer that they need to submit a urine sample for testing. The sample is then sent to a laboratory for analysis and the results are reported back to the governing athletic agency. For some substances, blood samples may be required.

Gas chromatography (GC) and mass spectrometry (MS) are the most common methods of chemical analysis. These tests can be done on urine and blood samples. In gas chromatography, the sample is vaporized in the presence of a gaseous solvent and introduced into the instrument. Each substance dissolves differently in the gas and stays in the gas phase for a unique, specific time, called the retention time. Typically the substance comes out of the gas and is absorbed on to a solid or liquid, which is then analysed by a detector. When the sample is analysed, the retention time is plotted to create a chromatogram. Standard samples of drugs are run, as well as the urine/blood samples, so that specific drugs can be identified and quantified in the chromatograms of the samples.

Utilization: Forensic investigations at crime scenes

Forensic analytical science conducts analyses, identification, and interpretation of physical criminal evidence. Experts in forensic science can provide their services to a criminal court as they can interpret and consult on the results of their analytical techniques. There are many techniques forensic scientists use, and the type of analytical method used depends on the type of sample and the type of results needed.

Gas chromatography/mass spectrometry, more commonly known as GC/MS, is used by forensic scientists for drug identification. The GC/MS instrument is able to detect all chemical substances in a given sample; therefore, this technique is useful in determining types of drugs present in a sample for a criminal investigation.

Immunoassays combine chemistry and immunology to test for specific analytes. Immunoassays detect antibody–antigen reaction. These tests are used in forensic science to analyse biological specimens for the presence of alcohol, drugs, toxins and poisons, and to determine causes of death in criminal investigations.

High-performance liquid chromatography, or HPLC, is an analytical technique capable of detecting specific components in a sample. In forensic science this test is used for drug analysis, toxicology (study of poisons), explosives analysis, ink analysis, fibres and plastics.

Forensic science also deals with testing for DNA analysis. DNA analysis is required in order to identify the source of bodily fluids: blood and semen. The PCR-based techniques include different types of analytical techniques including mass spectrometry. PCR (polymerase chain reaction) is an enzyme-based technique for amplifying DNA sequences.

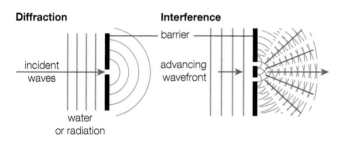

■ **Figure 21.25** Diffraction and interference in waves

■ X-ray crystallography

X-rays have a wavelength of about 0.1 nm, comparable with interatomic distances in molecules. If a beam of monochromatic X-rays (that is, X-rays with a single wavelength) is directed onto a molecular crystal, the atoms in the crystal lattice behave like a diffraction grating. In some directions, the X-ray waves reinforce each other (constructive interference), and in other directions the waves cancel out (destructive interference), forming an interference pattern (Figure 21.25). The diffraction of the X-rays is due to the presence of electrons around the atom (or ions). A greater number of electrons around an atom (or ion) leads to greater scattering of X-rays. Since hydrogen atoms only have one electron they hardly scatter X-rays and have little effect on an X-ray diffraction pattern.

When a beam of X-rays falls on a crystal plane composed of regularly arranged atoms, molecules or ions, the X-rays are diffracted. Waves from the diffracted X-rays may produce constructive or destructive interference. For constructive interference, the path difference must be equal to an integral multiple of the wavelength (Figure 21.26).

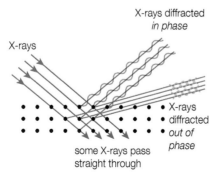

■ **Figure 21.26** Diffraction in X-rays

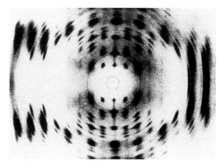

■ **Figure 21.27** Diffraction photograph of sodium chloride, NaCl

By studying the diffraction pattern (Figure 21.27) the structure and arrangement of the particles (atoms, ions and molecules) in the crystalline solid can be deduced (Chapter 4). The unit cell and the distance between atoms, as well as bond angles within molecules, can also be determined. This technique known as X-ray crystallography is based on Bragg's law and is discussed in Chapter 22 on the accompanying website. It can also be used to establish the structures of metals and ionic solids, which are also discussed in Chapter 22.

One common technique used in modern X-ray crystallography is single-crystal X-ray crystallography (Figure 21.28). A small single pure crystal is rotated, under computer control, in the beam of X-rays. The positions and intensities of the maxima are recorded by detectors placed around the crystal. Analysis of the results is performed with a computer, and it is now possible to determine the structure of complex molecules, including proteins. X-ray diffraction patterns of hydrated DNA strongly suggested it had a double helix structure (see Chapter 23 on the accompanying website).

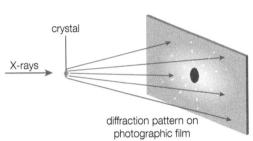

■ **Figure 21.28** Single-crystal X-ray crystallography

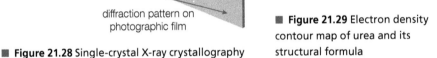

■ **Figure 21.29** Electron density contour map of urea and its structural formula

One method of presenting the results of X-ray diffraction analysis is an electron density map, with contours joining positions of equal electron density (electrons per cubic nanometre). Figure 21.29 shows the electron density contour map of urea (carbamide) compared with its structural formula. The positions of the carbon, nitrogen and oxygen atoms are clearly visible (due to their high electron density) but not the hydrogen atoms (due to their low electron density). An electron density contour map gives information about bond lengths and angles, and provides evidence for bond polarity (Chapter 4). The main drawback is that the hydrogen atoms have low electron density and are not visible.

Sharing of structural information electronically

The international chemical community often shares structural information via the internet. The Cambridge Structural Database, ChemSpider and the Worldwide Protein Data Bank are three widely used online resources that contain structural information.

■ The Cambridge Structural Database (CSD) is a repository for information about small molecule crystal structures. Scientists use single-crystal X-ray crystallography to determine the crystal structure of a compound. Once the structure is determined, information about the structure is deposited in electronic form in the CSD. Other scientists can search and retrieve structures from the database.

■ ChemSpider (Figure 21.30) was developed by the Royal Society of Chemistry (RSC). It is a free chemical structures database that provides rapid test and structure search access to over 30 million structures from hundreds of data sources.

■ The Worldwide Protein Data Bank (www.wwPDB.org) consists of a number of organisations that act as deposition, data processing and distribution centres for the PDB data. Its mission is to maintain a single PDB archive of macromolecular structural data that is freely and publicly available to the global community.

■ **Figure 21.30**
ChemSpider front
screen

■ *Examination questions –
a selection*

Paper 1 IB style questions

Q1 What is being probed during ^{1}H NMR
spectroscopy?
A nuclei   C ions
B electrons   D covalent bonds

Q2 Which molecule does **not** give a single peak in its
^{1}H NMR spectrum?
A methoxymethane, $H_3C-O-CH_3$
B benzene, C_6H_6
C phenol (hydroxybenzene), C_6H_5OH
D methanal (H_2CO)

Q3 How many peaks will be present in the ^{1}H NMR
spectrum of 1,4-dimethylbenzene?
A 1   C 3
B 2   D 4

Q4 Which region of the electromagnetic spectrum
corresponds to the energy of molecular
vibrations?
A infrared
B ultraviolet
C visible
D microwaves

Q5 What structural information is provided by
infrared spectroscopy about an organic molecule?
A molar mass
B number of hydrogen atoms
C number of carbon atoms
D functional groups

Q6 Which one of the following techniques may be
used to reveal the crystalline components of paints
on the basis of their crystal structure?
A infrared spectroscopy
B mass spectrometry
C microwave spectroscopy
D X-ray diffraction

Paper 2 IB style questions

Q1 **a** Outline the basic principle of **all** chromatographic techniques. [2]

b Paper chromatograms formed by two orange food colourings, A and B, are shown below.

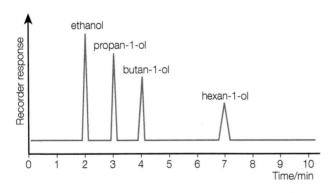

i Which of these food colourings is a mixture of dyes? [1]

ii Which of these food colourings is a pure substance? [1]

iii Explain whether the same dye is present in each of the food colourings. [2]

iv Calculate the R_f value of the substance responsible for the red spot in the chromatogram of A. [1]

The R_f value is the ratio of the distance moved by the solute/distance moved by solvent.

c The results of a thin-layer chromatography separation on silica gel are shown below.

Compound	Distance travelled/cm
Compound 1	1.6
Compound 2	9.2
Compound 3 (solvent)	12.6

i Calculate the R_f values of the compounds 1 and 2 and comment on their values. [3]

ii State **one** advantage of thin-layer chromatography over paper chromatography. [1]

Q2 The diagram shows a GLC chromatogram for a mixture of four alcohols – ethanol, propan-1-ol, butan-1-ol and hexan-1-ol.

a Explain how retention times are measured. [1]

b Explain how the areas under the component peaks are used. [1]

c **i** Which component has a retention time of 7 minutes? [1]

ii Which component is present in the largest amount? [1]

d State **two** factors or variables that affect retention times. [1]

e **i** Suggest why GLC would be unsuitable for analysing a drug which contains paracetamol (m.p. 151 °C) and caffeine (m.p. 238 °C). [2]

ii Suggest another chromatographic technique that would be suitable for performing the analysis. [1]

Q3 There are four structural isomers that are alcohols with the formula C_4H_9OH.

a Explain why the infrared spectra of all four alcohols show very similar absorptions around 3350 cm^{-1} and 2900 cm^{-1}. [2]

b Describe how these alcohols can be distinguished using their infrared spectra. [1]

c Explain why the mass spectra of all four alcohols show a peak at $m/z = 74$. [1]

d Suggest the formulas of the fragments formed from C_4H_9OH with the following m/z values:

i $m/z = 57$

ii $m/z = 45$ [2]

e The numbers of peaks, and the areas under them, in the ^1H NMR spectra of these alcohols can be used to identify them.

i Explain why the ^1H NMR spectrum of $(CH_3)_2CHCH_2OH$ has four peaks. Predict the ratio of the areas under the peaks. [2]

ii Deduce the structure of the alcohol whose ^1H NMR spectrum has two peaks with areas in the ratio 9 : 1. [1]

Q4 Deduce and draw the high-resolution ^1H NMR spectrum of propan-1-ol and explain why two triplets at different chemical shifts are observed in this spectrum. [5]

Index